Thomas W. Wieting
March, 1965

INTERSCIENCE MONOGRAPHS IN PHYSICS AND ASTRONOMY

Edited by R. E. MARSHAK

Volume I: E. R. Cohen, K. M. Crowe, J. W. M. DuMond
THE FUNDAMENTAL CONSTANTS OF PHYSICS

Volume II: G. J. Dienes and G. H. Vineyard
RADIATION EFFECTS IN SOLIDS

Volume III: N. N. Bogoliubov and D. V. Shirkov
INTRODUCTION TO THE THEORY OF QUANTIZED FIELDS

Additional volumes in preparation

INTERSCIENCE MONOGRAPHS IN PHYSICS AND ASTRONOMY

Edited by R. E. MARSHAK
University of Rochester, Rochester, New York

VOLUME III

INTRODUCTION TO THE THEORY OF QUANTIZED FIELDS

N. N. BOGOLIUBOV
D. V. SHIRKOV
Steklov Mathematical Institute, Academy of Sciences, Moscow, U.S.S.R.
Joint Institute for Nuclear Research, Dubna, U.S.S.R.

Authorized English Edition
Revised and Enlarged by the Authors
Translated from the Russian by

G. M. Volkoff
Department of Physics, University of British Columbia
Vancouver, B. C., Canada

INTERSCIENCE PUBLISHERS, INC., NEW YORK
Interscience Publishers Ltd., London **1959**

First Published 1959

Library of Congress Catalog Card Number 59-10445

INTERSCIENCE PUBLISHERS, INC., 250 Fifth Avenue, New York 1, N. Y.
For Great Britain and Northern Ireland:
INTERSCIENCE PUBLISHERS LTD., 88/90 Chancery Lane, London W. C. 2

PRINTED IN THE NETHERLANDS
BY DIJKSTRA'S DRUKKERIJ N.V., VOORHEEN BOEKDRUKKERIJ GEBR. HOITSEMA, GRONINGEN

Preface to the First Russian Edition

This monograph is an attempt to give a systematic presentation of the modern theory of quantized fields from its foundations right up to its most recent achievements.

In writing this book the authors were guided by their intention to present field theory from a unified point of view combining internal logical consistency and closure with completeness of the material covered. We also aimed, wherever possible, to introduce the maximum degree of clarity into the basic assumptions of the theory employed at the present stage of its development. At the same time, naturally, particular attention was devoted to the mathematical correctness of the arguments, as a result of which the extent of coverage of the applications of the theory to calculations of specific physical phenomena can be claimed to be only methodologically complete.

The authors also wanted to treat sufficiently fully the most promising approaches developed quite recently. We hope that because of this, the book will prove to be useful not only to persons first undertaking the study of quantum field theory, but also to theoreticians working in this domain of physics.

The chapter "Dispersion Relations," which presents the most recent results, was included in the book as a supplement in view of the current interest in this topic.

The authors wish to thank the staff and the post-graduate students of the Division of Theoretical Physics of the V. A. Steklov Mathematical Institute of the Academy of Sciences, U.S.S.R., and of the Chair of Statistical Physics and Mechanics of the Physics Faculty of the M. V. Lomonosov Moscow State University, for their remarks and suggestions made during the preparation of the manuscript. We are particularly grateful to B. V. Medvedev, who contributed a number of valuable comments on different parts of the book.

February, 1957
Moscow

N. N. Bogoliubov
D. V. Shirkov

Translator's Note

The translator wishes to express his gratitude to the authors for providing him with a pre-publication copy of the manuscript which permitted the translation to be started several months prior to the publication of the Russian edition, and also for supplying some additional new material which does not appear in the Russian edition: a Mathematical Appendix containing the proof of the important theorem quoted without proof in 51.3, a new Section 51.4, two new paragraphs at the end of 49.2, and numerous minor revisions, in particular those on pp. 547, 548, 580, 608, and 609, and corrections of typographical errors. Thanks are also due to Gostekhizdat for airmailing freshly printed copies of the Russian edition for final checking of the translation. This cooperation has made possible the early appearance in English of the present enlarged and corrected edition.

July, 1958
Vancouver, Canada

G. VOLKOFF

Contents

CHAPTER III The Scattering Matrix

§ 1. Introduction

1.1. *A Survey of the Present State of Field Theory*

This is the tenth year since the date of publication of the work by Bethe (7) which marked the beginning of the rapid development of modern quantum field theory. During these years the principal domain of quantum field theory — quantum electrodynamics — has turned into a quite well-developed theory which is in excellent agreement with experiment.

The basic equations of quantum electrodynamics have already been known since the late 1920's when the classical papers of Dirac, Heisenberg, and Pauli appeared. At the same time an approach to the solution of these equations by the method of perturbation theory was formulated which appeared to be a quite natural one in view of the existence of a small parameter — the fine structure constant $\alpha = 1/137$. However, the application of the methods of perturbation theory to the solution of problems in electrodynamics was confronted by an essential obstacle. It turned out that only the main approximation of perturbation theory led to results that were in definite agreement with experiment. A calculation of successive approximations not only gave no improvement in the preceding results but led to mathematically meaningless divergent expressions (products of high powers of the fine structure constant α and integrals whose integrands fall off slowly for large values of virtual momenta).

If we assume that the theory is incorrect at high energies and formally restrict the region of integration by some limiting energy, for example of the order mc^2, then we shall find that the contribution of such "cut-off" integrals will be small because of the small factors α^n. Because of this it appeared to be quite natural to attempt to improve the theory by introducing various kinds of so-called *form factors* which cut off the divergent integrals at high energies. However, all attempts based on the introduction of form factors, or of elementary lengths in space-time "explaining" such form factors, have not led to any significant results.

Nevertheless, it was clear that the basic foundations of the theory are correct, that the principal approximations are in satisfactory agreement with experiment, and that one must only get rid of divergent expressions in the radiation corrections which are given by the higher-order approximations of perturbation theory.

This difficulty was solved by the introduction of the so-called *subtraction formalism.* Its basic idea is founded on the fact that not all the radiation corrections obtained in higher approximations are observable. This is related to the fact that in using perturbation theory we are forced to regard as the initial state the situation when $\alpha = 0$, i.e., when the interaction of the electron with the electromagnetic field is entirely absent. In this approximation we have to ascribe to the electron a certain mass m and charge e. If we then calculate in the second approximation, say, the self-energy of the electron, we shall obtain for it an expression of the form $(m + \alpha m_1)c^2$ which contains the radiation correction αm_1 to the mass, where m_1 is given by a divergent integral. It is clear in this case that m — the mass of the fictitious noninteracting or "bare" electron — is not an observable quantity, and neither is αm_1. Only the sum $m_0 = m + \alpha m_1$ is an observable representing the mass of the actual electron which interacts with the electromagnetic field. Therefore, in the calculation of various effects one should express the desired quantities not in terms of m, but in terms of the observable mass m_0. This simple argument is the one that led to the creation of the subtraction formalism which made possible the elimination of all the divergences from the radiation corrections by means of compensating for them by a suitable choice of the initial m and e.

On the basis of such concepts Bethe succeeded in carrying out a calculation of the Lamb shift of the $2S_{1/2}$ and $2P_{1/2}$ levels in the hydrogen atom, and in this way a start was made on the problem of determining the radiation corrections to various observable effects.

These ideas received a more systematic and consistent development in the work of Schwinger (104)–(106). By representing the mass and charge of the "bare" electron in the form

$$m_0 - \alpha m_1, \qquad e_0 - \alpha e_1$$

he showed that one may so choose the divergent expressions for m_1 and e_1 that they completely compensate all divergences in the radiation corrections of the second order.

The special covariant form of the fundamental field equations developed by Tomonaga (126) and by Schwinger (104) turned out to be particularly convenient for carrying out this program. As is well known, in the usual form of these equations the wave function of the dynamic system is considered to be a function of the time which thus plays a special role from the outset. The proposal made by Tomonaga and by Schwinger was to consider the wave function as a functional of the spacelike surface σ and to introduce in place of the usual Schrödinger equation

$$i\,\frac{\partial \Phi(t)}{\partial t} = H(t)\Phi(t)$$

the covariant equation in terms of functional derivatives

$$i\,\frac{\delta \Phi(\sigma)}{\delta \sigma(x)} = H(x \mid \sigma)\Phi(\sigma),$$

where $H(x \mid \sigma)$ is the Hamiltonian density at the space-time point x lying on the surface σ. This form of writing down the fundamental equations is completely equivalent to the usual one and essentially gives nothing new, but historically it has played an important role in the development of a fully covariant form of perturbation theory which facilitated carrying out the program of compensating for infinities.

At the same time, but starting from a different basis, the covariant perturbation theory was developed in a form very convenient for practical applications by Feynman (40), (41). Feynman utilized the special approach to quantum mechanics developed by him (39), which is based on the idea of representing the quantum-mechanical probability amplitude in the form of a *continuous integral* over the set of all the virtual trajectories of

$\exp\{iA\}$, where A is the classical action. With the aid of these concepts, which he expressed in simple graphical form, Feynman developed a set of prescriptions for constructing the probability amplitude in any approximation. Of great practical convenience is the symbolic graphical representation which he introduced for complicated integral expressions in the form of diagrams which give a schematic description of the nature of the process being investigated. The technique of Feynman diagrams has turned out to be an important contribution to the development of quantum field theory and has now achieved universal use.

These papers by Tomonaga, Schwinger, and Feynman were then generalized by Dyson (33), (34) who on the one hand succeeded in deriving Feynman's prescriptions from the Tomonaga-Schwinger theory, and on the other hand outlined the methodology of the subtraction formalism used in the evaluation of the elements of the scattering matrix in approximations of arbitrarilily high order. As a result of the subsequent development of Dyson's work, the prescriptions of the subtraction formalism in electrodynamics have now been completely worked out. The calculations of radiation corrections carried out with the aid of these prescriptions fully agree within the limits of error with the experimental data available today. Thus, for example, the calculated value of the radiation correction to the magnetic moment of the electron in units of the Bohr magneton is equal to 0.001145 while experiment gives 0.001146 ± 0.000012.

Although at present serious doubts are expressed with respect to the convergence, and even with respect to the summability, of the series utilized in perturbation theory, nevertheless these series have a definite asymptotic character, and their first terms fall off rapidly because of the existence of a small parameter.

Thus at present quantum electrodynamics represents a fully developed theory that contains prescriptions for the calculation of physical quantities of interest to us by means of power series (in powers of a small parameter α); the first several terms of these series lead in all cases to results which to a high degree agree with experimental data.

Quite a different situation exists in meson theories. Although the methodology of the subtraction formalism was immediately generalized to the renormalizable meson theories among which is included the now generally accepted pseudoscalar theory with pseudoscalar coupling, the corresponding perturbation theory expansions have turned out to be of no practical significance. The reason for this lies in the fact that the parameter $g^2/\hbar c$ which plays here the role of the fine structure constant α has turned out to be equal to approximately 15, as a result of which expansions in powers of this parameter have no meaning, while attempts made to study various effects by means of the first few approximations have not led even to qualitative agreement with experimental data. In this way it was definitely established that perturbation theory methods based on expansions in powers of the coupling constant are not applicable to meson theories.

In view of this, there has naturally arisen the problem of going beyond the framework of perturbation theory. Investigations devoted to this question may be tentatively grouped as belonging to one of two fundamental approaches. In one of these, the problem was considered of deriving approximate equations, whose degree of accuracy is not directly related to the smallness of the coupling constant, and of making calculations based on these equations of specific effects, mainly of processes of scattering of mesons by nucleons. Typical of this approach is the so-called Tamm-Dancoff method proposed in the papers of Fock (43), Tamm (124), and Dancoff (29). A definite degree of success has been achieved in its application to the problems of the scattering of mesons by nucleons: thus in its first approximation the Tamm-Dancoff method gives a good description of p-scattering. However, further development of this method has encountered a number of difficulties in principle: for example, up to the present time no one has succeeded in solving, in the case of this method, the problem of the removal of infinities with at least the same degree of consistency which has been achieved for perturbation theory.

The investigations representative of the second approach deal primarily with theoretical problems of the qualitative investigation of the properties of Green's functions which play a fundamental role in quantum field theory. In these papers some interesting results have been obtained, in particular spectral representations of Green's functions, and also a number of arguments have been advanced which lead one to suspect the existence of internal contradictions within the whole modern quantum field theory.

Since meson theories appeared to show very little promise, some investigators have already begun to consider that there can be no further development of field theory without a radical revision of its fundamental principles.

However, very recently a number of investigations utilizing a new, very interesting and deep approach has appeared. Without being tied down to any specific variant of meson theory this work is based on the general properties of covariance, unitarity, and causality of the scattering matrix, from which it is possible to obtain a number of so-called dispersion relations between quantities determined from experiments on the scattering of particles. These relations have received important application in the reduction of experimental data by means of phase analysis.

In our opinion the most important significance of these relations lies in the fact that they provide in principle a possibility of experimentally testing the existence of some sort of "elementary lengths" of magnitude corresponding to energies now attainable. The possibility indicated above is related to the fact that these relations hold only in the case of strict locality and are modified in a quite definite way in the case of a deviation from locality. However, it should be emphasized that investigations representative of this approach are only beginning to be developed.

In summary, it may be said that at the present time quantum field theory has completed a certain stage of its development which is characterized by the creation of a methodology of calculations within the framework of perturbation theory which has found application in quantum electrodynamics, and the limits on the applicability of this methodology are already becoming delineated.

In connection with this in our opinion the time has come to give a critical exposition of the basic foundations and methods of quantum field theory, and this is what we shall attempt to do in the present monograph.

1.2. *Plan of Presentation*

In order to present all the material from a unified point of view, we begin this book with a survey of the foundations of the classical and the quantum theory of free fields (Chapters I and II).

In order to make the presentation correspond closely to the actual state of affairs, the greatest amount of attention is devoted to a systematic presentation of perturbation theory. In doing this we have found it most advantageous to follow the ideas of Heisenberg, of Feynman, and particularly of Stueckelberg and to discuss the problem of determining the scattering matrix without the usual introduction of the Hamiltonian formalism but by taking as our basis the physical requirements of covariance, unitarity and causality. Proceeding in this manner it is possible to develop a method of obtaining convergent expressions for the coefficients of the power series for the S-matrix without having to deal at intermediate stages with obviously meaningless divergent expressions and without having to resort to purely formal considerations in compensating for infinities. This program for determining the scattering matrix and of obtaining convergent expressions for the functions appearing as coefficients in it is carried out in Chapters III and IV.

In Chapter V, applications to various specific cases of the regularized perturbation theory developed previously are considered with the largest amount of attention being devoted to spinor electrodynamics with all the essential arguments in this case being presented in quite a detailed manner.

In Chapter VI it is shown how, by starting from any given scheme, one may obtain an equation (of the type of Schrödinger's equation) for the state amplitude and how one may determine the principal dynamic variables of a system of mutually interacting quantized fields. In the same chapter solutions of a number of now classical problems of the motion of an electron in a given external field are also presented: polarization of the vacuum, anomalous magnetic moment of the electron, and the radiation shift of levels in the hydrogen atom. This concludes the presentation of topics related to perturbation theory.

The next part contains a presentation of those principal possibilities of going beyond the framework of perturbation theory which are now becoming clarified. In Chapter VII, Feynman's method of *continuous integration* and of the representation in terms of it of fundamental Green's functions is considered. Chapter VIII contains an analysis of the so-called *renormalization group* which allows us to improve in an effective way the formulas given by perturbation theory for electrodynamic Green's functions in the domains of the ultraviolet and the infrared catastrophes where these functions have singularities. The final Chapter, IX, is devoted to dispersion relations.

In presenting the aforementioned material, the authors wished to stress the methodological aspects of the theory. Therefore, the concrete examples which have been considered are of an illustrative nature in contrast, for example, to Heitler's book (60).

1.3. *Some Notation*

We now add a few words with respect to the notation adopted.

The components of all the four-vectors have been chosen to be real. The metric is defined by means of Minkowski's tensor (taken with reversed sign) g^{mn}:

$$g^{mn} = 0 \quad \text{for} \quad m \neq n, \; g^{00} = -g^{11} = -g^{22} = -g^{33} = 1,$$

i.e., the product of two four-vectors a and b with components a^0, a^1, a^2, a^3 and b^0, b^1, b^2, b^3 is defined in the following manner:

$$ab \equiv \sum_{0 \leq m,\, n \leq 3} g^{mn} a^m b^n = a^0 b^0 - a^1 b^1 - a^2 b^2 - a^3 b^3 = a^0 b^0 - \mathbf{ab}.$$

Bold type ($\mathbf{a}$, $\mathbf{b}$) is used to denote the ordinary three-vectors. Indices representing summation over all four components 0, 1, 2, 3 are usually denoted by Latin letters, while indices representing summation over the three space components 1, 2, 3 are denoted by Greek letters. For example

$$ab = \sum_{m,n} g^{mn} a^m b^n, \qquad \mathbf{ab} = \sum_{\alpha} a^\alpha b^\alpha.$$

The upper indices are, as usual, contravariant, while the lower ones are covariant (for details see § 2.4). Raising and lowering indices are accomplished with the aid of the metric tensor, e.g.

$$a_n = \sum_m g_{mn} a^m, \qquad a^m = \sum_n g^{mn} a_n;$$

with

$$g_{mn} = g^{mn}.$$

Throughout the book the system of units is used in which the velocity of light and Planck's constant divided by 2π are taken equal to unity, i.e.,

$$c = \hbar = 1.$$

In this system of units energy, momentum, and mass have the dimensions of a reciprocal length, while the time x^0 has the dimensions of length.

References to the literature appear in parentheses. The complete list of references appears at the end of the book.

CHAPTER I

Classical Theory of Free Fields

§ 2. Lagrangian Formalism and Field Invariants

2.1. *Fields and Particles*

In Chapter I, classical field theory, i.e., one not involving quantization, is considered.

A well-known example of a wave field is the electromagnetic field which describes the interaction of electrically charged particles. The classical description of the electromagnetic field based on Maxwell's equations leads us to purely wave theoretic concepts of electromagnetism. Also, it sometimes turns out to be convenient to regard the continuous system of the electromagnetic field as a discrete mechanical system with an infinite number of degrees of freedom, more precisely as an infinite number of so-called field oscillators. Such an approach permits one to use the apparatus of classical mechanics for the study of the field.

The transition to the corpuscular point of view, or more precisely to a unified corpuscular-wave point of view, is accomplished by means of the so-called *quantization* procedure in the course of which discrete energy quanta are ascribed to the field corresponding to various possible energy states of the field oscillators. In doing so, one says that the electromagnetic quanta are particles which describe the interaction between the electrically charged particles. The rest mass of the quanta of the electromagnetic field turns out to be equal to zero.

It also turns out that it is possible to associate wave fields with particles of rest mass different from zero (electrons, nucleons, mesons, etc.). Such particles are identified with the quanta of the corresponding fields and describe the interaction between other particles which serve as sources of the given wave field. A well-known example of such a correspondence is given by the π-mesons which are the quanta of the nuclear (or the meson) field which describes the interaction between nucleons (protons and neutrons). In this connection it is said that nuclear forces are "transmitted" by π-mesons. Thus a quantum theory of interacting wave fields actually represents a theory of *interaction between elementary particles.*

In presenting the theory of wave fields, the order of presentation which is the simplest one and which was developed historically (although it is not the most satisfactory one — see § 17) is the following one which we also adopt. We first consider the classical theory of wave fields, then the quantum theory of free fields, and finally the quantum theory of interacting fields. Naturally the presentation of the classical and the quantum theories of free fields is of an auxiliary character, and claims only to be methodologically complete.

2.2. *Hamiltonian and Lagrangian Formalisms*

By treating the field as a mechanical system with an infinite number of degrees of freedom we are led to the possibility of formulating a theory of the field by analogy with the classical mechanics of a particle. In this procedure, the field is described by means of a so-called *field function* which corresponds to an infinite number of degrees of freedom. The equations for the field functions may be obtained from the Lagrangian function of the system by means of a variational principle of stationary action, and the dynamic variables may be obtained by means of introducing quantities similar to the corresponding expressions occurring in the formalism of classical mechanics.

In analogy with mechanics two methods of constructing a theory of wave fields turn out to be possible.

In the canonical (or the Hamiltonian) formalism the fundamental quantities are the generalized coordinates and momenta and also the Hamiltonian function for the system which is constructed with the aid of the Lagrangian function and the generalized coordinates and momenta. The canonical equations and the dynamic variables are obtained directly from the Hamiltonian function, and this method of formulating the field theory permits a detailed formal analogy with classical mechanics to be carried through.

However, in spite of its straightforwardness, the Hamiltonian formalism has an essential disadvantage: since time is singled out, the presentation loses its relativistic invariance which is particularly inconvenient in the case of quantum field theory.

The second method of presenting field theory, to which we shall refer as the Lagrangian formalism, is based on the fact that the introduction of generalized coordinates and momenta as well as of the Hamiltonian function is not unavoidable. Starting with the Lagrangian of the system, one may obtain the equations of motion by means of a variational principle, while the dynamic variables, such as energy-momentum and charge, are defined as invariants corresponding to various transformations of the system of coordinates and of the field functions. While in the canonical formalism time is the fundamental independent variable and coordinate variables play the role of parameters, all four coordinates appear in the Lagrangian formalism in a perfectly symmetric way. The individual features of a detailed analogy with a mechanical system of particles become less sharply emphasized, but the presentation of the theory becomes relativistically covariant from the outset. Naturally the final results are equivalent in the two cases. We shall develop our presentation on the basis of the Lagrangian formalism.

2.3. *The Lagrangian Function and the Principle of Stationary Action*

The field equations and their invariants are obtained directly from the Lagrangian function. Let us therefore first of all formulate the fundamental requirements to be imposed on this function. A prominent place among them is occupied by the requirement of relativistic invariance, or the condition of invariance with respect to the full inhomogeneous Lorentz group. In this connection let us recall the definition of the Lorentz group. As is well known, the full Lorentz group is the group of homogeneous linear transformations of the coordinates of 4-dimensional space-time which leave invariant the quadratic form representing the square of a 4-interval:

$$s^2 = \sum_n g^{nn}(x^n)^2 \equiv (x^0)^2 - (x^1)^2 - (x^2)^2 - (x^3)^2, \qquad (2.1)$$

and which do not reverse the direction of time.[1] This group includes spatial rotations in the three planes $x^1\, x^2$, $x^2\, x^3$, $x^3\, x^1$, the Lorentz rotations in the three planes $x^0\, x^1$, $x^0\, x^2$, $x^0\, x^3$, the reflections of the three space axes x^1, x^2, x^3 and all the products of these transformations. The determinants of the transformations of rotation are equal to $+1$, while the determinants of the reflections of the axes are equal to -1. Therefore the proper Lorentz group of transformations with the determinant $+1$ is separated from the full group and includes the six rotations and the reflections of an even number of space axes which are equivalent to rotations.

It is often convenient to consider the full Lorentz group together with transformations of translation along all four coordinate axes. For brevity we shall denote this combined set of transformations by the name of the inhomogeneous Lorentz group.

We return now to the Lagrangian function. It is a function of the time, and in mechanics it is expressed as a sum over all the material points of the system. For a continuous system of the type of a wave field, this sum is expressed by a spatial integral of the Lagrangian density function

$$\Lambda(x^0) = \int d\mathbf{x}\, \mathscr{L}(x^0, \mathbf{x}). \qquad (2.2)$$

However, the variational principle deals not with the Lagrangian function Λ, but with the action A obtained from it by integrating over x^0. Therefore the noncovariant expression (2.2) in the Lagrangian formalism in fact turns out to be only an intermediate step, and it is quite sufficient to consider the Lagrangian density function

$$\mathscr{L}(x^0, \mathbf{x}) = \mathscr{L}(x),$$

[1] *Translator's note.* In American literature the "full Lorentz group" is usually taken to include time reversal $t \to -t$.

which depends on all four space-time variables. For brevity we shall in future refer to $\mathscr{L}(x)$ as the Lagrangian,

Usually the Lagrangian $\mathscr{L}$ is taken to be a real function[2] of the field variables $u_i(x)$ and of their first derivatives[3] $\partial u_i/\partial x^k$ which does not explicitly depend on the coordinates x^k and which is invariant with respect to transformations of coordinates belonging to the inhomogeneous Lorentz group.

If the Lagrangian $\mathscr{L}(x)$ depends only on the state of the fields in an infinitely small neighborhood of the point x, i.e., on the values of u_i and of a finite number of their partial derivatives evaluated at the point x, then it is called a local Lagrangian, and the corresponding theory is said to be a local theory. In the opposite case when, for example, $\mathscr{L}(x)$ is represented in the form

$$\int dy\, F\left(u(x),\ u(y),\ \frac{\partial u(x)}{\partial x^k},\ \frac{\partial u(y)}{\partial y^m}\right),$$

we obtain so-called nonlocal theories which are not discussed in this book.

Thus we may write down the local Lagrangian in the form

$$\mathscr{L}(x) = \mathscr{L}\left(u_i(x),\ \frac{\partial u_i(x)}{\partial x^k}\right).$$

The integral of the Lagrangian over a certain volume in space-time

$$A = \int \mathscr{L}(x)\, dx \qquad (dx = dx^0\, d\mathbf{x}) \tag{2.3}$$

is given the name of *action.*

From the variational principle of stationary action

$$\delta A = 0,$$

together with the assumption that the variations of the field functions vanish at the surface of the four-volume over which the

[2] On the subject of the physical meaning of the requirement of reality (or more accurately of the hermiticity) of the Lagrangian, refer to the theory of the scattering matrix (§ 18).

[3] The requirement that $\mathscr{L}$ should depend only on U, and $\partial u_i/\partial x^k$ leads to the field equations being differential equations of the second order.

integral is taken, one obtains, using integration by parts, the Lagrange-Euler equations

$$\frac{\delta A}{\delta u_i(x)} = \frac{\partial \mathscr{L}}{\partial u_i(x)} - \sum_k \frac{\partial}{\partial x^k} \frac{\partial \mathscr{L}}{\partial(\partial u_i/\partial x^k)} = 0, \tag{2.4}$$

which are the equations determining the field functions $u_i(x)$, i.e., the field equations.

2.4. *Transformation Properties of the Field Functions. Tensors and Spinors*

Before proceeding to the construction of field invariants we shall examine the transformation properties of the field functions. In other words, we must establish the laws governing the transformation of the field functions describing the wave fields when the coordinates are subjected to transformations belonging to the inhomogeneous Lorentz group

$$\left.\begin{aligned} x \to x' &= Lx, \\ x'^k &= \sum_l g^{ll} \Omega^{kl} x^l + a^k. \end{aligned}\right\} \tag{2.5}$$

The field function $u(x)$ is understood to be either one function (a single-component field function) or several functions (a many-component field function) of the four coordinates x^k defined in every coordinate system. A transition from one coordinate system x to another x' which is related to x by the Lorentz transformation (2.5) corresponds to a linear homogeneous transformation of the components of the field function

$$u(x) \to u'(x') = \Lambda u(x), \tag{2.6}$$

with the matrix of the transformation Λ of the functions being completely determined by the matrix of the Lorentz transformation L. We emphasize that the above transformation (2.6) is not restricted to a replacement of the argument x by x', and describes a transformation from one coordinate system to another, rather than a displacement from one point of space to another.

Thus to each Lorentz transformation L there corresponds a linear transformation Λ_L, it being evident that to the identity element of the group L there corresponds the identity transformation $\Lambda = 1$, and that to a product of two elements of the Lorentz group there corresponds the product of two transformations

$$\Lambda_{L1\,L2} = \Lambda_{L1}\Lambda_{L2}.$$

The system of operators Λ possessing such properties is denoted in group theory by the term linear representation of the group. The operators Λ evidently may be represented in the form of matrices whose rank is determined by the number of components of the field function u. In the case when the number of components of u is finite, it is said that the group of transformations Λ forms a finite-dimensional representation of the Lorentz group, while in the opposite case we obtain an infinite-dimensional representation of this group. In view of the fact that all the principal physical fields are usually described by functions with a finite number of components, we shall limit ourselves in the following to a discussion of only the finite-dimensional representations of the Lorentz group.

Thus we may regard the transformations Λ as operators operating in the finite-dimensional space of the components of the field functions and represent them by square matrices of finite rank.

Sometimes it happens that the space of the components of the field functions within which the representation Λ operates breaks up into subspaces invariant with respect to all the transformations belonging to a given representation (i.e., into subspaces that transform into themselves under the operation Λ). Such a representation is said to be reducible. In the opposite case the representation is irreducible. If the process of separating out invariant subspaces in the space of a reducible representation is carried out to the end, i.e., if the whole space is divided into invariant subspaces which themselves do not contain invariant subspaces, then it is clear that the initial representation will be broken up into irreducible representations operating in the corresponding invariant subspaces. Thus the study of any reducible representation may be replaced by an equivalent study of the irreducible representations of the given group. Thus all possible types of wave functions and their laws of transformation (2.6) may be obtained by means of investigating the finite-dimensional representations of the Lorentz group.

The investigation referred to above forms a special division of the theory of representations of continuous groups and may be briefly summarized as follows. The finite-dimensional representations of the Lorentz group may be single-valued or double-valued. This is related to the fact that the correspondence $L \to \Lambda_L$ need not be necessarily single-valued, since, generally speaking, the field functions are not directly experimentally observable quantities (however, the observable quantities may always be expressed in the form of *bilinear combinations* of the field functions). However, the lack of single-valuedness of the operator Λ_L corresponding to the transformation L must always be such that the observable quantities transform in a completely single-valued manner under any arbitrary Lorentz transformation L. Moreover, it is necessary that the operators Λ_L should be continuous functions of the parameters of the transformation L, i.e., that an infinitesimal transformation of the coordinate system should correspond to an infinitesimal transformation of the field functions. The combined requirements stated above lead to the representations of the Lorentz group being divided into two categories. The first category is characterized by the *single-valuedness of the correspondence* $L \to \Lambda_L$ and contains the single-valued so-called *tensor* and *pseudotensor* [4] *representations.* The field functions which transform in accordance with the tensor representation are called tensors (pseudotensors) and in some cases may be observable themselves (the electromagnetic field). In the second case this correspondence turns out to be double-valued: $L \to \pm \Lambda_L$.

The transformation law for a (pseudo) tensor of the Nth rank

$$T^{i_1, i_2, \ldots, i_N}$$

under continuous transformations of coordinates (transformations

[4] The distinction between tensors and pseudotensors is related to the transformations of the reflection of space axes and is discussed more fully later.

involving the reflections of an odd number of axes will be discussed later separately) has the form

$$T'^{i_1, i_2, \ldots, i_N}(x') = \sum_{(j)} \frac{\partial x'^{i_1}}{\partial x^{j_1}} \cdots \frac{\partial x'^{i_N}}{\partial x^{j_N}} T^{j_1, \ldots, j_N}(x) \qquad (2.7)$$

or using the notation of (2.5)

$$T'^{i_1, \ldots, i_N}(x') = \sum_{(j)} g^{j_1 j_1} \ldots g^{j_N j_N} \Omega^{i_1 j_1} \ldots \Omega^{i_N j_N} T^{j_1, \ldots, j_N}(x).$$

The double-valued representations are referred to as spinor representations, and the corresponding quantities are called *spinors.* The transformation law for spinor quantities has a more complex structure and is given for the simplest spinors in § 6. We merely note that the transformation law for tensor quantities which follows from (2.7)

$$u(x) \rightarrow u'(x') = u(x)$$

in the case of the transformation of translation

$$x'^k = x^k + a^k$$

also holds for spinors.

We shall now give the simplest tensor representations and the quantities which correspond to them. The tensor of zero rank which under any continuous transformation transforms in accordance with the law

$$u'(x') = u(x), \qquad (2.8)$$

is an invariant and is called a *scalar* (pseudoscalar).

The tensor of the first rank which under a rotation of coordinates transforms in accordance with the law

$$u'^k(x') = \sum_m g^{mm} \Omega^{km} u^m(x), \qquad (2.9)$$

is called a *contravariant vector* (pseudovector). The covariant vector associated with it

$$u_k(x) = \sum_m g^{km} u^m(x)$$

transforms in accordance with the law

$$u'^k(x') = g^{kk} \sum_m \Omega^{km} u_m(x). \tag{2.10}$$

Corresponding formulas may be written down without any difficulty for covariant and contravariant tensors of second and higher ranks.

As we have pointed out already, relations of the type (2.7)–(2.10) establish the transformation laws of tensor quantities only for transformations of a continuous type. The laws governing their transformation under a reflection of an odd number of space axes are not determined by these expressions and must be formulated separately. Because the consecutive twofold application of such a reflection must correspond to the identity operator as a result of the single-valuedness of the tensor representation, the transformation laws in question may have only the forms

$$u'(x') = u(x) \tag{2.11}$$

or

$$u'(x') = -u(x). \tag{2.12}$$

Those quantities which change sign on reflection, i.e., which transform according to (2.12) in contrast to quantities transforming in accordance with (2.11), are called *pseudoquantities* (pseudoscalar, pseudovector, pseudotensor, etc.).

The distinction between the transformation laws (2.11) and (2.12) seems at first glance to have a somewhat formal character. However, as we shall see later (§ 8), the *concept of parity* defined by these relations plays an essential role in determining the possible forms of interaction between various fields.

2.5. *Noether's Theorem*

For the construction of field invariants, we shall use Noether's theorem. The theorem states that to every continuous transformation of coordinates which makes the variation of the action equal to zero, and for which the transformation law of the field functions is also given, there corresponds a definite invariant, i.e., a combination of the field functions and of their derivatives which remains conserved.

To prove Noether's theorem we shall consider the infinitesimal transformation of coordinates

$$x^k \to x'^k = x^k + \delta x^k, \quad \delta x^k = \sum_{1 \leqq j \leqq s} X_j^k \delta\omega^j \tag{2.13}$$

with s infinitesimal parameters

$$\delta\omega_i \quad (i = 1, 2, \ldots, s),$$

which, for example, in the case of a transformation from the inhomogeneous Lorentz group include the infinitesimal translations δa^k and the infinitesimal rotations $\delta\omega^{ik}$. The transformation law of the wave functions (2.6) in the case of the transformation (2.13) may be written in the form

$$u_i(x) \to u_i'(x') = u_i(x) + \delta u_i(x), \quad \delta u_i(x) = \sum_{1 \leqq j \leqq s} \Psi_{ij}(x)\delta\omega^j. \tag{2.14}$$

In (2.13) and (2.14) the quantities X_j^k and Ψ_{ij} are the transformation matrices, and $\delta u_i(x)$ is the variation in the field function due both to the change in the form of the function and to the change in its argument. The variation in the form of the function $\bar{\delta} u_i$ is therefore equal to

$$\bar{\delta} u_i \equiv u_i'(x) - u_i(x) = \sum_j \left(\Psi_{ij} - \sum_k \frac{\partial u_i(x)}{\partial x^k} X_j^k\right) \delta\omega^j. \tag{2.15}$$

We now find the variation of the action

$$\delta A = \delta \int \mathscr{L}(x) dx.$$

It is made up of the sum of the variation of the Lagrangian $\mathscr{L}(x)$ and of the variation in the range of integration. Similarly to the manner in which, in the one-dimensional case, we may symbolically represent the variation in the limits $\delta b - \delta a$ of the integral $\int_a^b dt$ in the form

$$\int_a^b \delta(dt) = \int_a^b dt \, \frac{\partial \delta(t)}{\partial t},$$

we may write in the four dimensional case under discussion

$$\delta A = \int \delta\mathscr{L}(x) dx + \int \mathscr{L}(x) \delta(dx),$$

where the symbol $\delta(dx)$ denotes the variation in the region of integration

$$\delta(dx) = \sum_l \frac{dx}{dx^l}\,\delta(dx^l) = dx \sum_l \frac{\partial \delta x^l}{\partial x^l}.$$

The second term in the expression for δA may, of course, also be written in the form of a surface integral over the boundary of the region of integration. By varying the Lagrangian we obtain

$$\delta \mathscr{L} = \mathscr{L}'(x') - \mathscr{L}(x) = \bar{\delta}\mathscr{L} + \sum_n \frac{\partial \mathscr{L}}{\partial x^n}\,\delta x^n,$$

with the variation in the form of the Lagrangian having the form

$$\bar{\delta}\mathscr{L} = \sum_i \frac{\partial \mathscr{L}}{\partial u_i}\,\delta u_i + \sum_{i,k} \frac{\partial \mathscr{L}}{\partial(\partial u_i/\partial x^k)}\,\bar{\delta}\left(\frac{\partial u_i}{\partial x^k}\right).$$

Using equations (2.4) and the fact that the operations δ and $\partial/\partial x$ commute we find from this

$$\bar{\delta}\mathscr{L} = \sum_{i,k} \frac{\partial}{\partial x^k}\left(\frac{\partial \mathscr{L}}{\partial(\partial u_i/\partial x^k)}\right)\bar{\delta} u_i + \sum_{i,k} \frac{\partial \mathscr{L}}{\partial(\partial u_i/\partial x^k)}\,\frac{\partial}{\partial x^k}(\bar{\delta} u_i)$$

$$= \sum_{i,k} \frac{\partial}{\partial x^k}\left(\frac{\partial \mathscr{L}}{\partial(\partial u_i/\partial x^k)}\,\bar{\delta} u_i\right).$$

Collecting terms we obtain the following expressions for the variation of the action

$$\left.\begin{aligned}
\delta A &= \int dx \left(\delta \mathscr{L} + \mathscr{L} \sum_n \frac{\partial \delta x^n}{\partial x^n}\right) \\
&= \int dx \sum_k \frac{\partial}{\partial x^k}\left\{\sum_i \frac{\partial \mathscr{L}}{\partial(\partial u_i/\partial x^k)}\,\bar{\delta} u_i + \mathscr{L}\delta x^k\right\} = -\int dx \sum_{k,j} \frac{\partial \theta_j^k}{\partial x^k}\,\delta\omega^j, \\
&\text{where} \\
\theta_i^k &= \sum_j \frac{\partial \mathscr{L}}{\partial(\partial u_j/\partial x^k)}\left(\sum_n \frac{\partial u_j}{\partial x^n} X_i^n - \Psi_{ji}\right) - \mathscr{L} X_i^k.
\end{aligned}\right\} \quad (2.16)$$

From the requirement that the variation of the action must vanish we obtain, after setting equal to zero the functional derivatives of the action with respect to the parameters $\delta\omega^j$:

$$\frac{\delta A}{\delta \omega^i} = -\sum_k \frac{\partial \theta_i^k}{\partial x^k} = 0. \qquad (2.17)$$

From equations (2.17) one may obtain by means of Gauss'

theorem the laws of conservation of the corresponding surface integrals. Integrating (2.17) over a volume of infinite extent in the spacelike directions and limited in the timelike directions by spacelike three-dimensional surfaces σ_1 and σ_2, we shall obtain, after assuming that at the boundaries of the spacelike volume the field is practically equal to zero:

$$\sum_k \int_{\sigma_1} d\sigma_k \theta_i^k - \sum_k \int_{\sigma_2} d\sigma_k \theta_i^k = 0.$$

Here $d\sigma_k$ is the projection of an element of the surface σ on the three-plane perpendicular to the x^k axis. The equation which we have obtained shows that the surface integrals

$$C_i(\sigma) = \sum_k \int_\sigma d\sigma_k \theta_i^k \tag{2.18}$$

do not actually depend on the surface σ. In the particular case when the surfaces σ represent the three-planes $x^0 = t = \text{const}$, the integration in (2.18) takes place over a three-dimensional configuration space and the integrals

$$C_i(x^0) = \int d\mathbf{x}\, \theta_i^0 \tag{2.19}$$

do not depend on the time.

It has thus been shown that to each continuous s-parametric transformation of coordinates (2.13) and of the field function there corresponds a certain invariant (2.19) $C_i (i = 1, 2, \ldots, s)$ which is independent of the time.

The quantity θ_i^k is not unique. To it we may add an expression of the form

$$\sum_m \frac{\partial}{\partial x^m} f_i^{mk}$$

subject to the condition that

$$f_i^{mk} = - f_i^{km}.$$

This property is sometimes used for the symmetrization of θ. The degree of arbitrariness indicated above, however, does not affect the value of the integrals (2.18) and (2.19) which are conserved.

We now proceed to consider concrete examples of the quantity θ and of the conservation laws (2.19) connected with it.

2.6. *The Energy-Momentum Vector*

In the case of infinitesimal space-time translations

$$x'^k = x^k + \delta x^k,$$

by choosing for the parameters of the transformation $\delta\omega^i$ the quantities δx^k and by taking into account the law of transformation (2.8) we find

$$X_l^k = \delta_l^k, \qquad \Psi_{il} = 0 \quad (l = 0,\ 1,\ 2,\ 3),$$

and θ becomes the second rank tensor

$$T_l^k = \sum_i \frac{\partial \mathscr{L}}{\partial(\partial u_i/\partial x^k)} \frac{\partial u_i}{\partial x^l} - \mathscr{L}\delta_l^k \quad (k,\ l = 0,\ 1,\ 2,\ 3).$$

In the fully contravariant form this tensor is given by

$$T^{kl} = g^{ll} \sum_i \frac{\partial \mathscr{L}}{\partial(\partial u_i/\partial x^k)} \frac{\partial u_i}{\partial x^l} - \mathscr{L} g^{kl}. \tag{2.20}$$

Integrals of the type (2.19) involving T^{kl} represent a four-vector constant in time

$$P^l = \int T^{0l}\, d\mathbf{x}. \tag{2.21}$$

The zero component of this vector P^0 in classical mechanics represents the Hamiltonian function, i.e., the energy. It therefore follows from considerations of covariance that the four-vector (2.21) represents energy momentum, and the tensor (2.20) is the energy-momentum tensor.

We note here that we shall be interested principally in the integrated dynamic quantities similar to the energy momentum four-vector P^l. The structure of the tensor T^{kl}, which in our presentation is not even unique, becomes of interest in itself only in a consistent theory which takes into account gravitational effects. However, it is well known that such a unified theory does not exist at present, and therefore we shall not touch upon such questions here.

2.7. *The Angular Momentum Tensor and the Spin Tensor*

In the case of the infinitesimal four-rotations

$$x'^n = x^n + \sum_{m \neq n} g^{mm} x^m \delta\omega^{nm}$$

in virtue of the antisymmetry of the quantities

$$\delta\omega^{nm} = -\delta\omega^{mn}$$

we may take for the parameters of the transformation the six linearly independent quantities

$$\delta\omega^{nm}, \qquad n < m.$$

Here the indices (n, m) denote the plane in which the rotation with the parameter ω^{nm} takes place. We see that in formula (2.13) the lower index j is replaced by two indices

$$j \to (n, m),$$

and we find, taking the antisymmetry of ω^{nm} into account:

$$\delta x^k = \sum_j X^k_j \delta\omega^j = \sum_{n>m} X^k_{(nm)} \delta\omega^{(nm)} = \sum_l g^{ll} x^l \delta\omega^{kl} = \sum_{m,l} g^{ll} x^l \delta\omega^{ml} \delta^k_m$$
$$= \sum_{m<l} g^{ll} x^l \delta\omega^{ml} \delta^k_m + \sum_{m>l} g^{ll} x^l \delta\omega^{ml} \delta^k_m = \sum_{m<l} \delta\omega^{ml} (g^{ll} x^l \delta^k_m - g^{mm} x^m \delta^k_l),$$

from which it follows that

$$X^k_{(nm)} = g^{mm} x^m \delta^k_n - g^{nn} x^n \delta^k_m \qquad (n \leqq m). \tag{2.22}$$

We represent the total variation of the field function in the form

$$u'_i(x') = u_i(x) + \delta u_i, \qquad \delta u_i = \sum_{j,k<l} A^j_{i(kl)} (u_j(x) \delta\omega^{kl}.$$

For a scalar field

$$A^j_{i(kl)} = 0, \tag{2.23}$$

for a covariant vector field

$$A^j_{i(kl)} = g_{ik} \delta^j_l - g_{il} \delta^j_k, \qquad k \leqq l. \tag{2.24}$$

Substituting the values of $X^k_{(nm)}$ from (2.22) and

$$\Psi_{i(nm)} = \sum_j A^j_{i(nm)} u_j(x) = g_{in} u_m(x) - g_{im} u_n(x)$$

into (2.16) we obtain the angular momentum tensor

$$M^k_{(lm)} = \sum_i \frac{\partial \mathscr{L}}{\partial(\partial u_i/\partial x^k)} \left\{\frac{\partial u_i}{\partial x^l} g^{mm} x^m - \frac{\partial u_i}{\partial x^m} g^{ll} x^l\right\} + \mathscr{L}(g^{ll} x^l \delta^k_m$$

$$-g^{mm}x^m\delta^k_l) - \sum_{i,i} \frac{\partial \mathscr{L}}{\partial(\partial u_i/\partial x^k)} A^j_{i(lm)} u_j(x) = (g^{mm}x^m T^k_l - g^{ll}x^l T^k_m)$$

$$- \sum_{i,j} \frac{\partial \mathscr{L}}{\partial(\partial u_i/\partial x^k)} A^j_{i(lm)} u_j(x). \tag{2.25}$$

From formula (2.25) we can clearly see the connection between the symmetry properties of the energy-momentum tensor T^k_l and the structure of the angular-momentum tensor $M^k_{(l,m)}$. In the case of a scalar field, the second term in (2.25) is absent and the relation between M and T takes on a form similar to that which occurs in the mechanics of a particle. Therefore the term

$$M_0^{k,lm} = x^m T^{kl} - x^l T^{km} \tag{2.26}$$

should be identified with the intrinsic orbital angular momentum of the wave field. In the case of a single-component field this angular momentum is conserved

$$\sum_k \frac{\partial M_0^{k,lm}}{\partial x^k} = 0.$$

Substituting (2.26) into this expression, we find that the energy-momentum tensor for the scalar field turns out to be symmetric with respect to its indices:

$$T^{kl} = T^{lk}.$$

In the case of a multicomponent (vector, spinor) field the expression for M^k_{lm} has the form (2.25). The second term of this expression

$$S^k_{lm} \equiv - \sum_{i,j} \frac{\partial \mathscr{L}}{\partial(\partial u_i/\partial x^k)} u_j(x) A^j_{i,lm} \tag{2.27}$$

characterizes the polarization properties of the field and, as follows from quantum theory (see Chapter II), corresponds to the spin angular momentum of particles described by the quantized field.

For the spatial density of the orbital and the spin angular momenta we obtain:

$$M_0^{0,lm} = x^m T^{0l} - x^l T^{0m},$$

$$S_{lm}^0 = -\sum_{i,j} \frac{\partial \mathscr{L}}{\partial(\partial u_i/\partial x^0)} u_j(x) A^j_{i,lm}.$$

Integrating these expressions over the configuration space we obtain the tensors of the orbital and the spin angular momenta in the form

$$M_0^{lm} = \int M_0^{0,lm} d\mathbf{x} = \int d\mathbf{x} (x^m T^{0l} - x^l T^{0m}), \tag{2.28}$$

$$S^{lm} = g^{ll} g^{mm} \int S_{lm}^0 d\mathbf{x} = -g^{ll} g^{mm} \int d\mathbf{x} \sum_{i,j} \frac{\partial \mathscr{L}}{\partial(\partial u_i/\partial x^0)} u_j(x) A^j_{i,lm}. \tag{2.29}$$

2.8. *The Charge and the Current Vector*

Finally, in the case of complex fields which, as we shall see later, correspond in the simplest cases to charged particles the Lagrangian turns out to be invariant with respect to a so-called gauge transformation of the first kind which acts only on the field functions and does not operate on the coordinates.

The point is that in virtue of the property of reality (hermiticity) the Lagrangian, as well as the dynamic variables may depend on the complex fields only through quadratic forms of the type u^*u where u and u^* are complex conjugate functions or their derivatives. From this it immediately follows that the complex wave functions u may be multiplied by an arbitrary unitary phase factor of the form $\exp(i\alpha)$ which does not lead to any change in the quadratic form u^*u and consequently does not lead to any observable effects.

Treating u and u^* as linearly independent functions we may write the gauge transformation of the first kind in the form

$$u_j \to e^{i\alpha} u_j, \qquad u_j^* \to e^{-i\alpha} u_j^*. \tag{2.30}$$

Assuming α to be an infinitesimal quantity we obtain from this:

$$u_j \to u_j + i\alpha u_j, \qquad u_j^* \to u_j^* - i\alpha u_j;$$

from which it follows that

$$\Psi_j = i u_j \qquad \text{for all} \quad u_j,$$
$$\Psi_j = -i u_j^* \qquad \text{for all} \quad u_j^*,$$

and also that $X_l^k = 0$. Substituting these expressions into (2.16) we arrive at an expression that has the tensor dimensionality of a vector

$$J^k(x) = i \sum_j \left(\frac{\partial \mathscr{L}}{\partial(\partial u_j^*/\partial x^k)} u_j^*(x) - \frac{\partial \mathscr{L}}{\partial(\partial u_i/\partial x^k)} u_j(x) \right). \quad (2.31)$$

This four-vector satisfies the equation of continuity

$$\sum_k \frac{\partial J^k}{\partial x^k} = - \frac{\delta A}{\delta \alpha} = 0 \quad (2.32)$$

and therefore is usually identified with the four-vector of the current, while the integral over all space of its zero component, which in accordance with (2.19) is independent of the time,

$$Q = \int J^0(x) d\mathbf{x} = i \int d\mathbf{x} \sum_j \left(\frac{\partial \mathscr{L}}{\partial(\partial u_j^*/\partial x^0)} u_j^*(x) - \frac{\partial \mathscr{L}}{\partial(\partial u_j/\partial x^0)} u_j(x) \right) = \text{const} \quad (2.33)$$

is identified with the charge of the field. [5]

We now proceed to the study of various specific wave fields to which we shall apply the general formalism developed above. In Chapter I we shall consider the following most important free wave fields: (a) the scalar (pseudoscalar) field which corresponds to the pseudoscalar π-mesons; (b) the vector field; (c) the electromagnetic field; and (d) the simplest spinor field which corresponds to electrons and positrons, nucleons, μ-mesons, and apparently also to hyperons.

We emphasize that it would be incorrect to state that the free fields "describe" the corresponding particles, since a complete description of the elementary particles with all their physical characteristics (for example, their magnetic moments) may be obtained only from a theory of interacting fields. Therefore it is more correct to say that the individual free fields "correspond" to the different particles and give a basis for the description of these particles within the framework of the theory of interacting fields.

[5] We emphasize that the charge Q need not necessarily be identified with the electric charge. Thus, formulas of the type (2.33) may, for example, describe nucleonic charge (for details on this point see § 8).

§ 3. The Scalar Field

As was already noted in § 2, it is usually assumed that the Lagrangian depends only on the field functions and on their partial derivatives of order not higher than the first. This requirement leads to the corresponding field equations being differential equations of order not higher than the second.

An important property of the Lagrangians of free fields follows from the requirements of linearity and homogeneity of the free field equations. It may be easily shown that only Lagrangians quadratic in the field functions and their derivatives lead to such equations.

These conditions together with considerations of relativistic invariance and of the transformation properties of the field functions actually determine the Lagrangian except for the coefficients.

In beginning a discussion of the simplest of all wave fields — the scalar field — we shall consider two variants: 1. the real scalar field which describes neutral scalar mesons, and 2. the complex scalar field which describes charged scalar mesons.

3.1. *Lagrangian Formalism for a Real Scalar Field*

The simplest wave field is described by a single-component real wave function $\varphi(x)$ which transforms under Lorentz transformations like a scalar or a pseudoscalar. As was noted in the preceding section, the difference between a scalar and a pseudoscalar lies in their transformation properties under an odd number of reflections of the coordinate axes, and this becomes apparent only in the form of the possible laws of interaction (more precisely in the form of the interaction Lagrangian) with other fields. Therefore, in the theory of free fields we shall not make a distinction between scalars and pseudoscalars, vectors and pseudovectors, etc., and shall in fact discuss them simultaneously.

Let us consider the real scalar field which describes neutral spinless particles (neutral (pseudo) scalar mesons with spin zero).

The Lagrangian of this field

$$\mathscr{L} = \tfrac{1}{2} \sum_k g^{kk} \left(\frac{\partial \varphi}{\partial x^k}\right)^2 - \frac{m^2}{2} \varphi^2(x) \tag{3.1}$$

is determined by the conditions formulated above up to its coefficients which are chosen in such a way that the formulas (2.4) lead to the Klein-Gordon equation

$$-\sum_k g^{kk}\frac{\partial^2\varphi(x)}{\partial x^k\partial x^k}-m^2\varphi=(\square-m^2)\varphi(x)=0, \qquad (3.2)$$

which is obviously the only invariant equation of the second order. Here $\square$ is the d'Alembertian operator

$$\square\equiv-\sum_k g^{kk}\frac{\partial^2}{\partial x^k\partial x^k}=\frac{\partial^2}{\partial x^1\partial x^1}+\frac{\partial^2}{\partial x^2\partial x^2}+\frac{\partial^2}{\partial x^3\partial x^3}-\frac{\partial_2}{\partial x^0\partial x^0}. \qquad (3.3)$$

Substituting the Lagrangian (3.1) into (2.19) we obtain the energy-momentum tensor of the real scalar field in the form

$$T^{kl}=g^{kk}g^{ll}\frac{\partial\varphi}{\partial x^k}\frac{\partial\varphi}{\partial x^l}-g^{kl}\mathscr{L}. \qquad (3.4)$$

From this we find the energy density

$$T^{00}=\tfrac{1}{2}\sum_k\left(\frac{\partial\varphi}{\partial x^k}\right)^2+\frac{m^2}{2}\varphi^2 \qquad (3.5)$$

and the density of the momentum vector

$$T^{0\alpha}=-\frac{\partial\varphi}{\partial x^0}\frac{\partial\varphi}{\partial x^\alpha} \qquad (\alpha=1,\ 2,\ 3). \qquad (3.6)$$

With the aid of (2.25) we obtain the expression for the angular-momentum tensor

$$M^k_{lm}=g^{kk}\frac{\partial\varphi}{\partial x^k}\left(g^{mm}x^m\frac{\partial\varphi}{\partial x^l}-g^{ll}x^l\frac{\partial\varphi}{\partial x^m}\right)+\mathscr{L}(g^{ll}x^l\delta^k_m-g^{mm}x^m\delta^k_l). \quad (3.7)$$

Setting $k=0$ in this expression we obtain the spatial density of the angular-momentum tensor conserved in time:

$$M^0_{lm}=\frac{\partial\varphi}{\partial x^0}\left(g^{mm}x^m\frac{\partial\varphi}{\partial x^l}-g^{ll}x^l\frac{\partial\varphi}{\partial x^m}\right)+\mathscr{L}(g^{ll}x^l\delta^0_m-g^{mm}x^m\delta^0_l). \quad (3.8)$$

The spin angular momentum of a scalar field is equal to zero since it has only a single component. Since the field is real the current four-vector is also equal to zero.

3.2. *Momentum Representation and Positive- and Negative-Frequency Components*

The expressions for the dynamic variables assume a more suggestive form in the momentum representation. For this purpose we write the field function $\varphi(x)$ in the form of a four-dimensional Fourier integral

$$\varphi(x) = \frac{1}{(2\pi)^{3/2}} \int dk\, e^{ikx} \tilde{\varphi}(k), \tag{3.9}$$

where

$$dk = dk^0\, d\mathbf{k} = dk^0\, dk^1\, dk^2\, dk^3,$$
$$kx = \sum_n g^{nn} k^n x^n = k^0 x^0 - \mathbf{k}\mathbf{x},$$

while the factor 2π has been taken to the power $-\frac{3}{2}$ for the sake of convenience in a later transition to a three-dimensional integral.

The condition that $\varphi(x)$ should be real leads to the following property of complex conjugation for $\tilde{\varphi}$

$$\tilde{\varphi}^*(k) = \tilde{\varphi}(-k). \tag{3.10}$$

Substituting the expansion (3.9) into the field equation (3.2) we find that the function $\tilde{\varphi}$ satisfies the equation

$$(k^2 - m^2)\tilde{\varphi}(x) = 0$$

and may therefore be represented in the form

$$\tilde{\varphi}(k) = \delta(k^2 - m^2)\varphi(k). \tag{3.11}$$

The factor $\delta(k^2 - m^2)$ establishes the relation between the "energy" variable k^0, the "momentum" variable $\mathbf{k}$ and the term m^2 which therefore represents the square of the mass:

$$k^2 - m^2 = (k^0)^2 - \mathbf{k}^2 - m^2 = 0.$$

If (3.11) is taken into account, the expansion (3.9) takes on the form

$$\varphi(x) = \frac{1}{(2\pi)^{3/2}} \int dk \delta(k^2 - m^2) e^{ikx} \varphi(k). \tag{3.12}$$

Because of the presence under the integral sign of the δ-function the integration is in fact carried out not over the whole four-dimensional space but only over the two three-dimensional hyperboloids

$$k^0 = \pm \sqrt{\mathbf{k}^2 + m^2}, \tag{3.13}$$

one of which lies entirely within the upper light cone and the other entirely within the lower one. Noting further that the two hyperboloids are separately Lorentz-invariant we arrive at the following Lorentz-invariant decomposition of the integral (3.12) into two terms:

$$\varphi(x) = \varphi^{(+)}(x) + \varphi^{(-)}(x), \tag{3.14}$$

$$\varphi^{(+)}(x) = \frac{1}{(2\pi)^{3/2}} \int dk e^{ikx} \delta(k^2 - m^2) \varphi^{(+)}(k), \tag{3.15}$$

$$\varphi^{(-)}(x) = \frac{1}{(2\pi)^{3/2}} \int dk e^{-ikx} \delta(k^2 - m^2) \varphi^{(-)}(k). \tag{3.16}$$

Here

$$\varphi^{(+)}(k) = \theta(k^0) \varphi(k) \text{ and } \varphi^{(-)}(k) = \theta(k^0) \varphi(-k), \tag{3.17}$$

while θ is the well-known step function

$$\theta(x) = \begin{cases} 1, & x > 0, \\ 0, & x < 0. \end{cases} \tag{3.18}$$

The functions $\varphi^{(+)}(x)$ and $\varphi^{(-)}(x)$ will in the future be referred to, in accordance with the indices introduced above, as the positive-frequency and negative-frequency parts of the function $\varphi(x)$. As may be easily seen the sign of the frequency is determined by the sign of the product kx (or more precisely by the sign of the "frequency" term $k^0x^0 = + x^0 (\mathbf{k}^2 + m^2)^{1/2}$) in the exponent of the integrand. In this connection we note that in the contemporary literature the converse notation is often used, i.e., the sign of the frequency being taken the same as that of the form

$$k_\mu x_\mu = \mathbf{kx} + k_4 x_4 = - kx.$$

We have abandoned such a notation because (as will be seen in Chapter II) expressions of the type (3.15) correspond in quantum theory to the creation of the field particles, while expressions of the type (3.16) correspond to their annihilation. Therefore in the system of notation adopted by us the signs (+) and (—) not only correspond to the sign of the frequency, but also symbolize the physical meaning of the corresponding quantum operators with $(+)$ referring to creation and $(-)$ to annihilation.[6]

As will be shown later, the above decomposition also turns out to be very convenient for writing down the dynamic variables in the momentum representation, since they may be expressed as quadratic forms in $\varphi^{(+)}(k)$ and $\varphi^{(-)}(k)$.

We also note that as a result of $\varphi(x)$ being real the rules of complex conjugation for $\varphi^{(+)}(k)$ and $\varphi^{(-)}(k)$ take on the form

$$(\varphi^{(+)}(k))^* = \varphi^{(-)}(k), \quad (\varphi^{(-)}(k))^* = \varphi^{(+)}(k). \tag{3.19}$$

Carrying out in expressions (3.12) and (3.13) the integration over k^0 we obtain:

$$\left.\begin{aligned} \varphi^{(+)}(x) &= \frac{1}{(2\pi)^{3/2}} \int \frac{d\mathbf{k}}{2k^0} e^{ikx} \varphi^{(+)}(k), \\ \varphi^{(-)}(x) &= \frac{1}{(2\pi)^{3/2}} \int \frac{d\mathbf{k}}{2k^0} e^{-ikx} \varphi^{(-)}(k). \end{aligned}\right\} \quad (k^0 = +\sqrt{\mathbf{k}^2 + m^2}). \tag{3.20}$$

Here it is convenient to renormalize the three-dimensional Fourier amplitudes. For this we introduce the notation

$$\varphi^{(+)}(\mathbf{k}) = \frac{\varphi^{(+)}(k)}{\sqrt{2k^0}} \tag{3.21}$$

$$\varphi^{(-)}(\mathbf{k}) = \frac{\varphi^{(-)}(k)}{\sqrt{2k^0}} \tag{3.22}$$

$$(k^0 = +\sqrt{\mathbf{k}^2 + m^2}),$$

and then expressions (3.20) will take on the form

$$\varphi^{(+)}(x) = \frac{1}{(2\pi)^{3/2}} \int \frac{d\mathbf{k}}{\sqrt{2k^0}} e^{ikx} \varphi^{(+)}(\mathbf{k}), \tag{3.23}$$

$$\varphi^{(-)}(x) = \frac{1}{(2\pi)^{3/2}} \int \frac{d\mathbf{k}}{\sqrt{2k^0}} e^{-ikx} \varphi^{(-)}(\mathbf{k}). \tag{3.24}$$

The choice of the normalizing constant in (3.21) and (3.22)

[6] The same system of notation has also been adopted in the last edition of Heitler's book (60).

will become clear from the expressions for the dynamic variables (see (3.26) below).

Substituting (3.11), (3.23), and (3.24) into the expression (3.4) for the energy density and integrating over the configuration space we obtain

$$P^0 = \int T^{00}\, d\mathbf{x} = \tfrac{1}{2}\int \left[\sum_k \left(\frac{\partial\varphi}{\partial x^k}\right)^2 + m^2\varphi^2\right] d\mathbf{x}$$

$$= \tfrac{1}{2}\int d\mathbf{x}\left\{\sum_k \left(\frac{\partial\varphi^{(+)}}{\partial x^k}\frac{\partial\varphi^{(+)}}{\partial x^k} + 2\frac{\partial\varphi^{(+)}}{\partial x^k}\frac{\partial\varphi^{(-)}}{\partial x^k} + \frac{\partial\varphi^{(-)}}{\partial x^k}\frac{\partial\varphi^{(-)}}{\partial x^k}\right)\right.$$

$$\left. + m^2(\varphi^{(+)}(x)\,\varphi^{(+)}(x) + 2\varphi^{(+)}(x)\,\varphi^{(-)}(x) + \varphi^{(-)}(x)\,\varphi^{(-)}(x))\right\}$$

$$= \int d\mathbf{x}\left\{\sum_k \frac{\partial\varphi^{(+)}}{\partial x^k}\frac{\partial\varphi^{(-)}}{\partial x^k} + m^2\varphi^{(+)}(x)\,\varphi^{(-)}(x)\right\}. \tag{3.25}$$

Since, for example,

$$\int d\mathbf{x}\left\{\sum_n \frac{\partial\varphi^{(+)}}{\partial x^n}\frac{\partial\varphi^{(+)}}{\partial x^n} + m^2\varphi^{(+)}(x)\,\varphi^{(+)}(x)\right\}$$

$$= \int \frac{d\mathbf{k}\, d\mathbf{k}'}{2\sqrt{k^0 k'^0}}\, \varphi^{(+)}(\mathbf{k})\varphi^{(+)}(\mathbf{k}')e^{i(k^0+k'^0)x^0}$$

$$\cdot\, (m^2 - \sum_n k^n k'^n)\,\frac{1}{(2\pi)^3}\int d\mathbf{x}e^{-i(\mathbf{k}+\mathbf{k}')\mathbf{x}}$$

$$= \int \frac{d\mathbf{k}}{2k^0}\, \varphi^{(+)}(\mathbf{k})\,\varphi^{(+)}(-\,\mathbf{k})\, e^{2ik^0x^0}\,(m^2 - k^0k^0 + \mathbf{k}\mathbf{k})$$

and, since

$$m^2 - k^0k^0 + \mathbf{k}\mathbf{k} = m^2 - k^2 = 0,$$

we obtain:

$$\int d\mathbf{x}\left\{\sum_n \frac{\partial\varphi^{(+)}}{\partial x^n}\frac{\partial\varphi^{(+)}}{\partial x^n} + m^2\varphi^{(+)}(x)\,\varphi^{(+)}(x)\right\} = 0.$$

An analogous relation holds for the quadratic form in $\varphi^{(-)}$. A calculation quite similar to the one just completed leads to:

$$P^0 = \int d\mathbf{k}\cdot k^0\varphi^{(+)}(\mathbf{k})\varphi^{(-)}(\mathbf{k}) \qquad (k^0 = +\sqrt{\mathbf{k}^2 + m^2}).$$

The corresponding expression for the momentum vector has the form

$$P^{\alpha} = \int T^{0\alpha}\, d\mathbf{x} = \int d\mathbf{k}\cdot k^{\alpha}\varphi^{(+)}(\mathbf{k})\,\varphi^{(-)}(\mathbf{k}) \qquad (\alpha = 1,\ 2,\ 3).$$

Combining these expressions, we write them in the form which would also hold in the case that throughout the whole calculation the functions $\varphi^{(+)}$ and $\varphi^{(-)}$ were treated as noncommuting:

$$P^{n} = \tfrac{1}{2}\int d\mathbf{k}\cdot \mathbf{k}^{n}(\varphi^{(+)}(\mathbf{k})\,\varphi^{(-)}(\mathbf{k}) + \varphi^{(-)}(\mathbf{k})\,\varphi^{(+)}(\mathbf{k})). \qquad (3.26)$$

Such a representation will turn out to be useful for the quantization of the scalar field.

We now see the point of choosing the particular normalization in (3.21) and (3.22). The amplitudes $\varphi^{+}(\mathbf{k})$ and $\varphi^{(-)}(\mathbf{k})$ have been so chosen that the products $\varphi^{(+)}(\mathbf{k})\varphi^{(-)}(\mathbf{k})$ may be interpreted as the average density of particles of momentum $\mathbf{k}$, energy k^0 and mass $m = \sqrt{(k^0)^2 - \mathbf{k}^2}$ having no charge or spin. An example of such uncharged spinless particles are the neutral pseudoscalar π^0-mesons.

With the aid of the four-dimensional amplitudes $\varphi^{(+)}(k)$ and $\varphi^{(-)}(k)$ the energy-momentum four-vector may be written in the manifestly covariant form

$$P^{n}=\tfrac{1}{2}\int dk\cdot k^{n}\theta(k^{0})\delta(k^{2}-m^{2})(\varphi^{(+)}(k)\varphi^{(-)}(k)+\varphi^{(-)}(k)\varphi^{(+)}(k)). \quad (3.27)$$

3.3. *The Discrete Momentum Representation*

Sometimes the *discrete momentum representation* is used which is convenient in a number of cases. In this case it assumed that the field is contained within a spatial cube of volume $V = L^3$, where L is the length of the cube edge. From the condition that φ should be periodic along each space coordinate with a period L we find that φ may be represented in the form of the sum

$$\varphi(x) = \frac{1}{L^{3/2}}\sum_{n_1, n_2, n_3}\frac{\varphi^{(+)}_{n_1, n_2, n_3}}{\sqrt{2k^0}}\exp\left[\frac{2\pi i}{L}(n_0x^0 - n_1x^1 - n_2x^2 - n_3x^3)\right]$$

$$+\frac{1}{L^{3/2}}\sum_{n_1, n_2, n_3}\frac{\varphi^{(-)}_{n_1, n_2, n_3}}{\sqrt{2k^0}}\exp\left[-\frac{2\pi i}{L}(n_0x^0 - n_1x^1 - n_2x^2 - n_3x^3)\right], \quad (3.28)$$

with n_1, n_2, and n_3 in this expression taking on all integral values from $-\infty$ to $+\infty$ and with

$$k^0 = \frac{2\pi}{L} n_0, \quad n_0 = \sqrt{n_1^2 + n_2^2 + n_3^2 + \frac{L^2 m^2}{4\pi^2}}\,.$$

In (3.28) the summation is carried out over momenta whose components are integral multiples of the quantity $2\pi/L$. By letting the dimensions L of the cube tend to infinity, it is evidently possible in the limit to go over to the continuous representation. For such a limiting process

$$\left(\frac{2\pi}{L}\right)^3 \to d\mathbf{k}, \tag{3.29}$$

and also

$$\left(\frac{L}{2\pi}\right)^{3/2} \varphi_n \to \varphi(\mathbf{k}). \tag{3.30}$$

Using these rules for the transition to the limit it is not difficult to show that the energy-momentum four-vector (3.26) takes on the following form in the discrete representation

$$P^m = \sum_{n_1, n_2, n_3} k^m \varphi^{(+)}_{n_1, n_2, n_3} \varphi^{(-)}_{n_1, n_2, n_3}\,. \tag{3.31}$$

Expression (3.31) permits one to treat the field confined within the volume L^3 as a system with an infinite number of degrees of freedom — a collection of an infinite number of particles, which from the point of view of the Hamiltonian formalism are usually treated by means of introducing canonical coordinates and momenta as field oscillators with energy

$$k^0 = \frac{2\pi}{L} \sqrt{n_1^2 + n_2^2 + n_3^2 + \frac{L^2 m^2}{4\pi^2}}$$

and momentum

$$\mathbf{k} = \frac{2\pi}{L} \mathbf{n} \qquad (\mathbf{n} = n_1, n_2, n_3).$$

The quadratic combination of amplitudes $\varphi^{(+)}_n \varphi^{(-)}_n$ plays in such a case the role of the average number of particles with given energy and momentum.

3.4. *The Complex Scalar Field*

The theory of the complex scalar field is constructed by analogy with the theory of the real scalar field. The difference consists of the fact that the complex scalar field is described by the complex function

$$\varphi(x) = \varphi_1(x) + i\varphi_2(x),$$

i.e., essentially by two independent real functions φ_1 and φ_2. However, the formalism becomes more convenient if instead of φ_1 and φ_2 their combinations φ and $\varphi^* = \varphi_1 - i\varphi_2$ are used.

We write down the Lagrangian of the complex field in a

form analogous to that of the Lagrangian of the real field

$$\mathscr{L} = \sum_n g^{nn} \frac{\partial \varphi^*}{\partial x^n} \frac{\partial \varphi}{\partial x^n} - m^2 \varphi^*(x)\varphi(x). \tag{3.32}$$

Taking the variations of the functions φ and φ^* to be independent we may obtain from this expression with the aid of the formulas of § 3: the field equations

$$(\Box - m^2)\varphi(x) = 0, \quad (\Box - m^2)\varphi^*(x) = 0;$$

the energy-momentum tensor

$$T^{kl} = g^{kk} g^{ll} \left(\frac{\partial \varphi^*}{\partial x^k} \frac{\partial \varphi}{\partial x^l} + \frac{\partial \varphi^*}{\partial x^l} \frac{\partial \varphi}{\partial x^k} \right) - g^{kl} \mathscr{L}; \tag{3.33}$$

the density of the energy-momentum four-vector

$$T^{00} = \sum_k \frac{\partial \varphi^*}{\partial x^k} \frac{\partial \varphi}{\partial x^k} + m^2 \varphi^* \varphi, \quad T^{0\alpha} = -\left(\frac{\partial \varphi^*}{\partial x^0} \frac{\partial \varphi}{\partial x^\alpha} + \frac{\partial \varphi^*}{\partial x^\alpha} \frac{\partial \varphi}{\partial x^0} \right) \tag{3.34}$$

and the current four-vector

$$J^k = i g^{kk} \left(\varphi^* \frac{\partial \varphi}{\partial x^k} - \frac{\partial \varphi^*}{\partial x^k} \varphi \right). \tag{3.35}$$

The spin angular momentum of the complex scalar field turns out to be equal to zero in analogy with the same situation for the real scalar field.

Carrying out the decomposition into positive- and negative-frequency parts and the transition to the momentum representation

$$\varphi^{(\pm)}(x) = \frac{1}{(2\pi)^{3/2}} \int dk \delta(k^2 - m^2)\, e^{\pm ikx} \varphi^{(\pm)}(k),$$

$$\varphi^{*(\pm)}(x) = \frac{1}{(2\pi)^{3/2}} \int dk \delta\,(k^2 - m^2)\, e^{\pm ikx} \varphi^{*(\pm)}(k),$$

we find after performing the integration with respect to the variable k^0:

$$\varphi^{(\pm)}(x) = \frac{1}{(2\pi)^{3/2}} \int \frac{d\mathbf{k}}{\sqrt{2k^0}}\, e^{\pm ikx} \varphi^{(\pm)}(\mathbf{k}), \tag{3.36}$$

$$\varphi^{*(\pm)}(x) = \frac{1}{(2\pi)^{3/2}} \int \frac{d\mathbf{k}}{\sqrt{2k^0}}\, e^{\pm ikx} \varphi^{*(\pm)}(\mathbf{k}), \tag{3.37}$$

where by analogy with the previously considered case of the real field we have introduced the three-dimensional amplitudes

$$\left.\begin{aligned} \varphi^{(\pm)}(\mathbf{k}) &= \frac{\varphi^{(\pm)}(k)}{\sqrt{2k^0}}, \\ \varphi^{*(\pm)}(\mathbf{k}) &= \frac{\varphi^{*(\pm)}(k)}{\sqrt{2k^0}}. \end{aligned}\right\} \quad (k^0 = \sqrt{\mathbf{k}^2 + m^2}).$$

The notation for the positive- and negative-frequency functions in the k-representation has been so introduced that, for example, $\varphi^{*(+)}(k)$ denotes not the function which is complex conjugate to $\varphi^{(+)}(k)$, but the positive-frequency part of $\varphi^*(k)$. Therefore the rules for complex conjugation in the momentum representation have the form

$$(\varphi^{(+)}(k))^* = \varphi^{*(-)}(k), \quad (\varphi^{(-)}(k))^* = \varphi^{*(+)}(k). \tag{3.38}$$

Substituting the expansions (3.36) and (3.37) into the expressions for the energy-momentum density (3.34) and for the charge (3.35) we find after integrating over the configuration space:

$$\left.\begin{aligned} P^l &= \int d\mathbf{k} \cdot k^l \{\varphi^{*(+)}(\mathbf{k})\, \varphi^{(-)}(\mathbf{k}) + \varphi^{*(-)}(\mathbf{k})\, \varphi^{(+)}(\mathbf{k})\} \\ &(l = 0,\ 1,\ 2,\ 3, \quad k^0 = \sqrt{\mathbf{k}^2 + m^2}), \end{aligned}\right\} \tag{3.39}$$

$$Q = \int d\mathbf{k} \{\varphi^{*(+)}(\mathbf{k})\, \varphi^{(-)}(\mathbf{k}) - \varphi^{*(-)}(\mathbf{k})\, \varphi^{(+)}(\mathbf{k})\}. \tag{3.40}$$

From these expressions for the energy-momentum four-vector and for the charge it follows that the product $\varphi^{*(-)}(\mathbf{k})\varphi^{(+)}(\mathbf{k})$ may be interpreted as the density of the average number of particles of mass m, energy k^0, momentum $\mathbf{k}$, and charge -1, while the product $\varphi^{*(+)}(\mathbf{k})\varphi^{(-)}(\mathbf{k})$ may be interpreted as the density of the average number of particles of energy k^0, momentum $\mathbf{k}$, and charge $+1$.

Corresponding to the above, after quantization (§ 10) $\varphi^{*(+)}(k)$ will describe the creation of a particle of mass m, momentum $\mathbf{k}$, and charge 1, while $\varphi^{(-)}$ will describe its annihilation. A similar correspondence also exists for $\varphi^{(+)}$ and $\varphi^{*(-)}$.

Thus, the complex scalar field describes positively and negatively charged spinless particles. Examples of such particles are pseudoscalar π^+- and π^--mesons.

§ 4. The Vector Field

4.1. *Lagrangian, Subsidiary Condition, and Invariants*

The function which describes the vector field consists of four components U_0, U_1, U_2, and U_3 which together form a covariant four-vector, i.e., which transforms under the Lorentz rotations

$$x'^k = x^k + \delta x^k, \quad \delta x^k = \sum_n g^{nn} x^n \omega^{kn}, \quad \omega^{kn} + \omega^{nk} = 0$$

in accordance with the formulas

$$U'_k(x') = U_k(x) + \delta U_k, \quad \delta U_k = g^{kk} \sum_n U_n(x) \omega^{nk}. \tag{4.1}$$

The simplest possibility of generalizing for a vector field the formalism developed in the preceding section, consists of choosing the Lagrangian of the vector field in the form (for simplicity we shall at first consider only the real vector field)

$$\mathscr{L} = -\tfrac{1}{2} \sum_{n,m} g^{nn} g^{mm} \frac{\partial U_n}{\partial x^m} \frac{\partial U_n}{\partial x^m} + \frac{m^2}{2} \sum_k g^{kk} U_k U_k, \tag{4.2}$$

i.e., in the form of a covariant sum of four "Lagrangians" each separately corresponding to the components U_0, U_1, U_2, and U_3. Such a Lagrangian obviously leads to Klein-Gordon equations for each of the components U_k and to dynamic variables which are natural generalizations of the corresponding expressions for the scalar field. However, it is easy to see that such a formulation leads also to negative terms in the expression for the energy which correspond to the U_0 component. The way out of this difficulty consists of imposing on the components U_k the invariant subsidiary condition [7]

[7] This condition is the only possible invariant condition linear in the field functions.

$$\sum_k g^{kk} \frac{\partial U_k}{\partial x^k} = 0. \tag{4.3}$$

This condition reduces the number of linearly independent components from four to three and, as will be shown later, guarantees that the energy of the vector field is positive definite. The three remaining components correspond to the three possible values of the component of the spin along a given axis which are respectively 1, 0, − 1, i.e., which describe particles with spin one. The imposition of the subsidiary condition (4.3) corresponds to the exclusion of a particle of spin zero which in this formulation leads to a negative energy.

Therefore, for the presentation of the theory of the vector field the Lagrangian is usually chosen (Wentzel (133), Pauli (91a)) in such a way that in addition to the field equations the automatic fulfilment of the subsidiary condition (4.3) is also guaranteed. We refer the reader to the literature cited for the detailed calculations and merely state here that such a program may be based on the following Lagrangian:

$$\mathscr{L} = -\tfrac{1}{4} \sum_{n,m} \left(\frac{\partial U_n}{\partial x^m} - \frac{\partial U_m}{\partial x^n}\right)^2 g^{nn} g^{mm} + \frac{m^2}{2} \sum_n g^{nn} U_n U_n, \tag{4.4}$$

which differs from (4.2) by the term

$$\tfrac{1}{2} \sum_{n,m} g^{nn} g^{mm} \frac{\partial U_n}{\partial x^m} \frac{\partial U_m}{\partial x^n}. \tag{4.5}$$

The arbitrariness in the choice of the Lagrangian is evidently related to the possibility of constructing several different invariants using first derivatives of the components of the vector.

A similar arbitrariness occurs in the choice of the Lagrangian for the electromagnetic field, which is also described by a vector potential. However, in the theory of the electromagnetic field, because the mass m is equal to zero it is not possible to construct a formalism in such a way as to guarantee that the subsidiary condition (4.3) should hold automatically. Therefore, in the classical theory the fulfilment of condition (4.3) is usually guaranteed by means of a suitable gauge transformation (see § 5). However, when the electromagnetic field is quantized (see Chapter II, § 13) it is not possible to satisfy condition (4.3) in the form of a functional relationship between the components of the quantized potential since it turns out to be incompatible with the commutation relations. In that case one has to impose on the allowed states certain conditions that are equivalent to condition (4.3) holding only for average values.

Thus, in the theory of the electromagnetic field the imposition of the subsidiary condition is carried out *independently* of the Lagrangian formalism. It therefore appears natural in the case of the vector field also *not to associate* the subsidiary condition (4.3) with the Lagrangian formalism. For example, it is possible to use a Lagrangian of type (4.2) and to impose condition (43) independently of it.

Here the problem arises of the lack of uniqueness in the structure of the Lagrangian and of the influence of this lack of uniqueness on the dynamic variables. We note in this connection that the action which corresponds to the difference (4.5) between the two Lagrangians given above reduces to zero after integration by parts with condition (4.3) being taken into account, and consequently the actions corresponding to Lagrangian (4.2) and (4.4) coincide. The Lagrangians (4.2) and (4.4) lead to different energy-momentum tensors, angular-momentum tensors, etc. However, as will be shown on the example of the energy-momentum tensor, the differences between these quantities may be represented, after the subsidiary condition and the field equations have been taken into account, in the form of corresponding divergences, as a result of which the dynamic variables of the type of the energy-momentum vector turn out to be equal. This will be sufficient for us, since, according to a remark made in § 2, the problem of the unique definition of quantities of the type of the energy-momentum tensor falls outside the range of the topics being discussed here.

Proceeding to the construction of the Lagrangian formalism of the vector field, we note that in agreement with general properties the real vector field describes neutral particles and the complex field describes charged particles. For brevity we shall limit our discussion to the complex vector field, keeping in mind that the corresponding calculations for the real field will lead to essentially different results only in the calculations of the current and the charge.

In accordance with the preceding, we shall choose the Lagrangian of the vector field in the form

$$\mathscr{L} = - \sum_{k,n} g^{kk} g^{nn} \frac{\partial U_k^*}{\partial x^n} \frac{\partial U_k}{\partial x^n} + m^2 \sum_n g^{nn} U_n^* U_n \tag{4.6}$$

and shall impose independently of it the subsidiary conditions on U and U^*:

$$\sum_n g^{nn} \frac{\partial U_n}{\partial x^n} \equiv \left(\frac{\partial U}{\partial x}\right) = 0, \quad \sum_n g^{nn} \frac{\partial U_n^*}{\partial x^n} \equiv \left(\frac{\partial U^*}{\partial x}\right) = 0.$$

From the Lagrangian (4.6) we find with the aid of the formulas of § 2 the field equations:

$$(\Box - m^2) U_n(x) = 0, \quad (\Box - m^2) U_n^*(x) = 0;$$

the energy-momentum tensor

$$T^{kl} = - g^{kk} g^{ll} \sum_n g^{nn} \left(\frac{\partial U_n^*}{\partial x^k} \frac{\partial U_n}{\partial x^l} + \frac{\partial U_n^*}{\partial x^l} \frac{\partial U_n}{\partial x^k}\right) - g^{kl} \mathscr{L}; \tag{4.7}$$

the current vector

$$J^k = - i g^{kk} \sum_m g^{mm} \left(U_m^* \frac{\partial U_m}{\partial x^k} - \frac{\partial U_m^*}{\partial x^k} U_m\right) \tag{4.8}$$

and the spin angular-momentum tensor

$$S_{lm}^k = g^{kk} \left(U_m^* \frac{\partial U_l}{\partial x^k} + \frac{\partial U_l^*}{\partial x^k} U_m - U_l^* \frac{\partial U_m}{\partial x^k} - \frac{\partial U_m^*}{\partial x^k} U_l\right). \tag{4.9}$$

In accordance with the remark made earlier, the energy-momentum tensor (4.7) while being symmetric in the indices k and l nevertheless does not coincide with the usual symmetric energy-momentum tensor corresponding to the Lagrangian of type (4.4) and having the form[8]

$$\begin{aligned} \theta^{kl} = &- g^{kk} g^{ll} \sum_m (H_{km}^* H_{lm} + H_{lm}^* H_{km}) g^{mm} \\ &+ \tfrac{1}{2} g^{kl} \sum_{n,m} g^{nn} g^{mm} H_{nm}^* H_{nm} + m^2 g^{kk} g^{ll} (U_l^* U_k + U_k^* U_l) \\ &- m^2 g^{kl} \sum_n g^{nn} U_n^* U_n, \end{aligned} \tag{4.10}$$

[8] See, for example, Pauli (91a), or Wentzel (133).

where we have introduced the notation

$$H_{mn} = \frac{\partial U_n}{\partial x^m} - \frac{\partial U_m}{\partial x^n}, \quad H^*_{mn} = \frac{\partial U^*_n}{\partial x^m} - \frac{\partial U^*_m}{\partial x^n}.$$

However, it may be easily seen that this difference is not significant. Indeed, the difference between the tensors (4.7) and (4.10) may be represented in the form

$$T^{kl} - \theta^{kl} = \sum_n \frac{\partial}{\partial x^n} f_1^{kn,l} + g^{kk} g^{ll} f_{2,kl} + g^{kk} g^{ll} f_{3,kl}.$$

The tensor

$$f_1^{kn,l} = \tfrac{1}{2} \sum_m U^*_m \left(g^{kl} g^{nn} \frac{\partial U_n}{\partial x^m} - g^{nl} g^{kk} \frac{\partial U_k}{\partial x^m} \right)$$

$$+ \tfrac{1}{2} \sum_m \left(g^{kl} g^{nn} \frac{\partial U^*_n}{\partial x^m} - g^{nl} g^{kk} \frac{\partial U^*_k}{\partial x^m} \right) U_m + g^{kk} g^{nn} g^{ll} (U^*_l H_{nk} + H^*_{nk} U_l)$$

$$+ \tfrac{1}{2} g^{kk} g^{nn} g^{ll} \left\{ \left(U^*_n \frac{\partial U_k}{\partial x^l} - U^*_k \frac{\partial U_n}{\partial x^l} \right) + \left(\frac{\partial U^*_k}{\partial x^l} U_n - \frac{\partial U^*_n}{\partial x^l} U_k \right) \right\}$$

appearing under the divergence sign of the above expression is antisymmetric in the indices k and n:

$$f_1^{kn,l} = - f_1^{nk,l}$$

and in accordance with a remark made in § 2 has no effect on the value of the energy-momentum four-vector. The other two tensors

$$f_{2,kl} = \tfrac{1}{2} \left\{ U^*_k \frac{\partial}{\partial x^l} \left(\frac{\partial U}{\partial x} \right) - \left(\frac{\partial U^*}{\partial x^l} \right) \frac{\partial U_k}{\partial x^l} + \frac{\partial}{\partial x^l} \left(\frac{\partial U^*}{\partial x} \right) U_k \right.$$

$$\left. - \frac{\partial U^*_k}{\partial x^l} \left(\frac{\partial U}{\partial x} \right) \right\} - \tfrac{1}{2} g^{kl} \sum_m \left\{ U^*_m \frac{\partial}{\partial x^m} \left(\frac{\partial U}{\partial x} \right) + \frac{\partial}{\partial x^m} \left(\frac{\partial U^*}{\partial x} \right) U_m \right\}$$

$$+ U^*_l \frac{\partial}{\partial x^k} \left(\frac{\partial U}{\partial x} \right) + \frac{\partial}{\partial x^k} \left(\frac{\partial U^*}{\partial x} \right) U_l$$

and

$$f_{3,kl} = U^*_l (\Box U_k - m^2 U_k) + (\Box U^*_k - m^2 U^*_k) U_l$$

give no contribution at all to the above expression, since in view of the imposed subsidiary condition and of the field equations they become identically equal to zero. Thus the tensor (4.7) together with the subsidiary conditions leads to the usual expression for the energy-momentum four-vector, as we will also show later by means of a direct calculation.

Similar arguments can of course also be made for expressions (4.8) and (4.9) which do not agree with the corresponding expressions of the usual presentation.

Setting $k = 0$ in (4.7) we obtain the spatial density of the energy-momentum four-vector

$$\left.\begin{aligned} T^{00} &= -\sum_{k,n} g^{nn} \frac{\partial U_n^*}{\partial x^k} \frac{\partial U_n}{\partial x^k} - m^2 \sum_n g^{nn} U_n^* U_n, \\ T^{0\alpha} &= \sum_n g^{nn} \left(\frac{\partial U_n^*}{\partial x^0} \frac{\partial U_n}{\partial x^\alpha} + \frac{\partial U_n^*}{\partial x^\alpha} \frac{\partial U_n}{\partial x^0} \right), \quad \alpha = 1,\ 2,\ 3. \end{aligned}\right\} \tag{4.11}$$

Similarly, starting from formulas (4.8) and (4.9), we obtain the charge density

$$J^0 = -i \sum_n g^{nn} \left(U_n^* \frac{\partial U_n}{\partial x^0} - \frac{\partial U_n^*}{\partial x^0} U_n \right) \tag{4.12}$$

and the spatial density of the components of the spin vector S

$$S_1 = \int S_{23}^0 d\mathbf{x}, \quad S_2 = \int S_{31}^0 d\mathbf{x}; \quad S_3 = \int S_{12}^0 d\mathbf{x},$$

$$S_{\alpha\beta}^0 = U_\beta^* \frac{\partial U_\alpha}{\partial x^0} + \frac{\partial U_\alpha^*}{\partial x^0} U_\beta - U_\alpha^* \frac{\partial U_\beta}{\partial x^0} - \frac{\partial U_\beta^*}{\partial x^0} U_\alpha . \tag{4.13}$$

4.2. *Transition to the Momentum Representation*

For further calculation of dynamic variables we shall go over, as is usually done, to the momentum representation

$$U_n(x) = \frac{1}{(2\pi)^{3/2}} \int dk e^{ikx} \delta(k^2 - m^2) U_n(k),$$

$$U_n^*(k) = \frac{1}{(2\pi)^{3/2}} \int dk e^{ikx} \delta(k^2 - m^2) U_n^*(k)$$

and shall decompose the potentials U, U^* into their positive- and negative-frequency parts:

$$U_n(x) = U_n^{(+)}(x) + U_n^{(-)}(x), \quad U_n^*(x) = U_n^{*(+)}(x) + U_n^{*(-)}(x).$$

Integrating over the variable k^0 we shall obtain the three-dimensional momentum representation of the potentials in the form

$$\left.\begin{aligned} U_n^{(\pm)}(x) &= \frac{1}{(2\pi)^{3/2}} \int \frac{d\mathbf{k}}{\sqrt{2k^0}} e^{\pm ikx} U_n^{(\pm)}(\mathbf{k}), \\ U_n^{*(\pm)}(x) &= \frac{1}{(2\pi)^{3/2}} \int \frac{d\mathbf{k}}{\sqrt{2k^0}} e^{\pm ikx} U_n^{*(\pm)}(\mathbf{k}). \end{aligned}\right\} \tag{4.14}$$

Here we have introduced our usual notation

$$\left.\begin{aligned} &U_n^{(\pm)}(\mathbf{k}) = \frac{U_n^{(\pm)}(k)}{\sqrt{2k^0}}, \quad U_n^{*(\pm)}(\mathbf{k}) = \frac{U_n^{*(\pm)}(k)}{\sqrt{2k^0}} \quad (k^0 = \sqrt{\mathbf{k}^2 + m^2}), \\ &U_n^{(\pm)}(k) = \theta(k^0) U_n(\pm k), \quad U_n^{*(\pm)}(k) = \theta(k^0) U_n^*(\pm k). \end{aligned}\right\} \tag{4.15}$$

We recall that in accordance with the definitions of momentum amplitudes the conditions of complex conjugation have the form

$$(U_n(k))^* = U_n^*(-k)$$

and, consequently, (4.16)

$$(U_n^{(\pm)}(k))^* = U^{*(\mp)}(k).$$

Substituting the expansions (4.14) into expressions (4.11), (4.12), and (4.13), and carrying out the integration over dx we shall obtain the energy-momentum four-vector

$$\begin{aligned} P^n &= \int T^{0n} d\mathbf{x} \\ &= -\int d\mathbf{k} \cdot k^n \{\sum_m g^{mm} (U_m^{*(-)}(\mathbf{k}) U_m^{(+)}(\mathbf{k}) + U_m^{*(+)}(\mathbf{k}) U_m^{(-)}(\mathbf{k}))\}, \end{aligned} \tag{4.17}$$

the charge

$$Q = \int J^0 d\mathbf{x} = -\int d\mathbf{k} \sum_n g^{nn} (U_n^{*(+)}(\mathbf{k}) U_n^{(-)}(\mathbf{k}) - U_n^{*(-)}(\mathbf{k}) U_n^{(+)}(\mathbf{k})) \tag{4.18}$$

and the spin vector

$$\mathbf{S} = i \int d\mathbf{k} \{[\mathbf{U}^{*(+)}(\mathbf{k}) \times \mathbf{U}^{(-)}(\mathbf{k})] + [\mathbf{U}^{*(-)}(\mathbf{k}) \times \mathbf{U}^{(+)}(\mathbf{k})]\}. \tag{4.19}$$

It may be seen that the spin vector (4.19) is an invariant due to the *symmetry* of the energy-momentum tensor (4.7).

Taking into account the conditions of complex conjugation (4.16) we note that according to (4.17) the term with $m = 0$ in the expression for the energy P^0 turns out to be negative as a result of which the energy is not positive definite. As was noted above, this difficulty is removed by imposing the subsidiary conditions which in the three-dimensional momentum representation (4.14) take on the form

$$\sum_n k^n U_n^{(\pm)}(\mathbf{k}) = 0, \quad \sum_n k^n U_n^{*(\pm)}(\mathbf{k}) = 0. \tag{4.20}$$

In virtue of these conditions the components U_n are no longer independent. By finding with the aid of (4.20) an expression for the component U_0 in terms of the others:

$$U_0^{(\pm)}(\mathbf{k}) = -\frac{1}{k^0} \sum_\alpha k^\alpha U_\alpha^{(\pm)}(\mathbf{k}), \quad U_0^{*(\pm)}(\mathbf{k}) = -\frac{1}{k^0} \sum_\alpha k^\alpha U_\alpha^{*(\pm)}(\mathbf{k})$$
$$(\alpha = 1, 2, 3),$$

we obtain the following expression for the quadratic form in the integrand of (4.17) which depends only on the "space" components of the potential:

$$-\sum_n g^{nn} U_n^{*(\pm)}(\mathbf{k}) U_n^{(\mp)}(\mathbf{k}) = \sum_\alpha U_\alpha^{*(\pm)}(\mathbf{k}) U_\alpha^{(\mp)}(\mathbf{k})$$
$$-\frac{1}{(k^0)^2} \left(\sum_\alpha k^\alpha U_\alpha^{*(\pm)}(\mathbf{k})\right) \left(\sum_\beta k^\beta U_\beta^{(\mp)}(\mathbf{k})\right). \tag{4.21}$$

The form (4.21) may be diagonalized by means of the linear substitution

$$\mathbf{U}(k) = \mathbf{e}_1 a_1(k) + \mathbf{e}_2 a_2(k) + \frac{\mathbf{k}}{|\mathbf{k}|} \frac{k^0}{m} a_3(k), \tag{4.22}$$

which represents a decomposition of the potential U_α into a longitudinal and a transverse component. Here $\mathbf{e}_1$ and $\mathbf{e}_2$ are complex unit vectors orthogonal to the wave vector $\mathbf{k}$ and to each other:

$$(\mathbf{e}_1 \cdot \mathbf{e}_1) = (\mathbf{e}_2 \cdot \mathbf{e}_2) = 1, \quad (\mathbf{e}_r \cdot \mathbf{k}) = (\mathbf{e}_r^* \cdot \mathbf{k}) = (\mathbf{e}_r \cdot \mathbf{e}_s) = (\mathbf{e}_r \cdot \mathbf{e}_s^*) = 0$$
$$(r, s = 1, 2),$$

and representing transverse polarization vectors.

Substituting (4.22) into (4.21) we find after a simple calculation:

$$-\sum_n g^{nn} U_n^{*(\pm)}(\mathbf{k}) U_n^{(\mp)}(\mathbf{k}) = \sum_\alpha a_\alpha^{*(\pm)}(\mathbf{k})\, a_\alpha^{(\mp)}(\mathbf{k}).$$

Substituting this expression into (4.17) and (4.18) we obtain diagonal expressions for the energy momentum and for the charge, with the energy turning out to be manifestly positive definite in terms of the new variables:

$$P^l = \int d\mathbf{k} \cdot k^l \{\sum_\alpha a_\alpha^{*(+)}(\mathbf{k})\, a_\alpha^{(-)}(\mathbf{k}) + \sum_\beta a_\beta^{*(-)}(\mathbf{k})\, a_\beta^{(+)}(\mathbf{k})\}, \tag{4.23}$$

$$Q = \int d\mathbf{k} \{\sum_\alpha a_\alpha^{*(+)}(\mathbf{k})\, a_\alpha^{(-)}(\mathbf{k}) - \sum_\beta a_\beta^{*(-)}(\mathbf{k})\, a_\beta^{(+)}(\mathbf{k})\}. \tag{4.24}$$

4.3. *Spin of the Vector Field*

In order to make clear the connection between the amplitudes a and the spin variable, we shall consider the component of the spin vector along the direction of the propagation vector. Substituting (4.22) into (4.19) we shall obtain

$$S_3 = i \int d\mathbf{k} \{a_1^{*(+)}(\mathbf{k}) a_2^{(-)}(\mathbf{k}) - a_2^{*(+)}(\mathbf{k}) a_1^{(-)}(\mathbf{k}) + a_2^{*(-)}(\mathbf{k}) a_1^{(+)}(\mathbf{k}) - a_1^{*(-)}(\mathbf{k}) a_2^{(+)}(\mathbf{k})\}. \tag{4.25}$$

This expression may be diagonalized by means of the linear transformation

$$a_1^{(\pm)} = \frac{b_1^{(\pm)} + b_2^{(\pm)}}{\sqrt{2}}, \quad a_2^{(\pm)} = \frac{b_1^{(\pm)} - b_2^{(\pm)}}{i\sqrt{2}}, \quad a_3^{(\pm)} = b_3^{(\pm)},$$
$$a_1^{*(\pm)} = \frac{b_1^{*(\pm)} + b_2^{*(\pm)}}{\sqrt{2}}, \quad a_2^{*(\pm)} = i\, \frac{b_1^{*(\pm)} - b_2^{*(\pm)}}{\sqrt{2}}, \quad a_3^{*(\pm)} = b_3^{*(\pm)}, \tag{4.26}$$

which does not change the diagonal form of P and Q:

$$P^n = \int d\mathbf{k} \cdot k^n \sum_\alpha (b_\alpha^{*(-)}(\mathbf{k}) b_\alpha^{(+)}(\mathbf{k}) + b_\alpha^{*(+)}(\mathbf{k}) b_\alpha^{(-)}(\mathbf{k})), \tag{4.27}$$

$$Q = \int d\mathbf{k} \sum_\alpha (b_\alpha^{*(+)}(\mathbf{k}) b_\alpha^{(-)}(\mathbf{k}) - b_\alpha^{*(-)}(\mathbf{k}) b_\alpha^{(+)}(\mathbf{k})), \tag{4.28}$$

$$S_3 = \int d\mathbf{k}[b_1^{*(+)}(\mathbf{k})b_1^{(-)}(\mathbf{k}) - b_1^{*(-)}(\mathbf{k})b_1^{(+)}(\mathbf{k}) + b_2^{*(-)}(\mathbf{k})b_2^{(+)}(\mathbf{k}) - b_2^{*(+)}(\mathbf{k})b_2^{(-)}(\mathbf{k})]. \qquad (4.29)$$

From these formulas, it may be seen that the quadratic combinations of the amplitudes $b^{*(\pm)}$ and $b^{(\pm)}$ may be considered as the densities of the average number of particles which have definite values of energy, momentum, charge, and component of spin along the direction of motion. Thus, for example, the quantity $b_2^{*(-)}(\mathbf{k})\ b_2^{(+)}(\mathbf{k})$ represents the density of particles with momentum $\mathbf{k}$, energy k^0, charge -1, and component of spin along the direction of motion equal to $+1$; similarly $b_3^{*(-)}(\mathbf{k})b_3^{(+)}(\mathbf{k})$ is the density of particles with momentum $\mathbf{k}$, energy k^0, charge -1, zero component of spin, etc. As we shall see later (cf. Chapter II) after quantization, the amplitude $b_2^{(+)}(\mathbf{k})$ describes the creation of a particle of energy k^0, momentum $\mathbf{k}$, charge -1, spin component $+1$, while the amplitude $b_2^{*(-)}(\mathbf{k})$ describes its annihilation, etc.

Returning to the amplitudes $a_{1,2}$ we find that in accordance with (4.24) they correspond to *circularly polarized* oscillations.

Thus the complex vector field describes positively and negatively charged particles of mass

$$m = \sqrt{(k^0)^2 - \mathbf{k}^2}$$

and with three possible values of the component of the spin vector along the direction of motion equal respectively to 1, 0, -1. A rigorous foundation for this correspondence can, of course, be provided only by quantum theory.

4.4. *Klein-Gordon Equations Written in the Form of a System of First-Order Equations*

We note that in the general case the system of equations

$$(\Box - m^2)u_i(x) = 0 \qquad (i = 1, 2, \ldots, s) \qquad (4.30)$$

may be replaced by a system of equations of the first order of the form

$$\left(i \sum_n \Gamma^n \frac{\partial}{\partial x^n} - M\right) u(x) = 0, \qquad (4.31)$$

where Γ and M are certain square matrices and the number $r (r > s)$ of components of the function u is equal to the rank of the matrices Γ and M whose properties are determined by the transformation laws of the function

u (by its tensor character) and by the conditions of covariance of equations (4.31).

In particular, if the matrices Γ are determined by the conditions

$$\Gamma^n\Gamma^m + \Gamma^m\Gamma^n = 2g^{mn},$$

while M is diagonal, then, as will be shown in § 6, the rank of the only irreducible representation of Γ is equal to four, and the function u is a four-component spinor.

The case when Γ are defined by the relations

$$\Gamma^k\Gamma^n\Gamma^m + \Gamma^m\Gamma^n\Gamma^k = g^{kn}\Gamma^m + g^{mn}\Gamma^k, \tag{4.32}$$

while the matrix M is diagonal has been investigated by Duffin (32) and by Kemmer (69) (see also Pauli (91a)). In this case, the rank of the matrices turns out to be equal to sixteen. The corresponding representation may be decomposed into three irreducible ones. In the first of these u has a single component equal to zero, in the second it has five components, and in the third it has ten components. The five-component function gives a scalar representation, corresponds to a scalar and its four-gradient, and describes particles of zero spin. The ten-component function gives a vector representation, corresponds to a four-vector U and to the six components of the tensor

$$H_{mn} = \frac{\partial U_n}{\partial x^m} - \frac{\partial U_m}{\partial x^n},$$

and describes particles of spin one.

The conditions of covariance of equations of type (4.31) under Lorentz transformations impose on the matrices Γ certain relations which establish the connection between the matrices Γ and the transformation laws of the wave function u. We shall examine the infinitesimal rotation transformation (under a transformation of translation equations (4.31) are trivially covariant):

$$x^n \to x'^n = x^n + \sum_k g^{kk} x^k \omega^{nk}, \qquad \omega^{nk} + \omega^{kn} = 0,$$

under which the function u transforms in accordance with

$$u'(x') = \Lambda u(x). \tag{4.33}$$

As a result of the demand of covariance, equation (4.31) must retain its old form in terms of the new variables:

$$\left(i \sum_n \Gamma^n \frac{\partial}{\partial x'^n} - M\right) u'(x') = 0.$$

If we express the derivatives with respect to the transformed coordinates x' occurring in the above expression in terms of the derivatives with respect to the original coordinates x, and then multiply on the left by Λ^{-1} and equate terms of the first order in the parameters ω, we shall obtain the relations between the transformation matrix Λ and the coefficients Γ and M of the preceding equation

$$\left.\begin{aligned} \Lambda^{-1}M\Lambda &= M, \\ \Lambda^{-1}\Gamma^k\Lambda &= \Gamma^k + \sum_n g^{nn}\Gamma^n\omega^{kn}, \end{aligned}\right\} \tag{4.34}$$

which guarantee the covariance of the equation under discussion.

Thus the tensor transformation laws of the field functions in the Duffin-Kemmer formalism take on the form given by (4.33), while the transformation matrix Λ turns out to be related to the matrix coefficients of the field equation. The tensor transformation law seems to take on "the external appearance" of a transformation of the spinor type. This fact is, of course, connected with the transition to a new system of "independent components" of the field function, which are in fact linear combinations of the components of the tensor and of their first derivatives.

Equation (4.31) may also be obtained by the variational method from a Lagrangian of the form

$$\mathscr{L} = \frac{i}{2}\sum_n \left(\bar{u}\Gamma^n \frac{\partial u}{\partial x^n} - \frac{\partial \bar{u}}{\partial x^n}\Gamma^n u\right) - \bar{u}Mu. \tag{4.35}$$

The function $\bar{u}$ occurring in this expression is said to be "adjoint" to u, satisfies the equation

$$i\sum_n \frac{\partial \bar{u}}{\partial x^n}\Gamma^n + \bar{u}M = 0,$$

and is linearly related to the function u^*, which is complex-conjugate to u, by means of the matrix equation

$$\bar{u} = u^*\Gamma. \tag{4.36}$$

The matrix Γ of this last transformation is determined in terms of Γ^k and Γ^m by means of the condition that the Lagrangian (4.35) should be real. In this way we obtain:

$$(\Gamma)^{-1}\Gamma^{*k}\Gamma^* = \Gamma^k, \qquad (\Gamma)^{-1}M^*\Gamma^* = M.$$

It is also evident that expressions for the dynamic variables may be obtained in the usual way from the Lagrangian (4.35).

§ 5. The Electromagnetic Field

5.1. *Potential of the Electromagnetic Field*

The electromagnetic field is described by the well-known Maxwell equations which have been repeatedly checked by experiment

$$\operatorname{curl}\mathbf{E} = -\frac{\partial \mathbf{H}}{\partial x^0}, \qquad \operatorname{curl}\mathbf{H} = \frac{\partial \mathbf{E}}{\partial x^0},$$

$$\operatorname{div}\mathbf{H} = 0, \qquad \operatorname{div}\mathbf{E} = 0.$$

For a more symmetric description of the electromagnetic field, a real covariant four-vector electromagnetic potential A_n

($n = 0, 1, 2, 3$) is introduced in such a way that

$$\mathbf{E} = \text{grad}\, A_0 - \frac{\partial \mathbf{A}}{\partial x^0}, \qquad \mathbf{H} = \text{curl}\, \mathbf{A}.$$

The components of the "four-dimensional curl" of the potential A form the well-known antisymmetric tensor of the electromagnetic field

$$H_{kl} = \frac{\partial A_l}{\partial x^k} - \frac{\partial A_k}{\partial x^l}, \tag{5.1}$$

whose components are related to the components of the vectors representing the electric and magnetic field strengths by means of the expressions

$$E_\alpha = H_{\alpha 0} \quad (\alpha = 1,\ 2,\ 3); \quad H_1 = H_{23}, \quad H_2 = H_{31}, \quad H_3 = H_{12}.$$

It is convenient to exhibit this relationship in the following explicit form

$$H_{kl} = \begin{pmatrix} 0 & -E_1 & -E_2 & -E_3 \\ E_1 & 0 & H_3 & -H_2 \\ E_2 & -H_3 & 0 & H_1 \\ E_3 & H_2 & -H_1 & 0 \end{pmatrix}.$$

Maxwell's equations may be rewritten with the aid of the tensor H_{kl} in the form

$$\sum_k g^{kk} \frac{\partial H_{kl}}{\partial x^k} = 0 \qquad (k,\ l = 0,\ 1,\ 2,\ 3), \tag{5.2}$$

$$\frac{\partial H_{kl}}{\partial x^m} + \frac{\partial H_{mk}}{\partial x^l} + \frac{\partial H_{lm}}{\partial x^k} = 0 \qquad (k,\ l,\ m) = \begin{cases} 0,\ 1,\ 2, \\ 1,\ 2,\ 3, \\ 2,\ 3,\ 0, \\ 3,\ 0,\ 1. \end{cases} \tag{5.3}$$

In making the further transition in these equations from H_{kl} to the potential A_l we see that the four equations (5.3) are a consequence of the definition (5.1), and do not lead to any equation for A_l, while the four equations (5.2) yield:

$$\sum_k g^{kk} \frac{\partial^2 A_n}{(\partial x^k)^2} - \sum_k g^{kk} \frac{\partial^2 A_k}{\partial x^k\, \partial x^n} = 0. \tag{5.4}$$

From this it follows that the formulation of the equations of the electromagnetic field in terms of the potential A_n is really simple, symmetric, and manifestly covariant.

5.2. *Gauge Transformation of the Second Kind and the Lorentz Condition*

We note further that the method of introducing the potential A is *nonunique to a high degree.* The point is that in Maxwell's theory the observable quantities, such as the vectors **E**, **H**, the tensor H_{kl} and also the equations of the electromagnetic field are all invariant under a so-called *gauge transformation of the second kind of the potential* A:

$$A_n(x) \to A'_n(x) = A_n(x) + \frac{\partial f(x)}{\partial x^n}. \tag{5.5}$$

Therefore the potential A is not an observable quantity and is not unique. In (5.5) $f(x)$ is an arbitrary function which has partial derivatives of the first and second order.

This lack of uniqueness of the potential A may be used in such a way as to satisfy some subsidiary condition. The so-called *Lorentz condition*

$$\sum_k g^{kk} \frac{\partial A_k}{\partial x^k} \equiv \left(\frac{\partial A}{\partial x}\right) = 0, \tag{5.6}$$

which is the only possible invariant condition linear in A is usually chosen as such a subsidiary condition. It is not difficult to show that $f(x)$ may always be chosen in such a way as to satisfy condition (5.6).

If the Lorentz condition is taken into account, the field equations (5.4) assume the form

$$-\sum_k g^{kk} \frac{\partial^2 A_l}{(\partial x^k)^2} \equiv \Box A_l = 0. \tag{5.7}$$

However, the additional Lorentz condition still does not completely determine the potential A. Equations (5.6) and (5.7) are invariant with respect to the "special gauge transformation of the second kind"

$$A_n(x) \to A'_n(x) = A_n(x) + \frac{\partial f_0(x)}{\partial x^n}, \tag{5.8}$$

which is characterized by the requirement that the arbitrary function $f_0(x)$ must satisfy D'Alembert's equation

$$\Box f_0 = 0.$$

In any particular Lorentz frame of reference the function f_0 may be chosen so that some one of the components of A, for example the "scalar" potential A_0, vanishes. In this case the Lorentz condition assumes the form

$$\sum_{\alpha=1,2,3} \frac{\partial A_\alpha}{\partial x^\alpha} \equiv \operatorname{div} \mathbf{A} = 0. \tag{5.9}$$

In order to establish the physical meaning of equation (5.9), it is convenient to go over to the momentum representation

$$A_n(x) = \frac{1}{(2\pi)^{3/2}} \int dk \delta(k^2)\, e^{ikx} A_n(k). \tag{5.10}$$

Substituting (5.10) into (5.9) we find:

$$\sum_\alpha k_\alpha A_\alpha(k)|_{k^2=0} = (\mathbf{k} \cdot \mathbf{A}(k))|_{k^2=0} = 0. \tag{5.11}$$

Equation (5.11) is the condition that the *electromagnetic field is transverse.* Thus, in spite of the fact that the electromagnetic field is described by a four-component potential, only *the two linearly independent components* orthogonal to the propagation vector have physical meaning. It is important to stress that although the condition of transversality is not covariant, it is possible to arrange that it should be satisfied in any arbitrary particular Lorentz frame of reference by means of a suitable special gauge transformation (5.8).

We note further that the actual reduction of the four-component field to a two-component one, which takes place in consequence of the condition of invariance under a gauge transformation, is closely connected with the fact that the *rest mass* of the particles corresponding to this field, i.e., photons, *is zero.* It is precisely because of this important property that the potential A disappears from the field equations and the invariance of the electromagnetic field under gauge transformations is brought about.

5.3. *Lagrangian Formalism*

In going over to the Lagrangian formalism we note that, as we shall see subsequently (cf. Chapter II), when the electromagnetic field is quantized it will no longer be possible to satisfy the subsidiary Lorentz condition (5.6) as a relation between the components of the quantized potential A_n. In the quantum theory of the electromagnetic field the Lorentz condition will have to be replaced by a certain condition on the wave function subjected to second quantization which guarantees only that the average value of the operator $(\partial A/\partial x)$ taken over the allowed states will be equal to zero.

Therefore, as in the case of the vector field, and in contrast to the usual presentation, we shall not introduce the Lorentz condition into the Lagrangian formalism. We shall choose the Lagrangian function following the example of the corresponding function for the vector field in which we set $m = 0$:

$$\mathscr{L} = -\tfrac{1}{2}\sum_{m,n} g^{mm} g^{nn} \frac{\partial A_m}{\partial x^n}\frac{\partial A_m}{\partial x^n}. \tag{5.12}$$

This Lagrangian actually corresponds to the Lagrangian of Dirac, Fock, and Podolsky (31) (cf. also Wentzel (133)):

$$\mathscr{L} = -\tfrac{1}{4}\sum_{k,l} g^{kk} g^{ll} H_{kl} H_{kl} - \tfrac{1}{2}\left(\frac{\partial A}{\partial x}\right)^2,$$

from which it differs by the divergence

$$\sum_{k,l} \tfrac{1}{2}\frac{\partial}{\partial x^l}\left[A_k \frac{\partial A_l}{\partial x^k} - A_l \frac{\partial A_k}{\partial x^k}\right].$$

The Lagrangian (5.12) differs from the generally used gauge-invariant expression

$$\mathscr{L} = -\tfrac{1}{4}\sum_{k,l} g^{kk} g^{ll} H_{kl} H_{kl} \tag{5.13}$$

by a quantity which, after being integrated over all space-time and after the Lorentz condition has been taken into account, reduces to zero giving no contribution to the action of the system.

In a similar manner, the Lagrangian (5.12) leads to quantities of the type of the energy-momentum tensor which do not agree with the usual gauge-invariant expressions. However, as in the case of the vector field, the differences between the corresponding expressions may be expressed in the form of divergences, and after the field equations and the Lorentz condition have been taken into account, do not give any contributions to the dynamic characteristics of the system of the type of the energy-momentum four-vector. Concerning the uniqueness of the energy-momentum tensor (and of other quantities analogous to it) we note that, in accordance with the remarks made in § 2, this question falls outside the framework of this presentation.

From the Lagrangian (5.12) we obtain by the usual methods, and with the aid of formulas (2.4), (2.20), and (2.27), the following expressions: the field equations

$$\Box A_k = 0;$$

the energy-momentum tensor

$$T^{kl} = - g^{kk} g^{ll} \sum_n g^{nn} \frac{\partial A_n}{\partial x^k} \frac{\partial A_n}{\partial x^l} - g^{kl} \mathscr{L};$$

the spatial energy-momentum density

$$T^{00} = - \tfrac{1}{2} \sum_{k,n} g^{nn} \left(\frac{\partial A_n}{\partial x^k}\right)^2, \quad T^{0\alpha} = \sum_n g^{nn} \frac{\partial A_n}{\partial x^0} \frac{\partial A_n}{\partial x^\alpha} \qquad (\alpha = 1,\ 2,\ 3); \tag{5.14}$$

the spin angular-momentum tensor

$$S^k_{lm} = g^{kk} \left(A_m \frac{\partial A_l}{\partial x^k} - A_l \frac{\partial A_m}{\partial x^k} \right)$$

and the spatial density of the spin vector

$$S^0_{\alpha\beta} = A_\beta \frac{\partial A_\alpha}{\partial x^0} - A_\alpha \frac{\partial A_\beta}{\partial x^0}. \tag{5.15}$$

To complement the Lagrangian formalism we shall impose the Lorentz condition

$$\left(\frac{\partial A}{\partial x}\right) = 0.$$

We note that the above Lorentz condition refers only to the unquantized theory of the electromagnetic field and, as we shall see later (in Chapter II), must be replaced upon quantization by certain conditions on the wave functions of the allowed states, which are equivalent to the Lorentz condition only in an average sense.

The expressions for the energy-momentum and angular-momentum tensors obtained in this way differ, as may be expected, from the corresponding gauge-invariant expressions commonly used in the theory of the electromagnetic field which are obtained from the gauge-invariant Lagrangian (5.13). However, it may be shown, in complete analogy to the procedure used earlier (§ 4) in the case of the vector field, that the differences between the corresponding tensors may be represented in the form of a sum of the corresponding antisymmetric divergences and of terms which reduce to zero after the field equations and the Lorentz condition have been taken into account, and consequently lead to expressions for the dynamic characteristics of the system that agree with the usual ones.

In order to calculate the dynamic characteristics, we shall decompose the components of the potential into their positive- and negative-frequency parts

$$A_n(x) = A_n^{(+)}(x) + A_n^{(-)}(x)$$

and go over to the momentum representation. We write down directly the formula for the three-dimensional momentum representation, keeping in mind the fact that the three-dimensional momentum amplitudes $A(\mathbf{k})$ are related to the four-dimensional amplitudes $A(k)$ by the usual expressions of type (4.15) and satisfy the following complex conjugate conditions:

$$(A_n^{(\pm)}(\mathbf{k}))^* = A_n^{(\mp)}(\mathbf{k}).$$

5.4. *Transverse, Longitudinal, and Time Components*

We now introduce a frame of reference associated with the momentum vector $\mathbf{k}$, i.e., we shall go over to a special frame of reference in momentum space by representing $A(\mathbf{k})$ in the form of a sum of a time, a longitudinal and a transverse component:

$$A_n^{(\pm)}(\mathbf{k}) = e_n^1 a_1^{(\pm)}(\mathbf{k}) + e_n^2 a_2^{(\pm)}(\mathbf{k}) + e_n^3 a_3^{(\pm)}(\mathbf{k}) + e_n^0 a_0^{(\pm)}(\mathbf{k}). \quad (5.16)$$

Here e^1 and e^2 are spatial unit polarization vectors orthogonal to each other and to the unit vector e^3 in the direction of the momentum vector:

$$(\mathbf{e}^\alpha \mathbf{e}^\beta) = \delta_{\alpha\beta}(\alpha, \beta = 1, 2, 3), \; e_0^\alpha = 0, \quad \mathbf{e}^3 = \frac{\mathbf{k}}{|\mathbf{k}|},$$

$$[\mathbf{e}^1 \mathbf{e}^2] = \mathbf{e}^3, \quad [\mathbf{e}^2 \mathbf{e}^3] = \mathbf{e}^1, \quad [\mathbf{e}^3 \mathbf{e}^1] = \mathbf{e}^2,$$

while $\mathbf{e}^0$ is a unit time vector which has the properties

$$e_n^0 = \delta_{n0}, \quad \mathbf{e}^0 \mathbf{e}^0 = 1, \quad \mathbf{e}^0 \mathbf{e}^\alpha = 0 \qquad (\alpha = 1, 2, 3).$$

It may be easily verified that under the transformation (5.16) the basic quadratic form which determines the energy-momentum four-vector [cf. (5.14)] does not change its form

$$\sum_n g^{nn} A_n^{(+)}(\mathbf{k}) A_n^{(-)}(\mathbf{k}) = \sum_m g^{mm} a_m^{(+)}(\mathbf{k}) a_m^{(-)}(\mathbf{k}). \quad (5.17)$$

On further substituting the expansion (5.16) into the Lorentz subsidiary condition written separately for the positive- and the negative-frequency components:

$$\sum_n k^n A_n^{(+)}(\mathbf{k}) = 0, \qquad \sum_n k^n A_n^{(-)}(\mathbf{k}) = 0,$$

we shall obtain two relations

$$|\mathbf{k}| \, a_3^{(\pm)}(\mathbf{k}) + k^0 a_0^{(\pm)}(\mathbf{k}) = 0.$$

Noting that since the mass m is equal to zero, $|\mathbf{k}| = k^0$, we obtain from this

$$a_3^{(+)}(\mathbf{k}) \, a_3^{(-)}(\mathbf{k}) - a_0^{(+)}(\mathbf{k}) a_0^{(-)}(\mathbf{k}) = 0. \quad (5.18)$$

The preceding relation (5.18) means that because of the Lorentz condition the average number $a_3^{(+)} a_3^{(-)}$ of "longitudinal" photons is equal to the average number $a_0^{(+)} a_0^{(-)}$ of "timelike" photons, and that their contributions to the energy-momentum four-vector are of opposite sign. One may therefore speak of the "longitudinal" and "timelike" photons as if "compensating" each other. Substituting (5.18) into (5.17), we obtain

$$-\sum_n g^{nn} A_n^{(+)}(\mathbf{k})\, A_n^{(-)}(\mathbf{k}) = \sum_{\nu=1,\,2} a_\nu^{(+)}(\mathbf{k})\, a_\nu^{(-)}(\mathbf{k}). \tag{5.19}$$

Further, on computing the energy-momentum four-vector

$$P^n = \int d\mathbf{k} \cdot k^n \{-\sum_m g^{mm} A_m^{(+)}(\mathbf{k})\, A_m^{(-)}(\mathbf{k})\}$$
$$= \sum_{\mu=1,\,2} \int d\mathbf{k} \cdot k^n a_\mu^{(+)}(\mathbf{k})\, a_\mu^{(-)}(\mathbf{k}), \tag{5.20}$$

we find that in the case under consideration, as in the case of the vector field, the energy turns out to be positive definite only in virtue of the Lorentz subsidiary condition.

5.5. *Spin*

If we next determine the spin vector

$$S_\alpha = \int S^0_{\beta\gamma}\, dx \quad (\alpha,\ \beta,\ \gamma) = (1,\ 2,\ 3),$$

$$\mathbf{S} = i\int d\mathbf{k}[\mathbf{A}^{(+)}(\mathbf{k}) \times \mathbf{A}^{(-)}(\mathbf{k})] = i\int d\mathbf{k}\ [\mathbf{a}^{(+)}(\mathbf{k}) \times \mathbf{a}^{(-)}(\mathbf{k})], \tag{5.21}$$

which remains constant in time because of the symmetry of the tensor T^{kl}, we find its component along the direction of the propagation vector $\mathbf{k}$ in the form

$$S_3 \sim i(a_1^{(+)}(\mathbf{k})\, a_2^{(-)}(\mathbf{k}) - a_2^{(+)}(\mathbf{k})\, a_1^{(-)}(\mathbf{k})). \tag{5.22}$$

Introducing the new amplitudes $b_1^{(\pm)}$ and $b_2^{(\pm)}$ as in § 4 we obtain for P^n and S_3 the "diagonal" expressions

$$P^n = \int d\mathbf{k} \cdot k^n (b_1^{(+)}(\mathbf{k})\, b_1^{(-)}(\mathbf{k}) + b_2^{(+)}(\mathbf{k})\, b_2^{(-)}(\mathbf{k})), \tag{5.23}$$

$$S_3 = \int d\mathbf{k} (b_1^{(+)}(\mathbf{k})\, b_1^{(-)}(\mathbf{k}) - b_2^{(+)}(\mathbf{k}) b_2^{(-)}(\mathbf{k})), \tag{5.24}$$

from which it follows directly that the products

$$b_i^{(+)}(\mathbf{k})\, b_i^{(-)}(\mathbf{k}) \qquad (i = 1,\ 2)$$

may be regarded as average numbers of particles of zero mass, momentum $\mathbf{k}$, energy $k^0 = |\mathbf{k}|$, having a component of spin angular momentum along the direction of the propagation vector equal to $+1 (i = 1)$ and to $-1 (i = 2)$. We are in fact dealing with *photons*.

Thus the transition to the momentum representation allows one to see directly that the electromagnetic field describes transverse photons with two possible values of the component of spin along the direction of motion. A rigorous foundation of this correspondence is, of course, given by the theory only as a result of second quantization.

§ 6. The Spinor Field. Dirac Matrices and Transformation Laws of Spinor Functions

6.1. *Linearization of the Klein-Gordon Operator*

We now proceed to examine the simplest spinor field which, as will be shown below, is characterized by the fact that it describes charged particles of spin $\frac{1}{2}$, for example, electrons and positrons. Following Dirac we shall obtain the corresponding equations by means of the "linearization" of the Klein-Gordon operator:

$$\Box - m^2 = \sum_n g^{nn} P^n P^n - m^2, \tag{6.1}$$

where for convenience the usual quantum mechanical notation

$$P^n = i g^{nn} \frac{\partial}{\partial x^n}.$$

has been adopted. The operator (6.1) is quadratic in the derivatives $\partial/\partial x^n$, and, as may be easily seen, cannot be represented in the form of two factors linear in P^n with numerical coefficients. Indeed, if by analogy with the formula for factoring the difference of two squares, one attempts to write (6.1) in the form

$$\Box - m^2 = (P - m)(P + m),$$

where P is some linear combination of the operators P^k with coefficients γ^k

$$P = \sum_k g^{kk} P^k \gamma^k,$$

then one must demand that the relation

$$\sum_n g^{nn} P^n P^n = (\sum_k g^{kk} P^k \gamma^k)^2,$$

should hold, on expanding the right-hand side of which one finds the condition determining the coefficients γ:

$$\gamma^n \gamma^m + \gamma^m \gamma^n = 2g^{mn}. \tag{6.2}$$

Since, in accordance with this condition, the quantities γ^k with different indices anticommute, they are not ordinary numbers and may be obtained in the form of matrices.

With the aid of these quantities the Klein-Gordon operator may be represented in the form of a product of two commuting matrix operators:

$$\Box - m^2 = \left(i \sum_n \gamma^n \frac{\partial}{\partial x^n} + m\right)\left(i \sum_k \gamma^k \frac{\partial}{\partial x^k} - m\right), \tag{6.3}$$

and in order that the field function should satisfy the Klein-Gordon equation

$$(\Box - m^2)\psi = 0, \tag{6.4}$$

we may demand that it should also satisfy one of the two first-order equations:

$$\left(i \sum_n \gamma^n \frac{\partial}{\partial x^n} + m\right)\psi(x) = 0, \quad \left(i \sum_u \gamma^n \frac{\partial}{\partial x^n} - m\right)\psi(x) = 0. \tag{6.5}$$

Equations (6.5) are, of course, less general than (6.4), and although every solution of one of equations (6.5) also satisfies equation (6.4) the converse does not hold.

It is important to note that equations (6.5) are actually quite new equations, since the functions which satisfy them give a *spinor* representation of the Lorentz group.

One may therefore expect that equations (6.5) contain more detailed information than equation (6.4). As is well known, this is actually the case, since with the aid of just these equations (6.5) Dirac for the first time succeeded in describing electron spin equal to $\frac{1}{2}$. Equations (6.5) are called *Dirac equations*, and the matrices γ defined by equations (6.2) are called the *Dirac matrices.*

A common property of all the solutions of the Klein-Gordon equation which we have considered until now, and which correspond to single-valued representations of the Lorentz group, is the fact that the particles described by them have integral spin (0 and 1 in the cases examined so far). For a description of particles with half-integral spin one has to employ spinor representations, the simplest of which corresponds to equations (6.5) and (6.2).

In view of the matrix character of the operators in equations (6.5) the wave function ψ which satisfies them is a many-component one, with the number of its components determined by the rank of the matrices γ.

6.2. *Dirac Matrices*

We now turn to a study of the properties of the four hyper-complex numbers γ^n defined by the relations (6.2). The rank of the irreducible representation of these quantities may be established on the basis of the following considerations.

If to the above four quantities we add all their possible products (including multiple ones) and all the linear combinations with all possible complex coefficients of all the hypercomplex numbers obtained in this way, we evidently shall obtain a set of elements for which the operations of addition of one element to another and of multiplication of an element by an element or by a complex number are defined. As it is usually stated, we obtain a certain *algebra A* over the field of complex numbers. In addition, we shall have to assume that a finite dimensional matrix representation exists in this case.

By using a number of algebraic theorems [9] it may be shown that the rank n of an irreducible matrix representation of a given system of hypercomplex numbers is related to the number h of linearly independent elements of algebra A by

$$h = n^2. \tag{6.6}$$

Going over to the matrix representation of the quantities γ it may be easily seen that this relation expresses the simple fact that the number h of linearly independent square matrices of rank n is equal to the number of elements of these matrices.

Let us find the number h. From the four matrices γ^k one may construct by multiplying them together sixteen linearly independent matrices:

[9] cf., for example, Van-der-Waerden (129), Ch. 2.

$$\left.\begin{array}{l}\text{the unit matrix } I = g^{kk}\gamma^k\gamma^k \\ \text{the four matrices } \gamma^k (k = 0, 1, 2, 3) \\ \text{the six matrices } \Gamma^{kl} = \gamma^k\gamma^l (k < l) \\ \text{the four matrices } D^{kln} = \gamma^k\gamma^l\gamma^n (k < l < n) \\ \text{the single matrix}^{10}\ \gamma^5 = \gamma^0\gamma^1\gamma^2\gamma^3\end{array}\right\} \qquad (6.7)$$

It may be easily seen that all other products of the matrices (6.2), and consequently all the linear combinations of such products, i.e., the whole algebra A, can be expressed by linear relations in terms of the matrices (6.7). Thus, for example, after suitable commutations have been performed we have

$$\gamma^2\gamma^1 = -\Gamma^{12},\ \gamma^1\gamma^2\gamma^3\gamma^2\gamma^0 = D^{013} \text{ etc.}$$

As may be easily shown, the matrices (6.7) are linearly independent. To prove this property, we must examine the traces of the matrices (6.7). Remembering that by definition the trace of a matrix is the sum of its diagonal elements, we arrive at the possibility of cyclic permutation of matrix factors under the trace (or spur) sign. Thus, for example:

$$\mathrm{Sp}\, ABC \equiv \sum_{\alpha,\beta,\gamma} A_{\alpha\beta}B_{\beta\gamma}C_{\gamma\alpha} = \sum_{\alpha,\beta,\gamma} C_{\gamma\alpha}A_{\alpha\beta}B_{\beta\gamma} = \mathrm{Sp}\, CAB. \qquad (6.8)$$

Using this property and the definition (6.2) we shall show that the traces of all the matrices (6.7) with the exception of the unit matrix are equal to zero.

Let us consider, for example, the trace of one of the matrices $\gamma^k (k = 0, 1, 2, 3)$. We multiply γ^k on the left by $g^{nn}\gamma^n\gamma^n = 1 (n \neq k)$ and use the cyclic property. We then have:

$$\mathrm{Sp}\,\gamma^k = g^{kk}\,\mathrm{Sp}\,\gamma^n\gamma^n\gamma^k = g^{nn}\,\mathrm{Sp}\,\gamma^n\gamma^k\gamma^n,$$

from which we obtain with the aid of (6.2):

$$\mathrm{Sp}\,\gamma^k = \tfrac{1}{2} g^{nn}\,\mathrm{Sp}\,\gamma^n\,(\gamma^k\gamma^n + \gamma^n\gamma^k)|_{n\neq k} = 0. \qquad (6.9)$$

In a similar way one can show that all the other traces are also equal to zero. To illustrate the methods we also calculate the

[10] The symbol γ^4 is usually reserved for the matrix which differs from γ^0 by the factor i, i.e., $\gamma^4 = i\gamma^0$.

trace of the matrix γ^5. By a cyclic permutation of the matrix γ^0 which appears as a factor in γ^5 we have:

$$\mathrm{Sp}\,\gamma^5 = \mathrm{Sp}\,\gamma^0 D^{123} = \mathrm{Sp}\,D^{123}\gamma^0. \tag{6.10}$$

However, the result of a direct commutation of γ^0 and D^{123} yields

$$\gamma^0 D^{123} = -D^{123}\gamma^0,$$

from which it follows directly that the trace of the matrix γ^5 is equal to zero.

We shall now show that the linear independence of the matrices (6.7) follows from the fact that all their traces, except that of the unit matrix, are zero. To obtain the proof we assume the converse. Let

$$F = a\mathbf{I} + \sum_n b^n\gamma^n + \sum_{m,k} c^{mk}\Gamma^{mk} + \sum_{l,m,n} d^{lmn}D^{lmn} + e\gamma^5 = 0,$$

where a, b, c, d, and e are certain complex coefficients. Taking the trace of F we find $a = 0$. Then taking the trace of $\gamma^k F$ we find that $b^k = 0$. In a similar manner by successively taking the traces of the products of F with each of the matrices (6.7), we convince ourselves that all the coefficients in F are zero. Thus the number of linearly independent matrices of the algebra under consideration is sixteen, and the rank of the irreducible representation of the matrices γ^k is equal to four in accordance with (6.6).

Thus the hypercomplex numbers γ^k may be represented in the form of *square matrices of four rows and columns.* From the definition (6.2) it follows that the four matrices γ^k may be chosen to be unitary, if the condition of being Hermitean conjugate is imposed in the form

$$\gamma^{\dagger k} = g^{kk}\gamma^k. \tag{6.11}$$

(Here the matrix $a^\dagger$ which is Hermitean conjugate to a is taken to be as usual the matrix which is obtained from a by the operation of taking the complex conjugate of each of its elements followed by an interchange of rows and columns, i.e., $a^\dagger_{\alpha\beta} = a^*_{\beta\alpha}$.)

It may also be easily seen that the matrix γ^5 introduced above anticommutes with γ^0, γ^1, γ^2, γ^3, while its square is equal to -1, i.e.,

$$\gamma^k \gamma^l + \gamma^l \gamma^k = 2g^{kl} \qquad (k,\ l = 0,\ 1,\ 2,\ 3,\ 5), \qquad (6.12)$$

where by definition

$$g^{55} = -1. \qquad (6.13)$$

Also

$$\gamma^{\dagger k} = g^{kk} \gamma^k \qquad (k = 0,\ 1,\ 2,\ 3,\ 5). \qquad (6.14)$$

From the fact that the matrices γ have four rows it follows that the trace of the unit matrix is equal to four, i.e.,

$$\mathrm{Sp}\, \mathbf{I} = g^{kk}\, \mathrm{Sp}\, \gamma^k \gamma^k = 4. \qquad (6.15)$$

Taking into account the fact demonstrated above that the traces of the matrices γ^k, and also of their products Γ^{kl}, D^{kln} are equal to zero, and using the basic formula (6.2), we arrive after some additional computation at the following set of formulas

$$\begin{aligned} \mathrm{Sp}\, \gamma^k &= 0, \\ \mathrm{Sp}\, \gamma^k \gamma^l &= 4g^{kl}, \\ \mathrm{Sp}\, \gamma^k \gamma^l \gamma^m \gamma^n &= 4g^{kl} g^{mn} + 4g^{lm} g^{kn} - 4g^{km} g^{ln} \\ & \qquad (k,\ l,\ m,\ n = 0,\ 1,\ 2,\ 3) \qquad (6.16) \end{aligned}$$

etc.

As a general rule, we find that the traces of the products of an odd number of matrices γ are always equal to zero, while traces of an even number of such matrices are up to a factor 4 equal to the antisymmetrized sums of products of a corresponding number of factors g^{kl}, with the signs of the individual terms of such sums being determined by whether the corresponding permutation of indices is odd or even.

In concluding our discussion of the Dirac matrices, we note that the basic relations (6.2), and all the properties of the matrices found above, are invariant under a unitary transformation

$$\gamma^k \to O \gamma^k O^{-1}, \qquad (6.17)$$

where O is an arbitrary nonsingular matrix (i.e., one having an inverse) which may be regarded as unitary.

From this it follows that in general the matrices are determined only up to a unitary transformation, and the specific representation of the matrices may be chosen in a number of different ways. It is customary to use that representation of the

Dirac matrices in which γ^0 is diagonal:

$$\left.\begin{aligned}
&\gamma^0 = \begin{pmatrix} 1 & 0 & 0 & 0 \\ 0 & 1 & 0 & 0 \\ 0 & 0 & -1 & 0 \\ 0 & 0 & 0 & -1 \end{pmatrix}, \quad \gamma^2 = \begin{pmatrix} 0 & 0 & 0 & -i \\ 0 & 0 & i & 0 \\ 0 & i & 0 & 0 \\ -i & 0 & 0 & 0 \end{pmatrix}, \\
&\gamma^1 = \begin{pmatrix} 0 & 0 & 0 & 1 \\ 0 & 0 & 1 & 0 \\ 0 & -1 & 0 & 0 \\ -1 & 0 & 0 & 0 \end{pmatrix}, \quad \gamma^3 = \begin{pmatrix} 0 & 0 & 1 & 0 \\ 0 & 0 & 0 & -1 \\ -1 & 0 & 0 & 0 \\ 0 & 1 & 0 & 0 \end{pmatrix}, \\
&\gamma^5 = \begin{pmatrix} 0 & 0 & -i & 0 \\ 0 & 0 & 0 & -i \\ -i & 0 & 0 & 0 \\ 0 & -i & 0 & 0 \end{pmatrix}
\end{aligned}\right\} \tag{6.18}$$

This representation of the matrices γ is related to the frequently used matrices[11] α, β, and[12] σ, ρ by means of the relations

$$\begin{aligned}
&\alpha_n = \gamma^0\gamma^n \qquad (n = 1,\ 2,\ 3),\ \beta = \gamma^0, \\
&\sigma_\nu = i\gamma^5\gamma^0\gamma^\nu (\nu = 1,\ 2,\ 3), \quad \sigma_1 = i\gamma^2\gamma^3, \quad \sigma_2 = i\gamma^3\gamma^1, \quad \sigma_3 = i\gamma^1\gamma^2, \\
&\rho_1 = i\gamma^5, \quad \rho_2 = -\gamma^5\gamma^0, \quad \rho_3 = \gamma^0.
\end{aligned} \tag{6.19}$$

All the other representations may be obtained from (6.18) by means of the transformation (6.17).

6.3. *The Dirac Equation*

Let us now return to an examination of Dirac's equations (6.5). By noting that the set of Dirac matrices is invariant with respect to a change of sign of γ (transformation (6.17) with $O = \gamma^5$), we conclude that the sign in front of the mass term in the Dirac operator is not significant. Usually the fundamental Dirac equation is written in the form

$$\left(i \sum_n \gamma^n \frac{\partial}{\partial x^n} - m\right) \psi(x) = 0. \tag{6.20}$$

[11] cf., for example, W. Pauli (91).
[12] cf., for example, Dirac (30).

The second conjugate Dirac equation may be obtained from (6.20) in the following way. By taking the Hermitean conjugate expression of (6.20) we obtain in virtue of (6.14)

$$i \sum_n \frac{\partial \psi^*}{\partial x^n} \gamma^{*n} + m\psi^* = i \sum_n g^{nn} \frac{\partial \psi^*}{\partial x^n} \gamma^n + m\psi^* = 0.$$

This equation for ψ^*, however, does not have the correct form, since it differs from the first equation in (6.5) by the factor g^{nn} under the summation sign. In order to remove this deficiency we may, for example, multiply this equation on the right by the matrix γ^0. After carrying out the commutation of Dirac matrices under the summation sign we obtain the equation

$$i \sum_n \frac{\partial \bar{\psi}}{\partial x^n} \gamma^n + m\bar{\psi} = 0, \tag{6.21}$$

which has the correct form. The function $\bar{\psi}$ which appears in this equation is defined by the relation

$$\bar{\psi}(x) = \psi^*(x)\gamma^0 \tag{6.22}$$

and is referred to as the *adjoint* (or the *Dirac-conjugate*) function with respect to ψ. In a similar fashion equation (6.21) is said to be "adjoint" with respect to (6.20). It will be shown later (see § 7) that in analogy to (4.36) the function $\bar{\psi}$ enables us to introduce a Lagrangian and to construct dynamic variables.

Since the rank of the Dirac matrices is equal to four, the wave functions ψ and $\bar{\psi}$ are *four-component* ones, and are sometimes represented by a four-component column or row vector respectively. In spite of its simple appearance the representation of ψ and $\bar{\psi}$ in the form of rows and columns may, however, lead to a certain amount of confusion (for example in the introduction of the operation of charge conjugation — see § 12 of Chapter II), and therefore we shall not use it. It will be sufficient for us to keep in mind that by writing out in detail the matrix form of Dirac equation (6.20), we shall obtain the four equations

$$\sum_\beta \left(i \sum_n \gamma^n_{\alpha\beta} \frac{\partial}{\partial x^n} - m\mathbf{I}_{\alpha\beta} \right) \psi_\beta(x) = 0$$

for the four components $\psi_\alpha(\alpha = 1, 2, 3, 4)$. Obviously the adjoint equation (6.21) may also be written out in component form.

6.4. *Transformation Properties of the Spinor Field*

We now turn to an examination of the transformations of the spinor wave functions under Lorentz transformations of the coordinates. We note that in contrast to the tensor representations considered earlier, for which the field equations were automatically covariant due to the covariance of the Klein-Gordon operator, the conditions for the covariance of the Dirac equations (6.20), (6.21) must be investigated separately.

As is well known, an equation is said to be *covariant* if after a transformation, i.e., in terms of the transformed coordinates and functions, it has the same form as before the transformation.

Thus, for example, under the space-time translations

$$x \to x' = x^k + a^k$$

the Dirac operator is not altered

$$i \sum_n \gamma^n \frac{\partial}{\partial x^n} - m = i \sum_n \gamma^n \frac{\partial}{\partial x'^n} - m$$

and therefore, in accordance with the remark made in § 2, one should set

$$\psi'(x') = \psi(x),$$

since this will make the equation have the old form in terms of the new variables:

$$\left(i \sum_n \gamma^n \frac{\partial}{\partial x'^n} - m\right) \psi'(x') = 0, \qquad (6.23)$$

i.e., it remains covariant.

Under the infinitesimal rotations

$$x \to x' = x + \delta x, \; \delta x^k = \sum_n g^{nn} x^n \omega^{kn}, \;\; \omega^{kn} + \omega^{nk} = 0 \qquad (6.24)$$

the Dirac operator is no longer covariant

$$\left(i \sum_k \gamma^k \frac{\partial}{\partial x'^k} - m\right) = i \sum_n \gamma^n \left(\frac{\partial}{\partial x^n} - g^{nn} \sum_k \omega^{kn} \frac{\partial}{\partial x^k}\right) - m,$$

in view of which the transformation law for the spinor wave function has a more complicated matrix form

$$\psi'(x') = \Lambda\psi(x). \tag{6.25}$$

In order to establish the connection between the transformation matrix Λ and the Dirac matrices and the transformation parameters we shall start from the condition of covariance of the Dirac equation, and assume that it has the form (6.23) in terms of the transformed variables. On multiplying (6.23) on the left by Λ^{-1} we shall obtain the original equation (6.20) provided the following relation holds:

$$\Lambda^{-1}\gamma^n\Lambda = \gamma^n + \sum_k g^{kk}\gamma^k\omega^{nk} \quad (n, k = 0, 1, 2, 3). \tag{6.26}$$

Here all terms of the first order in ω mutually cancel, and neglecting terms of the second order we obtain:

$$\Lambda^{-1}\left(i\sum_k \gamma^k \frac{\partial}{\partial x'^k} - m\right)\psi'(x') = \left(i\sum_k \gamma^k \frac{\partial}{\partial x^k} - m\right)\psi(x) = 0.$$

By representing the matrix Λ in the form

$$\Lambda = 1 + \sum_{i,k} \lambda_{ik}\omega^{ik}, \tag{6.27}$$

where the expansion coefficients λ_{ik} have the property of being antisymmetric

$$\lambda_{ik} = -\lambda_{ki},$$

we find that in view of (6.26) they satisfy the relations

$$\gamma^k\lambda_{kl} - \lambda_{kl}\gamma^k = g^{ll}\gamma^l;$$

which together with the conditions of antisymmetry yield

$$\lambda_{kl} = \tfrac{1}{2}g^{kk}g^{ll}\gamma^k\gamma^l. \tag{6.28}$$

Formulas (6.27) and (6.28) give us the explicit form of the transformation matrix Λ for the infinitesimal rotation transformations. However, it turns out that with the aid of these formulas one may also obtain the explicit form of the matrix Λ for finite transformations. To achieve this we make use of the *group* property of the operator $\Lambda(\varphi)$ where φ is the angle of rotation in one of the planes $x^k x^l$. From the additive property of rotations it follows that

$$\Lambda(\varphi_1 + \varphi_2)\psi = \Lambda(\varphi_1)\Lambda(\varphi_2)\psi,$$

i.e.,

$$\Lambda(\varphi_1 + \varphi_2) = \Lambda(\varphi_1)\Lambda(\varphi_2).$$

Setting $\varphi_1 = \varphi$, $\varphi_2 = d\varphi$ in the above expressions after a short calculation

$$\Lambda(\varphi + d\varphi) = \Lambda(\varphi)\Lambda(d\varphi), \qquad \frac{\Lambda(\varphi + d\varphi) - \Lambda(\varphi)}{d\varphi} = \Lambda(\varphi)\,\frac{\Lambda(d\varphi) - 1}{d\varphi}$$

we obtain the differential equation for the group of rotations

$$\frac{d\Lambda(\varphi)}{d\varphi} = \Lambda(\varphi)\lambda_{ik}.$$

On integrating this equation, taking into account (6.28) and the initial condition $\Lambda(0) = 1$ which arises from (6.27), we find:

$$\Lambda_{ik}(\varphi) = \exp \tfrac{1}{2}[g^{ii} g^{kk} \gamma^i \gamma^k \varphi]. \tag{6.29}$$

The calculation carried out above with the aid of which we have obtained formula (6.28) is a special case of an argument, well known in group theory, by means of which the group as a whole is reconstructed from the operators of infinitesimal rotation transformations.

Let us examine special cases of formula (6.29). For a space rotation in the plane $x^\alpha x^\beta (\alpha \neq \beta,\ \alpha,\ \beta = 1,\ 2,\ 3)$

$$x'^\alpha = x^\alpha \cos\varphi - x^\beta \sin\varphi, \quad x'^\beta = x^\beta \cos\varphi + x^\alpha \sin\varphi; \tag{6.30}$$

and from this we obtain

$$\psi'(x') = \Lambda_{\alpha\beta}\psi(x),$$

$$\left.\begin{aligned} \Lambda_{\alpha\beta} &= e^{\frac{\varphi}{2}\gamma^\alpha\gamma^\beta} = \cos\frac{\varphi}{2} + \gamma^\alpha\gamma^\beta \sin\frac{\varphi}{2}, \\ \Lambda^{-1}_{\alpha\beta} &= e^{-\frac{\varphi}{2}\gamma^\alpha\gamma^\beta} = \cos\frac{\varphi}{2} - \gamma^\alpha\gamma^\beta \sin\frac{\varphi}{2}. \end{aligned}\right\} \tag{6.31}$$

For a Lorentz rotation in the plane $x^0x^\alpha(\alpha = 1, 2, 3)$

$$\left.\begin{aligned} x'^0 &= x^0 \operatorname{ch} \varphi - x^\alpha \operatorname{sh} \varphi, \\ x'^\alpha &= x^\alpha \operatorname{ch} \varphi - x^0 \operatorname{sh} \varphi \end{aligned}\right\} (\operatorname{tg} \varphi = v) \tag{6.32}$$

we shall correspondingly obtain

$$\left.\begin{aligned} \Lambda_{0\alpha} &= e^{-\frac{1}{2}\varphi\gamma^0\gamma^\alpha} = \operatorname{ch} \frac{\varphi}{2} - \gamma^0\gamma^\alpha \operatorname{sh} \frac{\varphi}{2}, \\ \Lambda_{0\alpha}^{-1} &= e^{\frac{1}{2}\varphi\gamma^0\gamma^\alpha} = \operatorname{ch} \frac{\varphi}{2} + \gamma^0\gamma^\alpha \operatorname{sh} \frac{\varphi}{2}. \end{aligned}\right\} \tag{6.33}$$

As may be seen from (6.26) the expression $\Lambda^{-1} \gamma^n \Lambda$ in the case of the infinitesimal transformation (6.24) is given in terms of the matrices γ^n by the same linear form which gives the transformed coordinates x' in terms of x. Forming the expressions $\Lambda^{-1}\gamma^n\Lambda$ with the aid of (6.31) and (6.33), and comparing them with (6.30) and (6.32), we find that the same holds for the finite rotation transformations.

The *nonuniqueness* of spinor functions follows directly from the formulas of space rotation (6.31). Setting $\varphi = 2\pi$ in these formulas we find that the transformation matrix $\Lambda(2\pi) = -1$ corresponds to a complete space rotation of the coordinate system, i.e., the field function changes sign under such a transformation. However, since the transformation of rotation through an angle 2π brings the coordinate system into its original position, i.e., coincides with the identity transformation, it follows that the *spinor wave functions are always determined up to their sign.*

We also exhibit the form of the matrix Λ for the transformations of *reflection* of different number of coordinate axes. Noting that the transformation formulas for reflections of an even number of different space axes, which reduce to rotations, follow from (6.31), we shall restrict ourselves to the transformation of reflection of all three space axes

$$\left.\begin{aligned} x'^\alpha &= -x^\alpha (\alpha = 1, 2, 3), \; x'^0 = x^0, \\ \psi'(x') &= \Lambda_{123}\psi(x), \quad \Lambda_{123} = \gamma^0, \end{aligned}\right\} \tag{6.34}$$

and to the transformation of reflection of the time axis

$$\left.\begin{aligned} &x'^0 = x^0,\ x'^\alpha = x^\alpha\ (\alpha = 1,\ 2,\ 3), \\ &\psi'(x') = \Lambda_0\psi(x),\ \Lambda_0 = \gamma^1\gamma^2\gamma^3 = \gamma^0\gamma^5. \end{aligned}\right\} \qquad (6.35)$$

The transformation properties of the adjoint spinor $\bar{\psi}$ follow from its definition (6.22). Taking the Hermitean conjugate of (6.25), and multiplying it on the right by γ^0 we obtain:

$$\psi^{*\prime}(x')\gamma^0 = \bar{\psi}'(x') = \psi^* \Lambda^\dagger \gamma^0 = \bar{\psi}(x)\gamma^0 \Lambda^\dagger \gamma^0,$$

i.e., we find that the adjoint spinor is transformed by means of the matrix $\gamma^0\Lambda^\dagger\gamma^0$. Further, it may be easily seen that for any transformation of the Lorentz group, the following relation always holds

$$\gamma^0\Lambda^\dagger\gamma^0 = \Lambda^{-1}, \qquad (6.36)$$

in virtue of which the transformation law for the adjoint spinor, for transformations of the Lorentz group will have the form

$$\bar{\psi}'(x') = \bar{\psi}(x)\Lambda^{-1}. \qquad (6.37)$$

To prove (6.36) we note that it obviously holds under a transformation of reflection of space axes (6.34), while its validity under rotations may be established with the aid of the relation

$$\gamma^0\gamma^{\dagger k}\gamma^0 = \gamma^k \qquad (6.38)$$

which follows from (6.2) and (6.15). Since in accordance with (6.31) and (6.33) the transformation matrices of the rotations are linear functions of quadratic combinations of Dirac's matrices, we find with the aid of (6.38)

$$\begin{aligned} \gamma^0\Lambda^\dagger(\gamma^k\gamma^l)\gamma^0 = \gamma^0\Lambda(\gamma^{\dagger l}\gamma^{\dagger k})\gamma^0 &= \Lambda(\gamma^0\gamma^{\dagger l}\gamma^0 \cdot \gamma^0\gamma^{\dagger k}\gamma^0) \\ &= \Lambda(\gamma^l\gamma^k) = \Lambda(-\gamma^k\gamma^l), \end{aligned}$$

which is equivalent [13] to (6.36) in accordance with the second formulas of (6.31) and (6.33).

On the basis of the above considerations one may say that under an arbitrary homogeneous Lorentz transformation of the coordinate system

[13] By carrying out a similar calculation for a transformation which includes a reflection of the time axis we would have obtained in place of (37) the relation

$$\bar{\psi}'(x') = -\bar{\psi}(x)\Lambda^{-1}. \qquad (6.39)$$

$$x' = Lx, \; x'^n = \sum_m L^{nm} x^m \tag{6.40}$$

the spinor wave function $\psi(x)$, and the function $\bar{\psi}(x)$ adjoint to it, transform with the aid of mutually inverse matrix operators Λ and Λ^{-1} which have the property

$$\Lambda^{-1} \gamma^n \Lambda = \sum_m L^{nm} \gamma^m. \tag{6.41}$$

We shall now show that from the transformation laws (6.25), (6.37) taken together with expression (6.41) it follows that quadratic forms of spinors ψ and $\bar{\psi}$ transorm in accordance with tensor representations of the Lorentz group.

In order to do this, we consider the quadratic form

$$\bar{\psi}(x) O \psi(x), \tag{6.42}$$

where O is a certain, as yet arbitrary, matrix constructed from products of the γ matrices. Under a Lorentz transformation (6.40) we find on the basis of (6.25) and (6.37):

$$\bar{\psi}'(x') O \psi'(x') = \bar{\psi}(x) \Lambda^{-1} O \Lambda \psi(x).$$

Let us consider the simplest special cases: (a) $O = 1$; $\bar{\psi}'(x')\psi'(x') = \bar{\psi}(x)\psi(x)$, from which it is clear that the form $\bar{\psi}\psi$ is a scalar; (b) $O = \gamma^n$ $(n = 0, 1, 2, 3)$; with the aid of (6.41) we find:

$$\bar{\psi}'(x') \gamma^n \psi'(x') = \sum_m L^{nm} \bar{\psi}(x) \gamma^m \psi(x),$$

from which it follows that the four quantities $\bar{\psi}\gamma^n\psi$ form a covariant four-vector.

In a similar way it may be shown that the quantities

$$\bar{\psi}(x) \frac{\gamma^n \gamma^m - \gamma^m \gamma^n}{2} \psi(x)$$

represent the components of an antisymmetric covariant tensor of the second rank, etc.

Of particular interest are those cases when the matrix γ^5 occurs as a factor in O. The point is that, as may be easily shown, under proper Lorentz transformations γ^5 commutes with Λ:

$$\Lambda^{-1} \gamma^5 \Lambda = \gamma^5,$$

while under improper Lorentz transformations they anticommute

$$\Lambda^{-1}\gamma^5\Lambda = -\gamma^5.$$

Therefore the form $\bar{\psi}(x)\gamma^5\psi(x)$ behaves like a scalar in the former case and changes sign in the latter. It is clear that it is a pseudoscalar. In a similar fashion the four quantities

$$\bar{\psi}(x)\gamma^5\gamma^n\psi(x)$$

transform under rotations like the components of a four-vector, while under reflections they in addition change sign. They form a pseudovector.

By analogous arguments one may without difficulty establish the tensor nature also of more complicated forms of type (6.42). However, we shall conclude with these examples our examination of the properties of the γ matrices and of the transformation laws of spinor functions, since the material presented above will turn out to be sufficient for the purposes of our further discussion.[14]

§ 7. The Spinor Field. Properties of the Solutions and Dynamic Variables

7.1. *Momentum Representation and Matrix Structure*

We now proceed to discuss the properties of the solutions of the Dirac matrix equation (6.20)

$$\left(i\sum_n \gamma^n \frac{\partial}{\partial x^n} - m\right)\psi(x) = 0.$$

Since the rank of the matrices γ^n is equal to four the field function ψ has four components. Each of these components satisfies the Klein-Gordon equation. Indeed, applying the operator $(i\hat{\partial} + m)$ from the left to (6.20) we find, on taking (6.3) into account, that

$$\left(i\sum_n \gamma^n \frac{\partial}{\partial x^n} + m\right)\left(i\sum_n \gamma^n \frac{\partial}{\partial x^n} - m\right)\psi(x)$$
$$= (i\hat{\partial} + m)(i\hat{\partial} - m)\psi(x) = (\Box - m^2)\psi(x) = 0.$$

[14] We recommend to the reader who is interested in a more detailed and complete presentation of the transformation laws of spinor functions the review article by I. S. Shapiro (111).

Therefore $\psi(x)$ may be represented in the form

$$\psi(x) = \frac{1}{(2\pi)^{3/2}} \int dk e^{ikx} \delta(k^2 - m^2) \psi(k), \tag{7.1}$$

with the momentum amplitude $\psi(k)$ by definition satisfying the equation

$$(\hat{k} + m)\psi(k)|_{k^2=m^2} = 0. \tag{7.2}$$

Here we have introduced the notation

$$\hat{a} = \sum_n g^{nn} a^n \gamma^n = (a\gamma) = a^0 \gamma^0 - \mathbf{a}\gamma,$$

which we shall frequently employ in the subsequent discussion.

Decomposing, as usual, the function $\psi(x)$ into its positive- and negative-frequency parts

$$\psi(x) = \psi^{(+)}(x) + \psi^{(-)}(x), \tag{7.3}$$

$$\psi^{(\pm)}(x) = \frac{1}{(2\pi)^{3/2}} \int dk e^{ikx} \delta(k^2 - m^2) \theta(\pm k^0) \psi(k), \tag{7.4}$$

and integrating over k^0, we obtain the formulas for the three-dimensional momentum representation in the form

$$\psi^{(\pm)}(x) = \frac{1}{(2\pi)^{3/2}} \int d\mathbf{k} e^{\pm ikx} \psi^{(\pm)}(\mathbf{k}). \tag{7.5}$$

Here we have adopted the notation

$$\left.\begin{aligned} \psi^{(+)}(\mathbf{k}) &= \frac{\theta(k^0)\psi(k)}{2k^0}, \\ \psi^{(-)}(\mathbf{k}) &= \frac{\theta(k^0)\psi(-k)}{2k^0} \end{aligned}\right\} \quad (k^0 = \sqrt{\mathbf{k}^2 + m^2}). \tag{7.6}$$

The three-dimensional amplitudes $\psi^{(+)}(\mathbf{k})$ and $\psi^{(-)}(\mathbf{k})$ satisfy the matrix equations

$$(m + \hat{k})\psi^{(+)}(\mathbf{k}) = 0, \quad (m - \hat{k})\psi^{(-)}(\mathbf{k}) = 0. \tag{7.7}$$

The different signs of $\hat{k}$ in these equations arise from the difference in signs of the exponents in the integrands in formulas (7.5).

The matrix structure of $\psi^{(+)}$ and $\psi^{(-)}$ depends on the representation of the Dirac matrices γ and may be determined in the following manner. In view of the covariance of equation (7.2) established above, it may be discussed in some fixed system of coordinates, having in mind that we can always go over to any other system with the aid of the transformations discussed in the preceding section. Choosing as such a system the system in which $\mathbf{k} = 0$, we find from (7.2) and (7.7)

$$(\gamma^0 k^0 + m)\psi(k^0)_{k^0=m} = 0,$$
$$(\gamma^0 + \mathbf{I})\psi^{(+)}(0) = 0,$$
$$(\gamma^0 - \mathbf{I})\psi^{(-)}(0) = 0.$$

From this we obtain in the representation (6.18)

$$\left.\begin{aligned}\psi_\alpha^{(+)}(0) &= c_3\delta_\alpha^3 + c_4\delta_\alpha^4, \\ \psi_\beta^{(-)}(0) &= c_1\delta_\beta^1 + c_2\delta_\beta^2.\end{aligned}\right\} \tag{7.8}$$

Here α, β are matrix indices, and δ_k^i are Kronecker's symbols.

The solution for an arbitrary k different from zero may be obtained from (7.8) by means of an appropriate Lorentz transformation.

The equations satisfied by $\psi^{(+)}$ and $\psi^{(-)}$ may also be written in the form

$$\left.\begin{aligned}(\gamma^0 k^0 + \boldsymbol{\gamma}\mathbf{k} + m)\,\psi^{(+)}(\mathbf{k}) &= 0, \\ (-\gamma^0 k^0 + \boldsymbol{\gamma}\mathbf{k} + m)\,\psi^{(-)}(-\mathbf{k}) &= 0\end{aligned}\right\} \quad (k^0 = +\sqrt{\mathbf{k}^2 + m^2}),$$

in which they differ from each other only by the sign of k^0. As has just been shown, each of them has two linearly independent solutions. From this it follows that the Dirac equation has only *two linearly independent solutions* for each given value of the four-vector k (the sign of the k^0 component being fixed!).

It is now not difficult to establish the transformation nature of the functions $\psi^{(+)}$ and $\psi^{(-)}$. To do this we consider the set of transformations consisting of the three-dimensional purely spatial rotations and reflections of the space axes. This set of transformations forms a group G which is a subgroup of the Lorentz group. Since the transformations of the group G do not act on the time coordinate x^0, they also leave invariant the matrix structure of the decomposition (7.3) of the field function into its positive- and negative-frequency parts. In other words, under three-dimensional rotations and spatial reflections the two-component quantities $\psi^{(+)}$ and $\psi^{(-)}$ transform independently of each other. Therefore each of them provides a two-dimensional representation of the rotation group and of reflections in three-dimensional space. This representation is said to be a *spinor* representation, and quantities which transform in accordance with it are called *spinors in three-dimensional space.*

Thus the four-component field function ψ, which transforms in accordance with the spinor representation of the Lorentz group and which therefore represents a *spinor in four-dimensional pseudo-Euclidean space* over which the Lorentz group is defined, *decomposes with respect to the group of three-dimensional reflections and rotations into two irreducible parts which are spinors in three-dimensional space.*[15]

The fact that the positive- and negative-frequency components of the field function $\psi^{(+)}$ and $\psi^{(-)}$ transform independently of each other under three-dimensional rotations and reflections may be directly checked in the representation (6.18) used by us in the following manner.

In accordance with (7.8), the field function ψ may be represented in the form

$$\psi = \begin{pmatrix} \psi^{(-)} \\ \psi^{(+)} \end{pmatrix}, \tag{7.9}$$

where $\psi^{(-)}$ and $\psi^{(+)}$ are two-component functions.

On the other hand, writing Dirac's matrices (6.18) with the aid of the *two-rowed Pauli matrices*

$$\left.\begin{aligned} \sigma_1 = \begin{pmatrix} 0 & 1 \\ 1 & 0 \end{pmatrix}, \quad \sigma_2 = \begin{pmatrix} 0 & -i \\ i & 0 \end{pmatrix}, \quad \sigma_3 = \begin{pmatrix} 1 & 0 \\ 0 & -1 \end{pmatrix}, \\ \sigma_1 \sigma_2 = -\sigma_2 \sigma_1 = i\sigma_3, \ldots \end{aligned}\right\} \tag{7.10}$$

in the "split-up form"[16]

$$\gamma^0 = \begin{pmatrix} \mathbf{I} & \mathbf{0} \\ \mathbf{0} & -\mathbf{I} \end{pmatrix}, \quad \gamma^\alpha = \begin{pmatrix} \mathbf{0} & \sigma_\alpha \\ -\sigma_\alpha & \mathbf{0} \end{pmatrix} \quad (\alpha = 1, 2, 3), \tag{7.11}$$

we see that the transformation matrices of the three-dimensional rotations and reflections turn out, in accordance with (6.31) and (6.34), also to be diagonal in the "split-up" representation (7.9):

$$\gamma^1\gamma^2 = -i\begin{pmatrix} \sigma_3 & \mathbf{0} \\ \mathbf{0} & \sigma_3 \end{pmatrix}, \quad \gamma^2\gamma^3 = -i\begin{pmatrix} \sigma_1 & \mathbf{0} \\ \mathbf{0} & \sigma_1 \end{pmatrix}, \quad \gamma^3\gamma^1 = -i\begin{pmatrix} \sigma_2 & \mathbf{0} \\ \mathbf{0} & \sigma_2 \end{pmatrix}, \quad \gamma^0 = \begin{pmatrix} \mathbf{I} & \mathbf{0} \\ \mathbf{0} & -\mathbf{I} \end{pmatrix}, \tag{7.12}$$

from which the independence of the transformations $\psi^{(+)}$ and $\psi^{(-)}$ follows directly.

[15] We note that the terminology that we employ has been adopted from Cartan's book (28). Some authors use the term "spinor" to refer to the two-component spinor in three-dimensional space. In such cases, the four-component spinor of the Lorentz group is called a "bispinor."

[16] Here we have also adopted the abbreviated notation for the two-rowed unity and zero matrices

$$\mathbf{I} = \begin{pmatrix} 1 & 0 \\ 0 & 1 \end{pmatrix}, \quad \mathbf{0} = \begin{pmatrix} 0 & 0 \\ 0 & 0 \end{pmatrix},$$

Corresponding to this, the adjoint spinor $\bar{\psi}$ also has two linearly independent solutions for a definite sign of the frequency. Since the preceding solutions of Dirac's equation are complex, one may say that they describe positively and negatively charged particles. Since two linearly independent solutions exist, it follows now that these particles may exist in two different states which, as will be shown below, differ in the *sign of the component of spin* along the direction of motion.

7.2. *Decomposition into Spin States and Normalization and Orthogonality Relations*

Denoting the normalized linearly independent solutions for $k^0 > 0$, i.e., of the first of equations (7.7), by $v^{\nu,+}(\mathbf{k})$, and those for $k^0 < 0$, i.e., of the second of equations (7.7), by $v^{\nu,-}(\mathbf{k})$ $(\nu = 1, 2)$, we shall write the expansions of the functions $\psi^{(+)}(\mathbf{k})$ and $\psi^{(-)}(\mathbf{k})$ into spin states in the form

$$\psi_\alpha^{(\pm)}(\mathbf{k}) = \sum_{\nu=1,\,2} a_\nu^\pm(\mathbf{k})\, v_\alpha^{\nu,\,\pm}(\mathbf{k}). \tag{7.13}$$

Similarly for the adjoint spinor

$$\bar{\psi}^{(\pm)}(\mathbf{k}) = \sum_{\nu=1,\,2} a_\nu^{*\pm}(\mathbf{k})\bar{v}^{\nu,\,\pm}(\mathbf{k}). \tag{7.14}$$

Since $\bar{\psi}^{(+)}$ and $\bar{\psi}^{(-)}$ represent here, as elsewhere throughout this book, the positive- and negative-frequency parts of the function $\bar{\psi}$ the conditions of Hermitean conjugation for the normalized spinors v have the form

$$(v^{\nu,\,\pm}(\mathbf{k}))^* = v^{*\nu,\,\mp}(\mathbf{k}). \tag{7.15}$$

Therefore the conditions for the orthonormality of the spinors v may be written in the form

$$v^{*\nu,\,\pm}(\mathbf{k})v^{\mu,\,\mp}(\mathbf{k}) \equiv \sum_{\alpha=1,\,2,\,3,\,4} v_\alpha^{*\nu,\,\pm}(\mathbf{k})v_\alpha^{\mu,\,\mp}(\mathbf{k}) = \delta^{\mu\nu}. \tag{7.16}$$

By means of purely algebraic transformations, one may obtain from (7.6), (7.15), and the Dirac equations a number of relations for quadratic forms in the spinors v and $\bar{v} = v^*\gamma^0$, the most important of which are the following:

the condition of orthonormality for the adjoint spinors

$$\bar{v}^{\nu,\pm}(\mathbf{k})v^{\mu,\mp}(\mathbf{k}) = v^{*\nu,\pm}(\mathbf{k})\,\gamma^0 v^{\mu,\mp}(\mathbf{k}) = \pm\frac{m}{k^0}\,\delta^{\mu\nu}; \tag{7.17}$$

the condition of mutual orthogonality for the spinors v with arguments differing only in their sign

$$v^{*\nu,\pm}(\mathbf{k})\,v^{\mu,\pm}(-\mathbf{k}) = 0; \tag{7.18}$$

the relations

$$\left.\begin{aligned} & v^{*\pm}(\mathbf{k})[(k^\alpha\gamma^\beta - k^\beta\gamma^\alpha) - m\gamma^\alpha\gamma^\beta]v^{\pm}(-\mathbf{k}) = 0, & \text{(7.19a)}\\ & \sum_{\alpha=1,2,3} k^\alpha[v^{*\nu,\pm}(\mathbf{k})\,(\gamma^\alpha\gamma^\beta - \gamma^\beta\gamma^\alpha)\,v^{\mu,\mp}(\mathbf{k})] = 0 & \text{(7.19b)}\end{aligned}\right\}(\alpha, \beta = 1, 2, 3)$$

and, finally, the formulas for summation over the spin index

$$\left.\begin{aligned} & \sum_{\nu=1,2} v_\alpha^{\nu,+}(\mathbf{k})\,\bar{v}_\beta^{\nu,-}(\mathbf{k}) = \frac{(\hat{k}-m)_{\alpha\beta}}{2k^0}, & \text{(7.20)}\\ & \sum_{\nu=1,2} v_\alpha^{\nu,-}(\mathbf{k})\bar{v}_\beta^{\nu,+}(\mathbf{k}) = \frac{(\hat{k}+m)_{\alpha\beta}}{2k^0} & \text{(7.21)}\end{aligned}\right\}(k^0 = +\sqrt{\mathbf{k}^2 + m^2}).$$

To prove relation (7.17) we begin with the Dirac equations

$$\left.\begin{aligned} (\gamma^0 k^0 - \boldsymbol{\gamma}\mathbf{k} + m)\,v^{\nu,+}(\mathbf{k}) &= 0,\\ (\gamma^0 k^0 + \boldsymbol{\gamma}\mathbf{k} - m)\,v^{\mu,-}(-\mathbf{k}) &= 0 \end{aligned}\right\}(\mathbf{k}^0 = \sqrt{\mathbf{k}^2 + m^2}). \tag{7.22}$$

Multiplying the first of these on the left by $v^{*\mu,-}(\mathbf{k})$ we obtain:

$$k^0\bar{v}^{\mu,-}(\mathbf{k})\,v^{\nu,+}(\mathbf{k}) - \mathbf{k}v^{*\mu,-}(\mathbf{k})\boldsymbol{\gamma}v^{\nu,+}(\mathbf{k}) + mv^{*\mu,-}(\mathbf{k})v^{\nu,+}(\mathbf{k}) = 0.$$

Taking the Hermitean conjugate, and making use of the Hermitean properties of the Dirac matrices (7.15), we obtain the expression

$$k^0\bar{v}^{\nu,-}(\mathbf{k})\,v^{\mu,+}(\mathbf{k}) + \mathbf{k}v^{*\nu,-}(\mathbf{k})\boldsymbol{\gamma}v^{\mu,+}(\mathbf{k}) + mv^{*\nu,-}(\mathbf{k})\,v^{\mu,+}(\mathbf{k}) = 0,$$

a comparison of which with the original expression leads directly to

$$v^{*\nu,-}(\mathbf{k})\,\gamma^0 v^{\mu,+}(\mathbf{k}) = -\frac{m}{k^0}\,\delta^{\mu\nu}.$$

The second of relations (7.17) is proved in a similar manner.

To prove the orthogonality properties (7.18) we multiply the first of equations (7.22) on the left by $\bar{v}^{\mu,+}(-\mathbf{k})$:

$$k^0 v^{*\mu,+}(-\mathbf{k})\,v^{\nu,+}(\mathbf{k}) - v^{*\mu,+}(-\mathbf{k})\,(\gamma^0\boldsymbol{\gamma}\mathbf{k} - m\gamma^0)\,v^{\nu,+}(\mathbf{k}) = 0.$$

Multiplying the second of equations (7.22) on the left by $\bar{v}^{\nu,-}(\mathbf{k})$ and taking the Hermitean conjugate we arrive at the relation

$$k^0 v^{*\mu,+}(-\mathbf{k})\,v^{\nu,+}(\mathbf{k}) + v^{*\mu,+}(-\mathbf{k})\,(\gamma^0\boldsymbol{\gamma}\mathbf{k} - m\gamma^0)\,v^{\nu,+}(\mathbf{k}) = 0,$$

a comparison of which with the preceding one yields directly one of relations (7.18):

$$v^{*\mu,+}(-\mathbf{k})\, v^{\nu,+}(\mathbf{k}) = 0.$$

The derivation of relations (7.19a) and (7.19b) is accomplished by means of the same methods of multiplying the Dirac equations by products of the γ^n matrices and adjoint spinors and of taking the Hermitean conjugate of the expressions so obtained. In view of the relative awkwardness of such calculations we omit the derivation of expressions (7.19).

To obtain formulas (7.20), (7.21) for summing over spins, we consider the usual Green's function for the Dirac equation (7.2) which satisfies the inhomogeneous equation

$$G(k)(\hat{k} + m) = (\hat{k} + m)G(k) = 1 \tag{7.23}$$

and which consequently has the form

$$G(k) = (\hat{k} + m)^{-1} = \frac{\hat{k} - m}{k^2 - m^2}. \tag{7.24}$$

In the last two equations k^0 is not equal to the root $\pm(\mathbf{k}^2 + m^2)^{1/2}$ which we shall denote here by λ

$$\lambda(\mathbf{k}) = \sqrt{\mathbf{k}^2 + m^2}.$$

On the contrary, the number $\pm\lambda$ has for k^0 the nature of an eigenvalue of the corresponding homogeneous equation. Therefore $G(k)$ is not even defined for $k^0 = \pm\lambda$. However, for $k^0 \neq \pm\lambda$ $G(k)$ may be expanded in terms of the complete system of solutions of the homogeneous equation

$$(\hat{k} + m)v = 0,$$

which, in accordance with (7.22), consists of the four solutions $v^{\nu,+}(\mathbf{k})$, $v^{\nu,-}(\mathbf{k})$ $(\nu = 1, 2)$. We then obtain the expansion

$$G_{\alpha\beta}(k) = \sum_{\nu=1,2} (v_\alpha^{\nu,+}(\mathbf{k})\, w_\beta^{\nu,+}(k) + v_\alpha^{\nu,-}(\mathbf{k})\, w_\beta^{\nu,-}(\mathbf{k})).$$

If we substitute it into (7.23):

$$(\gamma^0 k^0 - \boldsymbol{\gamma}\mathbf{k} + m)\Big[\sum_{\nu=1,2} (v_\alpha^{\nu,+}(\mathbf{k})\, w_\beta^{\nu,+}(k) + v_\alpha^{\nu,-}(\mathbf{k})\, w_\beta^{\nu,-}(\mathbf{k}))\Big] = 1$$

and use the field equations

$$(\boldsymbol{\gamma}\mathbf{k} - m)\, v^{\nu,+}(\mathbf{k}) = \gamma^0\lambda v^{\nu,+}(\mathbf{k}); \qquad (\gamma k - m)\, v^{\nu,-}(-\mathbf{k}) = -\gamma^0\lambda v^{\nu,-}(-\mathbf{k}),$$

we obtain:

$$(k^0 - \lambda)\gamma^0 \sum_\nu v^{\nu,+}(\mathbf{k})\, w^{\nu,+}(k) + (k^0 + \lambda)\gamma^0 \sum_\nu v^{\nu,-}(-\mathbf{k})\, w^{\nu,-}(k) = 1. \tag{7 25}$$

Multiplying (7.25) on the left by $\bar{v}^{\mu,+}(-\mathbf{k})$ and taking into account the properties of normalization (7.16) and of orthogonality (7.18), we obtain an expression for the coefficient $w^{\nu,+}$:

$$w^{\nu,-}(k) = \frac{\bar{v}^{\nu,+}(-\mathbf{k})}{k^0 + \lambda(\mathbf{k})}.$$

Determining in a similar way the second coefficient $w^{\nu,+}$ we arrive at the following expression for G:

$$G(k) = \sum_{\nu} \frac{(k^0+\lambda)\, v^{\lambda,+}(\mathbf{k})\, \bar{v}^{\nu,-}(\mathbf{k}) + (k^0-\lambda)\, v^{\nu,-}(-\mathbf{k})\, \bar{v}^{\nu,+}(-\mathbf{k})}{(k^0)^2 - \lambda^2}. \tag{7.26}$$

Recalling then that $\lambda^2 = \mathbf{k}^2 + m^2$, and comparing (7.26) with (7.24) in the limits $k^0 \to +\lambda$ and $k^0 \to -\lambda$ we obtain formulas (7.20) and (7.21) respectively.

We shall need the relations (7.17)–(7.19) for the calculation of the dynamic variables of the spinor field (this section), while formulas (7.20) and (7.21) will be useful for the quantization of the spinor field (Chapter II) and for the calculation of the squares of matrix elements in the theory of interacting fields (Chapter III).

7.3. *Lagrangian Formalism and Invariants*

We now turn to the Lagrangian formalism. Dirac equations (6.20) and (6.21) may be obtained by means of the variational principle from the following Lagrangian:

$$\mathscr{L} = \frac{i}{2} \sum_n \left(\bar{\psi}(x)\, \gamma^n \frac{\partial \psi}{\partial x^n} - \frac{\partial \bar{\psi}}{\partial x^n} \gamma^n \psi(x) \right) - m\bar{\psi}(x)\, \psi(x). \tag{7.27}$$

In contrast to the Lagrangian of fields considered earlier, the Lagrangian of the spinor field (7.27) reduces to zero if the functions ψ and $\bar{\psi}$ occurring in it satisfy the field equations. [17]

In the usual way we obtain from (7.27) the energy momentum tensor

$$T^{kl} = \frac{i}{2} g^{ll} \left(\bar{\psi}(x)\, \gamma^k \frac{\partial \psi}{\partial x^l} - \frac{\partial \bar{\psi}}{\partial x^l} \gamma^k \psi(x) \right) \tag{7.28}$$

and the current four-vector

$$J^k(x) = \bar{\psi}(x)\, \gamma^k \psi(x). \tag{7.29}$$

In order to calculate the spin tensor, we note that after carrying out the summation over the spin indices, the formula (7.25) for the spinor field may be written in the form

[17] The Lagrangians of all other fields of the form (7.9) have the same property.

$$S^{k,\,lm} = -\frac{\partial \mathscr{L}}{\partial(\partial\psi/\partial x^k)} A^{\psi,\,lm}\psi(x) - \bar{\psi}(x)\,A^{\bar{\psi},\,lm}\frac{\partial \mathscr{L}}{\partial\,(\partial\bar{\psi}/\partial x^k)}.$$

The coefficients A^{ψ} and $A^{\bar{\psi}}$ occurring above may be defined with the aid of formulas (6.27), (6.28), and of the rules for obtaining an adjoint spinor, in the following form

$$A^{\psi,\,lm} = \frac{i}{2}\,\sigma^{lm}, \qquad A^{\bar{\psi},\,lm} = -\frac{i}{2}\,\sigma^{lm},$$

where σ is the so-called "matrix spin tensor"

$$\sigma^{lm} = \frac{\gamma^l\gamma^m - \gamma^m\gamma^l}{2i}. \tag{7.30}$$

With the aid of the formulas given above, we obtain from the Lagrangian (7.27) the following expression for the spin angular momentum tensor of the spinor field

$$S^{k,\,lm} = \tfrac{1}{4}\,\bar{\psi}(x)\,\{\gamma^k\sigma^{lm} + \sigma^{lm}\gamma^k\}\,\psi(x). \tag{7.31}$$

In order to carry out the integration over three-dimensional space and to obtain the dynamic variables, it is convenient to go over in the usual manner to the three-dimensional momentum representation

$$\psi^{(\pm)}(x) = \frac{1}{(2\pi)^{3/2}}\int d\mathbf{k}e^{\pm ikx}\sum_{\nu=1,\,2} a_\nu^{\pm}(\mathbf{k})\,v^{\nu,\pm}(\mathbf{k}), \tag{7.32}$$

$$\bar{\psi}^{(\pm)}(x) = \frac{1}{(2\pi)^{3/2}}\int d\mathbf{k}e^{\pm ikx}\sum_{\nu=1,\,2} a_\nu^{*\pm}(\mathbf{k})\bar{v}^{\nu,\,\pm}(\mathbf{k}). \tag{7.33}$$

Substituting (7.32), (7.33) into (7.28), setting $k = 0$ in that expression, and integrating over three-dimensional space after taking into account the conditions of orthonormality (7.16), we obtain the energy-momentum four-vector

$$P^l = \int d\mathbf{x}\cdot T^{0l} = \int d\mathbf{k}\cdot k^l\sum_{\nu=1,2}(a_\nu^{*+}(\mathbf{k})a_\nu^{-}(\mathbf{k}) - a_\nu^{*-}(\mathbf{k})a_\nu^{+}(\mathbf{k})), \tag{7.34}$$

where, as is always the case in this book,

$$k^0 = \sqrt{\mathbf{k}^2 + m^2}.$$

Taking into account the fact that in accordance with (7.32)

and (7.33) the rules of Hermitean conjugation of the amplitudes $a^{\pm}$ and $a^{*\pm}$ have the form

$$(a^{+})^{*} = a^{*-} \text{ and } (a^{-})^{*} = a^{*+}, \tag{7.35}$$

we see that in the classical theory the energy of the spinor field

$$P^0 = \int d\mathbf{k} \cdot k^0 \sum_{\nu} (a_{\nu}^{*+}(\mathbf{k})a_{\nu}^{-}(\mathbf{k}) - a_{\nu}^{*-}(\mathbf{k})a_{\nu}^{+}(\mathbf{k})) \tag{7.36}$$

is not positive definite. The positive definite nature of the energy of the spinor field is achieved in the quantum theory by means of Fermi-Dirac quantization.[18]

Proceeding to the calculation of the spin vector we note that in accordance with (6.19) the components of the spin tensor σ^{lm} may be expressed in terms of the α_i and σ_i matrices in the following manner

$$\sigma^{lm} = \begin{pmatrix} \mathbf{0} & -i\alpha_i & -i\alpha_2 & -i\alpha_3 \\ i\alpha_1 & \mathbf{0} & -\sigma_3 & \sigma_2 \\ i\alpha_2 & \sigma_3 & \mathbf{0} & -\sigma_1 \\ i\alpha_3 & -\sigma_2 & \sigma_1 & \mathbf{0} \end{pmatrix}. \tag{7.37}$$

Therefore, setting $k = 0$ and $l, m = 1, 2, 3$ in (7.31) we see that the spatial density of the spin vector is given by the matrix "vector" $\boldsymbol{\sigma}$:

$$\mathbf{S} = \tfrac{1}{2} \int \psi^{*}(x)\boldsymbol{\sigma}\psi(x)d\mathbf{x}. \tag{7.38}$$

In contrast to the spins of the vector and the electromagnetic fields, the spin vector of the spinor field (7.38) is not conserved in time (which is related to the lack of symmetry in the energy-momentum tensor). However, in the case that the field functions ψ, $\bar{\psi}$ do not depend on some of the coordinates x^0, x', . . . it is possible to achieve that the "equation of continuity" should hold for some of the components of the tensor S, and consequently that the corresponding integrals remain conserved in time. Thus, setting $\partial/\partial x^1 = \partial/\partial x^2 = 0$ we obtain

$$\sum_k \frac{\partial S^{k,12}}{\partial x^k} = 0,$$

[18] For a more detailed discussion of this point refer to § 12.

from which it follows that the component of the spin vector along the x^3 axis

$$S_3 = \int dx \cdot S^{0,12}$$

is conserved in time. In the momentum representation, this statement is equivalent to "the conservation of the component of the spin vector along the direction of motion."

By passing in (7.38) to the three-dimensional momentum representation, and carrying out the integration over the three-dimensional configuration space we obtain:

$$\begin{aligned}\mathbf{S} = \tfrac{1}{2}\int d\mathbf{k}\{&\psi^{*(+)}(\mathbf{k})\boldsymbol{\sigma}\psi^{(-)}(\mathbf{k}) \\ &+ \psi^{*(-)}(\mathbf{k})\boldsymbol{\sigma}\psi^{(+)}(\mathbf{k}) + e^{2ik^0x^0}\psi^{*(+)}(\mathbf{k})\boldsymbol{\sigma}\psi^{(+)}(-\mathbf{k}) \\ &+ e^{-2ik^0x^0}(\psi^{*(-)}(\mathbf{k})\boldsymbol{\sigma}\psi^{(-)}(\mathbf{k})\}.\end{aligned} \tag{7.39}$$

Restricting ourselves to the consideration of only the S_3 component we make use of relation (7.19) which we write in the form

$$v^{*(\pm)}(\mathbf{k})\boldsymbol{\sigma}v^{(\pm)}(-\mathbf{k}) = \frac{i}{m}v^{*(\pm)}(\mathbf{k})[\mathbf{k}\times\gamma]v^{(\pm)}(-\mathbf{k}).$$

In virtue of this relation the time-dependent terms in S_3 disappear in the coordinate system in which $k_1 = k_2 = 0$, and we obtain an expression of the following form

$$\begin{aligned}\tfrac{1}{2}\sum_{\nu,\mu}\{&a_\nu^{*+}(\mathbf{k})a_\mu^-(\mathbf{k})\,v^{*\nu,+}(\mathbf{k})\,\sigma_3\,v^{\mu,-}(\mathbf{k}) \\ &+ a_\nu^{*-}(\mathbf{k})a_\mu^+(\mathbf{k})v^{*\nu,-}(\mathbf{k})\,\sigma_3\,v^{\mu,+}(\mathbf{k})\},\end{aligned} \tag{7.40}$$

for the further specification of which it is convenient to choose some special concrete representation of the Dirac matrices. In the representation (6.18) used by us the matrix σ_3 has the form

$$\sigma_3 = \begin{pmatrix}1 & 0 & 0 & 0\\ 0 & -1 & 0 & 0\\ 0 & 0 & 1 & 0\\ 0 & 0 & 0 & -1\end{pmatrix}.$$

Choosing the normalized spinors in the coordinate system $k_1 = k_2 = 0$ in the form

$$\left.\begin{aligned} v^{1,+} &= N^{-1}\left(\frac{k^3}{k^0+m}, \quad 0, \quad 1, \quad 0\right), \\ v^{2,+} &= N^{-1}\left(0, \quad -\frac{k^3}{k^0+m}, \quad 0, \quad 1\right), \\ v^{1,-} &= N^{-1}\left(1, \quad 0, \quad \frac{k^3}{k^0+m}, \quad 0\right), \\ v^{2,-} &= N^{-1}\left(0, \quad 1, \quad 0, \quad -\frac{k^3}{k^0+m}\right), \end{aligned}\right\} \quad (7.41)$$

where N is the normalization constant equal to

$$N = \sqrt{1+\left(\frac{k^3}{k^0+m}\right)^2} = \sqrt{\frac{2k^0}{k^0+m}},$$

we find that (7.40) assumes the form

$$\tfrac{1}{2}(a_1^{*+}a_1^- - a_2^{*+}a_2^- + a_1^{*-}a_1^+ - a_2^{*-}a_2^+). \qquad (7.42)$$

Comparing expressions (7.34) for energy momentum, (7.41) for the component of the spin vector, and the expression for the charge

$$Q = \int \psi^*(x)\psi(x)d\mathbf{x} = \int d\mathbf{k} \sum_\nu (a_\nu^{*+}(\mathbf{k})\, a_\nu^-(\mathbf{k}) + a_\nu^{*-}(\mathbf{k})\, a_\nu^+(\mathbf{k})), \quad (7.43)$$

which follows directly from (7.29) we find[19] that the spinor field describes charged particles with the possible values of the component of the spin along any given axis being equal to $\pm \frac{1}{2}$. A more detailed classification of the possible values of energy-momentum, charge, and spin component will be given after quantization (§12), where it will receive a complete and unambiguous foundation.

§ 8. Lagrangian of a System of Fields

In this section without essentially raising the questions of the interaction of various fields we shall consider briefly the general structure of the Lagrangians for systems of fields, and we shall obtain certain dynamic variables of such systems.

[19] Taking into account the fact that after quantization of the spinor field (cf. § 12) expressions (7.34), (7.42), and (7.43) retain their structure, changing only the signs of some of their terms.

8.1. *The Interaction Lagrangian and Invariants of a System of Fields*

In considering problems connected with the interaction between different fields, one starts with the Lagrangian

$$\mathscr{L}_{\text{tot}} = \mathscr{L}_{\text{free}} + \mathscr{L}_{\text{int}}, \tag{8.1}$$

which consists of the sum $\mathscr{L}_{\text{free}}$ of the appropriate Lagrangians of the free fields and the term $\mathscr{L}_{\text{int}}$ which describes the interaction and which is called the *interaction Lagrangian.*

The interaction Lagrangian $\mathscr{L}_{\text{int}}$ must satisfy the main physical requirement — it must be relativistically invariant. It must therefore have the form of any arbitrary *invariant* algebraic or integral combination of the field functions of the interacting fields. Leaving aside the integral Lagrangians which lead to nonlocal theories which we are not going to consider, we conclude that the interaction Lagrangian $\mathscr{L}_{\text{int}}$ may be formed from the field functions by means of contracting a product of two quantities of the same tensor dimensionality; e.g., two scalars, two pseudoscalars, or two vectors.

Thus the interaction of a scalar field $\varphi(x)$ with a spinor field $\psi(x)$ may be chosen to be of the scalar-scalar type

$$\bar{\psi}(x)\,\psi(x)\,\varphi(x), \tag{8.2}$$

of the vector-vector type

$$\sum_n \bar{\psi}(x)\,\gamma^n\,\psi(x)\,\frac{\partial\varphi(x)}{\partial x^n} \tag{8.3}$$

etc. Similarly, the simplest forms of interaction of a pseudoscalar field $\varphi(x)$ with a spinor field $\psi(x)$ are the following:

$$\bar{\psi}(x)\,\gamma^5\,\psi(x)\,\varphi(x), \tag{8.4}$$

$$\sum_n \bar{\psi}(x)\,\gamma^5\gamma^n\,\psi(x)\,\frac{\partial\varphi(x)}{\partial x^n}. \tag{8.5}$$

We now turn to a consideration of the invariants of a system of fields. Because of the relativistic invariance of the interaction Lagrangian, the total Lagrangian of the system is an invariant with respect to four translations and six rotations of the coordinate system. The invariants corresponding to these transformations — energy-momentum and angular-momentum — are determined by formulas which follow from Noether's theorem.

Of particular interest is the case in which $\mathscr{L}_{\text{int}}$ does not depend on the derivatives of the field functions. In this case, in accordance with formulas (2.20) and (2.29), the momentum and the spin of the system of fields are equal to the sum of the momenta and the sum of the spins of the individual fields, while the energy density of the system of fields is equal to the sum of the energy densities of the individual fields minus $\mathscr{L}_{\text{int}}$, i.e.,

$$\mathbf{P} = \sum_i \mathbf{P}_i, \quad P^0 = \sum_i P_i^0 - \int \mathscr{L}_{\text{int}}(x)\, dx,$$
$$\mathbf{S} = \sum_i \mathbf{S}_i. \tag{8.6}$$

8.2. *Invariants under Gauge Transformations*

The gradient transformation of the 1st kind (*gauge transformation*) must be considered separately. The point is that the invariance of $\mathscr{L}_{\text{int}}$ under transformations of type (2.30) is not *a priori* necessary. Actually such a requirement is imposed on $\mathscr{L}_{\text{int}}$ in the case when it is desired to require for this system of fields the conservation of some physical quantity of the type of electric charge.

For example, the interaction Lagrangian of the electromagnetic field (5.12) and the electron-positron field (7.21) has the form

$$\mathscr{L}_{\text{int}}(x) = e \sum_n \bar{\psi}(x)\, \gamma^n\, \psi(x)\, A_n(x) = e \sum_n J^n(x)\, A_n(x). \tag{8.7}$$

The total Lagrangian for the system, equal to the sum of expressions (5.12), (7.27), and (8.7):

$$\mathscr{L}(x) = \mathscr{L}_0(x) + \mathscr{L}_{\text{int}}(x)$$

($\mathscr{L}_0$ is the sum of the Lagrangians of free fields), is invariant under the transformation

$$\psi(x) \to e^{i\alpha}\psi(x),$$
$$\bar{\psi}(x) \to \bar{\psi}(x)e^{-i\alpha}.$$

Since $\mathscr{L}_{\text{int}}$ is independent of $\partial\psi/\partial x$ the corresponding invariant (2.33) is identical with the charge of the free electron-positron field (7.43).

Here is another example. Consider the system of four fields: proton, neutron, electron-positron, and neutrino fields. We shall describe protons, neutrons, electrons, and neutrinos by means of a spinor field of the type (7.27). Then

$$\mathscr{L} = \mathscr{L}_0 + \mathscr{L}_{\text{int}}$$

$$\mathscr{L}_0 = \mathscr{L}_P + \mathscr{L}_N + \mathscr{L}_e + \mathscr{L}_\nu,$$

$$\mathscr{L}_P = \frac{i}{2}\sum_n\left(\overline{\Psi}_P(x)\,\gamma^n\,\frac{\partial \Psi_P}{\partial x^n} - \frac{\partial \overline{\Psi}_P}{\partial x^n}\gamma^n\,\Psi_P(x)\right) - M\overline{\Psi}_P(x)\,\Psi_P(x),$$

$$\mathscr{L}_N = \frac{i}{2}\sum_m\left(\overline{\Psi}_N(x)\gamma^m\,\frac{\partial \Psi_N}{\partial x^m} - \frac{\partial \overline{\Psi}_N}{\partial x^m}\gamma^m\,\Psi_N(x)\right) - M\overline{\Psi}_N(x)\,\Psi_N(x),$$

$$\mathscr{L}_e = \frac{i}{2}\sum_k\left(\bar{\psi}(x)\,\gamma^k\,\frac{\partial \psi}{\partial x^k} - \frac{\partial \bar{\psi}}{\partial x^k}\gamma^k\,\psi(x)\right) - m\bar{\psi}(x)\,\psi(x),$$

$$\mathscr{L}_\nu = \frac{i}{2}\sum_l\left(\bar{u}_\nu(x)\,\gamma^l\,\frac{\partial u_\nu}{\partial x^l} - \frac{\partial u_\nu}{\partial x^l}\gamma^l\,u_\nu(x)\right).$$

Here M is the nucleon mass, m is the electron mass, Ψ_P is the proton wave function, Ψ_N is the neutron wave function, ψ is the electron-positron function, u_ν is the neutrino function.

The interaction Lagrangian of these four fields which describes β-processes is usually taken in the following form:

$$\mathscr{L}_{\text{int}} = g_\beta[(\overline{\Psi}_P O \Psi_N)(\bar{\psi} O u_\nu) + (\overline{\Psi}_N O \Psi_P)(\bar{u}_\nu O \psi)], \tag{8.8}$$

where O are the Dirac matrices which determine the form of the interaction. For example, for vector coupling $O = \gamma$ and $\mathscr{L}_{\text{int}}$ has the form

$$\mathscr{L}_{\text{int}} = g_\beta \sum_n g^{nn}[(\overline{\Psi}_P\gamma^n\Psi_N)(\bar{\psi}\gamma^n u_\nu) + (\overline{\Psi}_N\gamma^n\Psi_P)(\bar{u}_\nu\gamma^n\psi)].$$

The total Lagrangian $\mathscr{L}_0$ is invariant with respect to several independent gauge transformations of the first kind; for example:

$$\left.\begin{array}{lll} (1) & \psi(x) \to e^{-i\alpha}\psi(x), & \bar{\psi}(x) \to e^{i\alpha}\bar{\psi}(x), \\ & \Psi_P(x) \to e^{i\alpha}\Psi_P(x), & \overline{\Psi}_P(x) \to e^{-i\alpha}\overline{\Psi}_P(x), \\ & \Psi_N(x) \to \Psi_N(x), & \overline{\Psi}_N(x) \to \overline{\Psi}_N(x), \\ & u_\nu(x) \to u_\nu(x), & \bar{u}_\nu(x) \to u_\nu(x). \end{array}\right\} \tag{8.9}$$

The corresponding invariant is equal to the difference between the charges of the Ψ_P and ψ fields and represents electric charge.

$$\left.\begin{array}{ll} \Psi_P \to e^{i\beta}\Psi_P, & \overline{\Psi}_P \to e^{-i\beta}\overline{\Psi}_P, \\ \Psi_N \to e^{i\beta}\Psi_N, & \overline{\Psi}_N \to e^{-i\beta}\overline{\Psi}_N, \\ \psi \to \psi, & \bar{\psi} \to \bar{\psi}, \\ u_\nu \to u_\nu, & \bar{u}_\nu \to \bar{u}_\nu. \end{array}\right\} \quad (2) \qquad (8.10)$$

The corresponding invariant is equal to the sum of the charges of the Ψ_P and Ψ_N fields, and is called the nucleonic (or nuclear) charge.

We emphasize that the properties of invariance of the Lagrangians under various gauge transformations differ somewhat from their invariance under Lorentz rotations and translations. The invariance of any Lagrangian under rotations and translations is a general physical requirement. The invariance of any Lagrangian under some kind or another of gauge transformation is determined by the existence of a definite physical conservation law. Thus from the law of conservation of electric charge, which is a firmly established law of nature, it follows that all fields may be divided into three groups:

u_{+z} fields which describe electrically positive z-fold (in units of e) charged particles,

$u_{-z'}$ fields which describe electrically negative z'-fold (in units of e) charged particles,

u_0 fields which describe electrically neutral particles.

It also follows that all possible Lagrangians[20] are invariant under a gauge transformation:[21]

$$\left.\begin{array}{ll} u_{+z} \to e^{i\alpha z}u_{+z}, & u^\dagger_{+z} \to e^{-i\alpha z}u^\dagger_{+z}, \\ u_{-z'} \to e^{-i\alpha z'}u_{-z'}, & u^\dagger_{-z'} \to e^{i\alpha z'}u^\dagger_{-z'}, \\ u_0 \to u_0, & u^\dagger_0 \to u^\dagger_0. \end{array}\right\} \qquad (8.11)$$

[20] More briefly, the "total Lagrangian" which is the sum of the Lagrangians of all the existing free fields (both those already known, and those as yet unknown).

[21] The symbol † is used here and later to denote the operation of "generalized" conjugation, for example of the type used to obtain $\overline{\psi}$ from ψ in the case of the spinor field.

The transformations (8.9) are special cases of the transformations (8.11).

Similarly, in accordance with experimental data, the number of nucleons either remains constant in elementary processes, or changes as a result of the creation and annihilation of nucleon-antinucleon pairs. Therefore, if one ascribes a "nucleonic" charge of $+1$ to the proton and the neutron, and -1 to the antiproton and antineutron, one may speak of the conservation of nucleonic charge.

By assuming that the nucleonic charge is conserved in all processes without exception, we thereby assume that the "total Lagrangian" is invariant under some gauge transformation of the form

$$u_A \to u_A e^{iy_A\beta}, \qquad u_A^\dagger \to e^{-iy_A\beta} u_A^\dagger, \tag{8.12}$$

where the index y_A indicates the magnitude and the sign of the nucleonic charge of the particles of the given field u_A. Transformations (8.10) are special cases of the transformations (8.12) with

$$y(\Psi_P) = 1, \qquad y(\Psi_N) = 1,$$
$$y(\psi) = 0, \qquad y(u_\nu) = 0.$$

We thus see that the conservation laws referred to above have two aspects. On the one hand the law of conservation of electric charge is verified directly experimentally. On the other hand the law of conservation of electric charge appears as a certain mathematical property of the "total Lagrangian," or more accurately, as a selection rule for the possible types of elementary processes.

There exists a simple correspondence between the form of the interaction Lagrangian and the type of elementary process described by this Lagrangian, which may be put on a rigorous basis by means of the theory of second quantization (Chapter III).

As is shown in § 9, the field functions u, $u^\dagger$ are decomposed into creation and annihilation operators. The function $u(x)$ is decomposed into an annihilation operator for the basic particle and a creation operator for the antiparticle; $u^\dagger(x)$ is decomposed into an annihilation operator for the antiparticle and the creation operator for the basic particle. Therefore a combination of functions of the type

$$u_1(x)u_2^\dagger(x)\ \ldots\ u_k(x)$$

describes a process in which an antiparticle of the field u_1, is created (or a particle of the field u_1 is absorbed), a particle of the field u_2 is created (or an antiparticle of the field u_2 is absorbed), etc.

For example, the interaction Lagrangian for the electron-positron and the electromagnetic fields

$$\mathscr{L}_{\text{int}}(x) = e \sum_k \bar{\psi}(x)\gamma^k\psi(x)A_k(x)$$

describes elementary processes of the type shown in Fig. 1.

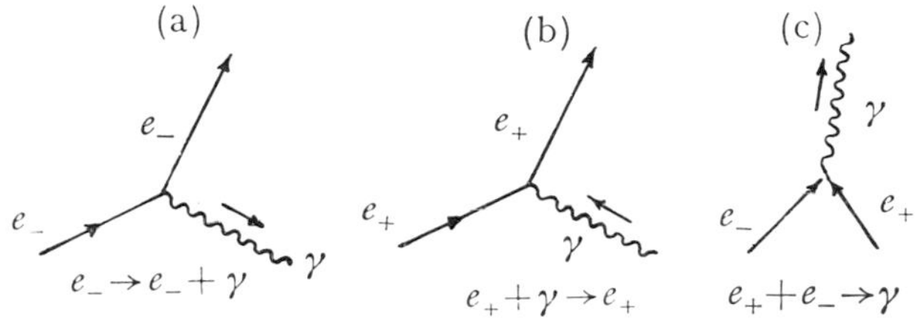

Fig. 1. (a) Emission of photon γ by electron e_-. (b) Absorption of photon γ by positron e_+. (c) Annihilation of an electron-positron pair with emission of a photon.

It may be easily seen with the aid of the above correspondence rules that the invariance of the given interaction Lagrangian under the transformation (8.10) guarantees the conservation of electric charge in the corresponding processes.

CHAPTER II

Quantum Theory of Free Fields

§ 9. General Principles of Quantization of Wave Fields

9.1. *Operator Nature of the Field Functions and the Transformation Law of the State Amplitude*

Until now we have considered the various fields as being classical ones. The classical description of fields is characterized by the fact that the theory does not explicitly concern itself with the processes of creation and annihilation (more accurately with processes of mutual transformation) of particles corresponding to these fields. In quantum mechanics the square of the wave function gives the probability of finding the particles of the field in a g ven state. In the quantum theory of wave fields, the wave functions of the fields describe sets of particles the *processes of mutual transformations* of which are explicitly contained in the theory. Corresponding to this, the wave functions of quantum fields *take on an operator meaning and are decomposed into particle creation and annihilation operators* between which commutation relations are set up. The operator wave functions are defined by the field equations and by the commutation relations up to a unitary transformation.

The field functions are therefore no longer functions in the classical sense but become operators which operate on a wave function common to all the fields which we shall call the *state amplitude.* [22] In the quantized theory, the expectation values and the probabilities of states are given by quadratic forms of the state amplitude.

[22] The state amplitude may be thought of as a vector in some Hilbert space in consequence of which in American literature it is usually called the *state vector*.

Let us consider the transformation of the state amplitude Φ under a certain transformation of coordinates L from the inhomogeneous Lorentz group which consists of the Lorentz group itself and of the four translations

$$x \rightarrow x' = Lx = x + \delta x; \quad \delta x^k = a^k + \sum_n g^{nn} x^n \omega^{kn}. \tag{9.1}$$

In so doing we must, of course, assume that the transformation of the state amplitude which is of interest to us

$$\Phi \rightarrow \Phi' = U_L \Phi \tag{9.2}$$

is accomplished by means of the unitary operator U_L:

$$U_L U_L^* = 1, \tag{9.3}$$

which guarantees the invariance of the norm of the state amplitude $\Phi^*\Phi$. In particular, in the case of the infinitesimal transformation of type (9.1) we have:

$$\Phi' = (1 + \delta U_L)\Phi, \tag{9.4}$$

in which the quantity δU_L must be anti-Hermitean in virtue of (9.3). On the other hand, it must obviously be a linear combination of the infinitesimal parameters a^k and ω^{kl}. Let us therefore write

$$\delta U_L = i \sum_k g^{kk} P^k a^k + \frac{i}{2} \sum_{k,n} g^{kk} g^{nn} M^{kn} \omega^{kn}. \tag{9.5}$$

The metric tensor g has been introduced into the coefficients of the above expression in order that the operators P and M should have the correct transformation properties of a vector and a tensor respectively. In view of the anti-Hermitean nature of δU_L the operators P and M introduced above will be Hermitean.

In order to establish their physical meaning we consider in ordinary quantum mechanics the wave function φ which depends on the coordinates $\mathbf{x}$ and the time x^0. The transformation law for such a scalar function has in accordance with (2.8) the form

$$\varphi'(x') = \varphi(x).$$

By carrying out a displacement of the arguments $x \rightarrow L^{-1}x$ and by taking into account the smallness of the transformation parameters and the antisymmetry of ω^{kn} we find:

$$\varphi'(x) = \varphi(L^{-1}x) = \varphi(x) - \sum_n a^n \frac{\partial \varphi}{\partial x^n} - \sum_{k,n} g^{nn} x^n \omega^{kn} \frac{\partial \varphi}{\partial x^k}$$

$$= \left[1 - \sum_n a^n \frac{\partial}{\partial x^n} - \tfrac{1}{2} \sum_{k,n} \left(g^{nn} x^n \frac{\partial}{\partial x^k} - g^{kk} x^k \frac{\partial}{\partial x^n}\right) \omega^{kn}\right] \varphi(x), \quad (9.6)$$

from which it may be seen that the transformation of $\varphi(x)$ may also be represented in the form (9.4), (9.5), while for P and M we obtain the expressions

$$P^n = i g^{nn} \frac{\partial}{\partial x^n}, \quad (9.7)$$

$$M^{kn} = i\left(x^n g^{kk} \frac{\partial}{\partial x^k} - x^k g^{nn} \frac{\partial}{\partial x^n}\right). \quad (9.8)$$

Thus in the case (9.6) considered above in virtue of the usual quantum-mechanical *correspondence principle* the quantities P and M should be identified with the energy-momentum four-vector and the angular momentum tensor respectively.

Therefore it is natural to interpret P as the energy-momentum four-vector and M as the angular momentum tensor also in the case of (9.5). Of course in quantum field theory when the amplitude Φ does not depend explicitly on the coordinates, we cannot use formulas (9.7), (9.8) but must choose for P and M certain operators which operate on the state amplitude.

9.2. *Quantization Postulate for Wave Fields*

As the fundamental postulate for the quantization of wave fields we shall assume that the energy-momentum four-vector P and the angular momentum tensor M are expressed in terms of the operator field functions by the same relations of the type (2.21), (2.25) as in the classical theory of wave fields, with the operator factors of course being arranged in this case in appropriate order. This postulate is a further application of the correspondence principle and determines the law of transformation of the second-quantized state amplitudes.

Let us now investigate the question of the connection between the transformation properties of operator wave functions established in § 2 and the transformation properties of the state amplitudes under a Lorentz transformation (9.1). For this purpose let us take the expectation value of the transformed operator field function $u'(x)$ in the state described by the amplitude Φ. This quantity may be written in the form

$$\Phi^* u'(x) \Phi.$$

In accordance with the meaning of transformation (9.2), this expectation value may be calculated from the untransformed function $u(x)$ but with the aid of the transformed state amplitudes Φ'. We have therefore

$$\Phi^* u'(x) \Phi = \Phi^{*\prime} u(x) \Phi'.$$

Expressing the amplitudes Φ' and $\Phi^{*\prime}$ with the aid of (9.2) in terms of Φ and Φ^*, we obtain from the above

$$u'(x) = U_L^* u(x) U_L. \tag{9.9}$$

This relation represents a condition of compatibility of the transformation properties of the operator field functions and of the state amplitudes. It imposes on the field operators a number of operator conditions, which must be satisfied by the operators of any arbitrary wave field irrespective of the specific form of commutation relations. We will now proceed to formulate these operator conditions.

Remembering that for the infinitesimal transformation

$$x' = x + \delta x, \quad \delta x^k = \sum_i X_i^k \delta\omega^i$$

the operator U_L has in accordance with (9.4) the form

$$U_L = 1 + \delta U_L; \quad \delta U_L = i \sum_j U_j \delta\omega^j,$$

where δU_L is anti-Hermitean, we obtain from (9.9)

$$u'(x) = u(x) - \delta U_L u(x) + u(x) \delta U_L = u(x) + [u(x), \delta U_L].$$

This relation may also be written in the form

$$\bar{\delta} u(x) = [u(x), \delta U_L], \tag{9.10}$$

where $\bar{\delta} u$, just as in § 2, denotes the variation of the form of the function u:

$$\bar{\delta} u(x) \equiv u'(x) - u(x).$$

Utilizing for δu the expression (2.15), we find

$$i\left(\Psi_{ij} - \sum_n \frac{\partial u_i(x)}{\partial x^n} X_j^n\right) = [U_j, u_i]. \tag{9.11}$$

Relations (9.11) are the operator conditions on the field operators which we seek. Let us examine the concrete form of formula (9.11) for various transformations.

Under a transformation of the displacement of the coordinate system, when

$$X_j^n = \delta_j^n, \quad \Psi_{ij} = 0, \quad U_k = P^k g^{kk},$$

we find: [23]

$$i g^{nn} \frac{\partial u_i}{\partial x^n} = [u_i(x), P^n]. \tag{9.12}$$

Under transformations of rotation (spatial and Lorentz) of the coordinate axes, when

$$\left.\begin{aligned} X^k_{(mn)} &= g^{nn} x^n \delta^k_m - g^{mm} x^m \delta^k_n, \\ \Psi_{i(mn)} &= \sum_j A^j_{i(mn)} u_j, \quad U_{(mn)} = g^{mm} g^{nn} M^{mn} \end{aligned}\right\} (m \leqq n),$$

we obtain similarly

$$i\left\{\sum_j A^j_{i(mn)} u_j - \sum_k \frac{\partial u_i}{\partial x^k}(g^{nn} x^n \delta^k_m - g^{mm} x^m \delta^k_n)\right\} = [M_{mn}, u_i]. \tag{9.14}$$

[23] When the theory is presented on the basis of the canonical formalism, the zero component of this equation is usually postulated (91a), (133)

$$i\frac{\partial u}{\partial t} = [u, H], \tag{9.13}$$

where $t = x^0$, and $H = P^0$ is the Hamiltonian operator. Such a postulate is likewise based on the correspondence principle. Indeed, in classical mechanics the following equation holds for conservative systems

$$\frac{\partial u}{\partial t} = \{H, u\},$$

where

$$\{a, b\} = \sum_i \left(\frac{\partial a}{\partial q_i}\frac{\partial b}{\partial p_i} - \frac{\partial a}{\partial p_i}\frac{\partial b}{\partial q_i}\right)$$

are the classical Poisson brackets. In this case, the quantization postulate consists of the replacement of the classical Poisson brackets by the quantum Poisson brackets

$$\{a, b\} \to i[a, b],$$

which leads to (9.13).

On the right-hand side of the above equation, we have the angular-momentum operator which in the classical theory was represented in the form of a sum of orbital and spin angular momenta

$$M = M_0 + S. \tag{9.15}$$

We shall assume that this relation is not changed in the course of the process of quantization and that the operator S_{mn} expressed in a suitable manner in terms of the operator field functions by a relation of the type (2.27) is the spin operator.

In the case of a complex field, we must also investigate the gauge transformation of the first kind. As was established in § 8, the field function which corresponds to particles of charge z, transforms in accordance with

$$\left.\begin{aligned} u(x) &\to u'(x) = e^{i\alpha z}u(x), \\ u^\dagger(x) &\to u^{\dagger\prime}(x) = e^{-i\alpha z}u^\dagger(x). \end{aligned}\right\} \tag{9.16}$$

The corresponding transformation of the state amplitude

$$\Phi' = U_\alpha \Phi \tag{9.17}$$

is accomplished by means of the unitary operator U_α which, in the case when the parameter of the transformation α is infinitesimal, assumes the form

$$U_\alpha = 1 + \delta U_\alpha, \quad \delta U_\alpha = iQ\alpha,$$

where Q is a certain Hermitean operator whose physical meaning may be determined with the aid of the correspondence principle. For an infinitesimal α equations (9.16)

$$\begin{aligned} u'(x) &= (1 + i\alpha z)u(x), \\ u^{\dagger\prime}(x) &= (1 - i\alpha z)u^\dagger(x) \end{aligned}$$

agree in form with (9.17) with the charge z playing in them the role of the operator Q. Therefore, in virtue of the correspondence principle, the quantity Q must be identified with the charge. Naturally in the case under discussion one should interpret the expression Q not as the charge z itself, but as the charge operator expressed in terms of the operator wave functions of the field by a relation of the type (2.33).

Thus for a gauge transformation of the first kind

$$X_i^k = 0, \quad U_i = Q,$$

$$\Psi_{ij} = \begin{cases} iu_i & \text{for all } u, \\ -iu_i^\dagger & \text{for all } u^\dagger. \end{cases}$$

Substituting these values into (9.11) we arrive at equations

$$\left. \begin{aligned} zu(x) &= [u(x),\ Q], \\ -zu^\dagger(x) &= [u^\dagger(x),\ Q]. \end{aligned} \right\} \tag{9.18}$$

We have obtained equations of three types, (9.12), (9.14), and (9.18), which represent operator conditions on quantized functions of wave fields that do not depend on the concrete form of the commutation relations. By investigating these equations, we shall now formulate certain more detailed properties of the field operators.

9.3. *The Physical Meaning of the Positive- and Negative-Frequency Components and of Adjoint Functions*

From equations (9.12) we obtain directly the physical meaning of the positive-frequency and the negative-frequency parts of the operator field function (105). Let us consider the field of particles of mass m, described by the function $u(x)$:

$$u(x) = u^{(+)}(x) + u^{(-)}(x),$$

$$u^{(+)}(x) = \int_{k^0>0} e^{ikx}\delta(k^2 - m^2)\,u(k)\,dk,$$

$$u^{(-)}(x) = \int_{k^0>0} e^{-ikx}\delta(k^2 - m^2)\,u(-k)\,dk.$$

Substituting separately $u^{(+)}$ and $u^{(-)}$ into condition (9.12) we find:

$$\left. \begin{aligned} [u^{(+)}(x),\ P^n] &= -\int_{k^0>0} e^{ikx}k^n\,\delta(k^2 - m^2)\,u(k)\,dk, \\ [u^{(-)}(x),\ P^n] &= \int_{k^0>0} e^{-ikx}k^n\,\delta(k^2 - m^2)\,u(-k)\,dk, \end{aligned} \right\} \tag{9.19}$$

from which it follows that:

$$[u^{(+)}(k),\ P^n] = -k^n u^{(+)}(k), \tag{9.20}$$

$$[u^{(-)}(k),\ P^n] = k^n u^{(-)}(k). \tag{9.21}$$

Here we have introduced the notation

$$u^{(+)}(k) = u(k)|_{k^0>0}, \quad u^{(-)}(k) = u(-k)|_{k^0>0}.$$

We now introduce a state with a definite value p^n of the energy-momentum four-vector described by the amplitude Φ_p

$$P^n \Phi_p = p^n \Phi_p. \tag{9.22}$$

Multiplying (9.20) on the right by Φ_p and taking into account (9.22), we obtain

$$P^n u^{(+)}(k) \Phi_p = (p^n + k^n) u^{(+)}(k) \Phi_p. \tag{9.23}$$

By the same method we find that from (9.21)

$$P^n u^{(-)}(k) \Phi_p = (p^n - k^n) u^{(-)}(k) \Phi_p, \tag{9.24}$$

with $k^0 = (\mathbf{k}^2 + m^2)^{1/2}$ in both cases.

From the equations obtained above, it follows that the expression $u^{(+)}(k)\Phi_p$ represents the amplitude of the state with the energy momentum $k + p$, while $u^{(-)}(k)\Phi_p$ corresponds to the state with the energy momentum $p - k$. Since at the same time the relation $\mathbf{k}^2 = m^2$ holds, one may consider that the operator $u^{(+)}(k)$ describes the creation of a particle of mass m and four-momentum k, while the operator $u^{(-)}(k)$ corresponds to the annihilation of such a particle.

We emphasize that this property of the positive- and negative-frequency parts of the field operators is quite general and valid for fields of arbitrary tensor dimensionality, both real and complex, and does not depend on the specific form of the commutation relations.

Proceeding to the investigation of equation (9.14) we note that it explicitly contains the transformation matrix A of the components of the field functions which is determined by the tensor dimensionality of the field and gives a finite-dimensional representation of the Lorentz group. A detailed analysis of equation (9.14) leads to the decomposition of the operator field function into states with definite values of the total angular momentum, which corresponds to an expansion in spherical harmonics.

Let us also investigate equations (9.18). Introducing the

amplitude Φ_q of the state with the definite value of the charge q

$$Q\Phi_q = q\Phi_q,$$

we obtain with the aid of (9.18) two equations:

$$\left.\begin{aligned} Qu\Phi_q &= (q - z)u\Phi_q, \\ Qu^\dagger\Phi_q &= (q + z)u^\dagger\Phi_q, \end{aligned}\right\} \qquad (9.25)$$

from which it follows that the operator $u^\dagger$ increases the charge of the field by z, while the operator u decreases it by the same amount. Similar properties hold, of course, separately for the positive- and negative-frequency parts of the operators $u^\dagger$ and u.

9.4. *The Vacuum State and the Amplitude of the State with a Given Number of Particles*

On the basis of the preceding investigation, we may in a natural way define the vacuum state and establish rules for constructing amplitudes which correspond to states with a definite number of various particles.

We shall consider a dynamic system consisting of several noninteracting quantized fields characterized by the operator functions

$$u_1(x), \ldots, u_n(x).$$

For convenience of notation, we shall also include in this sequence the corresponding adjoint functions in those cases in which they differ from u_i.

Let us define the *vacuum state* Φ^0 for the given dynamic system. Since there are no particles in the vacuum, the energy and the momentum of the vacuum are equal to zero. Since the negative-frequency operators $u^{(-)}$ diminish both the energy and the momentum, and the energy cannot be negative, the following relations must hold for all x

$$u_1^{(-)}(x)\Phi_0 = \ldots = u_n^{(-)}(x)\Phi_0 = 0. \qquad (9.26)$$

Going over to the momentum representation we obtain the corresponding relations

$$u_1^{(-)}(k_1)\Phi_0 = \ldots = u_n^{(-)}(k_n)\Phi_0 = 0 \qquad (9.27)$$

for all k_i such that $k_i^2 = m_i^2$, where m_i is the mass of the particle of the ith kind.

Relations (9.27) and their adjoint relations

$$\Phi_0^* u_1^{\dagger(+)}(k_1) = \ldots = \Phi_0^* u_n^{\dagger(+)}(k^n) = 0 \tag{9.28}$$

together with the normalization condition

$$\Phi_0^* \Phi = 1 \tag{9.29}$$

may be considered to be *the definition of the vacuum state of free fields.*

The amplitude of any arbitrary state of the dynamic system under consideration may now be represented with the aid of the vacuum amplitude introduced above and the creation operators for the appropriate particles. Thus the amplitude of the state which contains exactly s particles of the $j_1, \ldots, j_s$ kinds respectively will be given by an expression of the form

$$\Phi = \int F_s(k_1, \ldots, k_s)\,\delta(k_1^2 - m_{j_1}^2) \ldots \delta(k_s^2 - m_{j_s}^2)\, u_{j_1}^{(+)}(k_1) \ldots \\ \ldots u_{j_s}^{(+)}(k_s)\, dk_1 \ldots dk_j \Phi_0. \tag{9.30}$$

Here F_s is a weighting function which characterizes the particle distribution with respect to the continuous state parameters—the energies and the momenta, while the indices $j_1, \ldots, j_s$ correspond to the discrete state characteristics (for example the charge of the particles and the values of the spin components along a given direction).

The general amplitude for an arbitrary state will be given by a superposition of such expressions

$$\Phi = \sum_{\left(\substack{j_1, \ldots, j_s \\ s \geqq 0}\right)} \int F_s(k_1, \ldots, k_s)\delta(k_1^2 - m_{j_1}^2) \ldots \delta(k_s^2 - m_{j_s}^2) u_{j_1}^{(+)}(k_1) \ldots \\ \ldots u_{j_s}^{(+)}(k_s)\, dk_1 \ldots dk_s \cdot \Phi_0. \tag{9.31}$$

Expression (9.31) may also be written in the configuration representation. In order to do this we shall first carry out the integration over all k_i^0:

$$\Phi = \sum_{\left(\substack{j_1, \ldots, j_s \\ s \geqq 0}\right)} \int F_s(\mathbf{k}_1, \ldots, \mathbf{k}_s) u_j^{(+)}(\mathbf{k}_1) \ldots u_j^{(+)}(\mathbf{k}_s) d\mathbf{k}_1 \ldots d\mathbf{k}_s \cdot \Phi_0, \tag{9.32}$$

where, as usual,

$$u^{(+)}(\mathbf{k}) = \frac{\theta(k^0)u(k)}{\sqrt{2k^0}} \qquad (k^0 = \sqrt{\mathbf{k}^2 + m^2}),$$

and also

$$F_s(\mathbf{k}_1, \ldots, \mathbf{k}_s) = \frac{F_s(k_1, \ldots, k_s)}{\prod\limits_{1 \leq i \leq s} \sqrt{2k_i^0}} \qquad (k_i^0 = \sqrt{\mathbf{k}_i^2 + m_i^2}).$$

Going over to the configuration representation with the aid of the relations

$$F_s(\mathbf{k}_1, \ldots, \mathbf{k}_s) = \frac{1}{(2\pi)^{3s/2}} \int e^{i\sum_j (\mathbf{k}_j \mathbf{x}_j)} \varphi_s(\mathbf{x}_1, \ldots, \mathbf{x}_s) d\mathbf{x}_1 \ldots d\mathbf{x}_s,$$

$$u^{(+)}(\mathbf{k}) = \frac{1}{(2\pi)^{3/2}} \int e^{ikx} u^{(+)}(0, \mathbf{x}) d\mathbf{x},$$

$$u^{(+)}(0, \mathbf{x}) = u^{(+)}(x)|_{x^0=0}$$

we shall obtain for the state amplitude the following expression in place of (9.31):

$$\Phi = \sum_{\left(\substack{j_1, \ldots, j_s \\ s \geq 0}\right)} \int \varphi_s(\mathbf{x}_1, \ldots, \mathbf{x}_s) u_{j_1}^{(+)}(0, \mathbf{x}_1) \ldots u_{j_s}^{(+)}(0, \mathbf{x}_s) d\mathbf{x}_1 \ldots d\mathbf{x}_s \cdot \Phi_0. \tag{9.33}$$

The functions $\varphi_s(x_1, \ldots, x_s)$ occurring in the above expression are to be interpreted as ordinary wave functions for a system of s particles in configuration space. If we had a state in which exactly s particles were present, then the state amplitude would be completely characterized by one such function. In the general case, when the number of particles is not fixed, the state amplitude is characterized by a sequence of functions φ_s. We shall here in fact obtain the *Fock representation* for the state amplitude.

It should be emphasized that the dependence of Φ on the time has dropped out in the above, which is quite natural, since in the representation chosen by us, the state amplitude in the absence of interaction turns out to be constant.

§ 10. Setting Up the Commutation Relations

10.1. *Types of Commutation Relations*

We now proceed to set up the commutation relations for the operator wave functions.

In the classical theory of free fields with a quadratic Lagrangian, the canonical formalism is introduced by expressing the field functions linearly in terms of mutually conjugate generalized coordinates and momenta. The classical Poisson brackets for the field functions

$$\{u_\alpha(x), \quad u_\beta(y)\}$$

turn out to be certain functions of x and y independent of u. Therefore, starting with the correspondence principle, it is customary to assume in the quantum theory of a free field that the commutation rule for the operator field functions has one of the two following forms: either

$$\{u_\alpha(x), \ u_\beta(y)\}_- = u_\alpha(x)u_\beta(y) - u_\beta(y)u_\alpha(x) = \Delta_{\alpha\beta},$$

or

$$\{u_\alpha(x), \ u_\beta(y)\}_+ = u_\alpha(x)u_\beta(y) + u_\beta(y)u_\alpha(x) = \Delta_{\alpha\beta},$$

i.e., it is assumed that either the commutator or the anticommutator of two field operators is a c-number $\Delta_{\alpha\beta}$.

Relations of the first type are called Bose-Einstein commutation relations, while relations of the second type are called Fermi-Dirac commutation relations.

From considerations of invariance under translations, it follows that $\Delta_{\alpha\beta}$ may depend only on the difference $x - y$. We shall therefore write

$$\{u_\alpha(x), \ u_\beta(y)\}_\pm = \frac{1}{i} \Delta_{\alpha\beta}(x - y), \tag{10.1}$$

having for convenience factored out i^{-1}.

From equation (10.1) it follows directly that the positive- and negative-frequency parts of the operator wave functions of the same frequency signature always strictly commute or anticommute, i.e.,

$$\{u^{(+)}(x),\ u^{\dagger(+)}(y)\} = \{u^{(+)}(x),\ u^{(+)}(y)\} = \{u^{\dagger(+)}(x),\ u^{\dagger(+)}(y)\} =$$
$$= \{u^{(-)}(x),\ u^{\dagger(-)}(y)\} = \{u^{(-)}(x),\ u^{(-)}(y)\} = \{u^{\dagger(-)}(x),\ u^{\dagger(-)}(y)\} = 0. \tag{10.2}$$

Indeed, in order that the commutator (anticommutator), for example, of two positive-frequency functions

$$\{u_\alpha^{(+)}(x),\ u_\beta^{(+)}(y)\} = \frac{1}{(2\pi)^3} \int e^{i(kx+ly)}\,\theta(k^0)\theta(l^0)\delta(k^2-m^2)\delta(l^2-m^2) \times \{u_\alpha^{(+)}(k),\ u_\beta^{(+)}(l)\} dk\, dl$$

should turn out to depend on the difference $x - y$ it is necessary that

$$k = -l,$$

which is impossible due to the presence of the factor $\theta(k^0)\theta(l^0)$.

Relations (10.2) have a simple physical meaning. They correspond to the fact that the acts of creation of particles of any field do not interfere with one another, and neither do the acts of annihilation of particles of any field.

The exact form of the commutator functions $\Delta_{\alpha\beta}(x - y)$ for any arbitrary field is determined by the equations (9.12), (9.13), (9.20), (9.21) and by the structure of the operator of the energy-momentum four-vector of the given field. From the classical theory of free fields, we know that the four-momentum P^n may always be represented in the form of a sum of integrals of the following form (compare (3.26), (3.39), (4.23), (5.20), and (7.34):

$$P^n = \sum_\alpha \int d\mathbf{k} \cdot k^n (a_\alpha^{*(+)}(\mathbf{k}) a_\alpha^{(-)}(\mathbf{k}) \pm a_\alpha^{*(-)}(\mathbf{k}) a_\alpha^{(+)}(\mathbf{k})), \tag{10.3}$$

the integrands in which are quadratic in the independent amplitudes $a^{(\pm)}$ related to $u^{(\pm)}(\mathbf{k})$ by linear expressions of the form

$$u^{(\pm)}(\mathbf{k}) = \sum_\alpha v_\alpha^{(\pm)}(\mathbf{k}) a_\alpha^{(\pm)}(\mathbf{k}). \tag{10.4}$$

In quantum field theory the functions $a^{(+)}$ and $a^{(-)}$ are mutually noncommuting operators in view of which the order of factors in expressions of type (10.3) becomes important.

10.2. *Normal Product of Operators and the Form of Dynamic Variables*

We introduce the concept of an operator written in normal form and the concept of the normal product of operators.

The normal form of an operator is said to be the form in which in each term all the creation operators $u^{(+)}$ (or correspondingly $a^{(+)}$) in the momentum representation are written to the left of all the annihilation operators $u^{(-)}$ (or correspondingly $a^{(-)}$).

It is easy to see that the normal form of operators is the most convenient one from the point of view of carrying out calculations. Indeed, in order to calculate the matrix element $\Phi^* A \Phi$ of any arbitrary operator A in its normal form, it is necessary merely to commute all the operators $u^{(-)}$ occurring in A with all the $u^{(+)}$ occurring in the state amplitude Φ, and all the $u^{(+)}$ occurring in A with all the $u^{(-)}$ occurring in Φ^* until one of the $u^{(-)}$ operates on Φ_0, or one of the $u^{(+)}$ operates on Φ_0^*, which gives zero.

We consider an example. We write down in normal form the product of two Bose operators $u^*(x)$ and $u(y)$. We then obtain in turn:

$$
\begin{aligned}
u^*(x)u(y) &= u^{*(-)}(x)\,u^{(+)}(y) + u^{*(+)}(x)\,u^{(-)}(y) + u^{*(-)}(x)\,u^{(+)}(y) \\
&\qquad + u^{*(+)}(x)\,u^{(-)}(y) \\
&= u^{(+)}(x)\,u^{(+)}(y) + u^{*(+)}(x)\,u^{(-)}(y) + u^{(+)}(y)\,u^{*(-)}(x) \\
&\qquad + u^{*(-)}(x)\,u^{(-)}(y) - i\Delta^{(-)}(x-y).
\end{aligned}
$$

It is evident that in the more general case by reducing to the normal form the product of a certain number of operator wave functions u, we shall obtain a sum of products of the components $u^{(+)}$, $u^{(-)}$ and of commutator $\Delta^{(-)}$-functions. The general prescription for such a product is considered by us later (§ 16) and forms the content of an important theorem due to Wick.

The whole expression may be conventionally regarded as a "polynomial" in powers of $\Delta^{(-)}$-functions. The zero degree term of this polynomial, i.e., the sum of terms not involving any $\Delta^{(-)}$-functions, is called the normal product of the original operator wave functions. The normal product may also be defined as the original product reduced to its normal form with all the commutator functions being taken equal to zero in the process of reduction.

The normal product of the operators $u_1 u_2 \ldots u_n$ is denoted by the symbol

$$:u_1 u_2 \ldots u_n:.$$

As another example we write down the normal product of two operators $u^\dagger(x)$ and $u(y)$ obeying Fermi-Dirac quantization rules. We obviously have

$$:u^\dagger(x) u(y): = u^{\dagger(+)}(x) u^{(+)}(y) + u^{\dagger(+)}(x) u^{(-)}(y) - u^{(+)}(y) u^{\dagger(-)}(x) + u^{\dagger(-)}(x) u^{(-)}(y).$$

We now agree by definition to express all the dynamic variables which depend quadratically on operators of the same arguments, such as the Lagrangian, energy momentum and current in the form of normal products. For example, we shall write the Lagrangian for a scalar field in the form

$$\mathscr{L} = \tfrac{1}{2} \sum_n : \frac{\partial \varphi^*}{\partial x^n} \frac{\partial \varphi}{\partial x^n} : g^{nn} - \frac{m^2}{2} : \varphi^* \varphi :.$$

It is easy to see that because of the definition of the vacuum amplitude Φ_0

$$\varphi^{(-)}(x)\Phi_0 = 0, \quad \varphi^{*(-)}(x)\Phi_0 = 0$$

and of the conjugate relation

$$\Phi_0^* \varphi^{(+)}(x) = 0, \quad \Phi_0^* \varphi^{*(+)}(x) = 0$$

it follows from the preceding that the expectation values of all the dynamic variables vanish for the vacuum state, i.e.,

$$\Phi_0^* P^n \Phi_0 = 0,$$

$$\Phi^* Q \Phi_0 = 0 \text{ etc.}$$

By this method we exclude from the theory at the outset pseudophysical quantities of the type of zero-point energy, zero-point charge, etc., which usually arise in the process of quantization. At the same time it is quite clear that all the conservation laws established in the classical theory for the dynamic variables introduced above are also retained here, since in the course of proving them we used algebraic identities which remain valid for normal products.

10.3. *Requirement that Energy Should Be Positive*

Writing the expression for the energy-momentum four-vector in normal form we now obtain

$$P^n = \sum_\alpha \int d\mathbf{k} \cdot k^n \{a_\alpha^{*(+)}(\mathbf{k}) a_\alpha^{(-)}(\mathbf{k}) \pm a_\alpha^{(+)}(\mathbf{k}) a_\alpha^{*(-)}(\mathbf{k})\}, \qquad (10.5)$$

where the sign in front of the second term in the above equation agrees with the sign in (10.3) in the case of Bose-Einstein quantization, and differs from it in the case of Fermi-Dirac quantization. The sign of the second term in (10.5), and consequently the method of quantization, is uniquely determined by the requirement that *the expectation value of the energy should be positive.* Noting that in accordance with our notation we always have

$$(a^{(+)})^* = a^{*(-)},$$

we see that the second term in (10.5) is an expression of the form AA^*. Rewriting this expression in matrix form

$$\sum_k A_{mk} A^*_{kn},$$

we convince ourselves that its matrix elements

$$\sum_{k,\, m,\, n} u^*_m A_{mk} A_{kn} u_n = \sum_k \left| \sum_n u^*_n A_{nk} \right|^2$$

are always positive.

Thus the fact that the expectation value of the energy should be positive definite is guaranteed only by the upper sign $+$, and for any arbitrary field we obtain the expression for the four-momentum

$$P^n = \sum \int_\alpha d\mathbf{k} \cdot k^n \{a_\alpha^{*(+)}(\mathbf{k}) a_\alpha^{(-)}(\mathbf{k}) + a_\alpha^{(+)}(\mathbf{k}) a_\alpha^{*(-)}(\mathbf{k})\}, \qquad (10.6)$$

which is evidently symmetric with respect to particles of both signs of charge. Comparing (10.6) with (3.26), (3.39), (4.23), (5.20), and (7.36) we find that the scalar, vector, and electromagnetic fields must be qunatized according to Bose-Einstein rules, while the spinor field must be quantized according to Fermi-Dirac rules.[24] We also note that particles which correspond to fields quantized according to Bose-Einstein rules are called bosons while those corresponding to fields quantized according to Fermi-Dirac rules are called fermions.

Prior to establishing the specific form of the commutation relations, we note that in the case of complex fields in addition to relations (10.2) the commutators (anticommutators) of operators referring to particles of different sign also vanish, i.e.,

$$\{u^{(+)}(x),\ u^{(-)}(y)\} = \{u^{\dagger(+)}(x),\ u^{\dagger(-)}(y)\} = 0. \tag{10.7}$$

In order to do this we consider the state with a definite value of the charge q:

$$Q\Phi_q = q\Phi_q. \tag{10.8}$$

Applying the operator Q to the amplitudes

$$u_\alpha^{(+)}(x)\, u_\beta^{(-)}(y)\, \Phi_q \text{ and } u_\beta^{(-)}(y)\, u_\alpha^{(+)}(x)\, \Phi_q,$$

and with the aid of equation

$$zu^{(\pm)}(x) = [u^{(\pm)}(x),\ Q]$$

we evidently obtain

$$Qu_\alpha^{(+)}(x)\, u_\beta^{(-)}(y)\Phi_q = (q - 2z)\, u_\alpha^{(+)}(x)\, u_\beta^{(-)}(y)\Phi_q$$

and

$$Qu_\beta^{(-)}(y)\, u_\alpha^{(+)}(x)\Phi_q = (q - 2z)\, u_\beta^{(-)}(y)\, u_\alpha^{(+)}(x)\Phi_q.$$

Adding and subtracting these relations we find:

$$Q\{u_\alpha^{(+)}(x),\ u_\beta^{(-)}(y)\}\Phi_q = (q - 2z)\{u_\alpha^{(+)}(x),\ u_\beta^{(-)}(y)\}\Phi_q.$$

We note that the c-number

[24] Our reasoning was based on the difference in the signs of the second term in the "classical" expression for the energy. It should be emphasized that, as has been shown by Pauli (91a), this circumstance in turn depends on the various transformation properties of the field components (integral or half-integral spin). Schwinger (109) showed that a deeper reason for the difference in quantization procedure is related to the requirement of invariance under a reflection of the time axis. See also Pauli's article (91b).

$$\{u_\alpha^{(+)}(x),\quad u_\beta^{(-)}(y)\}$$

cannot be different from zero, since in this case after cancelling this number we would obtain

$$Q\Phi_q = (q - 2z)\Phi_q,$$

which contradicts equation (10.8). The second of equations (10.7) is proved in a similar manner.

The physical meaning of relations (10.7) consists of the mutual independence of the acts of creation and annihilation of particles with different charge.

We have established in this manner that for any arbitrary (complex) field only the *c*-numbers

$$\{u^{\dagger(-)}(x),\ u^{(+)}(y)\}\ \text{and}\ \{u^{(-)}(x),\quad u^{\dagger(+)}(y)\}$$

may differ from zero.

10.4. *Fermi-Dirac and Bose-Einstein Commutation Relations*

Equations (9.12) together with the expression (10.6) for the energy-momentum four-vector uniquely determine these *c*-numbers.[25] Substituting (10.6) into equations (9.12) written in terms of the field operators in the momentum representation $a^{(\pm)}$, we obtain:

$$\left.\begin{aligned}
&-k^n a_i^{(+)}(\mathbf{k})\\
&= \int d\mathbf{k}' \cdot k'^n [a_i^{(+)}(\mathbf{k}),\ \sum_j (a_j^{*(+)}(\mathbf{k}')a_j^{(-)}(\mathbf{k}') + a_j^{(+)}(\mathbf{k}')\, a_j^{*(+)}(\mathbf{k}'))],\\
&\quad k^n a_i^{(-)}(\mathbf{k})\\
&= \int d\mathbf{k}' \cdot k'^n [a_i^{(-)}(\mathbf{k}),\ \sum_j (a_j^{*(+)}(\mathbf{k}')\, a_j^{(+)}(\mathbf{k}') + a_j^{(+)}(\mathbf{k}')a_j^{*(-)}(\mathbf{k}'))].
\end{aligned}\right\} \tag{10.9}$$

From (10.2) and (10.7) it follows that

$$[a_i^{(+)}(\mathbf{k}),\quad a_j^{*(+)}(\mathbf{k}')\, a_j^{(-)}(\mathbf{k}')] = 0,$$
$$[a_i^{(-)}(\mathbf{k}),\quad a_j^{(+)}(\mathbf{k}')a_j^{*(-)}(\mathbf{k}')] = 0.$$

Equations (10.9) therefore lead to the relations

[25] The argument presented here follows that of Sokolov — see (**114**), part 1, § 18.

$$\left.\begin{aligned}\sum_j [a_i^{(+)}(\mathbf{k}),\ a_j^{(+)}(\mathbf{k}')\, a_j^{*(-)}(\mathbf{k}')] &= -\,\delta(\mathbf{k}-\mathbf{k}')\, a_i^{(+)}(\mathbf{k}),\\ \sum_j [a_i^{(-)}(\mathbf{k}),\ a_j^{*(+)}(\mathbf{k}')\, a_j^{(-)}(\mathbf{k}')] &= \delta(\mathbf{k}-\mathbf{k}')\, a_i^{(-)}(\mathbf{k}).\end{aligned}\right\} \qquad (10.10)$$

Assuming that the operators of the same frequency signature anticommute (spinor field) we obtain from (10.10):

$$-\sum_j a_j^{(+)}(\mathbf{k}')[a_i^{(+)}(\mathbf{k}),\ a_j^{*(-)}(\mathbf{k}')]_+ = -\,\delta(\mathbf{k}-\mathbf{k}')\, a_i^{(+)}(\mathbf{k}),$$

$$\sum_j [a_i^{(-)}(\mathbf{k}),\ a_j^{*(+)}(\mathbf{k}')]_+ a_j^{(-)}(\mathbf{k}') = \delta(\mathbf{k}-\mathbf{k}')\, a_i^{(-)}(\mathbf{k}),$$

from which follow the Fermi-Dirac commutation relations for the spinor field

$$\left.\begin{aligned}[a_i^{(+)}(\mathbf{k}),\ a_j^{*(-)}(\mathbf{k}')]_+ &= \delta(\mathbf{k}-\mathbf{k}')\delta_{ij}\\ [a_i^{(-)}(\mathbf{k}),\ a_j^{*(+)}(\mathbf{k}')]_+ &= \delta(\mathbf{k}-\mathbf{k}')\delta_{ij}\,.\end{aligned}\right\} \qquad (10.11)$$

Assuming that the operators of the same frequency signature commute we obtain from (10.10)

$$\sum_j a_j^{(+)}(\mathbf{k}')[a_j^{*(-)}(\mathbf{k}'),\ a_i^{(+)}(\mathbf{k})]_- = \delta(\mathbf{k}-\mathbf{k}')a_i^{(+)}(\mathbf{k}),$$

$$\sum_j [a_i^{(-)}(\mathbf{k}),\ a_j^{*(+)}(\mathbf{k}')]_-\ a_j^{(-)}(\mathbf{k}') = \delta(\mathbf{k}-\mathbf{k}')a_i^{(-)}(\mathbf{k}),$$

from which follow the Bose-Einstein commutation relations for all the other fields considered by us:

$$\left.\begin{aligned}[a_j^{*(-)}(\mathbf{k}'),\ a_i^{(+)}(\mathbf{k})]_- &= \delta(\mathbf{k}-\mathbf{k}')\delta_{ij}\,,\\ [a_i^{(-)}(\mathbf{k}),\ a_j^{*(+)}(\mathbf{k}')]_- &= \delta(\mathbf{k}-\mathbf{k}')\delta_{ij}\,.\end{aligned}\right\} \qquad (10.12)$$

The commutator functions $\Delta_{\alpha\beta}$ in the x-representation may be obtained from (10.11) and (10.12) by taking into account the specific properties of the coefficients $v(\mathbf{k})$ in the expansions (10.4).

In order to write down the commutation relations in a relativistically invariant form we shall go over to the four-dimensional operators by means of the relations

$$a^{(\pm)}(\mathbf{k}) = \frac{\theta(k^0)a(\pm\, k)}{\sqrt{2k^0}} \qquad (k^0 = \sqrt{\mathbf{k}^2 + m^2}),$$

from which it also follows that:

$$a^{(\pm)}(\mathbf{k}) = \int \sqrt{2k^0}\,\theta(k^0)\,\delta(k^2 - m^2)\,a(\pm k)\,dk^0.$$

Therefore, by representing the right-hand terms of (10.11) and (10.12) in the form

$$\delta_{ij} \int dk^0 \int dk'^0\, 2k^0\,\theta(k^0)\,\delta(k - k')\,\delta(k^2 - m^2),$$

we shall obtain by equating the integrands

$$\begin{aligned} &\theta(k^0)\,\theta(k'^0)\,\delta(k^2 - m^2)\,\delta(k'^2 - m^2)\{a_i^*(-k),\ a_j(k')\} \\ &= \theta(k^0)\,\theta(k'^0)\,\delta(k^2 - m^2)\,\delta(k'^2 - m^2)\{a_i(-k),\ a_j^*(k')\} \\ &= \delta_{ij}\,\delta(k - k')\,\delta(k^2 - m^2)\,\theta(k^0). \end{aligned}$$

From this it follows that for the Fermi-operators

$$\delta(k^2 - m^2)\,\delta(k'^2 - m^2)\{a_i(k),\ a_j^*(k')\}_+ = \delta_{ij}\,\delta(k + k')\,\delta(k^2 - m^2) \tag{10.13}$$

and for the Bose-operators

$$\begin{aligned} &\delta(k^2 - m^2)\,\delta(k'^2 - m^2)\{a_i(k),\ a_j^*(k')\}_- \\ &\qquad = -\,(\theta(k^0) - \theta(-k'^0))\,\delta_{ij}\,\delta(k + k')\,\delta(k^2 - m^2). \end{aligned} \tag{10.14}$$

10.5. *Commutation Relations in the Discrete Momentum Representation*

We shall also give the form of the commutation relations in the discrete momentum representation mentioned in § 3. Using the discrete expansion for the field functions of the type (3.28)

$$u(x) = \frac{1}{L^{3/2}} \sum_{(n_1, n_2, n_3)} \left(\frac{u^{(+)}(\mathbf{n})}{\sqrt{2k^0}}\, e^{\frac{2\pi i}{L}(nx)} + \frac{u^{(-)}(\mathbf{n})}{\sqrt{2k^0}}\, e^{-\frac{2\pi i}{L}(nx)} \right)$$

and the discrete representation of the energy-momentum four-vector of the type (3.31)

$$P^m = \sum_{(\alpha, n)} \left(a_\alpha^{*(+)}(\mathbf{n})\, a_\alpha^{(-)}(\mathbf{n}) + a_\alpha^{(+)}(\mathbf{n})\, a_\alpha^{*(-)}(\mathbf{n})\right) k^m,$$

with

$$u(\mathbf{n}) = u(n_1,\ n_2,\ n_3), \qquad a(\mathbf{n}) = a(n_1,\ n_2,\ n_3),$$

$$k^\alpha = \frac{2\pi}{L}\, n^\alpha (\alpha = 1,\ 2,\ 3) \text{ and } k^0 = \frac{2\pi}{L} \sqrt{n_1^2 + n_2^2 + n_3^2 + \frac{L^2}{4\pi^2} m^2},$$

we obtain after a calculation similar to the one given above the following discrete commutation relations:

in the case of the spinor field

$$\{a_\alpha^{(+)}(\mathbf{n}),\ a_\beta^{*(-)}(\mathbf{n}')\}_+ = \{a_\alpha^{(-)}(\mathbf{n}),\ a_\beta^{*(+)}(\mathbf{n}')\}_+ = \delta_{\alpha\beta}\delta_{\mathbf{nn}'}, \tag{10.15}$$

in the case of all the other fields

$$\{a_\alpha^{(-)}(\mathbf{n}),\ a_\beta^{*(+)}(\mathbf{n}')\}_- = \{a_\alpha^{*(-)}(\mathbf{n}),\ a_\beta^{(+)}(\mathbf{n}')\}_- = \delta_{\alpha\beta}\delta_{\mathbf{nn}'}. \tag{10.16}$$

Here $\delta_{\mathbf{nn}'}$ is the product of Kronecker symbols

$$\delta_{\mathbf{nn}'} = \delta_{n_1n_1'}\delta_{n_2n_2'}\delta_{n_3n_3'},$$

while the discrete operators $a(\mathbf{n})$ are related to the continuous $a(\mathbf{k})$ in the limit of large L by expressions of type (3.30):

$$\lim_{L\to\infty}\left(\frac{L}{2\pi}\right)^{3/2} a(\mathbf{n}) = a(\mathbf{k}).$$

In the second quantization theory, quadratic combinations of the discrete creation and annihilation operators of the type

$$a^{(-)}a^{*(+)},\quad a^{*(-)}a^{(+)}$$

play the role of operators for the number of particles. Let us examine the case of quantization according to Bose-Einstein rules. We shall then obtain from (10.16)

$$a^{(-)}a^{*(+)} - a^{*(+)}a^{(-)} = 1. \tag{10.17}$$

Denoting the operator $a^{*(+)}a^{(-)}$ by n:

$$n = a^{*(+)}a^{(-)}, \tag{10.18}$$

we shall show that the eigenvalues N of the operator n

$$n\Phi = N\Phi \tag{10.19}$$

are integers. To see this we consider the expression

$$(\Phi^\dagger(a^{*(+)})^k(a^{(-)})^k\Phi). \tag{10.20}$$

After carrying out successive commutations of the operators $a^{*(+)}$ and $a^{(-)}$ and taking into account the relation

$$a^{*(+)}n = (n-1)a^{*(+)},$$

which follows from (10.17) and (10.18), we obtain successively:

$$a^{*(+)}a^{*(+)}a^{(-)}a^{(-)} = a^{*(+)}na^{(-)} = (n-1)a^{*(+)}a^{(-)} = n(n-1),$$
$$a^{*(+)}a^{*(+)}a^{*(+)}a^{(-)}a^{(-)}a^{(-)} = a^{*(+)}n(n-1)a^{(-)}$$
$$= (n-1)a^{*(+)}(n-1)a^{(-)} = n(n-1)(n-2),$$

. . . .

. . . .

. . . .

from which it follows that

$$(\Phi^*(a^{*(+)})^k(a^{(-)})^k\Phi) = (\Phi^* n(n-1)\dots(n-k+1)\Phi)$$
$$= N(N-1)\dots(N-k+1)(\Phi^*\Phi). \tag{10.21}$$

Since the operator

$$(a^{*(+)})^k (a^{(-)})^k$$

represents the product of an operator and its conjugate, the matrix element (10.20) cannot be negative. On the other hand for a nonintegral N a value of k may be found

$$k > N + 1,$$

for which (10.21) will become less than zero, which is impossible. Therefore N is an integer.

As may be easily seen, in the discrete representation the four-momentum and the charge are expressed by sums of the type

$$\sum_{\nu} \omega_{\nu} n_{\nu},$$

where ω_{ν} is the four-momentum or the charge of a single particle in the state ν. It is therefore natural to consider n_{ν} as an operator which represents the number of particles in the given state.

We now turn to the Fermi-Dirac quantization rule:

$$a^{(-)} a^{*(+)} + a^{*(+)} a^{(-)} = 1. \tag{10.22}$$

Denoting

$$a^{*(+)} a^{(-)} = n,$$

we shall investigate the eigenvalues N of the operator n. In order to do this we examine the expression

$$\Phi^* n^2 \Phi = N^2 \Phi^* \Phi.$$

Commuting the operators $a^{(-)}$ and $a^{*(+)}$ and taking into account the relations

$$a^{(-)} n = (1 - n) a^{(-)}, \quad a^{(-)} a^{(-)} + a^{(-)} a^{(-)} = 0,$$

we obtain:

$$\begin{aligned} n^2 = a^{*(+)} a^{(-)} a^{*(+)} a^{(-)} &= a^{*(+)} a^{(-)} n \\ &= a^{*(+)} (1 - n) a^{(-)} = n - a^{*(+)} a^{*(+)} a^{(-)} a^{(-)} = n, \end{aligned}$$

i.e.,

$$\Phi^* n^2 \Phi = \Phi^* n \Phi,$$

from which it follows that

$$N^2 = N,$$

and consequently N may equal either 1, or 0, i.e.,

$$N = 0,\ 1. \tag{10.23}$$

Using the expressions for the energy-momentum and the charge operators, we further find without difficulty that the numbers N_{ν} which correspond to the operators

$$n_{\nu} = a_{\nu}^{*(+)} a_{\nu}^{(-)}, \qquad n_{\nu}^* = a_{\nu}^{(+)} a_{\nu}^{*(-)},$$

are indeed equal to the number of particles with the corresponding momenta and charge, and the operators n_ν and n_ν^* are therefore the operators for the number of particles.

We therefore see that quantization in accordance with Bose-Einstein rules leads to quite a different physical picture from that obtained from quantization in accordance with Fermi-Dirac rules. When quantization is carried out according to (10.17), the occupation numbers N may take on arbitrarily large integral values. In the case of Bose-Einstein statistics, an arbitrarily large number of particles may exist in the same state (characterized by a given four-momentum, charge and spin). On the other hand, when quantization is carried out in accordance with (10.22), the occupation numbers may only take on the two values 0 and 1 in accordance with (10.23). Relation (10.23) is an expression of the Pauli exclusion principle: in a system of particles obeying Fermi-Dirac statistics, not more than one particle may exist in any given state.

We have briefly examined the usual discrete representation of the field functions which was used primarily in the earlier articles on quantum field theory. Its virtues are the simplicity and the directness of the method of introducing the occupation numbers and the possibility of expressing the state amplitude as a function of these numbers.

However, since it is noncovariant, we shall not use it in our presentation, but we shall work with the continuous representation.

It is not difficult to see that in this case the operator expressions

$$a^{*(+)}(\mathbf{k})\, a^{(-)}(\mathbf{k}), \quad a^{(+)}(\mathbf{k})\, a^{*(-)}(\mathbf{k})$$

play the role of the density of the number of particles in three-dimensional momentum space.

§ 11. Scalar and Vector Fields

In this section we shall examine the simplest fields quantized according to Bose-Einstein rules — the complex and the real scalar fields and the complex form of the vector field.

11.1. *The Real Scalar Field*

The real scalar field is described by a single real function φ. This function may be represented as the sum of its positive- and negative-frequency parts $\varphi^{(+)}$ and $\varphi^{(-)}$ which, in accordance with the analysis given in § 9, describe the creation and annihilation of neutral particles corresponding to the field.

In § 10 it was also established that the scalar field is quantized in accordance with Bose-Einstein rules. We must therefore take

$$[\varphi^{(-)}(\mathbf{k}), \quad \varphi^{(+)}(\mathbf{k}')]_- = \delta(\mathbf{k} - \mathbf{k}') \tag{11.1}$$

and also (see formula (10.2))

$$[\varphi^{(-)}(\mathbf{k}),\ \varphi^{(-)}(\mathbf{k}')]_- = [\varphi^{(+)}(\mathbf{k}),\ \varphi^{(+)}(\mathbf{k}')]_- = 0. \qquad (11.2)$$

Using as our starting point formulas (11.1) and (11.2), which give the commutation relations in the momentum representation, we shall determine the form of the commutation functions in the x-representation. Using the expansions (3.20) for this purpose we find:

$$[\varphi^{(-)}(x),\ \varphi^{(+)}(y)]_- = \frac{1}{(2\pi)^3}\int d\mathbf{k}\int d\mathbf{l}\ \frac{e^{i(ly-kx)}}{\sqrt{2k^0}\sqrt{2l^0}}\ [\varphi^{(-)}(\mathbf{k}),\ \varphi^{(+)}(\mathbf{l})]_-$$

$$= \frac{1}{(2\pi)^3}\int \frac{e^{ik(y-x)}}{2k^0}\ d\mathbf{k}$$

$$= \frac{1}{(2\pi)^3}\int e^{-ik(x-y)}\,\delta(k^2 - m^2)\,\theta(k^0)\,dk = \frac{1}{i}\,D^{(-)}(x-y), \qquad (11.3)$$

where we have introduced the notation

$$D^{(-)}(x) = \frac{i}{(2\pi)^3}\int e^{ikx}\,\delta(k^2 - m^2)\theta(-k^0)dk. \qquad (11.4)$$

From (11.3) it also follows that

$$[\varphi^{(+)}(x),\ \varphi^{(-)}(y)]_- = \frac{1}{i}\,D^{(+)}(x-y), \qquad (11.5)$$

where

$$D^{(+)}(x) = -D^{(-)}(-x) = \frac{1}{(2\pi)^3 i}\int e^{ikx}\,\delta(k^2 - m^2)\theta(k^0)dk. \qquad (11.6)$$

Adding (11.3) and (11.5) (taking into account the commutativity of components of the same frequency signature), we obtain the expression for the commutator of the complete field functions

$$[\varphi(x),\ \varphi(y)]_- = \frac{1}{i}\,D(x-y). \qquad (11.7)$$

On the right-hand side of the above expression we have the well-known Pauli-Jordan commutation function

$$D(x) = D^{(+)}(x) + D^{(-)}(x) = \frac{1}{(2\pi)^3 i}\int e^{ikx}\,\delta(k^2 - m^2)\,\varepsilon(k^0)dk, \qquad (11.8)$$

in which

$$\varepsilon(k^0) = \theta(k^0) - \theta(-k^0) = \begin{cases} +1 \text{ for } k^0 > 0, \\ -1 \text{ for } k^0 < 0. \end{cases}$$

The meaning of the indices (+) and (−) in the left-hand sides of formulas (11.4) and (11.6) now also becomes clear since the functions $D^{(+)}$ and $D^{(-)}$ introduced there represent the positive- and negative-frequency parts of the "complete commutation function" D.

We shall obtain the principal dynamic variables of the quantized real scalar field from the general prescription of § 10 by rewriting the corresponding expressions for the unquantized field in terms of normal products:

$$\left.\begin{aligned} \mathscr{L} &= \tfrac{1}{2}\sum_n g^{nn} : \frac{\partial \varphi}{\partial x^n}\frac{\partial \varphi}{\partial x^n} : - \frac{m^2}{2} : \varphi^2 :, \\ T^{mn} &= g^{mm} g^{nn} : \frac{\partial \varphi}{\partial x^m}\frac{\partial \varphi}{\partial x^n} : - g^{mn}\mathscr{L}, \\ P^n &= \int d\mathbf{k}\, k^n \varphi^{(+)}(\mathbf{k})\,\varphi^{(-)}(\mathbf{k}). \end{aligned}\right\} \qquad (11.9)$$

We note that the arguments of § 9 which established the meaning of the positive- and negative-frequency parts of the field function $\varphi^{(+)}$ and $\varphi^{(-)}$ did not determine their normalization. This normalization may now be determined by means of expression (11.9) for the energy-momentum four-vector. We consider the amplitude of the state which contains one scalar particle with an unnormalized momentum distribution function $c(\mathbf{k})$

$$\Phi_1 = \int c(\mathbf{k})\,\varphi^{(+)}(\mathbf{k})\, d\mathbf{k}\Phi_0, \qquad (11.10)$$

and we calculate the expectation value of the operator (11.9) for this state. After carrying out the commutations of the operators, we obtain

$$\langle P^n \rangle_1 \equiv \frac{\Phi_1^* P^n \Phi_1}{\Phi_1^* \Phi_1} = \frac{\int c^*(\mathbf{k}) c(\mathbf{k}) k^n d\mathbf{k}}{\int c^*(\mathbf{k}) c(\mathbf{k}) d\mathbf{k}}. \qquad (11.11)$$

The transition to a state with a given value of the four-momentum k^n may be carried out in (11.10) and (11.11) by means of localizing the function $c(\mathbf{k})$ in a small region around the value $\mathbf{k} = \mathbf{K}$ (for example by means of a limiting process of the type $c(\mathbf{k}) \rightarrow \sim \delta(\mathbf{k}-\mathbf{K})$). In the above $k^n \rightarrow K^n$ and we obtain

$$\langle P^n \rangle_1 \rightarrow K^n.$$

Thus the expectation value of the operator P^n for a state with the given value of the four-momentum K^n is exactly equal to K^n (which corresponds to the results of the preceding section, compare pp. 109–112), and, consequently, the normalization of the operators $\varphi^{(+)}$ and $\varphi^{(-)}$ in expression (11.9) is correct.

11.2. *The Complex Scalar Field*

In contrast to the real field the complex scalar field is characterized by two mutually conjugate functions φ and φ^* and describes charged particles of two signs of charge.

Proceeding to the examination of the positive- and negative-frequency parts of the functions φ and φ^*, we find, in accordance with the properties established in § 10 of the function φ decreasing and of the function φ^* increasing the charge of the field, that the operator $\varphi^{(+)}$ describes the creation of a particle of negative charge, the operator $\varphi^{(-)}$ describes the annihilation of a particle of positive charge, the operator $\varphi^{*(+)}$ describes the creation of a particle of positive charge, and the operator $\varphi^{*(-)}$ describes the annihilation of a particle of negative charge.

It was also shown in § 10 that the scalar field is quantized according to Bose-Einstein rules and that the operators which refer to particles of different sign always (anti) commute among themselves. From this it follows that the commutation rules for the operators of the complex scalar field have the following form

$$\left.\begin{aligned} [\varphi^{*(-)}(\mathbf{k}),\ \varphi^{(+)}(\mathbf{k}')]_- &= \delta(\mathbf{k}-\mathbf{k}'),\\ [\varphi^{(-)}(\mathbf{k}),\ \varphi^{*(+)}(\mathbf{k}')]_- &= \delta(\mathbf{k}-\mathbf{k}'), \end{aligned}\right\} \tag{11.12}$$

while all the other commutators are equal to zero.

In going over to the x-representation by means of the formulas of § 3 we find from the above that

$$[\varphi^{*(-)}(x),\ \varphi^{(+)}(y)]_- = \frac{1}{i} D^{(-)}(x-y) \tag{11.13}$$

and

$$[\varphi^{*(+)}(x),\ \varphi^{(-)}(y)]_- = \frac{1}{i} D^{(+)}(x - y). \qquad (11.14)$$

Adding (11.13) and (11.14), and taking into account the fact that components of the same frequency signature of φ and φ^* commute among themselves, and that the Pauli-Jordan function is odd

$$D(x) = - D(- x), \qquad (11.15)$$

as follows from (11.8), we obtain the following formulas:

$$[\varphi(x),\ \varphi^*(y)]_- = [\varphi^*(x),\ \varphi(y)]_- = \frac{1}{i} D(x - y). \qquad (11.16)$$

We shall obtain the principal dynamic variables of the complex scalar field, just as in the case of the real scalar field, by rewriting the corresponding expressions from § 3 for the unquantized field in terms of normal products. We obtain in this way:

$$\mathscr{L} = \sum_n g^{nn} : \frac{\partial \varphi^*}{\partial x^n} \frac{\partial \varphi}{\partial x^n} : - m^2 : \varphi^* \varphi :, \qquad (11.17)$$

$$T^{mn} = g^{mm} g^{nn} : \left(\frac{\partial \varphi^*}{\partial x^m} \frac{\partial \varphi}{\partial x^n} + \frac{\partial \varphi^*}{\partial x^n} \frac{\partial \varphi}{\partial x^m} \right) : - g^{mn} \mathscr{L}, \qquad (11.18)$$

$$P^n = \int d\mathbf{k} \cdot k^n (\varphi^{*(+)}(\mathbf{k}) \varphi^{(-)}(\mathbf{k}) + \varphi^{(+)}(\mathbf{k}) \varphi^{*(-)}(\mathbf{k})), \qquad (11.19)$$

$$Q = \int d\mathbf{k} (\varphi^{*(+)}(\mathbf{k}) \varphi^{(-)}(\mathbf{k}) - \varphi^{(+)}(\mathbf{k}) \varphi^{*(-)}(\mathbf{k})). \qquad (11.20)$$

It follows from the structure of the operators P^n and Q that $\varphi^{*(+)}(\mathbf{k})$ is the operator for the creation of a particle with energy-momentum k and charge $+ 1$; $\varphi^{(-)}(\mathbf{k})$ is the annihilation operator for the same particle; $\varphi^{(+)}(\mathbf{k})$ is the creation operator for a particle with energy-momentum k and charge $- 1$; $\varphi^{*(-)}(\mathbf{k})$ is the annihilation operator for the same particle.

11.3. *The Complex Vector Field*

In quantizing the vector field we shall limit ourselves to an examination of the complex vector field as we have done in § 4. In doing so, we note that the transition to the real vector field in the formulas that we shall obtain below may be carried out provided the change in the form of the commutation relations is taken into account (compare the transition from (11.12) to (11.1)).

In order to set up the quantization rules for the four-potential of the vector field, we note that a mechanical generalization to this case of the quantization rules of the scalar field, i.e., the independent quantization of each component of the potential U_n following the example of the scalar field, turns out to be impossible, since such a procedure does not guarantee that the expectation value of the energy will be positive and turns out to be incompatible with the subsidiary condition (4.3).

The quantization procedure must therefore take cognizance of the subsidiary condition which, as we have seen in § 4, automatically guarantees that P^0 shall be positive. In particular, it was shown that as a result of going over from U_n to the longitudinal and transverse components in accordance with formula (4.22) the energy-momentum four-vector may be expressed in terms of three linearly independent amplitudes $a_\alpha(\mathbf{k})$ in the following manner:

$$P^n = \int d\mathbf{k} \cdot k^n \sum_{\alpha=1,2,3} (a_\alpha^{*(+)}(\mathbf{k})a_\alpha^{(-)}(\mathbf{k}) + a_\alpha^{*(-)}(\mathbf{k})a_\alpha^{(+)}(\mathbf{k})). \quad (4.23)$$

This form of writing down the classical four-momentum takes into account the subsidiary condition (4.3) and guarantees that the unquantized P^0 shall be positive. It is also clear that the quantization of the three independent amplitudes a_α directly in accordance with Bose-Einstein rules will guarantee that the expectation value of the energy operator will be positive definite.

As a result of this, the operators a_α must be made to satisfy the following commutation relations:

$$\left.\begin{aligned} &[a_\alpha^{(-)}(\mathbf{k}),\ a_\beta^{*(+)}(\mathbf{k}')]_- = \delta_{\alpha\beta}\delta(\mathbf{k}-\mathbf{k}'), \\ &[a_\alpha^{*(-)}(\mathbf{k}),\ a_\beta^{(+)}(\mathbf{k}')]_- = \delta_{\alpha\beta}\delta(\mathbf{k}-\mathbf{k}') \end{aligned}\right\} \quad (11.21)$$

(all the other commutators are equal to zero).

Rewriting in normal form the expressions for the energy-momentum four-vector (4.27), for the charge (4.28), and for the component of the spin vector along the direction of motion (4.29), all expressed in terms of the amplitudes b_α (which are related to a_α by expressions (4.26)), we obtain:

$$P^n = \int d\mathbf{k} \cdot k^n \sum_\alpha \left(b_\alpha^{*(+)}(\mathbf{k})b_\alpha^{(-)}(\mathbf{k}) + b_\alpha^{(+)}(\mathbf{k})b_\alpha^{*(-)}(\mathbf{k})\right), \tag{11.22}$$

$$Q = \int d\mathbf{k} \sum_\alpha \left(b_\alpha^{*(+)}(\mathbf{k})b_\alpha^{(-)}(\mathbf{k}) - b_\alpha^{(+)}(\mathbf{k})b_\alpha^{*(-)}(\mathbf{k})\right), \tag{11.23}$$

$$S_3 = \int d\mathbf{k}\{b_1^{*(+)}(\mathbf{k})b_1^{(-)}(\mathbf{k}) - b_1^{(+)}(\mathbf{k})b_1^{*(-)}(\mathbf{k}) + b_2^{(+)}(\mathbf{k})b_2^{*(-)}(\mathbf{k}) - b_2^{*(+)}(\mathbf{k})b_2^{(-)}(\mathbf{k})\}. \tag{11.24}$$

By evaluating the corresponding expectation values we convince ourselves that $b_1^{*(+)}(\mathbf{k})$ and $b_1^{(-)}(\mathbf{k})$ are respectively the creation and annihilation operators for a particle of momentum **k**, charge $+ 1$, and component of spin along the direction of motion $+ 1$, $b_2^{*(+)}(\mathbf{k})$, $b_2^{(-)}(\mathbf{k})$ are the creation and annihilation operators for a particle of momentum **k**, charge $+ 1$ and spin component $- 1$, $b_3^{*(+)}(\mathbf{k})$ and $b_3^{(-)}(\mathbf{k})$ are the creation and annihilation operators for a particle of momentum **k**, charge $+ 1$ and zero spin component. The meaning of the operators $b_\alpha^{(+)}$ and $b_\alpha^{*(-)}$ may be obtained from the foregoing by means of the following rule: "the transition from $b_\alpha^{(\pm)}$ to $b_\alpha^{*(\pm)}$ corresponds to a change in the sign of the charge and in the sign of the spin component."

Thus, for example, if we calculate the expectation values of the operators (11.22), (11.23), (11.24) for a single-particle state described by an amplitude of type (11.10)

$$\Phi_1 = \int c(\mathbf{k})\, b_1^{(+)}(\mathbf{k})\, d\mathbf{k}\, \Phi_0,$$

taking into account the rule for finding Hermitean conjugates $(b_1^{(+)})^* = b_1^{*(-)}$, we obtain as a result of going over to $c(\mathbf{k})$ localized in the neighborhood of $\mathbf{k} = \mathbf{K}$

$$\langle P^n\rangle_1 = K^n, \quad \langle Q\rangle_1 = 1, \quad \langle S_3\rangle_1 = - 1 \text{ etc.}$$

We see from the above that the vector field (4.3), (4.6), describes charged particles of mass m and with three possible values of the component of spin $(1, 0, - 1)$ along a given direction. More briefly, it is said that this field describes vector mesons of spin 1.

The amplitudes a_α also have a simple meaning. Thus the amplitudes a_3 correspond to particles of zero spin component, while a_1 and a_2 describe linear combinations of states with spin components 1 and -1 which correspond to circular polarization.

We also write down the commutation relations for the four dependent amplitudes U_n. With the aid of (4.26) we find without difficulty the commutation relations for the three amplitudes $U_\alpha(\mathbf{k})$ ($\alpha = 1, 2, 3$):

$$[U_\alpha^{*(-)}(\mathbf{k}), U_\beta^{(+)}(\mathbf{k}')]_- = [U_\alpha^{(-)}(\mathbf{k}), U_\beta^{*(+)}(\mathbf{k}')]_- = \delta(\mathbf{k}-\mathbf{k}')\left(\delta_{\alpha\beta} + \frac{k_\alpha k_\beta}{m^2}\right).$$

Utilizing the relation between U_0 and U_α

$$U_0(\mathbf{k}) = -\frac{1}{k^0}\sum_\alpha k^\alpha U_\alpha(\mathbf{k}),$$

we then determine the commutators which involve U_0

$$[U_0^{*(-)}(\mathbf{k}),\ U_\alpha^{(+)}(\mathbf{k}')]_- = [U_0^{(-)}(\mathbf{k}), U_\alpha^{*(+)}(\mathbf{k}')]_- = -\frac{k^0 k^\alpha}{m^2}\delta(\mathbf{k}-\mathbf{k}'),$$

$$[U_0^{*(-)}(\mathbf{k}), U_0^{(+)}(\mathbf{k}')]_- = [U_0^{(-)}(\mathbf{k}), U_0^{*(+)}(\mathbf{k}')]_- = \left(\frac{k^0 k^0}{m^2} - 1\right)\delta(\mathbf{k}-\mathbf{k}').$$

Bringing together all the expressions obtained above we obtain the formula

$$[U_n^{*(-)}(\mathbf{k}),\ U_l^{(+)}(\mathbf{k}')]_- = [U_n^{(-)}(\mathbf{k}),\ U_l^{*(+)}(\mathbf{k}')]_-$$
$$= \left(-g^{nl} + g^{nn}g^{ll}\frac{k^n k^l}{m^2}\right)\delta(\mathbf{k}-\mathbf{k}'), \qquad (11.25)$$

which is relativistically symmetric and compatible with the subsidiary condition (4.3). Going over to the coordinate representation we obtain from the above:

$$[U_l^{*(-)}(x),\ U_n^{(+)}(y)]_- = [U_l^{(-)}(x),\ U_n^{*(+)}(y)]_-$$
$$= \left(g^{ln} + \frac{1}{m^2}\frac{\partial^2}{\partial x^l\,\partial x^n}\right) iD^{(-)}(x-y), \qquad (11.26)$$

$$[U_l^*(x),\ U_n(y)]_- = \left(g^{ln} + \frac{1}{m^2}\frac{\partial^2}{\partial x^l\,\partial x^n}\right) iD(x-y), \qquad (11.27)$$

where, as usual, $D(x-y)$ is the Pauli-Jordan commutation function, while $D^{(-)}$ is its negative-frequency part.

It is not difficult to verify that the commutation relations

(11.27) are compatible both with the field equations and with the subsidiary conditions. Thus, operating on both sides of (11.27) with the Klein-Gordon operator $\Box_x - m^2$ we obtain the identity $0 = 0$, since according to (11.8)

$$(\Box_x - m^2) D(x-y) = 0.$$

Applying the operation

$$\sum_l g^{ll} \frac{\partial}{\partial x^l}$$

to (11.27) we obtain a similar result, since

$$\sum_l g^{ll} \frac{\partial}{\partial x^l} \left(g^{ln} + \frac{1}{m^2} \frac{\partial^2}{\partial x^l \partial x^n} \right) D(x-y) = \left(\frac{\partial}{\partial x^n} - \frac{\Box}{m^2} \frac{\partial}{\partial x^n} \right) D(x-y) = 0.$$

§ 12. The Spinor Field

12.1. *Fermi-Dirac Quantization and Commutation Functions*

It may be seen from the structure of the energy-momentum four-vector of the spinor field

$$P^n = \int d\mathbf{k} \cdot k^n \sum_{\nu=1,2} \left(a_\nu^{*+}(\mathbf{k}) a_\nu^-(\mathbf{k}) - a_\nu^{*-}(\mathbf{k}) a_\nu^+(\mathbf{k}) \right) \tag{7.34}$$

that the independent amplitudes a_ν may be subjected to quantization.

As we have mentioned earlier, the requirement that the expectation value of the energy operator P^0 should be positive leads to the demand that the spinor field must be quantized in accordance with Fermi-Dirac rules. Therefore the Fourier amplitudes of the spinor field $a_\nu(\mathbf{k})$ should be regarded as operators which satisfy the Fermi-Dirac commutation relations

$$\left. \begin{aligned} [a_\nu^{*-}(\mathbf{k}), \ a_\mu^+(\mathbf{k}')]_+ &= \delta_{\nu\mu} \delta(\mathbf{k} - \mathbf{k}'), \\ [a_\nu^-(\mathbf{k}), \ a_\mu^{*+}(\mathbf{k})]_+ &= \delta_{\nu\mu} \delta(\mathbf{k} - \mathbf{k}') \end{aligned} \right\} \tag{12.1}$$

(all the other anticommutators are equal to zero).

The commutation relations for the operators $\psi(x)$ will be obtained from the above with the aid of formulas (7.5), (7.13), (7.14), (7.20), (7.21). We obtain in turn (α, β are spinor indices):

$$[\psi_\alpha^{(-)}(x),\ \bar{\psi}_\beta^{(+)}(y)]_+ = \frac{1}{(2\pi)^3}\int d\mathbf{k}\int d\mathbf{l}\ e^{i(ly-kx)}[\psi_\alpha^{(-)}(\mathbf{k}),\ \bar{\psi}_\beta^{(+)}(\mathbf{l})]_+$$

$$= \frac{1}{(2\pi)^3}\int d\mathbf{k}\int d\mathbf{l}\ e^{i(ly-kx)}\sum_{\nu,\,\mu} v_\alpha^{\nu,-}(\mathbf{k})\,\bar{v}_\beta^{\mu,+}(\mathbf{l})\,[a_\nu^-(\mathbf{k}),\ a_\mu^{*+}(\mathbf{l})]_+$$

$$= \frac{1}{(2\pi)^3}\int d\mathbf{k}\ e^{ik(y-x)}\sum_\nu v_\alpha^{\nu,-}(\mathbf{k})\bar{v}_\beta^{\nu,+}(\mathbf{k}) = \frac{1}{(2\pi)^3}\int d\mathbf{k}\ e^{ik(y-x)}\frac{(\hat{k}+m)_{\alpha\beta}}{2k^0}$$

$$= \frac{1}{(2\pi)^3}\int dk(\hat{k}+m)_{\alpha\beta}\,\delta(k^2-m^2)\,\theta(k^0)e^{ik(y-x)}$$

$$= \left(i\sum_n \gamma^n\frac{\partial}{\partial x^n}+m\right)_{\alpha\beta} iD^{(+)}(y-x)$$

or in virtue of the symmetry of the D-function (11.6)

$$[\psi^{(-)}(x),\ \bar{\psi}^{(+)}(y)]_+ = \left(i\sum_n \gamma^n\frac{\partial}{\partial x^n}+m\right)\frac{1}{i}D^{(-)}(x-y). \qquad (12.2)$$

By methods similar to the above it may be shown that

$$[\psi^{(+)}(x),\ \bar{\psi}^{(-)}(y)]_+ = \left(i\sum_n \gamma^n\frac{\partial}{\partial x^n}+m\right)\frac{1}{i}D^{(+)}(x-y). \qquad (12.3)$$

Introducing the notation

$$S_{\alpha\beta}^{(\pm)}(x) = \left(i\sum_n \gamma^n\frac{\partial}{\partial x^n}+m\right)_{\alpha\beta} D^{(\pm)}(x),$$

we obtain from (12.2) and (12.3)

$$[\psi(x),\ \bar{\psi}(y)]_+ = \frac{1}{i}S(x-y), \qquad (12.4)$$

where

$$S(x) = \left(i\sum_n \gamma^n\frac{\partial}{\partial x^n}+m\right)D(x) = \frac{i}{(2\pi)^3}\int e^{ikx}\delta(k^2-m^2)\varepsilon(k^0)(\hat{k}-m)dk. \qquad (12.5)$$

The commutation relations (12.2)–(12.4) are compatible with the field equations since

$$\left(i\sum_n \gamma^n \frac{\partial}{\partial x^n} - m\right) S(x-y) = \left(i\sum_n \gamma^n \frac{\partial}{\partial x^n} - m\right)\left(i\sum_k \gamma^k \frac{\partial}{\partial x^k} + m\right) D(x-y)$$
$$= (\Box - m^2) D(x-y) = 0.$$

In order to write the commutation relations (12.1) in a manifestly invariant form we shall represent expansions of the type (see (7.13) and (7.14))

$$\psi_\alpha^{(\pm)}(k) = \sum_{\nu=1,2} a_\nu^\pm(\mathbf{k})\, v_\alpha^{\nu,\pm}(\mathbf{k})$$

in the form

$$\psi_\alpha(\pm k) = \sum_\nu a_\nu(\pm k) v_\alpha^\nu(\pm k) \quad (k^0 = \sqrt{\mathbf{k}^2 + m^2}),$$

by using the relations

$$\left.\begin{aligned} \psi^{(\pm)}(\mathbf{k}) &= \frac{\psi^{(\pm)}(k)}{\sqrt{2k^0}} = \frac{\theta(k^0)\psi(\pm k)}{\sqrt{2k^0}}, \\ a_\nu^\pm(\mathbf{k}) &= \frac{a_\nu^{(\pm)}(k)}{\sqrt{2k^0}} = \frac{\theta(k^0)\, a_\nu(\pm k)}{\sqrt{2k^0}}, \\ v_\alpha^{\nu,\pm}(\mathbf{k}) &= v_\alpha^{\nu,\pm}(k) = \theta(k^0) v_\alpha^\nu(\pm k) \end{aligned}\right\} \quad k^0 = \sqrt{\mathbf{k}^2 + m^2}.$$

The operators $a_\nu(k)$ are relativistically covariant and satisfy commutation relations which are analogous to the relations that hold for the scalar field (10.13):

$$\delta(k^2 - m^2)\delta(k'^2 - m^2)[a_\nu^{*-}(k),\ a_\mu^+(k')] = \delta_{\mu\nu}\delta(k - k')\delta(k^2 - m^2),$$
$$\delta(k^2 - m^2)\delta(k'^2 - m^2)[a_\nu^-(k),\ a_\mu^{*+}(k')] = \delta_{\mu\nu}\delta(k - k')\delta(k^2 - m^2).$$

By going over to $a_\nu(\pm k)$ in these expressions we obtain

$$\delta(k^2 - m^2)\delta(k'^2 - m^2)[a_\nu^*(k), a_\mu(k')] = \delta_{\mu\nu}\delta(k + k')\delta(k^2 - m^2). \tag{12.6}$$

12.2. *Dynamic Variables*

If we define the Lagrangian of the spinor field in terms of the normal product

$$\mathscr{L} = \frac{i}{2} : \sum_n \left(\bar\psi(x)\gamma^n \frac{\partial\psi}{\partial x^n} - \frac{\partial\bar\psi}{\partial x^n}\gamma^n\psi(x)\right) : - m : \bar\psi(x)\psi(x) :, \tag{12.7}$$

we shall obtain the following expressions for the dynamic variables:

the energy-momentum density tensor

$$T^{kl} = \frac{i}{2} g^{ll} : \left(\bar{\psi} \gamma^k \frac{\partial \psi}{\partial x^l} - \frac{\partial \bar{\psi}}{\partial x^l} \gamma^k \psi \right) : ;$$

the spin tensor

$$S^{k(ml)} = \tfrac{1}{4} : \bar{\psi}(x) \gamma^k \sigma^{ml} \psi(x) : + \tfrac{1}{4} : \bar{\psi}(x) \sigma^{ml} \gamma^k \psi(x) : ; \qquad (12.8)$$

the current vector

$$J^k(x) = : \bar{\psi}(x) \gamma^k \psi(x) :. \qquad (12.9)$$

The corresponding integrated expressions in the momentum representation in accordance with (7.34), (7.42), and (7.41) will take on the following form:
the energy-momentum four-vector

$$P^n = \int d\mathbf{k} \cdot k^n \sum_\nu \left(a_\nu^{*+}(\mathbf{k}) a_\nu^-(\mathbf{k}) + a_\nu^+(\mathbf{k}) a_\nu^{*-}(\mathbf{k}) \right); \quad (12.10)$$

the charge

$$Q = \int d\mathbf{k} \sum_\nu \left(a_\nu^{*+}(\mathbf{k}) a_\nu^-(\mathbf{k}) - a_\nu^+(\mathbf{k}) a_\nu^{*-}(\mathbf{k}) \right); \qquad (12.11)$$

the component of the spin along the direction of motion

$$S_3 \sim \tfrac{1}{2} \left(a_1^{*+}(\mathbf{k}) a_1^-(\mathbf{k}) - a_2^{*+}(\mathbf{k}) a_2^-(\mathbf{k}) - a_1^+(\mathbf{k}) a_1^{*-}(\mathbf{k}) + a_2^+(\mathbf{k}) a_2^{*-}(\mathbf{k}) \right). \qquad (12.12)$$

From expressions (12.10)–(12.12), it follows that the operators $a_\nu^{*+}(\mathbf{k})$ and $a_\nu^-(\mathbf{k})$ are respectively the creation and annihilation operators for particles of momentum $\mathbf{k}$, mass $m (k^2 = m^2)$, charge $+1$, and component of spin along the z axis equal to $\frac{1}{2} (\nu = 1)$ or $-\frac{1}{2} (\nu = 2)$.

The operators $a_\nu^+(\mathbf{k})$ and $a_\nu^-(\mathbf{k})$ correspond to particles which differ from those described above only by the sign of the charge (-1) and by the sign of the spin (i.e., $\frac{1}{2} (\nu = 2)$ and $-\frac{1}{2} (\nu = 1)$). In other words, the spinor field describes charged particles of half-integral spin. Such particles are electrons, protons, neutrons, μ-mesons, and, apparently, the neutrino and the hyperons.

As has just been shown, each of the spinor fields describes simultaneously two kinds of particles with electric charge of opposite sign (electron and positron, μ^+ and μ^--mesons, etc.).

In accordance with the now-established terminology, one of these particles is considered to be the fundamental one (electron, proton, μ^-), while the second particle is called the antiparticle (positron, antiproton, μ^+). The antiparticle differs physically from the fundamental particle by the sign of its charge[25a] and by the direction of its spin.

Moreover, the antiparticles are sometimes treated as "holes" in the completely occupied sea of negative energy levels. However, the picture of a completely filled sea of "negative" energies cannot be made to be completely satisfactory[26] and historically it arose as an attempt to avoid the inconsistencies contained in the unquantized theory of the spinor field. Indeed, if one ascribes to expression (7.34) a direct physical meaning then the antiparticle density

$$\rho_{\text{anti}}(\mathbf{k}) = a_\nu^{*-}(\mathbf{k})\, a_\alpha^+(\mathbf{k})$$

occurs in the expression for the energy-momentum four-vector with a minus sign, which leads us to speak of "negative" energies.

As we have seen the difficulty of "negative" energies is contained only in the classical theory, and does not arise in the quantized theory of the spinor field.

It is also considered that the picture of a sea of "negative" energy levels gives an easily visualizable description of the processes of the creation and annihilation of a particle-antiparticle pair. However, such processes (taking into account emission of a photon during pair annihilation, and annihilation of a photon during pair creation) are special cases of processes of mutual transformation of elementary particles which are subject only to the laws of conservation of energy and momentum, and do not require any special models for their interpretation.

We thus see that the concept of the sea of negative energy levels is connected with the lack of a well-defined physical meaning for the classical spinor field. In contrast, the physical meaning of the quantum theory of the spinor field is entirely clear, and allows one to avoid introducing additional concepts such as a completely filled sea of "negative" energy levels, of "holes" in it, etc.

12.3. *Charge Conjugation*

We now introduce the additional operation of charge conjugation of a spinor field. If we consider the fields describing charged particles which we have discussed earlier, i.e., the complex scalar

[25a] This refers, of course, to all types of charge. See footnote 5, p. 27.
[26] See, for example, (60).

and the complex vector fields, then it follows from the structure of the dynamic variables and the commutation relations that the transformation

$$\varphi(x) \to \varphi'(x) = \varphi^*(x), \quad \varphi^*(x) \to \varphi^{*\prime}(x) = \varphi(x) \qquad (12.13)$$

to the new wave functions $\varphi'(x)$, $\varphi^{*\prime}(x)$ leaves all the physical quantities, with the exception of the current, unchanged, and changes the sign of the current four-vector. Thus the transformation (12.13) corresponds to a transition to particles having charges of opposite sign with respect to the original particles.

A transformation of type (12.13) is therefore called the transformation of charge conjugation. The charge conjugation of a spinor field is more complicated than transformation (12.13) because of the matrix character (multicomponent nature) of spinor wave functions; it is a matrix transformation of the following form [26a]

$$\psi(x) = C\bar{\psi}'(x), \quad \bar{\psi}(x) = C^{-1}\psi'(x) = \psi'(x)\overset{\mathrm{T}}{C}{}^{-1}. \qquad (12.14)$$

This abbreviated method of writing it is equivalent to the following statement in terms of components:

$$\psi_\alpha = \sum_\beta C_{\alpha\beta}\bar{\psi}'_\beta, \quad \bar{\psi}_\alpha = \sum_\beta C^{-1}_{\alpha\beta}\psi'_\beta = \sum_\beta \psi'_\beta(\overset{\mathrm{T}}{C}{}^{-1})_{\beta\alpha},$$

since in virtue of the definition of a transposed matrix we always have

$$(C)_{\alpha\beta} = (\overset{\mathrm{T}}{C})_{\beta\alpha}.$$

The transformation inverse to (12.14) is similarly given by

$$\psi'(x) = C\bar{\psi}(x), \quad \bar{\psi}'(x) = C^{-1}\psi(x) = \psi(x)\overset{\mathrm{T}}{C}{}^{-1}. \qquad (12.15)$$

We thus see that charge conjugation defined by (12.14) in addition to the obvious property that the twice-iterated transformation is the identity transformation, also has the property of "mirror" symmetry, i.e., its form coincides with that of the inverse transformation.

We shall determine the explicit form of the matrices C by

[26a] In order that (12.14) should be consistent we must demand that

$$CC^\dagger = 1. \qquad (12.14a)$$

requiring that the Lagrangian of the free field and, consequently, the energy-momentum four-vector should not change their form, while the current four-vector should change its sign, i.e., that the following relations should hold

$$\mathscr{L}(\psi) = \mathscr{L}(\psi'), \quad T(\psi) = T(\psi') \text{ and } J^k(\psi) = - J^k(\psi').$$

For this it will be sufficient to demand that the following two relations should hold:

$$: \bar{\psi}_1(x)\gamma^k\psi_2(x) : = - : \bar{\psi}_2'(x)\gamma^k\bar{\psi}_1(x) : \tag{12.16}$$

and

$$: \bar{\psi}(x)\psi(x) : = : \bar{\psi}'(x)\psi'(x) :, \tag{12.17}$$

where $\psi_1(x)$ and $\psi_2(x)$ are either equal to the function ψ itself, or to its derivatives $\partial\psi/\partial x^k$. In any case

$$\psi_i = C\bar{\psi}_i'(x), \qquad \bar{\psi}_i = \overset{\mathrm{T}}{\psi_i'}C^{-1} \qquad (i = 1, 2). \tag{12.18}$$

Indeed, if we first set

$$\psi_1(x) = \psi(x), \quad \psi_2(x) = \frac{\partial\psi}{\partial x},$$

and then set

$$\psi_1 = \frac{\partial\psi}{\partial x}, \quad \psi_2 = \psi,$$

we shall obtain from (12.16)

$$: \bar{\psi}(x)\gamma^k \frac{\partial\psi}{\partial x^k} : = - : \frac{\partial\bar{\psi}'(x)}{\partial x^k}\gamma^k\psi'(x) :,$$

$$: \frac{\partial\bar{\psi}}{\partial x^k}\gamma^k\psi(x) : = - : \bar{\psi}'(x)\gamma^k\frac{\partial\psi'}{\partial x^k} :,$$

which together with (12.17) give:

$$\mathscr{L}(\psi) = \mathscr{L}(\psi') \text{ and } T(\psi) = T(\psi').$$

Setting in (12.16)

$$\psi_1 = \psi \text{ and } \psi_2 = \psi,$$

we also obtain

$$J(\psi) = - J(\psi').$$

Let us now examine the restrictions imposed on the matrix C by the conditions (12.16) and (12.17).

Substituting (12.18) into (12.16) we shall obtain:

$$:\bar{\psi}_1(x)\gamma^k\psi_2(x): \; = \; :\psi_1'(x)\overset{T}{C}{}^{-1}\gamma^k C\bar{\psi}_2'(x):.$$

Taking into account the fact that the quantized spinors ψ' and $\bar{\psi}'$ anticommute, we obtain from the preceding the expression

$$:\bar{\psi}_1(x)\gamma^k\psi_2(x): \; = - \; :\bar{\psi}_2'(x)\overset{T}{C}\overset{T}{\gamma}{}^k C^{-1}\psi_1'(x):,$$

from the comparison of which with (12.16) we obtain the first condition on the matrix C

$$\overset{T}{C}\overset{T}{\gamma}{}^k C^{-1} = \gamma^k$$

or in transposed form

$$\overset{T}{C}{}^{-1}\gamma^k C = \overset{T}{\gamma}{}^k. \qquad (12.19)$$

Similarly by substituting (12.18) into (12.17) we obtain:

$$:\bar{\psi}(x)\psi(x): \; = \; :\psi'(x)\overset{T}{C}{}^{-1}C\bar{\psi}'(x): \; = - \; :\bar{\psi}'(x)\overset{T}{C}C^{-1}\psi'(x):,$$

from which we find the second condition on the matrix C

$$\overset{T}{C}C^{-1} = -1 \qquad (12.20)$$

or

$$\overset{T}{C} = -C. \qquad (12.21)$$

Utilizing (12.21) we may also write (12.19) in the form

$$C^{-1}\gamma^k C = -\overset{T}{\gamma}{}^k. \qquad (12.22)$$

From equation (12.22) we can determine the form of the matrix C in the representation of the Dirac matrices γ^k (6.18). In this representation

$$\overset{T}{\gamma}{}^0 = \gamma^0, \quad \overset{T}{\gamma}{}^1 = -\gamma^1, \quad \overset{T}{\gamma}{}^2 = \gamma^2, \quad \overset{T}{\gamma}{}^3 = -\gamma^3.$$

We now note that equation (12.22) on being written in the form

$$C^{-1}\gamma^k C = \pm\,\gamma^k \quad \begin{pmatrix} + \text{ for } k = 1,\ 3, \\ - \text{ for } k = 0,\ 2 \end{pmatrix}$$

coincides with equation (6.26), which defines the form of the matrix Λ of the transformation of reflection of the x^0 and x^2 axes. Therefore the matrix C in the representation (6.18) coincides with the matrix Λ of the transformation indicated above, i.e., (see (6.33)):

$$C = \Lambda_{02}(-\,i\pi) = e^{\frac{i\pi}{2}\gamma^0\gamma^2} = \gamma^0\gamma^2 = \alpha_2. \tag{12.23}$$

In the representation (6.18) α_2 has the form

$$\alpha_2 = \begin{pmatrix} 0 & 0 & 0 & -i \\ 0 & 0 & i & 0 \\ 0 & -i & 0 & 0 \\ i & 0 & 0 & 0 \end{pmatrix}.$$

The property (12.21) is thus also satisfied.

As has been previously indicated the specific form of the matrix C depends on the representation of the Dirac-matrices. In going over from the representation (6.18) to some other γ'^k by means of the formulas

$$\gamma'^k = O\gamma^k O^{-1}, \tag{12.24}$$

we shall obtain the new matrix C' for the transformation of charge conjugation from the relation

$$C' = OC\overset{\mathrm{T}}{O}, \tag{12.25}$$

whose validity may be easily verified by substituting expressions (12.24), (12.25) into (12.19) and (12.21).

§ 13. The Electromagnetic Field

13.1. *Singularities of the Electromagnetic Field and the Quantization Procedure*

In the quantization of the electromagnetic field, it is necessary to satisfy simultaneously the requirements of positive energy density, the Lorentz subsidiary condition, and the condition of transversality. Moreover, the whole formulation should have the property of being relativistically covariant.

We encountered a similar situation in the quantization of the vector meson field. The difference consists of the fact that vector mesons may exist in three spin states while photons, because of their transversality, may exist only in two spin states, and also of the fact that, in contrast to mesons, the mass of the photons is equal to zero. The first of the above two circumstances leads to the fact that the components of the potential of the electromagnetic field contain, to an even greater extent than in the case of the vector field, "superfluous" variables, since we have four components and only two states in which real photons may exist.

The second difference ($m = 0$) leads to the impossibility of applying to the electromagnetic field the procedure used for the quantization of the vector field. Indeed, the quantization of a hypothetical vector field with vanishingly small mass, i.e., of a field which differs from the electromagnetic field by not having a gauge transformation and therefore having three components, already meets with fundamental difficulties. In attempting to carry out such a quantization we obtain meaningless expressions first of all when we diagonalize the energy momentum by means of the substitution (4.22), and second of all in setting up commutation relations for the components of the potential A_n (11.25)–(11.27) due to the appearance of the vanishingly small mass in the denominators of the expressions enumerated above.

Therefore the quantization of the electromagnetic field is carried out in the following manner. We regard the components of the vector potential as independent quantities, thereby giving up the Lorentz condition in operator form. Then, in accordance with the general prescription for quantization (§ 9), starting with the structure of the energy-momentum four-vector expressed in terms of its longitudinal, transverse, and timelike components $a_n(\mathbf{k})$

$$P^n = \int d\mathbf{k} \cdot k^n \Big(- \sum_m g^{mm} a_m^{(+)}(\mathbf{k})\, a_m^{(-)}(\mathbf{k})\Big), \tag{13.1}$$

we arrive at the commutation relations

$$[a_m^{(-)}(\mathbf{k}),\ a_n^{(+)}(\mathbf{k}')]_- = -\, g^{mn}\,\delta(\mathbf{k} - \mathbf{k}'), \tag{13.2}$$

from which with the aid of expansions (5.10) and (5.16) we find:

$$[A_m^{(-)}(x),\ A_n^{(+)}(y)]_- = ig^{mn} D_0^{(-)}(x-y),$$

where $D^{(-)}$ is the usual negative-frequency commutation function for zero mass:

$$D_0^{(-)}(x) = \frac{i}{(2\pi)^3}\int dk\delta(k^2)\,\theta(-k^0)\,e^{ikx}.$$

The complete commutator for the components A_n has the following form:

$$\begin{aligned}[A_n(x),\ A_m(y)]_- &= ig^{mn}D_0(x-y),\\ D_0(x) &= \frac{1}{(2\pi)^3 i}\int e^{ikx}\,\delta(k^2)\,\varepsilon\,(k^0)\,dk.\end{aligned} \tag{13.3}$$

The quantization (13.2) evidently does not guarantee that the expectation value of the energy should be positive. We shall leave this question open for the time being, and shall return to it later when we formulate the Lorentz subsidiary condition.

The quantization (13.2) allows us to regard the operators $a_n^{(\pm)}$ as creation and annihilation operators for four independent kinds of photons—two transverse kinds, "longitudinal" and "timelike." However, the following difficulty arises in such a quantization. The component a_0 satisfies the relation

$$[a_0^{(-)}(\mathbf{k}),\ a_0^{(+)}(\mathbf{k}')]_- = -\,\delta(\mathbf{k}-\mathbf{k}'),$$

a comparison of which with (10.12) shows that the creation and annihilation operators for the "timelike" photons behave as if they had interchanged places, which occurs as a result of the term $a_0^{(+)}a_0^{(-)}$ in expression (13.1) having a negative sign.

However, such a situation is incompatible with the assumption that the field is real. Indeed, it follows from (13.3) that

$$[A_0^{(-)}(x),\ A_0^{(+)}(y)]_- = -\int e^{-ik(x-y)}\,\theta(k^0)\,\delta(k^2)\,dk. \tag{13.4}$$

The left-hand side of this relation may be represented in the form of a matrix element for the vacuum state

$$\Phi_0^*[A_0^{(-)}(x),\ A_0^{(+)}(y)]_-\Phi_0 = \Phi_0^*\,A_0^{(-)}(x)A_0^{(+)}(y)\,\Phi_0 = \Phi_0^*A_0(x)A_0(y)\Phi_0.$$

Multiplying this matrix element by $h(x)h(y)$ where h is a real function and integrating over x and y, we obtain the obviously positive quantity

$$\Phi_0^* \int A_0(x)\, h(x)\, dx \int A_0(y)\, h(y)\, dy\, \Phi_0 = \Phi_0^* \left| \int A_0(x)\, h(x)\, dx \right|^2 \Phi_0 > 0.$$

On the other hand, carrying out the same operation on the right-hand side of (13.4) we arrive at the obviously negative expression

$$- \int dk \int dx\, h(x) \int dy\, h(y)\, e^{-ik(x-y)}\, \theta(k^0)\, \delta(k^2)$$
$$= - \int dk\, \theta(k^0)\, \delta(k^2) \left| \int e^{ikx}\, h(x)\, dx \right|^2 < 0,$$

which contradicts the foregoing.

13.2. *Indefinite Metric*

In order to eliminate the difficulty outlined above we shall use a formal approach (11) (55) which is essentially based on the fact that the "timelike photons" that correspond to the zero component of the potential do not actually exist, but that their appearance in the intermediate steps of the argument is connected with the transition from observable quantities (the vectors **E** and **H**) to the nonobservable four-potential A, which was made in order that the theory should be relativistically symmetric and covariant.

We shall now assume that the a_0 component, in contrast to the other components, is anti-Hermitean, i.e.,

$$a_n^* = - g^{nn} a_n$$

(this assumption is equivalent to introducing a Hermitean a_4, $a_0 = ia_4$). We then obtain the usual commutation relations

$$[a_m^{*(-)}(\mathbf{k}),\ a_n^{(+)}(\mathbf{k}')]_- = \delta(\mathbf{k} - \mathbf{k}')\, \delta_{nm},$$

$$[A_m^*(x),\ A_n(y)]_- = \delta_{nm} \frac{1}{i} D_0(x - y).$$

In order to retain the self-conjugate property for the operator a_n we shall have to introduce an indefinite metric in the space of the state amplitudes. In order to do this we introduce the Hermitean operator η defined by the relations

$$\eta a_n = -g^{nn} a_n \eta, \quad \eta^2 = 1, \quad \eta\Phi_0 = \Phi_0, \tag{13.5}$$

i.e., one which commutes with a_α ($\alpha = 1, 2, 3$) and anticommutes with a_0. By introducing a new definition for the adjoint state amplitude

$$\Phi^\dagger = \Phi^* \eta, \tag{13.6}$$

i.e., by defining the expectation value as

$$\langle f \rangle = \Phi^* \eta f \Phi = \Phi^\dagger f \Phi, \tag{13.7}$$

we obtain the self-conjugate property for the operator a_n

$$(\Phi^\dagger a_n \Phi)^* = (\Phi^* \eta a_n \Phi)^* = \Phi^{**} a_n \eta \Phi = \Phi^* \eta a_n \Phi = \Phi^\dagger a_n \Phi.$$

Let us now consider the question of the subsidiary condition. In the course of quantization we assumed that the A_n are independent, and consequently we may not impose the Lorentz condition on the operators A_n. It may be easily seen that it is likewise impossible to impose the Lorentz condition on the allowed state amplitudes, i.e., to demand that

$$\sum_n g^{nn} \frac{\partial A_n(x)}{\partial x^n} \Phi = 0,$$

for such a condition would, for example, contradict the definition of the vacuum state. Indeed, by setting $\Phi = \Phi_0$ we obtain:

$$\left(\frac{\partial A}{\partial x}\right) \Phi_0 = \left(\frac{\partial A^{(+)}}{\partial x}\right) \Phi_0 = 0.$$

Multiplying on the left by $A_k^{*(-)}(y)$ we obtain:

$$A_k^{*(-)}(y) \sum_n g^{nn} \frac{\partial A_n^{(+)}(x)}{\partial x^n} \Phi_0 = \sum_n g^{nn} \frac{\partial}{\partial x^n} (A_k^{*(-)}(y) A_n^{(+)}(x)) \Phi_0$$

$$= \sum_n g^{nn} \frac{\partial}{\partial x^n} (A_n^{(+)}(x) A_k^{*(-)}(y)) \Phi_0 - \sum_n g^{nn} \frac{\partial}{\partial x^n} D_n^{(+)}(x-y) g^{nk} \Phi_0$$

$$= -\frac{\partial}{\partial x^k} D_0^{(+)}(x-y) \Phi_0 \neq 0,$$

which is a contradiction.

Therefore we shall formulate the Lorentz condition as a condition on allowed states but in a weaker form:

$$\sum_n g^{nn} \frac{\partial A_n^{(-)}(x)}{\partial x^n} \Phi \equiv \left(\frac{\partial A^{(-)}}{\partial x}\right) \Phi = 0, \tag{13.8}$$

and its adjoint relation in the form

$$\Phi^\dagger \left(\frac{\partial A^{(+)}}{\partial x}\right) = 0. \tag{13.9}$$

These conditions guarantee that the Lorentz condition is satisfied on the average

$$\left\langle\left(\frac{\partial A}{\partial x}\right)\right\rangle = \Phi^\dagger \left(\frac{\partial A}{\partial x}\right) \Phi = 0,$$

which is quite sufficient to establish correspondence with the classical field.

Let us now turn to the question of the positive value of the observed energy density. For this we rewrite the subsidiary conditions in the momentum representation. We obviously have

$$(k^0 a_0^{(-)}(\mathbf{k}) + |\mathbf{k}|\, a_3^{(-)}(\mathbf{k}))\, \Phi = 0,$$
$$\Phi^\dagger (k^0 a_0^{(+)}(\mathbf{k}) + |\mathbf{k}|\, a_3^{(+)}(\mathbf{k})) = 0,$$

or taking into account that $k^0 = |\mathbf{k}|$

$$(a_0^{(-)}(\mathbf{k}) + a_3^{(-)}(\mathbf{k}))\, \Phi = 0, \tag{13.10}$$

$$\Phi^\dagger (a_0^{(+)}(\mathbf{k}) + a_3^{(+)}(\mathbf{k})) = 0. \tag{13.11}$$

From this it follows that in the allowed states the total energy and momentum of the longitudinal and timelike pseudophotons are equal to zero, since

$$\begin{aligned}\langle a_3^{(+)} a_3^{(-)} - a_0^{(+)} a_0^{(-)} \rangle &= \Phi^\dagger (a_3^{(+)} a_3^{(-)} - a_0^{(+)} a_0^{(-)})\, \Phi \\ &= \Phi^\dagger (a_3^{(+)} + a_0^{(+)})\, a_3^{(-)} \Phi = 0.\end{aligned}$$

We therefore obtain for the energy-momentum vector

$$\begin{aligned}\langle P^n \rangle &= \int d\mathbf{k}\, k^n \langle -\sum_m g^{mm} a_m^{(+)}(\mathbf{k})\, a_m^{(-)}(\mathbf{k}) \rangle \\ &= \int d\mathbf{k} \cdot k^n \langle a_1^{(+)}(\mathbf{k})\, a_1^{(-)}(\mathbf{k}) + a_2^{(+)}(\mathbf{k})\, a_2^{(-)}(\mathbf{k}) \rangle.\end{aligned} \tag{13.12}$$

This guarantees that the expectation value of the energy will be positive. We shall now show that the newly defined norm (13.7) gives the same results for the expectation values of observable quantities as the old norm. In order to do this we shall represent the vector potential with the aid of (3.10) in the form

$$g^{nn} A_n^{(-)}(k)$$
$$= \left\{ \sum_{\sigma=1,2} e_\sigma^n a_\sigma^{(-)}(\mathbf{k}) + \left(\frac{k^n}{|\mathbf{k}|} - e_0^n \right) a_3^{(-)}(\mathbf{k}) + e_0^n (a_0^{(-)} + a_3^{(-)}) \right\};$$

from which it follows that

$$A_n^{(-)}(x)\Phi = \left\{ A_n^{\mathrm{tr}(-)}(x) + \frac{\partial \Lambda}{\partial x^n} + g^{n0} F^{(-)}(x) \right\} \Phi, \quad (13.13)$$

where $F^{(-)}(x)\Phi = 0$ and $\partial\Lambda/\partial x^n$ is a quantity which may be made to vanish by means of a gauge transformation. Therefore

$$A_n^{(-)}(x)\,\Phi = A_n^{\mathrm{tr}(-)}(x)\,\Phi$$

and similarly

$$\Phi^\dagger A_n^{(+)}(x) = \Phi^\dagger A_n^{\mathrm{tr}(+)}(x).$$

Thus we always have

$$\Phi^\dagger A_n(x)\Phi = \Phi^\dagger A_n^{\mathrm{tr}}(x)\,\Phi.$$

It is not difficult to show that the more general assertion holds

$$\Phi^\dagger K \Phi = \Phi^\dagger K^{\mathrm{tr}} \Phi, \quad (13.14)$$

where K is an operator of the form

$$K = \sum_\alpha Z\left(\frac{\partial}{\partial x_1}, \ldots, \frac{\partial}{\partial x_s}\right) A_{\alpha_1}(x_1) \ldots A_{\alpha_s}(x_s),$$

Z is a polynomial function, and

$$K^{\mathrm{tr}} = \sum_\alpha Z\left(\frac{\partial}{\partial x_1}, \ldots, \frac{\partial}{\partial x_s}\right) A_{\alpha_1}^{\mathrm{tr}}(x_1) \ldots A_{\alpha_s}^{\mathrm{tr}}(x_s).$$

Indeed by representing A_n in the form (13.13) and discarding the gradient terms, we see that we must carry out the commutations of terms of the form A^{tr} and $F = a_0 + a_3$. However, F and A^{tr} commute, $F^{(+)}$ and $F^{(-)}$ also commute, and $\Phi_0^\dagger F^{(+)} = F^{(-)}\Phi_0 = 0$.

Thus only the commutators of $A^{\mathrm{tr}(-)}$ and $A^{\mathrm{tr}(+)}$ are left. Consequently we have proved the validity of (13.14). We shall now show that

$$\Phi^\dagger K^{\mathrm{tr}} \Phi = \Phi_{\mathrm{tr}}^\dagger K^{\mathrm{tr}} \Phi_{\mathrm{tr}} = \Phi_{\mathrm{tr}}^* K^{\mathrm{tr}} \Phi_{\mathrm{tr}} \tag{13.15}$$

where Φ_{tr} is the amplitude of the pure photon state, i.e., of a state which does not contain longitudinal or timelike pseudophotons. Indeed, the amplitude of an arbitrary state may be represented in the form of a linear combination of a pure photon state and of terms containing various numbers of pseudophotons. In virtue of the subsidiary conditions the latter terms may contain the operators a_0 and a_3 only in the combination

$$a_3 - a_0,$$

i.e.,

$$\Phi = \{1 + \sum_n c_n \prod_{1 \leqq j \leqq n} (a_3^{(+)}(\mathbf{k}_j) - a_0^{(+)}(\mathbf{k}_j))\}\Phi_{\mathrm{tr}},$$

$$\Phi^\dagger = \Phi_{\mathrm{tr}}^\dagger\{1 + \sum_n c_n \prod_{1 \leqq j \leqq n} (a_3^{(-)}(\mathbf{k}_j) - a_0^{(-)}(\mathbf{k}_j))\}.$$

We shall refer to the state Φ_{tr} as the pseudophoton vacuum. But since the combinations

$$\tilde{F}^{(+)} = a_0^{(+)} - a_3^{(+)} \text{ and } \tilde{F}^{(-)} = a_0^{(-)} - a_3^{(-)}$$

commute with K^{tr} and with each other we have

$$\begin{aligned} \Phi^\dagger K^{\mathrm{tr}} \Phi &= \Phi_{\mathrm{tr}}^\dagger\{1 + \sum_n c_n \prod_j \tilde{F}^{(-)}(\mathbf{k}_j)\} K^{\mathrm{tr}} \{1 + \sum_m c_m \prod_i \tilde{F}^{(+)}(\mathbf{k}_i)\} \Phi_{\mathrm{tr}} \\ &= \Phi_{\mathrm{tr}}^\dagger\{1 + \sum_m c_m \prod_i \tilde{F}^{(+)}(\mathbf{k}_i)\} K_{\mathrm{tr}} \{1 + \sum_n c_n \prod_j \tilde{F}^{(-)}(\mathbf{k}_j)\} \Phi_{\mathrm{tr}} \\ &= \Phi_{\mathrm{tr}}^\dagger K^{\mathrm{tr}} \Phi_{\mathrm{tr}} = \Phi_{\mathrm{tr}}^* \eta K^{\mathrm{tr}} \Phi_{\mathrm{tr}} = \Phi_{\mathrm{tr}}^* K^{\mathrm{tr}} \eta \Phi_{\mathrm{tr}} = \Phi_{\mathrm{tr}}^* K^{\mathrm{tr}} \Phi_{\mathrm{tr}}, \end{aligned}$$

since

$$\Phi_{\mathrm{tr}}^\dagger a_{3,0}^{(+)} = 0, \quad a_{3,0}^{(-)} \Phi_{\mathrm{tr}} = 0$$

and

$$K^{\mathrm{tr}} \eta = \eta K^{\mathrm{tr}}, \quad \eta \Phi_{\mathrm{tr}} = \Phi_{\mathrm{tr}}.$$

Thus we have established that the expectation value of K over the indefinite metric is equal to the ordinary expectation value of K^{tr}.

We conclude that the use of the indefinite metric in calculating real observable quantities cannot lead to any paradoxical results such as "negative probabilities."

In future for convenience we shall always use the usual notation Φ^* in place of $\Phi^\dagger$.

13.3 *The Form of the Basic Quantities*

In conclusion we list the forms of the fundamental quantities belonging to the quantized electromagnetic field:
the Lagrangian

$$\mathscr{L}(x) = -\tfrac{1}{2}\sum g^{mm} g^{nn} : \frac{\partial A_m}{\partial x^n} \frac{\partial A_m}{\partial x^n} :, \tag{13.16}$$

the field equations

$$\Box A_n = 0, \tag{13.17}$$

the Lorentz subsidiary condition

$$\left(\frac{\partial A^{(-)}}{\partial x}\right)\Phi \equiv \sum_n g^{nn} \frac{\partial A_n^{(-)}}{\partial x^n} \Phi = 0, \tag{13.8}$$

the general expression for the operator of the energy-momentum four-vector

$$P^n = \int d\mathbf{k} \cdot k^n \left(-\sum_n g^{nn} a_n^{(+)}(\mathbf{k})\, a_n^{(-)}(\mathbf{k})\right) \tag{13.18}$$

and its expectation value over allowed states

$$\langle P^n \rangle = \Phi \int d\mathbf{k} \cdot k^n \sum_{\nu=1,\,2} a_\nu^{(+)}(\mathbf{k})\, a_\nu^{(-)}(\mathbf{k})\, \Phi, \tag{13.12}$$

the commutator of the field functions

$$[A_m(x),\ A_n(y)]_- = i g^{mn} D_0(x-y), \tag{13.3}$$

the spin-angular momentum vector

$$\mathbf{S} = i \int d\mathbf{k} [\mathbf{a}^{(+)}(\mathbf{k}) \times \mathbf{a}^{(-)}(\mathbf{k})]. \tag{13.19}$$

§ 14. Green's Functions [27]

14.1. *Definition*

In the process of quantizing wave fields we have obtained the following commutation functions: the commutation function for

[27] A tabulation of singular functions is given in the Appendix.

a scalar field (the Pauli-Jordan function)

$$D(x) = \frac{1}{(2\pi)^3 i}\int dk e^{ikx}\,\varepsilon\,(k^0)\,\delta(k^2 - m^2) \tag{14.1}$$

and the commutation functions for the electromagnetic, the spinor, and the vector fields which may be expressed in terms of $D(x)$ and of its partial derivatives:

$$D_0(x) = D(x)\mid_{m=0} = \frac{1}{(2\pi)^3 i}\int dk e^{ikx}\varepsilon(k^0)\,\delta(k^2), \tag{14.2}$$

$$\begin{aligned} S_{\alpha\beta}(x) &= (i\hat{\partial} + m)_{\alpha\beta} D(x) \\ &= \frac{1}{(2\pi)^3 i}\int dk e^{-ikx}(\hat{k} + m)_{\alpha\beta}\varepsilon(k^0)\,\delta(k^2 - m^2), \end{aligned} \tag{14.3}$$

$$\begin{aligned} D_{ln}(x) &= \left(g^{ln} + \frac{1}{m^2}\frac{\partial^2}{\partial x^l\,\partial x^n}\right) D(x) \\ &= \frac{1}{(2\pi)^3 i}\int dk e^{ikx}\left(g^{ln} - \frac{k_l k_n}{m^2}\right)\varepsilon(k^0)\delta(k^2 - m^2). \end{aligned} \tag{14.4}$$

The functions enumerated above are solutions of the homogeneous equations of the corresponding fields and may be decomposed in a relativistically invariant manner into sums of their positive- and negative-frequency parts, each of which separately also satisfies the corresponding homogeneous equation.

We shall now establish the relation between the commutation functions listed above and the solutions of the corresponding inhomogeneous field equations with point sources, i.e., with the Green's functions. Since the commutation functions for all the fields may be reduced to $D(x)$ and its partial derivatives, we shall first of all investigate the relationship indicated using the example of the scalar field.

We shall define *Green's function for the scalar field* as usual in the following way:[28]

$$(\Box_x - m^2)\,G(x - y) = -\,\delta(x - y). \tag{14.5}$$

[28] For the sake of definiteness we shall adopt the convention of choosing the sign of the δ-function on the right-hand side of the equations for Green's functions in agreement with the sign of the mass m (or m^2) in the operator of the left-hand side of the equation.

Going over to the momentum representation

$$G(x - y) = \frac{1}{(2\pi)^4} \int e^{ik(x-y)} G(k)\, dk, \tag{14.6}$$

we shall obtain for G the following formal expression:

$$G(k) = \frac{1}{m^2 - k^2}, \tag{14.7}$$

$$G(x) = \frac{1}{(2\pi)^4} \int \frac{e^{ikx}}{m^2 - k^2}\, dk. \tag{14.8}$$

Expression (14.8) is actually not defined until we have specified the way in which we go around the poles at $k^2 = m^2$. This indefiniteness is related to the fact that the complete solution of equation (14.5) may be written in the form of a sum of the particular solution of the inhomogeneous equation and of solutions $D^{(+)}$ and $D^{(-)}$ of the homogeneous equation with arbitrary coefficients which may be uniquely determined by imposing boundary conditions on G.

14.2. *"Retarded" and "Advanced" Green's Functions for a Scalar Field*

An important role in field theory is played by the so-called "retarded" Green's function defined by the condition

$$D^{\text{ret}}(x - y) = 0 \text{ for } x^0 - y^0 < 0. \tag{14.9}$$

In order to write $D^{\text{ret}}(x - y)$ in a form closely similar to (14.7) we note that if this function is multiplied by $\exp[-\varepsilon(x^0 - y^0)]$ where $\varepsilon > 0$ then in accordance with (14.9) it shall not acquire any additional singularities:

$$D^{\text{ret}} \cdot e^{-\varepsilon(x^0 - y^0)} = G_\varepsilon, \tag{14.10}$$

as a result of which it may be written in the following form:

$$D^{\text{ret}}(x - y) = \lim_{\varepsilon \to 0} G_\varepsilon. \tag{14.11}$$

In accordance with its definition (14.10) G_ε satisfies the equation

$$\left\{\Delta - \left(\frac{\partial}{\partial t} + \varepsilon\right)^2 - m^2\right\} G_\varepsilon = -\delta(x - y) \tag{14.12}$$

and therefore in the momentum representation in the limit $\varepsilon \rightarrow 0$ it has the form

$$\frac{1}{m^2 - (k^0 - i\varepsilon)^2 + k} \rightarrow \frac{1}{m^2 - k^2 + 2i\varepsilon k^0}.$$

Thus in accordance with (14.11) the retarded Green's function may be represented in the form[29]

$$D^{\mathrm{ret}}(x - y) = \frac{1}{(2\pi)^4} \int \frac{e^{ik(x-y)}}{m^2 - k^2 + 2i\varepsilon k^0}\, dk. \qquad (14.13)$$

It may be easily verified that expression (14.13) does actually satisfy condition (14.9). Indeed the term $2i\varepsilon k^0$ in the denominator indicates the rule for going around the poles

$$(k^0)_1 = \sqrt{\mathbf{k}^2 + m^2} + i\varepsilon,$$
$$(k^0)_2 = -\sqrt{\mathbf{k}^2 + m^2} + i\varepsilon,$$

which are therefore situated above the path of integration (see

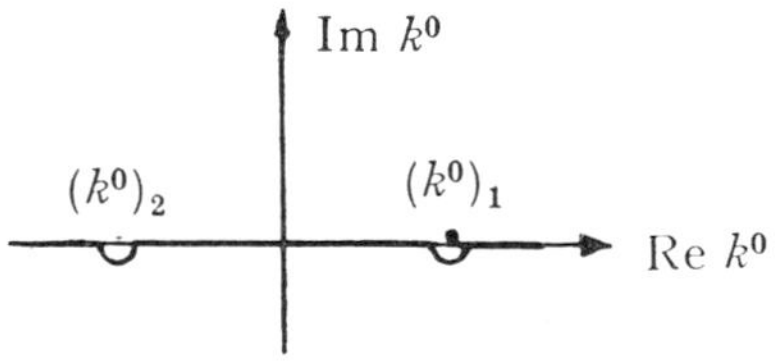

Fig. 2. The path of integration for the function D_{ret} in the complex k^0 plane.

Fig. 2). Therefore for $x^0 - y^0 < 0$, when the contour of integration must be closed in the lower half plane ($k^0 = \mathrm{Re}\, k^0 - i\, \mathrm{Im}\, k^0$, $x^0 - y^0 = -\,|\, x^0 - y^0 \,|$, $ik^0 \,|\, x^0 - y^0 \,| \rightarrow -\, \mathrm{Im}\, k^0 \,|\, x^0 - y^0 \,|$), there are no poles inside it and we obtain formula (14.9). In the opposite case when $x^0 - y^0 > 0$ the path of integration is closed in the upper half plane and the integral over k^0 turns out to be equal

[29] In this expression, and also in all the following similar expressions, the limiting process is not explicitly indicated by the symbol lim because the significance of the terms which depend on ε is only to indicate the direction of going around the poles.

to the sum of the residues at the poles $(k^0)_1$ and $(k^0)_2$:

$$\int_{-\infty}^{+\infty} \frac{dk^0\, e^{ik^0(x^0-y^0)}}{\left(k^0-(k^0)_1\right)\left(k^0-(k^0)_2\right)} = 2\pi i\, \frac{e^{i(k^0)_1(x^0-y^0)}}{(k^0)_1-(k^0)_2} + 2\pi i\, \frac{e^{i(k^0)_2(x^0-y^0)}}{(k^0)_2-(k^0)_1}$$

$$= \frac{\pi i}{k^0}\left(e^{ik^0(x^0-y^0)} - e^{-ik^0(x^0-y^0)}\right)\Big|_{k^0=+\sqrt{\mathbf{k}^2+m^2}}\,.$$

Therefore, for $x^0 - y^0 > 0$ we obtain:

$$D^{\mathrm{ret}}(x-y) = \frac{1}{(2\pi)^3 i}\int \frac{e^{ik^0(x^0-y^0)} - e^{-ik^0(x^0-y^0)}}{2k^0}\, e^{-i\mathbf{k}(\mathbf{x}-\mathbf{y})}\, d\mathbf{k}$$

$$= \frac{1}{(2\pi)^3 i}\int dk e^{ik(x-y)}\, \varepsilon(k^0)\,\delta(k^2-m^2) = D(x)$$

and we may therefore write

$$D^{\mathrm{ret}}(x) = \theta(x^0)\, D(x). \tag{14.14}$$

In the same way it may be shown that the "advanced" Green's function defined by the condition

$$D^{\mathrm{adv}}(x-y) = 0 \text{ for } x^0 - y^0 > 0 \tag{14.15}$$

and satisfying equation (14.5) has the form

$$D^{\mathrm{adv}}(x-y) = \frac{1}{(2\pi)^4}\int \frac{e^{ik(x-y)}}{m^2-k^2-2i\varepsilon k^0}\, dk = -\theta(y^0-x^0)\, D(x-y). \tag{14.16}$$

We shall also give an expression for the integral (14.8) in terms of its principal value. In order to do this we take half the sum of (14.14) and (14.16) and, taking into account the well-known identity

$$\frac{1}{x+i\varepsilon k^0} = \frac{\mathscr{P}}{x} - i\pi\delta(x)\,\varepsilon(k^0), \tag{14.17}$$

where $\mathscr{P}$ denotes the principal value, we obtain the formula

$$\frac{\mathscr{P}}{(2\pi)^4}\int \frac{e^{ikx}}{m^2-k^2}\, dk = \tfrac{1}{2}\varepsilon(x^0)\, D(x). \tag{14.18}$$

14.3. *Causal Green's Function for a Scalar Field*

A particularly important role in quantum field theory is played by the *causal Green's function*[30] $D^c(x-y)$ which describes, as is commonly stated, the *causal relationship* between the processes of creation and annihilation of particles at different space-time points x and y. We shall establish the explicit form of the function D^c, restricting ourselves at first to the case of the scalar field.

The process of creation of a scalar particle at the point x and of its subsequent annihilation at the point y is described by the matrix element

$$\Phi_1^*(y)\Phi_1(x) = \Phi_0^*\varphi^{(-)}(y)\varphi^{(+)}(x)\Phi_0 = \frac{1}{i}D^{(-)}(y-x) = iD^{(+)}(x-y). \tag{14.19}$$

In the preceding equation one should obviously assume that $y^0 > x^0$. Conversely, if $x^0 > y^0$, the particle is created at the point y and annihilated at the point x. The expression

$$\Phi_1^*(x)\Phi_1(y) = \frac{1}{i}D^{(-)}(x-y). \tag{14.20}$$

corresponds to this latter process.

Thus the causal function $D^c(x-y)$ must be proportional to the function $D^{(-)}(x-y)$ for $x^0 > y^0$, while for $x^0 < y^0$ it must be proportional to the function $D^{(+)}(x-y)$. In order to obtain the explicit form of this function we shall make use of the fact already noted earlier that an arbitrary solution of equation (14.5) may be represented as a sum of its particular solution and of a linear combination of the solutions of the homogeneous equation. For example, taking the retarded Green's function as such a particular solution, we shall obtain the formula for the arbitrary solution of equation (14.5) in the following form:

$$G(x) = D^{\text{ret}}(x) + a_1 D^{(+)}(x) + a_2 D^{(-)}(x), \tag{14.21}$$

where a_1 and a_2 are certain arbitrary numerical coefficients.

[30] This was apparently introduced for the first time by Stueckelberg and Rivier (119).

Setting $a_1 = -1$, $a_2 = 0$ in this expression we obtain the expression

$$D^{\text{ret}}(x-y) - D^{(+)}(x-y)$$
$$= \theta(x^0 - y^0) D^{(-)}(x-y) - \theta(y^0 - x^0) D^{(+)}(x-y),$$

which satisfies all the conditions imposed on D^c.

In order to obtain an expression for the causal function

$$D^c(x) = \theta(x^0) D^{(-)}(x) - \theta(-x^0) D^{(+)}(x) \tag{14.22}$$

in the momentum representation we note that the difference $D^{\text{ret}} - D^{(+)}$ in accordance with (14.17) may be represented in the form

$$\frac{1}{m^2 - k^2 + 2i\varepsilon k^0} + 2\pi i\theta(k^0)\delta(k^2 - m^2)$$
$$= \frac{\mathscr{P}}{m^2 - k^2} + \left(2\theta(k^0) - \varepsilon(k^0)\right)\pi i\delta(k^2 - m^2)$$
$$= \frac{\mathscr{P}}{m^2 - k^2} + i\pi\delta(k^2 - m^2) = \frac{1}{m^2 - k^2 - i\varepsilon},$$

which gives

$$D^c(x) = \frac{1}{(2\pi)^4} \int \frac{e^{ikx}}{m^2 - k^2 - i\varepsilon} dk. \tag{14.23}$$

The causal function D^c may be directly expressed in terms of matrix elements of the type (14.19), (14.20). In order to do this we shall introduce the chronological product (or the *T-product*) of two field operators $T(u(x)u(y))$, which is equal to the product of these operators taken in the order from right to left which corresponds to an increase in the time arguments, with due regard being paid to the overall sign, which may change if the operators are quantized in accordance with Fermi-Dirac rules, i.e.,[31]

$$T(u(x)u(y)) = \begin{cases} u(x)u(y) & \text{for } x^0 > y^0, \\ \pm\, u(y)u(x) & \text{for } x^0 < y^0 \end{cases} \tag{14.24}$$

(+ for Bose-operators, − for Fermi-operators).

[31] For a more detailed investigation of T-products and of their various properties, refer to the theory of the scattering matrix (Chapter III).

Calculating the matrix element of (14.24) in the vacuum state for the scalar field under consideration we shall obtain with the aid of (14.19) and (14.20):

$$\Phi_0^* T(\varphi(x)\varphi(y))\Phi_0 = \begin{cases} \Phi_0^* \varphi(x)\varphi(y)\Phi_0 = \dfrac{1}{i} D^{(-)}(x-y) & \text{for } x^0 > y^0, \\ \Phi_0^* \varphi(y)\varphi(x)\Phi_0 = iD^{(+)}(x-y) & \text{for } x^0 < y^0. \end{cases}$$

Thus

$$D^c(x-y) = i\Phi_0^* T(\varphi(x)\varphi(y))\Phi_0 = i < T\varphi(x)\varphi(y) >_0. \quad (14.25)$$

14.4. *Causal Green's Functions for Various Fields*

From (14.23) it follows that in order that a function of the form (14.7) should have the property of "causality" it is sufficient to regard the square of the mass in the denominator of its momentum representation as containing an infinitesimal negative imaginary additional term.

Recalling that in accordance with (14.2)–(14.4) the commutation functions for the electromagnetic, the spinor, and the vector fields differ from the Pauli-Jordan function only by differential operators, we shall postulate by definition that the causal functions of the above fields differ from D^c by the same operators, i.e.,

$$D_0^c(x) = D^c(x)\,|_{m=0} = -\frac{1}{(2\pi)^4}\int \frac{e^{ikx}}{k^2 + i\varepsilon}\,dk, \quad (14.26)$$

$$S_{\alpha\beta}^c(x) = (i\hat{\partial} + m)_{\alpha\beta} D^c(x) = \frac{1}{(2\pi)^4}\int \frac{(m - \hat{p})_{\alpha\beta}}{m^2 - p^2 - i\varepsilon}\, e^{ipx}\,dp, \quad (14.27)$$

$$D_{nl}^c(x) = \left(g^{nl} + \frac{1}{m^2}\frac{\partial^2}{\partial x^n \partial x^l}\right) D^c(x) = \frac{1}{(2\pi)^4}\int \frac{\left(g^{nl} - \dfrac{k_n k_l}{m^2}\right)}{m^2 - k^2 - i\varepsilon}\, e^{ikx}\,dk. \quad (14.28)$$

The causal functions defined in this way may be expressed by analogy with the function D^c in terms of the expectation values over the vacuum state of the chronological products of the operators of the corresponding fields:

$$D_{mn}^c(x-y) = i\Phi_0^* T(U_m(x)U_n(y))\Phi_0, \quad (14.29)$$

$$-g^{mn}D_0^c(x-y)=i\Phi_0^* T(A_m(x)A_n(y))\Phi_0, \tag{14.30}$$

$$S_{\alpha\beta}^c(x-y)=i\Phi_0^* T(\psi_\alpha(x)\bar{\psi}_\beta(y))\Phi_0. \tag{14.31}$$

Formulas (14.29), (14.30) are obvious consequences of relations (14.2), (14.4), while for the proof of (14.31) we shall make use of the commutators for the spinor field (12.2), (12.3). In this way we obtain:

$$i(\Phi_0^* T(\psi(x)\bar{\psi}(y))\Phi_0)$$
$$=\begin{cases} i(\Phi_0^*\psi^{(-)}(x)\bar{\psi}^{(+)}(y)\Phi_0)=(i\hat{\partial}+m)\dfrac{1}{i}D^{(-)}(x-y) & \text{for } x_0>y_0,\\ i(\Phi_0^*\bar{\psi}^{(-)}(y)\psi^{(+)}(x)\Phi_0)=(i\hat{\partial}+m)\,iD^{(+)}(x-y) & \text{for } x^0<y^0,\end{cases}$$

which in view of (14.27) is equivalent to (14.31).

It is also clear that if in the denominators of formulas (14.26)–(14.28) we replace $-i\varepsilon$ by $2i\varepsilon k^0$, we shall obtain expressions which reduce to zero for $x^0<y^0$ and which consequently represent the retarded Green's functions for the corresponding fields.

We note that one should exercise a certain degree of caution in representing Green's functions of the various fields in terms of the commutation functions by relations of the type (14.14), (14.16), (14.18), (14.22). Thus, for example, the causal function of the vector field might have been written down in analogy with (14.22) in the form

$$\theta(x^0)D_{mn}^{(-)}(x)-\theta(-x^0)D_{mn}^{(+)}(x), \tag{14.32}$$

where

$$D_{ln}^{(\pm)}(x)=\frac{\pm 1}{(2\pi)^3 i}\int e^{ikx}\theta(\pm k^0)\,\delta(k^2-m^2)\left(g^{ln}-\frac{k_l k_n}{m^2}\right)dk.$$

However, a direct evaluation of expression (14.32) which may be easily carried out with the aid of the integral representation of the θ-function:

$$\theta(\pm x^0)=\frac{1}{2\pi}\int_{-\infty}^{+\infty}\frac{e^{ix^0\tau}}{\varepsilon\pm i\tau}d\tau, \tag{14.33}$$

leads to the expression

$$D_{ln}^c(x)-\frac{\delta_{l0}\,\delta_{n0}}{m^2}\delta(x),$$

which differs from $D_{ln}^c(x)$ in the neighborhood of the point $x=0$. Such a result is a consequence of an actual indefiniteness of expression (14.32) in an infinitesimal neighborhood of the point $x=0$.

This indefiniteness of the causal function may be particularly simply seen if the function is written in the form

$$i\Phi_0^* T(U_l(x)\, U_n(y))\, \Phi_0. \tag{14.34}$$

Indeed, expression (14.34) in accordance with (14.24) is uniquely defined for $x^0 < y^0$, and also for $y^0 < x^0$. Its meaning is also clear for $(x - y)^2 = -(x - y)^2 \neq 0$, since (14.34) may be written either in the form

$$i\Phi_0^* U_l(x)\, U_n(y)\, \Phi_0,$$

or in the form

$$i\Phi_0^* U_n(y)\, U_l(x)\, \Phi_0$$

since, for $(x - y)^2 < 0$ (refer to the discussion of the properties of the D and D^c-functions in § 15) the operators $U(x)$ and $U(y)$ commute:

$$[U_l(x),\ U_n(y)]_- = \frac{1}{i} D_{ln}(x - y)\,\big|_{(x-y)^2<0} = 0,$$

and both forms are equivalent. However, the meaning of expression (14.34) is entirely unclear in the case when the arguments are equal ($x = y$). From this it follows that the T-product is not defined at the point $x = y$, and that using different methods for its actual construction one can obtain expressions which differ from each other by terms proportional to $\delta(x - y)$ and its derivatives.

We shall encounter this circumstance once again in the theory of interacting fields (Chapter III), where it will be investigated in greater detail. For the time being, in order to avoid any indefiniteness, we shall agree to define chronological products of field operators not by means of expressions of type (14.32), but by means of formulas of type (14.26)-(14.28), in the form of Green's functions of inhomogeneous equations of the corresponding fields:

$$\Box D_0^c(x) = -\delta(x),$$

$$(i\hat{\partial} - m)\, S^c(x) = -\delta(x),$$

$$(\Box - m^2)\, D_{nl}^c(x) = -\left(g^{nl} + \frac{1}{m^2}\frac{\partial^2}{\partial x^n\, \partial x^l}\right)\delta(x).$$

The form of the right-hand side of the last equation is determined by the requirement of the compatibility of the causal function of the vector field with the subsidiary condition

$$\sum_n g^{nn}\frac{\partial U_n}{\partial x^n} = 0.$$

Analogous relations between the commutation and the causal functions may be established for an arbitrary field. In order to derive them it is convenient to start with the field equations written in Kemmer's form (see § 4.4):

$$\left(i\sum_n \Gamma^n \frac{\partial}{\partial x^n} - m\right) u(x) = 0.$$

Setting up the Lagrangian in the usual manner, and then with its aid the energy-momentum four-vector, one may obtain by using the method indicated in § 10 the commutation functions for the field $\Delta_{\alpha\beta}$. We shall then obtain for $\Delta_{\alpha\beta}(x)$ an expression of the form

$$\Delta_{\alpha\beta}(x) = \frac{1}{(2\pi)^3 i} \int P_{\alpha\beta}(k)\, e^{ikx} \delta(k^2 - m^2)\, \varepsilon(k^0) dk = P_{\alpha\beta}\left(-i \frac{\partial}{\partial x}\right) D(x), \tag{14.35}$$

where $P_{\alpha\beta}(k)$ is a certain polynomial in the components of k.

Repeating the arguments of that section we shall obtain the expression for the causal function $\Delta^c_{\alpha\beta}$ in the form

$$\Delta^c_{\alpha\beta}(x) = \frac{1}{(2\pi)^4} \int \frac{P_{\alpha\beta}(k)\, e^{ikx}\, dk}{m^2 - k^2 - i\varepsilon} = P_{\alpha\beta}\left(-i \frac{\partial}{\partial x}\right) D^c(x) \tag{14.36}$$

with the same polynomial $P_{\alpha\beta}$.

14.5. *Relation to the Notations of Stueckelberg and of Schwinger*

In conclusion we shall give for reference purposes formulas showing the correspondence between the commutation functions and the Green's functions used by us and the corresponding functions in the notation of Stueckelberg and Rivier (98), (119) and of Schwinger (104), (105).

In our system of notation we take the Pauli-Jordan function

$$D(x) = \frac{1}{(2\pi)^3 i} \int e^{ikx}\, \delta(k^2 - m^2)\, \varepsilon(k^0)\, dk$$

as our basis.

The symbols $D^{(+)}$ and $D^{(-)}$ denote its (+) and (−) frequency parts, i.e., parts with $k^0 > 0$ and $k^0 < 0$

$$D^{(\pm)}(x) = \frac{\pm 1}{(2\pi)^3 i} \int_{k^0 \gtrless 0} e^{ikx} (k^2 - m^2)\, dk.$$

In the notation of Stueckelberg the basic function is taken to be the Pauli-Jordan function denoted by $D^0(x)$

$$D^0(x) = D(x).$$

The symbols D^+ and D^- in the case of Stueckelberg and Rivier denote the positive- and negative-frequency parts of D^0 multiplied by $\pm 2i$, where the frequency signature is understood to be the sign in the exponent of the expression

$$k^\mu x^\mu \equiv k^1 x^1 + k^2 x^2 + k^3 x^3 + k^4 x^4 = \mathbf{kx} - k_0 x_0,$$

i.e., the sign which is opposite to the sign of the frequency k^0 itself. Therefore

$$\begin{aligned} D^+(x) &= -\ 2iD^{(-)}(x), \\ D^-(x) &= 2iD^{(+)}(x). \end{aligned} \tag{14.37}$$

In Schwinger's case the basic function is the function Δ defined in the following manner

$$\Delta(x) = \frac{1}{(2\pi)^3 i} \int e^{ik^\mu x^\mu} \delta(k^2 - m_2)\, \varepsilon(k^0)\, dk = \frac{i}{(2\pi)^3} \int e^{ikx} \delta(k^2 - m^2)\, \varepsilon(k^0)\, dk$$

which differs in its sign from the Pauli-Jordan function

$$\Delta(x) = -\ D(x). \tag{14.38}$$

In Schwinger's case, the symbols $\Delta^{(+)}$ and $\Delta^{(-)}$ denote the positive- and negative-frequency parts of Δ, (the frequency signature agrees with the sign of $k^\mu x^\mu$), which together with (11.38) gives:

$$\begin{aligned} \Delta^{(+)}(x) &= -\ D^{(-)}(x), \\ \Delta^{(-)}(x) &= -\ D^{(+)}(x). \end{aligned} \tag{14.39}$$

The auxiliary function

$$\Delta^{(1)}(x) = D^1(x) = \frac{1}{(2\pi)^3} \int e^{ikx} \delta(k^2 - m^2)\, dk$$

used by Stueckelberg and Rivier and by Schwinger has in our notation

$$D^1(x) = \Delta^{(1)}(x) = i(D^{(+)}(x) - D^{(-)}(x)). \tag{14.40}$$

The retarded and the advanced functions of Stueckelberg and Rivier and of Schwinger agree with ours:

$$\begin{aligned} D^{\text{ret}}(x) &= \Delta_R(x) = D_{\text{ret}}(x), \\ D^{\text{adv}}(x) &= \Delta_A(x) = D_{\text{adv}}(x). \end{aligned}$$

Finally, our notation for the causal Green's function agrees with Stueckelberg's notation, in Schwinger's notation has the form

$$D^c(x) = \Delta_+(x) \tag{14.41}$$

and is related in the following manner to the Dyson-Feynman "propagation function":

$$D^c(x) = \frac{i}{2} \Delta_F\,(x). \tag{14.42}$$

§ 15. Singularities of the Commutation and Causal Functions [32]

15.1. *Calculation of the $D^{(+)}$ and $D^{(-)}$ Functions*

We now proceed to investigate the singularities of the com-

[32] A summary of the principal results of this section is contained in the Appendix.

mutation functions and of Green's functions. In the preceding section it was shown that all of these functions may be expressed in terms of the positive- and negative-frequency parts of the Pauli-Jordan function. Therefore we begin by evaluating the integrals

$$D^{(+)}(x) = \frac{1}{(2\pi)^3 i} \int e^{ikx}\delta(k^2 - m^2)\theta(k^0)dk, \tag{15.1}$$

$$D^{(-)}(x) = \frac{i}{(2\pi)^3} \int e^{-ikx}\delta(k^2 - m^2)\theta(k^0)dk. \tag{15.2}$$

Carrying out the integration in (15.1) and (15.2) with respect to k^0 and with respect to the angle variables in $\mathbf{k}$-space we shall represent these expressions in the form

$$D^{(+)}(x) = \frac{1}{4\pi r}\frac{\partial}{\partial r} f(x), \quad D^{(-)}(x) = \frac{1}{4\pi r}\frac{\partial}{\partial r} f^*(x), \tag{15.3}$$

where

$$f(x) \equiv f(x^0, r) = \frac{i}{2\pi}\int_{-\infty}^{+\infty} \frac{e^{i(k^0x^0+kr)}}{k^0} dk, \quad k^0 = \sqrt{\mathbf{k}^2 + m^2}, \tag{15.4}$$

$$k = \sqrt{\mathbf{k}^2}, \quad r = \sqrt{\mathbf{x}^2},$$

while $f^*(x)$ is the function complex conjugate to $f(x)$. Thus the problem of determining $D^{(+)}$ and $D^{(-)}$ has been reduced to the evaluation of the one integral (15.4). By introducing the new variables

$$k = m \operatorname{sh} \varphi, \quad k^0 = m \operatorname{ch} \varphi, \tag{15.5}$$

in the above expression we obtain:

$$f(x) = \frac{i}{2\pi}\int_{-\infty}^{+\infty} d\varphi e^{im(x^0 \operatorname{ch}\varphi + r \operatorname{sh}\varphi)}. \tag{15.6}$$

Here four cases should be distinguished:

1. $x^0 > 0, \quad x^0 > r,$ 2. $x^0 > 0, \quad x^0 < r,$

3. $x^0 < 0, \quad |x^0| > r,$ 4. $x^0 < 0, \quad |x^0| < r.$

Carrying out respectively the substitutions

$$\begin{aligned}
&1.\quad x^0 = \sqrt{\lambda}\,\mathrm{ch}\,\varphi_0, && r = \sqrt{\lambda}\,\mathrm{sh}\,\varphi_0,\\
&2.\quad x^0 = \sqrt{-\lambda}\,\mathrm{sh}\,\varphi_0, && r = \sqrt{-\lambda}\,\mathrm{ch}\,\varphi_0,\\
&3.\quad x^0 = -\sqrt{\lambda}\,\mathrm{ch}\,\varphi_0, && r = \sqrt{\lambda}\,\mathrm{ch}\,\varphi_0,\\
&4.\quad x^0 = -\sqrt{-\lambda}\,\mathrm{sh}\,\varphi_0, && r = \sqrt{-\lambda}\,\mathrm{ch}\,\varphi_0
\end{aligned}$$

(here the notation $\lambda = x^2 = (x^0)^2 - r^2$ has been introduced), and using the well-known integral representation for the cylindrical functions,[33] we find

$$1.\qquad \frac{1}{2\pi i}\int_{-\infty}^{+\infty} d\varphi e^{im\sqrt{\lambda}\,\mathrm{ch}\,(\varphi+\varphi_0)} = \tfrac{1}{2}H_0^{(1)}(m\sqrt{\lambda})$$

$$= \tfrac{1}{2}J_0(m\sqrt{\lambda}) + \frac{i}{2}N_0(m\sqrt{\lambda}),$$

$$2.\qquad \frac{i}{2\pi}\int_{-\infty}^{+\infty} d\varphi e^{im\sqrt{-\lambda}\,\mathrm{sh}\,(\varphi+\varphi_0)} = \frac{i}{\pi}K_0(m\sqrt{-\lambda}),$$

$$3.\qquad \frac{i}{2\pi}\int_{-\infty}^{+\infty} d\varphi e^{-im\sqrt{\lambda}\,\mathrm{ch}\,(\varphi-\varphi_0)} = \tfrac{1}{2}H_0^{(2)}(m\sqrt{\lambda})$$

$$= \tfrac{1}{2}J_0(m\sqrt{\lambda}) - \frac{i}{2}N_0(m\sqrt{\lambda}),$$

$$4.\qquad \frac{i}{2\pi}\int_{-\infty}^{+\infty} d\varphi e^{-im\sqrt{-\lambda}\,\mathrm{sh}\,(\varphi-\varphi_0)} = \frac{i}{\pi}K_0(m\sqrt{-\lambda}),$$

from which it follows that

$$f(x) = \varphi(x^0, \lambda) = \begin{cases} \dfrac{1}{2i}N_0(m\sqrt{\lambda}) - \tfrac{1}{2}\varepsilon(x^0)J_0(m\sqrt{\lambda}) & \text{for } \lambda > 0,\\[2ex] \dfrac{i}{\pi}K_0(m\sqrt{-\lambda}) & \text{for } \lambda < 0. \end{cases} \qquad (15.7)$$

Here $J_0(z)$ is the Bessel function of zero order, $N_0(z)$ is the Neumann function of zero order, $K_0(z)$ is the Hankel function of imaginary argument of zero order, which are all defined in the usual way:

$$J_0(z) = \sum_{k=0}^{\infty}(-1)^k\frac{z^{2k}}{2^{2k}(k!)^2},$$

[33] Ryzhik and Gradshtein (100), formulas 6.431 and 6.446.1.

$$\pi N_0(z) = 2J_0(z)\left(\ln\frac{z}{2} + \mathbf{C}\right) - 2\sum_{k=1}^{\infty}\frac{(-1)^k z^{2k}}{2^{2k}(k!)^2}\left[\sum_{m=1}^{k}\frac{1}{m}\right],$$

$$K_0(z) = \frac{\pi i}{2} H_0^{(1)}(iz) = \frac{\pi i}{2}[J_0(iz) + iN_0(iz)]$$

($\mathbf{C}$ is Euler's constant equal to $0.577215\ldots$). We note that in the neighborhood of the point $z = 0$ these functions may be represented in the form

$$\left.\begin{aligned} J_0(z) &= 1 - \left(\frac{z}{2}\right)^2 + O(z^4), \\ N_0(z) &= \frac{2}{\pi}\left[1 - \left(\frac{z}{2}\right)^2\right]\ln\frac{z}{2} + \frac{2}{\pi}\mathbf{C} + O(z^2), \\ K_0(z) &= -\left[1 + \left(\frac{z}{2}\right)^2\right]\ln\frac{z}{2} - \mathbf{C} + O(z^2) \end{aligned}\right\} \tag{15.8}$$

and that for large z the following asymptotic formulas hold:

$$\left.\begin{aligned} J_0(z) &= -\frac{2}{\sqrt{\pi z}}\sin z, \\ N_0(z) &= \frac{2}{\sqrt{\pi z}}\sin z, \\ K_0(z) &= \sqrt{\frac{2}{\pi z}}\,e^{-z} \end{aligned}\right\} \quad (z \gg 1). \tag{15.9}$$

Replacing in (15.3) differentiation with respect to r by differentiation with respect to λ, and taking into account the discontinuity of the function f at the point $\lambda = 0$ (compare (15.8)), we obtain from (15.7) the following expressions for $D^{(+)}$ and $D^{(-)}$:

$$D^{(+)}(x) = \frac{1}{4\pi}\varepsilon(x^0)\delta(\lambda) - \frac{mi}{8\pi\sqrt{\lambda}}\theta(\lambda)\left[N_1(m\sqrt{\lambda}) - i\varepsilon(x^0)J_1(m\sqrt{\lambda})\right] + \theta(-\lambda)\frac{mi}{4\pi^2\sqrt{-\lambda}}K_1(m\sqrt{-\lambda}), \tag{15.10}$$

$$D^{(-)}(x) = \frac{1}{4\pi}\varepsilon(x^0)\delta(\lambda) - \theta(\lambda)\varepsilon(x^0)\frac{m}{8\pi\sqrt{\lambda}}J_1(m\sqrt{\lambda}) + \frac{mi}{8\pi\sqrt{\lambda}}\theta(\lambda)N_1(m\sqrt{\lambda}) - \theta(-\lambda)\frac{mi}{4\pi^2\sqrt{-\lambda}}K_1(m\sqrt{-\lambda}). \tag{15.11}$$

Formulas (15.10) and (15.11) will be our starting point for the investigation of the singularities of all the functions of interest to us.[34]

15.2. *Explicit Form and Singularities of the Functions $D(x)$ and $D^c(x)$*

Adding (15.10) and (15.11) we obtain the expression for the Pauli-Jordan function in the form

$$D(x) = \frac{1}{2\pi}\varepsilon(x^0)\,\delta(\lambda) - \frac{m}{4\pi\sqrt{\lambda}}\theta(\lambda)\,\varepsilon(x^0)\,J_1(m\sqrt{\lambda}). \qquad (15.13)$$

From this formula it follows that the Pauli-Jordan function has an extremely important property: *it vanishes outside the light cones* (for $\lambda < 0$). Therefore all the (anti) commutators of the field operators whose arguments differ by a spacelike interval also vanish. Physically this corresponds to the fact that events separated by a spacelike interval are independent, since the speed of propagation of a signal cannot exceed the speed of light.

In order to obtain the causal function we shall construct from formulas (15.10) and (15.11) the combination

$$\theta(x^0)\,D^{(-)}(x) - \theta(-x^0)\,D^{(+)}(x).$$

This gives:

$$D^c(x) = \frac{1}{4\pi}\delta(\lambda) - \frac{m}{8\pi\sqrt{\lambda}}\theta(\lambda)\,\{J_1(m\sqrt{\lambda}) - iN_1(m\sqrt{\lambda})\}$$
$$+ \frac{mi}{4\pi^2\sqrt{-\lambda}}\theta(-\lambda)\,K_1(m\sqrt{-\lambda}). \qquad (15.14)$$

Finally, for the retarded Green's function we obtain with the aid of (14.14) and (15.13) the expression:

$$D^{\text{ret}}(x) = \frac{\theta(x^0)}{2\pi}\left\{\delta(\lambda) - \frac{m}{2\sqrt{\lambda}}\theta(\lambda)\,J_1(m\sqrt{\lambda})\right\}. \qquad (15.15)$$

[34] We remind the reader that the cylindrical functions of the first order are related to those of zero order by the expression

$$Z_1(x) = -\frac{\partial}{\partial x}Z_0(x), \qquad (15.12)$$

where Z is any one of J, N, and K.

It is now evident that D^{ret} vanishes everywhere, except for the light cone, into the future.

We now turn to the investigation of the singularities of commutation functions and of Green's functions. From formulas (15.10), (15.11), (15.13)–(15.15) it follows that all the singularities of the functions under investigation are situated only on the light cones (for $\lambda = 0$) since when the argument tends to infinity in either the spacelike or the timelike directions, these functions in accordance with (15.9) and (15.12) fall off like

$$|\lambda|^{-3/4} \exp\left(- m\sqrt{|\lambda|}\right)$$

and $\lambda^{-3/4}$ respectively.

In order to investigate the regularity properties we shall therefore examine the behavior of the above functions in the neighborhood of the light cone. Utilizing for this purpose formulas (15.8) and (15.12) we find:[35]

$$D^{(\pm)}(x) = \frac{1}{4\pi}\varepsilon(x^0)\delta(\lambda) \pm \frac{i}{4\pi^2\lambda} \mp \frac{im^2}{8\pi^2}\ln\frac{m|\lambda|^{1/2}}{2} - \frac{m^2}{16\pi}\varepsilon(x^0)\theta(\lambda) + O(\sqrt{|\lambda|}\ln|\lambda|,) \tag{15.16}$$

$$D(x) = \frac{1}{2\pi}\varepsilon(x^0)\delta(\lambda) - \frac{m^2}{8\pi}\varepsilon(x^0)\theta(\lambda) + O(\lambda), \tag{15.17}$$

$$D^c(x) = \frac{1}{4\pi}\delta(\lambda) + \frac{1}{4\pi^2 i}\frac{1}{\lambda} - \frac{m^2}{16\pi}\theta(\lambda) + \frac{im^2}{8\pi^2}\ln\frac{m|\lambda|^{1/2}}{2} + O(\sqrt{|\lambda|}\ln|\lambda|), \tag{15.18}$$

$$D^{\mathrm{ret}}(x) = \frac{1}{2\pi}\theta(x^0)\delta(\lambda) - \frac{m^2}{8\pi}\theta(x^0)\theta(\lambda) + \theta(x^0)\theta(\lambda)O(\lambda). \tag{15.19}$$

Expressions (15.16)–(15.19) have four types of singularities on the light cone: a pole $1/\lambda$, $\ln|\lambda|$, a δ-function $\delta(\lambda)$, and a discontinuity $\theta(\lambda)$. The factors $\varepsilon(x^0)$ and $\theta(x^0)$ in the individual terms of (15.16), (15.17), (15.19) do not introduce any additional

[35] Setting $m = 0$ in (15.18) we obtain the well-known formula for the causal function of the electromagnetic field

$$D_0^c(x) = \frac{1}{4\pi}\left(\delta(\lambda) - \frac{i}{\pi\lambda}\right) = \frac{1}{4\pi}\delta_+(-\lambda) \equiv \frac{1}{4\pi^2}\int_0^\infty e^{ix(-\lambda)}\,dx. \tag{15.18a}$$

singularities outside the light cone since the adjoining factors $\delta(\lambda)$ and $\theta(\lambda)$ produce the result that the discontinuities $\varepsilon(x^0)$ and $\theta(x^0)$ appear only at the origin of coordinates, i.e., again on the light cone.

Thus the above commutation functions and Green's functions for quantum wave fields are singular functions which have quite strong singularities on the light cone.

15.3. *Regularization of Singular Functions by the Method of Pauli-Villars*

As will be shown later (Chapter III), in the theory of interacting fields we shall have to deal with expressions which contain products of varying numbers of the above singular functions. In certain cases (see also § 16) the singularities of the individual functions occurring in such products will be superimposed on top of one another leading to meaningless nonintegrable expressions. Later (Chapters IV and V), a method will be outlined for the removal of individual singularities from such expressions. In order that we should not have to deal with actual infinities in the intermediate stages, we shall find it convenient to use in such stages in place of the singular functions themselves certain regular approximations to them, and to carry out the transition to the limit that destroys the regularity only in the final expressions.

Using as our basis the preceding analysis of the singularities of commutation functions and of Green's functions, we shall now formulate a method of constructing such approximations to these functions which together with all their derivatives up to any given order will have no singularities on the light cone. An example of such a procedure is afforded by the so-called Feynman's regularization (39) of the causal photon Green's function which consists of replacing

$$D_0^c(k) = -\frac{1}{k^2}$$

by

$$\mathrm{reg}_F\, D_0^c(k) = D_0^c(k) - D_M^c(k) = -\frac{1}{k^2} - \frac{1}{M^2 - k^2} = -\frac{M^2}{k^2(M^2 - k^2)},$$

where M^2 is the square of an "auxiliary mass," which is evidently equivalent to the introduction of the factor

$$\frac{M^2}{M^2 - k^2}.$$

It is easy to show with the aid of (15.18) that the function $\text{reg}_F\, D_0^c$ in contrast to D_0^c does not have on the light cone the strongest singularities $\delta(\lambda)$ and λ^{-1}. On the other hand

$$\lim_{M \to \infty} \text{reg}_F\, D_0^c(k) = D_0^c(k).$$

We note now that in accordance with formulas (15.3) and (15.7) the above singular functions may be represented in the form

$$\frac{\partial}{\partial \lambda} f_1(m^2\lambda) = m^2 f_2(m^2\lambda). \tag{15.20}$$

The last assertion is correct up to factors $\varepsilon(x^0)$ and $\theta(x^0)$ which are contained in the individual terms of the above functions. We emphasize that our aim is to form such combinations of commutation functions and Green's functions which would have on the light cone zeros (with respect to λ) of sufficiently high order, which in turn would guarantee the absence of singularities in the appropriate number of derivatives with respect to λ (or, what is the same, with respect to the components x^k). As has been noted earlier, the singularities corresponding to $\varepsilon(x^0)$ and $\theta(x^0)$ make themselves felt because of the factors $\delta(\lambda)$ and $\theta(\lambda)$ only on the light cone, and will therefore be cancelled by a zero with respect to λ of sufficiently high order together with the singularities with respect to the variable λ. Therefore we are justified in the analysis of the singularities of the above singular functions to start with formula (15.20).

From this formula it follows directly that the singularities $1/\lambda$ and $\delta(\lambda)$ always appear with coefficients that do not depend on the mass, while the singularities $\ln(\lambda)$ and $\theta(\lambda)$ appear with coefficients proportional to m^2. Therefore, taking a linear combination of several functions Δ (we shall here denote by the symbol Δ any of the functions under discussion $D^{(+)}$, $D^{(-)}$, D, D^c, D^{ret} . . .) which correspond to fields characterized by different masses M:

$$c_1 \Delta_{M_1}(x) + c_2 \Delta_{M_2}(x) + \ldots + c_k \Delta_{M_k}(x_k),$$

the coefficients of which satisfy the conditions

$$c_1 + c_2 + \ldots + c_k = 0,$$
$$c_1 M_1^2 + c_2 M_2^2 + \ldots + c_k M_k^2 = 0,$$

we shall obtain an expression which contains no singularities on the light cone.

In order to obtain an expression which is continuous together with all its derivatives up to order $n - 1$ inclusive it is sufficient to construct a form which in the neighborhood of the point $\lambda = 0$ has a zero of order not less than n. This may be achieved by subjecting the coefficients c_i to a greater number $(n + 1)$ of conditions

$$\sum_i c_i = 0, \quad \sum_i c_i M_i^2 = 0, \ldots, \quad \sum_i c_i M_i^{2n} = 0.$$

Clearly the minimum required number of masses in the above does not exceed $n + 2$. [36]

In the preceding procedure, one of the auxiliary masses M is chosen equal to the fundamental mass of the field m, while the corresponding coefficient c is set equal to unity. In this way for any given singular field function $\Delta(x)$ with a mass m we obtain a corresponding function which is continuous together with all its derivatives up to order $n - 2$ inclusive

$$\text{reg}\,\{\Delta_m(x)\} = \Delta_m(x) + \sum_{i=1}^{n} c_i \Delta_{M_i}(x). \tag{15.21}$$

This function contains n auxiliary masses $M_1, \ldots, M_n$, while its n coefficients are subjected to the n conditions

$$1 + \sum_{i=1}^{n} c_i = 0, \; m^2 + \sum_i c_i M_i^2 = 0, \ldots, \; m^{2n-2} + \sum_i c_i M_i^{2n-2} = 0. \tag{15.22}$$

As will be shown in § 16, the compensating masses M_i may be so chosen that when their magnitudes are made to approach infinity in a certain prescribed way the coefficients c_i remain finite.

[36] We note that in practical calculations (see Chapter IV) in place of a complete elimination of the singularities of singular functions, it turns out to be sufficient to reduce these singularities to ones of integrable type; this leads to a reduction in the number of required auxiliary masses.

Then for large but finite masses we shall have the situation in which, in virtue of the asymptotic properties (15.9) of cylindrical functions mentioned before, the values of the auxiliary functions Δ_{M_i} will turn out to be vanishingly small everywhere except for a small region in the neighborhood of the light cone.

In the above since the coefficients c_i are finite the regularized function reg $\{\Delta\}$ will practically differ from the function Δ only in the small region in the neighborhood of the light cones in which reg $\{\Delta(x)\}$ in contrast to $\Delta(x)$ will be continuous together with a certain number of its derivatives. As the values of the auxiliary masses M_i increase the region in the neighborhood of the light cone in which the difference reg $\{\Delta\} - \Delta$ differs from zero becomes smaller, while the finite values of reg $\{\Delta(x)\}$ and of its derivatives become larger. In the limit $M_i \to \infty$ we obtain the situation in which the function reg $\{\Delta\}$ ceases to differ from Δ.

The above formal method of removing singularities from singular field functions by means of introducing auxiliary masses is one of the variants of the method known under the name of the *Pauli-Villars regularization* (93). This method is equivalent to the introduction of additional fields with masses which compensate for the singularities in the functions of the fundamental field.

However, we must emphasize that *physically the concept of "compensating" fields is quite without content*, since in expression (15.21) some of the functions Δ_{M_i} will necessarily have negative coefficients. (As was shown in § 13 a negative sign in front of a commutation function leads to a contradiction with the basic assumptions of the theory and is therefore inadmissible.) Therefore, we shall regard the Pauli-Villars method of the regularization of singular field functions as a formal procedure only.

Of course the preceding method of introducing an approximation is not the only one. One may, for example, obtain regularized approximations to the D-functions by limiting the region of integration in momentum-space or by introducing a cut-off factor (form factor).

However, we shall prefer the above method of obtaining a regularized approximation to all the others having in mind its following advantages: manifest relativistic invariance, nonoccurrence of mixing of positive- and negative-frequency parts of singular functions, and universality in the sense of the simultaneous regularization of the singular functions $D^{(+)}$, $D^{(-)}$, and D^c.

§ 16. Operator Expressions and Singular Functions

16.1. *The Coefficient Functions of Operator Expressions*

Before we present the theory of interacting fields, we shall have to familiarize ourselves with a number of properties, largely of algebraic character, of operator expressions which are made up of quantized field functions of the free fields.

Let us consider a typical operator expression which depends on the values of the positive- and negative-frequency parts of such functions at a number of space-time points $x_1, \ldots, x_n$ and represented in the normal form:

$$A(x_1, \ldots, x_n) = \sum K_{\ldots\alpha\ldots\beta\ldots}(x_1, \ldots, x_n) \ldots u_\alpha^{(+)}(x_r) \ldots u_\beta^{(-)}(x_s) \ldots \tag{16.1}$$

Here $\ldots u_\alpha(x) \ldots$ are the components of wave functions or their partial derivatives, $K_{\ldots\alpha\ldots\beta\ldots}(x_1, \ldots, x_n)$ are certain c-functions of the variables $x_1, \ldots, x_n$ which in view of the homogeneity of space-time are invariant under translations:

$$K_{\ldots\alpha\ldots\beta\ldots}(x_1 + a, \ldots, x_n + a) = K_{\ldots\alpha\ldots\beta\ldots}(x_1, \ldots, x_n). \tag{16.2}$$

We shall call these functions the coefficient functions of the given operator expression (16.1). Due to the singularity of the commutation relations, these functions will be, generally speaking, singular and their mathematical nature will be specifically discussed later. For the time being we shall note that it is not difficult to express directly in terms of the coefficient functions the matrix elements of the operator $A(x_1, \ldots, x_n)$ for the various states

$$\Phi_{\ldots\gamma\ldots p\ldots} = \ldots u_\gamma^{(+)}(p) \ldots \Phi_0, \tag{16.3}$$

which correspond to the presence of given kinds of particles with given momenta $p_1, \ldots, p_j$. In order to do this it will only be necessary to form matrix elements of the type:

$$\Phi^*_{\ldots\gamma\ldots p\ldots} \ldots u_\alpha^{(+)}(x_r) \ldots u_\beta^{(-)}(x_s) \ldots \Phi_{\ldots\gamma'\ldots p'\ldots}$$

$$= \int e^{i(\sum x_r k_r - \sum x_s k_s)} \Phi_0^* \ldots u_\gamma^{(-)}(p) \ldots u_\alpha^{(+)}(k_r) \ldots u_\beta^{(-)}(k_s) \ldots u_{\gamma'}^{(+)}(p') \ldots \Phi_0$$
$$\times (\prod \delta(k_r^2 - m_\alpha^2)\, dk_r)(\prod \delta(k_s^2 - m_\beta^2) dk_s), \quad (16.4)$$

and this can be easily carried out with the aid of the commutation relations written in the form:

$$\delta(k^2 - m^2)\{u_\alpha^{(+)}(k), u_\beta^{(-)}(p)\} = \delta(k-p)\, P_{\alpha\beta}(k)\ (p^0 = \sqrt{\mathbf{p}^2 + m^2}), \quad (16.5)$$

where $P_{\alpha,\beta}(k)$ are polynomials in the components of k.

Indeed, we shall commute the creation operators $u_\alpha^{(+)}(k_r)$ to the left and the annihilation operators $u_\beta^{(-)}(k_s)$ to the right until they shall either "cancel" themselves respectively against $\ldots u_\gamma^{(-)}(p) \ldots, \ldots u_{\gamma'}^{(+)}(p') \ldots$, or give zero by operating on the vacuum state amplitude. It may be seen that a result different from zero will be obtained in the preceding only when all the $u_\alpha^{(+)}(k_r)$ will cancel against $u_\gamma^{(-)}(p)$, and all the $u_\beta^{(-)}(k_s)$ will cancel against $u_{\gamma'}^{(+)}(p')$.

The δ-functions which appear as a result of such "cancellation" will enable us to carry out the integration over the variables k_r making them equal to $\ldots p' \ldots$. The functions $u_\gamma^{(-)}(p_\alpha) \ldots$, $u_{\gamma'}^{(+)}(p'_\alpha)$ which remain free must also mutually cancel as a result of which factors of the type

$$\theta(p_\omega^0)\, \delta(p_\omega^2 - m_\gamma^2)\, \delta(p_\omega - p'_\omega). \quad (16.6)$$

will appear.

As a result of these elementary operations we shall obtain for the matrix element (16.3) expressions of the form:

$$\sum P^{\ldots\alpha\ldots\beta\ldots}_{\ldots\gamma\ldots\gamma'\ldots}(\ldots p \ldots p' \ldots)\, e^{i(\sum p_\nu x_\nu - \sum p'_\lambda x_\lambda)} \quad (16.7)$$

or

$$\sum Z^{\ldots\alpha\ldots\beta\ldots}_{\ldots\gamma\ldots\gamma'\ldots}(\ldots p' \ldots p \ldots)\, e^{i(\sum p_\nu x_\nu - \sum p'_\lambda x_\lambda)}$$
$$\cdot \prod \{\theta(p_\omega^0)\, \delta(p_\omega^2 - m_\gamma^2)\, \delta(p_\omega - p'_\omega)\}, \quad (16.8)$$

in which $P^{\ldots\alpha\ldots\beta\ldots}_{\ldots\gamma\ldots\gamma'\ldots}$, $Z^{\ldots\alpha\ldots\beta\ldots}_{\ldots\gamma\ldots\gamma'\ldots}$ are polynomials in the components of $\ldots p \ldots p' \ldots$. We shall obtain expression (16.7) in the case when all the $u_\gamma^{(-)}$, $u_{\gamma'}^{(+)}$ are compensated by $u_\alpha^{(+)}$, $u_\beta^{(-)}$; in the opposite case we shall obtain formula (16.8).

Thus on the basis of (16.1) we shall finally obtain

$$\Phi^*_{\dots\gamma\dots p\dots} A(x_1, \dots, x_n) \Phi_{\dots\gamma'\dots p'}$$
$$= \sum P^{\dots\alpha\dots\beta\dots}_{\dots\gamma\dots\gamma'\dots}(\dots p \dots p' \dots) K_{\dots\alpha\dots\beta\dots}(x_1, \dots, x_n) e^{i(\sum p_\nu x_\nu - \sum p'_\lambda x_\lambda)}$$
$$+ \sum Z^{\dots\alpha\dots\beta\dots}_{\dots\gamma\dots\gamma'\dots}(\dots p \dots p' \dots) K'_{\dots\alpha\dots\beta\dots}(x_1, \dots, x_n) e^{i(\sum p_\nu x_\nu - \sum p'_\lambda x_\lambda}$$
$$\times \prod \{\theta(p^0_\omega)\, \delta(p^2_\omega - m^2_\gamma)\, \delta(p_\omega - p'_\omega)\}. \quad (16.9)$$

In view of the obvious convenience of the normal form of representation of operator expressions, for example for the determination of their matrix elements, the problem of the appropriate method of reduction becomes of interest. It is clear that for the reduction to the normal form of operator expressions which are polynomials in wave functions it is sufficient to be able to reduce products of the type $A_1(x_1) \dots A_n(x_n)$ in which $A_j(x)$ are "linear operators," i.e., linear combinations of the corresponding $u_j^{(+)}(x)$, $u_j^{(-)}(x)$.

Actually, in any given case, a direct transformation of such a product may be carried out without any fundamental difficulties. It is quite sufficient in order to achieve this to move in turn $u^{(+)}$ to the left and $u^{(-)}$ to the right, and to make use of the commutation relations in each such "displacement." Nevertheless, because of the large number of terms obtained in the above procedure even for relatively small values of n, it is useful to have a well-developed set of prescriptions for carrying out the operation of reduction to the normal form in as automatic a manner as possible.

Such a set of prescriptions follows from an important theorem due to Wick (134) which we shall now formulate.

16.2. *Wick's Theorem for Normal Products*

Let us consider first of all the case $n = 2$ in which we have the product of two linear operators $A_1(x_1) A_2(x_2)$. In this case, in order to reduce the product to the normal form, it is obviously sufficient to carry out not more than one displacement of the operators $u^{(-)}(x_1)$, $u^{(+)}(x_2)$, and therefore in the result we shall obtain terms with the "proper order" in the sequence of positive- and negative-frequency parts of wave functions, and a term in the commutation functions which no longer contains any operator expressions.

Thus the product under discussion may differ from the normal product

$$: A_1(x_1)\, A_2(x_2) :$$

only by a c-expression which we shall call a pairing and which we shall denote by means of bracketing below the line:

$$A_1(x_1)\, A_2(x_2) = \, : A_1(x_1)\, A_2(x_2) : + \underbracket{A_1(x_1)\, A_2}(x_2). \tag{16.10}$$

Since for the vacuum state the expectation value of the normal product is always equal to zero, we may define the pairing as the vacuum expectation value of the ordinary product:

$$\underbracket{A_1(x_1)\, A_2}(x_2) = \Phi_0^*\, A_1(x_1)\, A_2(x_2)\, \Phi_0 \equiv \langle A_1(x_1)\, A_2(x_2)\rangle_0. \tag{16.11}$$

As an example let us consider the real scalar field. Starting with the commutation relations:

$$\varphi(x)\, \varphi(y) - \varphi(y)\, \varphi(x) = -\, iD(x - y),$$

we have as usual

$$\varphi^{(-)}(x)\, \varphi^{(+)}(y) = \varphi^{(+)}(y)\, \varphi^{(-)}(x) - iD^{(-)}(x - y),$$

in view of which we shall obtain:

$$\begin{aligned} \varphi(x)\, \varphi(y) &= \left(\varphi^{(+)}(x) + \varphi^{(-)}(x)\right) \left(\varphi^{(+)}(y) + \varphi^{(-)}(y)\right) \\ &= \varphi^{(+)}(x)\, \varphi^{(+)}(y) + \varphi^{(+)}(y)\, \varphi^{(-)}(x) + \varphi^{(+)}(x)\, \varphi^{(-)}(y) \\ &\quad + \varphi^{(-)}(x)\, \varphi^{(-)}(y) - iD^{(-)}(x-y) \end{aligned}$$

or in accordance with the definition of the normal product,

$$\varphi(x)\, \varphi(y) = \, : \varphi(x)\, \varphi(y) : - \, iD^{(-)}(x - y).$$

We therefore obtain

$$\left.\begin{aligned} &\underbracket{\varphi(x)\, \varphi}(y) = \langle \varphi(x)\, \varphi(y)\rangle_0 = -\, iD^{(-)}(x - y), \\ &\underbracket{\varphi^{(+)}(x)\, \varphi^{(-)}}(y) = 0, \quad \underbracket{\varphi^{(-)}(x)\, \varphi^{(+)}}(y) = -\, iD^{(-)}(x - y). \end{aligned}\right\} \tag{16.12}$$

Similarly in the case of the electromagnetic field we shall obtain:

$$\underbrace{A_n(x)\, A_m(y)} = \langle A_n(x)\, A_m(y)\rangle_0 = ig^{nm} D_0^{(-)}(x-y). \tag{16.13}$$

Let us also consider a fermion field for which

$$\psi_\alpha(x)\,\bar\psi_\beta(y) + \bar\psi_\beta(y)\,\psi_\alpha(x) = -\,iS_{\alpha\beta}(x-y),$$
$$\psi_\alpha^{(-)}(x)\,\bar\psi_\beta^{(+)}(y) = -\,\bar\psi_\beta^{(+)}(y)\,\psi_\alpha^{(-)}(x) - iS_{\alpha\beta}^{(-)}(x-y).$$

Then

$$\psi(x)\,\bar\psi(y) = \psi^{(+)}(x)\,\bar\psi^{(+)}(y) - \bar\psi^{(+)}(y)\,\psi^{(-)}(x)$$
$$+\,\psi^{(+)}(x)\,\bar\psi^{(-)}(y) + \psi^{(-)}(x)\,\bar\psi^{(-)}(y) - iS^{(-)}(x-y)$$

or

$$\psi_\alpha(x)\,\bar\psi_\beta(y) = \,:\psi_\alpha(x)\,\bar\psi_\beta(y):\, - iS_{\alpha\beta}^{(-)}(x-y),$$

and therefore

$$\underbrace{\psi_\alpha(x)\,\bar\psi_\beta(y)} = -\,iS_{\alpha\beta}^{(-)}(x-y). \tag{16.14}$$

In a similar way we may show that

$$\underbrace{\psi_\alpha(x)\,\psi_\beta(y)} = -\,S_{\beta\alpha}^{(+)}(y-x). \tag{16.15}$$

Since $\psi(x)$ always anticommutes with $\psi(y)$, and $\bar\psi(x)$ with $\bar\psi(y)$ we shall in addition obtain:

$$\underbrace{\psi_\alpha(x)\,\psi_\beta(y)} = 0, \qquad \underbrace{\bar\psi_\alpha(x)\,\bar\psi_\beta(y)} = 0. \tag{16.16}$$

In order to be able to formulate Wick's theorem it is also necessary to introduce the concept of the normal product with pairing.

As we have already mentioned in § 9, the normal product $:A_1(x_1)\ldots A_n(x_n):$ may be defined as the result of reducing to the normal form the ordinary product $A_1(x_1)\ldots A_n(x_n)$ provided that during *the process of reduction* the quantized field functions are regarded as being strictly commuting or anticommuting and the value zero is assigned to all the commutation functions that appear. From this it follows directly that when the order of factors is altered in a normal product only its sign may change:

$$:A_{i_1}(x_{i_1})\ldots A_{i_n}(x_{i_n}): \,=\, \eta :A_1(x_1)\ldots A_n(x_n): \quad (\eta = (-1)^p),$$

where p is the parity of the permutation to which the Fermi operators are subjected in the transition from the initial sequence of the factors $1, \ldots, n$ to the sequence $i_1, \ldots, i_n$.

It is evident that the normal product is linear with respect to each of its factors:

$$
\begin{aligned}
&: A_1(x_1) \ldots (aA'_j(x_j) + bA''_j(x_j)) \ldots A_n(x_n) : \\
&= a : A_1(x_1) \ldots A'_j(x_j) \ldots A_n(x_n) : + b : A_1(x_1) \ldots A''_j(x_j) \ldots A_n(x_n) :,
\end{aligned}
$$

where a and b are arbitrary complex c-numbers.

We now introduce the normal product with pairing, setting by definition:

$$
\begin{aligned}
&: A_1(x_1) \ldots \underbrace{A_j(x_j) \ldots A_k(x_k)} \ldots A_n(x_n) : \\
&\qquad = \eta \underbrace{A_j(x_j)\, A_k(x_k)} : A_1(x_1) \ldots A_{j-1}(x_{j-1})\, A_{j+1}(x_{j+1}) \ldots \\
&\qquad\qquad \ldots A_{k-1}(x_{k-1})\, A_{k+1}(x_{k+1}) \ldots A_n(x_n) : \ (\eta = (-1)^p),
\end{aligned}
$$

where p is the parity of the Fermi permutations in going over from the sequence

$$1, \ldots, j-1, j, j+1, \ldots, k-1, k, k+1, \ldots, n$$

to the sequence

$$j, k, 1, \ldots, j-1, j+1, \ldots, k-1, k+1, \ldots, n.$$

In a completely analogous way we shall define the normal product with an arbitrary number of pairings:

$$: \underbrace{A_1(x_1)\, \overbrace{A_2(x_2)\, A_3(x_3)}}\, \overbrace{A_4(x_4) \ldots A_{n-1}(x_{n-1})}\, A_n(x_n) :$$

i.e., we shall take it to be equal to the product of all the pairings with the normal product of the remaining unpaired operators and with the number $\eta = (-1)^p$:

$$\eta \underbrace{A_1 A_3}\, \underbrace{A_2\, A_{n-1}} \ldots : A_4 \ldots A_n :,$$

where p is the parity of the permutations to which the Fermi operators are subjected in the process of bringing the pairings outside the normal product.

Thus for example:

$$
\begin{aligned}
&:\bar{\psi}_\alpha(x_1)\,\bar{\psi}_\beta(x_2)\,\psi_\gamma(x_3)\,\psi_\delta(x_4): \\
&\qquad = -\,\underbracket{\bar{\psi}_\alpha(x_1)\,\psi_\gamma(x_3)}\,\underbracket{\bar{\psi}_\beta(x_2)\,\psi_\delta(x_4)} = S^{(+)}_{\gamma\alpha}(x_3 - x_1)\,S^{(+)}_{\delta\beta}(x_4 - x_2).
\end{aligned}
$$

From the above definition it follows immediately that the normal product with pairing is linear with respect to its factors, and that when they are transposed within such a product without changing the pairings and without changing the order of paired operators in a given pair, this product is multiplied by $\eta = (-1)^p$.

We can now give a simple formulation of Wick's theorem. According to this theorem "the ordinary product of linear operators is equal to the sum of all the corresponding normal products with all possible pairings including the normal product without pairing":

$$
\begin{aligned}
A_1 \ldots A_n &= :A_1 \ldots A_n: + :\underbracket{A_1 A_2}\ldots A_n: + \ldots \\
&\quad + :\underbracket{A_1 \ldots A_{n-1}}A_n: + :\underbracket{A_1 \ldots A_n}: \\
&\quad + :\underbracket{A_1 A_2}\,\underbracket{A_3 A_4}\ldots A_n: + \ldots
\end{aligned} \tag{16.17}
$$

For the proof of the foregoing we shall need the following lemma: if $A_1, \ldots, A_n$, B are linear operators, then:

$$
:A_1 \ldots A_n:B = :A_1 \ldots :A_n B + \sum_{(1 \leq k \leq n)} :A_1 \ldots \underbracket{A_k \ldots A_n B}:. \tag{16.18}
$$

We note that the validity of this lemma will be completely established as soon as we have proved it for the special case in which each of the operators A_j, B is either a creation operator or an annihilation operator. Indeed, in the general case we may represent each such operator in the form of a sum of creation and annihilation operators. Making use of the linearity of the products under discussion with respect to their factors we shall represent them in the form of sums of products of creation and annihilation operators, i.e., of products which correspond to the special case mentioned above. Therefore, the validity of the lemma in the general case will follow from its validity in this special case.

Let us also note that the case when B is an annihilation operator is trivial. Indeed in such a case in the expression

$$:A_1 \ldots A_n:B$$

the operator B already occupies its "proper" place, so that this expression will be equal to

$$:A_1 \ldots A_n B:.$$

Moreover, since B is an annihilation operator it follows that $\underbracket{A_k B} = 0$.

Thus we only have to consider the case when B is a creation operator. But in such a case if some of the operators A_j are creation operators we may take them to the left outside the normal product symbols; their pairings with B are equal to zero, so that among the A_j inside the normal product symbols only the annihilation operators remain. Thus in order to prove the lemma quoted before we only have to prove it for the case when all the A_j are annihilation operators while B is a creation operator.

Since for $n = 1$ the validity of this lemma follows directly from the definition of pairing

$$A_1 B = :A_1 B: + \underbracket{A_1 B},$$

we may use the method of induction to prove the lemma.

We assume that the lemma holds for a certain number n of operators A_j. Then by multiplying equation (16.18) on the left by certain annihilation operator A_0 we shall obtain:

$$A_0 :A_1 \ldots A_n: B = A_0 :A_1 \ldots A_n B: + \sum_{(1 \leqq k \leqq n)} A_0 :A_1 \ldots \underbracket{A_k \ldots A_n B}:. \tag{16.19}$$

But the only creation operator B which occurs in the expression

$$:A_1 \ldots \underbracket{A_k \ldots A_n B}:$$

is paired, and therefore this expression is equal to a c-number multiplied into the normal product of annihilation operators only. On the other hand, the normal product of annihilation operators coincides with their ordinary product. Therefore

$$A_0 :A_1 \ldots \underbracket{A_k \ldots A_n B}: = :A_0 A_1 \ldots \underbracket{A_k \ldots A_n B}:. \tag{16.20}$$

We now turn to the analysis of the first term in the right-hand side of equation (16.19). We have:

$$:A_1 \ldots A_n B: = (-1)^p :BA_1 \ldots A_n: = (-1)^p B :A_1 \ldots A_n:,$$

where p is the parity of the Fermi permutations required to bring B from the extreme right-hand side to the extreme left-hand side position. From this we obtain:

$$\begin{aligned} A_0 :A_1 \ldots A_n B: &= (-1)^p A_0 B :A_1 \ldots A_n: \\ &= (-1)^p :A_0 B::A_1 \ldots A_n: + (-1)^p \underbracket{A_0 B} :A_1 \ldots A_n: \\ &= (-1)^p :A_0 B::A_1 \ldots A_n: + (-1)^p :\underbracket{A_0 B} A_1 \ldots A_n: \\ &= (-1)^{p+p'} :BA_0::A_1 \ldots A_n: + :\underbracket{A_0 A_1 \ldots A_n B}:, \end{aligned}$$

where p' is the parity of the Fermi permutations needed for A_0 to exchange places with B.

On the other hand, since B is a creation operator while all the A_i are annihilation operators, it follows that:

$$(-1)^{p+p'} : BA_0 : : A_1 \dots A_n : = (-1)^{p+p'} : BA_0A_1 \dots A_n :$$
$$= (-1)^p : A_0BA_1 \dots A_n : = : A_0A_1 \dots A_nB : .$$

We have therefore:

$$A_0 : A_1 \dots A_nB : = : A_0A_1 \dots A_nB : + : \underbrace{A_0A_1 \dots A_nB} : ,$$

using which, and in virtue of (16.20), we shall obtain from (16.19)

$$: A_0A_1 \dots A_n : B = : A_0A_1 \dots A_nB : + \sum_{(0 \leqq k \leqq n)} : A_0A_1 \dots \underbrace{A_k \dots A_nB} : .$$

Thus, having assumed the validity of equation (16.18) for the case when the number of operators A was n we have now established its validity also for the case when this number is $n + 1$. This concludes the proof of the lemma formulated above.

We further note that this lemma may be directly generalized also to the case of normal products with an arbitrary number of pairings. Indeed, since the normal product with pairings is always equal to the product of pairings by $(-1)^p$ and by the normal product of operators remaining unpaired we see that in equation (16.18) we may take in place of the "pure" normal product of the operators A their normal product with an arbitrary number of pairings.

We now begin the proof of Wick's theorem itself. It is evident that the theorem is trivial for the case $n=2$. We shall therefore use the method of induction. We assume that equation (16.17) which expresses Wick's theorem holds for the case of the product of n operators A, and we shall attempt to prove it for the case of the product of $n + 1$ linear operators. In order to do this we multiply equation (16.17) on the right by a certain linear operator A_{n+1}. We then express the ordinary product $A_1 \dots A_{n+1}$ in the form of a sum of all the normal products of the operators $A_1 \dots A_n$ with all possible pairings between them multiplied on the right, in the ordinary sense, by A_{n+1}. (We emphasize that among the terms with all possible pairings, the term with zero number of pairings is also included.)

But in accordance with the generalized lemma proved above the normal product of the operators $A_1, \dots, A_n$ with an arbitrary given number of pairings among them multiplied on the right, in the ordinary sense, by A_{n+1} is equal to the sum of normal products of the operators $A_1, \dots, A_{n+1}$ in which in addition to the pairings already occurring among $A_1, \dots, A_n$ we also take into account all possible (including zero) [37] pairings of the free operators $A_1, \dots, A_n$ with A_{n+1}. In this way, we

[37] i.e., the term containing no pairings of $A_1, \dots, A_n$ with A_{n+1}.

show that the ordinary product of $n + 1$ linear operators $A_1, \ldots, A_{n+1}$ may be represented in the form of a sum of their normal products with all possible pairings, which completes the proof by induction. The proof of Wick's theorem is thus completed.

It may be easily seen that this theorem is also applicable to the case when some of the factors themselves appear as normal products:

$$:A_1 \ldots A_{k_1}::A_{k_1+1} \ldots A_{k_2}:\ldots:A_{k_s} \ldots A_n:. \tag{16.21}$$

In this case, Wick's theorem is used in exactly the same way as for the "pure" product $A_1 \ldots A_n$ with the one obvious difference, that we now need not take into account pairings between those factors in (16.21) that belong to the same normal product. For example, the pairings between $A_1, \ldots, A_{k_1}$, the pairings between $A_{k_1+1}, \ldots, A_{k_2}$, need not be taken into account.

In order to illustrate the application of Wick's theorem in its general form we shall consider the products

$$:\bar{\psi}(x)\,\gamma^k\psi(x)::\bar{\psi}(y)\,\gamma^l\psi(y): \\ = \sum_{(\sigma,\,\sigma',\,\tau,\,\tau')} :\bar{\psi}_\sigma(x)\,\gamma^k_{\sigma\sigma'}\psi_{\sigma'}(x)::\bar{\psi}_\tau(y)\,\gamma^l_{\tau\tau'}\psi_{\tau'}(y):. \tag{16.22}$$

We have:

$$\begin{aligned} :\bar{\psi}_\sigma(x)\,\gamma^k_{\sigma\sigma'}\psi_{\sigma'}(x)::\bar{\psi}_\tau(y)\,\gamma^l_{\tau\tau'}\psi_{\tau'}(y): \\ = :\bar{\psi}_\sigma(x)\,\gamma^k_{\sigma\sigma'}\psi_{\sigma'}(x)\,\bar{\psi}_\tau(y)\,\gamma^l_{\tau\tau'}\psi_{\tau'}(y): \\ + \underbrace{\bar{\psi}_\sigma(x)\,\psi_{\tau'}(y)}\,\gamma^k_{\sigma\sigma'}\gamma^l_{\tau\tau'}:\psi_{\sigma'}(x)\,\bar{\psi}_\tau(y): \\ + \underbrace{\psi_{\sigma'}(x)\,\bar{\psi}_\tau(y)}\,\gamma^k_{\sigma\sigma'}\gamma^l_{\tau\tau'}:\bar{\psi}_\sigma(x)\,\psi_{\tau'}(y): \\ + \underbrace{\psi_{\sigma'}(x)\,\bar{\psi}_\tau(y)}\,\underbrace{\bar{\psi}_\sigma(x)\,\psi_{\tau'}(y)}\,\gamma^k_{\sigma\sigma'}\gamma^l_{\tau\tau'}, \end{aligned}$$

from which on the basis of the pairing formulas (16.14), (16.15), we shall obtain:

$$\begin{aligned} :\bar{\psi}_\sigma(x)\,\gamma^k_{\sigma\sigma'}\psi_{\sigma'}(x)::\bar{\psi}_\tau(y)\,\gamma^l_{\tau\tau'}\psi_{\tau'}(y): \\ = :\bar{\psi}_\sigma(x)\,\gamma^k_{\sigma\sigma'}\psi_{\sigma'}(x)\,\bar{\psi}_\tau(y)\,\gamma^l_{\tau\tau'}\psi_{\tau'}(y): \\ - i:\bar{\psi}_\tau(y)\,\gamma^l_{\tau\tau'}S^{(+)}_{\tau'\sigma}(y-x)\,\gamma^k_{\sigma\sigma'}\psi_{\sigma'}(x): \\ - i:\bar{\psi}_\sigma(x)\,\gamma^k_{\sigma\sigma'}S^{(-)}_{\sigma'\tau}(x-y)\,\gamma^l_{\tau\tau'}\psi_{\tau'}(y): \\ + \gamma^k_{\sigma\sigma'}S^{(-)}_{\sigma'\tau}(x-y)\,\gamma^l_{\tau\tau'}S^{(+)}_{\tau'\sigma}(y-x). \end{aligned}$$

Substituting this expression into (16.22) and carrying out the summation over the spinor indices we shall finally obtain:

$$:\bar{\psi}(x)\gamma^k\psi(x)::\bar{\psi}(y)\gamma^l\psi(y):$$
$$= :\bar{\psi}(x)\gamma^k\psi(x)\,\bar{\psi}(y)\gamma^l\psi(y): - i:\bar{\psi}(y)\gamma^l S^{(+)}(y-x)\gamma^k\psi(x):$$
$$-i:\bar{\psi}(x)\gamma^k S^{(-)}(x-y)\gamma^l\psi(y): + \mathrm{Sp}\,\{\gamma^k S^{(-)}(x-y)\gamma^l S^{(+)}(y-x)\}. \tag{16.23}$$

With the aid of Wick's theorem we are able to reduce in an almost automatic manner ordinary products of operators to sums of normal products multiplied by c-numbers. One should terminate the reduction to the normal form at this stage, since, generally speaking, it is not useful to express the normal products in the explicit normal form. The representation of operators in terms of linear combinations of normal products may in fact be regarded as the most convenient way of writing their representations in the normal form. For example, it is shorter to write

$$:\bar{\psi}(x)\,\psi(x):,$$

than the same expression in the expanded form

$$\bar{\psi}^{(+)}(x)\,\psi^{(+)}(x) + \bar{\psi}^{(+)}(x)\,\psi^{(-)}(x) - \psi^{(+)}(x)\,\bar{\psi}^{(-)}(x) + \bar{\psi}^{(-)}(x)\,\psi^{(-)}(x),$$

and this is even more true in the case of products containing a larger number of factors.

As we have seen, it is very easy to deal with normal products. For example, suppose that we have to evaluate a matrix element of the type:

$$\Phi^*_{\ldots\gamma\ldots p\ldots} : A_1(x_1)\ldots A_n(x_n) : \Phi_{\ldots\gamma'\ldots p'\ldots}$$
$$= \Phi_0^*\ldots u_\gamma^{(-)}(p)\ldots : A_1(x_1)\ldots A_n(x_n) : \ldots u_{\gamma'}^{(+)}(p')\ldots\Phi_0. \tag{16.24}$$

We note that in accordance with Wick's theorem the product

$$\ldots u_\gamma^{(-)}(p) : \ldots A_1(x_1)\ldots A_n(x_n) : \ldots u_{\gamma'}^{(+)}(p')\ldots$$
$$= :\ldots u_\gamma^{(-)}(p)\ldots : : A_1(x_1)\ \ A_n(x_n) : : \ldots u_{\gamma'}^{(+)}(p')\ldots :$$

is equal to the sum of the corresponding normal products with all possible pairings: $u_\gamma^{(-)}(p)$ with $A_j(x_j)$, $A_j(x_j)$ with $u_{\gamma'}^{(+)}(p')$, and

$u_\gamma^{(-)}(p)$ with $u_{\gamma'}^{(+)}(p')$. On the other hand, the vacuum expectation value of a normal product which contains at least one unpaired operator is equal to zero. We therefore see that the matrix element (16.24) consists of the sum of only those normal products for which all the operators are paired. It will therefore be given by a sum of terms of the type:

$$(-1)^p \prod \{u_{\gamma_\alpha}^{(-)}(p_\alpha) A_j(x_j)\} \prod \{A_j(x_j) u_{\gamma'_\beta}^{(-)}(p'_\beta)\} \prod \{u_{\gamma_\sigma}^{(-)}(p_\sigma) u_{\gamma'_\tau}^{(-)}(p'_\tau)\}.$$

16.3. *Improper Nature of Singular Functions*

We shall now discuss the question of the structure of the coefficient functions which appear when the operation of multiplication of operator expressions is carried out. We note that in accordance with Wick's theorem the coefficient functions which are obtained in evaluating products of linear operators $A_1(x_1) \ldots A_n(x_n)$ have the form

$$\prod_{(r<s)} D_{\alpha\beta}^{(-)}(x_r - x_s), \qquad (16.25)$$

where $D_{\alpha\beta}$ are commutation functions.

The product

$$A_1(x_1, \ldots, x_n)\, A_2(y_1, \ldots, y_m)$$

of any two arbitrary operators belonging to type (16.1) under investigation

$$\begin{aligned} A_1(x_1, \ldots, x_n) &= \sum K_{\ldots\alpha\ldots\beta\ldots}(x_1, \ldots, x_n) \ldots u_\alpha^{(+)}(x_r) \ldots u_\beta^{(-)}(x_s) \ldots, \\ A_2(y_1, \ldots, y_m) &= \sum Q_{\ldots\sigma\ldots\tau\ldots}(y_1, \ldots, y_m) \ldots u_\sigma^{(+)}(y_i) \ldots u_\tau^{(-)}(y_j) \ldots, \end{aligned} \qquad (16.26)$$

belongs to the same type and its coefficient functions may be expressed in the form

$$K(x_1, \ldots, x_n) Q(y_1, \ldots, y_m) \prod D_{\beta\sigma}^{(-)}(x_s - y_i). \qquad (16.27)$$

It should be noted, however, that the function $D^{(-)}(x)$ and to an even greater extent the functions

$$D_{\beta\sigma}^{(-)}(x) = P_{\beta\sigma}\left(\frac{\partial}{\partial x}\right) D^{(-)}(x)$$

have a high degree of singularity on the light cone, and therefore serious doubts may arise as to whether expressions such as (16.25), (16.27) which contain products of arbitrary numbers of these functions have any real meaning.

In this connection it is now useful to discuss the more general question as to the conditions which should be imposed on the coefficient functions appearing in the operator expressions of type (16.1) under consideration at present in order that a definite meaning may be ascribed to these expressions, or as is usually stated, that they should contain no "divergences."

First of all it is clear that we cannot demand that the coefficient functions $K(x_1, \ldots, x_n)$ should be functions in the generally accepted mathematical sense, since in that case we ought to exclude from consideration all "singular" or "improper" functions such as $\delta(x)$ and $D(x)$ with which we continually have to deal in relativistic quantum mechanics. It is therefore natural to regard the $K(x_1, \ldots, x_n)$ as being defined specifically as improper functions.[38]

We shall now attempt to present the ideas which are usually implied in this concept in publications on quantum mechanics, but which as a rule are not clearly formulated. It may be easily seen that in contrast to ordinary functions, singular or improper functions are defined not by giving their values for all the values of their arguments (for a certain set of values of their arguments they may be either infinite or, in general, not defined at all), but by prescribing rules for the integration of their products with sufficiently regular functions. For example, the δ-function is characterized by the rules of integration of its products with continuous functions; the derivatives of the δ-function are characterized by the rules of integration of their products with appropriately differentiable functions, etc.

In other words, an improper function is defined by specifying an appropriate linear functional in a suitable "linear space" of sufficiently regular functions. In recent years such a functional

[38] At present in the Soviet mathematical literature the name *generalized functions* has become commonly accepted for such functions. In foreign literature they are referred to as *distributions*.

point of view has been developed in the work of Sobolev (**113**) and of Schwartz (**103**) dealing with the creation of a new mathematical theory—the so-called "theory of distributions."

Of course we cannot undertake here a presentation of the general theory of improper functions in any detail, and we will therefore restrict ourselves to the principal formulations which refer only to those properties of specific coefficient functions that we shall need for direct use in subsequent sections.

We now formulate the definition of the coefficient functions $K(x_1, \ldots, x_n)$. In accordance with the commonly accepted point of view we shall consider $K(x_1, \ldots, x_n)$ as a given and integrable function if in a certain given linear space L of functions $F(x_1, \ldots, x_n)$, which are sufficiently smooth and which fall off sufficiently rapidly at infinity, a linear functional can be defined which we shall agree to represent symbolically in the form

$$\int K(x_1, \ldots, x_n)\, F(x_1, \ldots, x_n)\, dx_1 \ldots dx_n. \qquad (16.28)$$

Let us make this definition more precise. We introduce the class $C(q, r, n)$ of functions $F(x_1, \ldots, x_n)$ which are continuous together with all their partial derivatives up to the qth order inclusive, and for which all the products:

$$x_{i_1}^{\alpha_1} \ldots x_{i_s}^{\alpha_s} \frac{\partial^p F(x_1, \ldots, x_n)}{\partial x_{j_1}^{\beta_1} \ldots \partial x_{j_p}^{\beta_p}} \quad \left\} \begin{array}{c} (s = 0,\ 1, \ldots, r), \\ (p = 0,\ 1, \ldots, q), \\ (\beta, \alpha = 0,\ 1,\ 2,\ 3) \end{array} \right. \qquad (16.29)$$

are bounded. The linear space formed by the functions of this class for any arbitrary given q, r will be taken as the space L.

Thus the main requirement which will always be imposed on the coefficient functions is that the integral (16.28) should be defined as a linear functional in the linear space $C(q, r, n)$, in any case for sufficiently large q, r. We shall in future refer to this requirement as the condition of integrability.

Usually it is convenient to carry out the actual construction of the coefficient functions by means of an improper limiting process. We shall say that the sequence

$$K_M(x, \ldots, x_n) \qquad (M \to \infty), \qquad (16.30)$$

is convergent in an improper sense if the corresponding sequence of integrals

$$\int K_M(x_1, \ldots, x_n) F(x_1, \ldots, x_n) dx_1 \ldots dx_n \tag{16.31}$$

converges in the ordinary sense for each function $F(x_1, \ldots, x_n)$ from a certain fixed class $C(q, r, n)$. It is of course assumed in the above that all the functions (16.30) are integrable in the given $C(q, r, n)$. The usual notation $\rightarrow$, lim will be used to express the existence of improper convergence.

Since

$$\lim_{M\to\infty} \int K_M(x_1, \ldots, x_n)\, F(x_1, \ldots, x_n)\, dx_1 \ldots dx_n$$

will also be a linear functional in $C(q, r, n)$, then by agreeing to represent it symbolically in the form

$$\int \lim_{M\to\infty} K_M(x_1, \ldots, x_n)\, F(x_1, \ldots, x_n)\, dx_1 \ldots dx_n,$$

we thereby define the improper limit

$$\lim_{M\to\infty} K_M(x_1, \ldots, x_n)$$

as an integrable improper function. In virtue of this definition

$$\int \lim_{M\to\infty} K_M(x_1, \ldots, x_n)\, F(x_1, \ldots, x_n)\, dx_1 \ldots dx_n$$
$$= \lim_{M\to\infty} \int K_M(x_1, \ldots, x_n)\, F(x_1, \ldots, x_n)\, dx_1 \ldots dx_n$$

for any function $F(x_1, \ldots, x_n)$ from the class $C(q, r, n)$ with sufficiently high indices q, r.

It should be emphasized that the improper limiting process is actually continually being used in the investigation of singular functions in quantum mechanics, although, as a rule, no attention is paid to the fact that it differs from the limiting process in the ordinary sense. Thus, for example, when it is stated that $\delta(t)$ is the limit of the function

$$\delta_\varepsilon(t) = \begin{cases} 0 & \text{for } |t| > \varepsilon, \\ \dfrac{1}{2\varepsilon} & \text{for } |t| \leqq \varepsilon \end{cases}$$

for $\varepsilon \to +0$ the notion of the limit in this case must evidently be interpreted in the improper sense. In an exactly similar way the limiting process will be an improper one when $\varepsilon \to +0$ in the expression

$$\frac{P_{\alpha\beta}(p)}{m^2 - p^2 - i\varepsilon}$$

for the Fourier transform of the function $D^c_{\alpha\beta}$.

Let us now discuss from the above point of view the question of approximating the principal singular functions $D^{(\pm)}_{\alpha\beta}$, $D^c_{\alpha\beta}$ by means of regularized expressions. Let us take for example the function $D^{(-)}_{\alpha\beta}(x)$, defined by the formal relation

$$D^{(-)}_{\alpha\beta}(x) = P_{\alpha\beta}\left(i\frac{\partial}{\partial x}\right) D^{(-)}(x)$$
$$= \frac{i}{(2\pi)^3}\int e^{-ikx} P_{\alpha\beta}(k)\,\theta(k^0)\,\delta(k^2 - m^2)\,dk. \qquad (16.32)$$

Let us first of all determine the meaning which should be ascribed to integrals with infinite limits which occur in the above. As is well known, an ordinary integral taken over an infinite region is defined as the limit of integrals with finite regions of integration which are expanded indefinitely and in the limit include the whole given infinite region. It is therefore natural to define integrals of the type

$$K(x) = \int e^{-ikx} P(k)\,\theta(k^0)\,\delta(k^2 - m^2)\,dk \qquad (16.33)$$

with a polynomial $P(k)$ as the improper limit of the integral

$$K_G(x) = \int_G e^{-ikx} P(k)\,\theta(k^0)\,\delta(k^2 - m^2)\,dk$$

as the region G is expanded indefinitely.

It may be shown that such a limit actually exists. We take a sequence of regions G_n such that the size of the four-dimensional cube:

$$-L_n \leqq k^\alpha \leqq L_n \qquad (\alpha = 0, 1, 2, 3),$$

which is entirely contained within G_n tends to ∞ as n does and consider the integral

$$\int K_G(x) F(x)\,dx$$

with the function $F(x)$ chosen from a certain class $C(q, r, 1)$. We then have:

$$\int K_G(x)F(x)\,dx = \int_G \tilde{F}(k)P(k)\,\theta(k^0)\,\delta(k^2 - m^2)\,dk$$
$$= \int \theta(k;\,G)\tilde{F}(k)P(k)\,\theta(k^0)\,\delta(k^2 - m^2)\,dk,$$

where

$$\tilde{F}(k) = \int F(x)\,e^{-ikx}\,dx$$
$$\theta(k;\,G) = \begin{cases} 1 & \text{for } k \in G, \\ 0 & \text{for } k \,\bar{\in}\, G. \end{cases}$$

In going over to the three-dimensional integral we shall obtain:

$$\int K_G(x)F(x)\,dx = \int \theta(k^0, \mathbf{k}, G)\,F(k^0, \mathbf{k})\,P(k^0, \mathbf{k})\,\frac{d\mathbf{k}}{2k^0} \tag{16.34}$$
$$(k^0 = \sqrt{\mathbf{k}^2 + m^2}).$$

We now evaluate the rate at which $\tilde{F}(k)$ falls off at infinity. We assume that $F(x)$ belongs to the class $C(q, 5, 1)$. Then the expressions

$$|\,F(x)\,|, \qquad \left|\frac{\partial^p F(x)}{(\partial x^\alpha)^p}\right|,$$

$$\Big(\sum_\alpha |\,x^\alpha\,|\Big)^5\,|\,F(x)\,|, \qquad \Big(\sum_\alpha |\,x^\alpha\,|\Big)^5\left|\frac{\partial^p F(x)}{(\partial x^\beta)^p}\right| \qquad (p = 1, \ldots, q)$$

are bounded, as a result of which

$$\int |\,F(x)\,|\,dx < \infty, \qquad \int \left|\frac{\partial^p F(x)}{(\partial x^\beta)^p}\right| dx < \infty.$$

It is now clear that $\tilde{F}(k)$ will be continuous and bounded:

$$|\,\tilde{F}(k)\,| \leqq \int |\,F(x)\,|\,dx.$$

Integrating by parts we then obtain:

$$\tilde{F}(k) = \left(\frac{-ig^{\alpha\alpha}}{k^\alpha}\right)^q \int \frac{\partial^q F(x)}{(\partial x^\alpha)^q}\,e^{-ikx}\,dx,$$

from which it follows that

$$|\,k^\alpha\,|^q\,|\,\tilde{F}(k)\,| \leqq \int \left|\frac{\partial^q F(x)}{(\partial x^\alpha)^q}\right| dx \leqq \sum_\alpha \int \left|\frac{\partial^q F(x)}{(\partial x^\alpha)^q}\right| dx = \text{const} = C$$

and

$$\Big(\sum_\alpha |\,k^\alpha\,|\Big)^q\,|\,\tilde{F}(k)\,| \leqq 4^{q-1} \sum |\,k^\alpha\,|^q\,|\,\tilde{F}(k)\,| \leqq 4^q C. \tag{16.35}$$

Let ν denote the degree of the polynomial $P(k)$. We see that the expression $\tilde{F}(k)P(k)$ which is a continuous function of k falls off as $|k| \to \infty$ not slower than

$$\frac{\text{const}}{|k|^{q-\nu}}.$$

Therefore:

$$\int |\tilde{F}(k^0, \mathbf{k})P(k^0, \mathbf{k})| \frac{d\mathbf{k}}{k^0} < \infty$$

for any arbitrary function $F(x)$ from the class $C(q, 5, 1)$ with $q = \nu + 3$. Consequently we have

$$\left| \int \theta(k^0, \mathbf{k}; G_n)\tilde{F}(k^0, \mathbf{k})P(k^0, \mathbf{k}) \frac{d\mathbf{k}}{k^0} - \int \tilde{F}(k^0, \mathbf{k})\, P(k^0, \mathbf{k}) \frac{d\mathbf{k}}{k^0} \right|$$

$$= \left| \int \{\theta(k^0, \mathbf{k}; G_n) - 1\}\tilde{F}(k^0, \mathbf{k})P(k^0, \mathbf{k}) \frac{d\mathbf{k}}{k^0} \right| \leqq \int \left| \tilde{F}(k^0, \mathbf{k})P(k^0, \mathbf{k}) \frac{d\mathbf{k}}{k^0} \right|_{n\to\infty} \to 0$$

$$(\ldots |k^\alpha| \geqq L_n \ldots).$$

We can now assert on the basis of (16.34) that for every function $F(x)$ from the class $C(\nu + 3, 5, 1)$

$$\int K_{G_n}(x)\, F(x)\, dx \to \int \tilde{F}(k^0, \mathbf{k})P(k^0, \mathbf{k}) \frac{d\mathbf{k}}{2k^0}.$$

This proves the existence of the improper limit

$$\lim_{n\to\infty} K_{G_n}(x) = K(x),$$

for which

$$\int K(x)F(x)dx = \int \tilde{F}(k^0, \mathbf{k})P(k^0, \mathbf{k}) \frac{d\mathbf{k}}{2k^0}.$$

We shall adopt this improper limit, which evidently is independent of the particular choice of the sequence of expanding regions G_n, as the definition of the integral (16.33).

Thus relation (16.32) actually defines an integrable improper function $D^{(-)}_{\alpha\beta}(x)$ with

$$\int D^{(-)}_{\alpha\beta}(x)F(x)\, dx = \frac{i}{(2\pi)^3} \int \tilde{F}(k^0, \mathbf{k})\, P_{\alpha\beta}(-k^0, -\mathbf{k}) \frac{d\mathbf{k}}{2k^0}. \quad (16.36)$$

As has been just established, $D^{(-)}_{\alpha\beta}(x)$ is an improper limit of the sequence of functions

$$\frac{i}{(2\pi)^3} \int_{G_n} e^{-ikx} P_{\alpha\beta}(-k)\, \theta(k^0)\, \delta(k^2 - m^2)\, dk, \quad (16.37)$$

which, as may be easily seen, are regular and analytic.

However, such a method of approximation may turn out in a number of cases not to be sufficiently convenient. The point is that expressions (16.37) are not covariant since the region of integration changes under Lorentz transformations.

16.4. *Some Properties of the Pauli-Villars Regularization*

In order to be able to approximate $D^{(-)}_{\alpha\beta}(x)$, naturally in the improper sense, by means of continuous and at the same time covariant functions we shall make use of regularization of the Pauli-Villars type which was mentioned in § 15. We set

$$\left.\begin{aligned} \operatorname{reg}\,(D^{(-)}_{\alpha\beta}(x)) &= P_{\alpha\beta}\left(-\,i\frac{\partial}{\partial x}\right)\operatorname{reg}\,(D^{(-)}(x)), \\ \operatorname{reg}\,(D^{(-)}(x)) &= D^{(-)}(x) + \sum_{(1\leqq j\leqq l)} c_j D^{(-)}_{M_j}(x), \end{aligned}\right\} \tag{16.38}$$

where $D^{(-)}_{M}(x)$ is the negative frequency part of the Pauli function corresponding to mass M, while the numbers c_j are determined by equations

$$\left.\begin{aligned} 1 + \sum_{1\leqq j\leqq l} c_j &= 0, \\ m^2 + \sum_j M_j^2 c_j &= 0, \\ \cdots\cdots&\cdots\cdots \\ \cdots\cdots&\cdots\cdots \\ \cdots\cdots&\cdots\cdots \\ m^{2(l-1)} + \sum_j M_j^{2(l-1)} c_j &= 0. \end{aligned}\right\} \tag{16.39}$$

Since reg $(D^{(-)}(x))$ is continuous and has continuous partial derivatives up to the $(l-2)$th order inclusive we see that for $l > \nu + 2$ (ν is the degree of the polynomial $P_{\alpha\beta}$) the functions reg $(D^{(-)}_{\alpha\beta}(x))$ will be continuous.

We now show that the masses M may always be chosen in such a way that for $M \to \infty$ the coefficients c_j will remain bounded. We emphasize that in considering the limiting transition $M \to \infty$ the number l is always regarded as fixed. We take any arbitrary fixed *different* masses m_j. Then the determinant:

$$\begin{vmatrix} 1 & \dots & 1 \\ m_1^2 & \dots & m_l^2 \\ \cdot & \cdot & \cdot \\ m_1^{2(l-1)} & \dots & m_l^{2(l-1)} \end{vmatrix}$$

will differ from zero and therefore the equations:

$$\sum_{(1 \leqq j \leqq l)} a_j^{(\nu)} = \delta_{0\nu},$$

$$\cdots\cdots\cdots\cdots$$

$$\sum_{(1 \leqq j \leqq l)} a_j^{(\nu)} m_j^{2(l-1)} = \delta_{l-1,\,\nu} \qquad (\nu = 0, \ldots, l-1),$$

in which δ_{ij} denote the elements of the unit matrix, will have finite solutions $a_j^{(\nu)}$. We set

$$M_j = M m_j. \tag{16.40}$$

For such a system of masses we shall find from equations (16.39):

$$c_j = - \sum_{(0 \leqq \nu \leqq l-1)} a_j^{(\nu)} \left(\frac{m}{M}\right)^{2\nu}.$$

These c_j will evidently be uniformly bounded as $M \to \infty$. The special choice (16.40) for the masses M_j indicated above is not essential; for the following we require only that

$$| c_j | \underset{M \to \infty}{\leqq} \text{const.}$$

We can now prove the validity of the relation:

$$\text{reg}\,(D_{\alpha\beta}^{(-)}(x)) \underset{M \to \infty}{\to} D_{\alpha\beta}^{(-)}(x); \tag{16.41}$$

for this it is only necessary to show that for any arbitrary function from the class $C(\nu + 3, 5, 1)$ the following limiting relation holds

$$\int F(x)\, \text{reg}\,(D_{\alpha\beta}^{(-)}(x))\, dx \to \int F(x)\, D_{\alpha\beta}^{(-)}(x) dx. \tag{16.42}$$

We have:

$$\int F(x) \operatorname{reg} (D^{(-)}_{\alpha\beta}(x))dx - \int F(x)D^{(-)}_{\alpha\beta}(x)dx$$
$$= \sum_{1\leqq j\leqq l} c_j \int F(x)\, P_{\alpha\beta}\left(- i \frac{\partial}{\partial x}\right) D^{(-)}_{M_j}(x)dx,$$

and therefore since the c_j are bounded the proof of (16.41) will be completed as soon as we have shown that

$$\int F(x) \left\{ P_{\alpha\beta}\left(- i \frac{\partial}{\partial x}\right) D^{(-)}_{M_j}(x)\right\} dx \underset{M\to\infty}{\longrightarrow} 0.$$

But in virtue of (16.36) this integral is equal to

$$\frac{i}{(2\pi)^3} \int \tilde{F}(\sqrt{\mathbf{k}^2 + M_j^2},\ \mathbf{k})\, P_{\alpha\beta}(- \sqrt{\mathbf{k}^2 + M_j^2},\ - \mathbf{k})\, \frac{d\mathbf{k}}{2\sqrt{\mathbf{k}^2 + M_j^2}}. \qquad (16.43)$$

On the other hand, in virtue of the inequalities (16.35), we shall obtain for $q = \nu + 3$:

$$| \tilde{F}(k)\, P_{\alpha\beta}(- k) | \leq \frac{Q}{(\sum_\alpha | k^\alpha |)^3} \leq \frac{Q}{(k^0)^3} \qquad (Q = \text{const}).$$

Therefore in absolute value the integral (16.43) will be less than:

$$\frac{Q}{(2\pi)^3} \int \frac{dk}{(k^2 + M_j^2)^2} = \frac{Q}{(2\pi)^3 M_j} \int \frac{dp}{(p^2 + 1)^2} \underset{M\to\infty}{\longrightarrow} 0.$$

Thus the functions $D^{(-)}_{\alpha\beta}(x)$ are in fact approximated in the improper sense by the continuous functions

$$\operatorname{reg} \{D^{(-)}_{\alpha\beta}(x)\}, \qquad M \to \infty,$$

which obviously have the required properties of covariance.

We have considered above only the functions $D^{(-)}_{\alpha\beta}(x)$. However, it may be easily seen that all the above arguments may be immediately carried over also to the functions $D^{(+)}_{\alpha\beta}(x)$, $D^{c}_{\alpha\beta}(x)$.

16.5. *Multiplication of Singular Functions*

We now consider the investigation of the fundamental question regarding the definition of the products of pairings (16.25) with the aid of Wick's theorem. We emphasize that the necessity of a separate definition of products is, generally speaking, typical for improper functions. The point is that an improper function is defined by setting up rules for integrating its products only with sufficiently regular functions, and from such rules a prescription does not directly follow for the integration of products of several singular functions. However, we may use here the method of the improper limiting process and may define the expression (16.25) being discussed with the aid of a convergent sequence of regular functions. In order to construct such a sequence in the most natural way possible, we shall first make use of a purely formal approach typical of field theory. We shall use the representations (16.32) as our starting point and we shall set:

$$\prod_{(r<s)} D^{(-)}_{\alpha_r\beta_s}(x_r - x_s) = \prod_{(r<s)} \left\{ \frac{i}{(2\pi)^3} \int e^{-ik(x_r - x_s)} P_{\alpha\beta}(-k)\, \theta(k^0)\, \delta(k^2 - m^2_{\alpha\beta})\, dk \right\}.$$

Formally carrying out the multiplication of these integrals we shall obtain:

$$\prod_{(r<s)} D^{(-)}_{\alpha_r\beta_s}(x_r - x_s) = \left(\frac{i}{(2\pi)^3}\right)^N \int \exp i \sum_{(r<s)} \lambda_{\alpha_r\beta_s}(x_s - x_r) \times \prod_{(r<s)} \{P_{\alpha\beta}(-\lambda_{\alpha\beta})\, \theta(\lambda^0_{\alpha\beta})\, \delta(\lambda^2_{\alpha\beta} - m^2_{\alpha\beta})\, d\lambda_{\alpha\beta}\}$$

$$= \int \exp i \sum k_r x_r\, \Delta(k_1, \ldots, k_n)\, dk_1 \ldots dk_n, \qquad (16.44)$$

where N is the number of factors in the product under consideration and where

$$\Delta(k_1, \ldots, k_n) = \left(\frac{i}{(2\pi)^3}\right) \int \prod_r \delta(k_r + \sum_{(s<r)} \lambda_{\alpha_s\beta_r} - \sum_{(r<s)} \lambda_{\alpha_r\beta_s}) \times \prod_{(r<s)} \{P_{\alpha\beta}(-\lambda_{\alpha\beta})\, \theta(\lambda^0_{\alpha\beta})\, \delta(\lambda^2_{\alpha\beta} - m^2_{\alpha\beta})\, d\lambda_{\alpha\beta}\}. \qquad (16.45)$$

It may be shown that the region of integration in the integral (16.45) obtained above is in fact finite. Because of this it turns out to be possible to give a rigorous definition of the products (16.25) under discussion in the form of improper limits of a sequence of corresponding regular analytic functions. Choosing for such analytic functions the products of reg $\{D^{(-)}(x)\}$ we shall obtain:

$$\prod \{\text{reg}\, (D^{(-)}(x_r - x_s))\} \to \prod D^{(-)}(x_r - x_s). \qquad (16.46)$$

Indeed, the integration in (16.45) is carried out only over the set of points for which

$$\left.\begin{aligned} k_r &= \sum_{(r<s)} \lambda_{\alpha_r \beta_s} - \sum_{(s<r)} \lambda_{\alpha_s \beta_r}, \\ \lambda^0_{\alpha\beta} &> 0, \quad (\lambda_{\alpha\beta})^2 < (\lambda^0_{\alpha\beta})^2. \end{aligned}\right\} \tag{16.47}$$

Therefore, in particular:

$$\begin{aligned} k^0_1 &= \sum_{(s>1)} \lambda^0_{\alpha_1 \beta_s}, \\ k^0_2 &= \sum_{(s>2)} \lambda^0_{\alpha_2 \beta_s} - \sum_{(s<2)} \lambda^0_{\alpha_s \beta_2}, \\ k^0_3 &= \sum_{(s>3)} \lambda^0_{\alpha_3 \beta_s} - \sum_{(s<3)} \lambda^0_{\alpha_s \beta_3}, \end{aligned}$$

from which since $\lambda^0_{\alpha\beta}$ are positive we shall obtain in turn:

$$\begin{aligned} &\sum_{s} \lambda^0_{\alpha_1 \beta_s} \leqq k^0_1, \\ &\sum_{(s>2)} \lambda^0_{\alpha_2 \beta_s} = k^0_2 + \lambda^0_{\alpha_1 \beta_2} \leqq k^0_2 + k^0_1, \\ &\sum_{(s>3)} \lambda^0_{\alpha_3 \beta_s} = k^0_3 + \lambda^0_{\alpha_1 \beta_3} + \lambda^0_{\alpha_2 \beta_3} \leqq k^0_3 + k^0_1 + (k^0_2 + k^0_1), \\ &\cdots\cdots\cdots\cdots\cdots\cdots \\ &\sum_{(s>r)} \lambda^0_{\alpha_r \beta_s} \leqq k^0_r + k^0_{r-1} + 2k^0_{r-2} + 2^2 k^0_{r-3} + \ldots + 2^{r-2} k^0_1, \\ &\cdots\cdots\cdots\cdots\cdots\cdots \end{aligned}$$

so that in any case:

$$0 \leqq \lambda^0_{\alpha\beta} \leqq 2^{n-2}(|\, k^0_1 \,| + \ldots + |\, k^0_n \,|) \tag{16.48}$$

and consequently

$$|\, \lambda_{\alpha\beta} \,|^2 \leqq 2^{2(n-2)} (|\, k^0_1 \,| + \ldots + |\, k^0_n \,|)^2.$$

The fact that the region of integration in (16.45) is actually finite leads to an absence of divergences and to the possibility of a rigorous definition of the above expression (16.25) as an improper limit of the sequence of regular analytic functions:

$$K(x_1, \ldots, x_n \mid \Gamma_\omega) = \int_{\Gamma_\omega} e^{i\sum k_r x_r} \Delta(k_1, \ldots, k_n) dk_1 \ldots dk_n \tag{16.49}$$

as the region Γ_ω of the $4n$-dimensional space of the points $k_1, \ldots, k_n$ is expanded indefinitely and in the limit includes all this space.

In order to prove this assertion we shall prove the existence of such a limit and its independence of the particular choice of the sequence of regions Γ_ω. In order to do this we shall as usual consider the corresponding sequence of functionals

$$\int K(x_1, \ldots, x_n \mid \Gamma_\omega)\, F(x_1, \ldots, x_n) dx_1 \ldots dx_n \tag{16.50}$$

in the linear space $C(q, r, n)$ for fixed sufficiently large values of q, r. We shall have to evaluate the rate of falling off at infinity of the Fourier transform of the function F

$$\tilde{F}(k_1, \ldots, k_n) = \int e^{i \sum k_r x_r} F(x_1, \ldots, x_n) dx_1 \ldots dx_n.$$

Repeating in the present case $n > 1$ in exact detail the arguments which were given earlier we can easily see that if $F(x_1, \ldots, x_n)$ belongs to the class $C(q, 4n+1. n)$ then $\tilde{F}(k_1, \ldots, k_n)$ will be a continuous function which satisfies the inequality

$$|\tilde{F}(k_1, \ldots, k_n)| \leqq \frac{A}{(\sum |k_j^a|)^q} \quad (A = \text{const}). \tag{16.51}$$

By substituting (16.49) into (16.50) and introducing the function

$$\theta(k_1, \ldots, k_n | \Gamma_\omega) = \begin{cases} 1 \text{ inside the region } \Gamma_\omega \\ 0 \text{ outside the region } \Gamma_\omega \end{cases}$$

we shall obtain:

$$\begin{aligned} &\int K(x_1, \ldots, x_n \mid \Gamma_\omega)\, F(x_1, \ldots, x_n) dx_1 \ldots dx_n \\ &= \int_{\Gamma_\omega} \tilde{F}(k_1, \ldots, k_n)\, \Delta(k_1, \ldots, k_n) dk_1 \ldots dk_n \\ &= \int \theta(k_1, \ldots, k_n \mid \Gamma_\omega)\, \tilde{F}(k_1, \ldots, k_n)\, \Delta(k_1, \ldots, k_n) dk_1 \ldots dk_n \\ &= \frac{i^N}{(2\pi)^{3N}} \int \theta(k_1(\lambda), \ldots, k_n(\lambda) \mid \Gamma_\omega)\, \tilde{F}(k_1(\lambda), \ldots, k_n(\lambda)) \\ &\times \prod_{(r<s)} \{P_{\alpha\beta}(-\lambda_{\alpha\beta})\, \theta(\lambda^0_{\alpha\beta})\, \delta(\lambda^2_{\alpha\beta} - m^2_{\alpha\beta})\, d\lambda_{\alpha\beta}\}, \end{aligned}$$

where

$$k_r(\lambda) = \sum_{(r<s)} \lambda_{\alpha_r \beta_s} - \sum_{(s<r)} \lambda_{\alpha_s \beta_r}. \tag{16.52}$$

Since the region Γ_ω is expanded indefinitely and in the limit includes the whole $4n$-dimensional space, we can assert that for points outside Γ_ω

$$\sum_{(\alpha, r)} |k_r^\alpha| \geqq L_\omega \xrightarrow[\omega \to \infty]{} \infty.$$

Thus for those λ for which

$$1 - \theta(k_1(\lambda), \ldots, k_n(\lambda) \mid \Gamma_\omega) \neq 0,$$

we shall have:

$$2 \sum |\lambda^\gamma_{\alpha_r \beta_s}| \geqq \sum |k_r^\gamma| \geqq L_\omega.$$

Taking note of this we shall obtain:

$$\left| \int K(x_1, \ldots, x_n \mid \Gamma_\omega) F(x_1, \ldots, x_n) dx \right.$$

$$\left. - \frac{i^n}{(2\pi)^{3N}} \int \tilde{F}(k_1(\lambda), \ldots, k_n(\lambda)) \prod_{(r<s)} \{P_{\alpha\beta}(-\lambda_{\alpha\beta}) \theta(\lambda^0_{\alpha\beta}) \delta(\lambda^2_{\alpha\beta} - m^2_{\alpha\beta}) d\lambda_{\alpha\beta}\} \right| \leqq \varepsilon_\omega, \tag{16.53}$$

where

$$\varepsilon_\omega = (2\pi)^{-3N} \left| \int_{G_\omega} \tilde{F}(\ldots k_j(\lambda) \ldots) \mid \prod_{(r<s)} \mid P_{\alpha\beta}(-\lambda_{\alpha\beta}) \mid \theta(\lambda^0_{\alpha\beta}) \delta(\lambda^2_{\alpha\beta} - m^2_{\alpha\beta}) d\lambda_{\alpha\beta} \right|, \tag{16.54}$$

(Here G_ω denotes a region limited by the condition $\Sigma \mid \lambda^\gamma_{\alpha\beta} \mid \geqq \frac{1}{2} L_\omega$.)

But since the inequalities (16.48) follow from (16.47), we see that under the integral sign in (16.54)

$$(\lambda^0_{\alpha\beta})^2 \leqq 2^{2(n-2)} \left(\sum \mid k^0_j(\lambda) \mid\right)^2,$$

$$\sum (\lambda^0_{\alpha\beta})^2 \leqq 2^{2(n-2)} N \left(\sum \mid k^0_j(\lambda) \mid\right)^2,$$

and consequently:

$$\sum \mid k^0_j(\lambda) \mid \geqq 2^{-(n-2)} N^{-\frac{1}{2}} \sqrt{\sum \mid \lambda^0_{\alpha\beta} \mid^2}.$$

From this in virtue of (16.51) we shall obtain:

$$\mid \tilde{F}(\ldots k_j(\lambda) \ldots) \mid \leqq \frac{A \cdot 2^{n-2} \sqrt{N}}{\left(\sum \mid \lambda^0_{\alpha\beta} \mid^2\right)^{q/2}}$$

and therefore under the integral sign in (16.54)

$$\mid \tilde{F}(\ldots k_j(\lambda) \ldots) \prod P_{\alpha\beta}(-\lambda_{\alpha\beta}) \mid \leqq \frac{B}{\left(\sum \mid \lambda^0_{\alpha\beta} \mid^2\right)^{\frac{q-\nu}{2}}} \tag{16.55}$$

where ν is the sum of the degrees of all the polynomials $P_{\alpha\beta}$ and where $B = \text{const}$. It is now clear that

$$\varepsilon_\omega \leqq (2\pi)^{-3N} B \int_{G_\omega} \frac{\prod \{\theta(\lambda^0_{\alpha\beta}) \delta(\lambda^2_{\alpha\beta} - m^2_{\alpha\beta}) d\lambda_{\alpha\beta}\}}{\left(\sum \mid \lambda^0_{\alpha\beta} \mid^2\right)^{\frac{q-\nu}{2}}}$$

$$= \frac{(2\pi)^{-3N} B}{2^N} \int_{G_\omega} \frac{\ldots d\lambda_{\alpha\beta} \ldots}{\left\{\prod \sqrt{m^2_{\alpha\beta} + \lambda^2_{\alpha\beta}}\right\} \left\{\sum \left(m^2_{\alpha\beta} + \lambda^2_{\alpha\beta}\right)\right\}^{\frac{q-\nu}{2}}}.$$

Therefore if we take

$$q = \nu + 2N + 1,$$

then the integral on the right-hand side of this inequality is absolutely convergent and $\varepsilon_\omega \to 0$ as $\omega \to \infty$. Thus for any arbitrary function $F(x_1, \ldots, x_n)$ from the class $C(\nu + 2N + 1,\ 4n + 1,\ n)$ the expression on the left-hand side of the inequality (16.53) tends to zero.

We may therefore assert that the sequence of regular analytic functions (16.49) is a convergent one (in the improper sense), and that

$$\int \left\{ \lim_{\omega\to\infty} \int_{\Gamma_\omega} e^{i\sum k_r x_r} \Delta(k_1, \ldots, k_n) dk_1 \ldots dk_n \right\} F(x_1, \ldots, x_n) dx_1 \ldots dx_n$$

$$= \frac{i^N}{(2\pi)^{3N}} \int \tilde{F}(\ldots k_j(\lambda) \ldots) \prod_{(r<s)} \{P_{\alpha\beta}(-\lambda_{\alpha\beta})\, \theta(\lambda^0_{\alpha\beta})\, \delta(\lambda^2_{\alpha\beta} - m^2_{\alpha\beta}) d\lambda_{\alpha\beta}\}. \quad (16.56)$$

Since the right-hand side of this inequality is independent of the particular choice of the sequence of regions Γ_ω we see that as a result the expression

$$\lim_{\omega\to\infty} \int_{\Gamma_\omega} e^{i\sum k_r x_r} \Delta(k_1, \ldots, k_n) dk_1, \ldots dk_n,$$

is also independent of the choice of this sequence.

Thus the relation (16.44) does in fact define the expression

$$\prod_{(r<s)} D^{(-)}_{\alpha_r\beta_s}(x_r - x_s)$$

as an integrable improper function for which in view of (16.56):

$$\int \Big\{ \prod_{(r<s)} D^{(-)}_{\alpha_r\beta_s}(x_r - x_s) \Big\} F(x_1, \ldots, x_n) dx_1 \ldots dx_n$$

$$= \frac{i^N}{(2\pi)^{3N}} \int \tilde{F}(\ldots k_j(\lambda) \ldots) \prod_{(r<s)} \{P_{\alpha\beta}(-\lambda_{\alpha\beta})\, \theta(\lambda^0_{\alpha\beta})\, \delta(\lambda^2_{\alpha\beta} - m^2_{\alpha\beta}) d\lambda_{\alpha\beta}\}. \quad (16.57)$$

The product of singular functions $D^{(-)}_{\alpha\beta}$ under discussion may also be approximated by means of corresponding products of regularized functions reg $\{D^{(-)}_{\alpha\beta}\}$

$$\prod_{(r<s)} \text{reg}\, (D^{(-)}_{\alpha_r\beta_s}(x_r - x_s)) \to \prod_{(r<s)} D^{(-)}_{\alpha_r\beta_s}(x_r - x_s). \quad (16.46)$$

We shall prove this property by establishing that for every function $F(x_1, \ldots, x_n)$ from the class $C(\nu + 2N + 1,\ 4n + 1,\ n)$ the following limiting relation holds

$$\int F(x_1, \ldots, x_n) \Big\{ \prod_{(r<s)} \text{reg}\, D^{(-)}_{\alpha_r\beta_s}(x_r - x_s) \Big\} dx_1 \ldots dx_n$$

$$- \int F(x_1, \ldots, x_n) \Big\{ \prod_{(r<s)} D^{(-)}_{\alpha_r\beta_s}(x_r - x_s) \Big\} dx_1 \ldots dx_n \to 0 \text{ for } M \to \infty. \quad (16.58)$$

In consequence of the definition of the regularized functions (16.38) the above difference (16.58) is a sum of products of the coefficients c_j and integrals which are obtained from the integral on the right-hand side of (16.57) by replacing the masses m by the masses M. Since all the c_j remain bounded as $M \to \infty$ the proof of the relation (16.58) will be completed as soon as we have shown that such integrals tend to zero. Making use for this purpose of the inequality (16.55) we shall find that in absolute value they will be less than

$$(2\pi)^{-3N}\, 2^{-N}\, B \int \{\ldots + m_{\alpha\beta}^2 + \ldots + M_j^2 + \ldots + \sum \lambda_{\alpha\beta}^2\}^{-\frac{2N+1}{2}} \prod \left(\frac{d\lambda_{\alpha\beta}}{|\lambda_{\alpha\beta}|}\right). \quad (16.59)$$

But due to the presence of the masses M_j in the denominator of the integrand this integral tends to zero (as $M \to \infty$) and this completes the proof of expression (16.46).

The arguments presented above may also be extended to the general case of coefficient functions obtained by multiplying two operator functions of type (16.1) with different arguments, and the corresponding expressions:

$$K(x_1, \ldots, x_n)\, Q(y_1, \ldots, y_m) \prod D_{\beta\sigma}^{(-)}(x_s - y_j) \quad (16.60)$$

(in which $x_1, \ldots, x_n, y_1, \ldots, y_m$ are independent arguments, while K and Q are integrable coefficient functions invariant under translations) may be defined as integrable improper functions.

The following general theorem may be proved for expressions of this form.

If $K_M(x_1, \ldots, x_n), Q_M(y_1, \ldots, y_m)$ are coefficient functions invariant under translations, and if in the improper sense:

$$\left.\begin{aligned} K_M(x_1, \ldots, x_n) &\xrightarrow[M\to\infty]{} K(x_1, \ldots, x_n); \\ Q_M(y_1, \ldots, y_m) &\xrightarrow[M\to\infty]{} Q(y_1, \ldots, y_m), \end{aligned}\right\} \quad (16.61)$$

while the arguments $x_1, \ldots, x_n, y_1, \ldots, y_m$ are independent, then

$$K_M(x_1, \ldots, x_n)\, Q_M(y_1, \ldots, y_m) \prod \operatorname{reg} D_{\beta\sigma}^{(-)}(x_s - y_j)$$
$$\xrightarrow[M\to\infty]{} K(x_1, \ldots, x_n)\, Q(y_1, \ldots, y_m) \prod D_{\beta\sigma}^{(-)}(x_s - y_j). \quad (16.62)$$

The proof of this theorem is technically based on the same principle as the proof of the limiting relation (16.58).

In essence both these proofs are based on the simple fact that if the sum of the negative frequencies is bounded, then it follows that each individual frequency is bounded. We have examined at first the product of only the negative-frequency parts of the D-functions; our whole analysis may therefore be carried over in a trivial way also to the case when only the $D^{(+)}$ occur in place of the $D^{(-)}$.

Quite a different situation will arise if we consider in place of (16.25), for example, products of the type

$$\prod_{(r<s)} D^c_{\alpha_r \beta_s}(x_r - x_s), \tag{16.63}$$

since in $D^c(x)$ both positive- and negative-frequency components are present. It may be shown that in spite of the weakness of our condition of integrability (§ 16.3) which requires the existence of the integral of the product of the singular function under discussion only with functions from the class $C(q, r, n)$ with arbitrarily high indices q, r, the product (16.63) is not a definite integrable function and an improper limiting relation of type (16.58) does not hold in this case.

16.6. *Some Properties of Singular Functions*

We shall now say a few words about the properties of continuity, differentiability, etc. which the singular functions have for certain ranges of values of their arguments. Since we define a singular function merely as the symbolic "kernel" of a given linear functional, it may, in general, have no definite values anywhere. However, in a number of important cases singular functions have both definite finite values and various properties of regularity for certain ranges of values of their arguments. Thus, for example, $\delta(x) = 0$ for $x \neq 0$, the functions $D^{(\pm)}(x)$, $D^c(x)$ are continuous outside the light cone, etc.

It is therefore useful to introduce in this connection the following mathematical definition:

Let $K(x_1, \ldots, x_n)$ be an improper function integrable over a certain class $C(q, r, n)$, and let $f(x_1, \ldots, x_n)$ be an ordinary function continuous within a certain region O (of the space of the points $x_1, \ldots, x_n$); we shall then say that

$$K(x_1, \ldots, x_n) = f(x_1, \ldots, x_n)$$

in the region O and that K is continuous in this region if

$$\int \{K(x_1, \ldots, x_n) - f(x_1, \ldots, x_n)\} F(x_1, \ldots, x_n)\, dx_1 \ldots dx_n = 0$$

for every function F of the class $C(q, r, n)$ which vanishes outside

O together with all its partial derivatives up to the qth order inclusive.

We shall also agree to interpret in exactly the same sense the other regularity properties of the improper functions in the given region. In an analogous manner, one may also introduce the concept of improper convergence within a definite range of values of the arguments. We shall say that a sequence of improper functions $K_M(x_1, \ldots, x_n)$ integrable over a certain fixed class $C(q, r, n)$ converges in the improper sense within the region O if the sequence of integrals

$$\int K_M(x_1, \ldots, x_n)\, F(x_1, \ldots, x_n)\, dx_1 \ldots dx_n$$

converges for every function F in $C(q, r, n)$ which vanishes outside O together with all its partial derivatives up to the qth order inclusive.

With the aid of the definitions given above, the methods of dealing with ordinary functions may to a large extent be extended also to improper functions. These methods may be used for the investigation of those cases frequently encountered in quantum field theory when the purely formal operations with improper functions lead to expressions which do not have a definite meaning, for example, to expressions containing "divergences."

16.7. *Multiplication of Operator Functions*

We now proceed to investigate operator expressions represented by finite sums of the form (16.1). We note first of all that the existence of limiting relations (16.46) allows us to eliminate one possible objection to the proof of Wick's theorem given above which is based on the fact that in the course of the above proof we carried out multiplication of singular functions. A proof of Wick's theorem quite free of such objections may be given very simply, for example, in accordance with the following outline. We at first examine a fictitious case when the field functions satisfy commutation relations in which $D_{\alpha\beta}$ have been replaced by reg $D_{\alpha\beta}$, and for this case we carry out the proof of Wick's theorem in exactly the same form in which it was presented earlier. Since the regularized functions are continuous, such a proof will now be quite rigorous. For the transition to the actual case, it will now be sufficient to go to the limit $M \to \infty$ which removes the regularization.

In a similar manner with the aid of the more general limiting relations (16.62), it is not difficult to establish the validity of multiplying two integrable operator functions

$$A_1(x_1, \ldots, x_n)\, A_2(y_1, \ldots, y_m) \tag{16.64}$$

with independent arguments.

We call those operator expressions integrable which may be represented by finite sums of the type (16.1) in which all the coefficient functions satisfy the requirement of integrability.

In order to show that the product (16.64) is an integrable operator function of the arguments $x_1, \ldots, x_n, y_1, \ldots, y_m$, we again consider the fictitious case in which the commutation relations have been regularized, and in addition we shall replace all the coefficient functions K, Q of the operators A_1, A_2 by some continuous functions K_M, Q_M making sure only that the following improper limiting relations hold

$$K_M \to K, \; Q_M \to Q \text{ as } M \to \infty.$$

Then, having reduced to the normal form the product of the operator functions regularized in the manner indicated above, we shall obtain coefficient functions of the form:

$$\sum K_M(x_1, \ldots, x_n)\, Q_M(y_1, \ldots, y_m) \prod \operatorname{reg}\, \{D_{\alpha\beta}^{(-)}(x_s - y_j)\},$$

which in virtue of (16.62) form (as $M \to \infty$) a sequence which converges in the improper sense. We may therefore go to the limit which destroys the regularization and determine the coefficient functions of the actual product (16.64) as integrable singular functions. The theorem which we have established above, stating that the product of two (and consequently of any arbitrary number of) integrable operator functions with independent arguments is again an integrable operator function, will turn out to be quite useful.

We now consider a certain integrable operator function $A(x_1, \ldots, x_n)$ and take the integral

$$\int A(x_1, \ldots, x_n) F(x_1, \ldots, x_n) dx_1 \ldots dx_n, \tag{16.65}$$

in which $F(x_1, \ldots, x_n)$ is an arbitrary function of the class $C(\infty, \infty, n)$. We set up the matrix elements which characterize this operator integral

$$\Phi^*_{\ldots\gamma\ldots p\ldots} \int A(x_1, \ldots, x_n) F(x_1, \ldots, x_n) dx_1 \ldots dx_n \Phi_{\ldots\gamma'\ldots p'\ldots} \tag{16.66}$$

over all the possible states

$$\Phi_{\ldots\gamma\ldots p\ldots} = \ldots u^{(+)}_{\gamma}(p) \ldots \Phi_0,$$

which correspond to the presence of given kinds of particles with given momenta. In view of (16.9) we shall obtain for them the following expression:

$$\begin{aligned}\sum P^{\ldots\alpha\ldots\beta\ldots}_{\ldots\gamma\ldots\gamma'\ldots}(\ldots p \ldots p' \ldots) \int K_{\ldots\alpha\ldots\beta\ldots}(x_1, \ldots, x_n) \\ \times e^{i(\Sigma p_\nu x_\nu - \Sigma p'_\lambda x_\lambda)} F(x_1, \ldots, x_n) dx_1 \ldots dx_n \\ + \sum Z^{\ldots\alpha\ldots\beta\ldots}_{\ldots\gamma\ldots\gamma'\ldots}(\ldots p \ldots p' \ldots) \prod \{\theta(p^0_\omega)\delta(p^2_\omega - m^2_\gamma)\delta(p_\omega - p'_\omega)\} \\ \times \int K'_{\ldots\alpha\ldots\beta\ldots}(x_1, \ldots, x_n) e^{i(\Sigma p_\nu x_\nu - \Sigma p'_\lambda x_\lambda)} F(x_1, \ldots, x_n) dx_1 \ldots dx_n,\end{aligned} \tag{16.67}$$

where, as has been mentioned earlier, P and Z are polynomials in the components of p. We also point out that the δ-functions in the second sum allow for the possibility of the momenta p, p' being the same for particles of the same kind. Consequently, the second sum will not occur if the matrix element is evaluated between states for which the momenta for particles of the same kind are different; in such a case

$$\begin{aligned}\Phi^*_{\ldots\gamma\ldots p\ldots} \int A(x_1, \ldots, x_n) F(x_1, \ldots, x_n) dx_1 \ldots dx_n \Phi_{\ldots\gamma'\ldots p'\ldots} \\ = \sum P^{\ldots\alpha\ldots\beta\ldots}_{\ldots\gamma\ldots\gamma'\ldots}(\ldots p \ldots p' \ldots) \int K_{\ldots\alpha\ldots\beta\ldots}(x_1, \ldots, x_n) \\ \times e^{i(\Sigma p_\nu x_\nu - \Sigma p'_\lambda x_\lambda)} F(x_1, \ldots, x_n) dx_1 \ldots dx_n.\end{aligned} \tag{16.68}$$

Since the function F belongs to the class $C(\infty, \infty, n)$ then the function

$$e^{i(\Sigma p_\nu x_\nu - \Sigma p'_\lambda x_\lambda)} F(x_1, \ldots, x_n).$$

also belongs to the same class. Therefore, since the coefficient functions K are integrable, the integrals

$$\int K_{\dots\alpha\dots\beta\dots}(x_1, \dots, x_n)\, e^{i(\Sigma p_\nu x_\nu - \Sigma p'_\lambda x_\lambda)}\, F(x_1, \dots, x_n)\, dx_1 \dots dx_n \tag{16.69}$$

turn out to be finite. Moreover, since the differentiation of this integral with respect to p corresponds to multiplying F by the components of x, while the multiplication of F by an arbitrary polynomial in such components does not take it outside the class $C(\infty, \infty, n)$, we see that the integrals (16.69) are continuous functions of the momenta $\dots p \dots p' \dots$ which have continuous partial derivatives of arbitrary order.

Thus we see that the matrix elements (16.66) under consideration are linear combinations of terms of the type

$$f(\dots p \dots p' \dots),\quad f(\dots p \dots p' \dots) \prod \{\theta(p^0_\omega)\, \delta(p^2_\omega - m^2_\gamma)\, \delta(p_\omega - p'_\omega)\},$$

in which $f(\dots p \dots p' \dots)$ are continuous together with all their partial derivatives with respect to $\dots p \dots p' \dots$. In particular, in the region in which the momenta $\dots p \dots p' \dots$ are not the same for identical particles the matrix elements themselves will possess such properties of "smoothness." The operator integrals (16.65) may therefore be considered to be convergent.

Integrals of the type

$$\int A(x_1, \dots, x_n)\, F(x_2, \dots, x_n)\, dx_2 \dots dx_n \tag{16.70}$$

with "one incomplete integration" will also be convergent in the same sense.

Indeed in the present case the only difference will consist of the fact that instead of the integrals (16.69) appearing in the matrix element the integrals

$$\int K_{\dots\alpha\dots\beta\dots}(x, x_2, \dots, x_n)\, \varphi(x_2, \dots, x_n)\, dx_2 \dots dx_n,$$
$$\varphi(x_2, \dots, x_n) = e^{i(\Sigma p_\nu x_\nu - \Sigma p'_\lambda x_\lambda)}\, F(x_2, \dots, x_n), \tag{16.71}$$

will appear which, due to the invariance of the coefficient functions under translations, may be reduced in an elementary way to the form (16.69).

In fact, in virtue of this property we obtain:

$$\int K(x, x_2, \ldots, x_n)\varphi(x_2, \ldots, x_n)\,dx_2 \ldots dx_n$$
$$= \int K(x+\xi, x_2+\xi, \ldots, x_n+\xi)\varphi(x_2, \ldots, x_n)\,dx_2 \ldots dx_n.$$

We multiply both sides of the above equality by some function $\varphi(\xi)$ of the class $C(\infty, \infty, 1)$ for which

$$\int \varphi(\xi)\,d\xi = 1,$$

and integrate over ξ. We then find:

$$\int K(x, x_2, \ldots, x_n)\varphi(x_2, \ldots, x_n)\,dx_2 \ldots dx_n$$
$$= \int K(x+\xi, x_2+\xi, \ldots, x_n+\xi)\varphi(\xi)\varphi(x_2, \ldots, x_n)\,dx_2 \ldots dx_n\,d\xi.$$

We introduce a change of variables

$$x+\xi \to x_1, \quad x_2+\xi \to x_2, \ldots, x_n+\xi \to x_n.$$

Then

$$\xi \to x_1 - x, \; x_2 \to x_2 - x_1 + x, \ldots, x_n \to x_n - x_1 + x,$$

and we obtain:

$$\int K(x, x_2, \ldots, x_n)\varphi(x_2, \ldots, x_n)\,dx_2 \ldots dx_n$$
$$= \int K(x_1, x_2, \ldots, x_n)\varphi'(x_1, x_2, \ldots, x_n)\,dx_1 \ldots dx_n,$$

where

$$\varphi'(x_1, x_2, \ldots, x_n) = \varphi(x_1 - x)\varphi(x_2 - x_1 + x, \ldots, x_n - x_1 + x),$$

by means of which we reduce the integrals (16.71) to the type (16.69).

Having demonstrated the convergence of operator integrals of the form (16.65) and (16.70) we note, nevertheless, that due to the generality of our condition of integrability the class of operator integrals that are guaranteed to converge turns out to be somewhat narrow. Thus this class does not include the integrals

$$\int A(x_1, \ldots, x_n)\,dx_1 \ldots dx_n,$$

taken over the whole infinite space of the points $x_1, \ldots, x_n$ since they correspond to the function $F = 1$ which does not vanish at infinity.

The matrix elements of the operator integrals of the above form have to be defined separately by means of a limiting process starting with the corresponding sequence of functions of the class

$C(\infty, \infty, n)$ which approaches 1 over the indefinitely expanding region which in the limit includes the whole space of integration.

16.8. *Some Definitions*

Up until now we have been considering operator functions of points $x_1, \ldots, x_n$ which have been expressed in terms of positive- and negative-frequency parts of quantized field functions. An important role is played by a more specialized type of operator functions in which the quantized field functions appear, so to speak, "entirely" within the symbols for the normal product:

$$A(x_1, \ldots, x_n) = \sum K_{\ldots\alpha\ldots}(x_1, \ldots, x_n) : \ldots u_\alpha(x_j) \ldots :. \qquad (16.72)$$

If the Fermi field functions occur in the preceding expression only in even combinations, then we shall call such a sum a polylocal operator. From the definitions given before and from Wick's theorem, it follows immediately that the multiplication of several polylocal operators results again in a polylocal operator.

Polylocal operators have the following important property:

$$[A_1(x_1, \ldots, x_n); \quad A_2(y_1, \ldots, y_m)] = 0, \qquad (16.73)$$

if each of the x_j is spacelike with respect to any arbitrary y_i.

Indeed, since the Pauli-Jordan function vanishes inside the light cone, we have:

$$\{u_\alpha(x_j), u_\beta(y_i)\}_\pm = 0 \qquad (x_j \sim y_i).$$

Therefore, in view of Wick's theorem we obtain:

$$: \ldots u_\alpha(x_j) \ldots : : \ldots u_\beta(y_i) \ldots : = : \ldots u_\alpha(x_j) \ldots u_\beta(y_i) \ldots : \qquad (16.74)$$

But since the field functions occur only in even combinations, as mentioned before, we may bring $\ldots u_\beta(y_i) \ldots$ to the left of $\ldots u_\alpha(x_j) \ldots$ in the normal product on the left-hand side of (16.74) without introducing a change of sign. We shall therefore obtain,

$$[: \ldots u_\alpha(x_j) \ldots :, : \ldots u_\beta(y_i) \ldots :] = 0$$

for

$$(x_1, \ldots, x_n) \sim (y_1, \ldots, y_m),$$

from which follows the validity of equation (16.73).

We now consider the case when $n = 1$. In this case, the polylocal operator depends only on the behavior of the field functions (their derivatives may, of course, be included among them) at the single point x, as a result of which we shall call it a local operator. In view of (16.73) we have for two local operators:

$$[\mathscr{L}(x),\ \mathscr{L}(y)] = 0 \qquad (x \sim y). \tag{16.75}$$

We note that also in the case $n > 1$ the situation may occur such that a polylocal operator in fact depends on the behavior of the field functions at only a single point. Suppose that in fact in the sum (16.72) all the coefficient functions vanish for all $x_1, \ldots, x_n$ with the exception of those which satisfy the equality

$$x_1 = x_2 = \ldots = x_n.$$

It is clear that in this case K may be constructed only from the expression

$$\delta(x_1 - x_2) \ldots \delta(x_1 - x_n)$$

and its partial derivatives. Since the coefficient functions by definition must have the property of translational invariance, we see that the general expression for them in the above case must be

$$z\left(\ldots \frac{\partial}{\partial x} \ldots\right) \delta(x_1 - x_2) \ldots \delta(x_1 - x_n),$$

where $z(\ldots \partial/\partial x \ldots)$ is a certain polynomial in $\partial/\partial x_j^\alpha$ with *constant* coefficients. We shall call a polylocal operator with coefficient functions of this type a quasilocal operator. As may be easily seen integration of a quasilocal operator over all the points $x_1, \ldots, x_n$ except one will lead to an ordinary local operator.

CHAPTER III

The Scattering Matrix

§ 17. Fundamental Ideas of the Theory of Interacting Fields

17.1. *Representations of the Schrödinger Equation*

One of the methods most widely used in ordinary quantum mechanics to investigate the behavior of dynamical systems is the well-known Schrödinger representation. In this representation, the behavior of dynamical systems is described by means of a time-dependent wave function $\Psi(t)$ determined by the Schrödinger equation

$$i\frac{\partial\Psi(t)}{\partial t} = H\Psi(t) \qquad (t = x^0). \tag{17.1}$$

Here H is the Hamiltonian operator which corresponds to the total energy of the whole system and which does not depend on the time for closed systems. In general in this representation the dynamic variables of closed systems are described by operators that do not explicitly depend on the time. However, their expectation values

$$\bar{B}_t = \Psi^*(t)B\Psi(t) \tag{17.2}$$

may depend on the time through the wave functions $\Psi(t)$. If we consider the operator H to remain constant in time, we may formally integrate equation (17.1) and write

$$\Psi(t) = e^{\frac{Ht}{i}}\Psi,$$

where

$$\Psi = \text{const}$$

does not depend on the time.

Substituting this expression into (17.2) we obtain:

$$\bar{B}_t = \Psi^* e^{-\frac{Ht}{i}} B e^{\frac{Ht}{i}} \Psi. \tag{17.3}$$

Formula (17.3) may be interpreted as the expectation value with respect to the functions Ψ, which do not depend on the time, of the operator

$$B(t) = e^{-\frac{Ht}{i}} B e^{\frac{Ht}{i}}, \tag{17.4}$$

which depends on the time. In this way we arrive at the Heisenberg representation in which explicit dependence on the time is exhibited not by the wave functions but by the dynamic variables. It is evident that from the point of view of calculating observable values of dynamic variables the two representations are completely equivalent. After differentiating (17.4) with respect to time, we see that in the Heisenberg representation the time dependence of the dynamical variables is determined by the equation

$$\frac{\partial B}{\partial t} = i[H,\ B(t)], \tag{17.5}$$

where

$$i[a,\ b] = i(ab - ba) \tag{17.6}$$

are the quantum Poisson brackets.

It is of interest to note that in classical mechanics the time dependence of the dynamic variables is determined by the same equations (17.5) with classical Poisson brackets.

In applying the Schrödinger representation to the case which is of interest to us of the interaction of quantized fields we have to decompose the total Hamiltonian H into two parts:

$$H = H_0 + H_1, \tag{17.7}$$

where H_0 is the Hamiltonian of the free field, H_1 is the interaction Hamiltonian, and

$$H_0 = \int H_0(\mathbf{x})\, d\mathbf{x}, \quad H_1 = \int H_1(\mathbf{x})\, d\mathbf{x}.$$

In the preceding, the energy densities $H_0(\mathbf{x})$ and $H_1(\mathbf{x})$ are combinations of the basic field functions taken at a certain fixed instant of time, for example, $u(0, \mathbf{x}) = u(x)]_{x^0=0}$. Therefore in studying processes due to interactions of fields one usually starts with the Schrödinger equation written in the form

$$i \frac{\partial \Psi(t)}{\partial t} = (H_0 + H_1)\, \Psi(t). \tag{17.8}$$

One of the fundamental inadequacies of modern quantum theory of fields of real interacting particles is the necessity to introduce into the discussion fields of fictitious noninteracting particles and to treat the interaction as a given additional factor which alters the properties of the dynamical system and which may be "switched on" and "switched off." At first glance it might appear that this does not provide any special basis for criticism of the theory. Indeed, the particles interact intensely with each other only if they are sufficiently close. Therefore it would appear that at large distances between the particles the interaction between the fields is not essential and that in a certain approximation it is useful to neglect it and to regard the real particles as being free.

However, by arguing in this way we omit from consideration the fact that the particles continuously interact with the vacuum as if it were some sort of a physical "medium" through which they move.

It therefore appears to be desirable that in the course of developing a theory we should from the outset deal with real interacting particles without introducing any artificial concepts of fictitious free fields. However, since up to the present time no such program has been carried out, we must resort to the preceding method of decomposition.

17.2. *The Interaction Representation*

In the case when no interaction is present, the fundamental equation (17.8) assumes the form

$$i \frac{\partial \Psi(t)}{\partial t} = H_0 \Psi(t).$$

By carrying out the integration formally we obtain:

$$\Psi(t) = e^{\frac{H_0 t}{i}} \Phi. \tag{17.9}$$

In the study of free fields we have referred to the constant Φ as the state amplitude. In the case of interacting fields expression (17.9) will no longer satisfy the basic equation with Φ independent of the time. However, we may generalize it by setting

$$\Psi(t) = e^{\frac{H_0 t}{i}} \Phi(t) \tag{17.10}$$

and regarding $\Phi(t)$ as a new state amplitude. From the mathematical point of view we introduce a new unknown function by a method which is analogous to the method of variation of constants used in the theory of differential equations. On substituting (17.10) into the fundamental equation (17.8), we obtain:

$$H_0 e^{\frac{H_0 t}{i}} \Phi(t) + i e^{\frac{H_0 t}{i}} \frac{\partial \Phi(t)}{\partial t} = (H_0 + H_1) e^{\frac{H_0 t}{i}} \Phi(t),$$

from which it follows that

$$i \frac{\partial \Phi(t)}{\partial t} = e^{-\frac{H_0 t}{i}} H_1 e^{\frac{H_0 t}{i}} \Phi(t).$$

Let us discuss the meaning of the equation obtained above. In equation (17.7) the interaction energy density $H_1(x)$ is (cf. § 8) a linear combination of expressions of the type

$$H_i(\mathbf{x}) = u_\alpha(0, \mathbf{x}) \ldots u_\omega(0, \mathbf{x}).$$

But

$$e^{-\frac{H_0 t}{i}} H_i e^{\frac{H_0 t}{i}} = e^{-\frac{H_0 t}{i}} u_\alpha(0, \mathbf{x}) e^{\frac{H_0 t}{i}} \ldots e^{-\frac{H_0 t}{i}} u_\omega(0, \mathbf{x}) e^{\frac{H_0 t}{i}}.$$

Therefore the application of the operator

$$e^{-\frac{H_0 t}{i}} \ldots e^{\frac{H_0 t}{i}}$$

to H_1 corresponds to replacing the operator field functions $u(0, \mathbf{x})$ independent of the time by time-dependent operator functions

$$u(t, \mathbf{x}) = e^{-\frac{H_0 t}{i}} u(0, \mathbf{x}) e^{\frac{H_0 t}{i}}.$$

Consequently, we now go over to the Heisenberg representation for the operator functions of the free field that we discussed in § 9.

For the determination of $\Phi(t)$ we now have an equation of the form:

$$i \frac{\partial \Phi}{\partial t} = H_1(t) \Phi(t), \quad H_1(t) = \int H_1(t, \mathbf{x})\, d\mathbf{x}, \tag{17.11}$$

in which the operator $H_1(t, \mathbf{x})$ is obtained from $H_1(x)$ by replacing $u(0, \mathbf{x})$ by $u(t, \mathbf{x}) = u(x)$. Such a representation of the Schrödinger equation is called the interaction representation.

Let us examine the problem of obtaining expressions for the dynamic variables in the interaction representation. Substituting (17.10) into (17.2) we obtain:

$$\Psi^*(t)\, B \Psi(t) = \Phi^*(t)\, e^{-\frac{H_0 t}{i}} B e^{+\frac{H_0 t}{i}} \Phi(t),$$

i.e.,

$$\bar{B}_t = \Phi^*(t)\, B_{\text{int}}(t)\, \Phi(t),$$

where

$$B_{\text{int}}(t) = e^{-\frac{H_0 t}{i}} B e^{\frac{H_0 t}{i}}.$$

We thus see that in the interaction representation the operator expressions for the dynamic variables must be regarded as functions of field operators in the Heisenberg representation for the free field. In other words, the operators for the dynamic variables are expressed by forms which depend on the field functions

$$u(t, \mathbf{x}) = u(x),$$

that satisfy the homogeneous equations of the free fields.

The principal defect of all the preceding representations of the Schrödinger equation, including the interaction representation, is the distinctive role played by the time, and the consequent manifest noncovariance of the formulation. This formal defect of the theory was eliminated in a special modification of the interaction representation developed by Tomonaga (126) and by Schwinger (104). In this modification, instead of dealing with the surfaces $t = \text{const}$ in four-dimensional space-time, a more general class of spacelike surfaces σ is introduced. We shall deal with this in greater detail in Chapter VI.

17.3. *The Scattering Matrix*

We note that with the aid of equation (17.11) we may already introduce into our discussion a very important quantity characterizing the system, the so-called scattering matrix or the S-matrix. Let us study a process at the beginning and at the end of which we have only particles that are widely separated from each other and may be considered to be free.

In order to calculate the probability amplitude for the scattering and for the mutual transformations of particles occurring in this process, we shall examine the situation in which the interaction $H_1(t)$ is adiabatically switched on in the infinitely remote past and is adiabatically switched off in the infinitely remote future. By denoting the amplitude of the initial state by $\Phi(-\infty)$ and the amplitude of the final state by $\Phi(\infty)$, we may establish a connection between them by means of the relation

$$\Phi(\infty) = S\Phi(-\infty), \tag{17.12}$$

in which the operator S is called the scattering operator or the scattering matrix. The squares of the corresponding matrix elements of the operator S determine the transition probabilities and the effective cross sections of the various possible scattering and mutual transformation processes of the particles.

In order to obtain formulas suitable for calculations, one could, starting with equations (17.11), obtain its solution by the method of successive approximations in the form of an expansion in powers of the small interaction. One would then obtain a relation between $\Phi(-\infty)$ and $\Phi(\infty)$ of the type (17.12), with the operator S expressed in the form of the expansion

$$S = 1 - i\int_{-\infty}^{+\infty} H_1(t)\,dt + (-i)^2\int_{-\infty}^{+\infty} H_1(t)\,dt\int_{-\infty}^{t} H_1(t')\,dt' + \ldots$$

It is just by such a method that the investigation of the S-matrix is carried out in the majority of the presently available articles on quantum field theory (Tomonaga (126), Schwinger (104), Pauli and Villars (93), Dyson (33), (34), Akhiezer and Berestetski (2), Heitler (60)).

In our opinion, however, it is more useful to employ the method proposed by Stueckelberg (Stueckelberg and Rivier (119), Stueckelberg and Green (117)) in which the generalized scattering matrix is introduced without reference to the Hamiltonian formalism and to the Schrödinger equation. In their place, in order to obtain the explicit form of the S-matrix, one uses certain explicitly formulated physical conditions, among which the condition of causality plays an important role. Stueckelberg himself did not succeed in obtaining a sufficiently clear and general formulation of the causality condition as a result of which his ideas were not widely accepted.

We shall present below a new formulation of the condition of causality (Bogoliubov (16), Bogoliubov and Shirkov (21)) and a method based on it of constructing the scattering matrix in the quantum theory of interacting fields.[38a]

In developing this theory, we shall have to make use, as is done in the customary presentation, of the operations of "switching on" and "switching off" the interaction. In order to describe this operation mathematically, we shall introduce the function $g(x)$ with values in the range (0, 1) which represents the extent of switching on the interaction. In those regions where $g(x) = 0$, the interaction is absent, in those regions where $g(x) = 1$, it is switched on completely, and for $0 < g(x) < 1$, the interaction is switched on only partially. By replacing the actual interaction Lagrangian $\mathscr{L}(x)$ by the product $\mathscr{L}(x)g(x)$, we obtain an interaction "switched on with an intensity $g(x)$."

Now let $g(x)$ differ from zero only in a certain finite space-time region. In this case, in the sufficiently remote past and future the fields are free, and, therefore, the initial and final states of the dynamic system may be characterized by the usual constant state amplitudes introduced in Chapter II. These two quantities

[38a] See also, in this connection, the papers by Bogoliubov (14), (15), (16).

$\Phi(-\infty)$ and $\Phi(\infty)$ will be related by a certain operator $S(g)$ which transforms $\Phi(-\infty)$ into $\Phi(\infty)$ and which depends on the behavior of the function $g(x)$. By fixing the amplitude of the initial state $\Phi(-\infty) = \Phi$, we may regard the final amplitude as a functional of g:

$$\Phi(\infty) = \Phi(g) = S(g)\Phi. \tag{17.13}$$

In accordance with this definition, it is natural to interpret $S(g)$ as the scattering matrix for the case when the interaction is switched on with an intensity g. The actual case in which the interaction is switched on fully over the entire space-time must now be investigated within the given framework by means of a transition to the limit in which the region within which $g = 1$ is extended indefinitely and in the limit includes all space-time. In this case, the usual scattering matrix S may be defined by

$$S = S(1). \tag{17.14}$$

17.4. *Relativistic Covariance and Unitary Nature of the S-Matrix*

Let us now formulate a number of fundamental physical conditions which must be satisfied by the matrix S. As always, an important physical requirement is the *condition of relativistic covariance*. In order to formulate it explicitly let us consider a transformation L belonging to the inhomogeneous Lorentz group:

$$x \to x' = Lx. \tag{17.15}$$

In the absence of interaction in the theory of the free field, the transformation law for the state amplitude which corresponds to the transformation (17.15) had, in accordance with (9.2), the form

$$\Phi' = U_L\Phi. \tag{17.16}$$

In the present case, when $\Phi = \Phi(g)$ it is also necessary to take into account the fact that the function $g(x)$ itself, which may be regarded as a certain "classical field," undergoes the transformation (17.15); since the region of interaction described by the function g remains invariant under the transformation (17.15), the transition to new coordinates in the argument of g gives:

$$g(x) \to Lg(x) = g(L^{-1}x). \tag{17.17}$$

Therefore the transformation law for the amplitude $\Phi(g)$ will now be of the form:

$$\Phi(g) \rightarrow \Phi'(Lg) = U_L \Phi(g). \tag{17.18}$$

Considerations of relativistic covariance also make us require that the transformation law (17.13) from the initial to the final amplitude should not depend on the frame of reference, i.e., that

$$\Phi'(g) = S(g)\Phi'. \tag{17.19}$$

Substituting into this equation relation (9.2) and formula (17.18) with a displaced argument ($Lg \rightarrow g$) we shall find on taking (17.13) into account

$$U_L S(L^{-1}g)\Phi = S(g) U_L \Phi. \tag{17.20}$$

Since the amplitude of the initial state Φ is arbitrary this expression may be written in operator form

$$U_L S(L^{-1}g) = S(g) U_L,$$

or after displacing the arguments by L, multiplying on the right by U_L^{-1}, and taking into account the unitary nature of U_L:

$$S(Lg) = U_L S(g) U_L^{-1} = U_L S(g) U_L^{\dagger}. \tag{17.21}$$

Formula (17.21) expresses the condition of covariance of the operator $S(g)$.

We shall now formulate another general requirement—the requirement that the norm of the wave functions be conserved. In the present case we must demand that

$$\Phi^*(g)\Phi(g) = \Phi^*\Phi,$$

from which it follows that

$$S^{\dagger}(g) S(g) = 1, \tag{17.22}$$

i.e., the operator $S(g)$ must be *unitary*.

17.5. *The Condition of Causality*

We must also guarantee that the condition of causality is satisfied according to which any event occurring in the system may exert an influence on the evolution of the system only in the future and cannot exert any influence on the behavior of the system in the past at times preceding the given event. We must therefore require that the change in the interaction law in any space-time region can influence the evolution of the system only at subsequent times.

In order to formulate the condition of causality explicitly, we shall first consider the case when the space-time region G in which the function $g(x)$ differs from zero may be divided into two separate sub-regions G_1 and G_2 such that all points of one of them (G_1) lie in the past with respect to a certain time instant t, while all points of the other sub-region (G_2) lie in the future with respect to t. The function $g(x)$ may in this case be represented as a sum of two functions

$$g(x) = g_1(x) + g_2(x), \tag{17.23}$$

one of which (g_1) differs from zero only in G_1, while the second (g_2) differs from zero only in G_2.

At time t one may define a state characterized by the amplitude Φ_t which, because of considerations of causality, should not depend on the interaction in the region G_2 and which may therefore be written in the form

$$\Phi_t = S(g_1)\,\Phi, \tag{17.24}$$

where $S(g_1)$ is the scattering matrix for the case when the interaction is switched on with an intensity $g_1(x)$. The final state $\Phi(g)$ may now be obtained from Φ_t with the aid of the operator $S(g_2)$ which describes the interaction in the region G_2

$$\Phi(g) = S(g_2)\,\Phi_t. \tag{17.25}$$

Comparing (17.23)–(17.25) with (17.13) we find that

$$S(g_1 + g_2) = S(g_2)\,S(g_1) \quad \text{for } G_2 > G_1. \tag{17.26}$$

(The sense of the inequality $G_2 > G_1$ denotes that all points of the region G_2 lie at times later than all points of the region G_1.) Relation (17.26) represents the formulation of the principle of causality for the case $G_2 > G_1$.

We shall now consider two cases which differ from each other by the form of the interaction in the region G_2 and which are described by the same function in G_1, i.e.,

$$g'(x) = g_2'(x) + g_1(x), \quad g''(x) = g_2''(x) + g_1(x).$$

By constructing the expression $S(g'')S(g')$ we see without difficulty that it does not depend on the behavior of the functions g'' and g' in the region G_1 since according to (17.26)

$$S^\dagger(g_1 + g_2) = S^\dagger(g_1)\, S^\dagger(g_2),$$

and taking into account the unitary properties of the matrix S we obtain:

$$S(g'')\, S^\dagger(g') = S(g_2'')\, S(g_1)\, S^\dagger(g_1)\, S^\dagger(g_2') = S(g_2'')\, S^\dagger(g_2').$$

Thus the product $S(g'')S^\dagger(g')$ does not in fact depend on the behavior of the function g in the region G_1. This is due to the fact that the dependence on the state of the system prior to the time t which is contained in $S(g'')$ is eliminated by the corresponding part of the operator $S^\dagger(g')$.

Therefore, in the more general case, we shall also adopt the following formulation of the condition of causality: "if there are two functions $g''(y)$ and $g'(y)$ which coincide with each other for y^0 smaller than a certain t, then the product $S(g'')S^\dagger(g')$ must not depend on the state of the system for $y^0 < t$."

For the future use it will turn out to be very convenient to have the condition of causality formulated in differential form.

We shall often need to use the concept of the functional derivative which is a natural extension of the concept of a partial derivative. As is well known the partial derivative $\partial f/\partial z_i$ of a certain function of n variables $z_1, \ldots, z_n$ may be defined as the coefficient of dz_i in the sum

$$df = \sum_{(1 \leq i \leq n)} A_i\, dz_i, \tag{17.27}$$

which represents the differential of this function.

Let us now consider a certain functional $I(u)$ for which the variation $\delta I(u)$, defined as the principal part of the increment $I(u + \delta u) - I(u)$, may be represented by an integral of the form

$$\delta I(u) = \int_G A(x, u)\, \delta u\, dx,$$

where A is a functional of u which depends on the position of the point

x in the region G:

$$A = A(x, u),$$

in a manner similar to the way in which A_i in the sum (17.27) is a function of $z_1, \ldots, z_n$ depending on the index i. By analogy with the preceding definition of a partial derivative, we shall now introduce the concept of the functional derivative $\delta I(u)/\delta u(x)$ of the functional $I(u)$ with respect to u at the point x defining it by means of the relation

$$\frac{\delta I(u)}{\delta u(x)} = A(x, u).$$

In the same way we can also introduce functional derivatives of higher orders, and it is not difficult to see that functional derivatives possess the main properties of ordinary derivatives.

If we set

$$g'(y) = g(y) \text{ and } g'' = g(y) + \delta g(y),$$

where $\delta g(y)$ is an infinitesimal variation of the function $g(y)$ which differs from zero only for $y^0 > t$, then the matrix $S(g'')$ may be represented in the form

$$S(g'') = S(g) + \delta S(g), \tag{17.28}$$

where

$$\delta S(g) = \int_{y^0 > t} \frac{\delta S}{\delta g(y)} \delta g(y) \, dy.$$

It may now be seen that the expression

$$S(g'') S^\dagger(g') = S(g) S^\dagger(g) + \delta S(g) S^\dagger(g) = 1 + \delta S(g) S^\dagger(g)$$

does not depend on the behavior of the function $g(x)$ for $x^0 < t < y^0$.

By going over to the variational derivative, we may therefore formulate the condition of causality as the condition that the expression

$$\frac{\delta S(g)}{\delta g(y)} S^\dagger(g) \tag{17.29}$$

should be independent of the behavior of the function $g(x)$ at the point x for $x < y$. From considerations of covariance, it also follows from this that the operator (17.29) cannot depend on the behavior of the function $g(x)$ also at $x \sim y$ ($x \sim y$ denotes that the points x and y are separated by a spacelike interval).

The condition of causality may evidently be written in the form

$$\frac{\delta}{\delta g(x)}\left(\frac{\delta S(g)}{\delta g(y)} S^{\dagger}(g)\right) = 0 \quad \text{for } x \lessapprox y. \tag{17.30}$$

Relation (17.30) represents the *formulation of the principle of causality in differential form* which is the *most convenient one* for subsequent considerations.

We thus have conditions of relativistic covariance (17.21), unitary nature (17.22), and causality (17.30) which together provide a sufficient basis for the construction of the S-matrix. In § 18 we shall give, with the aid of these conditions and correspondence arguments, a method for the explicit determination of the coefficients in the expansion of $S(g)$ into a functional series in $g(x)$. We also note that one should also add to the preceding conditions the requirement that the energy of stationary states should be positive. In the theory of free fields, the fulfilment of this requirement was considered separately. However, at the present stage of our presentation we shall be unable to formulate this condition for the theory of interacting fields in view of the fact that at present we are confined within the framework of perturbation theory and therefore cannot consider bound states.

17.6. *"Classical Fields" as Arguments of Functionals*

In conclusion, we note that in the formulation of the theory adopted by us the function g, which characterizes the extent of switching on the interaction, appears to play the role of a certain "classical field" which permits us to examine different regions in space-time.

The usual scattering matrix (17.14) which corresponds to the interaction of quantized wave fields over the entire space-time does not depend on any ordinary functions, and therefore its matrix elements are numbers which contain no functional dependences. The introduction into the interaction Lagrangian of an unquantized function converts the S-matrix and its matrix elements into functionals. By computing functional derivatives of these functionals it turns out to be possible to examine the space-time properties of various quantities occurring in the theory (as has just been demonstrated in the formulation of the condition of causality). The "classical fields" (of the type g) introduced in this procedure play the role of auxiliary variables in the intermediate stages of the argument and are usually eliminated from the final expressions by a suitable limiting process (for example $g \to 1$).

The classical field $g(x)$ introduced above as a factor multiplying the interaction Lagrangian density (17.17) provides a convenient mathematical means for the formal expansion of the scattering matrix in powers of the interaction which we shall carry out in § 18.

Naturally, this method of introducing an auxiliary field is not the only one. In some cases it turns out to be more convenient to introduce such a field in a more "physical" way, for example, in the form of a given external field $u^{\text{ext}}(x)$ or of a given external flux of some kind of particles $J^{\text{ext}}(x)$. Thus, in order to obtain Schwinger's equations for Green's functions of spinor electrodynamics (Chapter VII), one introduces into the interaction Lagrangian[39] $\mathscr{L}(x)$ an external unquantized electromagnetic potential $A^{\text{ext}}(x)$ as a result of which $\mathscr{L}(x)$ takes on the form

$$\mathscr{L}(x) = e \sum_n :\bar{\psi}(x)\gamma^n \psi(x)\,[A_n(x) + A_n^{\text{ext}}(x)]: .$$

Here the classical field A^{ext} plays the role of an auxiliary functional argument which facilitates the analysis of the space-time properties of the theory, and in contrast to $g(x)$, the field A^{ext} (or more accurately its final limiting value) may have a direct physical meaning. The scattering matrix in this case turns out to be a functional of A^{ext} and by repeating without any appreciable changes the argument leading to (17.30), we can obtain in this case

$$\frac{\delta}{\delta A_n^{\text{ext}}(x)}\left[\frac{\delta S(A^{\text{ext}})}{\delta A_m^{\text{ext}}(y)}\,S^{\dagger}(A^{\text{ext}})\right] = 0 \quad \text{for } x \lesssim y. \tag{17.31}$$

[39] In future we shall always take L to stand for the interaction Lagrangian which was earlier denoted by L_{int}.

By analogy with the foregoing, it is not difficult to reformulate the condition of causality to correspond to any other method of introducing classical fields.

§ 18. The Interaction Lagrangian and the S-Matrix

18.1. *Expansion of the S-Matrix into a Power Series in Powers of the Interaction*

We now begin the actual construction of the scattering matrix from the interaction Lagrangian $\mathscr{L}(x)$. We shall seek $S(g)$ in the form of a formal functional expansion in powers of $g(x)$:

$$S(g) = 1 + \sum_{n \geqq 1} \frac{1}{n!} \int S_n(x_1, \ldots, x_n) g(x_1) \ldots g(x_n) dx_1 \ldots dx_n, \quad (18.1)$$

in which $S_n(x_1, \ldots, x_n)$ are operator expressions which depend on the complete field functions and on their partial derivatives at the points $x_1, \ldots, x_n$. In order to guarantee the scalar nature of S_n, we shall also assume that the Fermi field operators occur in S_n only in even combinations. In other words we shall require that the $S_n(x_1, \ldots, x_n)$ should be polylocal operators in the sense of the definition given in § 16. It should be emphasized that the requirement that S_n should depend on the complete field functions, and not separately on their positive- and negative-frequency parts, represents a special physical condition. When this requirement is satisfied, then the relation

$$[S_n(x_1, \ldots, x_n), \quad S_m(y_1, \ldots, y_m)] = 0, \quad (18.2)$$

holds when all the x_i are spacelike with respect to all the y_j. Therefore, if the two functions $g_1(x)$ and $g_2(x)$ are localized in such space-time regions that any point of one region is spacelike with respect to all the points of the other region, then $S(g_1)$ commutes with $S(g_2)$. This essentially expresses the fact (which is also a manifestation of the principle of causality) that a signal cannot be propagated with a speed greater than that of light and that the processes of switching on the interaction within two regions g_1 and g_2 which are spacelike with respect to one another do not interfere with each other. It is solely in order to guarantee this important physical property that we shall assume that S_n is a polylocal operator.

In order to guarantee the convergence at least of the individual terms of expansion (18.1) we shall assume that S_n are integrable operator functions. Indeed, for sufficiently smooth and sufficiently rapidly decreasing functions $g(x)$, the individual integrals in (18.1) will converge. Naturally, the convergence of the individual terms of the series (18.1) has no relation to the convergence of the series as a whole. In connection with some recent investigations (Dyson (35), Thirring (125), Edwards (36), Ioffe (63)) there exist some fairly good reasons to expect that this series may even turn out to be divergent. At best, one may hope, in the case of a weak interaction, that by taking a certain small number of terms in the expansion we shall obtain an approximation whose accuracy improves as the interaction is made weaker. In other words, in certain cases one may regard the series (18.1) as a *source of asymptotic approximations.* One such case of practical importance is the case of electrodynamics.

However, even in the case of an interaction which is definitely known not to be weak (for example, the meson-nucleon interaction) the investigation of the formal expansion (18.1) is of considerable interest, since in this way we shall be able to arrive fairly simply at a number of quantitative as well as qualitative properties of the matrix $S(g)$ in order to attempt to establish them on a more rigorous basis at a later stage. Consequently, the study of this formal series must be of definite heuristic value which is enhanced by the fact that all attempts made to go beyond the framework of perturbation theory until now have so far led only to very limited results. We shall later present (see Chapters VII and VIII) a number of considerations with the aid of which it may turn out to be possible to construct a theory of interacting fields without making use of such formal expansions.

By returning to expression (18.1), we see that without restricting the generality of the argument $S_n(x_1, \ldots, x_n)$ may be considered to be *symmetric* functions of their arguments $x_1, \ldots, x_n$, since the weighting functions $g(x_1) \ldots g(x_n)$ enter the expressions in a symmetric manner.

18.2. *Conditions of Covariance, Unitarity, and Causality for S_n*

We shall now make use of the conditions that are satisfied by the matrix $S(g)$ in order to determine the explicit form of the functions S_n.

From the condition (17.21) of relativistic covariance of $S(g)$ we have:

$$\int U_L S_n(x_1, \ldots, x_n) U_L^\dagger g(x_1) \ldots g(x_n) dx_1 \ldots dx_n$$
$$= \int S_n(x_1, \ldots, x_n) g(L^{-1}x_1) \ldots g(L^{-1}x_n) dx_1 \ldots dx_n. \qquad (18.3)$$

Introducing a change of variables $x \to Lx$ in the right-hand side, we obtain:

$$\int U_L S_n(x_1, \ldots, x_n) U_L^\dagger g(x_1) \ldots g(x_n) dx_1 \ldots dx_n$$
$$= \int S_n(Lx_1, \ldots, Lx_n) g(x_1) \ldots g(x_n) dx_1 \ldots dx_n,$$

from which we arrive at the condition of Lorentz covariance for S_n

$$\left.\begin{aligned} U_L S_n(x_1, \ldots, x_n) U_L^\dagger &= S_n(Lx_1, \ldots Lx_n) \\ \text{or} \quad S_n(x_1, \ldots, x_n) &= U_L^\dagger S_n(Lx_1, \ldots, Lx_n) U_L. \end{aligned}\right\} \qquad (18.4)$$

In order to take into account the unitary nature (17.22) of the S-matrix we shall multiply the expansion (18.1) by its conjugate

$$S^\dagger(g) = 1 + \sum_{n \geqq 1} \frac{1}{n!} \int S_n^\dagger(x_1, \ldots, x_n) g(x_1) \ldots g(x_n) dx_1 \ldots dx_n \qquad (18.5)$$

and after introducing for the sake of symmetry of the resulting expressions the notation

$$S_0 = 1,$$

we shall obtain:

$$1 = \sum_{(k,\, m \geqq 0)} \frac{1}{k!m!} \int S_k(x_1, \ldots, x_k) g(x_1) \ldots g(x_k) dx_1 \ldots dx_k$$
$$\times \int S_m^\dagger(x_{k+1}, \ldots, x_{k+m}) g(x_{k+1}) \ldots g(x_{k+m}) dx_{k+1} \ldots dx_{k+m}$$
$$= \sum_{(k,\, n)} \frac{1}{k!(n-k)!} \int S_k(x_1, \ldots, x_k) S_{n-k}^\dagger(x_{k+1}, \ldots, x_n)$$
$$g(x_1) \ldots g(x_n) dx_1 \ldots dx_n. \qquad (18.6)$$

On collecting terms in (18.6) of the same "degree" in $g(x)$, we shall for $n = 0$ obtain the identity $(1 = 1)$, while for $n > 0$ we shall obtain:

$$\sum_{0 \leqq k \leqq n} \frac{1}{k!(n-k)!} \int S_k(x_1, \ldots, x_k)\, S^\dagger_{n-k}(x_{k+1}, \ldots, x_n) \\ g(x_1) \ldots g(x_n)\, dx_1 \ldots dx_n = 0. \quad (18.7)$$

From the relation (18.7) for arbitrary $g(x)$, one cannot as yet conclude that the expression

$$\sum_k \frac{1}{k!(n-k)!} S_k(x_1, \ldots, x_k)\, S^\dagger_{n-k}(x_{k+1}, \ldots, x_n) \quad (18.8)$$

is equal to zero.

Such a conclusion could have been reached if the expression (18.8) had turned out to be symmetric in all its arguments $x_1, \ldots, x_n$. Actually symmetry exists in each term of (18.8) only within each of the two groups of arguments: $x_1, \ldots, x_k$ and $x_{k+1}, \ldots, x_n$. In order to achieve the complete symmetrization of an expression of type (18.8) we shall introduce the symbol

$$P\left(\frac{x_1, \ldots, x_k}{x_{k+1}, \ldots, x_n}\right),$$

which denotes the sum over all the $n!/k!(n-k)!$ ways of breaking up the set of points $x_1, \ldots, x_n$ into two sets of k and $n - k$ points. Permutations within each of these two sets are not taken into account since the functions S_k are symmetric in their arguments. For example,

$$P\left(\frac{x_1}{x_2}\right) S_1(x_1)\, S_1(x_2) = S_1(x_1)\, S_1(x_2) + S_1(x_2)\, S_1(x_1),$$

$$P\left(\frac{x_1, x_2}{x_3}\right) S_2(x_1, x_2)\, S_1(x_3) = S_2(x_1, x_2)\, S_1(x_3) + S_2(x_1, x_3)\, S_1(x_2) \\ + S_2(x_2, x_3)\, S_1(x_1).$$

In order to symmetrize (18.7), we shall rewrite it $n!$ times, each time altering the notation for the arguments in such a way that the set of points $x_1, \ldots, x_n$ would be distributed among the arguments of the functions S_k and $S^\dagger_{n-k}$ in a different way. On adding the relations obtained in this way, we shall then obtain, because the weighting factor $g(x_1) \ldots g(x_n)$ remains unaltered,

$$\sum_k \int P\left(\frac{x_1, \ldots, x_k}{x_{k+1}, \ldots, x_n}\right) S_k(x_1, \ldots, x_k)\, S^\dagger_{n-k}(x_{k+1}, \ldots, x_n) \times g(x_1) \ldots g(x_n)\, dx_1 \ldots dx_n = 0,$$

from which it follows that the expression

$$\sum_{0 \leqq k \leqq n} P\left(\frac{x_1, \ldots, x_k}{x_{k+1}, \ldots, x_n}\right) S_k(x_1, \ldots, x_k)\, S^\dagger_{n-k}(x_{k+1}, \ldots, x_n)$$

vanishes due to its symmetry with respect to all n arguments. Remembering that $S_0 = 1$ we obtain from the above:

$$S_n(x_1, \ldots, x_n) + S^\dagger_n(x_1, \ldots, x_n) + \sum_{(1 \leqq k \leqq n-1)} P\left(\frac{x_1, \ldots, x_k}{x_{k+1}, \ldots, x_n}\right) S_k(x_1, \ldots, x_k) S^\dagger_{n-k}(x_{k+1}, \ldots, x_n) = 0. \quad (18.9)$$

We now turn to the condition of causality (17.30). We note from the outset that it is more convenient to deal not with the quantity

$$\frac{\delta S(g)}{\delta g(y)}\, S^\dagger(g),$$

which in view of the condition of unitarity

$$\frac{\delta}{\delta g(y)}(SS^\dagger) = \frac{\delta S}{\delta g(y)}\, S^\dagger + S\, \frac{\delta S^\dagger}{\delta g(y)} = 0$$

is anti-Hermitean, but with the expression

$$H(y;g) = i\, \frac{\delta S(g)}{\delta g(y)}\, S^\dagger(g) \quad (18.10)$$

which is evidently Hermitean. Utilizing (18.1) we find:

$$H(y; g) = i \sum_{n \geqq 0} \frac{1}{n!} \int S_{n+1}(y, x_1, \ldots, x_n)\, g(x_1) \ldots g(x_n)\, dx_1 \ldots dx_n$$

$$\times \sum_{m \geqq 0} \frac{1}{m!} \int S^\dagger_m(x_{n+1}, \ldots, x_{n+m})\, g(x_{n+1}) \ldots g(x_{n+m})\, dx_{n+1} \ldots dx_{n+m}$$

$$= \sum_{n \geqq 0} \frac{1}{n!} \int H_n(y, x_1, \ldots, x_n)\, g(x_1) \ldots g(x_n)\, dx_1 \ldots dx_n, \quad (18.11)$$

into which we have introduced the quantities

$$H_n(y, x_1, \ldots, x_n) =$$
$$= i \sum_{0 \leqq k \leqq n} P\left(\frac{x_1, \ldots, x_k}{x_{k+1}, \ldots, x_n}\right) S_{k+1}(y, x_1, \ldots, x_k) S^{\dagger}_{n-k}(x_{k+1}, \ldots, x_n)$$
$$= iS_{n+1}(y, x_1, \ldots, x_n)$$
$$+ i \sum_{0 \leqq k \leqq n-1} P\left(\frac{x_1, \ldots, x_k}{x_{k+1}, \ldots, x_n}\right) S_{k+1}(y, x_1, \ldots, x_k)\, S^{\dagger}_{n-k}(x_{k+1}, \ldots, x_n), \tag{18.12}$$

which are symmetric in all their arguments with the exception of the first. On calculating the functional derivative $\delta/\delta g(x)$ of expression (18.9) we obtain:

$$i \frac{\delta}{\delta g(x)}\left(\frac{\delta S(g)}{\delta g(y)}\, S^{\dagger}(g)\right)$$
$$= \sum_{n \geqq 1} \frac{1}{n!} \int H(y, x, x_1, \ldots, x_{n-1}) g(x_1) \ldots g(x_{n-1}) dx_1 \ldots dx_{n-1},$$

from which, in view of the condition of causality (17.30) and on the basis of the symmetry of the functions H_n with respect to all their arguments with the exception of the first, it follows that

$$H_n(y, x_1, x_2, \ldots, x_n) = 0, \tag{18.13}$$

if for at least one x_j $(j = 1, \ldots, n)$ $y \gtrsim x_j$.

18.3. *Determination of the Explicit Form of* $S_1(x)$ *and* $S_2(x, y)$

Thus from the conditions of covariance, unitarity, and causality for the complete matrix $S(g)$ we have obtained the conditions of covariance, unitarity, and causality for the functions $S_n(x_1, \ldots, x_n)$. We shall now show that the set of these conditions (18.4), (18.9), and (18.13) together with certain additional considerations which express the correspondence principle turns out to be sufficient to determine the explicit form of the functions $S_n(x_1, \ldots, x_n)$.

It turns out that formulas (18.9) and (18.13) regarded as recurrent relations enable us to determine any arbitrary function S_n in terms of the "preceding" S_k $(k = 1, 2, \ldots, n - 1)$ with the unitarity condition (18.9) serving to determine the Hermitean part of the function S_n, while the condition of causality (18.13) determines the anti-Hermitean part of S_n. Because of this, the construction of the functions $S_n(x_1, \ldots, x_n)$ may be carried out by the method of induction, but for this it is necessary to have an explicit expression for $S_1(x)$. This function may be determined from considerations of correspondence.

Let us therefore consider the function $S_1(x)$. The condition of causality cannot be formulated as yet for a single function, but, as we shall see later, it follows from the condition of causality for $n = 1$ that $S_1(x)$ and $S_1(y)$ must commute at points which are spacelike with respect to one another:

$$[S_1(x), S_1(y)] = 0 \text{ for } x \sim y, \tag{18.14}$$

for which it is evidently sufficient that $S_1(x)$ should satisfy the condition of locality (in the sense of the definition given in § 16).

By writing the condition of unitarity for $n = 1$ we have:

$$S_1(x) + S_1^\dagger(x) = 0, \tag{18.15}$$

from which it follows that $S_1(x)$ may be represented in the form

$$S_1(x) = i\Lambda_1(x), \tag{18.16}$$

where $\Lambda_1(x)$ is an Hermitean operator. Finally, the condition of relativistic covariance (18.4) gives

$$S_1(x) = U_L^\dagger S_1(Lx) U_L. \tag{18.17}$$

Thus $\Lambda_1(x)$ must be an Hermitean relativistically covariant operators atisfying the condition of locality.

We shall now relate $\Lambda_1(x)$ to the interaction Lagrangian $\mathscr{L}(x)$. As is well known, in classical theory the interaction is taken into account by means of adding to the free field Lagrangian $\mathscr{L}_0(x)$ the interaction Lagrangian $\mathscr{L}(x)$, and the "equations of motion" may be obtained with the aid of the principle of stationary action. Let us examine the action A of a system of classical fields in the case when the interaction is switched on with an intensity $g(x)$. We have then:

$$A = \int \mathscr{L}_0(x)\, dx + \int \mathscr{L}(x)\, g(x)\, dx, \tag{18.18}$$

where $\mathscr{L}_0$ and $\mathscr{L}$ contain field functions which satisfy appropriate equations of motion. In particular, by regarding $g(x)$ as an infinitesimal of the first order we shall find that these field functions will differ from the free field functions also by infinitesimals of the first order. On the other hand, from the fact that the free field equations are obtained from the condition:

$$\delta \int \mathscr{L}_0(x)\, dx = 0,$$

it follows that if the field functions under the integral sign in the first term on the right-hand side of (18.18) are expressed with an accuracy up to infinitesimal terms of the first order, then this will lead to an error of the second order of smallness in the value of the integral $\int \mathscr{L}_0\, dx$.

Therefore, if the interaction is switched on with an infinitesimal intensity $g(x)$ the action of the system will be altered by an amount $\int \mathscr{L}(x) g(x) dx$ in which $\mathscr{L}(x)$ depends on the free field functions.

As is well known[40] in the quasi-classical case the solution of the ordinary Schrödinger equation for the wave function ψ

$$i \frac{\partial \psi}{\partial t} = H\psi$$

takes on the form $\psi = \exp(iA)$ where A is the action of the system. The transition from the unperturbed expression

$$A_0 = \int \mathscr{L}_0(x)\, dx \tag{18.19}$$

to the action (18.18) will evidently correspond to the transformation of the wave function

$$\psi_0 = e^{iA_0} \to \psi = e^{iA} = e^{i\int \mathscr{L}(x)\, g(x)\, dx}\, \psi_0.$$

Thus on taking into account the smallness of the quantity g, this transition will correspond to the following transformation of the wave function:

$$\psi \to \psi' = \psi + \delta\psi, \quad \delta\psi = i \int \mathscr{L}(x)\, g(x)\, dx\, \psi.$$

[40] See, for example, Blokhintsev (13), Pauli (91).

By utilizing considerations of *correspondence,* we shall demand that the transformation law for the second quantized state amplitude Φ should have the same form, i.e.,

$$\Phi \to \Phi' = \Phi + \delta\Phi, \quad \delta\Phi = i \int \mathscr{L}(x)\, g(x) dx\, \Phi.$$

In other words we shall assume that for an infinitesimal g the matrix $S(g)$ shall have the form

$$S(g) = 1 + i \int \mathscr{L}(x) g(x) dx.$$

By comparing this formula with (18.1) we see that $S_1(x)$ actually does have the form (18.16) in which $\Lambda_1(x)$ is equal to the interaction Lagrangian:

$$S_1(x) = i\mathscr{L}(x). \tag{18.20}$$

It now follows from relations (18.14), (18.15), (18.17) that the *interaction Lagrangian must be a local, Hermitean, and relativistically covariant combination of operator field functions.* We note here that, as may be easily shown, scalar combinations of operator functions satisfying condition (9.9) automatically lead to the condition of relativistic covariance being satisfied, while the conditions of the Hermitean nature

$$\mathscr{L}^{\dagger}(x) = \mathscr{L}(x) \tag{18.21}$$

and of the local nature

$$[\mathscr{L}(x),\ \mathscr{L}(y)] = 0 \text{ for } x \sim y \tag{18.22}$$

of $\mathscr{L}$ represent subsidiary conditions which restrict the choice of the interaction Lagrangian.

We now proceed to the determination of $S_2(x, y)$. From the condition of causality (18.13) for $n = 1$ we obtain for $x \gtrsim y$

$$H_1(x,y) = iS_2(x,y) + iS_1(x)S_1^{\dagger}(y) = 0,$$

from which on taking (18.15) into account we obtain

$$S_2(x,y) = -\mathscr{L}(x)\mathscr{L}(y) \text{ for } x \gtrsim y. \tag{18.23}$$

In view of the symmetry of S_2 we also have:

$$S_2(x,y) = S_2(y,\ x) = -\mathscr{L}(y)\mathscr{L}(x) \text{ for } y \gtrsim x. \tag{18.24}$$

The regions within which formulas (18.23) and (18.24) are defined overlap for $x \sim y$, and this leads us to the condition of compatibility of the form (18.14) or (18.22) which represents the condition of locality for S_1 or $\mathscr{L}$.

Thus we have obtained the definition of the function $S_2(x, y)$ in the following form:

$$S_2(x, y) = \begin{cases} -\mathscr{L}(x)\mathscr{L}(y) & (x \gtrsim y), \\ -\mathscr{L}(y)\mathscr{L}(x) & (y \gtrsim x). \end{cases} \tag{18.25}$$

By taking the Hermitean conjugate we shall obtain in view of (18.21)

$$S_2^\dagger(x, y) = \begin{cases} -\mathscr{L}(y)\mathscr{L}(x) & (x \gtrsim y), \\ -\mathscr{L}(x)\mathscr{L}(y) & (y \gtrsim x). \end{cases} \tag{18.26}$$

The symmetry and the polylocal nature of $S_2(x, y)$ follows from the above form in which it is expressed. It is evident that expression (18.25) satisfies the requirements of covariance. Also, it is not difficult to verify that the unitarity condition is satisfied. Corresponding to (18.9) we must now check the relation

$$S_2(x, y) + S_2^\dagger(x, y) + S_1(x)\, S_1^\dagger(y) + S_1(y)\, S_1^\dagger(x) = 0.$$

Its validity follows directly from (18.20), (18.21), (18.25), (18.26). Indeed, we have, for example, for $x \gtrsim y$

$$\begin{aligned} &S_2(x,y) + S_2^\dagger(x,y) + S_1(x)\, S_1^\dagger(y) + S_1(y)\, S_1^\dagger(x) \\ &\quad = -\mathscr{L}(x)\mathscr{L}(y) - \mathscr{L}(y)\mathscr{L}(x) + \mathscr{L}(x)\mathscr{L}(y) + \mathscr{L}(y)\mathscr{L}(x) = 0. \end{aligned}$$

In a similar way we verify the validity of the above expression for $y \gtrsim x$. We have thus established that expression (18.25) satisfies all the requirements imposed on S_2.

18.4. *Chronological Product of Local Operators*

Before undertaking the construction of further functions $S_k (k = 3, 4, \ldots)$, it is useful to introduce the concept of the *ordered* or the *chronological product of operators*. For the time being we shall introduce it only for local opeators. The chronological product of a number of local operators $A_1(x_1) \ldots A_n(x_n)$

is denoted by the symbol $T(A_1(x_1) \ldots A_n(x_n)$ and by definition[41] is equal to the ordinary product of these operators taken in a definite order which corresponds to the decrease of the time components of the arguments of the factors from left to right, i.e.,

$$T(A_1(x_1) \ldots A_n(x_n)) = A_{j_1}(x_{j_1}) A_{j_2}(x_{j_2}) \ldots A_{j_n}(x_{j_n}), \quad (18.27)$$

where the sequence $x_j, \ldots, x_{jn}$ is determined by

$$x^0_{j_1} \geqq x^0_{j_2} \geqq \ldots \geqq x^0_{j_n}.$$

For brevity we shall often refer to a chronological product as a T-product. We shall also need the concept of an *antichronological product* which by definition corresponds to an increase in the time components of the arguments from left to right. Taking, for example, the Hermitean conjugate of the right-hand side of (18.27) we shall obtain the expression

$$A^\dagger_{j_n}(x_{j_n}) \ldots A^\dagger_{j_1}(x_{j_1}) \quad (x^0_{j_n} \leqq x^0_{j_{n-1}} \leqq \ldots \leqq x^0_{j_1}),$$

which may be conveniently called the antichronological product (or $T^\dagger$-product) of the operators $A^\dagger_1(x_1) \ldots A^\dagger_n(x_n)$. We shall therefore set

$$T^\dagger(A_1(x_1) \ldots A_n(x_n)) = A_{j_1}(x_{j_1}) A_{j_2}(x_{j_2}) \ldots A_{j_n}(x_{j_n}) \quad (18.28)$$
$$(x^0_{j_1} \leqq x^0_{j_2} \leqq \ldots \leqq x^0_{j_n}).$$

We shall show that the definition of the T-product is covariant in spite of the distinctive role played by the time. The chronological order of the points $x_1, \ldots, x_n$ which may change in going over from one Lorentz frame to another under a Lorentz rotation is of significance for the value of the T-product. At first glance it might seem that such a transition might alter the value of the T-product, however this does not occur. Indeed, let us consider that the preceding transformation is carried out by means of a large number of small transformations which is always possible in view of the continuous nature of Lorentz rotations. The process of the change in the chronological order of the points $x_1, \ldots, x_n$ will then be broken up into a certain number of stages

[41] Compare with the definition of the chronological product of two field operators in § 14.

during each of which there will occur the simultaneous change in the time order within a certain group $x_j, \ldots, x_k$ (of two or more) points. But the chronological order of a number of points $x_j, \ldots, x_k$ may be altered by a Lorentz rotation only if these points have a spacelike relation to one another. The corresponding operators $\Lambda_j(x_j) \ldots \Lambda_k(x_k)$ will in this case commute among themselves in virtue of the property of locality, and their order is immaterial. Therefore, at each stage of the transformation the value of the T-product will not be altered, and, consequently, it will not be altered in general.

It is also not difficult to see that in accordance with the definition (18.27) *the local operators may be commuted within the T-product without changing its value.* From this it follows, in particular, that if all the operators Λ are the same, then the T-product turns out to be a symmetric function of its arguments.

Returning to (18.25) we see that with the aid of the T-product S_2 may be rewritten in the form

$$S_2(x, y) = -T(\mathscr{L}(x)\mathscr{L}(y)). \tag{18.29}$$

Corresponding to this, (18.26) will take on the form

$$S_2^\dagger(x, y) = -T^\dagger(\mathscr{L}(x)\mathscr{L}(y)). \tag{18.30}$$

18.5 *Determination of the Functions S_n for Arbitrary n.*

We shall now show that in general the expression

$$S_n(x_1, \ldots, x_n) = i^n T(\mathscr{L}(x_1) \ldots \mathscr{L}(x_n)), \tag{18.31}$$

which is a natural generalization of formulas (18.20) and (18.29) satisfies all the formal conditions imposed on S_n. The conditions of symmetry, covariance, and polylocality are now evidently satisfied, and we need only to check whether the conditions of unitarity and causality are likewise satisfied.

In order to do this, we shall find it more convenient to deal not with (18.31) but with the operator $S(g)$ as a whole. Substituting (18.31) into (18.1) we obtain:

$$S(g) = 1 + \sum_{n \geq 1} \frac{i^n}{n!} \int T(\mathscr{L}(x_1) \ldots \mathscr{L}(x_n))\, g(x_1) \ldots g(x_n)\, dx_1 \ldots dx_n. \tag{18.32}$$

We shall now examine some properties of the coefficients of the expansion (18.32). However, just as it is frequently more convenient in the theory of special functions to derive the interrelationship of the functions not from their explicit structure but from a certain general generating function, so in the present case it turns out to be simpler to verify the conditions of unitarity and causality for the series (18.32) as a whole. In order to do this we shall rewrite expression (18.32) in a slightly different form: we shall represent the nth term of the series in the form

$$\frac{i^n}{n!} T\left(\int \mathscr{L}(x_1) g(x_1)\, dx_1 \ldots \int \mathscr{L}(x_n) g(x_n)\, dx_n\right) = \frac{i^n}{n!} T\left(\left\{\int \mathscr{L}(x) g(x)\, dx\right\}^n\right). \quad (18.33)$$

The series (18.32) may now be formally summed by introducing the *T-exponential* (Feynman (42)):

$$S(g) = T\left\{1 + \sum_{n \geqq 1} \frac{i^n}{n!}\left[\int \mathscr{L}(x) g(x)\, dx\right]^n\right\} = T\left(\exp i \int \mathscr{L}(x) g(x) dx\right). \quad (18.34)$$

We have thus obtained a new expression for the scattering matrix $S(g)$.

We may introduce the important concept of the T-exponential from a different point of view. Let us divide the region within which the interaction is switched on described by the function $g(x)$ into an infinite number of infinitely thin layers Δ_j by means of spacelike surfaces $t = \text{const}$. We then have:

$$T\left(\exp i \int \mathscr{L}(x) g(x)\, dx\right) = T\left(\exp i \sum_j \int_{\Delta_j} \mathscr{L}(x) g(x)\, dx\right) = T\left(\prod_j \exp i \int_{\Delta_j} \mathscr{L}(x) g(x) dx\right).$$

It is then natural to define the T-exponential (18.34) as the limit of the T-product:

$$T\left(\exp i \int \mathscr{L}(x) g(x) dx\right) = \lim_{\Delta_j \to 0} T\left\{\prod_j\left(1 + i \int_{\Delta_j} \mathscr{L}(x) g(x) dx\right)\right\}. \quad (18.35)$$

The proof of the unitary nature of the matrix $S(g)$ becomes obvious from the representation (18.35). Indeed, the right-hand side of (18.35) is an ordinary product

$$\prod_j \left(1 + i \int_{\Delta_j} \mathscr{L}(x)\, g(x)\, dx\right),$$

taken in the appropriate chronological sequence of the layers Δ_j. But for sufficiently small Δ_j each factor of this product is unitary up to quantities of a higher order of smallness, and therefore the product as a whole is unitary. This completes the proof of the unitary nature of $S(g)$.

Let us now check the condition of causality. By calculating the variational derivative of $S(g)$ at the point y we shall obtain:

$$- i \frac{\delta S(g)}{\delta g(y)} = T\left(\mathscr{L}(y) \exp i \int \mathscr{L}(x)\, g(x)\, dx\right).$$

We divide the four-dimensional space into two parts G_+ and G_- by means of a spacelike surface $x^0 = \text{const} = y^0$ with respect to which G_+ lies in the "future," while G_- lies in the "past." We then have:

$$- i \frac{\delta S(g)}{\delta g(y)} = T\left(\mathscr{L}(y) \exp i \int_{G_+} \mathscr{L}(x)\, g(x)\, dx \exp i \int_{G_-} \mathscr{L}(z)\, g(z)\, dz\right)$$

$$= T\left(\mathscr{L}(y) \exp i \int_{G_+} \mathscr{L}(x)\, g(x)\, dx\right) T\left(\exp i \int_{G_-} \mathscr{L}(z) g(z) dz\right). \quad (18.36)$$

On the other hand, we obtain in a completely analogous manner

$$S(g) = T(\exp[\, i \int_{G_+} \mathscr{L}(x)\, g(x)\, dx + i \int_{G_-} \mathscr{L}(z)\, g(z)\, dz])$$

$$= T(\exp i \int_{G_+} \mathscr{L}(x)\, g(x) dx)\, T(\exp i \int_{G_-} \mathscr{L}(z)\, g(z)\, dz),$$

and likewise

$$S^\dagger(g) = \{T\, (\exp i \int_{G_-} \mathscr{L}(x)\, g(x)\, dx)\}^\dagger \{T \exp i \int_{G_+} \mathscr{L}(z)\, g(z)\, dz)\}^\dagger.$$

From this, taking into account the unitary nature of the expression $T\, (\exp i \int_{G_-} \mathscr{L}(x) g(x)\, dx)$, we shall obtain on the basis of (18.36)

$$- i \frac{\delta S(g)}{\delta g(y)} S^\dagger(g) = T(\mathscr{L}(y) \exp i \int_{G_+} \mathscr{L}(z) g(z) dz)$$
$$\{T(\exp i \int_{G_+} \mathscr{L}(z) g(z) dz)\}^\dagger.$$

Thus the product

$$- i \frac{\delta S(g)}{\delta g(y)} S^\dagger(g)$$

does not depend on the behavior of the function $g(x)$ in the region G_-, i.e., for $x^0 < y^0$. From considerations of covariance the same also holds for $x \sim y$. The condition of causality is therefore satisfied.

The preceding proofs that the conditions of causality and unitarity are satisfied by the operator $S(g)$ are very simple and direct. However, it should be noted that from the purely mathematical point of view they are not quite consistent. Indeed, in the course of the argument we have associated the question of the validity in the case of the product (18.31) of the elementary relations (18.9) and (18.12) with the entirely unclear problems of summing the series (18.1) as a whole, of making transitions to the limit, etc. Strictly speaking, all these points are not at all required for the proof. Instead of dealing with the T-exponential we may deal with the "T-exponential accurate up to a given order in g," and in this way all the problems connected with the summation of the series are automatically avoided.

18.6. *Analysis of the Arbitrariness in the Functions S_n and the Most General Form of $S(g)$*

We have thus verified that the expression

$$S_n(x_1, \ldots, x_n) \equiv i^n T(\mathscr{L}(x_1) \ldots \mathscr{L}(x_n))$$

is an acceptable one in the sense that it satisfies all the requirements imposed on S_n. However, it turns out that *this expression is not the most general one* that satisfies all the above requirements. Let us therefore investigate the problem of constructing the most general expression for $S_n(x_1, \ldots, x_n)$ which satisfies the conditions of symmetry, covariance, causality, and unitarity and thus completely solve the given problem of constructing the operator $S(g)$.

In order, to do this, let us first of all investigate the procedure of determining the function $S_n(x_1, \ldots, x_n)$ being given the preceding functions $S_1, S_2, \ldots, S_{n-1}$. As a consequence of the condition of unitarity (18.9) S_n is determined in terms of them up to a certain anti-Hermitean operator which we shall denote by $i\Lambda_n(x_1, \ldots, x_n)$. Moreover, the quantity $\Lambda_n(x_1, \ldots, x_n)$ must be a symmetric function of its arguments. The condition of causality (18.13) completely determines the operator function $S_n(x_1, \ldots, x_n)$ in terms of the preceding functions within the domain of definition of its arguments in which $x_1 \gtrsim x_j$ (for at least one of $j = 2, 3, \ldots, n$).

Therefore the anti-Hermitean operator $i\Lambda_n(x_1, \ldots, x_n)$ must vanish in the aforementioned region. Because it is symmetric in all its arguments, it follows that it must also vanish whenever for at least one pair of arguments x_i and x_j

$$x_i \neq x_j ,$$

and consequently it may differ from zero only when all its arguments coincide:

$$x_1 = x_2 = \ldots = x_n .$$

Thus it follows from the conditions of causality, unitarity, and symmetry that the Hermitean operator $\Lambda_n(x_1, \ldots, x_n)$ is a quasi-local operator in the sense of the definition given in § 16, and its coefficient functions have the form

$$Z\left(\ldots \frac{\partial}{\partial x_i} \ldots\right) \delta(x_1 - x_2) \ldots \delta(x_1 - x_n),$$

where due to considerations of invariance under translation Z cannot depend on x_i.

We have thus established that the conditions of invariance, symmetry, unitarity, and causality determine S_n when $S_1, S_2, \ldots, S_{n-1}$ are given up to $i\Lambda_n$ where $\Lambda_n(x_1, \ldots, x_n)$ is a Hermitean symmetric quasi-local operator which transforms like a scalar. Therefore in order to obtain expressions for $S_1, S_2, \ldots, S_n$ one must specify in addition to the operator $\mathscr{L}(x)$

a sequence of quasi-local operators

$$\Lambda_2(x_1, x_2), \ldots, \Lambda_n(x_1, \ldots, x_n).$$

We have thus arrived at results which at first glance seem somewhat strange. In order to completely determine the matrix $S(g)$ it turns out to be insufficient to specify the interaction Lagrangian, but it is also necessary to specify in addition an infinite sequence of quasi-local operators:

$$\Lambda_2(x_1, x_2), \Lambda_3(x_1, x_2, x_3), \ldots, \Lambda_n(x_1, \ldots, x_n) \ldots \quad (18.37)$$

In order to clarify this situation, let us approach this problem from a slightly different point of view. Let us consider the expression

$$T\left(\exp i \int \mathscr{L}(x; g)\, dx\right), \quad (18.38)$$

in which the "Lagrangian" $\mathscr{L}(x; g)$ is defined by the relation

$$\mathscr{L}(x; g) = \mathscr{L}(x)g(x) + \sum_{\nu \geqq 2} \frac{1}{\nu!} \int \Lambda_\nu(x, x_1, \ldots, x_{\nu-1}) g(x) g(x_1) \ldots g(x_{\nu-1}) dx_1 \ldots dx_{\nu-1}. \quad (18.39)$$

In view of the quasilocal nature of the functions Λ_ν, all the integrations in (18.39) disappear and $\mathscr{L}(x; g)$ in fact depends on the field functions $u(x)$ at the point x, and is therefore a local operator. In addition to the field operators $u(x)$ the expression $\mathscr{L}(x; g)$ also depends on the functions $g(x)$ which may be regarded as a "classical" field. Consequently (18.38) satisfies all the conditions imposed on $S(g)$, including the correspondence condition (18.16), and may be regarded as the expression for the scattering matrix $S(g)$. By expanding (18.38) into a series in powers of g we shall obtain expressions for $S_n(x_1, \ldots, x_n)$ which satisfy all the requirements imposed on them. We obtain:

$$T\left(\exp i \int \mathscr{L}(x; g)\, dx\right) = 1 + \sum_{m \geqq 1} \frac{i^m}{m!} \int T(\mathscr{L}(x_1; g) \ldots \mathscr{L}(x_m; g))\, dx_1 \ldots dx_m.$$

By substituting the expansion (18.39) into the foregoing expression, we obtain:

$$T\left(\exp i\int \mathscr{L}(x;\, g)dx\right)$$
$$= 1 + \sum_{\substack{m\geq 1 \\ (\nu_1\geq 0,\ldots,\nu_m\geq 0)}} \frac{i^m}{m!}\frac{1}{\nu_1!\ldots\nu_m!}\int T\,(\Lambda_{\nu_1}(x_1,\ldots,x_{\nu_1})\ldots$$
$$\ldots\Lambda_{\nu_m}(x_{\nu_1+\ldots+\nu_{m-1}+1},\ldots,x_{\nu_1+\ldots+\nu_m}))$$
$$\cdot\, g(x_1)\ldots g(x_{\nu_1+\ldots+\nu_m})dx_1\ldots dx_{\nu_1+\ldots+\nu_m},$$

in which we have set $\mathscr{L}(x) = \Lambda_1(x)$ in accordance with (18.16) and (18.20). The symbol

$$T(\Lambda_{\nu_1}(x_1,\ldots,x_{\nu_1})\ldots\Lambda_{\nu_s}(x_{\lambda+1},\ldots,x_{\lambda+\lambda_s}))$$

denotes the product of the operators $\Lambda_{\nu_1},\ldots,\Lambda_{\nu_s}$, taken in the chronological order of their time arguments. The multiplicity of arguments for each of Λ_ν should give us no concern since by definition Λ_ν differs from zero only when all its arguments coincide.

Let us now rearrange this series in powers of $g(x)$ by collecting terms in which $g(x)$ occurs raised to a definite nth power and which contain exactly n integrations:

$$T\left(\exp i\int \mathscr{L}(x;g)dx\right)$$
$$= 1 + \sum_{n\geq 1}\sum_{\substack{(1\leq m\leq n) \\ \sum\nu_i=n}} \frac{i^m}{m!}\frac{1}{\nu_1!\ldots\nu_m!}\int T\,(\Lambda_{\nu_1}(x_1,\ldots,x_{\nu_1})\ldots$$
$$\ldots\Lambda_{\nu_m}(x_{\nu_1+\ldots+\nu_{m-1}+1},\ldots,x_n))\,g(x_1)\ldots g(x_n)\,dx_1\ldots dx_n.$$

This last expansion still differs from the expansion (18.1) by the unsymmetric nature of the coefficients of the various "powers" of the function $g(x)$. In order to symmetrize them, let us by making use of the symmetry of the weighting factor $g(x_1)\ldots g(x_n)$ for any given n and of the symmetry of the functions Λ_ν interchange the designations of the variables $x_1,\ldots,x_n$ $n!/(\nu_1!\ldots\nu_m!)$ times so that after taking into account the symmetry of Λ_ν the sum of all the expressions thus obtained would be a symmetric function of all the arguments $x_1, \ldots, x_n$. After dividing the result by the number $n!/(\nu_1! \ldots \nu_m!)$ we arrive at the expression

$$T\left(\exp i \int \mathscr{L}(x; g)dx\right)$$

$$= 1 + \sum_{n \geq 1} \sum_{\left(\substack{1 \leq m \leq n \\ \Sigma \nu_i = 1}\right)} \frac{i^m}{n!\,m!} \int P(x_1, \ldots, x_{\nu_1} \mid x_{\nu_1+1} \ldots \mid \ldots, x_n)$$

$$\times T(\Lambda_{\nu_1}(x, \ldots, x_{\nu_1}) \ldots \Lambda_{\nu_m}(\ldots, x_n))\, g(x_1) \ldots g(x_n)dx_1 \ldots dx_n,$$

where $P(x_1, \ldots, x_{\nu_1} \mid x_{\nu_1+1} \ldots \mid \ldots, x_n)$ is the symmetrization operator over the arbitrary decompositions of the set of n points into $n!/(\nu_1! \ldots \nu_m!)$ possible combinations of $\nu_1, \nu_2, \ldots, \nu_m$ points at a time $(\Sigma \nu_i = n)$. This operator is a natural generalization of the operator introduced above

$$P\left(\frac{x_1, \ldots, x_\nu}{x_{\nu+1}, \ldots, x_n}\right) = P(x_1, \ldots, x_\nu \mid x_{\nu+1}, \ldots, x_n).$$

Thus the matrix (18.38) is written in the form (18.1) where the coefficients S_n have the form

$$S_n(x_1, \ldots, x_n) = \sum_{\left(\substack{1 \leq m \leq n \\ \Sigma \nu_i = n}\right)} \frac{i^m}{m!} P(x_1, \ldots, x_{\nu_1} \mid x_{\nu_1+1}, \ldots \mid \ldots, x_n)$$

$$\times T(\Lambda_{\nu_1}(x_1, \ldots x_{\nu_1}) \ldots \Lambda_{\nu_m}(\ldots x_n)).$$

Remembering that $\Lambda_1(x) = \mathscr{L}(x)$ we may rewrite S_n in the form

$$S_n(x_1, \ldots, x_n) = i^n T(\mathscr{L}(x_1) \ldots \mathscr{L}(x_n))$$

$$+ \sum_{\left(\substack{2 \leq m \leq n-1 \\ \Sigma \nu_i = n}\right)} \frac{i^m}{m!} P(x_1, \ldots, x_{\nu_1} \mid x_{\nu_1+1} \ldots \mid \ldots, x_n)$$

$$\times T[\Lambda_{\nu_1}(x_1, \ldots, x_{\nu_1}) \ldots \Lambda_{\nu_m}(\ldots x_n)] + i\Lambda_n(x_1, \ldots, x_n). \quad (18.40)$$

Let us examine several simple specific cases of the preceding formula. For $n = 2$ we obtain:

$$S_2(x_1, x_2) = i^2 T(\mathscr{L}(x_1)\, \mathscr{L}(x_2)) + i\Lambda_2(x_1, x_2).$$

For $n = 3$ we correspondingly obtain: [42]

$$S_3(x_1, x_2, x_3) = i^3 T(\mathscr{L}(x_1)\mathscr{L}(x_2)\mathscr{L}(x_3))$$

$$+ \sum_{\binom{\nu_1+\nu_2=3}{m=2}} \frac{i^2}{2!} P(x_1, x_{\nu_1}|\ldots, x_3) T(\Lambda_{\nu_1}(x_1, x_{\nu_1})\Lambda_{\nu_2}(\ldots x_3)) + i\Lambda_3(x_1, x_2, x_3)$$

$$= -iT(\mathscr{L}(x_1)\mathscr{L}(x_2)\mathscr{L}(x_3)) - T(\mathscr{L}(x_1)\Lambda_2(x_2, x_3))$$

$$- T(\mathscr{L}(x_2)\Lambda_2(x_1, x_3)) - T(\mathscr{L}(x_3)\Lambda_2(x_1, x_2)) + i\Lambda_3(x_1, x_2, x_3).$$

From this we see that each successive function S_n is expressed in terms of the preceding $S_1, \ldots, S_{n-1}$ up to a symmetric, anti-Hermitean, quasi-local operator $i\Lambda_n(x_1, \ldots, x_n)$. Therefore expression (18.40) is the most general expression for S_n, while the expression

$$S(g) = T\left(\exp i \int \mathscr{L}(x; g) dx\right),$$

where $\mathscr{L}(x; g)$ is defined by the expansion (18.39), is the most general expression for the scattering matrix. Thus the *sequence of quasi-local operators* (18.37) which must be given in order that the scattering matrix $S(g)$ should be completely determined may in fact be included in the interaction "Lagrangian."

The question now arises as to the physical meaning of the linear combination (18.39) of $\mathscr{L}(x)g(x)$ and of the integrals over quasi-local operators which plays the role of the most general acceptable Lagrangian. The structure and the interrelationship of expressions (18.39) and (18.40) which contain arbitrary quasi-local operators is determined by a purely mathematical property of expansions occurring in perturbation theory in general which had been previously noted by Poincaré.

In order to illustrate the aforementioned property, let us consider the differential equation

$$\frac{dy(x)}{dx} = \varepsilon y(x), \tag{18.41}$$

[42] The form of the second line of this formula (under the summation sign) is somewhat schematic. However, its meaning is clear from (18.40) and from subsequent material.

whose solution $y(x)$ contains one arbitrary constant C:

$$y(x) = Ce^{\varepsilon x}.$$

Considering ε to be a small parameter we shall solve equation (18.41) by the method of successive approximations. At each stage of the approximation we shall obtain on integration an arbitrary constant of the corresponding order of smallness in ε. Thus, in solving equation (18.41) by the method of perturbation theory, we shall obtain in place of a single arbitrary constant C an infinite set of arbitrary constants of various orders of smallness in ε:

$$C_0, \varepsilon C_1, \ldots, \varepsilon^n C_n, \ldots$$

This is essentially equivalent to the constant C being expanded into a series in powers of ε, i.e.,

$$C = C_0 + \varepsilon C_1 + \ldots + \varepsilon^n C_n + \ldots$$

In an exactly similar manner we have utilized in our argument the nonphysical operation of "switching on" the interaction. It turns out that in this procedure a part of the Lagrangian was "switched on" in the first approximation, a part in the second, a part in the nth approximation, and the interaction Lagrangian turned out to be broken up into a sequence of separate pieces. However, only the situation when the interaction has been switched on completely has a physical meaning. In this case, the function $g(x)$ is equal to unity and the expression (18.39) takes on the form

$$\mathscr{L}(x; 1) = \mathscr{L}(x) + \sum_{\nu \geqq 2} \frac{1}{\nu!} \int \Lambda_\nu(x, x_1, \ldots, x_{\nu-1}) dx_1 \ldots dx_{\nu-1}, \quad (18.42)$$

$$S(1) = S = T(\exp i \int \mathscr{L}(x; 1) dx). \quad (18.43)$$

Therefore the actual *scattering matrix* $S(1)$ *is completely characterized by the actual interaction Lagrangian of the system* $\mathscr{L}(x; 1)$ which in perturbation theory is sometimes represented in the form of a series.

In the usual presentation of field theory, starting with Schrödinger's equation, a representation for the scattering matrix is obtained in the form

$$T(\exp [- i \int H(x)dx]), \tag{18.44}$$

where $H(x)$ is the interaction Hamiltonian density. However, $H(x)$ coincides with $-\mathscr{L}$ only in particularly simple cases when $\mathscr{L}$ does not depend on the derivatives of the field functions (cf. (8.6)). In the general case H contains in addition to the term $-\mathscr{L}$ certain other noncovariant terms. By means of a fairly complicated procedure (85), these terms are completely eliminated and expression (18.44) is brought to the form (18.43).

§ 19. Evaluation of Chronological Products

19.1. *Chronological Pairing*

Since we now have an explicit expression for the scattering matrix, we may proceed to evaluate its matrix elements between different states. In the course of this calculation we shall have to reduce the terms of the matrix to the normal form, i.e., to such a form that in each individual term all the annihilation operators are placed to the right and all the creation operators to the left.

Let us therefore express the T-products of local operators $\mathscr{L}(x)$ in terms of the normal products of the corresponding field operators. In this connection we shall find it convenient to extend the notion of the T-product to the case of the general system of linear operators defined in § 16.

We define [43] the chronological or the ordered product

$$T(A_1(x_1) \ldots A_n(x_n))$$

of linear operators $A_1(x_1) \ldots A_n(x_n)$ as their ordinary product in chronological order multiplied by $\eta = (-1)^p$ where p is the parity of the Fermi-permutations in the transition from the order $1, \ldots, n$ to the chronological order, i.e.,

$$\begin{gathered} T(A_1(x_1) \ldots A_n(x_n)) = \eta A_{j_1}(x_{j_1}) \ldots A_{j_n}(x_{j_n}) \\ (x^0_{j_1} \geqq x^0_{j_2} \geqq \ldots \geqq x^0_{j_n}), \end{gathered} \tag{19.1}$$

[43] This definition is a natural generalization of the definition of the T-product of two field operators given in § 14.

where p is the parity of the permutation of the Fermi operators in the transition from the order $(1, 2, \ldots, n)$ to the order $(j_1, j_2, \ldots, j_n)$.

The prescription for the evaluation of such products is given by *Wick's theorem for T-products* which is the analog of Wick's theorem for ordinary products. Before beginning the proof of this theorem we shall introduce the important concept of the *chronological pairing of operators.*

In order to do this, we examine (19.1) in the case of two field operators. Then

$$T(u_1(x_1)\,u_2(x_2)) = \begin{cases} u_1(x_1)\,u_2(x_2) & (x_1^0 > x_2^0), \\ \eta u_2(x_2)\,u_1(x_1) & (x_2^0 > x_1^0). \end{cases}$$

In accordance with the definition or ordinary pairing

$$u_1(x_1)\,u_2(x_2) = \,:u_1(x_1)\,u_2(x_2):\, + \underbracket{u_1(x_1)\,u_2(x_2)}$$

the above expression may be brought into the form

$$T(u_1(x_1)\,u_2(x_2)) = \begin{cases} :u_1(x_1)\,u_2(x_2):\, + \underbracket{u_1(x_1)\,u_2(x_2)} & (x_1^0 > x_2^0), \\ \eta\,:u_2(x_2)\,u_1(x_1):\, + \eta\,\underbracket{u_2(x_2)\,u_1(x_1)} & \\ = \,:u_1(x_1)\,u_2(x_2):\, + \eta\,\underbracket{u_2(x_2)\,u_1(x_1)} & (x_2^0 > x_1^0). \end{cases} \tag{19.2}$$

From this it may be seen that in any arbitrary case $T(u_1(x_1)\,u_2(x_2))$ differs from $:u_1(x_1)\,u_2(x_2):$ by a c-number which we shall call the *chronological pairing* $\overbracket{u_1(x_1)\,u_2(x_2)}$, i.e., by definition

$$T(u_1(x_1)\,u_2(x_2)) = \,:u_1(x_1)\,u_2(x_2):\, + \overbracket{u_1(x_1)\,u_2(x_2)} \tag{19.3}$$

and

$$\overbracket{u_1(x_1)\,u_2(x_2)} = \begin{cases} \underbracket{u_1(x_1)\,u_2(x_2)} & \text{for } x_1^0 > x_2^0, \\ \eta\,\underbracket{u_2(x_2)\,u_1(x_1)} & \text{for } x_2^0 > x_1^0. \end{cases} \tag{19.4}$$

First of all, let us note an important property of chronological pairing. *It is permissible to interchange the order of factors within a chronological pairing* just as it is permissible to do so within a normal product:

$$\overline{u_1(x_1)\, u_2(x_2)} = \eta\, \overline{u_2(x_2)\, u_1(x_1)},$$

which follows directly from (19.4).

We shall now define chronological pairings for the operators of the principal wave fields. To do this we note that by evaluating the vacuum expectation value $\Phi_0^* \ldots \Phi_0 = \langle \quad \rangle_0$ of (19.3), and taking into account the fundamental property of the normal product and the normalization of the amplitude of the vacuum state, we shall obtain

$$\langle T(u_1(x_1)\, u_2(x_2))\rangle_0 = \overline{u_1(x_1)\, u_2(x_2)}, \tag{19.5}$$

i.e., that the chronological pairing of two field operators is equal to the vacuum expectation value of the chronological product of these operators. On the other hand, it was established in § 14 that such expectation values are equal up to a factor i to causal Green's functions of the corresponding fields. By using formulas obtained in that section we find:

for the scalar field

$$\overline{\varphi(x)\,\varphi(y)} = \langle T(\varphi(x)\,\varphi(y))\rangle_0 = \frac{1}{i}\, D^c(x-y) = \frac{1}{(2\pi)^4 i}\int \frac{e^{ik(x-y)}}{m^2-k^2-i\varepsilon}\,dk, \tag{19.6}$$

for the electromagnetic field

$$\overline{A_l(x) A_n(y)} = \langle T(A_l(x) A_n(y))\rangle_0 = i g^{ln} D_0^c(x-y) = \frac{g^{ln}}{(2\pi)^4 i}\int \frac{e^{ik(x-y)}}{k^2+i\varepsilon}\,dk, \tag{19.7}$$

for the vector field

$$\overline{U_n(x) U_l(y)} = \langle T(U_n(x)\, U_l(y))\rangle_0 = \frac{1}{i}\, D_{nl}^c(x-y)$$

$$= \frac{1}{(2\pi)^4 i}\int \frac{\left(g^{nl} - \dfrac{k_n k_l}{m^2}\right)}{m^2-k^2-i\varepsilon}\, e^{ik(x-y)}\,dk, \tag{19.8}$$

for the spinor field

$$\overbracket{\psi_\alpha(x)\bar{\psi}_\beta(y)} = \langle T(\psi_\alpha(x)\bar{\psi}_\beta(y))\rangle_0 = \frac{1}{i} S^c_{\alpha\beta}(x-y)$$

$$= \frac{1}{(2\pi)^4 i}\int \frac{(m-\hat{p})_{\alpha\beta}}{m^2-p^2-i\varepsilon}\, e^{ip(x-y)}\, dp. \quad (19.9)$$

However, we note that the formulas which lead to (19.6)–(19.9) were derived in § 14 only for $x^0 > y^0$ and for $x^0 < y^0$. From the property of covariance of T-products established in § 18 it follows that these formulas are also valid for $x \sim y$. Thus formulas (19.6)–(19.9) may be considered to hold everywhere for $x \neq y$.

The rules for integrating these expressions over an infinitesimal neighborhood of the point $x = y$ *may be fixed arbitrarily.* Thus, for example, it is always possible to add to the right-hand side of each of these expressions an arbitrary coefficient function of a quasi-local operator

$$P\left(\frac{\partial}{\partial x}\right)\delta(x-y),$$

where $P(\partial/\partial x)$ is a polynomial in $\partial/\partial x^\alpha$. This necessity of making an additional definition of pairing in an infinitesimal neighborhood of the point $x = y$ is a particular expression of the arbitrariness contained in the T-product. Indeed, the T-products are completely specified by our formal "definition" (18.26) and (19.2) only when their arguments are all different. Therefore, it is necessary to complete their definition within infinitesimal neighborhoods of those points at which the arguments coincide by specifying the rules for integrating their coefficient functions, i.e., in other words, the coefficient functions of T-products should be defined as integrable improper functions.

Thus we arrive at the conclusion that it is necessary not only to choose an interaction Lagrangian, but also at the same time to supplement the definitions of the T-products.

However, it should be noted that the influence on $S(g)$ of a change in the T-product may be taken into account by changing the Lagrangian $\mathscr{L}(x)$. Indeed by changing the T-products of field functions we introduce into the T-products of the interaction

Lagrangians various quasi-local operators which, as was shown in the preceding section, is equivalent to the addition of certain expressions to the interaction Lagrangian.

Consequently *in order to obtain the matrix elements of the scattering matrix* $S(g)$ *that determine the structure of physical processes, it is necessary to specify simultaneously the interaction Lagrangian and the rules for integrating* T*-products.* If the rules for integrating T-products are already specified, then the interaction Lagrangian $\mathscr{L}(x)$ should be chosen in a way *consistent* with these rules.

The dependence of the form of the Lagrangian on certain subsidiary considerations is by no means a specific peculiarity of quantum field theory. For example, in classical physics in order to determine the form of the Lagrangian, it is necessary first of all to choose independent dynamic variables (compare the treatments of the scalar field in the usual way (§ 3) and in Kemmer's formalism (§ 4.4)).

Thus, we must first of all complete the definition of all the pairings, and also of their products, in such a way that the products are integrable functions. As a result of this requirement, the T-products will turn out to be completely determined and it will then be possible to determine the Lagrangian.

We shall give a detailed treatment of these problems, which are connected with the problem of the regularization of the S-matrix, in the next chapter. For the present we shall restrict ourselves to completing the definition of the pairings of field functions. We shall adopt the convention that if for $x \neq y$ the pairing coincides with a certain Green's function

$$\Delta^c_{\alpha\beta}(x-y) = P_{\alpha\beta}\left(\frac{\partial}{\partial x}\right) D^c(x-y),$$

then it also coincides with this function in an infinitesimal neighborhood of the point $x = y$. In particular, we shall consider that formulas (19.6)–(19.9) are also valid in the infinitesimal neighborhood of the point $x = y$.

Let us also consider the general case when the field is described by a system of equations of the first order. As we have seen in

§ **14** the field functions in such a case satisfy the commutation relations

$$[u_\alpha(x),\ u^\dagger_\beta(y)] = \frac{1}{i} \Delta_{\alpha\beta}(x - y) = \frac{1}{i} P_{\alpha\beta}\left(\frac{\partial}{\partial x}\right) D(x - y),$$

$$[u^{(\pm)}_\alpha(x),\ u^{\dagger(\mp)}_\beta(y)] = \frac{1}{i} \Delta^{(\pm)}_{\alpha\beta}(x - y) = \frac{1}{i} P_{\alpha\beta}\left(\frac{\partial}{\partial x}\right) D^{(\pm)}(x - y).$$

Therefore on calculating the ordinary pairing we obtain:

$$\underbracket{u_\alpha(x) u^\dagger_\beta}(y) = \frac{1}{i} \Delta^{(-)}_{\alpha\beta}(x - y),$$

from which we find by standard methods the following expressions for chronological pairing

$$\overbracket{u_\alpha(x) u^\dagger_\beta}(y) = \begin{cases} -i\Delta^{(-)}_{\alpha\beta}(x - y) & (x^0 > y^0), \\ i\Delta^{(+)}_{\alpha\beta}(x - y) & (y^0 > x^0), \end{cases}$$

which for $x \neq y$ coincide with

$$\frac{1}{i} \Delta^c_{\alpha\beta}(x - y) = \frac{1}{i} P_{\alpha\beta}\left(\frac{\partial}{\partial x}\right) D^c(x - y).$$

We therefore assume that for arbitrary x and y

$$\overbracket{u_\alpha(x) u^\dagger_\beta}(y) = \frac{1}{i} \Delta^c_{\alpha\beta}(x - y). \tag{19.10}$$

In a number of cases derivatives of field functions may appear in the interaction Lagrangian. It is therefore useful to give here a complete definition of their pairings. After noting that for $x^0 \gtrless y^0$

$$\overbracket{\frac{\partial^k u_\alpha(x)}{(\partial x^0)^{k_0} \dots (\partial x^3)^{k_3}} \frac{\partial^q u^\dagger_\beta}{(\partial y^0)^{q_0} \dots (\partial y^3)^{q_3}}}(y)$$

$$= \frac{\partial^k}{(\partial x^0)^{k_0} \dots (\partial x^3)^{k_3}} \frac{\partial^q}{(\partial y^0)^{q_0} \dots (\partial y^3)^{q_3}} \overbracket{u_\alpha(x) u^\dagger_\beta}(y), \tag{19.11}$$

we assume that by definition (19.11) is valid for arbitrary x and y.

We also note some properties of chronological pairings and T-products.

As may be easily seen, the free field operators which occur in the normal products and in the ordinary pairings remain "free" in the sense that the above expressions reduce to zero when acted upon by the differential operators of the free field equations. Thus, for the scalar field

$$(\Box_x - m^2) : \varphi(x)\varphi(y) : = 0, \tag{19.12}$$

$$(\Box_x - m^2)\, \underbrace{\varphi(x)\varphi(y)} = 0. \tag{19.13}$$

It might seem that this property should also be retained by the chronological pairing defined in (19.4) in terms of ordinary pairings, and consequently also by the T-product. However, in fact (because the definition (19.4) is not satisfied at the point $x = y$) this does not occur. Indeed, as we have just shown, chronological pairings may be expressed in terms of causal Green's functions satisfying inhomogeneous field equations. Thus for a scalar field we have in accordance with (19.5):

$$(\Box_x - m^2)\overbrace{\varphi(x)\varphi}(y) = i\delta(x - y). \tag{19.14}$$

The same consequently holds also in the case of T-products. In particular, for a scalar field we find, for example, with the aid of (19.3), (19.12), and (19.14):

$$(\Box_x - m^2)T(\varphi(x)\varphi(y)) = i\delta(x - y). \tag{19.15}$$

Thus in the interaction representation the field operators within a T-product should be regarded as not satisfying the homogeneous field equations.

19.2. *Wick's Theorem for Chronological Products*

Wick's theorem for chronological products asserts that the T-product of a system of n linear operators is equal to the sum of their normal products with all possible chronological pairings (including the term with no pairings).

The proof in fact reduces to the proof of Wick's theorem for ordinary products. Indeed, according to the definition (19.1) a T-product is equal to a certain ordinary product

$$T(A_1(x_1) \ldots A_n(x_n)) = \eta A_{j_1}(x_{j_1}) \ldots A_{j_n}(x_{j_n}).$$

By applying Wick's theorem to this ordinary product, we see that it is equal to the sum of the normal products of the operators $A_{j_1}(x_{j_1}) \ldots A_{j_n}(x_{j_n})$ with all possible ordinary pairings. But since the order in the sequence $x_{j_1}, \ldots, x_{j_n}$ is chronologically correct the ordinary pairings will coincide with the chronological ones, i.e., $T(A_1(x_1) \ldots A_n(x_n))$ is equal to the product of η and the sum of the normal products of the operators $A_{j_1}(x_{j_1}) \ldots A_{j_n}(x_{j_n})$ with all possible chronological pairings.

As has been noted before, linear operators within a chronological pairing may be commuted (taking possible changes of sign into account). As a result we may reestablish the normal order of the factors 1, 2, . . ., n within normal products with all possible chronological pairings, at the same time leaving out the factor η. This completes the proof of the theorem.

Let us now consider the T-product of several normal products of linear field operators $A_i(x) \ldots D_j(z)$

$$T(:A_1(x)A_2(x) \ldots A_n(x): \ldots :D_1(z) \ldots D_m(z):). \tag{19.16}$$

T-products of just this form will be needed for the evaluation of T-products of local operators, since, by definition, the local operator $\mathscr{L}(x)$ is expressed as a linear combination of terms of the type

$$:A_1(x)A_2(x) \ldots A_n(x):.$$

The formulation of Wick's theorem for T-products of the type (19.16) has only the single special feature that mutual chronological pairings of operators occurring within the same normal product should not be taken into account.

For illustration let us reduce to the normal form the T-product of two current operators for the spinor field

$$J^m(x) = :\bar{\psi}(x)\gamma^m\psi(x): \text{ and } J^n(y) = :\bar{\psi}(y)\gamma^n\psi(y):.$$

Utilizing Wick's theorem, taking into account the vanishing of the pairings $\overline{\psi(x)\psi(y)}$ and $\overline{\bar{\psi}(x)\bar{\psi}(y)}$, and not taking into account the pairings $\overline{\psi(x)\bar{\psi}(x)}$ and $\overline{\psi(y)\bar{\psi}(y)}$ we obtain:

$$\begin{aligned} T(J^m(x), J^n(y)) &= T(:\bar{\psi}(x)\gamma^m\psi(x):, :\bar{\psi}(y)\gamma^n\psi(y):) \\ &= :\bar{\psi}(x)\gamma^m\psi(x)\bar{\psi}(y)\gamma^n\psi(y): + :\overline{\bar{\psi}(x)\gamma^m\psi(x)\bar{\psi}(y)\gamma^n\psi(y)}: \\ &+ :\bar{\psi}(x)\gamma^m\overline{\psi(x)\bar{\psi}(y)}\gamma^n\psi(y): + :\overline{\bar{\psi}(x)\gamma^m\overline{\psi(x)\bar{\psi}(y)}\gamma^n\psi(y)}:. \end{aligned}$$

Taking into account the fact that according to (19.8)

$$\overbrace{\psi(x)\,\bar{\psi}(y)} = \frac{1}{i}\, S^c(x-y)$$

and

$$\overbrace{\bar{\psi}(x)\,\psi(y)} = -\,\overbrace{\psi(y)\,\bar{\psi}(x)} = iS^c(y-x),$$

and carrying out the summation over the spinor indices we finally obtain:

$$T(J^m(x), J^n(y)) = :J^m(x)\, J^n(y): \; -i :\bar{\psi}(y)\,\gamma^n S^c(y-x)\,\gamma^m\,\psi(x): \\ -i :\bar{\psi}(x)\gamma^m S^c(x-y)\gamma^n\psi(y): + \mathrm{Sp}(S^c(x-y)\gamma^n S^c(y-x)\gamma^m). \quad (19.17)$$

In conclusion we note that starting with (19.16) one may also define a T-product of normal products of a more general type

$$T(: A_1(x_1) \ldots A_n(x_n) : \ldots : D(z_1) \ldots D_m(z_m) :) \quad (19.18)$$

as a sum of normal products of the operators

$$A_1(x_1) \ldots D_m(z_m)$$

with all possible pairings, excluding mutual pairings of operators occurring in the same normal product.

On the basis of such a definition of the T-product, it is possible to introduce the T-product of polylocal operators

$$T(A(x_1, \ldots, x_n) \ldots D(z_1, \ldots, z_m)), \quad (19.19)$$

by expressing it as a linear combination of expressions of type (19.18). The direct definition of the T-product (19.19) using the chronological criterion is not convenient in the present case because of the multiplicity of arguments of the operators $A, \ldots, D$.

It may be seen from the above that in effect the T-product represents a new algebraic operation which may be introduced independently of ordinary products.

From the mathematical point of view the T-product is particularly attractive due to the fact that, in contrast to ordinary products, the operators within a T-product may be permuted as if they commute or anticommute exactly.

§ 20. Reduction of the S-Matrix to the Normal Form

20.1. *Structure of the Coefficients of the Scattering Matrix*

We now proceed to formulate a convenient set of prescriptions for reducing to the normal form T-products of Lagrangians which define the operator expressions $S_n(x_1, \ldots, x_n)$ occurring in the scattering matrix. For the sake of simplicity, it is convenient to begin our presentation by considering a specific case. Let us therefore consider the interaction between the electromagnetic and the spinor electron-positron fields. In accordance with well-established tradition, we shall take the electrons to be the fundamental particles of the spinor field and the positrons to be the antiparticles. Therefore the operators of the spinor field $a^{*\nu,+}$ and $a^{\nu,-}$ (see § 12) describe creation and annihilation of electrons, while the operators $a^{\nu,+}$ and $a^{*\nu,-}$ refer to positrons. Naturally, in view of the complete symmetry of our presentation, one could just as well regard positrons as the fundamental particles, and electrons as the antiparticles. In such a case the roles played by the operators $a^{*\nu,+}$, $a^{\nu,-}$ and $a^{\nu,+}$, $a^{*\nu,-}$ would be interchanged, and one would only need to change the sign of the electric current, which, in the usual form adopted by us, appears as follows:

$$j^m(x) = -eJ^m(x) = -e:\bar{\psi}(x)\gamma^m\psi(x):. \tag{20.1}$$

Here e is the magnitude of the charge of the electron multiplied by $\sqrt{4\pi}$ and is equal to

$$e = \sqrt{\frac{4\pi}{137}} \tag{20.2}$$

in the natural system of units which we employ (§ 1).[44]

In accordance with formula (8.7), the interaction Lagrangian for the electromagnetic and the electron-positron fields has the form

$$\mathscr{L}(x) = -\sum_n :j^n(x)A_n(x): = e\sum_n :\bar{\psi}(x)\gamma^n\psi(x)A_n(x):. \tag{20.3}$$

Taking into account the elementary chronological pairings (19.7) and (19.9)

$$\overbracket{A_m(x)A_n(y)} = ig^{mn}D_0^c(x-y),$$

$$\overbracket{\psi_\sigma(x)\bar{\psi}_\rho(y)} = -\overbracket{\bar{\psi}_\rho(y)\psi_\sigma(x)} = \frac{1}{i}S^c_{\sigma\rho}(x-y),$$

[44] A more accurate value is $\alpha = \dfrac{e^2}{4\pi} = \dfrac{1}{137.036}$.

we consider the process of reduction to the normal form of the individual terms of the S-matrix

$$S(1) = 1 + \sum_{n \geqq 1} \frac{1}{n!} \int S_n(x_1, \ldots, x_n) dx_1 \ldots dx_n,$$

$$S_n(x_1, \ldots, x_n) = i^n T(\mathscr{L}(x_1) \ldots \mathscr{L}(x_n)), \qquad (18.31)$$

which depend on the Lagrangian (20.3). The first-order term is already written in the normal form:

$$S_1(x) = i\mathscr{L}(x) = ie : \bar{\psi}(x) \hat{A}(x) \psi(x) :. \qquad (20.4)$$

In the second order we obtain:

$$S_2(x, y) = i^2 T(\mathscr{L}(x) \mathscr{L}(y)) = -e^2 \sum_{m,n} T(: J^m(x) A_m(x) :: J^n(y) A_n(y) :).$$

Since the operators of the electromagnetic field commute with those of the electron-positron field, the aforementioned T-product may be expressed as a product of two T-products:

$$T(J^m(x) J^n(y)) T(A_m(x) A_n(y)).$$

The first factor $T(J^m(x) J^n(y))$ was evaluated by us in the preceding section (19.17), while the second factor may be evaluated in an elementary way by means of formula (19.3) and of the pairing of the electromagnetic field (19.7). We therefore obtain

$$\begin{aligned} S_2(x, y) = & - e^2 \sum_{m,n} (: A_m(x) A_n(y) : + i g^{mn} D_0^c(x - y)) \\ & \times \{: J^m(x) J^n(y) : - i : \bar{\psi}(y) \gamma^n S^c(y - x) \gamma^m \psi(x) : \\ & - i : \bar{\psi}(x) \gamma^m S^c(x - y) \gamma^n \psi(y) : + \mathrm{Sp}\, (S^c(x - y) \gamma^n S^c(y - x) \gamma^m)\} \\ = & -e^2 \sum_{m,n} \{: J^m(x) A_m(x) J^n(y) A_n(y) : + i : J^m(x) J^n(y) : g^{mn} D_0^c(x-y) \\ & - i : \bar{\psi}(y) \gamma^n A_n(y) S^c(y - x) \gamma^m A_m(x) \psi(x) : \\ & - i : \bar{\psi}(x) \gamma^m A_m(x) S^c(x-y) \gamma^n A_n(y) \psi(y) : + g^{mn} : \bar{\psi}(y) \gamma^n S^c(y-x) \\ & \times D_0^c(x - y) \gamma^m \psi(x) : + g^{mn} : \bar{\psi}(x) \gamma^m S^c(x - y) D_0^c(x - y) \gamma^n \psi(y) : \\ & + \mathrm{Sp} : (S^c(x - y) \gamma^n A_n(y) S^c(y - x) \gamma^m A_m(x) : + i g^{mn} D_0^c(x - y) \\ & \times \mathrm{Sp}\, (S^c(x - y) \gamma^n S^c(y - x) \gamma^m)\}. \end{aligned} \qquad (20.5)$$

In expressions (20.4) and (20.5) we have adopted the order of writing down the matrix operators such that within a normal product the spinor operators $\bar{\psi}$ and ψ are always ordered in accordance with a definite principle. In accordance with (20.3) each $\mathscr{L}$ contains one spinor $\bar{\psi}$ and one spinor ψ. Therefore, the nth order term of a T-product contains n operators $\bar{\psi}$ and n operators ψ. In the process of reducing the T-product to the normal form certain pairs of operators $\bar{\psi}(x_i)\psi(x_j)$ will be replaced by the corresponding pairings. Thus, after the individual terms of the T-product have been reduced to the normal form, each of the terms of the resulting expression (for example, the terms (20.5)) will contain the same number of operators $\bar{\psi}$ and ψ. Moreover, each $\bar{\psi}(x_k)$ may be made to correspond to a definite $\psi(x_{j_k})$ by following through the sequence of the arguments of the pairings

$$\overline{\psi(x_k)\bar{\psi}(x_{i_k})},\ \overline{\psi(x_{i_k})\bar{\psi}(x_{l_k})},\ \ldots,\ \overline{\psi(x_{m_k})\bar{\psi}(x_{j_k})}. \tag{20.6}$$

The free operators ψ and $\bar{\psi}$ occurring in the normal products may therefore always be divided into pairs with the same arguments (in the case if both operators ψ and $\bar{\psi}$ from some $\mathscr{L}(x)$ did not undergo pairing) or with arguments related by a sequence of arguments of corresponding S_c-functions.

We shall agree to write down the free operators in such a way that the operators forming pairs should be next to each other (only c-functions may stand between them), and that within each pair $\bar{\psi}(x_k)$ should always be to the left of $\psi(x_{j_k})$, i.e., in the form

$$:\bar{\psi}(x_1)\psi(x_{j_1})\bar{\psi}(x_2)\psi(x_{j_2})\ldots\bar{\psi}(x_k)\psi(x_{j_k}):. \tag{20.7}$$

Permutations of pairs among themselves do not alter the value of the normal product and therefore the order of the pairs is immaterial. All the terms in (20.4) and (20.5) are written in the form (20.7). In the future we shall always make use of this method of writing our formulas; this will enable us to obtain in a simple way the rule for determining the sign of any arbitrary term obtained as a result of evaluating a T-product of the form (18.31).

Expressions having a structure similar to (20.5) may also be obtained without difficulty for higher order terms. Using Wick's theorem for T-products, it may be immediately shown that the coefficient S_n (up to a factor i^n) is equal to the sum of normal products of Lagrangians $\mathscr{L}(x_1) \ldots \mathscr{L}(x_n)$ with all possible pairings. With the aid of this theorem it is also possible to formulate rules for automatically writing down the elements of the scattering matrix in normal form, and, consequently, also the matrix elements.

20.2. *Feynman Diagrams and the Rules of Correspondence*

In order to obtain such rules the elements of the S-matrix are made to correspond to certain graphical diagrams first introduced by Feynman (**40**, **41**) which we shall call "Feynman diagrams."

In order to introduce Feynman diagrams, it is necessary to establish certain definite rules of correspondence. As we have established above, the operator functions $S_n(x_1, \ldots, x_n)$ may be represented in accordance with Wick's theorem in the form of a sum of terms each of which is a product of a certain number of pairings of the electromagnetic field $\overbracket{A(x)\,A(y)}$ and the spinor field $\overbracket{\psi(x)\,\bar{\psi}(y)}$ by the normal product of the free operators $\bar{\psi}$, ψ, A and a certain number of matrices γ^n.

It is obvious that in order to give a graphical description of the terms of the scattering matrix in the above case (20.3) at present under consideration it is sufficient to specify the graphical representation of the two pairings

$$\overbracket{A_m(x_i)\,A_n(x_j)}, \quad \overbracket{\psi(x_k)\,\bar{\psi}(x_l)},$$

of the three free operators

$$\psi(x_i), \quad \bar{\psi}(x_j), \quad A_n(x_k)$$

and of the Dirac matrices γ^n.

We therefore agree to represent in our diagram the pairing

$$\overbracket{A_m(x_i)\,A_n(x_j)} = \overbracket{A_n(x_j)\,A_m(x_i)} = i g^{mn} D_0^c(x_i - x_j),$$

which is symmetrical in its arguments x_i and x_j, by a wavy line connecting the points x_i and x_j:

which may be considered to be a representation of the motion of a photon between the points x_i and x_j.

The nonsymmetric pairing

$$\overbrace{\psi(x_k)\,\bar{\psi}(x_l)} = \frac{1}{i} S^c(x_k - x_l)$$

we shall make correspond in the diagram to a directed line connecting the points x_i and x_j. It is convenient to choose the direction of this line by a direct inspection of the situation. We have already agreed to adopt the convention that the operator $\psi(x)$ describes the creation of a positron and the annihilation of an electron at the point x, while the operator $\bar{\psi}(y)$ describes the creation of an electron and the annihilation of a positron at the point y. In the other words, the operator $\psi(x)$ appears to correspond to an electron arriving at the point x, while $\bar{\psi}(x)$ appears to correspond to an electron leaving the point x (and *vice versa* for a positron).

Since electrons are taken to be the fundamental particles of the spinor field ψ it is natural to make the pairing $\overbrace{\psi(x_k)\bar{\psi}(x_l)}$ correspond in the diagram to a line directed from the point x_l to the point x_k, i.e.,

The directed lines introduced in this manner may be regarded as representing the motion of an electron between the points x_l and x_k of the diagram (or as representing the motion of a positron from the point x_k to the point x_l).[45]

We shall make the free operators $A(x)$, $\psi(x)$ and $\bar{\psi}(x)$ correspond to lines connecting the point x with the edge of the diagram. In so doing we make the operator $A_m(x)$ correspond to an undirected wavy (photon) line:

[45] Refer to the following section with respect to the correspondence of the diagrams introduced in the foregoing manner to actually occurring processes.

the operator $\psi(x)$ to a directed (electron) line entering the point x:

and the operator $\bar{\psi}(x)$ to a directed (electron) line leaving the point x:

To the Dirac matrix γ^k from the Lagrangian $\mathscr{L}(x_i)$ multiplied by the interaction constant e, we shall make correspond in the diagram the point x_i in which one photon line, one entering electron line and one emerging electron line all meet:

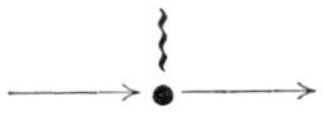

x_i

We shall call such points the *vertices* (or *junctions*) of the diagram. Table I gives a summary of the rules of correspondence between the various factors of the terms of the operator functions S_n and the elements of Feynman diagrams.

The rules of correspondence have been chosen in such a way that the diagram corresponding to one of the terms expressed in the normal form which occurs in the expression for the operator function $S_n(x_1, \ldots, x_n)$ consists of n vertices and of a certain number of internal and external photon and electron lines. In virtue of the local nature of the interaction Lagrangian (20.3) one electron line enters and one electron line leaves each vertex. Thus the electron lines of the complete diagram are continuous at the vertices and form either closed loops or continuous zig-zag lines which begin and end at the edges of the diagram. The sequence of the arguments of the pairings (20.6) determines the sequence of the vertices of the individual electron lines of the diagram, while the pairs of free operators $\bar{\psi}(x_i)\psi(x_{j_i})$ within a normal product correspond to the beginning (x_{j_i}) and to the end (x_i) of individual electron lines which do not form loops. A

Table I. Rules of Correspondence

Factor in the scattering matrix	Element of a Feynman diagram
1. Pairing of operators of the electromagnetic field $\overline{A_n(x)A_m(y)} = ig^{mn}D_0^c(x-y)$	1. Internal photon line 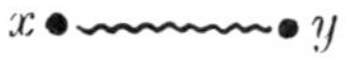
2. Pairing of operators of the spinor field $\overline{\psi_\alpha(x)\bar{\psi}_\beta(y)} = \frac{1}{i} S^c_{\alpha\beta}(x-y)$	2. Internal electron line 
3. Free operator $A_m(x)$ inside a normal product	3. External photon line 
4. Free operator $\psi(x)$ inside a normal product	4. Entering external electron line 
5. Free operator $\bar{\psi}(x)$ inside a normal product	5. Emerging external electron line 
6. Dirac matrix γ^k from the Lagrangian $\mathscr{L}(x)$ multiplied by e: $e\gamma^k$	6. Vertex 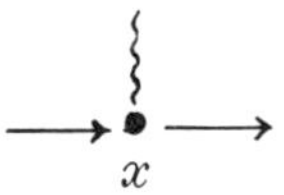

characteristic feature of the rules of correspondence is the fact that the coefficient functions $K_i(x_1, \ldots, x_n)$ of the operator expressions $S_n(x_1, \ldots, x_n)$:

$$S_n(x_1, \ldots, x_n) = \sum_i K_i(x_1, \ldots, x_n) : \ldots A(x_j) \ldots \bar{\psi}(x_k) \ldots \psi(x_l) \ldots :,$$

which consist entirely of chronological pairings of the operators ψ, $\bar{\psi}$ and A, correspond to the internal lines of the diagram, while the free operators within a normal product correspond to external lines.

As an example we consider one of the second-order terms

which occurs in the expression (20.5) for $S_2(x, y)$

$$\begin{aligned} & i^2 e^2 : \bar{\psi}(x)\,\hat{A}(x)\psi(x)\,\bar{\psi}(y)\hat{A}(y)\,\psi(y): \\ & \qquad = e^2\,\mathrm{Sp}\,\{i : S^c(y-x)\,\hat{A}(x)\,iS^c(x-y)\,\hat{A}(y):\} \\ & \qquad = -\,e^2\,\mathrm{Sp}\,\{: S^c(y-x)\,\hat{A}(x)\,S^c(x-y)\,\hat{A}(y):\}. \qquad (20.8) \end{aligned}$$

Utilizing the rules of correspondence we obtain the appropriate Feynman diagram (Fig. 3) (the so-called "photon self-energy diagram"; for more details see § 24).

Fig. 3. Photon self-energy diagram.

As a second example, let us consider one of the third-order terms occurring in $S_3(x, y, z)$

$$\begin{aligned} & (ie)^3 \sum_{m,\,n} : \bar{\psi}(x)\,\gamma^m A_m(x)\,\psi(x)\,\bar{\psi}(y)\,\hat{A}(y)\,\psi(y)\,\bar{\psi}(z)\,\gamma^n A_n(z)\,\psi(z): \\ & = -\,e^3 \sum_n g^{nn} D_0^c(x-z) :\bar{\psi}(x)\gamma^n S^c(x-y)\hat{A}(y) S^c(y-z)\gamma^n \psi(z):. \qquad (20.9) \end{aligned}$$

In this case the rules of correspondence lead us to the diagram shown in Fig. 4.

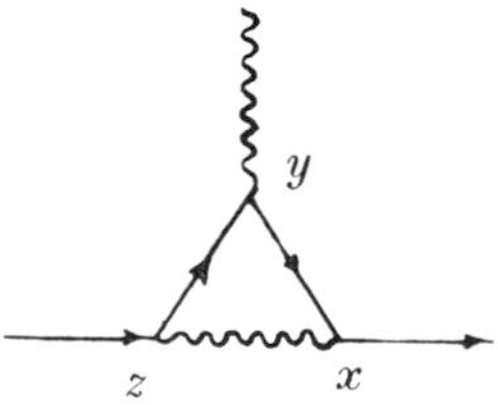

Fig. 4. Vertex diagram of the third order.

An examination of these simplest diagrams (Figs. 3 and 4) shows that motion along an electron line corresponds exactly to the order of the matrix elements from right to left in the corresponding term of the S-matrix. For example, in the second case by representing the diagram of Fig. 4 in the form of Fig. 5 we obtain exactly the same order of noncommuting matrix factors as in (20.9).

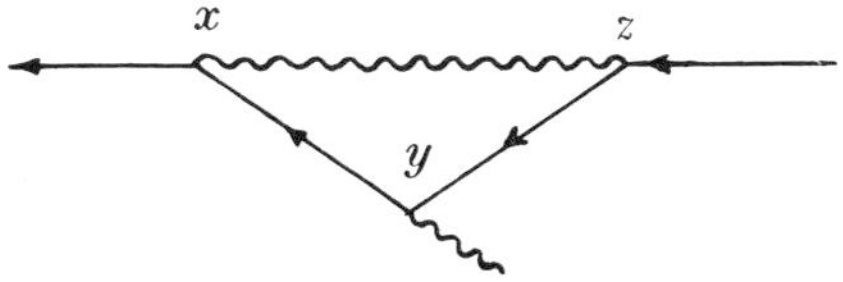

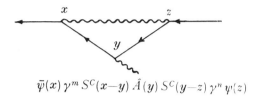

$$\bar{\psi}(x)\,\gamma^m\, S^C(x-y)\,\hat{A}(y)\,S^C(y-z)\,\gamma^n\,\psi(z)$$

Fig. 5.

We note that the construction of normal products with pairings corresponding to various diagrams in accordance with the rules formulated above may lead to an error in sign. Therefore the rules of correspondence established above must be supplemented by a sign rule.

In order to formulate this rule, we note that the error in sign occurs only in expressions which correspond to closed electron loops. Indeed, in accordance with the rules of correspondence, the diagram of Fig. 3 corresponds to the expression

$$(ie)^2\,\overbrace{\psi(x)\,\bar{\psi}(y)}\,\overbrace{\psi(y)\,\bar{\psi}(x)},$$

which differs in sign from (20.8). It is also evident that in the more general case such a difference in sign will occur for any arbitrary group of pairings corresponding to each of the closed loops of the diagram irrespectively of the order of these loops. From this it follows that the expression which is obtained by means of the rules of correspondence must in addition be multiplied by

$$\eta = (-1)^l, \tag{20.10}$$

where l is the number of closed loops in the diagram under consideration.

20.3. *Examples*

We shall illustrate by means of examples the application of the rules of correspondence together with the sign rule (20.10). We construct the term of the fourth-order operator function $S_4(x, y, z, t)$ which corresponds

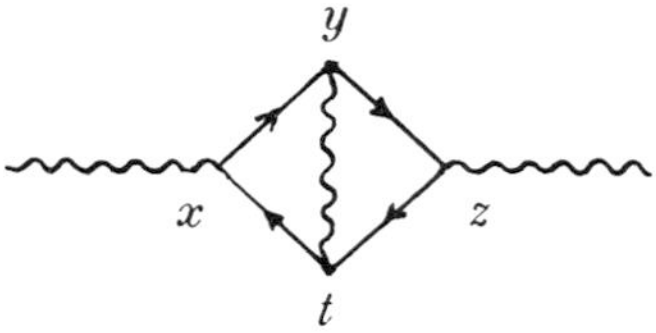

Fig. 6.

to the diagram of Fig. 6. By following along the electron loop from the point x we obtain the matrix factors

$$\begin{array}{ccccccccc} x & & t & & z & & y & & x \\ \bullet & \longleftarrow & \bullet & \longleftarrow & \bullet & \longleftarrow & \bullet & \longleftarrow & \bullet \\ ie\gamma^l; & & ie\gamma^k; & & ie\gamma^n; & & ie\gamma^m; & & \end{array}$$

$$\begin{array}{cccc} \frac{1}{i} S^c(x-t) & \frac{1}{i} S^c(t-z) & \frac{1}{i} S^c(z-y) & \frac{1}{i} S^c(y-x) \\ = -\psi(x)\,\overline{\psi}(t); & = -\psi(t)\,\overline{\psi}(z); & = -\psi(z)\,\overline{\psi}(y); & = -\psi(y)\,\overline{\psi}(x). \end{array} \tag{20.11}$$

By multiplying the product (20.11) by the photon factors

$$A_n(z), \quad ig^{mk}\, D_0^c(y-t), \quad A_l(x)$$

and by

$$\eta = (-1)^1 = -1,$$

we obtain after carrying out the summation over the spinor indices and over the polarization indices of the electromagnetic field (k, l, m, n):

$$-ie^4 \sum_{k,n} \mathrm{Sp}\,[:\,(S^c(x-t)\gamma^k g^{nk} D_0^c(t-y)\, S^c(t-z)\,\hat{A}(z)\, S^c(z-y)\gamma^n S^c(y-x)\,\hat{A}(x))\,:]$$

$$= -e^4 \sum_{k,n} \mathrm{Sp}\,[:\,\psi(x)\,\overline{\psi}(t)\gamma^k A_k(t)\,\psi(t)\,\overline{\psi}(z)\,\hat{A}(z)\,\psi(z)\,\overline{\psi}(y)\gamma^n A_n(y)\,\psi(y)\,\overline{\psi}(x)\,\hat{A}(x)\,:]$$

$$= i^4 e^4 \sum_{k,n} :\,(\overline{\psi}(t)\,\gamma^k A_k(t)\,\psi(t)\,\overline{\psi}(z)\,\hat{A}(z)\,\psi(z)\,\overline{\psi}(y)\,\gamma^n A_n(y)\,\psi(y)\,\overline{\psi}(x)\,\hat{A}(x)\,\psi(x))\,:,$$

i.e., one of the terms in the expansion of the function

$$S_4(x, y, z, t) = i^4 T(\mathscr{L}(x)\,\mathscr{L}(y)\,\mathscr{L}(z)\,\mathscr{L}(t))$$

into normal products with chronological pairings.

As a second example we shall construct the term of the fifth-order operator function $S_5(x, y, z, t, u)$ which corresponds to the diagram with

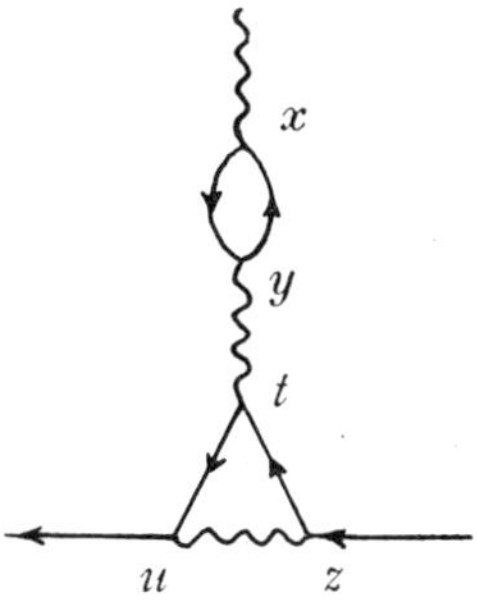

Fig. 7.

two electron loops (Fig. 7). We write out in turn the matrix factors which correspond to the closed cycle

$$\overset{y}{\bullet}\longleftarrow\overset{x}{\bullet}\longleftarrow$$

$$ie\gamma^l \frac{1}{i} S^c(y-x)\; ie\gamma^k \frac{1}{i} S^c(x-y)$$

and to the open cycle

$$\longleftarrow\overset{u}{\bullet}\longleftarrow\overset{t}{\bullet}\longleftarrow\overset{z}{\bullet}\longleftarrow$$

$$\overline{\psi}(u);\quad ie\gamma^p;\quad \frac{1}{i} S^c(u-t);\quad ie\gamma^m;\quad \frac{1}{i} S^c(t-z);\quad ie\gamma^n;\quad \psi(z)$$

On multiplying them by the photon factors

$$\overset{x}{\sim\bullet}\qquad \overset{y}{\bullet}\sim\sim\overset{t}{\bullet}\qquad \overset{z}{\bullet}\sim\sim\overset{u}{\bullet}$$

$$A_k(x);\qquad ig^{lm} D_0^c(y-t);\qquad ig^{np} D_0^c(z-u)$$

and by

$$\eta = (-1)^1 = -1,$$

we obtain, after carrying out the summation over the polarization indices (k, l, n, m, p) and the spinor indices, the expression

$$-(ie)^5 \sum_{l,n,m,p} : \mathrm{Sp}\left(\gamma^l \frac{1}{i} S^c(y-x)\hat{A}(x) \frac{1}{i} S^c(x-y)\, ig^{lm} D_0^c(y-t)\right.$$

$$\left. \times\; \overline{\psi}(u)\gamma^p \frac{1}{i} S^c(u-t)\gamma^m \frac{1}{i} S^c(t-z) ig^{np} D_0^c(z-u)\gamma^n \psi(z)\right) :$$

$$= -(ie)^5 \sum_{l,n,m,p} : \mathrm{Sp}\,(\gamma^l \psi(y)\,\overline{\psi}(x)\,\hat{A}(x)\,\psi(x)\,\overline{\psi}(y))\, A_l(y)\, A_m(t)$$

$$\times\; \overline{\psi}(u)\,\gamma^p\psi(u)\,\overline{\psi}(t)\,\gamma^m\,\psi(t)\,\overline{\psi}(z)\,A_n(z)\,A_p(u)\,\gamma^n\,\psi(z):$$

$$= (ie)^5 \sum_{l,n,m,p} : \overline{\psi}(u)\gamma^p$$

$$\times A_p(u)\psi(u)\overline{\psi}(t)\gamma^m A_m(t)\psi(t)\overline{\psi}(z)\gamma^n A_n(z)\,\psi(z)\overline{\psi}(y)\gamma^l A_l(y)\psi(y)\overline{\psi}(x)\,\hat{A}\,(x)\psi(x):,$$

which corresponds exactly to one of the terms in the expansion into normal products with chronological pairings of the function

$$S_5(x, y, z, t, u) = i^5 T(\mathscr{L}(x)\mathscr{L}(y)\mathscr{L}(z)\mathscr{L}(t)\mathscr{L}(u)).$$

20.4. *Concluding Remarks*

We have thus shown that the rules of correspondence together with the sign rule do in fact enable us to write down automatically the terms of the functions $S_n(x_1, \ldots, x_n)$ in normal form. It is evident that in order to obtain the complete expression for the operator function of the nth order $S_n(x_1, \ldots, x_n)$ it is necessary to write out in accordance with Wick's theorem all the normal products which correspond to all the possible diagrams of the nth order, i.e., to all the possible diagrams containing n vertices. For example, for $n = 2$ it is necessary to construct terms which correspond to all those diagrams (Fig. 8) which exhaust all

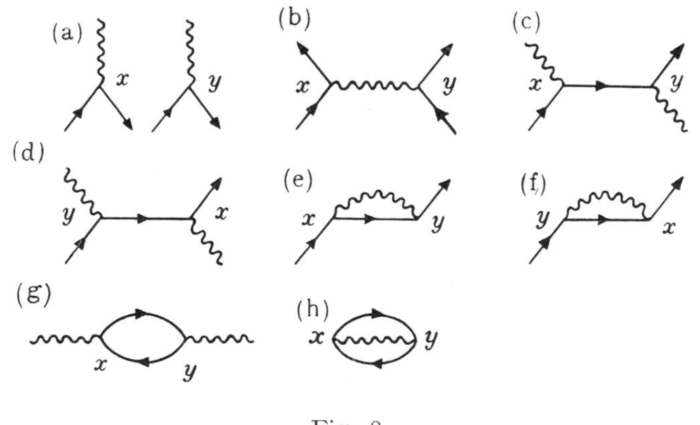

Fig. 8.

possible second-order diagrams. The sum of the corresponding normal products gives exactly the expression (20.5) for $S_2(x, y)$.

We have carried out a detailed analysis of the structure of the terms of the S-matrix which depends on the interaction Lagrangian for the electromagnetic and the electron-positron fields (20.3). It is quite clear that the method described above for the construction of the terms of the S-matrix with the aid of Feynman diagrams may be applied without difficulty to any other arbitrary local interaction. Of course, the rules of correspondence must be suitably modified. For example, the Lagrangian for the pseudoscalar interaction of a nucleon spinor field and a pseudoscalar meson field has the form

$$\mathscr{L}(x) = g \sum_{i=1,2,3} :\overline{\Psi}(x)\,\gamma^5\tau_i\,\Psi(x)\,\varphi_i(x):, \tag{20.12}$$

where g is the interaction constant, Ψ and $\overline{\Psi}$ are the eight component spinors for the nucleons, τ_i are the three isotopic spin matrices, φ_i are the three field functions for positively and negatively charged and neutral mesons (for details of this see § 33.1). The rules of correspondence for this Lagrangian are completely analogous to the rules given in Table I. The role of the spinors ψ is now played by the nucleon spinors Ψ, the potential A has been replaced by φ, and the matrices $e\gamma^n$ by $g\gamma^5\tau_i$. At each vertex of the corresponding diagrams one meson and two nucleon lines will meet.

In the study of β-processes Lagrangians of the type (8.8) are used:

$$\mathscr{L}(x) = g' :\overline{\Psi}(x)\,O\Psi(x)\,\bar{\psi}(x)\,O\nu(x):, \tag{20.13}$$

which contain three kinds of spinor fields — the nucleon field Ψ, the electron-positron field ψ, and the neutrino field ν. The rules of correspondence in this case must be formulated for the operators Ψ, $\overline{\Psi}$, ψ, $\bar{\psi}$, ν, $\bar{\nu}$ and for the pairings between them. At the vertices of the corresponding diagrams four lines will meet — two nucleon lines, one electron line, and one neutrino line. Only the nucleon lines of such a diagram will be continuous.

Complex processes in which interactions of different nature are combined are also of interest. The magnetic moment of an electrically neutral particle such as a neutron apparently should be represented as the result of a multistage process of interaction between the neutron and the electromagnetic field of the following type. At first the neutron is virtually transformed into a π-meson and a proton, then one of the charged particles (π^- or p) interacts with the electromagnetic field and finally the π^- and the proton are transformed back into a neutron. The process may be pictorially represented in the form of the diagram shown in Fig. 9.

The corresponding term of the S-matrix obviously corresponds to the T-product of two Lagrangians $\mathscr{L}_{\text{mes}}$ of the form (20.12)

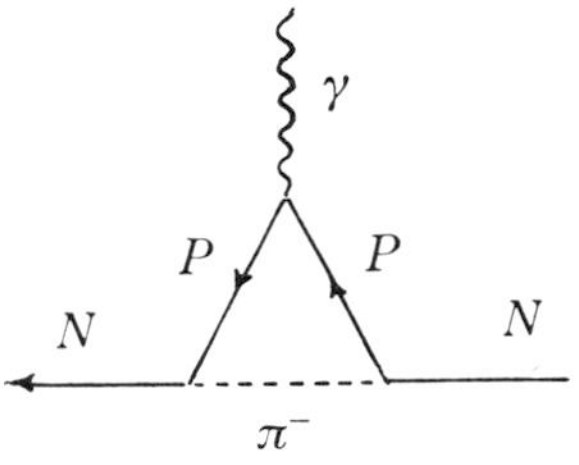

Fig. 9.

and of one Lagrangian $\mathscr{L}_{\text{e.d.}}$ of the form (20.3)

$$T(\mathscr{L}_{\text{mes}}(x)\,\mathscr{L}_{\text{e.d.}}(y)\,\mathscr{L}_{\text{mes}}(z)).$$

The rules of correspondence for such diagrams and for the terms of the S-matrix are given by the sum of the rules of correspondence for the Lagrangians (20.3) and (20.12).

We thus see that the representation of the terms of the S-matrix by means of Feynman diagrams is a universal method which is suitable for any arbitrary local interaction Lagrangians and which enables us to obtain automatically the terms of the S-matrix corresponding to any arbitrary process of interest to us.

§ 21. Feynman's Rules for the Evaluation of Matrix Elements of the Scattering Matrix

21.1. *Transition to the Momentum Representation*

We shall now investigate the process of evaluating matrix elements of the scattering matrix which occupies a prominent place in the calculation of effective cross sections for various processes of scattering and of mutual transformation of particles.

The evaluation of matrix elements is most conveniently carried out in the momentum representation, since, in this representation, the field operators $u(x)$ and the causal functions $\Delta^c(x-y)$ have a simple structure:

$$u(x) = \frac{1}{(2\pi)^{3/2}} \int e^{ikx} \delta(k^2 - m^2)\, u(k)\, dk,$$

$$u(k) = \sum_{\sigma} v^{\sigma}(k)\, a_{\sigma}(k),$$

$$\Delta^c(x - y) = \frac{1}{(2\pi)^4} \int e^{ikx} \Delta(k)\, dk,$$

$$\Delta(k) = \frac{P(k)}{m^2 - k^2 - i\varepsilon}.$$

We write the S-matrix in the momentum representation. After reduction to the normal form the nth-order term of the scattering matrix may be expressed in accordance with Wick's theorem as a sum of terms of the form

$$\int dx_1 \ldots \int dx_n K_{\ldots\alpha\ldots\beta\ldots}(x_1, \ldots, x_n) : \ldots u_{\alpha}(x_j) \ldots u_{\beta}^{\dagger}(x_i) \ldots :. \qquad (21.1)$$

The coefficient functions $K_{\ldots\alpha\ldots\beta\ldots}(x_1, \ldots, x_n)$ in the preceding expression correspond to the internal lines of Feynman diagrams and consist of multiple products of pairings occurring in the investigation of field functions. The normal product

$$: \ldots u_{\alpha}(x_j) \ldots u_{\beta}^{\dagger}(x_i) \ldots ; \qquad (21.2)$$

contains free operators corresponding to the external lines of the diagram.

For the sake of definiteness, let us again restrict ourselves to the case of interacting electromagnetic and electron-positron spinor fields described by the Lagrangian

$$\mathscr{L}(x) = e : \bar{\psi}(x)\, \hat{A}(x)\, \psi(x) :. \qquad (20.3)$$

In this case the coefficient functions are products of pairings of the electromagnetic field

$$\left.\begin{aligned} \overbrace{A_m(x) A_n}(y) &= i g^{mn} D_0^c(x - y), \\ D_0^c(x - y) &= -\frac{1}{(2\pi)^4} \int \frac{e^{ik(x-y)}}{k^2 + i\varepsilon}\, dk \end{aligned}\right\} \qquad (21.3)$$

and of pairings of the electron-positron field

$$\left.\begin{aligned} \overline{\psi_\alpha(x)\bar{\psi}_\beta(y)} &= \frac{1}{i} S^c_{\alpha\beta}(x-y), \\ S^c_{\alpha\beta}(x-y) &= \frac{1}{(2\pi)^4}\int e^{ip(x-y)} \frac{(m-\hat{p})_{\alpha\beta}}{m^2-p^2-i\varepsilon}\,dp, \end{aligned}\right\} \tag{21.4}$$

while the normal products (21.2) contain operator functions of the electromagnetic and the electron-positron fields which have the following momentum expansions

$$\begin{aligned} A_m(x) &= A_m^{(+)}(x) + A_m^{(-)}(x), \\ A_m^{(\pm)}(x) &= \frac{1}{(2\pi)^{3/2}}\int e^{\pm kx}\,\delta(k^2) A_m^{(\pm)}(k)\,dk, \\ A_m^{(\pm)}(k) &= \sum_{\nu=0,1,2,3} e^\nu_m a_\nu^{(\pm)}(k); \end{aligned} \tag{21.5}$$

$$\begin{aligned} \psi(x) &= \psi^{(+)}(x) + \psi^{(-)}(x), \\ \psi_\sigma^{(\pm)}(x) &= \frac{1}{(2\pi)^{3/2}}\int e^{\pm ipx}\,\delta(p^2-m^2)\,\psi_\sigma^{(\pm)}(p)\,dp, \\ \psi_\sigma^{(\pm)}(p) &= \sum_{\nu=1,2} v_\sigma^{\nu,\pm}(p) a_\nu^{\pm}(p); \end{aligned} \tag{21.6}$$

$$\begin{aligned} \bar{\psi}(x) &= \bar{\psi}^{(+)}(x) + \bar{\psi}^{(-)}(x), \\ \bar{\psi}_\sigma^{(\pm)}(x) &= \frac{1}{(2\pi)^{3/2}}\int e^{\pm ipx}\,\delta(p^2-m^2)\,\bar{\psi}_\sigma^{(\pm)}(p)\,dp, \\ \bar{\psi}_\sigma^{(\pm)}(p) &= \sum_{\nu=1,2} \bar{v}_\sigma^{\nu,\pm}(p)\, a_\nu^{*\pm}(p). \end{aligned} \tag{21.7}$$

Substituting expressions (21.3)–(21.7) into (21.1) we see that the integration over the variables $x_1, \ldots, x_n$ now reduces to the evaluation of independent integrals of the form

$$\int dx_j\, e^{ix_j(p_1-p_2+k)} = (2\pi)^4\,\delta(p_1-p_2+k). \tag{21.8}$$

We could at this point establish the rules of correspondence governing the construction of the elements of the S-matrix in the momentum representation. However, it is more convenient to investigate the process of evaluating the matrix elements of the terms of the S-matrix and to formulate directly the rules of correspondence for the construction of the matrix elements. These rules were first proposed by Feynman (40), (41) and are known as *Feynman's rules.*

21.2. *Evaluation of the Matrix Elements*

We examine the matrix elements of the normal products (21.2) taken between various states containing particles with given momenta. As was shown in § 9, the amplitude of the state containing n particles of different kinds with definite values of the momenta is given by an expression of the form

$$\Phi_{\dots k \dots} = a_1^{(+)}(\mathbf{k}_1)\, a_2^{(+)}(\mathbf{k}_2) \dots a_n^{(+)}(\mathbf{k}_n)\, \Phi_0$$

$$= \int dk_1^0 \sqrt{2k_1^0}\, \delta(k_1^2 - m^2)\, a_1^{(+)}(k_1) \dots \int dk_n^0 \sqrt{2k_n^0}\, \delta(k_n^2 - m_n^2)\, a_n^{(+)}(k_n) \Phi_0. \tag{21.9}$$

In the evaluation of the matrix element

$$\Phi^*_{\dots k' \dots} : \dots u_\alpha(x_j) \dots u_\beta^\dagger(x_i) \dots : \Phi_{\dots k \dots} \tag{21.10}$$

the creation operators $u^{(+)}$ and $u^{\dagger(+)}$ must be conmuted with the annihilation operators $a_i^{(-)}$ from the amplitude $\Phi^*_{\dots k' \dots}$ while the operators $u^{(-)}$ and $u^{\dagger(-)}$ must be commuted with the operators $a_i^{(+)}$ from the amplitude $\Phi_{\dots k \dots}$ until one of them acts on Φ_0 or on Φ_0^*, which yields zero.

The process of calculating such matrix elements was examined in detail at the beginning of § 16. It was established there that the matrix element (21.10) differs from zero if for each operator

$$u(x) = u^{(+)}(x) + u^{(-)}(x)$$

occurring in the normal product one can find an operator $a^{*(+)}$ in Φ or $a^{*(-)}$ in Φ^* corresponding to the same field which will "cancel" the operator u as a result of being commuted with it. Thus (21.10) will differ from zero in the case when the sum of the number of particles of each field in the initial state $\Phi_{\dots k' \dots}$ and in the final state $\Phi_{\dots k \dots}$ will be exactly equal to the number of operator functions of the given field in the normal product

(21.2). The matrix element (21.10) turns out also to differ from zero in the case when in addition to the operators which "cancel" the normal product $\Phi_{\dots k'\dots}$ and $\Phi_{\dots k\dots}$ also contain operators which cancel one another. The total number of particles in the states $\Phi^*_{\dots k'\dots}$ and $\Phi_{\dots k\dots}$ exceeds the number of operators in (21.1) by some even number. However, as was shown in § 16, such matrix elements differ from zero only in the case that the momenta of the above "extra" particles are the same in states $\Phi_{\dots k'\dots}$ and $\Phi_{\dots k\dots}$.

By restricting ourselves to the case when for no particles the momentum in the initial state equals the momentum in the final state, we arrive at the conclusion that the matrix element (21.10) may be represented in the form of a product of the results of commuting the operators

$$u^{(-)}(x_j) \text{ with } \int \theta(k^0)\, a_\rho^{*(+)}(k)\, \delta(k^2 - m^2)\sqrt{2k^0}\, dk^0 = a_\rho^{(+)}(\mathbf{k})$$

and

$$u^{(+)}(x_l) \text{ with } \int \theta(k^0)\, a_\sigma^{*(-)}(k)\, \delta(k^2 - m^2)\sqrt{2k^0}\, dk^0 = a_\sigma^{(-)}(\mathbf{k}),$$

which on being evaluated with the aid of the commutation relations written in the form

$$\delta(p^2 - m^2)\, \delta(k^2 - m^2)\, \{a_\sigma^{(-)}(p)\, a_\rho^{*(+)}(k)\} = \delta_{\sigma\rho}\, \delta(p - k)\, \delta(k^2 - m^2),$$

yield

$$\{u^{(-)}(x_j),\, a_\rho^{*(+)}(\mathbf{k})\} = \frac{1}{(2\pi)^{3/2}} \int dk^0\, \theta(k^0)\sqrt{2k^0} \int dp e^{-ipx_j} \sum_\sigma v^{\sigma,-}(p)$$

$$\times \{a_\sigma^{(-)}(p),\, a_\rho^{*(+)}(k)\}\, \delta(k^2 - m^2)\, \delta(p^2 - m^2)$$

$$= \frac{1}{(2\pi)^{3/2}} \int dk^0\, \theta(k^0)\sqrt{2k^0} \int dp e^{-ipx_j} \sum_\sigma v^{\sigma,-}(p)\, \delta(p-k)\, \delta(k^2-m^2)\delta_{\sigma\rho}$$

$$= \frac{1}{(2\pi)^{3/2}} \int dk^0 \theta(k^0)\sqrt{2k^0}\delta(k^2-m^2)e^{-ikx_j} v^{\rho,-}(k) = \frac{1}{(2\pi)^{3/2}} v^{\rho,-}(\mathbf{k})e^{-ikx_j}, \tag{21.11}$$

where

$$v^{\rho,-}(\mathbf{k}) = \frac{v^{\rho,-}(k)}{\sqrt{2k^0}}\Bigg|_{k^0 = \sqrt{k^2 + m^2}}$$

and also by means of a similar calculation

$$\{a_\rho^{*(-)}(\mathbf{k}),\ u^{(+)}(x_i)\} = \frac{1}{(2\pi)^{3/2}} v^{\rho,+}(\mathbf{k}) e^{ikx_i}. \qquad (21.12)$$

Thus, after the commutations have been carried out the matrix element (21.10) is in fact expressed in the form of the product

$$\prod_{(k)} \frac{v^-(\mathbf{k})}{(2\pi)^{3/2}} e^{-ikx_j} \prod_{(k')} \frac{v^+(\mathbf{k}')}{(2\pi)^{3/2}} e^{ik'x_i}, \qquad (21.13)$$

where the factors $(2\pi)^{-3/2} e^{-ikx} v^-(\mathbf{k})$ correspond to particles in the initial state, while the factors $(2\pi)^{-3/2} e^{ik'x} v^+(\mathbf{k}')$ correspond to particles in the final state.

Let us discuss the above results from the point of view of their correspondence with Feynman diagrams. Of greatest significance is the fact that from the point of view of the structure of the matrix elements to each external line of the diagram there corresponds a real particle either in the initial or in the final state. This circumstance allows us to regard Feynman diagrams as a schematic representation of actually occurring processes involving the interaction of elementary particles. The nature of these processes is determined by the structure of the vertices of the diagram which in turn depends on the interaction Lagrangian.

The vertices of the Lagrangian of spinor electrodynamics $e\bar{\psi}\hat{A}\psi$ may evidently be regarded as schematic representations of the processes either of absorption or emission of a photon by a positron or an electron, and of the processes of the creation or

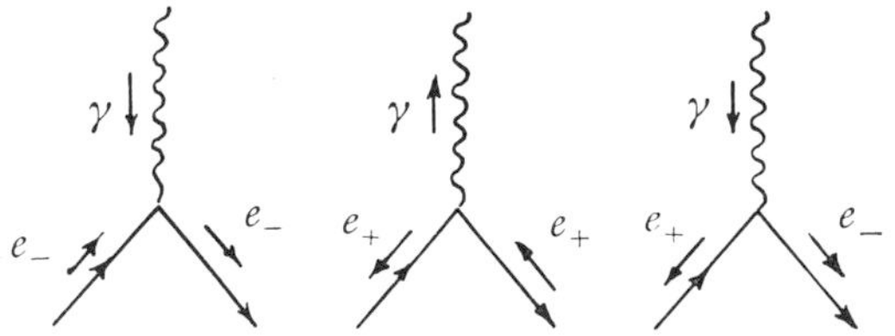

Fig. 10.

annihilation of an electron-positron pair with the absorption or emission of a photon, i.e., of processes of the type shown in Fig. 10 (see also Fig. 1). The vertices of the Lagrangian of β-

interactions describe interaction events in which four particles take part simultaneously: two nucleons, an electron (positron), and a neutrino. A detailed classification of these processes was made in § 8 (see (8.8)).

δ-functions of the type $\delta(p - p' + k \ldots)$ which arise in the transition to the momentum representation (21.8) evidently express the law of conservation of energy-momentum of the interacting particles in each individual event. By adding together the arguments of all such functions we obtain the condition

$$\sum p - \sum p' = 0, \qquad (21.14)$$

which expresses the law of conservation of the total energy-momentum four-vector for all the real particles participating in the process under consideration.

For the formulation of specific rules of correspondence between matrix elements and Feynman diagrams, we shall return to the case of spinor electrodynamics (20.3). It may be easily seen that an electron in the initial state with momentum $\mathbf{p}$ corresponds to the result of commuting $\psi(x)$ with $a_\nu^{*+}(\mathbf{p})$ which is equal to

$$\frac{1}{(2\pi)^{3/2}} v^{\nu,-}(\mathbf{p})\, e^{-ipx}.$$

A positron with momentum $\mathbf{p}$ corresponds to the factor

$$\frac{1}{(2\pi)^{3/2}} \bar{v}^{\nu,-}(\mathbf{p})\, e^{-ipx},$$

an electron in the final state corresponds to the factor

$$\frac{1}{(2\pi)^{3/2}} \bar{v}^{\nu,+}(\mathbf{p})\, e^{ipx},$$

a positron in the final state corresponds to the factor

$$\frac{1}{(2\pi)^{3/2}} v^{\nu,+}(\mathbf{p})\, e^{ipx},$$

a photon in the initial state with momentum $\mathbf{k}$ and polarization e_n corresponds to the result of commuting $A_m(x)$ with $a_n^+(\mathbf{k})$

which is equal to

$$-\frac{1}{(2\pi)^{3/2}}\frac{g^{nn}e^n_m}{\sqrt{2k^0}}e^{-ikx},$$

and, finally, a photon in the final state corresponds to the factor

$$-\frac{1}{(2\pi)^{3/2}}\frac{g^{nn}e^n_m}{\sqrt{2k^0}}e^{ikx}.$$

We see from the above that particles which arrive at the point x with momentum $\mathbf{k}$ always correspond to the negative-frequency exponential $\exp(-ikx)$, while particles emerging from the point x correspond to the factor $\exp(ikx)$. It is therefore convenient to adopt a similar convention also for the internal lines of the diagram.

In connection with the fact that the pairing $\overbrace{\psi(x)\bar{\psi}(y)}$ describes the process of the motion of an electron from the point y to the point x, it is more convenient in this case to use in place of the expansion (21.4) the formula

$$\overbrace{\psi(x)\bar{\psi}(y)} = \frac{1}{(2\pi)^4 i}\int e^{-ip(x-y)}\frac{m+\hat{p}}{m^2-p^2-i\varepsilon}dp. \qquad (21.15)$$

In the preceding the four-momentum p may be interpreted as the four-momentum of an electron leaving the point y (the factor $\exp(ipy)$) and arriving at the point x (the factor $\exp(-ipx)$). Formula (21.15) is evidently more convenient for describing the motion of an electron, while formula (21.4) is more convenient for a positron. However, in future we shall use (21.15) also in the case of a positron taking into account the fact that in this case the four-momentum p in this expression is equal to the four-momentum of the positron with the opposite sign.

Carrying out the integration over the variables $x_1, \ldots, x_n$ in accordance with formulas (21.8) we arrive at the rules of correspondence given in Table II.

Table II. Correspondence Rules for Matrix Elements in the Momentum Representation

(The sign rule and the symmetry properties have not been taken into account.)

No.	Particle and its state	Factor in the matrix element	Element of the diagram
1.	Electron in the initial state with momentum **p**	$\dfrac{v^{\nu,-}(\mathbf{p})}{(2\pi)^{3/2}}$	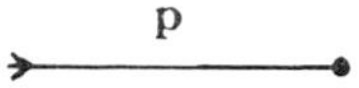
2.	Positron in the initial state with momentum **p**	$\dfrac{\bar{v}^{\nu,-}(\mathbf{p})}{(2\pi)^{3/2}}$	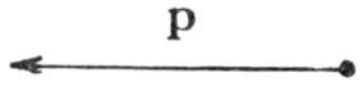
3.	Electron in the final state with momentum **p**	$\dfrac{\bar{v}^{\nu,+}(\mathbf{p})}{(2\pi)^{3/2}}$	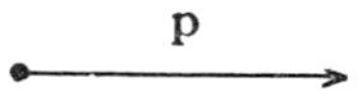
4.	Positron in the final state with momentum **p**	$\dfrac{v^{\nu,+}(\mathbf{p})}{(2\pi)^{3/2}}$	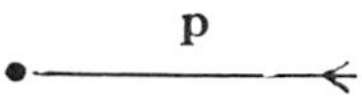
5.	Photon in the initial or final state with polarization e_n and momentum **k**	$\dfrac{-g^{nn}e^n_m}{(2\pi)^{3/2}\sqrt{2k^0}} = \dfrac{e^n_m}{(2\pi)^{3/2}\sqrt{2k^0}}\ (n\neq 0)$	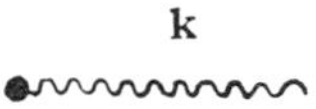
6.	Motion of an electron from 1 to 2 (or of a positron from 2 to 1)	$\dfrac{1}{(2\pi)^4 i}\,\dfrac{m+\hat{p}}{m^2-p^2-i\varepsilon}$	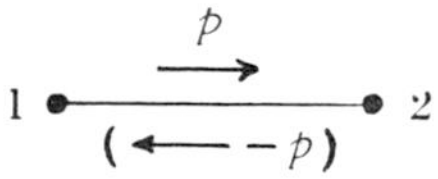
7.	Motion of a photon between vertices with summation indices m and n	$\dfrac{g^{mn}}{(2\pi)^4 i}\,\dfrac{1}{k^2+i\varepsilon}$	
8.	Vertex with summation index m with electron line p_1 and photon line k entering, and electron line p_2 emerging.	$ie\gamma^m(2\pi)^4 \times\delta(p_2-p_1-k)$	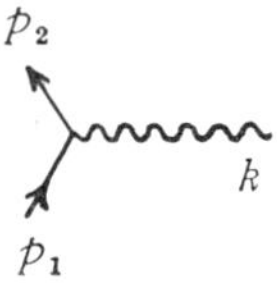

21.3. *Taking Account of Symmetry Properties*

In constructing matrix elements in the momentum representation it is also necessary to take into account the symmetry properties of the coefficients $S_n(x_1, \ldots, x_n)$ of the scattering matrix. For example, the symmetry of the coefficient $S_2(x_1, x_2)$ with respect to its arguments x_1 and x_2 leads to the fact that to diagrams of the Compton scattering type (Fig. 8c, d) there correspond two terms of $S_2(x_1, x_2)$ in the x-representation:

$$:\bar{\psi}(x_1)\hat{A}(x_1)\overbrace{\psi(x_1)\bar{\psi}(x_2)}\hat{A}(x_2)\psi(x_2):$$

and

$$:\overbrace{\bar{\psi}(x_1)\hat{A}(x_1)\psi(x_1)\bar{\psi}(x_2)\hat{A}(x_2)\psi(x_2)}:$$
$$= :\bar{\psi}(x_2)\hat{A}(x_2)\overbrace{\psi(x_2)\bar{\psi}(x_1)}\hat{A}(x_1)\psi(x_1):,$$

which lead to identical expressions after the integration over x_1 and x_2 has been carried out. It may be easily seen that in the general case the symmetry property of $S_n(x_1, \ldots, x_n)$ leads to the necessity of multiplying the matrix elements of the corresponding diagrams, in which a certain number of vertices $m < n$ appears in an unsymmetric fashion, by the factor $n!/(n-m)!$. In the case when among the n vertices of the diagram there are k groups of $\nu_1, \nu_2, \ldots, \nu_k$ vertices which occur symmetrically the whole expression must be multiplied by the factor

$$\frac{n!}{\nu_1!\,\nu_2!\ldots\nu_k!}.$$

One should separately discuss the case when the initial and final states both contain several particles of the same nature (several photons, several electrons, etc.). Let us for the sake of simplicity consider the situation when the final state contains N identical particles. The annihilation operators from the amplitude

$$\Phi_{\ldots p'\ldots} = \Phi_0^* a^{(-)}(\mathbf{p}_1)\ldots a^{(-)}(\mathbf{p}_N) \tag{21.16}$$

can then commute with the corresponding operators $a_i^{(+)}(p)$ from the normal product (21.2) in $N!$ different ways. Each of the terms of the expression so obtained will correspond to a diagram which differs in the fixed values of the momenta of the external lines. For example, the two-photon annihilation of an electron-positron pair is described by a sum of matrix elements which correspond to the two diagrams of Fig. 11 in which p_1 is the electron momentum, p_2 is the positron momentum, k_1 and k_2 are the momenta

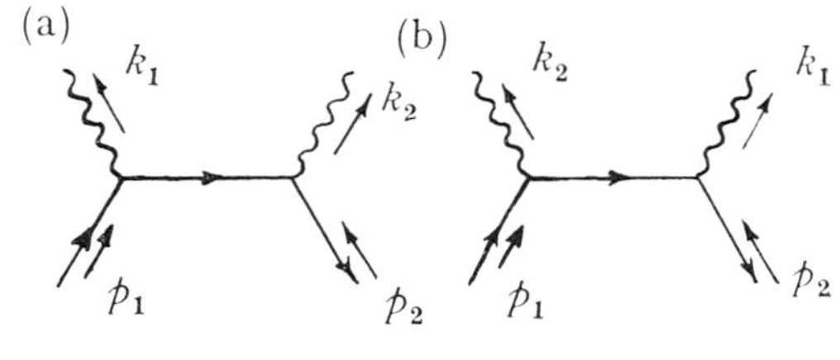

Fig. 11.

of the final photons. Thus the calculation of the matrix elements leads to no difficulties in this case. It is only necessary to take into account the fact that the normalized amplitude (for details see § 22) of the state containing N identical particles has the form

$$\Phi_{\dots p \dots} = \frac{a^{(+)}(\mathbf{p}_1) \dots a^{(+)}(\mathbf{p}_N)}{\sqrt{N!}} \Phi_0 \tag{21.17}$$

and that in case identical fermions are present the resulting matrix element must be antisymmetric with respect to an interchange of any two Fermi particles.

In summarizing the results of the preceding discussion, we see that in order to write down the matrix element for any process of scattering or of mutual transformation of particles it is necessary to represent this process schematically in the form of one or several Feynman diagrams, to find in accordance with the rules of correspondence of the type given in Table II the appropriate matrix elements, to determine their sign by means of the rule (20.10), to multiply the expression so obtained by the additional factor

$$\frac{1}{\nu_1! \dots \nu_k!} \frac{1}{\prod_j (\sqrt{N_j!})} \tag{21.18}$$

and to check the antisymmetry with respect to identical Fermi particles.

It should be noted that the Feynman diagrams introduced above in fact describe several processes simultaneously.

Thus the diagram of Fig. 11a describes first of all a process in which the electron p_1 initially emits a photon k_1, and then annihilates with the positron p_2, emitting the photon k_2. In addition, the same diagram describes the process in which the positron p_2 initially emits the photon k_2 and then annihilates with the electron p_1 emitting a photon k_1. In the first case, the internal electron line describes the motion of an electron in the direction of the electron line, in the second case it describes the motion of a positron in the opposite direction.

In the general case one may consider that each internal electron line describes either an electron with four-momentum p (with $p^0 > 0$) or a positron with four-momentum $-p$ (with $p^0 < 0$), while each internal photon line describes photons moving in one of the two possible directions as long as the whole overall picture of the motion of the particles does not contradict the energy-momentum conservation laws

$$p - p' \pm k = 0,$$

which follow from the structure of the vertex parts of the matrix element. In such a case the positive-frequency part of the causal function Δ^c describes motion in one direction, while the negative-frequency part describes motion in the opposite direction.

Those particles which in this method of description appear only in the intermediate states (for example, the photon in a diagram of the type of Fig. 8b) are called virtual particles. The intermediate states of real particles such as the electron state $p_1 - k_1$ (or the positron state $p_2 - k_2 = -(p_1 - k_1)$) in the diagram of Fig. 11a are called virtual states.

Virtual states of real particles and states of virtual particles differ from states of real particles by the fact that in such states the energy and the momentum are independent of each other, i.e., in virtual states the following condition does not hold

$$p^2 - m^2 = 0.$$

21.4. *Scattering by External Fields*

We now turn to the structure of matrix elements for processes of scattering of particles by external classical fields. Such fields are described by an unquantized potential $u^{\text{ext}}(x)$ which is a given function of the space coordinates $\mathbf{x}$ and the time x^0. For example, an external classical electromagnetic field is described by the potential $A_n^{\text{ext}}(x)$. The complete interaction Lagrangian for spinor electrodynamics which we are considering can now be represented in the form

$$\mathscr{L}(x) = -\sum_n j^n(x)\,(A_n(x) + A_n^{\text{ext}}(x)). \tag{21.19}$$

Corresponding to this terms will appear in the scattering matrix which contain the external unquantized field A^{ext}. The matrix elements will now contain momentum representations of the external potential

$$A_n^{\text{ext}}(x) = \frac{1}{(2\pi)^{3/2}}\int e^{iqx} A_n^{\text{ext}}(q)\,dq, \tag{21.20}$$

which in view of their nonoperator nature need not commute with the photon operators of the state amplitudes and are not connected with real particles represented by external lines in Feynman diagrams.

We shall therefore agree to make the factor

$$\frac{1}{(2\pi)^{3/2}} A^{\text{ext}}(k) \tag{21.21}$$

correspond to a wavy line leaving a vertex of the diagram which corresponds to the term $j^n(x)A_n^{\text{ext}}(x)$ in the Lagrangian and terminating in a shaded circle which we will use to denote symbolically a scattering center (Fig. 12).

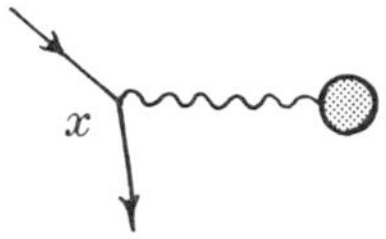

Fig. 12.

The representation of the interaction with a classical field by means of a virtual photon which the interacting particle (in this case an electron) exchanges with the source of the classical field corresponds to the physical nature of the phenomenon. The classical field differs from a quantized field only by the fact that it is specified in advance and that the interaction processes do not affect it. Such a field may be regarded as the limit of an ordinary quantized field as its intensity is made infinitely large. The interaction with such a field is actually brought about even in the limiting case by virtual photons whose process of propagation is described in the limiting case not by a causal photon function D_0^c but by a given potential A^{ext}.

If in going over to the momentum representation we carry out the integrations over the variables x_i we obtain as a result of integrating the expression

$$j^n(x_k)\, A_n^{\text{ext}}(x_k) \tag{21.22}$$

over the variable x_k the factor $\delta(p_1 - p_2 + q)$ which expresses the transfer of a part of the energy and of the momentum to the virtual photon. Thus the law of conservation of energy-momentum for the real particles (21.14) does not hold for processes of scattering by a classical field.

Let us examine in greater detail the important special case of scattering by a *stationary* classical field

$$A_n^{\text{ext}}(x) = a_n(\mathbf{x}),$$

$$a_n(\mathbf{x}) = \frac{1}{(2\pi)^{3/2}} \int e^{-i\mathbf{q}x}\, \varphi_n(\mathbf{q})\, d\mathbf{q}. \tag{21.23}$$

The variable q^0 is absent in the expansion of the stationary potential, and therefore the virtual photons which describe the interaction with a stationary field have the energy $q^0 = 0$ and transfer only momentum. Integrating (21.30) over x we obtain a δ-function

$$\delta(p - p' + \mathbf{q}) = \delta(p^0 - p'^0)\delta(\mathbf{p} - \mathbf{p}' + \mathbf{q}),$$

which expresses the law of conservation of energy ($p^0 = p'^0$) and the law of transfer of momentum ($\mathbf{p}' - \mathbf{p} = \mathbf{q}$). The second factor $\delta(\mathbf{p} - \mathbf{p}' + \mathbf{q})$ is then removed by integration over $\mathbf{q}$. Corresponding to this, the complete conservation law (21.14) will no longer hold and will be replaced by the law of conservation of the energy alone

$$\sum p^0 - \sum p'^0 = 0. \tag{21.24}$$

21.5. *General Structure of the Matrix Elements*

We shall examine in general terms the structure of the matrix elements of the scattering matrix

$$S = S(1),$$

defined in § 17 as the limit of the matrix $S(g)$ when the region in which $g(x) = 1$ is expanded indefinitely to include the whole space-time.

It is therefore necessary also to investigate the structure of the matrix elements of the matrix $S(g)$

$$\Phi^*_{\dots p' \dots} S(g) \Phi_{\dots p \dots} \tag{21.25}$$

and the singularities of the limiting transition $g(x) \to 1$.

From the structure of the matrix $S(g)$ represented in the form

$$S(g) = T\left(\exp i \int \mathscr{L}(x;\, g)\, dx\right), \tag{18.38}$$

it follows that the matrix elements (21.24) differ from the already investigated matrix elements

$$\Phi^*_{\dots p' \dots} S(1) \Phi_{\dots p \dots}$$

only by the presence of an additional factor $g(x)$ in the interaction Lagrangian $\mathscr{L}(x)$. Therefore $g(x)$ may be tentatively regarded as a certain external classical field, an interaction with which takes place at each vertex of a Feynman diagram. The Fourier transform of the g-field

$$\tilde{g}(\kappa) = \frac{1}{(2\pi)^4} \int e^{-i\kappa x} g(x)\, dx \tag{21.26}$$

may be made to correspond in the diagrams to lines similar to the one shown in Fig. 13 which emerge from each vertex but which do not reach the edge of the diagram. Such a line may be shown, for example, as a dotted line (Fig. 13). Moreover, the introduction into the Lagrangian of the function $g(x)$ evidently violates the law of conservation of energy-momentum at each vertex, and consequently in the diagram as a whole.

By means of Wick's theorem the matrix elements (21.25)

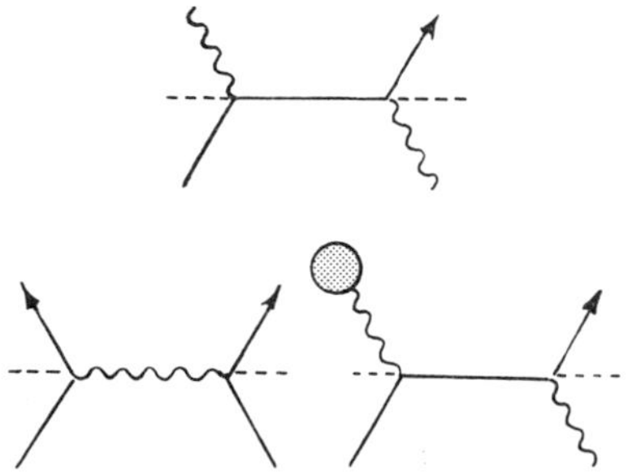

Fig. 13.

may be represented in the form

$$\Phi^*_{\dots p' \dots} S(g) \Phi_{\dots p \dots} = \sum_{(n, j_n)} \int K_{j_n}(x_1, \dots, x_n) g(x_1) \dots$$
$$\times \dots g(x_n) \Phi^*_{\dots p' \dots} : u_\alpha(x_j) \dots : \Phi_{\dots p \dots} dx_1 \dots dx_n. \quad (21.27)$$

The matrix elements appearing on the right-hand side yield, after the commutations have been performed:

$$\Phi^*_{\dots p' \dots} : \dots u_\alpha(x_j) \dots : \Phi_{\dots p \dots}$$
$$= \sum A(\dots p' \dots p \dots) \exp\{i(p_1' x_{j_1} + \dots + p_s' x_{j_s} - p_1 x_{i_1} - \dots - p_r x_{i_r})\}$$
$$(i, j = 1, \dots, n). \quad (21.28)$$

Because the coefficient functions $K(x_1, \dots, x_n)$ are invariant under translations their momentum representation contains a δ-function:

$$K(x_1, \dots, x_n) = \int \delta(\sum k_j) Q(k_1, \dots, k_n) e^{i \sum_j k_j x_j} dk_1 \dots dk_n.$$

Making use also of relation (21.26) we obtain from the above:

$$K(x_1, \dots, x_n) g(x_1) \dots g(x_n)$$
$$= \int \delta(\sum k_j) Q(k_1, \dots, k_n) \tilde{g}(k_1') \dots \tilde{g}(k_n') e^{i \sum (k_j + k'_j) x_j} \dots dk \dots dk' \dots$$
$$= \int K_g(k_1, \dots, k_n) e^{i \sum k_j x_j} \dots dk \dots, \quad (21.29)$$

where

$$K_g(k_1, \ldots, k_n)$$
$$= \int \delta(\sum k_j - \sum k'_j)\, Q(k_1 - k'_1, \ldots, k_n - k'_n)\, \tilde{g}(k'_1) \ldots \tilde{g}(k'_n) \ldots dk' \ldots . \tag{21.30}$$

Substituting (21.28) and (21.29) into (21.27) we obtain:

$$\Phi_{\ldots p' \ldots} S(g) \Phi_{\ldots p \ldots} = (2\pi)^{4n} \sum A(\ldots p' \ldots p \ldots) K_g(\ldots k \ldots), \tag{21.31}$$

where each k is equal either to one of the p', or to one of the p, or to the difference between p and p', or to zero. In any case,

$$\sum k_j = \sum p' - \sum p.$$

As was already mentioned, the function $g(x)$ is a function of the region in four-space in which the interaction occurs. If we assume that the process occurs within a volume V and within a time interval T we obtain that

$$g(x) = 1 \text{ for } \mathbf{x} \in V,\ x^0 \in T$$

and that it approaches zero sufficiently rapidly near the boundaries of this region. By increasing without limit the dimensions of the region V and the value of T we shall in the limit arrive at the situation in which the interaction is switched on in the infinitely remote past, is switched off in the infinitely remote future, and is effective over all space. The scattering matrix $S(1)$ is usually defined by means of such a transition to the limit.

In the above the Fourier transform $\tilde{g}(k)$ approaches a quantity which is proportional to $\delta(k)$. In order to obtain the coefficient of proportionality we note that

$$\int \tilde{g}(k) dk = g(0) = 1,$$

and therefore we have approximately

$$\tilde{g}(k) \cong \delta(k). \tag{21.32}$$

Now carrying out the integrations in (21.30) we find on making use of (21.32),

$$K_g(k_1, \ldots, k_n)$$
$$= \int Q(k_2' + \ldots + k_n' - k_2 - \ldots - k_n, k_2 - k_2', \ldots, k_n - k_n')$$
$$\times \tilde{g}(\sum k_j - \sum k_j' + k_1') \tilde{g}(k_2') \ldots \tilde{g}(k_n') \, dk_2' \ldots dk_n'$$
$$\approx \tilde{g}(\sum k_j) Q(-k_2 - \ldots - k_n, \ldots, k_2, \ldots, k_n)$$
$$\approx \tilde{g}(\sum k_j) Q(k_1, \ldots, k_n). \quad (21.33)$$

In order to carry out this integration it is important that the function Q should be continuous in the neighborhood of the point $(k_1, \ldots, k_n)$.

Substituting (21.33) into (21.31) we now obtain:

$$\Phi^*_{\ldots p' \ldots} S(g) \Phi_{\ldots p \ldots} \approx \tilde{g}(\sum p - \sum p') F(p', p), \quad (21.34)$$

and therefore in view of (21.32)

$$\Phi^*_{\ldots p' \ldots} S(1) \Phi_{\ldots p \ldots} = \delta(\sum p - \sum p') F(p', p). \quad (21.35)$$

In determining the probabilities of the various scattering processes one has to evaluate squares of matrix elements of the type

$$| \Phi^*_{\ldots p' \ldots} S \Phi_{\ldots p \ldots} |^2, \quad (21.36)$$

which may be naturally defined as the asymptotic forms as $V \to \infty$, $T \to \infty$ of the expressions

$$| \Phi^*_{\ldots p' \ldots} S(g) \Phi_{\ldots p \ldots} |^2 \approx | \tilde{g}(\sum p - \sum p') |^2 | F(p', p) |^2.$$

In order to determine $|\tilde{g}(k)|^2$ we note that just as in the case of $\tilde{g}(k)$ it must be proportional to $\delta(k)$, and by obtaining the coefficient of proportionality from the requirement that the norm must be conserved

$$\int | \tilde{g}(k)|^2 \, dk = \frac{1}{(2\pi)^4} \int | g(x)|^2 \, dx = \frac{VT}{(2\pi)^4},$$

we find approximately:

$$| \tilde{g}(k) |^2 \approx \frac{VT}{(2\pi)^4} \delta(k).$$

For the square of the matrix element (21.36) in which we are interested we now obtain a limiting expression of the form

$$|\Phi^*_{\dots p' \dots} S(1) \Phi_{\dots p \dots}|^2 = \frac{VT}{(2\pi)^4} \delta(\sum p - \sum p') \, |F(p', p)|^2. \quad (21.37)$$

A similar calculation may be carried out for the scattering of particles by a classical stationary field of the type (21.23). In this case, as we have already established, momentum is not conserved, but only energy is conserved, and in place of (21.35) and (21.37) we obtain:

$$\Phi^*_{\dots p' \dots} S(1) \Phi_{\dots p \dots} = \delta(\sum p^0 - \sum p'^0) \, F(p', p), \quad (21.38)$$

$$|\Phi^*_{\dots p' \dots} S(1) \Phi_{\dots p \dots}|^2 = \frac{T}{2\pi} \delta(\sum p^0 - \sum p'^0) \, |F(p', p)|^2. \quad (21.39)$$

§ 22. Probabilities of Scattering Processes and Effective Cross Sections

22.1. *Normalization of the State Amplitude*

We shall now establish the connection between the matrix elements of the S-matrix and the probabilities of scattering processes. We first consider the case when the interaction is switched on with an intensity $g(x)$ localized within a finite space-time region and discuss the usual problem of scattering theory in which prior to switching on the interaction there are s fluxes of particles with precisely determined momenta $\mathbf{p}_1, \dots, \mathbf{p}_s$ and inner quantum numbers $\sigma_1, \dots, \sigma_s$ characterizing the mass, the charge, and the spin, and in which it is required to find the average number of scattered particles with momenta lying within the infinitesimal intervals $d\mathbf{p}'_1, \dots, d\mathbf{p}'_r$ and with inner quantum numbers $\sigma'_1, \dots, \sigma'_r$.

First of all it is evident that just as in the case of analogous problems of ordinary quantum mechanics, we are here dealing with nonnormalizable state amplitudes and must therefore use normalization per unit volume. In order to obtain the state amplitude with such normalization, it is natural to make use of a limiting transition and to consider a sequence of state amplitudes with an indefinitely increasing ordinary norm.

We first obtain this amplitude for the case of a single particle.

We take the amplitude of the single particle state

$$\Phi_1 = \int \chi_\sigma(\mathbf{p})\, a_\sigma^+(\mathbf{p})\, d\mathbf{p}\, \Phi_0, \tag{22.1}$$

and note that its norm is equal to

$$\Phi_1^* \Phi = \int |\chi_\sigma(\mathbf{p})|^2 d\mathbf{p} = N. \tag{22.2}$$

Therefore by setting $N = 1$ we may consider that the expression

$$|\chi_\sigma(\mathbf{p})|^2 d\mathbf{p}$$

gives the probability that the particle characterized by the inner quantum number σ has its momentum within the interval $d\mathbf{p}$ about the average value $\mathbf{p}$. The function $\chi(\mathbf{p})$ itself is thus the wave function of the particle in the momentum representation. Therefore its Fourier transform

$$\varphi_\sigma(\mathbf{x}) = \frac{1}{(2\pi)^{3/2}} \int e^{i\mathbf{px}} \chi_\sigma(\mathbf{p})\, d\mathbf{p} \tag{22.3}$$

is the wave function in the configuration representation with a norm equal to

$$\int |\varphi_\sigma(\mathbf{x})|^2 d\mathbf{x} = \int |\chi_\sigma(\mathbf{p})|^2 d\mathbf{p} = N.$$

In the case of $N = 1$ one may interpret the quantity

$$|\varphi(\mathbf{x})|^2 d\mathbf{x} \tag{22.4}$$

as the probability in configuration space. By setting N equal to the number of particles much larger than unity we find that the expression (22.4) is the average number of particles within the infinitesimal volume element $d\mathbf{x}$.

Now by letting the normalization N increase indefinitely in such a way that $\chi_\sigma(\mathbf{p})$ tends to the expression

$$(2\pi)^{3/2} \delta(\mathbf{p} - \mathbf{p}_0),$$

we shall obtain a wave packet of increasingly better defined momentum. From (22.3) we find that

$$|\varphi_\sigma(\mathbf{x})| \to 1,$$

and that therefore also

$$|\varphi_\sigma(\mathbf{x})|^2 \to 1,$$

and we obtain in the limit the situation in which there is one particle per unit volume.

By going to the limit in (22.1) we obtain the expression for the amplitude of the single particle state normalized per unit volume:

$$\Phi_1 = (2\pi)^{3/2} a_\sigma^+(\mathbf{p})\,\Phi_0. \tag{22.5}$$

In the case of several different particles it is necessary to consider instead of (22.1) the expression

$$\Phi_s = \int \chi_{\sigma_1}(\mathbf{p}_1)\, a_{\sigma_1}^+(\mathbf{p}_1)\, d\mathbf{p}_1 \ldots \int \chi_{\sigma_s}(\mathbf{p}_s)\, a_{\sigma_s}^+(\mathbf{p}_s)\, d\mathbf{p}_s \Phi_0, \tag{22.6}$$

where all the σ_i $(i = 1, 2, \ldots, s)$ are different. The norm of such an amplitude will obviously be given by the product of the norms of s single particle states:

$$\Phi_s^* \Phi_s = \prod_{1 \leq i \leq s} \int |\chi_{\sigma_i}(\mathbf{p}_i)|^2 d\mathbf{p}_i = \prod_i N_i. \tag{22.7}$$

By repeating the argument given above separately for each of the factors in (22.6) and (22.7) we conclude that the amplitude of the many particle state normalized per unit volume for each of the particles present in this state has the form

$$\Phi_s = (2\pi)^{\frac{3s}{2}} a_{\sigma_1}^+(\mathbf{p}_1)\, a_{\sigma_2}^+(\mathbf{p}_2) \ldots a_{\sigma_s}^+(\mathbf{p})\,\Phi_0. \tag{22.8}$$

We have to consider separately the case when among the inner quantum numbers $\sigma_1, \ldots, \sigma_s$ there are some identical ones, i.e., when among the s particles there are several groups of identical particles. We assume that the first ν quantum numbers are the same:

$$\sigma_1 = \sigma_2 = \ldots = \sigma_\nu = \sigma.$$

Then in the course of evaluating the norm (22.7) the corresponding operators

$$a_\sigma^+(\mathbf{k}_1), \ldots, a_\sigma^+(\mathbf{k}_\nu)$$

from Φ may commute with the operators $a_\sigma(\mathbf{k}_1'), \ldots, a_\sigma(\mathbf{k}_\nu')$ from

Φ^* in $\nu!$ different ways. In the case of several groups of $\nu_1, v_2, \ldots, \nu_\alpha$ identical particles we shall correspondingly obtain:

$$\Phi^*\Phi = \prod (\nu!) \prod_i \int |\chi_{\sigma_i}(\mathbf{p}_i)|^2 d\mathbf{p}_i = \prod (\nu!) \prod_i N_i, \quad (22.9)$$

where the following notation has been used

$$\prod (\nu!) = \nu_1! \, \nu_2! \ldots \nu_\alpha!.$$

Therefore the amplitude of the many particle state normalized per unit volume will now assume the form

$$\Phi = \frac{(2\pi)^{\frac{3s}{2}}}{\sqrt{\Pi(\nu!)}} a^+_{\sigma_1}(\mathbf{p}_1) \, a^+_{\sigma_2}(\mathbf{p}_2) \ldots a^+_{\sigma_s}(\mathbf{p}_s) \, \Phi_0. \quad (22.10)$$

However, in this case we shall also use expression (22.8) since we have already taken the factor $[\Pi(\nu!)]^{-1/2}$ into account in Feynman's rules (21.18).

22.2 *Calculation of Transition Probabilities*

Upon returning to the problem stated at the beginning of this section, we see that as a result of the interaction, the system will go over from the state (22.8) into the state described by the amplitude

$$S(g)\,(2\pi)^{\frac{3s}{2}} \Phi_{\mathbf{p}_1\sigma_1 \ldots \mathbf{p}_s\sigma_s},$$

where

$$\Phi_{\mathbf{p}_1\sigma_1 \ldots \mathbf{p}_s\sigma_s} = a^+_{\sigma_1}(\mathbf{p}_1) \ldots a^+_{\sigma_s}(\mathbf{p}_s) \, \Phi_0, \quad (22.11)$$

and therefore the average number of particles which will be found in the final state described by the normalized amplitude Φ_α is equal, in accordance with the general rule of quantum mechanics, to

$$(2\pi)^{3s} \frac{|\Phi^*_\alpha S(g) \, \Phi_{\mathbf{p}_1\sigma_1 \ldots \mathbf{p}_s\sigma_s}|^2}{\Phi^*_\alpha \Phi_\alpha}. \quad (22.12)$$

In the preceding it is assumed in connection with the choice of normalization that in the initial state the average numbers of the various particles per unit volume are equal to unity.

In the case that these numbers are respectively equal to $n_1, \ldots, n_s$ expression (22.12) should be replaced by

$$n_1 n_2 \ldots n_s (2\pi)^{3s} \frac{|\Phi_\alpha^* S(g) \Phi_{\mathbf{p}_1\sigma_1 \ldots \mathbf{p}_s\sigma_s}|^2}{\Phi_\alpha^* \Phi_\alpha}. \tag{22.13}$$

We are now interested in the number of particles scattered into the momentum intervals $\Delta\mathbf{p}_1', \ldots, \Delta\mathbf{p}_r'$ centered about $\mathbf{p}_1', \ldots, \mathbf{p}_r'$. In carrying out this calculation we shall assume, as was mentioned in § 21.5, that the momentum of each particle has different values in the initial and the final states. Experimentally this requirement corresponds to the fact that particles with unchanged momentum are always included in the primary beam, while only those particles whose momentum has been altered are considered as scattered particles.

We shall therefore take the amplitude of the final state Φ_α in the form

$$\Phi_\alpha = (2\pi)^{\frac{3r}{2}} \int_G \Phi_{\mathbf{k}_1\sigma_1 \ldots \mathbf{k}_r\sigma_r} d\mathbf{k}_1 \ldots d\mathbf{k}_r,$$

where the region G is equal to the product of the volumes $\Delta\mathbf{p}_1', \ldots, \Delta\mathbf{p}_r'$. On calculating the norm of Φ_α, we now find

$$\Phi_\alpha^* \Phi_\alpha = (2\pi)^{3r} \Delta\mathbf{p}_1' \ldots \Delta\mathbf{p}_r',$$

while in place of (22.13) we obtain the expression

$$\frac{n_1 \ldots n_s (2\pi)^{3s}}{\Delta\mathbf{p}_1' \ldots \Delta\mathbf{p}_r'} \int_G d\mathbf{k}_1 \ldots d\mathbf{k}_r (\Phi^*_{\mathbf{k}_1\sigma_1 \ldots \mathbf{k}_r\sigma_r} S(g) \Phi_{\mathbf{p}_1\sigma_1 \ldots \mathbf{p}_s\sigma_s})^*$$
$$\times \int_G d\mathbf{k}_1' \ldots d\mathbf{k}_r' (\Phi^*_{\mathbf{k}'_1\sigma_1 \ldots \mathbf{k}'_r\sigma_r} S(g) \Phi_{\mathbf{p}_1\sigma_1 \ldots \mathbf{p}_s\sigma_s}),$$

which in virtue of the definition of the region G is equal to

$$n_1 \ldots n_s (2\pi)^{3s} |\Phi^*_{\ldots\mathbf{p}'\ldots} S(g) \Phi_{\ldots\mathbf{p}\ldots}|^2 \Delta\mathbf{p}_1' \ldots \Delta\mathbf{p}_r', \tag{22.14}$$

where for the sake of brevity the notation $\Phi_{\mathbf{p}_1\sigma_1 \ldots \mathbf{p}_r\sigma_r}$ has been replaced by $\Phi_{\ldots\mathbf{p}\ldots}$.

The structure of the squares of matrix elements of the type

$$|\Phi^*_{\ldots\mathbf{p}'\ldots} S(g) \Phi_{\ldots\mathbf{p}\ldots}|^2$$

and the limiting transition $g(x) \to 1$ have been investigated in

§ 21. By substituting into (22.14) the expression (21.37) obtained earlier and dividing it by VT we obtain the number of particles scattered into the interval $d\mathbf{p}'_1 \ldots d\mathbf{p}'_r$ per unit time and per unit volume:

$$(2\pi)^{3s-4}\, n_1 \ldots n_s\, |F(p', p)|^2\, \delta(\sum p - \sum p')\, d\mathbf{p}'_1 \ldots d\mathbf{p}'_r. \qquad (22.15)$$

Making use of formula (21.39) we also find the corresponding expression for scattering per unit time by a stationary classical field in the form

$$(2\pi)^{3s-1}\, n_1 \ldots n_s\, |F(p', p)|^2\, \delta(\sum p^0 - \sum p'^0)\, d\mathbf{p}'_1 \ldots d\mathbf{p}'_r. \qquad (22.16)$$

We emphasize once again that the above formulas (22.15), (22.16) have meaning only under the condition that the function $F(p', p)$ is *continuous* in the neighborhood of the given values of the momenta p', p. In specific calculations we obtain for $F(p', p)$ an expression in the form of a sum of several terms corresponding to a perturbation theory expansion. Therefore the appearance of singularities in $F(p', p)$ may lead to the inapplicability of perturbation theory.

Thus, in order to calculate the number of scattered particles or the corresponding probabilities, it is first of all necessary to calculate the matrix element (21.37) (or (21.39)) and to substitute the resulting function $F(p', p)$ which multiplies the δ-function into (22.15) (or (22.16)). The final result will have meaning only in the case that $F(p', p)$ is continuous in the neighborhood of the given values of its arguments.

Let us consider the process of the scattering of a particle by a particle. In this case $r = 2$, $s = 2$. Instead of (22.15) we obtain the expression

$$(2\pi)^2 n_1 n_2\, |F(p', p)|^2\, \delta(p_1 + p_2 - p'_1 - p'_2)\, d\mathbf{p}'_1 d\mathbf{p}'_2,$$

whose dimensionality in the system of units adopted by us is given by

$$[V^{-1} T^{-1}] = cm^{-4}.$$

Because $\mathbf{p}'_1$ is completely determined by $\mathbf{p}'_2$, and vice versa, we obtain on carrying out the integration over $\mathbf{p}'_2$:

$$(2\pi)^2 n_1 n_2\, |F(p', p)|^2\, \delta(p^0_1 + p^0_2 - p'^0_1 - p'^0_2)\, d\mathbf{p}'_1, \qquad (22.17)$$

where in F we have set

$$\mathbf{p}_2' = \mathbf{p}_1 + \mathbf{p}_2 - \mathbf{p}_1'.$$

22.3. *Differential and Total Effective Cross Sections*

Expression (22.17) is usually represented in the form of the product

$$n_1 \cdot n_2 \cdot v_1 \cdot d\sigma,$$

where v_1 is the absolute value of the velocity of the particle with four-momentum p_1 which is equal to unity for photons and to $|\mathbf{p}_1|/p_1^0$ for particles with rest mass different from zero.

The factor $d\sigma_1$ has the dimensions of an area (cm^2), is proportional to the element of solid angle containing the particle with momentum $\mathbf{p}_1'$ after scattering and is called the differential effective cross section. The integral of $d\sigma_1$ over all solid angles is called the total effective cross section.

Thus the differential effective cross section for the scattering of a particle by a particle has the form

$$d\sigma_1 = \frac{(2\pi)^2}{v_1} |F(p', p)|^2 d\mathbf{p}_1' \delta(E_1 + E_2 - E_1' - E_2')$$

$$= \frac{(2\pi)^2}{v_1} |F(p', p)|^2 \delta(E_1 + E_2 - E_1' - E_2') p_1'^2 dp_1' d\Omega_1' \quad (E_i = p_i^0, p_i' = |\mathbf{p}_i'|).$$

In order to eliminate the δ-function in the foregoing we note that in virtue of the relation

$$(E_1')^2 - (\mathbf{p}_1')^2 = m^2 \tag{22.18}$$

we may replace the integration over dp_1' by integration over dE_1' since

$$p_1' dp_1' = E_1' dE_1'.$$

In carrying out the integration over E_1' it is necessary to keep in mind that the energies E_1, E_2, E_1', and E_2' are, generally speaking, interdependent functions since each of them is related to the corresponding momentum by a relation of type (22.18), while the sum of the momenta is equal to zero. Therefore by setting

$$E_1' + E_2' - E_1 - E_2 = f(E_1'),$$

we obtain after carrying out the integration

$$d\sigma_1 = \frac{(2\pi)^2 p_1' E_1'}{v_1 \, | \, f'(E_1') \, |} \, | \, F(p', \, p) \, |^2 \, d\Omega_1' \, |_{p_1+p_2-p_2'-p_2'=0}, \qquad (22.19)$$

where

$$f'(E_1') = \frac{\partial f}{\partial E_1'} \, .$$

We obtain the total effective cross section by integrating (22.19) over $d\Omega_1'$:

$$\sigma_1(p_2, \, p_1') = \frac{(2\pi)^2}{v_1} \int_\Omega \frac{p_1' E_1'}{| \, f'(E_1') \, |} \, | \, F(p', \, p)|^2 d\Omega_1'. \qquad (22.20)$$

We note also that usually in calculating differential and total scattering cross sections, one is not interested in the spin states of the particles. Therefore a summation is carried out over the spin indices of the scattered particles, and an average is taken over the spin indices of the incident particles. By denoting these operations for the sake of brevity by the symbol Σ_σ we obtain the formula for the differential effective cross section in the form

$$d\sigma_1 = \frac{(2\pi)^2 p_1' E_1'}{v_1 \, | \, f'(E_1') \, |} \sum_\sigma |F(p_1', \, p)|^2 \, d\Omega_1' \, |_{p_1+p_2-p_1'-p_2'=0}. \quad (22.21)$$

In a similar manner one may obtain from the general formulas (22.15) and (22.16) expressions for the probabilities and for the cross sections of various other possible processes. We now also obtain the formula for the scattering of a particle of momentum p_1 by a stationary external field. For the sake of definiteness we shall examine the case when the particle on being scattered by the potential creates an additional particle k, i.e., a process of the bremsstrahlung type. On setting $s = 1$, $r = 2$, in (22.16) we obtain the expression

$$(2\pi)^2 n_1 \, | \, F(p', \, p)|^2 \, \delta(E_1 - E_1' - E_k) \, d\mathbf{p}_1' d\mathbf{k}, \qquad (22.22)$$

which in the system of units employed by us has the dimensionality $[T^{-1}] = cm^{-1}$; by representing (22.22) in the form $n_1 \, v_1 \, d\sigma_1$ we find after carrying out the integration over dE_1', and also the summation and averaging over the spin indices, the differential effective cross section

$$d\sigma_1 = \frac{(2\pi)^2}{v_1} |F(p', p)|^2 p_1' E_1' d\Omega_1' d\mathbf{k} |_{E-E_1'-E_k=0}. \quad (22.23)$$

§ 23. Examples of Calculation of Second-Order Processes

As examples of the application of the methods presented in § 22 we shall calculate in the first nonvanishing approximation the cross sections for the Compton scattering, for the two-photon annihilation of an electron-positron pair, and for the bremsstrahlung of an electron in the field of a nucleus. Since the formulas obtained below are well known, we shall not go into a discussion of them.

23.1 *Compton Scattering.*

We shall calculate the cross section for the scattering of a photon by a free electron. The initial state contains a photon of momentum $\mathbf{k}_1$, energy $k_1 = |\mathbf{k}_1|$, and an electron of four-momentum p_1. Without loss of generality we shall assume that the electron is at rest, i.e., $\mathbf{p}_1 = 0$, $p_1^0 = m$. In the final state we have the scattered photon of momentum $\mathbf{k}_2$ and energy $k_2 = |\mathbf{k}_2|$, and an electron which has received the recoil momentum $\mathbf{p}_2 = \mathbf{k}_1 - \mathbf{k}_2$ and which has the energy

$$p_2^0 = E_2 = \sqrt{(\mathbf{k}_1 - \mathbf{k}_2)^2 + m^2} = \sqrt{\mathbf{k}_1^2 + \mathbf{k}_2^2 - 2\mathbf{k}_1\mathbf{k}_2 \cos\theta + m^2},$$

where θ is the angle between the vectors $\mathbf{k}_1$ and $\mathbf{k}_2$.

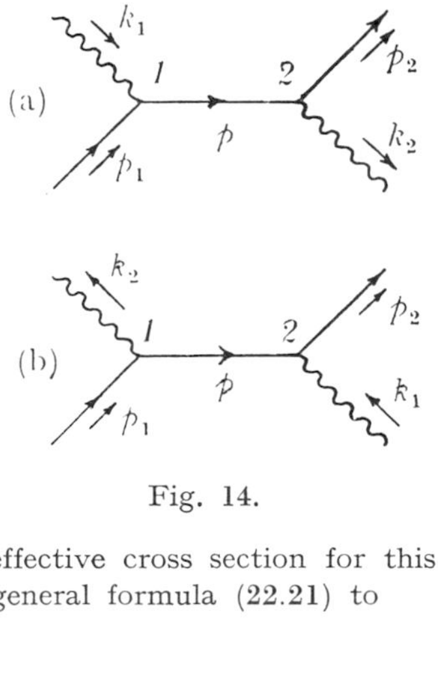

Fig. 14.

The differential effective cross section for this process is equal in accordance with the general formula (22.21) to

$$d\sigma = (2\pi)^2 \frac{k_2^2}{|f'(k_2)|} \sum_\sigma |F(p', p)|^2 d\boldsymbol{\Omega} = (2\pi)^2 \frac{k_2^3 E_2}{k_1 m} \sum_\sigma |F(p', p)|^2 d\boldsymbol{\Omega}. \tag{23.1}$$

The matrix element $F(p', p)$ is determined from formula (21.35). In order to calculate it we shall restrict ourselves to the possible diagrams of the second order shown in Fig. 14. The matrix elements corresponding to these diagrams can be obtained from the rules of correspondence formulated in § 21.

We shall write down in detail the matrix element for the diagram of Fig. 14a. The factor

$$(2\pi)^{-3/2} \bar{v}^{\nu,+}(\mathbf{p}_2),$$

will be taken to correspond to the external line of the electron emerging from the vertex 2 with the four-momentum p_2, while the factor

$$\frac{1}{(2\pi)^{3/2}} \frac{e_m^2}{\sqrt{2k_2}} \quad (m \neq 0)$$

will be taken to correspond to the external line of the photon emerging from the vertex 2 with momentum $\mathbf{k}_2$. Since the factor

$$ie\gamma^n (2\pi)^4 \delta(p - k_2 - p_2),$$

corresponds to this vertex the product of the last two factors gives

$$\delta(p - k_2 - p_2) \frac{ie}{\sqrt{2k_2}} (2\pi)^{5/2} \sum_{\alpha=1,2,3} e_2^\alpha \gamma^\alpha = -\delta(p - k_2 - p_2) \frac{ie(2\pi)^{5/2}}{\sqrt{2k_2}} \hat{e}_2.$$

The factor

$$\frac{1}{(2\pi)^4 i} \frac{m + \hat{p}}{m^2 - p^2 - i\varepsilon},$$

corresponds to the internal electron line, the expression

$$-\delta(p_1 + k_1 - p) \frac{ie(2\pi)^{5/2}}{\sqrt{2k_1}} \hat{e}_1,$$

corresponds to vertex 1 together with the external photon line k_1, and finally, the factor

$$(2\pi)^{-3/2} v^{\nu',-}(\mathbf{p}_1)$$

corresponds to the external electron line p_1.

Multiplying together all the preceding factors in the sequence corresponding to the motion along the electron line, and integrating over p, we shall obtain the expression

$$\delta(p_1 + k_2 - p_2 - k_2) F_a(p, k),$$

where

$$F_a(p, k) = \frac{e^2}{8\pi^2 i} \frac{1}{\sqrt{k_1 k_2}} \bar{v}^{\nu,+}(\mathbf{p}_2)\hat{e}_2 \frac{\hat{p}_1 + \hat{k}_1 + m}{(p_1 + k_1)^2 - m^2} \hat{e}_1 v^{\nu',-}(\mathbf{p}_1).$$

The diagram of Fig. 14b yields an analogous term

$$F_b(p, k) = \frac{e^2}{8\pi^2 i} \frac{1}{\sqrt{k_1 k_2}} \bar{v}^{\nu,+}(\mathbf{p}_2)\hat{e}_1 \frac{\hat{p}_1 - \hat{k}_2 + m}{(p_1 - k_2)^2 - m^2} \hat{e}_2 v^{\nu',-}(\mathbf{p}_1).$$

Noting that

$$(p_1 + k_1)^2 - m^2 = 2(p_1 k_1) = 2mk_1,$$
$$(p_1 - k_2)^2 - m^2 = -2(p_1 k_2) = -2mk_2,$$

we obtain on adding F_a and F_b,

$$F(p, k) = \frac{e^2}{16\pi^2 i} \frac{1}{m(k_1 k_2)^{3/2}} \bar{v}^{\nu,+}(\mathbf{p}_2) M v^{\nu',-}(\mathbf{p}_1), \tag{23.2}$$

where

$$M = k_2 \hat{e}_2(\hat{p}_1 + \hat{k}_1 + m)\hat{e}_1 - k_1 \hat{e}_1(\hat{p}_1 - \hat{k}_2 + m)\hat{e}_2.$$

In calculating $\Sigma_\sigma |F|^2$ we note that we must average over the initial spin index ν', and sum over the final spin index ν. Therefore we obtain with the aid of relations (7.20) and (7.21):

$$\sum_\sigma |F|^2 = \frac{1}{2}\sum_{\nu,\nu'} FF^*$$
$$= \frac{e^4}{2(4\pi)^4 m^2 (k_1 k_2)^3} \sum_{\nu\nu'} \bar{v}^{\nu,+}(\mathbf{p}_2) M v^{\nu',-}(\mathbf{p}_1) \bar{v}^{\nu',+}(\mathbf{p}_1) \bar{M} v^{\nu,-}(\mathbf{p}_2)$$
$$= \frac{e^4}{8(4\pi)^4 E_2 (mk_1 k_2)^3} \operatorname{Sp} A, \tag{23.3}$$

where

$$A = (\hat{p}_2 + m) M (\hat{p}_1 + m) \bar{M}. \tag{23.4}$$

Since the four-vectors k, p, and e are real, γ^0 is Hermitean, and $\boldsymbol{\gamma}$ is anti-Hermitean, we find that if $M = \Sigma_i c_i \hat{a}_1 \hat{a}_2 \dots \hat{a}_i$, then

$$\bar{M} = \sum_i c_i^* \hat{a}_i \hat{a}_{i-1} \dots \hat{a}_1,$$

where $a_1, \dots, a_i$ are vectors of the type k, p, and e.

Before evaluating (23.4) let us simplify M somewhat. Since in accordance with the definition of the Dirac matrices

$$\hat{a}\hat{b} + \hat{b}\hat{a} = 2(ab),$$

we may represent M in the form

$$M = k_2 \hat{e}_2 \hat{k}_1 \hat{e}_1 - k_2 \hat{e}_2 \hat{e}_1 (\hat{p}_1 - m) + 2k_2 \hat{e}_2 (p_1 e_1) + k_1 \hat{e}_1 k_2 \hat{e}_2$$
$$+ k_1 \hat{e}_1 \hat{e}_2 (\hat{p}_1 - m) - 2k_1 \hat{e}_1 (p_1 e_2). \tag{23.5}$$

But since M occurs in the combination

$$\bar{v}^{\nu,+}(\mathbf{p}_2) M v^{\nu',-}(\mathbf{p}_1),$$

and, in accordance with the field equation,

$$(\hat{p}_1 - m)\, v^{\nu',-}(\mathbf{p}_1) = 0$$

and since

$$(p_1 e_2) = (p_1 e_1) = 0,$$

the matrix M may be represented in the form

$$M = k_2 \hat{e}_2 \hat{k}_1 \hat{e}_1 + k_1 \hat{e}_1 \hat{k}_2 \hat{e}_2.$$

The matrix A may now be written as the sum of three terms

$$A = A_1 + A_2 + A_3,$$

where

$$A_1 = (\hat{p}_1 + m)\, M (\hat{p}_1 + m)\, \bar{M}, \quad A_2 = (\hat{k}_1 - \hat{k}_2)\, M \hat{p}_1 \bar{M},$$
$$A_3 = m(\hat{k}_1 - \hat{k}_2)\, M\bar{M}.$$

For the calculation of traces we shall use the conditions of transversality of the electromagnetic field

$$(e_1 k_1) = (e_2 k_2) = 0$$

and the relations

$$(p_1 e_1) = (p_1 e_2) = 0, \quad (p_1 k_1) = mk_1, \quad (p_1 k_2) = mk_2,$$
$$(k_1 k_1) = (k_2 k_2) = 0, \quad e_1^2 = e_2^2 = -1.$$

The term A_3 contains the product of an odd number of Dirac matrices and therefore

$$\mathrm{Sp}\, A_3 = 0.$$

In order to calculate $\mathrm{Sp}\, A_1$ it is sufficient to commute the first two factors in A_1 and to use the third of formulas (6.16), which gives:

$$\mathrm{Sp}\, A_1 = 32 m^2 k_1^2 k_2^2 (e_1 e_2)^2 = 32 m^2 k_1^2 k_2^2 \cos^2\theta. \tag{23.6}$$

For the calculation of A_2 it is convenient to make use of the fact that the factors of a product whose trace is being sought may be cyclically interchanged, and to write A_2 in the form

$$A_2 = \bar{M}(\hat{k}_1 - \hat{k}_2)\, M\hat{p}_1 + \tilde{A}_2 \quad (\mathrm{Sp}\, \tilde{A}_2 = 0).$$

By carrying out the commutations in such a way that identical factors should turn out to be next to each other we obtain:

$$(\hat{k}_1 - \hat{k}_2)\, M = a + b,$$

where

$$a = k_2 \hat{e}_2 \hat{k}_2 \hat{k}_1 \hat{e}_1 - k_1 \hat{e}_1 \hat{k}_1 \hat{k}_2 \hat{e}_2,$$
$$b = 2(k_1 e_2)\, k_2 \hat{k}_1 \hat{e}_1 - 2(k_1 e_1)\, k_1 \hat{k}_2 \hat{e}_2.$$

Further we find:

$$\mathrm{Sp}\, \bar{M} a \hat{p}_1 = 8 k_1 k_2 m (k_1 k_2)(k_1 - k_2) + 8 k_1 k_2 m \{k_1 (k_2 e_1)^2 - k_2 (k_1 e_2)^2\}, \tag{23.7}$$
$$\mathrm{Sp}\, \bar{M} b \hat{p}_1 = 8 k_1 k_2 m \{k_2 (k_1 e_2)^2 - k_1 (k_2 e_1)^2\}. \tag{23.8}$$

By adding expressions (23.6)–(23.8) and by taking into account the following relation whose validity may be easily checked

$$(k_1 k_2) = m(k_1 - k_2),$$

we obtain

$$\mathrm{Sp}\, A = 8m^2 k_1^2 k_2^2 \left\{4 \cos^2\theta + \frac{k_1}{k_2} + \frac{k_2}{k_1} - 2\right\}.$$

By substituting this expression together with (23.3) into (23.1) we obtain for the differential effective cross section

$$d\sigma = \frac{e^4}{(8\pi)^2 m^2} \frac{k_2^2}{k_1^2} \left\{4 \cos^2\theta + \frac{k_1}{k_2} + \frac{k_2}{k_1} - 2\right\} d\boldsymbol{\Omega}.$$

Introducing the "electron radius"

$$r_0 = \frac{e^2}{4\pi m},$$

we obtain the well-known *Klein-Nishina formula*:

$$d\sigma = \frac{r}{4} \frac{k_2^2}{k_1^2} \left\{4 \cos^2\theta + \frac{k_1}{k_2} + \frac{k_2}{k_1} - 2\right\} d\boldsymbol{\Omega}. \tag{23.9}$$

23.2 *Annihilation of an Electron-Positron Pair*

We shall now investigate the process of mutual annihilation of an electron and a positron. The simplest diagram which corresponds to this process (Fig. 15) is the only first-order diagram.

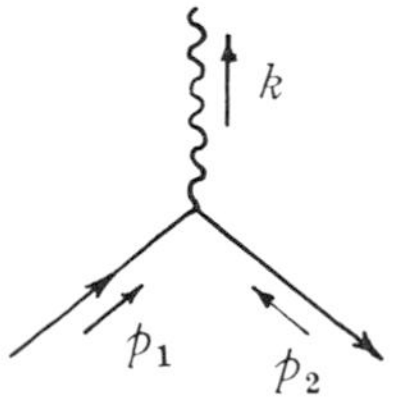

Fig. 15.

However, it may be easily seen that the one-photon annihilation described by this diagram is forbidden by the energy-momentum conservation laws. Indeed, the conservation laws give

$$\mathbf{k} = \mathbf{p}_1 + \mathbf{p}_2,$$
$$|\mathbf{k}| = \sqrt{|\mathbf{p}_1|^2 + m^2} + \sqrt{|\mathbf{p}_2|^2 + m^2},$$

and by going over, for example, into the system in which the center of mass of the electron and the positron is at rest ($\mathbf{p}_1 + \mathbf{p}_2 = 0$) we obtain an obvious contradiction.

The two-photon annihilation is described by the two second-order diagrams shown in Fig. 11.

We shall carry out the calculation in the system in which the center of mass of the electron and the positron is at rest. Then by setting

$$\mathbf{p}_1 = \mathbf{p}, \quad \mathbf{p}_2 = -\mathbf{p}, \quad \mathbf{k}_1 = \mathbf{k}, \quad \mathbf{k}_2 = -\mathbf{k},$$

we obtain:

$$\begin{aligned} &\text{electron: } (E_p = \sqrt{\mathbf{p}^2 + m^2}, \ \mathbf{p}) \\ &\text{positron: } (E_p, \ -\mathbf{p}) \\ &\text{first photon: } (k^0 = |\mathbf{k}|, \ \mathbf{k}) \\ &\text{second photon: } (k^0, \ -\mathbf{k}). \end{aligned}$$

In accordance with the basic formula (22.21) and taking into account the normalization of the amplitude of the two-photon state and the relation $|f'(E')| = 2$, the cross section for the foregoing process is equal to

$$d\sigma = \frac{(2\pi)^2 (k^0)^2}{4v(p_1)} \sum_{\sigma} |F|^2 \, d\boldsymbol{\Omega} = (2\pi)^2 \frac{(k^0)^3}{4p} \sum_{\sigma} |F|^2 \, d\boldsymbol{\Omega}, \tag{23.10}$$

where we have used the notation $p = |\mathbf{p}|$.

Making use of the rules of correspondence we construct the matrix elements

$$F_a(p, k) = \frac{e^2}{8\pi^2 i k^0} \bar{v}^{\nu,-}(\mathbf{p}_2) \hat{e}_2 \frac{\hat{p}_1 - \hat{k}_1 + m}{(p_1 - k_1)^2 - m^2} \hat{e}_1 v^{\nu',-}(\mathbf{p}_1),$$

$$F_b(p, k) = \frac{e^2}{8\pi^2 i k^0} \bar{v}^{\nu,-}(\mathbf{p}_2) \hat{e}_1 \frac{\hat{p}_1 - \hat{k}_2 + m}{(p_1 - k_2)^2 - m^2} \hat{e}_2 v^{\nu',-}(\mathbf{p}_1);$$

and by adding them we find:

$$F(p, k) = \frac{ie^2}{8\pi^2 k^0} \frac{\bar{v}^{\nu,-}(\mathbf{p}_2) M v^{\nu',-}(\mathbf{p}_1)}{2(p_1 k_1)(p_1 k_2)},$$

where

$$M = (p_1 k_2) \hat{e}_2 (\hat{p}_1 - \hat{k}_1 + m) \hat{e}_1 + \hat{e}_1 (\hat{p}_1 - \hat{k}_2 + m) \hat{e}_2 (p_1 k_1).$$

By commuting $\hat{p}_1 \hat{e}_1$ and $\hat{p}_2 \hat{e}_2$ and by making use of the field equations

$$(\hat{p}_1 - m) v(\mathbf{p}_1) = 0,$$

we bring M into the form

$$M = (p_1 k_2)[2(p_1 e_1) \hat{e}_2 - \hat{e}_2 \hat{k}_1 \hat{e}_1] + (p_1 k_1)[2(p_1 e_2) \hat{e}_1 - \hat{e}_1 \hat{k}_2 \hat{e}_2],$$

from which it also follows that

$$\bar{M} = (p_1 k_2)[2(p_1 e_1) \hat{e}_2 - \hat{e}_1 \hat{k}_1 \hat{e}_2] + (p_1 k_1)[2(p_1 e_2) \hat{e}_1 - \hat{e}_2 \hat{k}_2 \hat{e}_1].$$

In calculating $\Sigma_\sigma |F|^2$ it is necessary to average over the spins of both the electron and the positron. Therefore by taking into account formulas (7.20) and (7.21) we obtain

$$\sum_{\sigma}|F|^2 = \frac{e^4}{(8\pi^2k^0)^2}\frac{1}{16(p_1k_1)^2(p_1k_2)^2}\sum_{\nu,\nu'}\bar{v}^{\nu,-}(\mathbf{p}_2)Mv^{\nu',-}(\mathbf{p}_1)\bar{v}^{\nu',+}(\mathbf{p}_1)\bar{M}v^{\nu,+}(\mathbf{p}_2)$$
$$= \frac{e^4}{(4\pi k^0)^4}\frac{1}{16(p_1k_1)^2(p_1k_2)^2}\operatorname{Sp} A, \tag{23.11}$$

where

$$A = (\hat{p}_2 - m)M(\hat{p}_1 + m)\bar{M}.$$

Making use of the law of conservation of four-momentum

$$p_2 = k_1 + k_2 - p_1,$$

we shall write A in the form of the sum

$$A = A_1 + A_2 + A_3,$$

where

$$A_1 = (k_1 + \hat{k}_2)M\hat{p}_1\bar{M},$$
$$A_2 = -(\hat{p}_1 + m)M(\hat{p}_1 + m)\bar{M},$$
$$\operatorname{Sp} A_3 = 0.$$

For the calculation of $\operatorname{Sp} A_1$ and $\operatorname{Sp} A_2$ we shall utilize (6.16) and the following relations which follow directly from the corresponding definitions:

$$(k_1e_1) = (k_2e_2) = (k_1e_2) = (k_2e_1) = 0,$$
$$(k_1k_2) = 2(k^0)^2,\ k_1^2 = k_2^2 = 0,$$
$$(k_1p_1) = (k^0)^2 - \mathbf{k}_1\mathbf{p}_1 = k^0(k^0 - p\cos\theta),$$
$$(k_2p_1) = (k^0)^2 - \mathbf{k}_2\mathbf{p}_1 = k^0(k^0 + p\cos\theta),$$

where θ is the angle between the vectors $\mathbf{k}_1$ and $\mathbf{p}_1$.

The general method of calculating traces consists, as in the preceding case, of successive displacements of identical matrix four-vectors towards each other. Omitting the elementary but tedious calculations we merely state the results:

$$\operatorname{Sp} A_1 = 32(k^0)^2(pk_1)(pk_2)\{2(e_1e_2)(pe_1)(pe_2) + k_0^2 + (pe_1)^2 + (pe_2)^2\},$$
$$\operatorname{Sp} A_2 = -32(k^0)^2(pk_1)(pk_2)\{2(e_1e_2)(pe_1)(pe_2) + (pe_1)^2 + (pe_2)^2\}$$
$$-32\{2(k^0)^2(pe_1)(pe_2) + (e_1e_2)(pk_1)(pk_2)\}^2,$$
$$\operatorname{Sp} A = 32(pk_1)^2(pk_2)^2\left\{\frac{(k^0)^4}{(pk_1)(pk_2)} - \frac{4(k^0)^4(pe_1)^2(pe_2)^2}{(pk_1)^2(pk_2)^2}\right.$$
$$\left.-\frac{4(k^0)^2(e_1e_2)(pe_1)(pe_2)}{(pk_1)(pk_2)} - (e_1e_2)^2\right\}.$$

By summing over the polarization directions of the photons and by taking into account the relations

$$\sum_{e_1}(pe_1)^2 = \sum_{e_2}(pe_2)^2 = p^2\sin^2\theta,\ \sum_{e_1,e_2}(pe_1)^2(pe_2)^2 = p^4\sin^4\theta,$$
$$\sum_{e_1,e_2}(e_1e_2)^2 = 2,\ \sum_{e_1,e_2}(e_1e_2)(pe_1)(pe_2) = -p^2\sin^4\theta,$$

we obtain:

$$\mathrm{Sp}\,A = 64(pk_1)^2(pk_2)^2\left[\frac{(k^0)^2+p^2+p^2\sin^2\theta}{(k^0)^2-p^2\cos^2\theta}\quad\frac{2p^4\sin^4\theta}{((k^0)^2-p^2\cos^2\theta)^2}\right].$$

By substituting this expression into (23.11) and (23.10) we obtian the well-known formula (60) for the differential effective cross section for the annihilation of an electron-positron pair:

$$d\sigma = \frac{e^4}{4(4\pi)^2k^0p}\left\{\frac{(k^0)^2+p^2+p^2\sin^2\theta}{(k^0)^2+p^2\cos^2\theta} - \frac{2p^4\sin^4\theta}{((k^0)^2-p^2\cos^2\theta)^2}\right\}d\Omega. \qquad (23.12)$$

23.3 *Bremsstrahlung*

We now discuss the bremsstrahlung of an electron in the field of a nucleus. The process consists of the fact that the electron in passing close by a nucleus emits a photon under the influence of the electric field of the nucleus. In this process, the nucleus takes up a part of the momentum required for the conservation of energy. By Coulomb's law the potential of a nucleus of charge Ze is equal to

$$a_0(\mathbf{x}) = \frac{Ze}{4\pi\,|\,\mathbf{x}\,|},$$

and therefore

$$\varphi_0(\mathbf{q}) = \frac{Ze}{(2\pi)^{3/2}\,|\,\mathbf{q}\,|^2}. \qquad (23.13)$$

In the lowest nonvanishing order of approximation the bremsstrahlung is described by the two second-order diagrams shown in Fig. 16 where

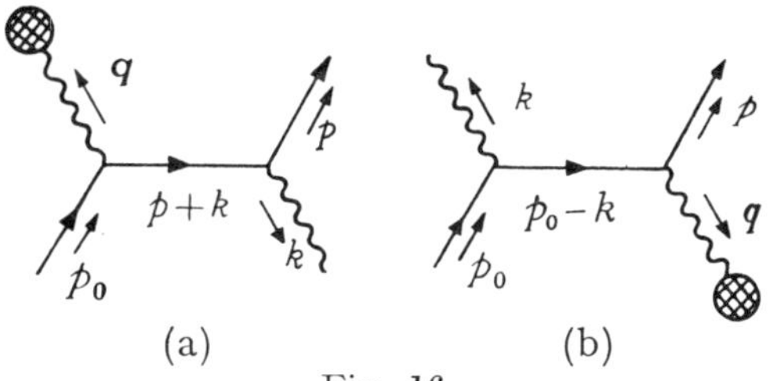

Fig. 16.

p_0 is the initial four-momentum of the electron, $\mathbf{q}$ is the momentum given up to the nucleus, p is the final four-momentum of the electron, and k is the momentum of the emitted photon.

In accordance with the basic formula (22.23) the cross section for this process is equal to

$$d\sigma = \frac{(2\pi)^2EE_0p}{p_0}\sum_\sigma|\,F(p',\,p)\,|^2\,d\Omega_p\,d\Omega_k\,(k_0)^2\,dk^0, \qquad (23.14)$$

where

$$p_0 = |\mathbf{p}_0| \text{ and } p = |\mathbf{p}|.$$

For the calculation of matrix elements we shall introduce a fictitious "polarization vector" of the timelike recoil pseudophoton e_q which has only a time component, i.e.,

$$e_q^{\mu} = \delta_{\mu 0}.$$

By applying the usual methods we then obtain

$$F(p', p) = \frac{e^2 \varphi(\mathbf{q})}{i(2\pi)^2} \bar{v}^{\nu,+}(\mathbf{p}) \left\{ \frac{\hat{e}}{\sqrt{2k^0}} \frac{\hat{p}+\hat{k}+m}{2(pk)} \hat{e}_q - \hat{e}_q \frac{\hat{p}_0-\hat{k}+m}{2(p_0 k)} \frac{\hat{e}}{\sqrt{2k^0}} \right\} v^{\nu',-}(\mathbf{p}_0)$$

or

$$F(p', p) = \frac{e^2 \varphi(\mathbf{q})}{2i(2\pi)^2 \sqrt{2k^0}} \bar{v}^{\nu,+}(\mathbf{p}) M v^{\nu',-}(\mathbf{p}_0), \tag{23.15}$$

where after the usual simplifications M may be brought into the form

$$M = \frac{a}{(pk)} + \frac{b}{(p_0 k)}$$
$$(a = \hat{e}\hat{k}\hat{e}_q + 2(ep)\hat{e}_q, \quad b = \hat{e}_q\hat{k}\hat{e} - 2(ep_0)\hat{e}_q).$$

On squaring (23.15), summing over the spin ν and the polarization e, and averaging over the spin ν', we obtain:

$$\sum_{\sigma} |F|^2 = \frac{Z^2 e^6}{64(2\pi)^7 k^0 E E_0} \frac{1}{(\mathbf{q}^2)^2} \operatorname{Sp} \tilde{A}, \tag{23.16}$$

where

$$A = (\hat{p} + m) M (\hat{p}_0 + m) \bar{M},$$

and where the tilde over A denotes summation over the polarization e.

We shall carry out the calculation of $\operatorname{Sp} \tilde{A}$ in three stages. We write A as a sum of three terms:

$$A = A_1 + A_2 + A_3,$$
$$A_1 = \frac{1}{(pk)^2} \{(\hat{p} + m) a (\hat{p}_0 + m) \bar{a}\}, \quad A_2 = \frac{1}{(p_0 k)^2} \{(\hat{p} + m) b (\hat{p}_0 + m) \bar{b}\},$$
$$A_3 = \frac{1}{(pk)(p_0 k)} \{(\hat{p} + m) a (\hat{p}_0 + m) \bar{b} + (\hat{p} + m) b (\hat{p}_0 + m) a\}.$$

We note that A_2 may be obtained from A_1 by carrying out the replacement

$$E \to -E_0, \quad \mathbf{p}_0 \to -\mathbf{p},$$
$$E_0 \to -E, \quad \mathbf{p} \to -\mathbf{p}_0.$$

Therefore by computing the traces

$$\operatorname{Sp} A_1 = \frac{8}{(pk)^2} \{(pk)(2E_0 k^0 - (p_0 k)) + 2(ep)^2 (2EE_0 - (pp_0) + m^2)$$
$$+ 2(ep)^2 (2E_0 k^0 - (p_0 k)) + 2(ep)(ep_0)(pk)\},$$

$$\begin{aligned}\operatorname{Sp} A_3 &= \frac{16(ep)(ep_0)}{(p_0k)(pk)}\{(p_0k) - (pk) - 2m^2 - 4EE_0 + 2(pp_0)\} \\ &+ \frac{16}{(p_0k)(pk)}\{k^0[k^0(pp_0) - E(p_0k) - E_0(pk)] \\ &+ (p_0k)(pk) - m^2(k^0)^2 + (ep)^2(p_0k) - (ep_0)^2(pk)\}\end{aligned}$$

and by summing over the photon polarization e and taking into account the relations

$$\left.\begin{aligned}&\sum_e (ep)^2 = p^2\sin^2\theta, \quad \sum_e (ep_0)^2 = p_0^2\sin^2\theta_0, \\ &\sum_e (ep_0)(ep) = pp_0\sin\theta\sin\theta_0\cos\varphi,\end{aligned}\right\} \tag{23.17}$$

where θ is the angle between $\mathbf{k}$ and $\mathbf{p}$, θ_0 is the angle between $\mathbf{k}$ and $\mathbf{p}_0$, φ is the angle between the planes $(\mathbf{k}, \mathbf{p})$ and $(\mathbf{k}, \mathbf{p}_0)$, we obtain:

$$\operatorname{Sp}\tilde{A} = \frac{8p^2\sin^2\theta}{(pk)^2}(4E^2 - q^2) + \frac{8p_0^2\sin^2\theta_0}{(p_0k)^2}(4E_0^2 - q^2)$$
$$- \frac{16pp_0\sin\theta\sin\theta_0\cos\varphi}{(pk)(p_0k)}[4EE_0 - q^2 + 2(k^0)^2] + 16(k^0)^2\frac{p_0^2\sin^2\theta_0 + p^2\sin^2\theta}{(pk)(p_0k)}.$$

Substituting (23.16) into (23.14) we have:

$$d\sigma = \frac{Z^2e^6}{64(2\pi)^5}\frac{p}{p_0}\frac{k^0dk^0d\boldsymbol{\Omega}_kd\boldsymbol{\Omega}_p}{\mathbf{q}^2\mathbf{q}^2}\operatorname{Sp}\tilde{A}.$$

By setting

$$d\boldsymbol{\Omega}_kd\boldsymbol{\Omega}_p = \sin\theta\,\mathrm{d}\theta\sin\theta_0\,\mathrm{d}\theta_0\,\mathrm{d}\varphi\,\mathrm{d}\varphi_0,$$

we obtain after integrating over $d\varphi_0$ the formula for the differential cross section in the form

$$\begin{aligned}d\sigma &= \frac{Z^2}{2\pi}\left(\frac{e^2}{4\pi}\right)^3\frac{p}{p_0}\frac{k_0dk_0\sin\theta\,d\theta\sin\theta_0\,d\theta_0\,d\varphi}{\mathbf{q}^2\mathbf{q}^2}\left\{\frac{p^2\sin^2\theta}{(pk)^2}(4E^2 - q^2)\right. \\ &+ \frac{p_0^2\sin^2\theta_0}{(p_0k)^2}(4E_0^2 - q^2) - \frac{2pp_0\sin\theta\sin\theta_0\cos\varphi}{(pk)(p_0k)}(4EE_0 - q^2 + 2k_0^2) \\ &\left.+ \frac{2(k^0)^2(p_0^2\sin^2\theta_0 + p^2\sin^2\theta)}{(pk)(p_0k)}\right\}.\end{aligned} \tag{23.18}$$

In view of the fact that

$$(pk) = k^0(p^0 - |p|\cos\theta),$$
$$(p_0k) = k^0(p_0 - |p|\cos\theta_0),$$

expression (23.18) agrees with the well-known formula (60).

CHAPTER IV

Removal of Divergences from the S-Matrix

§ 24. On the Divergences of the S-Matrix in Electrodynamics (Second Order)

Using the examples of Compton scattering, positron annihilation, and bremsstrahlung we have acquainted ourselves in detail with the type of matrix elements which correspond to one of the second-order diagrams.

The integrations of the corresponding matrix elements could be carried out in a trivial fashion with the aid of the vertex δ-functions (21.8) and the main labor consisted in the evaluation of the traces. When internal lines corresponding to virtual particles appear in a diagram the number of vertex δ-functions

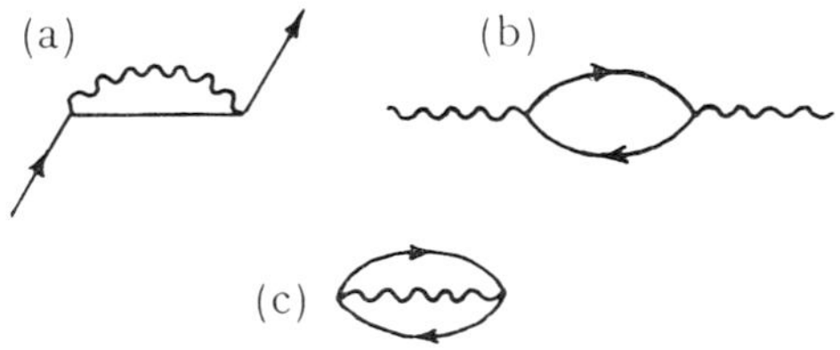

Fig. 17. Second-order divergent diagrams in electrodynamics.

turns out to be insufficient to carry out all the integrations and the function $F(p', p)$ in (21.35) is represented as a multiple integral. It turns out that such integrals in general *diverge for large momenta.* For example, matrix elements for Compton scattering and for pair annihilation diverge for higher orders in e^2 (e^4 and higher). Matrix elements of the second order which correspond to the diagrams shown in Fig. 17 also diverge.

24.1. *Divergent Diagram with Two External Electron Lines* Σ

We write the term in the scattering matrix which corresponds to the diagram of Fig. 17a

$$- e^2 : \bar{\psi}(x) \sum_n g^{nn} \gamma^n S^c (x - y) \gamma^n D_0^c(x - y) \psi(y) :, \qquad (24.1)$$

in the form [46]

$$- i : \bar{\psi}(x) \Sigma(x - y) \psi(y) :, \qquad (24.2)$$

where

$$\Sigma(x - y) = - ie^2 \sum_n g^{nn} \gamma^n S^c(x - y) \gamma^n D_0^c(x - y). \qquad (24.3)$$

A simple calculation shows that the Fourier transform $\Sigma(p)$ of the matrix $\Sigma(x - y)$

$$\Sigma(x - y) = \frac{1}{(2\pi)^4} \int e^{-ip(x-y)} \Sigma(p) \, dp \qquad (24.4)$$

appears in the matrix element of the S-matrix in the following way:

$$F(p', p) = (2\pi)^4 \bar{v}(p') \Sigma(p) v(p) \quad (p' = p), \qquad (24.5)$$

where $\bar{v}$ and v are spinor amplitudes corresponding to the field functions $\bar{\psi}$ and ψ. The convergence of the matrix element is therefore entirely determined by the convergence of the matrix $\Sigma(p)$. Recalling that in the momentum representation the causal functions have the form (compare (21.3) and (21.4))

$$D_0^c(k) = - \frac{1}{k^2 + i\varepsilon}, \qquad (24.6)$$

$$S^c(p) = \frac{m + \hat{p}}{m^2 - p^2 - i\varepsilon}, \qquad (24.7)$$

we find for $\Sigma(p)$:

[46] The factor $-i$ has been segregated here for convenience in subsequent calculations. With such normalization, the operator Σ in the momentum representation turns out to be real for $k^2 < 0$ (see § 31), and added to the electron mass m forms the mass operator in the equations for Green's functions (see § 34.3).

$$\Sigma(p) = \frac{e^2}{(2\pi)^4 i} \sum_n g^{nn} \int dk\, D_0^c(k)\, \gamma^n S^c(p-k)\, \gamma^n$$

$$= \frac{e^2}{(2\pi)^4 i} \sum_n g^{nn} \int \frac{dk}{k^2 + i\varepsilon} \gamma^n \frac{\hat{p} - \hat{k} + m}{(p-k)^2 - m^2 + i\varepsilon} \gamma^n. \qquad (24.8)$$

For large $|k|$ the integrand falls off like $|k|^{-3}$ and therefore the integral (24.8) diverges, generally speaking, linearly. We thus see that the purely formal rules for dealing with products of causal functions which we have adopted earlier in this case lead to a meaningless result.

Essentially this is a manifestation of the fact that we did not define a product of singular functions as an integrable singular function. In order to solve the problem of determining the coefficients of the chronological product

$$T(\mathscr{L}(x_1)\mathscr{L}(x_2))$$

as integrable improper functions we shall use the method of transition to the limit similar to the one which we have used in § 16. In order to do this we shall first of all consider an auxiliary fictitious case in which the field operator functions satisfy commutation relations in which the causal Δ^c-functions are replaced by reg (Δ^c).

The functions

$$\text{reg}\, D_0^c(k) = -\frac{1}{k^2 + i\varepsilon} - \sum_n c_M \frac{1}{k^2 + i\varepsilon - M^2}, \qquad (24.9)$$

$$\text{reg}\, S^c(p) = (m + \hat{p}) \left\{ \frac{1}{m^2 - p^2 - i\varepsilon} + \sum_M \frac{c_M}{M^2 - p^2 - i\varepsilon} \right\} \qquad (24.10)$$

should be substituted into the expression for $\Sigma(p)$ in place of (24.6) and (24.7).

It then turns out that in order to regularize $\Sigma(p)$ a single auxiliary mass M is sufficient. By setting

$$c_M = -1,$$

we have:

$$\text{reg}\, D_0^c(k) = -\frac{1}{k^2 + i\varepsilon} + \frac{1}{k^2 - M^2 + i\varepsilon} = \frac{M^2}{(k^2 + i\varepsilon)(k^2 - M^2 + i\varepsilon)},$$

$$\operatorname{reg} S^c(p) = \frac{m+\hat{p}}{m^2-p^2-i\varepsilon} - \frac{m+\hat{p}}{M^2-p^2-i\varepsilon} = \frac{(m+\hat{p})(M^2-m^2)}{(m^2-p^2-i\varepsilon)(M^2-p^2-i\varepsilon)}.$$

It may be easily seen that $\operatorname{reg} D_0^c(k)$ falls off as $|k|^{-4}$, while $\operatorname{reg} S^c(p)$ falls off as $|k|^{-3}$, and therefore the integral in the expression for $\operatorname{reg} \Sigma(p)$

$$\operatorname{reg} \Sigma(p) = \frac{e^2}{(2\pi)^4 i} \sum_n g^{nn} \int dk \operatorname{reg} D_0^c(k) \gamma^n \operatorname{reg} S^c(p-k) \gamma^n \tag{24.11}$$

for large values of $|k|$ behaves like

$$\int^k \frac{d^4k}{|k|^7} \sim \frac{1}{|k|^3}.$$

We now investigate the question of the behavior of $\operatorname{reg} \Sigma(p)$ as $M \to \infty$ in the course of the process of removing the regularization. It is convenient to conduct this investigation by explicitly calculating $\operatorname{reg} \Sigma(p)$.

We shall utilize the following auxiliary device for the calculation of the integral (24.11). We shall write the factors in the denominator of (24.11) in the form

$$\frac{1}{k^2 - m^2 + i\varepsilon} = \frac{1}{i} \int_0^\infty e^{i\alpha(k^2-m^2+i\varepsilon)} d\alpha. \tag{24.12}$$

In that case integration over k will reduce to the evaluation of integrals of the Gaussian type.

The fundamental four-dimensional integral of the Gaussian type has the form

$$\int e^{i(ak^2+bk)} dk = \frac{\pi^2}{ia^2} e^{-\frac{ib^2}{4a}} \qquad (a > 0). \tag{24.13}$$

Formula (24.13) may be obtained by considering the typical integral

$$\int_{-\infty}^\infty e^{i(at^2+bt)} dt \qquad (a > 0),$$

which we shall always regard as the limit of the expression

$$\int_{-\infty}^\infty e^{i(at^2+bt)-\eta t^2} dt \text{ for } \eta \to +0.$$

In order to evaluate it we introduce a change of variable

$$t = \frac{1+i}{\sqrt{2}} x - \frac{b}{2a}, \; i(at^2 + bt) = -ax^2 - \frac{ib^2}{4a},$$

which consists of a rotation of the coordinate system through an angle $-\pi/4$ and of a displacement of the origin. Then in the limit $\eta \to 0$ we shall obtain:

$$\int_{-\infty}^{\infty} e^{i(at^2+bt)} dt = \frac{1+i}{\sqrt{2}} e^{-\frac{ib^2}{4a}} \int_{-\infty}^{\infty} e^{-ax^2} dx = \frac{1+i}{\sqrt{2}} \sqrt{\frac{\pi}{a}} e^{-\frac{ib^2}{4a}} \; (a > 0). \tag{24.14}$$

The value of this integral for $a < 0$ may be obtained by taking the complex conjugate. We therefore have:

$$\int_{-\infty}^{\infty} e^{i(at^2+bt)} dt = \frac{1-i}{\sqrt{2}} \sqrt{\frac{\pi}{a}} e^{-\frac{ib^2}{4a}} \quad (a < 0). \tag{24.15}$$

We can now begin the evaluation of the required four-dimensional integrals of the type

$$\int e^{i(ak^2+bk)} dk,$$

where

$$k^2 = (k^0)^2 - \mathbf{k}^2, \; bk = b^0 k^0 - \mathbf{bk}, \; dk = dk^0 d\mathbf{k}.$$

With the aid of formulas (24.14), (24.15) we arrive directly at (24.13):

$$\int e^{i(ak^2+bk)} dk \equiv \int_{-\infty}^{\infty} e^{i(ak^{0^2}+b^0 k^0)} dk^0 \prod_{1 \leq \alpha \leq 3} \int_{-\infty}^{\infty} e^{-i(ak^{\alpha^2} + b^\alpha k^\alpha)} dk^\alpha$$

$$= \frac{1+i}{\sqrt{2}} \left(\frac{1-i}{\sqrt{2}}\right)^3 \frac{\pi^2}{a^2} e^{-\frac{i}{4a}(b^{0^2} - \mathbf{b}^2)} = \frac{\pi^2}{ia^2} e^{-\frac{ib^2}{4a}} \quad (a > 0).$$

The other integrals of this type which we shall require may be obtained from (24.13) by means of repeated differentiation with respect to the components of b. Thus, for example

$$\int e^{i(ak^2+bk)} k^n dk = \frac{ib^n}{2a} \left(\frac{\pi}{a}\right)^2 e^{-\frac{ib^2}{4a}} \quad (a > 0), \tag{24.16}$$

$$\int e^{i(ak^2+bk)} k^m k^n dk = \frac{2ag^{mn} - ib^n b^m}{4a^2} \left(\frac{\pi}{a}\right)^2 e^{-\frac{ib^2}{4a}} \quad (a > 0). \tag{24.17}$$

Formulas of this type for $a < 0$ may be obtained from (24.13), (24.16), and (24.17) by taking complex conjugates.

We return to the evaluation of the integral (24.11). Substituting into it integral representations for singular functions of the type (24.12)

$$\text{reg}\, D_0^c(k) = i\int_0^\infty e^{i\alpha k^2 - \varepsilon\alpha}(1 - e^{-i\alpha M^2})\, d\alpha, \tag{24.18}$$

$$\text{reg}\, S^c(p) = i(m + \hat{p})\int_0^\infty e^{i\alpha p^2 - \varepsilon\alpha}(e^{-i\alpha m^2} - e^{-i\alpha M^2})\, d\alpha, \tag{24.19}$$

performing the integration over dk with the aid of (24.13) and (24.16), we obtain, keeping in mind that

$$\sum_n g^{nn}\gamma^n \hat{p}\gamma^n = -2\hat{p} \text{ and } \sum_n g^{nn}\gamma^n\gamma^n = 4, \tag{24.20}$$

the following expression for reg $\Sigma(p)$:

$$\text{reg}\, \Sigma(p) = \frac{e^2}{8\pi^2}\int_0^\infty d\alpha \int_0^\infty d\beta\, \frac{e^{-\varepsilon(\alpha+\beta)}}{(\alpha+\beta)^2}\, e^{\frac{i\alpha\beta p^2}{\alpha+\beta}}$$

$$\times \left(2m - \hat{p}\,\frac{\alpha}{\alpha+\beta}\right)(1 - e^{-i\alpha M^2})\,(e^{-i\beta m^2} - e^{-i\beta M^2}). \tag{24.21}$$

By going over to the new variables

$$\alpha = \xi\lambda, \quad \beta = (1 - \xi)\lambda, \tag{24.22}$$

and taking into account the Jacobian

$$\frac{(\partial\alpha,\ \partial\beta)}{(\partial\xi,\ \partial\lambda)} = \lambda \tag{24.23}$$

we obtain:

$$\text{reg}\, \Sigma(p) = \frac{e^2}{8\pi^2}\int_0^1 (2m - \hat{p}\xi)\, J_\varepsilon(\xi,\ M)\, d\xi, \tag{24.24}$$

where the integral

$$J_\varepsilon(\xi, M) = \int_0^\infty \frac{d\lambda}{\lambda}\, e^{-\lambda\varepsilon + i\lambda\xi(1-\xi)p^2}(1 - e^{-i\xi\lambda M^2})\,(e^{-i(1-\xi)\lambda m^2} - e^{-i(1-\xi)\lambda M^2})$$

can be calculated by means of differentiating with respect to the parameter p^2. In this way we find in the limit $\varepsilon \to 0$

$$J_0(\xi, M) = \ln\left|\frac{M^2 - \xi p^2}{m^2}\right| + \ln\left|\frac{m^2}{m^2 - \xi p^2}\,\frac{\xi M^2 + (1-\xi)m^2 - \xi(1-\xi)p^2}{M^2 - \xi(1-\xi)p^2}\right|.$$

24.2. *Segregation of the Divergent Part of* Σ

Substituting the value obtained above for $J_0(\xi, M)$ into (24.24) we obtain

$$\operatorname{reg} \Sigma(p) = \frac{e^2}{8\pi^2}\int_0^1 d\xi\,(2m - \hat{p}\xi) \ln\left|\xi\,\frac{M^2 - \xi p^2}{m^2}\right|$$

$$+\frac{e^2}{8\pi^2}\int_0^1 d\xi\,(2m - \hat{p}\xi) \ln\left|\frac{m^2}{m^2 - \xi p^2}\,\frac{\xi M^2 + (1-\xi)m^2 - \xi(1-\xi)p^2}{M^2 - \xi^2(1-\xi)p^2}\right|; \tag{24.25}$$

the second term of which will converge as $M \to \infty$ to a definite limit equal to

$$\Sigma'(p) = \frac{e^2}{8\pi^2}\int_0^1 d\xi\,(2m - \hat{p}\xi) \ln\left|\frac{m^2}{m^2 - \xi p^2}\right|. \tag{24.26}$$

The decomposition in (24.25) is chosen in such a way that

$$\Sigma'(0) = 0 \quad \text{and} \quad \left.\frac{\partial \Sigma'(p)}{\partial p^n}\right|_{p=0} = 0. \tag{24.27}$$

The first term in (24.25) is evidently logarithmically divergent as $M \to \infty$.

In going over to the configuration representation we obtain for sufficiently large M

$$\operatorname{reg} \Sigma(x) = \frac{e^2}{(4\pi)^2}\left\{\ln\frac{M^2}{m^2}\left(4m - i\,\frac{\hat{\partial}}{\partial x}\right) + \left(\frac{i}{2}\,\frac{\hat{\partial}}{\partial x} - 4m\right)\right\}\delta(x) + \Sigma'_M(x), \tag{24.28}$$

with the Fourier transform of the function $\Sigma'_M(x)$ being given by the second term of expression (24.25). By repeating the argument of § 16 we see that for $M \to \infty$ $\Sigma'_M(x)$ converges in the improper sense to the integrable function

$$\lim \Sigma'_M(x) = \Sigma'(x),$$

whose Fourier transform is given by expression (24.26). Because of the factor $\ln (M/m)^2$ the function $\operatorname{reg} \Sigma(x)$ as a whole will not converge even in the improper sense. Since the first term of

(24.28) vanishes for $x \neq 0$ we may write:

$$\lim_{M\to\infty} \operatorname{reg} \Sigma(x) = \Sigma'(x) \text{ everywhere for } x \neq 0.$$

We have carried out above the segregation of the divergent part from the singular function $\Sigma(x)$. However, we emphasize that the operation of segregating the singularities is not unique. Indeed, we could have written (24.28), for example, in the form

$$\operatorname{reg} \Sigma(x) = \frac{e^2}{16\pi^2}\left\{\ln\left(\frac{M}{\mu}\right)^2\left(4m - i\frac{\hat{\partial}}{\partial x}\right) + \left(\frac{i}{2}\frac{\hat{\partial}}{\partial x} - 2m\right)\right\}\delta(x) + \Sigma''_M(x),$$

where

$$\Sigma''_M(x) = \frac{e^2}{16\pi^2}\ln\left(\frac{\mu}{m}\right)^2\left(4m - i\frac{\hat{\partial}}{\partial x}\right)\delta(x) + \Sigma'_M(x),$$

and μ is an arbitrary finite mass. We would have obtained for the regular part Σ''_M an expression differing from Σ'_M by terms proportional to $\delta(x)$ and to its first derivatives.

We can obtain a change of a similar nature in the finite part Σ'_M by going over to any other method of regularization. For example, if $\Sigma(p)$ is regularized by introducing into the integral (24.9) Feynman's cutoff factor (39), (41)

$$\frac{M^2}{M^2 - k^2},$$

which in our case is equivalent to regularizing only the photon D_0^c-function, then the result may be written in the form

$$\operatorname{reg}_F \Sigma(x) = \frac{e^2}{16\pi^2}\left\{\ln\left(\frac{M}{m}\right)^2\left(4m - i\frac{\hat{\partial}}{\partial x}\right) + \left(\frac{i}{2}\frac{\hat{\partial}}{\partial x} - 4m\right)\right\}\delta(x) + \Sigma'_F(x),$$

where the regular function Σ'_F differs in the momentum representation from Σ' by the quantity

$$\frac{e^2}{16\pi^2}\int_0^1 d\xi(\hat{p}\xi - 2m)\ln(1-\xi) = \frac{e^2}{16\pi^2}(2m - \tfrac{3}{4}\hat{p}).$$

In this way it may be seen that when the regularization is removed it is not $\operatorname{reg} \Sigma(p)$ which converges to a definite limit but, for example, the expression obtained by subtracting from it the first two terms of Maclaurin's series:

$$\operatorname{reg}\Sigma(p) - \operatorname{reg}\Sigma(0) - \sum_n \frac{\partial \operatorname{reg}\Sigma(p)}{\partial p^n}\bigg|_{p=0} \cdot p^n. \qquad (24.29)$$

This expression converges to a limit which does not depend on the method of regularization since the addition to $\operatorname{reg}\Sigma(p)$ of any arbitrary polynomial of the first degree in p does not alter the "residual" term (24.29).

We shall obtain the general expression for $\Sigma'(p)$ by adding to (24.29) an arbitrary polynomial of the first degree in p. From considerations of relativistic covariance this polynomial must have the form

$$c_1(\hat{p} - m) + c_2 m,$$

and consequently we obtain the general expression for $\Sigma'(p)$ in the form

$$\Sigma'(p) = \frac{e^2}{8\pi^2}\left\{\int_0^1 d\xi\,(2m - \hat{p}\xi)\ln\left|\frac{m^2}{m^2 - \xi p^2}\right| + c_1(\hat{p} - m) + c_2 m\right\}. \qquad (24.30)$$

Corresponding to the preceding, the expression for Σ' in the x-representation is determined up to the term

$$\frac{e^2}{8\pi^2}\left\{c_1\left(i\frac{\hat{\partial}}{\partial x} - m\right) + c_2 m\right\}\delta(x),$$

which vanishes for $x \neq 0$, i.e., as should have been expected from general considerations, the arbitrariness in the given term of the T-product manifests itself only in an infinitesimal neighborhood of the point $x = 0$.

24.3. *Divergent Diagram with Two External Photon Lines Π*

We now turn to the second divergent term in $S_2(x, y)$. The term of the scattering matrix which corresponds to the diagram of Fig. 17b may be represented in the form

$$-e^2 : \operatorname{Sp}(\hat{A}(x)\,S^c(x-y)\,\hat{A}(y)\,S^c(y-x)) :$$
$$= -i\sum_{m,n} : A_m(x)\,\Pi^{mn}(x-y)\,A_n(y) :,$$

where

$$\Pi^{mn}(x-y) = -ie^2 \operatorname{Sp} \gamma^m S^c(x-y)\gamma^n S^c(y-x). \qquad (24.31)$$

In going over to the momentum representation

$$\Pi^{mn}(x-y) = \frac{1}{(2\pi)^4}\int e^{ik(x-y)}\,\Pi^{mn}(k)\,dk, \qquad (24.32)$$

we find that the integral

$$\Pi^{mn}(k) = \frac{e^2}{(2\pi)^4 i}\int dp \operatorname{Sp}\left(\gamma^m \frac{\hat{p}+m}{p^2-m^2+i\varepsilon}\gamma^n \frac{\hat{p}-\hat{k}+m}{(p-k)^2-m^2+i\varepsilon}\right) \qquad (24.33)$$

diverges quadratically for large momenta.

For the explicit evaluation of $\Pi^{mn}(k)$ we shall use the same methods which were applied to the evaluation of $\Sigma(p)$. Utilizing the regularized S^c-functions (24.19) we carry out the integration over dp with the aid of formulas (24.13), (24.16), and (24.17). Also by calculating the trace in accordance with formula (6.16) we obtain:

$$\operatorname{reg}\Pi^{mn}(k)$$
$$= \frac{ie^2}{4\pi^2}\int_0^\infty d\alpha \int_0^\infty d\beta e^{-\varepsilon(\alpha+\beta)+\frac{i\alpha\beta k^2}{\alpha+\beta}}\left(e^{-i\alpha m^2}-e^{-i\alpha M^2}\right)\left(e^{-i\beta m^2}-e^{-i\beta M^2}\right)$$
$$\times \frac{1}{(\alpha+\beta)^2}\left\{\frac{i\alpha\beta}{(\alpha+\beta)^2}\left(2k^n k^m - k^2 g^{mn}\right) - g^{mn}\left(\frac{1}{\alpha+\beta}+im^2\right)\right\}.$$

By introducing the new variables

$$\alpha = \xi\lambda, \quad \beta = (1-\xi)\lambda$$

we shall transform this expression into the form

$$\operatorname{reg}\,\Pi^{mn}(k)$$
$$= \frac{ie^2}{4\pi^2}\int_0^1 d\xi \int_0^\infty \frac{d\lambda}{\lambda} e^{-\varepsilon\lambda}\left(e^{-i\xi\lambda m^2}-e^{-i\xi\lambda M^2}\right)\left(e^{-i(1-\xi)\lambda m^2}-e^{-i(1-\xi)\lambda M^2}\right)$$
$$\times\, e^{i\lambda\xi(1-\xi)k^2}\left\{i\xi(1-\xi)\left(2k^m k^n - g^{mn}k^2\right) - g^{mn}\left(\frac{1}{\lambda}+im^2\right)\right\}.$$

In order to carry out the integration over λ we shall write the term which contains λ^2 in the denominator in the form

$$\int_0^\infty \frac{d\lambda}{\lambda^2} e^{-\varepsilon\lambda} f(\lambda),$$

where

$$f(\lambda) = e^{i\lambda\xi(1-\xi)k^2}\left(e^{-i\xi\lambda m^2} - e^{-i\xi\lambda M^2}\right)\left(e^{-i(1-\xi)\lambda m^2} - e^{-i(1-\xi)\lambda M^2}\right),$$

and after integrating by parts and taking into account the fact that $f(\lambda)$ remains finite as $\lambda \to \infty$ and vanishes like λ^2 as $\lambda \to 0$, we find:

$$\int_0^\infty \frac{d\lambda}{\lambda^2} f(\lambda) e^{-\varepsilon\lambda} = \int_0^\infty \frac{d\lambda}{\lambda} \frac{\partial}{\partial\lambda}\left(e^{-\varepsilon\lambda} f(\lambda)\right) \xrightarrow[\varepsilon\to 0]{} \int_0^\infty \frac{d\lambda}{\lambda} e^{-\varepsilon\lambda} \frac{\partial f(\lambda)}{\partial\lambda}.$$

We therefore have:

$$\operatorname{reg} \Pi^{mn}(k) = \frac{ie^2}{4\pi^2} \int_0^1 d\xi \, F_\varepsilon(\xi, M),$$

where the integral

$$F_\varepsilon(\xi, M) = \int_0^\infty \frac{d\lambda}{\lambda} e^{-\varepsilon\lambda} \left\{ f(\lambda)\left[i\xi(1-\xi)(2k^n k^m - g^{mn} k^2) - im^2 g^{mn}\right] - g^{mn} \frac{\partial f}{\partial\lambda} \right\}$$

may be calculated by means of differentiation with respect to the parameter ε. In this way we obtain

$$\lim_{\varepsilon\to 0} F_\varepsilon(\xi, M) = F_0(\xi, M) = \left[2i\xi(1-\xi)(k^n k^m - g^{mn} k^2) - im^2 g^{mn}\right]$$

$$\times \left\{ \ln\left|\frac{(1-\xi)M^2+\xi m^2-\xi(1-\xi)k^2}{m^2-\xi(1-\xi)k^2}\right| - \ln\left|\frac{M^2-\xi(1-\xi)k^2}{\xi M^2+(1-\xi)m^2-\xi(1-\xi)k^2}\right| \right\}$$

$$+ig^{mn}\xi \left\{ m^2 \ln\left|\frac{(1-\xi)M^2+\xi m^2-\xi(1-\xi)k^2}{m^2-\xi(1-\xi)k^2}\right| \right.$$

$$\left. -M^2 \ln\left|\frac{M^2-\xi(1-\xi)k^2}{\xi M^2+(1-\xi)m^2-\xi(1-\xi)k^2}\right| \right\}$$

$$+ ig^{mn}(1-\xi) \left\{ m^2 \ln\left|\frac{\xi M^2+(1-\xi)m^2-\xi(1-\xi)k^2}{m^2-\xi(1-\xi)k^2}\right| \right.$$

$$\left. - M^2 \ln\left|\frac{M^2-\xi(1-\xi)k^2}{(1-\xi)M^2+\xi m^2-\xi(1-\xi)k^2}\right| \right\}.$$

In the limit $M \to \infty$ this expression takes on the form

$$\lim_{M\to\infty} F_0(\xi, M) = ig^{mn}(M^2-m^2)[\xi \ln \xi+(1-\xi) \ln (1-\xi)]$$
$$+ 2i\xi(1-\xi)\ln\frac{M^2}{m^2}(k^n k^m-g^{nm}k^2)$$
$$+ 2i\xi(1-\xi)(k^n k^m-g^{nm}k^2)\ln\left|\frac{\xi(1-\xi)m^2}{m^2-\xi(1-\xi)k^2}\right|$$
$$+ ig^{mn}[m^2-\xi(1-\xi)k^2].$$

24.4. *Segregation of the Divergences from Π and Gauge Invariance*

By integrating over ξ we find that in the limit of large M

$$\operatorname{reg}\Pi^{mn}(k)=\frac{e^2}{8\pi^2}g^{mn}(M^2-m^2)-\frac{e^2}{4\pi^2}\ln\frac{M^2}{m^2}\frac{k^n k^m-g^{nm}k^2}{3}+\Pi'^{mn}(k), \tag{24.34}$$

where

$$\Pi'^{mn}(k)=\frac{e^2}{2\pi^2}(k^n k^m-g^{nm}k^2)\int_0^1 d\xi\cdot\xi(1-\xi)\ln\left|\frac{m^2-\xi(1-\xi)k^2}{\xi(1-\xi)m^2}\right| \tag{24.35}$$

is a regular function.

In going over to the configuration representation we obtain for sufficiently large M

$$\operatorname{reg}\Pi^{mn}(x)=\frac{e^2}{8\pi^2}g^{mn}(M^2-m^2)\,\delta(x)$$
$$+\frac{e^2}{12\pi^2}\ln\frac{M^2}{m^2}\left(g^{nn}\frac{\partial}{\partial x^n}g^{mm}\frac{\partial}{\partial x^m}-g^{mn}\,\Box\right)\delta(x)+\Pi_M'^{mn}(x). \tag{24.36}$$

In the limit $M \to \infty$ the term $\Pi_M'^{mn}(x)$ converges in the improper sense to the integrable function $\Pi'^{mn}(x)$:

$$\lim_{M\to\infty}\Pi_M'^{mn}(x)=\Pi'^{mn}(x),$$

whose Fourier transform is given by formula (24.35). The segregation of the singularities from $\Pi^{mn}(x)$ has thus been completed. We note that, just as in the preceding case, the decomposition of $\operatorname{reg}\Pi^{mn}(x)$ into a singular and a finite part is not unique. Consequently the finite part $\Pi'^{mn}(x)$ is not unique. An arbitrary expression which is a polynomial in the components of k^n of degree not higher than the second may be added to $\Pi^{mn}(x)$ since the singular part in this case is a polynomial in k of the second degree.

In order to complete our analysis of the expression Π^{mn} we shall also formulate the condition of gauge invariance which must be satisfied by Π^{mn}. It may be easily seen that the function $\Pi^{mn}(k)$ appears in the matrix elements, similarly to the function $\Sigma(p)$, in the following combination with the potentials $A_m(k)$:

$$(2\pi)^4 \sum_{m,n} : A_m(k)\, \Pi^{mn}(k)\, A_n(k) : . \qquad (24.37)$$

As has been pointed out in § 6, the potentials of the electromagnetic field A_m are introduced from the beginning in such a way that all the physically observable quantities do not change their value under a gauge transformation of the potentials

$$A_m(x) \to A'_m(x) = A_m(x) + \frac{\partial f(x)}{\partial x^m}$$

or in the momentum representation

$$A_m(k) \to A'_m(k) = A_m(k) + i g^{mm} k^m f(k).$$

Therefore the requirement of the invariance of the matrix elements of the operators of the type (24.37)

$$\sum_{m,n} : A'_m(k)\, \Pi^{mn}(k) A'_n(k) : = \sum_{m,n} : A_m(k)\, \Pi^{mn}(k)\, A_n(k) :$$

leads us to the condition

$$\sum_n g^{nn} k^n \Pi^{mn}(k) = 0, \qquad (24.38)$$

from which it follows that the function Π^{mn} must have the form

$$\Pi^{mn}(k) = (k^m k^n - g^{mn} k^2)\, \pi(k^2). \qquad (24.39)$$

On returning to formulas (24.34) and (24.35) we see that because of the divergence of the function $\Pi^{mn}(k)$ the requirement of gauge invariance (24.38) may be imposed only on the regular part of $\Pi'^{mn}(k)$. It may be seen from (24.35) that in order for the function $\Pi'(k)$ to satisfy condition (24.38) it is necessary to add to it an expression of the type

$$c_3(k^n k^m - g^{mn} k^2),$$

i.e., the decomposition (24.36) should be replaced by the following one:

$$\operatorname{reg} \Pi^{mn}(x) = \frac{e^2}{8\pi^2} g^{mn}(M^2 - m^2)\,\delta(x) + \left(\frac{e^2}{12\pi^2} \ln \frac{M^2}{m^2} + \frac{e^2}{2\pi^2} c_3\right)$$
$$\times \left(g^{nn} \frac{\partial}{\partial x^n} g^{mm} \frac{\partial}{\partial x^m} - g^{mn} \square\right) \delta(x) + \Pi'^{mn}_{\text{inv}}(x),$$

where the finite part $\Pi'^{mn}_{\text{inv}}(x)$ is invariant under a gauge transformation and has in the momentum representation the form (24.39):

$$\Pi^{mn}_{\text{inv}}(k) = \frac{e^2}{2\pi^2} (k^m k^n - g^{mn} k^2) \left(c_3 + \int_0^1 d\xi \cdot \xi(1-\xi) \ln \left|\frac{m^2 - \xi(1-\xi) k^2}{\xi(1-\xi) m^2}\right|\right). \tag{24.40}$$

The term of the S-matrix which corresponds to the diagram of Fig. 17c may be investigated in a similar way. Without going into the details of the calculation, we shall merely note that after the regularization has been carried out the corresponding function $R(x_1 - x_2)$ may be written in the momentum representation in the form

$$R(k) = R'_M(k) + R_{\text{sing}}(M, k),$$

where as $M \to \infty$ the function $R'_M(k)$ converges to the integrable limit

$$\lim_{M \to \infty} R'_M(k) = R'(k),$$

while R_{sing} tends to a polynomial function of the components of the four-vector k which diverges like M^4.

24.5. *Construction of an Integrable S_2*

We arrive at the conclusion that the second-order term in the scattering matrix

$$S_2(x_1, x_2) = i^2 T(\mathscr{L}(x_1), \mathscr{L}(x_2))$$

in the regularized case ($M < \infty$) under consideration may be written in the form

$$i^2 T(\mathscr{L}(x_1)\mathscr{L}(x_2)) = i^2 T'_M[\mathscr{L}(x_1)\,\mathscr{L}(x_2)]$$

$$-i\Big\{a_2^M :\bar{\psi}(x_1)\Big(i\frac{\hat{\partial}}{\partial x_1} - m\Big)\delta(x_1 - x_2)\psi(x_2): - \delta m :\bar{\psi}(x_1)\,\delta(x_1 - x_2)\psi(x_2):$$

$$+ \delta\mu \sum_{n,\,m} g^{mn} : A_m(x_1)\,\delta(x_1 - x_2)\,A_n(x_2) :$$

$$+ a_3^M \sum_{m,\,n} : A_n(x_1)\Big(g^{nn}\frac{\partial}{\partial x_1^n} g^{mm}\frac{\partial}{\partial x_1^m} - \Box_1 g^{mn}\Big)\delta(x_1 - x_2)\,A_m(x_2) :$$

$$+ R_{\text{sing}}\Big(M, \frac{\partial}{\partial x}\Big)\,\delta(x_1 - x_2) + \text{the same terms with } x_1 \text{ replaced by } x_2\Big\}.$$

The constants a_2^M, a_3^M, δm, $\delta\mu$ in the above diverge for large M:

$$\left.\begin{aligned} a_2 &\sim \frac{e^2}{16\pi^2}\Big[\ln\frac{M^2}{m^2} - \frac{1}{2} - c_1\Big], \quad \delta m \sim \frac{e^2}{16\pi^2}\Big[3m\ln\frac{M^2}{m^2} - \frac{7m}{2} + c_2\Big], \\ a_3 &\sim \frac{e^2}{2\pi^2}\Big[\frac{1}{6}\ln\frac{M^2}{m^2} - c_3\Big], \quad \delta\mu \sim \frac{e^2}{8\pi^2}[M^2 - m^2], \end{aligned}\right\} \tag{24.42}$$

while in the construction of the coefficient functions of the expression T'_M the rules of correspondence should be somewhat altered: for the ordinary lines in Feynman diagrams the functions reg Δ^c should be used in place of Δ^c, while for closed diagrams the corresponding finite functions Σ'_M, $\Pi'^{mn}_{M,\text{inv}}$ and R'_M should be used. It is then evident that all the coefficient functions of the expression $T'_M(\mathscr{L}(x_1), \mathscr{L}(x_2))$ converge to a finite limit when the regularization is removed.

We see also that all the divergences in $S_2(x_1, x_2)$ come from terms proportional to $\delta(x_1 - x_2)$ and to its derivatives which differ from zero only in the infinitesimal neighborhood of the point $x_1 = x_2$. As was already mentioned in § 19, it is just in the neighborhood of the point $x_1 = x_2$ that the T-product $T(\mathscr{L}(x_1), \mathscr{L}(x_2))$ is not completely defined.

Therefore the possibility arises of defining this product in the neighborhood of the point $x_1 = x_2$ as the limit:

$$T'(\mathscr{L}(x_1)\,\mathscr{L}(x_2)) = \lim_{M\to\infty} T'_M(\mathscr{L}(x_1)\,\mathscr{L}(x_2)),$$

which will guarantee the *integrability* of $S_2(x_1, x_2)$.

There exists also another completely equivalent possibility. As has been established in § 18, the most general form of S_2 includes an arbitrary quasilocal operator:

$$S_2(x_1, x_2) = i^2 T(\mathscr{L}(x_1)\,\mathscr{L}(x_2)) + i\Lambda_2(x_1, x_2). \qquad (24.43)$$

Therefore it is possible without going to the limit $M \to \infty$ to define the quasilocal operator $i\Lambda_2(x_1, x_2)$ in such a way:

$$i\Lambda_2(x_1, x_2) = T(\mathscr{L}(x_1)\,\mathscr{L}(x_2)) - T'_M(\mathscr{L}(x_1)\,\mathscr{L}(x_2)), \qquad (24.44)$$

that it would compensate in expression (24.43) for all the singular terms from $T(\mathscr{L}(x_1), \mathscr{L}(x_2))$. Then after the transition to the limit $M \to \infty$ we shall obtain $S_2(x_1, x_2)$ in the form of an integrable polylocal operator

$$S_2(x_1, x_2) = -\,T'(\mathscr{L}(x_1)\mathscr{L}(x_2)).$$

As has been shown in § 18, the quasilocal operator $i\Lambda_2$ may be included into the total effective interaction Lagrangian. To accomplish this one must add to $\mathscr{L}(x)$ the additional terms $\mathscr{L}^{(2)}(x)$ which will compensate the singular terms in S_2 after integration over dx, i.e.,

$$i\int \mathscr{L}^{(2)}\,dx + \frac{i^2}{2}\int \{T(\mathscr{L}(x_1)\mathscr{L}(x_2)) - T'_M(\mathscr{L}(x_1)\mathscr{L}(x_2))\}\,dx_1\,dx_2 = 0.$$

By using (24.41) these *counter terms* may be represented after integration by parts in the form

$$\begin{aligned}\mathscr{L}^{(2)}(x) &= \frac{1}{2}\int \Lambda_2(x, y)\,dy \\ &= a_2^M \left\{\frac{i}{2}\sum_n : \left(\bar\psi(x)\,\gamma^n \frac{\partial\psi}{\partial x^n} - \frac{\partial\bar\psi}{\partial x^n}\gamma^n\,\psi(x)\right) : -\, m : \bar\psi\psi : \right\} \\ &\quad - \delta m : \bar\psi(x)\,\psi(x) : + \,\delta\mu \sum_n g^{nn} : A_n(x)\,A_n(x) : \\ &\quad + a_3^M \left\{\sum_{m,n} g^{mm} g^{nn} : \frac{\partial A_n}{\partial x^m}\frac{\partial A_n}{\partial x^m} : - : \left(\frac{\partial A}{\partial x}\right)^2 : \right\} + R, \qquad (24.45)\end{aligned}$$

where the constants a_2, a_3, δm, and $\delta\mu$ are of order e^2 and diverge as $M \to \infty$.

Thus after redefining $T(\mathscr{L}(x_1), \mathscr{L}(x_2))$ in the neighborhood of the point $x_1 = x_2$, or after adding the quasilocal operator (24.44), which is equivalent to the addition to the interaction Lagrangian of counter terms (24.45) of order e^2, and after going to the limit $M \to \infty$ we obtain for the terms of the S-matrix of order e^2 the regularized expression

$$\frac{i^2}{2!}\int dx_1\, dx_2\, T'(\mathscr{L}(x_1)\,\mathscr{L}(x_2)).$$

In the usual presentation (Dyson (34), Takeda (123), Matthews and Salam (86)) no mention is made of the transition to the limit and, in fact, meaningless divergent expressions are used as counter terms. Our presentation is essentially equivalent to the usual one and differs from it merely by a higher degree of rigor.

§ 25. On the Divergences of the S-Matrix in Electrodynamics (Third Order)

We have now completed our examination of the problem of the regularization of the matrix to the second order in e. However, it may be easily seen that a completely analogous procedure may be used to regularize higher-order terms of the S-matrix.

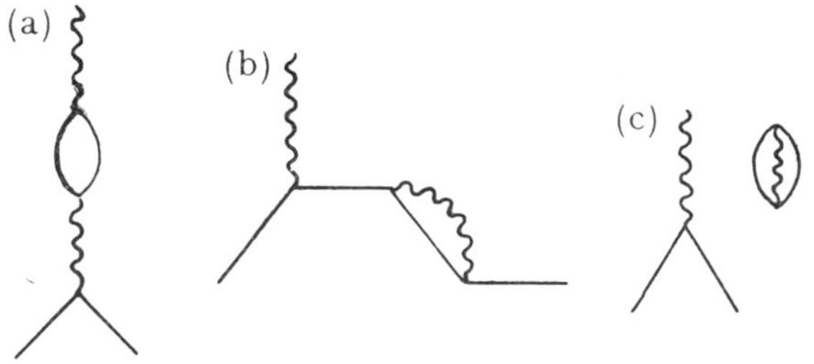

Fig. 18.

Let us consider the third-order term in the scattering matrix

$$S_3(x, y, z) = i^3 T(\mathscr{L}(x)\,\mathscr{L}(y)\,\mathscr{L}(z)). \tag{25.1}$$

Some of the divergent terms of S_3 which contain divergences of the second order corresponding, for example, to the diagrams shown in Fig. 18 are compensated for simultaneously with the removal of the divergences from S_2 by counter terms of the second order, i.e., by a redefinition of the T-product (25.1) at the points at which any two arguments coincide.

Specific divergences of the third order may therefore be contained only in those terms of S_3 which correspond to the diagrams shown in Figs. 19 and 20. However, terms which cor-

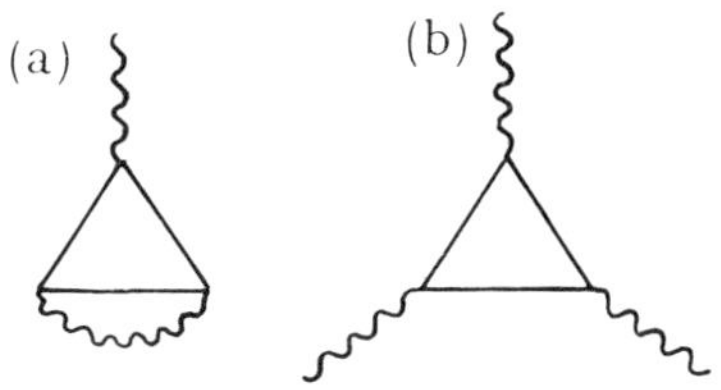

Fig. 19.

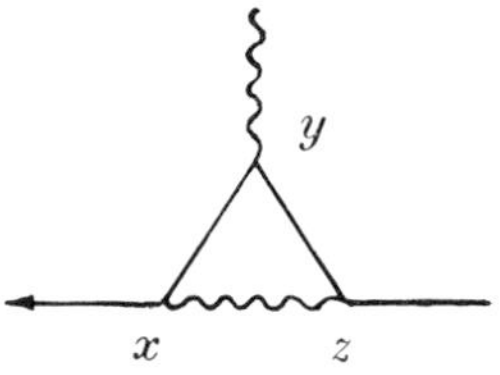

Fig. 20. Third-order divergent diagrams.

respond to diagrams of the type of Fig. 19a as well as terms which correspond to diagrams of the type of Fig. 19b always have their sum equal to zero. Indeed, these terms are proportional to e^3 and do not contain factors corresponding to free electrons and positrons. Therefore, under a transformation of charge conjugation (12.15) the corresponding matrix elements will change by a factor $(-1)^3 = -1$ and due to the absence of real electrons or positrons will describe the same processes. Consequently they are equal to zero.[47]

25.1. *Vertex Diagram of the Third Order*

It is therefore necessary to investigate only the third-order term corresponding to the diagram shown in Fig. 20. This term may be represented in the form

$$(ie)^3 : \bar{\psi}(x)\, \hat{A}(x) \psi(x) \bar{\psi}(y)\, \hat{A}(y) \psi(y) \bar{\psi}(z)\, \hat{A}(z)\, \psi(z) : \\ = ie \sum_n : \bar{\psi}(x)\, \Gamma^n(x, z \mid y)\, \psi(z)\, A_n(y) : ,$$

where we have introduced the *vertex function* of the third order

[47] This statement is a special case of Furry's theorem (see § 29).

$$\Gamma^n(x, z \mid y) = ie^2 \sum_k g^{kk} \gamma^k S^c(x-y) \gamma^n S^c(y-z) \gamma^k D_0^c(x-z). \quad (25.2)$$

By going over to the momentum representation

$$\Gamma^n(x,\ z,\ y) = \frac{1}{(2\pi)^8} \int e^{ip(z-x)+ik(y-x)} \Gamma^n(p,\ k) dp\, dk, \quad (25.3)$$

we obtain the following expression for the vertex function

$$\Gamma^n(p, k) = \frac{ie^2}{(2\pi)^4} \int dq\, D_0^c(p-q) \sum_k g^{kk} \gamma^k S^c(q+k) \gamma^n S^c(q) \gamma^k$$

$$= \frac{e^2}{(2\pi)^4 i} \sum_k g^{kk} \int \frac{dq}{(p-q)^2 + i\varepsilon} \gamma^k \frac{\hat{q}+\hat{k}+m}{(q+k)^2 - m^2} \gamma^n \frac{\hat{q}+m}{q^2-m^2} \gamma^k. \quad (25.4)$$

We note that the choice of the momentum variables in (25.3) and (25.4) corresponds to a diagram in which the incident electron line has the momentum p, the photon line has the momentum k, the emerging electron line has the momentum $p+k$, and the variable of integration q in (25.4) has been chosen equal to the difference of the four-momenta of the incident electron and the virtual photon as shown in Fig. 21.

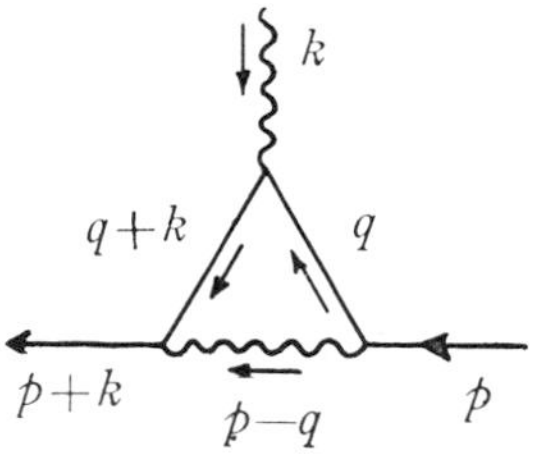

Fig. 21. Choice of notation for the momenta in a third-order vertex diagram.

The integral (25.3) diverges logarithmically for large q. In order to evaluate it we shall make use of the regularization procedure (24.18), (24.19) adopted earlier. Substituting the expressions for S^c and D_0^c into (25.3) we find, after some rearrangement of the Dirac matrices,

$$\text{reg}\, \Gamma^n(p, k) = \frac{e^2}{8\pi^4}\int_0^\infty \int_0^\infty \int_0^\infty d\alpha\, d\beta\, d\gamma\, e^{i\alpha p^2+i\beta k^2-\varepsilon(\alpha+\beta+\gamma)}$$
$$\times\ (1-e^{-i\alpha M^2})(e^{-i\beta m^2}-e^{-i\beta M^2})(e^{-i\gamma m^2}-e^{-i\gamma M^2})$$
$$\int dq e^{iq^2(\alpha+\beta+\gamma)+2iq(k\beta-p\alpha)}$$
$$\times\ [\gamma^n m^2 + \hat{q}\gamma^n(\hat{k}+\hat{q}) - 2m(k^n+2q^n)].$$

Carrying out the integration over q with the aid of (24.13), (24.16), and (26.17) and introducing the new variables x, y, λ:

$$\alpha = \lambda x, \quad \beta = \lambda y, \quad \gamma = \lambda(1-x-y), \tag{25.5}$$

we obtain from the above after integration over λ in the limit of large M

$$\text{reg}\, \Gamma^n(p, k) = \frac{e^2}{8\pi^2}\gamma^n\int_0^1 dx\int_0^{1-x} dy\left\{\ln\frac{M^2}{m^2} + \ln\frac{xy(1-x-y)}{(1-x)(1-y)(x+y)}\right.$$
$$\left. + \ln\left|\frac{m^2}{m^2(1-x)-x(1-x)p^2-y(1-y)k^2-2xy(pk)}\right|\right\} + \frac{e^2}{8\pi^2}\int_0^1 dx$$
$$\times\int_0^{1-x} dy\frac{\gamma^n m^2-2mk^n+(\hat{p}x-\hat{k}y)\gamma^n\hat{k}+4m(k^n y-p^n x)+(\hat{p}x-\hat{k}y)\gamma^n(\hat{p}x-\hat{k}y)}{m^2(1-x)-xp^2-yk^2+(xp-yk)^2}$$

25.2. *Segregation of the Divergence from Γ and Gauge Invariance*

We thus see that reg Γ may be written in the form of the sum

$$\text{reg}\, \Gamma^n(p, k) = \frac{e^2}{16\pi^2}\gamma^n\left[\ln\frac{M^2}{m^2}-\frac{1}{2}\right] + \Gamma'^n_M(p, k), \tag{25.6}$$

and that in the limit of large M the term Γ'^n_M converges to a finite limit which after some transformations may be represented in the form

$$\Gamma'^n(p, k) = \frac{e^2}{8\pi^2}\gamma^n\left\{\frac{(p+k)^2-m^2}{2(p+k)^2}-\frac{3}{4}-\frac{[(p+k)^2-m^2]^2}{2[(p+k)^2]^2}\ln\left(\frac{(p+k)^2-m^2}{m^2}\right)\right.$$
$$\left. -\int_0^1 dx\int_0^{1-x} dy\, y\frac{k^2(1-2y)+2xkp}{m^2(1-x)-xp^2-yk^2+(xp-yk)^2}\right\} + \frac{e^2}{8\pi^2}\int_0^1 dx \tag{25.7}$$
$$\times\int_0^{1-x} dy\frac{\gamma^n m^2-2mk^n+(\hat{p}x-\hat{k}y)\gamma^n\hat{k}+4m(k^n y-p^n x)+(\hat{p}x-\hat{k}y)\gamma^n(\hat{p}x-\hat{k}y)}{m^2(1-x)-xy(p+k)^2-x(1-x-y)p^2-y(1-x-y)k^2}.$$

In going over to the configuration representation we find that for such values of M the following relation holds

$$\operatorname{reg} \Gamma^n(x, z \mid y) = \frac{e^2}{16\pi^2}\gamma^n\left(\ln\frac{M^2}{m^2} - \frac{1}{2}\right)\delta(x-z)\delta(x-y) + \Gamma'^n_M(x, z \mid y), \tag{25.8}$$

where in the limit $M \to \infty$ the term Γ'^n_M converges to an integrable function Γ'^n which in the momentum representation is defined by formula (25.7). The first term in (25.8) diverges logarithmically as $M \to \infty$.

The decomposition (25.6) is of course not unique. In the given case it was chosen so that

$$\Gamma'^n(0,\ 0) = 0. \tag{25.9}$$

The degree of ambiguity is determined by the structure of the singular term. Therefore a constant proportional to the matrix γ^n may be added to the expression (25.7). However, this constant is not arbitrary and is determined by the condition of gauge invariance.

Let us investigate this condition applied to the third-order terms of the scattering matrix. These terms may be divided

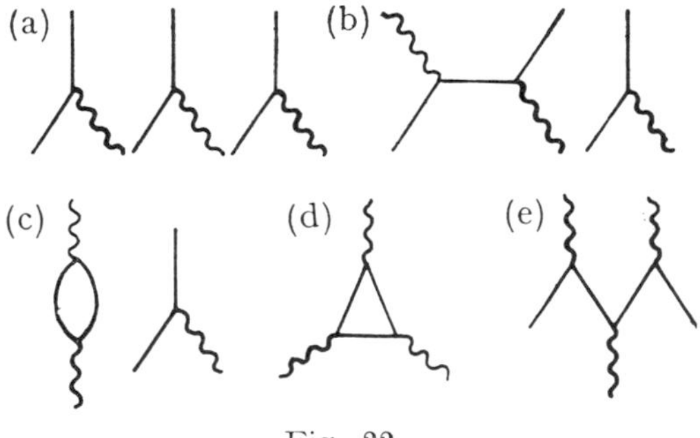

Fig. 22.

into two groups. One of these consists of terms containing three operators of the electromagnetic field $A(x)$, $A(y)$, $A(z)$ and not containing electromagnetic pairings D_0^c, while the other includes terms containing one operator A and one pairing D_0^c. The terms of the first group correspond to the diagrams shown in Fig. 22.

The terms which correspond to the diagrams of Figs. 22a–c, are normal products of the lowest order terms and are therefore manifestly gauge invariant. The term corresponding to Fig. 22d vanishes in accordance with Furry's theorem, and, finally, the gauge invariance of the term corresponding to Fig. 22e may be established by a direct calculation.

The sum of the terms of the second group which contain divergences of the third order may be written as a whole in the form

$$\sum_n : A_n(x) J^n(x, y, z) : + \sum_n : A_n(y) J^n(y, z, x) : + \sum_n : A_n(z) J^n(z, x, y) : .$$

The requirement of gauge invariance imposes on each term of this expression conditions of the form

$$\sum_n \int \frac{\partial f(x)}{\partial x^n} J^n(x, y, z) dx = 0,$$

which in view of the arbitrariness of the function f give:

$$\sum_n \frac{\partial}{\partial x^n} J^n(x, y, z) = 0. \qquad (25.10)$$

We now turn to the structure of the function $J^n(x, y, z)$. This function contains terms corresponding to the four diagrams (Fig. 23) and to four additional diagrams which differ from those shown by an interchange of the points z and y.

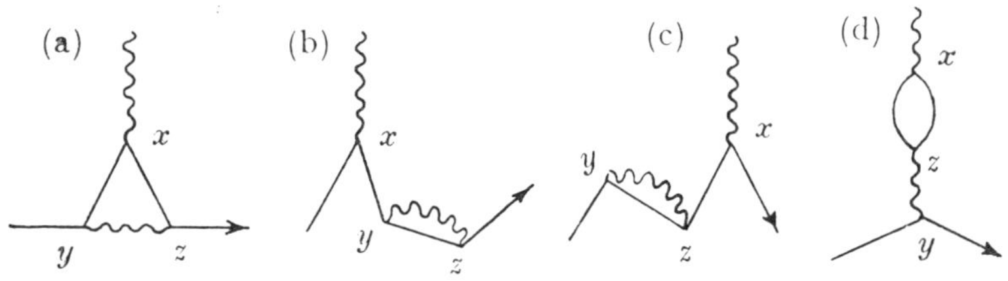

Fig. 23.

We note first of all that the terms J^n which correspond to the diagram of Fig. 23d

$$\left.\begin{aligned} J_d^m(x,y,z) \sim \{\sum_{n,k} \Pi^{mn}(x-z) g^{nk} : \bar\psi(y)\gamma^k\psi(y) : D_0^c(y-z) \\ + \text{ a term obtained by interchanging } z \text{ and } y, \end{aligned}\right\}$$

automatically give after the removal of divergences and in virtue of condition (24.38)

$$\sum_n \frac{\partial}{\partial x^n} J_d^n(x,y,z) = 0.$$

Therefore only the terms of S_3 which correspond to the first three diagrams of Fig. 23 remain to be investigated:

$$\begin{aligned} \sum_m g^{mm} \{ &: \bar\psi(z)\gamma^m S^c(z-x)\gamma^n S^c(x-y)\gamma^m\psi(y) : \\ &+ : \bar\psi(z)\gamma^m S^c(z-y)\gamma^m S^c(y-x)\gamma^n\psi(x) : \\ &+ : \bar\psi(x)\gamma^n S^c(x-z)\gamma^m S^c(z-y)\gamma^m\psi(y) : \} D_0^c(y-z). \end{aligned} \quad (25.11)$$

Differentiating them formally with respect to x^n and summing them after taking into account the equations

$$\left.\begin{aligned} \left(i\frac{\hat\partial}{\partial x} - m\right)\psi(x) = 0, \quad i\sum_n \frac{\partial\bar\psi}{\partial x^n}\gamma^n + m\bar\psi(x) = 0, \\ \left(i\frac{\hat\partial}{\partial x} - m\right) S^c(x) = i\sum_n \frac{\partial S^c(x)}{\partial x^n}\gamma^n - mS^c(x) = -\delta(x), \end{aligned}\right\} \quad (25.12)$$

we obtain:

$$\begin{aligned} D_0^c(y-z) \sum_m \{ &: \bar\psi(z)\gamma^m\delta(z-x) S^c(x-y)\gamma^m\psi(y) : \\ &- : \bar\psi(z)\gamma^m S^c(z-x)\delta(x-y)\gamma^m\psi(y) : \\ &+ : \bar\psi(z)\gamma^m S^c(z-y)\gamma^m\delta(y-x)\psi(x) : \\ &- : \bar\psi(x)\delta(x-z)\gamma^m S^c(z-y)\gamma^m\psi(y) : \} = 0. \end{aligned}$$

Thus the sum of the terms of the S-matrix which correspond to the diagrams of Figs. 23 a, b, c is indeed gauge invariant.

The verification of condition (25.10) carried out before was of a purely formal nature, since each of the terms of expression (25.11) is actually divergent. In fact, it is only necessary to verify that its finite part is gauge invariant. To make this verification more convenient, it is advantageous first to use Feynman's method of regularization and only then to go over to the method of regularization adopted by us. If we therefore regularize only the photon function

$$D_0^c(y-z) \to \text{reg } D_0^c(y-z),$$

we shall obtain the expression

$$\begin{aligned} \text{reg } D_0^c(y-z) \sum_m g^{mm}\{ &: \bar{\psi}(z)\gamma^m S^c(z-x)\gamma^n S^c(x-y)\gamma^m \psi(y) : \\ &+ : \bar{\psi}(z)\gamma^m S^c(z-y)\gamma^m S^c(y-x)\gamma^n \psi(x) : \\ &+ : \bar{\psi}(x)\gamma^n S^c(x-z)\gamma^m S^c(z-y)\gamma^m \psi(y) : \}, \end{aligned} \quad (25.13)$$

which as a whole clearly satisfies condition (25.10), since the factors being differentiated

$$\bar{\psi}(x),\ S^c(x-w),\ S^c(w-x),\ \psi(x) \quad (w = y,\ z)$$

are not changed.

The singular part of expression (25.13) for $M < \infty$ and after taking into account the expansions

$$\left.\begin{aligned} \text{reg}_F\, \Sigma(x-y) &= \Sigma'_F(x-y) - a_2^F\left(i\frac{\hat{\partial}}{\partial x} - m\right)\delta(x-y) - \delta m\,\delta(x-y), \\ \text{reg}_F\, \Gamma^n(x, y \mid \xi) &= a_1^F \gamma^n \delta(x-y)\delta(y-\xi) + \Gamma_F'^n(x, y \mid \xi) \end{aligned}\right\} \quad (25.14)$$

may be represented in the form

$$\begin{aligned} a_1^F &: \bar{\psi}(z)\gamma^n \delta(x-x)\delta(z-y)\psi(y) : \\ &+ a_2^F : \bar{\psi}(z)\left[\left(i\frac{\hat{\partial}}{\partial z} - m\right)\delta(z-y)\right] S^c(y-x)\gamma^n \psi(x) : \\ &- \delta m : \bar{\psi}(z)\delta(z-y) S^c(y-x)\gamma^n \psi(x) : \\ &+ a_2^F : \bar{\psi}(x)\gamma^n S(x-z)\left[\left(i\frac{\hat{\partial}}{\partial z} - m\right)\delta(z-y)\right]\psi(y) : \\ &- \delta m : \bar{\psi}(x)\gamma^n S^c(x-z)\delta(z-y)\psi(y) : . \end{aligned}$$

Differentiating this combination with respect to x^n, summing over n, and taking equations (25.12) into account we obtain the expression

$$(a_1^F - a_2^F)\Big\{:\bar{\psi}(z)\left(\frac{\hat{\partial}}{\partial x}\delta(z-x)\right)\delta(x-y)\,\psi(y):$$
$$+ :\bar{\psi}(z)\,\delta(z-x)\left(\frac{\hat{\partial}}{\partial x}\delta(x-y)\right)\psi(y):\Big\}.$$

25.3. *Ward's Identity*

Thus in order to guarantee the gauge invariance of the singular part of expression (25.14) it is necessary that

$$a_1^F = a_2^F. \tag{25.15}$$

Since expression (25.14) is gauge invariant as a whole the above condition guarantees the invariance of its finite part. Then by going to the limit $M \to \infty$ after a rearrangement of the effective Lagrangian we shall obtain for S_3 a gauge invariant expression not containing any infinities. The identity of the singular constants (25.15), which guarantees gauge invariance was first established in a somewhat more general form by Ward (132) and is known as Ward's identity.

We have obtained Ward's identity by using Feynman's regularization. We shall now show that it also holds in the case of the method of regularization usually employed by us. In order to do this we introduce for the sake of brevity the notation

$$\mathrm{reg}_F\,\Sigma \equiv \Sigma_F \text{ and } \mathrm{reg}_F\,\Gamma^n \equiv \Gamma_F^n\,,$$

and rewrite expressions (25.14) in the form

$$\Sigma_F(p) + a_2^F\hat{p} + ma_2^F + \delta m = \Sigma_F(p) - \Sigma_F(0)$$
$$- \sum_n \frac{\partial \Sigma_F(p)}{\partial p^n}\bigg|_{p=0}\cdot p^n + c_0^F + c_2^F\hat{p}, \tag{25.16}$$

$$\Gamma_F^n(p, k) - a_1^F\gamma^n = \Gamma_F^n(p, k) - \Gamma_F^n(0, 0) - c_1^F\gamma^n, \tag{25.17}$$

from which it follows that:

$$a_2^F\gamma^n = g^{nn}\frac{\partial \Sigma_F(p)}{\partial p^n}\bigg|_{p=0} - c_2^F\gamma^n = -\,\Gamma_F^n(0, 0) - c_1^F\gamma^n. \tag{25.18}$$

By means of a direct calculation it may be easily shown that

$$g^{nn}\frac{\partial \Sigma_F(p)}{\partial p^n} = -\Gamma_F^n(p, 0). \tag{25.19}$$

Therefore it follows from (25.18) that

$$c_1^F = c_2^F.$$

Now recalling that in accordance with (24.29) the combination

$$\Sigma_F(p) - \Sigma_F(0) - \sum_n \frac{\partial \Sigma_F}{\partial p^n}\bigg|_{p=0} \cdot p^n$$

does not depend on the method of regularization and in accordance with (24.27) is equal to expression (24.26), and also taking into account analogous considerations for the function Γ^n, we conclude that expressions

$$\Sigma'(p) + c_0 + c_2 \hat{p} \text{ and } \Gamma'^n(p, k) + c_1 \gamma^n$$

satisfy the requirement of gauge invariance under the condition

$$c_1 = c_2.$$

Therefore the singular parts of the functions $\Sigma(x)$ and $\Gamma(x, y | \xi)$, which are subtracted off in our usual method of regularization, may be written in the form

$$a_1\left(i\frac{\hat{\partial}}{\partial x} - m\right)\delta(x) + \delta m\, \delta(x), \tag{25.20}$$

$$-a_1 \gamma^n \delta(x-y)\,\delta(x-\xi), \tag{25.21}$$

where

$$a_1 = \frac{e^2}{16\pi^2}\left[\ln\frac{M^2}{m^2} - \frac{1}{2} - c_1\right], \tag{25.22}$$

$$\delta m = \frac{e^2}{16\pi^2}\left\{3m \ln\frac{M^2}{m^2} - \frac{7m}{2} + c_0\right\}. \tag{25.23}$$

Ward's identity thus also holds in the case of our method of regularization. In view of the fact that in the preceding argument we have used only the relations

$$\Sigma(0) = 0, \quad \frac{\partial \Sigma}{\partial p^n}\bigg|_{p=0} = 0, \quad \Gamma^n(0, 0) = 0,$$

this shows that Ward's identity does not in general depend on the method of regularization.

25.4. *Construction of an Integrable Function* S_3

We conclude that the third-order term in the scattering matrix may be written in the form

$$\begin{aligned}S_3(x_1, x_2, x_3) &= i^3 T'_M(\mathscr{L}(x_1)\mathscr{L}(x_2)\mathscr{L}(x_3)) - i^2 T(\mathscr{L}(x_1)\Lambda_2(x_2, x_3)) \\ &- i^2 T(\mathscr{L}(x_2)\Lambda_2(x_1, x_3)) - i^2 T(\mathscr{L}(x_3)\Lambda_2(x_1, x_2)) - i\Lambda_3(x_1, x_2, x_3),\end{aligned} \tag{25.24}$$

where T'_M is a regular operator function in the coefficient functions of which the function reg Δ^c should be used for the ordinary lines, the functions Π'_M and Σ'_M should be used for the closed diagrams shown in Fig. 17a,b and the function Γ'^n_M should be used for the vertex part (Fig. 20).

It is then clear that when the regularization is removed all the coefficient functions of the operator T'_M converge to finite limits which depend on Δ^c, Π', Σ', and Γ'. The terms in expression (25.24) containing the functions

$$i\Lambda_2(x_1, x_2) = T(\mathscr{L}(x_1)\mathscr{L}(x_2)) - T'_M(\mathscr{L}(x_1)\mathscr{L}(x_2)),$$

take into account divergences of the second order corresponding to diagrams of the type of Fig. 18, while the quasilocal operator

$$\left.\begin{aligned}\Lambda_3(x_1, x_2, x_3) &= -a_1 e\{:\bar{\psi}(x_1)\hat{A}(x_2)\psi(x_3):\delta(x_1-x_2)\delta(x_2-x_3)\\ &+ \text{terms which differ by interchanges of arguments}\end{aligned}\right\} \tag{25.25}$$

corresponds to the divergences of the vertex parts (Fig. 20).

After integration over x_1, x_2, x_3 the terms containing the functions Λ_2 give the contribution to the S-matrix

$$\frac{1}{2}\int dx_1\, dx_2\, dx_3\, T(\mathscr{L}(x_1)\Lambda_2(x_2, x_3)),$$

which is compensated by the terms in S_2, containing the counter terms $\mathscr{L}^{(2)}(x)$:

$$\frac{i^2}{2!}\int T(\mathscr{L}(x_1)\,\mathscr{L}^{(2)}(x_2))\,dx_1\,dx_2 + \frac{i^2}{2!}\int T(\mathscr{L}(x_2)\,\mathscr{L}^{(2)}(x_1))\,dx_1\,dx_2$$
$$= -\frac{1}{2}\int dx_1\,dx_2\,dx_3\,T(\mathscr{L}(x_1)\,\Lambda_2(x_2, x_3)).$$

The last divergent term of (25.24) must be compensated by adding to the interaction Lagrangian a new counter term of the third order in e:

$$\mathscr{L}^{(3)}(x) = -ea_1 :\bar{\psi}(x)\hat{A}(x)\psi(x): = \frac{1}{3!}\int \Lambda_3(x, x_2, x_3)\,dx_2\,dx_3. \quad (25.26)$$

Thus after introducing into the Lagrangian the additional counter terms $\mathscr{L}^{(2)}(x)$ and $\mathscr{L}^{(3)}(x)$ and going to the limit $M \to \infty$ we obtain for the second and third-order terms of the S-matrix the integrable expressions

$$T'(\mathscr{L}(x_1)\,\mathscr{L}(x_2)) \text{ and } T'(\mathscr{L}(x_1)\,\mathscr{L}(x_2)\,\mathscr{L}(x_3)). \quad (25.27)$$

We emphasize that the integrable expressions (25.27) for S_2 and S_3 may be obtained without making use of counter terms, by means of a suitable redefinition of T-products in the region in which their arguments coincide. This last possibility is preferable, since it turns out that the structure of the counter terms depends not only on the specific form of the auxiliary regularization but also on "the region of switching on" the interaction described by the function $g(x)$.

Up until now we have restricted ourselves to the consideration of the case when the interaction is completely switched on over all space-time and $g(x) = 1$. It is just this case when the actual switching on and switching off of the interaction refers to the remotely distant past and future which is important for the calculation of the matrix elements for the processes of scattering and of mutual transformation of particles.

However, it turns out that in those cases when we are interested in the properties of systems of particles existing in bound levels (energy levels, lifetimes, transition probabilities between bound states (for details see Chapter VI)), we have to examine the situation when the interaction is switched on only over a certain part of four-space and the function $g(x)$ increases from zero to unity within small regions near the surfaces bounding this part of four-space.

Keeping this last case in mind, we shall investigate the structure of the counter terms in the effective Lagrangian $\mathscr{L}(x; g)$ which guarantee that the operator

$$S(g) = T(\exp i \int \mathscr{L}(x; g)\, dx)$$

will be integrable.

Let us consider the second-order terms. The counter term $\mathscr{L}^{(2)}(x; g)$ is determined by the condition which is a natural generalization of relation (24.43):

$$\int \mathscr{L}^{(2)}(x;\, g)\, dx$$
$$= \frac{1}{2i}\int dx_1 dx_2 g(x_1) g(x_2) [T(\mathscr{L}(x_1)\mathscr{L}(x_2)) - T'_M(\mathscr{L}(x_1)\mathscr{L}(x_2))].$$

Substituting into the above equation the explicit expression for the difference $T - T'_M$ from (24.41) and integrating by parts we find:

$$\mathscr{L}^{(2)}(x;g) = \mathscr{L}^{(2)}(x)\, g^2(x) - ia_2 \sum_n :\bar{\psi}(x)\gamma^n \frac{\partial g(x)}{\partial x^n}\, \psi(x): g(x)$$
$$+ a_3 \sum_{m,n} g^{mm} g^{nn} \Big\{ : A_m(x)\, A_n(x) : \frac{\partial^2 g(x)}{\partial x^n\, \partial x^m} + : A_n(x) \frac{\partial A_m}{\partial x^n} : \frac{\partial g}{\partial x^m}$$
$$- : A_m(x) \frac{\partial A_n}{\partial x^n} : \frac{\partial g(x)}{\partial x^m} + : A_m(x)\, A_m(x) : \frac{\partial^2 g(x)}{\partial x^n\, \partial x^n} \Big\} g(x)$$
$$+ \{\text{terms containing } R \text{ and its derivatives}\} \qquad (25.28)$$

with the operator $\mathscr{L}^{(2)}(x)$ being determined by relation (24.44). It may also be easily seen that in the third order

$$\mathscr{L}^{(3)}(x;\, g) = \mathscr{L}^{(3)}(x)\, g^3(x),$$

with $\mathscr{L}^3(x)$ being determined by relation (25.26).

Thus in the process of integration by parts terms appear in $\mathscr{L}(x;\, g)$ which contain derivatives of the function $g(x)$ and which differ from the usual counter terms in their operator structure. This circumstance will turn out to be essential for the removal of divergences from Schrödinger's equation.

§ 26. General Rules for the Removal of Divergences from the S-Matrix

26.1. *Formulation of the Problem*

In § 24, § 25 the construction of integrable expressions for S_2 and S_3 was carried out using spinor electrodynamics as an example. We shall now undertake the formulation of the general method for the removal of divergences from the terms of the S-matrix of arbitrary order which is based on the same principle as the examples considered above (see Bogoliubov (16)). We shall first of all replace the true causal functions Δ^c by the regularized expressions reg Δ^c with a certain appropriate number of auxiliary masses M_i. For finite values of these masses the usual T-product of the Lagrangians

$$T(\mathscr{L}(x_1)\ldots\mathscr{L}(x_n)) \tag{26.1}$$

is quite definite and its coefficient functions are continuous. However, as we have just seen in specific cases, it is not possible to make the limiting transition $M \to \infty$ in (26.1) even if it were to be understood in the improper sense.

Speaking more accurately the coefficient functions of the operator (26.1) will converge in the improper sense only in those regions of space-time in which each of the arguments $x_1, x_2, \ldots, x_n$ differs from all the others. In order to segregate the "convergent part" from expression (26.1) it is necessary to apply to it, just as in the cases considered above, a certain subtraction procedure. In order to be able to formulate this procedure it is convenient to start with the general formula (18.40) which expresses $S_n(x_1, \ldots, x_n)$ in terms of the interaction Lagrangian $\mathscr{L}(x) = \Lambda_1(x)$ and the quasilocal operators Λ_ν $(\nu \geqq 2)$:

$$S_n(x_1, \ldots, x_n) = i^n T(\mathscr{L}(x_1)\ldots\mathscr{L}(x_n))$$
$$+ \sum_{\left(\substack{2 \leqq m \leqq n-1 \\ \Sigma\nu_i = n}\right)} \frac{i^m}{m!} P(x_1,\ldots,x_{\nu_1}|\ldots|\ldots,x_n) T(\Lambda_{\nu_1}(x_1,\ldots,x_{\nu_1})\ldots\Lambda_{\nu_m}(\ldots,x_n))$$
$$+ i\Lambda_n(x_1, \ldots, x_n). \tag{26.2}$$

As has been shown, this expression is the most general expression which satisfies all the conditions (of symmetry, covariance, unitarity, and causality) imposed on S_n for an arbitrary choice of Hermitean covariant quasilocal operators Λ_ν.

If we succeed in choosing the quasilocal operators Λ_ν in such a way that the expressions S_n will turn out to be convergent (we shall always understand the convergence of expressions of this type to be in the improper sense) then their limit as $M \to \infty$ will be first of all an integrable operator function (in the sense of the definition given in § 16), and secondly it will satisfy all the conditions imposed on S_n. Indeed, the condition of covariance (18.4) is of a linear nature and therefore the limiting transition for it is trivial, while the possibility of going to the limit in the conditions of unitarity (18.9) and of causality (18.12) is governed by the theorem of § 16 which states that the limit of the usual product of two operator functions is equal to the corresponding product of their limits.

Thus it is sufficient for us to set up a method of constructing from the given Lagrangian $\mathscr{L}(x) = \Lambda_1(x)$ a sequence of quasilocal operators Λ_ν $(\nu \geqq 2)$ which guarantee the convergence of expression (26.2). All the conditions imposed on S_n, including the condition of integrability, are automatically fulfilled for the limiting expressions obtained by the above method. In order to solve this problem it is obviously sufficient that we should choose for $\Lambda_\nu(x_1, \ldots, x_\nu)$ quasilocal operators of the same operator type as (26.1) (with $n = \nu$). In saying that Λ_ν belongs to the same operator type as (26.1) we mean that Λ_ν consists of the same operator terms

$$:\ldots u_\alpha(x_j) \ldots:, \tag{26.3}$$

as (26.1), and differs from it only by its coefficient functions. It now follows from (26.2) that $S_n(x_1, \ldots, x_n)$ will also be an expression of the same operator type as (26.1). In order to simplify the formulas it is convenient to set

$$i^{1-\nu}\Lambda_\nu(x_1, \ldots, x_\nu) = \Delta_\nu(x_1, \ldots, x_\nu), \quad \mathscr{L}(x) = \Lambda_1(x) = \Delta_1(x); \tag{26.4}$$

then

$$S_n = i^n T'_n, \tag{26.5}$$

where

$$T'_n = T(\mathscr{L}(x_1)\ldots\mathscr{L}(x_n))$$
$$+ \sum_{\substack{2\leq m\leq n-1\\ \Sigma\nu_i=n}} \frac{1}{m!} P(x_1,\ldots,x_{\nu_1}|\ldots|\ldots,x_n)\, T(\Delta_{\nu_1}(x_1,\ldots,x_{\nu_1})\ldots$$
$$\ldots\Delta_{\nu_m}(\ldots,x_n)) + \Delta_n(x_1,\ldots,x_n). \qquad (26.6)$$

Since T'_n belongs to the same operator type as (26.1) we may evidently develop a method for the actual construction of T'_n by means of a certain transformation of the coefficient functions of the operator T. In doing so, it turns out to be convenient to utilize graphical representations.

26.2. *Graphical Representation of the Subtraction Procedure and the Operation $\Delta(G)$*

The coefficient function for the T-product which corresponds to some particular diagram with ν vertices and with given internal lines is represented by a product of regularized causal functions of the type

$$\prod_l \{\text{reg}\, \Delta_l^c(x_a - x_b)\}. \qquad (26.7)$$

The coefficient functions of the quasilocal operator Δ_ν represent for the same diagram a product of δ-functions and of their derivatives. Therefore the whole set of points $x_1, \ldots, x_\nu$ behaves as a single entity in the diagram, as a result of which it is convenient in working with Δ_ν to introduce the concept of the generalized vertex G (see Fig. 24). We shall denote the

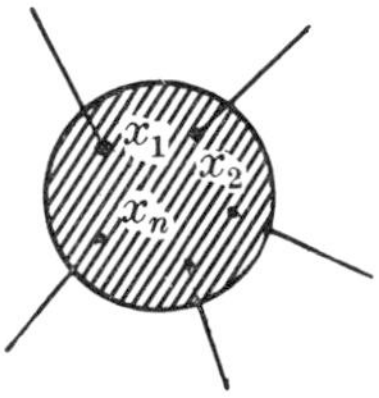

Fig. 24.

coefficient function of the operator Δ_ν which corresponds to the given generalized vertex G by means of $d_G(x_1, \ldots, x_\nu)$. We now consider an expression of the type

$$T(\Delta_\nu(x_1, \ldots x_\nu)\mathscr{L}(x_{\nu+1}) \ldots \mathscr{L}(x_n)). \qquad (26.8)$$

It is clear that its coefficient functions may be obtained from the coefficient functions of the operator (26.1) by means of the following procedure. Consider a diagram corresponding to the operator (26.8). By combining the points $x_1, \ldots, x_n$ in this diagram into the generalized vertex G we shall replace the product (26.7) which corresponds to the lines l internal with respect to G by the coefficient function $d_G(x_1, \ldots, x_\nu)$. We shall formally denote such a replacement operation by the symbol $\Delta(G)$. Then the coefficient functions of the operator (26.8) will be obtained from the coefficient functions of the operator (26.1) by the operation $\Delta(G)$.

It is also evident that in the more general case the coefficient functions of the expression

$$T(\Delta_{\nu_1}(x_1. \ldots, x_{\nu_1})\Delta_{\nu_2}(x_{\nu_1+1}, \ldots, x_{\nu_1+\nu_2}) \ldots \Delta_m(\ldots, x_n))$$

may be obtained from the coefficient functions of the operator (26.8) by means of the operation

$$\Delta(G_1) \ldots \Delta(G_m),$$

which consists of grouping the points $x_1, \ldots, x_\nu, x_{\nu_1+1}, \ldots, x_{\nu_1+\nu_2}, \ldots, x_n$ into the generalized vertices $G_1, G_2, \ldots, G_m$ and of replacing the factors of the product (26.7) which correspond to the internal lines of $G_1, \ldots, G_m$ by the corresponding $d_{G_1}, \ldots, d_{G_m}$ leaving unchanged the factors which correspond to the lines connecting different generalized vertices.

Thus T'_n may be obtained from T by applying the operation [48]

$$R(G) = 1 + \sum_{\substack{2 \leq m \leq n-1 \\ (G = G_1 * G_2 * \ldots * G_m)}} \frac{1}{m!}\Delta(G_1) \ldots \Delta(G_m) + \Delta(G). \qquad (26.9)$$

Here the summation is carried out over all possible ways of breaking up the set of points $x_1, \ldots, x_n$ of the diagram G into the generalized vertices $G_1, G_2, \ldots, G_m$. The symmetry of T'_n associated with the symmetrization operator P which appears

[48] The symbol $G_1 * G_2 * \ldots * G_n$ in this expression denotes the topological product of $G_1, G_2, \ldots, G_n$.

in (26.2) is taken into account in this case by making sure that in such a decomposition the points $x_1, \ldots, x_n$ appear in a perfectly symmetric way. We also emphasize that the generalized vertices cannot coincide with the ordinary vertices.

So far the operation $R(G)$ has been defined only purely formally. It will take on a concrete meaning after rules have been established for the actual determination of the function d_{G_a} for a given diagram G_a. By specifying d_G we thereby define Δ_ν and consequently T'_n. We shall choose d_G in such a way as to make T'_n integrable when $M \to \infty$.

Before undertaking the formulation of the method of construction of d_G we introduce the concept of the connectivity of the diagram. We shall say that a given diagram in unconnected if it may be decomposed into two parts not joined together by lines. In the opposite case the diagram will be said to be connected. We shall say that a connected diagram is weakly connected if by opening one line it may be changed into an unconnected one, and we shall say that it is strongly connected if this is not possible.

We now note that for an unconnected diagram the coefficient function of a T-product has the form of a product of two coefficient functions with different arguments. But the product of two functions with different arguments is convergent when each function is convergent separately. From this it follows that in an unconnected diagram, the divergences are automatically removed after they have been removed in its connected parts. Therefore the operator $\Delta(G)$ should be taken equal to zero for unconnected diagrams.

With such a choice of $\Delta(G)$ the operation $R(G)$ applied to a coefficient function of the T-product which corresponds to a diagram G consisting of two unconnected parts G_1 and G_2 decomposes into the product $R(G_1)R(G_2)$ of two operations which operate separately on the coefficient functions corresponding to the diagrams G_1 and G_2.

For weakly connected diagrams we obtain coefficient functions of the type

$$K_M(x_1, \ldots, x_k) \operatorname{reg} \Delta^c(x_a - y_b) Q_M(y_1, \ldots, y_s).$$

Since K and Q are invariant under translation, by setting

$$x - x_a = x', \quad y - y_b = y', \quad x_a - y_b = \xi,$$

we obtain a product of coefficient functions with independent arguments

$$K_M(x_1', \ldots, x_k') \operatorname{reg} \Delta^c(\xi) Q_M(y_1', \ldots, y_s'). \tag{26.10}$$

This expression will also converge as a whole if K and Q are convergent individually. Therefore for weakly connected diagrams we should also set $\Delta(G) = 0$.

Here, as in the preceding case, it is clear that with the above choice of the operator $\Delta(G)$ the coefficient functions of the operator T_n' for weakly connected diagrams have the same structure as (26.10). Thus in (26.9) we need only discuss the strongly connected decompositions of G into generalized vertices G_α.

26.3. *Index of the Diagram* $\omega(G)$ *and the Degree of Divergence*

In order to make the operator $\Delta(G)$ specific we also introduce the concept of the *index of the diagram.* In order to do this, we go over to the momentum representation. The coefficient functions of the T-product in the p-representation will obviously have the form

$$J_M(k) = \int \prod_{(1 \leqq q \leqq n)} \delta(\sum p - k_q) \prod_l \{\operatorname{reg} \Delta_l^c(p_l)\, dp_l\}. \tag{26.11}$$

Here the arguments of the δ-functions contain algebraic sums of the momenta of the internal lines of the diagram meeting at the vertex q to which the external momenta k_q have been added.

In accordance with the procedure of regularizing the Δ^c-functions which we have adopted we also have

$$\operatorname{reg} \Delta^c(p) = Z(p) \left\{ \frac{1}{m^2 - p^2 - i\varepsilon} - \sum_j c_j \frac{1}{M_j^c - p^2 - i\varepsilon} \right\},$$

where $Z(p)$ is the same polynomial which appears in the unregularized Δ^c-function.

If we go to the limit $M_j \to \infty$ in (26.11) then the whole integral will turn out to be, generally speaking, divergent for large momenta. We now compute its total degree of divergence. Since we are investigating connected diagrams $4(n-1)$ integrations may be carried out with the aid of δ-functions (the one remaining δ-function expresses the law of conservation of the total four-momentum) and we are left with $4(L-n+1)$ independent variables of integration where L denotes the total number of internal lines.

Just as in the case of integration over three-dimensional space one uses the radius as a variable of integration, we shall introduce the corresponding "radial" momentum p in carrying out the integration over the $4(L-n+1)$-dimensional space. Then the product of the independent differentials contained in $\Pi_l \mathrm{d}p_l$ gives the factor $P^{4(L-n+1)}\mathrm{d}P/P$. Taking into account only the terms of the highest degree in the function $\Delta^c(p)$ we obtain the factor

$$P^{\sum\limits_l r_l - 2L} = P^{\sum\limits_l (r_l - 2)}$$

and therefore in carrying out the integration over P the factor multiplying dP/P will for large P either increase or decrease as

$$P^{\sum\limits_l (r_l+2)-4(n-1)}.$$

Thus the integral over P will turn out to be divergent if

$$\sum_l (r_l + 2) - 4(n-1) \geqq 0,$$

and convergent if

$$\sum_l (r_l + 2) - 4(n-1) < 0.$$

We shall call the number

$$\omega(G) = \sum_l (r_l + 2) - 4(n-1) \tag{26.12}$$

the index of the diagram G.

Naturally the convergence of the integral over P does not yet imply that the integral of type (26.11) converges as a whole.

Here a situation may arise similar to the one occurring when in the course of evaluating the integral

$$\int_{-\infty}^{+\infty} dx \int_{-\infty}^{+\infty} dy \frac{x}{(y^2+1)^2}$$

the integral

$$\int \frac{\rho^2\, d\rho \cos^2 \varphi\, d\varphi}{(\rho^2 \sin^2 \varphi + 1)^2}$$

with respect to the radial variable ρ ($\rho = x/\cos\varphi = y/\sin\varphi$) converges while the remaining integration over φ turns out to be divergent because of singularities at the points $\varphi = 0$, $\varphi = \pi$.

The index of the diagram $\omega(G)$ may also be related to the conventional rate of increase with increasing momentum. In order to evaluate it we multiply all the external momenta and masses by some number a and determine the factor by which the integral (26.11) will be multiplied without taking regularization into account, and paying attention only to the highest power of a. It may be easily seen that this factor is just equal to

$$a^{\omega(G)}. \tag{26.13}$$

Thus the index of the diagram is exactly equal to the above conventional rate of increase.

We note that this rate of increase is referred to as conventional because the calculation leading to (26.13) is carried out purely formally without making a careful analysis of the convergence of the integral and does not take into account logarithmically divergent factors.

We now note that in breaking up G into s generalized vertices

$$G = G_1 * G_2 * \ldots * G_s,$$

we shall have

$$\omega(G) = \sum_{1 \leq j \leq s} \omega(G_j) + \sum_{l} (r_l + 2) - 4(s-1). \tag{26.14}$$

We now consider the coefficient function d_{G_j}. In the momentum representation it has the form

$$\delta(\sum p_j) Z_{G_j}(\ldots p \ldots),$$

where $Z_{G_j}(\ldots p \ldots)$ is a certain polynomial in the components of p.

As we shall see later, in order to compensate for the divergences of the T-product it is sufficient to choose for $Z_{G_j}(\ldots p \ldots)$ a polynomial of degree $\omega(G_j)$. It follows from (26.14) that with such a choice of d_{G_j} neither the total degree of divergence nor the conventional rate of increase with increasing momentum will be made larger by applying the operation $\Delta(G_1)\ldots\Delta(G_m)$, and that consequently $\omega(G)$ is not increased by applying the operation $R(G)$ as a whole.

As we have already seen in the examples just considered, it is convenient for the analysis and the evaluation of integrals of the type (26.11) to make use of the integral representation of causal functions (we shall refer to it below as the "α-representation")

$$\Delta^c(p) = Z(p)\, i \int_0^\infty e^{i\alpha(p^2-m^2+i\varepsilon)} d\alpha,$$

$$\text{reg}\, \Delta^c(p) = Z(p)\, i \int_0^\infty e^{i\alpha(p^2-m^2+i\varepsilon)} I(\alpha) d\alpha,$$

where

$$I(\alpha) = 1 + \sum_M c_M\, e^{-i\alpha(M^2-m^2)}.$$

It is convenient to write the factor $Z(p)$ in exponential form. To do this we shall make use of the relation

$$Z(p) = Z(-i\nabla q)\, e^{ipq}\,|_{q=0}\,.$$

With the aid of this representation the integration over the internal momenta in (26.11) is reduced to quadratures of Gaussian type

$$\prod_l Z(-i\nabla_{q_l}) \int e^{i\sum_l \alpha_l p_l^2 + i\sum_l p_l q_l} \prod_{1\leq q\leq n} \delta(\sum p + k_q) \prod_l dp_l\,|_{q_l=0}$$
$$= \delta(\sum k)\, f(\ldots k \ldots \alpha \ldots) \tag{26.15}$$

and only integrations over the variables α remain:

$$J_M(k) = \delta(\sum k) \int_0^\infty d\alpha_1 \ldots$$
$$\ldots \int_0^\infty d\alpha_L f(\ldots k \ldots \alpha \ldots)\, e^{-i\sum_l \alpha_l m_l^2 - \varepsilon \sum_l \alpha_l} \prod_{i\leq l\leq L} I(\alpha_l). \tag{26.16}$$

After carring out the integration over p_l we find that

$$f(\ldots k \ldots \alpha \ldots) = F(\ldots k \ldots \alpha \ldots)\, e^{i\sum_{a,b} A_{ab}(\ldots\alpha\ldots)(k_a k_b)}, \tag{26.17}$$

where F is a polynomial in k and a rational function of α which has nonintegrable poles when some of the α vanish. Since the convergence of the integral (26.16) is guaranteed for large α by the factors $\exp(-\varepsilon\Sigma_l \alpha_l)$ its possible divergences in the unregularized case are determined in the given representation just by the existence of these nonintegrable poles.

In order to determine the nature of the singularity we introduce the new variables

$$\alpha_j = \lambda\xi_j, \qquad \sum \xi_j = 1$$

and after fixing $\xi_j \neq 0$ we evaluate the order of the pole at the point $\lambda = 0$. By going over in (26.15) to the new "momenta"

$$p_l \sqrt{\lambda} = P_l; \qquad q_l \frac{1}{\sqrt{\lambda}} = Q_l; \qquad k_q \sqrt{\lambda} = K_q,$$

we find that

$$f(\ldots k \ldots \alpha \ldots)$$
$$= \lambda^{-\frac{4L-4(n-1)}{2}} \prod_l \left[Z\left(-\frac{i}{\sqrt{\lambda}}\nabla_Q\right)\right] \int e^{i\sum\limits_l P_l^2 + i\sum\limits_l (P_l Q_l)}$$
$$\times \prod_{1\leqq q\leqq n} \delta(\sum P + K_q) \prod_l dP_l \,|_{Q=0}.$$

By taking into account only the leading powers of λ in $\Pi\{Z(\ldots)\}$ we obtain for small λ

$$f(\ldots k \ldots \alpha \ldots) = \lambda^{-\frac{\omega(G)}{2}-L} F'(\ldots K \ldots)\, e^{i\sum\limits_{a,b} A'_{ab}(k_a k_b)}$$
$$= \lambda^{-\frac{\omega(G)}{2}-L} F'(\ldots \sqrt{\lambda} k \ldots)\, e^{i\sum\limits_{a,b} A'_{ab}(\xi)(k_a k_b)}. \qquad (26.18)$$

Thus the effective order of the pole with respect to λ for $\lambda = 0$ taking into account the value of the determinant

$$\frac{(\partial\alpha_1, \ldots, \partial\alpha_l)}{(\partial\xi_1, \ldots, \partial\xi_{l-1}, \partial\lambda)} = \lambda^{L-1}$$

is in fact determined by the index of the diagram $\omega(G)$.

26.4. *Structure of the Exponential Quadratic Form*

We now consider the structure of the quadratic form

$$A \equiv A_{ab}(\ldots \alpha_j \ldots) = \lambda A_{ab}(\ldots \xi_i \ldots).$$

It may be easily seen that it does not depend on the polynomials $Z(-i\nabla_q)$ and is a homogeneous function of the first degree in α_l.

Moreover, as we shall presently show, it is positive

$$\sum_{a,b} A_{ab} x_a x_b > 0 \qquad (\sum x^2 \neq 0) \tag{26.19}$$

and satisfies the condition

$$\sum_{a,b} A_{ab} x_a x_b < \sum_l \alpha_l \, (\sum_a |\, x_a \,|)^2. \tag{26.20}$$

Relations (26.19) and (26.20) may be conveniently verified by the method of induction, since their validity in the case of the simplest diagrams is evident (see the examples discussed in § **24** and § 25). We shall carry out the induction in two stages: (a) a new internal line is added for a given number of vertices; (b) a new vertex is added together with one line joining this vertex to one of the old vertices.

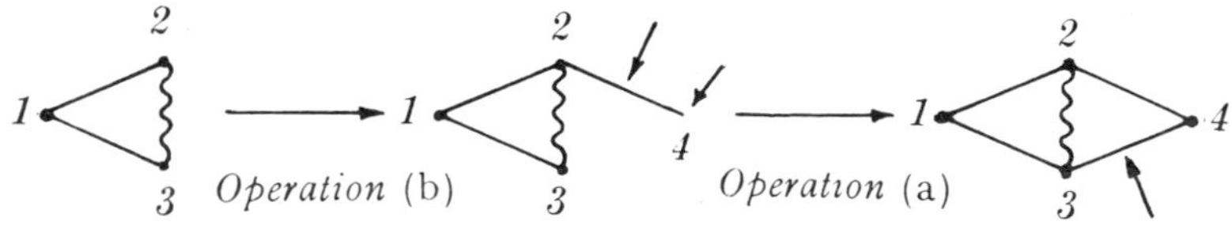

Fig. 25. Construction of the fourth-order photon self-energy diagram from the third-order vertex diagram.

It should be noted that considered individually the operations (a) and (b) are meaningless, but it may be easily seen that any diagram may be constructed from the simplest diagrams by means of successive application of the requisite number of such operations (see, for example, Fig. 25).

Let us consider operation (a). For the sake of definiteness

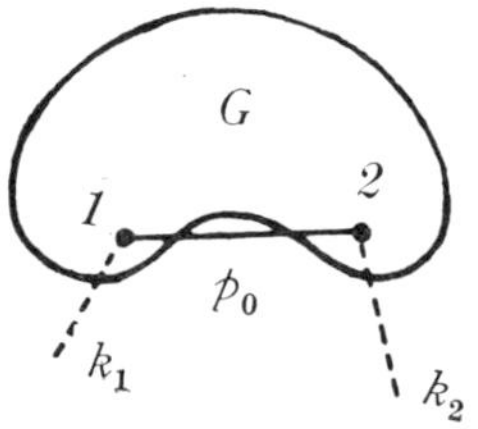

Fig. **26**. Addition of the internal line p_0 between the vertices 1 and 2.

we shall assume that the internal line with momentum p_0 is added between vertices 1 and 2 (as in Fig. 26). By neglecting factors of the type $Z(-i\nabla_q)$ which do not affect the structure of the exponential we can say that in expression (26.15) the factors

$$\delta(\textstyle\sum_1 p + k_1)\,\delta(\sum_2 p + k_2)$$

will be replaced by the factor

$$e^{i\alpha_0 p_0^2}\delta(\textstyle\sum_1 p + k_1 + p_0)\,\delta(\sum_2 p + k_2 - p_0)$$

and an integration over p_0 will be added. Thus the change in the integral (26.15) may be recorded in the form

$$\begin{aligned}f(k_1, k_2, \ldots | \ldots \alpha \ldots) \to \int e^{i\alpha_0 p_0^2} f(k_1 + p_0, k_2 - p_0, \ldots k \ldots | \ldots \alpha \ldots) dp_0 \\ = \int e^{i\alpha_0 p_0^2} F(k_1 + p_0,\ k_2 - p_0, \ldots k \ldots | \ldots \alpha \ldots) \\ \times \exp\{i \textstyle\sum A_{ab}(k_a + e_a p_0)(k_b + e_b p_0)\} dp_0,\end{aligned}$$

where the symbol e_a is defined as follows

$$e_1 = 1, \quad e_2 = -1, \quad e_q = 0 \quad (q > 2).$$

By writing the above integrals in the form (26.17) we see that because of its polynomial nature the function $F(k_1 + p_0, k_2 - p_0, \ldots, k \ldots | \ldots \alpha \ldots)$ does not influence the structure of the resulting exponential. Therefore by evaluating the integral

$$\begin{aligned}\int dp_0 \exp\{i\alpha_0 p_0^2 + i \textstyle\sum A_{ab}(k_a + e_a p_0)(k_b + e_b p_0)\} \\ = \int dp_0 \exp i\,\{(\alpha_0 + \textstyle\sum A_{ab} e_a e_b) p_0^2 + 2 \sum A_{ab} e_a (p_0 k_b) + \sum A_{ab} k_a k_b\},\end{aligned}$$

we obtain an exponential of the form

$$\exp i \left(\sum A_{ab} k_a k_b - \frac{(\sum A_{ab} k_b e_a)^2}{\alpha_0 + \sum A_{ab} e_a e_b} \right).$$

Thus when a new internal line is included in the diagram the exponent undergoes the following transformation:

$$\sum A_{ab} k_a k_b \to \sum A_{ab} k_a k_b - \frac{(\sum A_{ab} k_b e_a)^2}{\alpha_0 + \sum A_{ab} e_a e_b}. \tag{26.21}$$

Since the quadratic form (26.19) is positive for

$$x_a = k_a^n t_1 + e_a t_2 \qquad (n = 0,\ 1,\ 2,\ 3)$$

the fact that its discriminant is nonnegative leads us to the inequality

$$(\sum_{a,b} A_{ab} k_a^n k_b^n)(\sum_{a,b} A_{ab} e_a e_b) \geqq (\sum_{a,b} A_{ab} k_b^n e_a)^2,$$

which on being substituted into (26.21) rewritten for the individual nth component yields:

$$\sum A_{ab} k_a^n k_b^n \to \sum_{a,b} A_{ab} k_a^n k_b^n - \frac{(\sum A_{ab} k_b^n e_a)^2}{\alpha_0 + \sum A_{ab} e_a e_b}$$

$$\geqq \sum A_{ab} k_a^n k_b^n \frac{\alpha_0}{\alpha_0 + \sum A_{ab} e_a e_b} \geqq 0.$$

Thus we see that the property (26.19) is not violated by the inclusion of an extra internal line. Since the quadratic form is decreased by the transition (26.21) condition (26.20) is also not violated by the inclusion of an additional internal line.

Let us now consider the process of including in the diagram a new vertex and a line connecting it. For the sake of definiteness we shall assume that the new vertex 0 is connected by a line of momentum p_0 with the vertex 1 (Fig. 27).

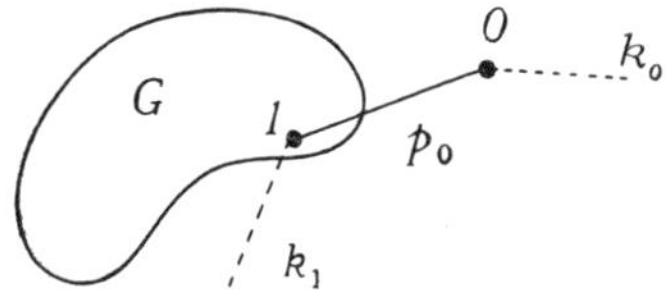

Fig. 27. Introduction of a new vertex 0 and of the line p_0 connecting it to G.

This will give rise in the integral (26.15) to the following replacement

$$\delta(\sum_1 p + k_1) \to e^{i\alpha_0 p_0^2} \delta(\sum_1 p + k_1 + p_0)\, \delta(k_0 - p_0)$$

and to the appearence of an additional integration over p_0, which may also be written in the form

$$f(\ldots k \ldots \alpha \ldots) \to \int dp_0 e^{i\alpha_0 p_0^2} f(k_1 + p_0, k_2, \ldots \alpha \ldots) \delta(p_0 - k_0)$$
$$= e^{i\alpha_0 k_0^2} f(k_0 + k_1, k_2, \ldots \alpha \ldots).$$

The change in the exponent is correspondingly given by:

$$\sum A_{ab} k_a k_b \to \alpha_0 k_0^2 + \sum A_{ab}(k_a + e_a k_a)(k_b + e_b k_0), \quad (26.22)$$

where $e_1 = 1$, $e_a = 0$ ($a \geqq 2$). In view of (26.20) we shall obtain from the above:

$$\alpha_0 x_0^2 + \sum_{a,b} A_{ab}(x_a + e_a x_0)(x_b + e_b x_0) \leqq \alpha_0 \sum_a (x_0 e_a + x_a)^2$$
$$+ \sum_{1 \leq l} \alpha_l \sum_{1 \leq a} (x_a + e_a x_0)^2 = \sum_{0 \leq l} \alpha_l \left| \sum_{1 \leq a} (x_a + e_a x_0) \right|^2 = \sum_{0 \leq l} \alpha_l \left(\sum_{0 \leq a} |x_a| \right)^2.$$

Thus condition (26.20) still holds after the addition of a new vertex and a line. Condition (26.19) is also retained since the quadratic form increases when the vertex is added.

The verification of the properties (26.19) and (26.20) is thus completed. We note that in the course of carrying this out we have in fact obtained the prescription for constructing the quadratic form which is embodied in formulas (26.21) and (26.22).

We now consider the changes which will take place in the coefficient functions of the T-products as a result of performing the operation $\Delta(G_j)$ in the integral "α-representation" (26.15) which we have adopted. We recall that in accordance with its definition the operation $\Delta(G_j)$ in the x-representation consists of replacing a part of the product $\Pi_l \Delta_l^c(x_a - x_b)$ which corresponds to the internal lines of G_j by the coefficient function of a quasilocal operator $d_{G_j}(\ldots x_a \ldots)$ which in the p-representation has the form of a polynomial multiplied by a δ-function:

$$\delta(\Sigma p) Z_{G_j}(\ldots p \ldots).$$

In going over to the integral representation (26.15), we shall use for the reduction of the polynomial Z_G to exponential form the relation

$$Z_G(\ldots p \ldots) = Z_G(\ldots -i\nabla_q \ldots)\, e^{i\Sigma(p_a q_a)}\big|_{q=0}, \quad (26.23)$$

which is a natural generalization of the formula for $Z_l(p)$ from $\Delta_l^c(p)$. It is evident that the quadratic form in the exponential will depend neither on Z_G nor on Z_l. Thus as a result of applying the operation $\Delta(G_j)$ we shall again obtain an expression of type (26.17) not containing any variables corresponding to the internal lines of G_j.

The "new" quadratic exponential form is obtained from the "old" one by setting equal to zero all the α_l corresponding to the internal lines of G_j. At the same time the momenta k_a which correspond to the vertices of the diagram united into a generalized vertex G_j automatically drop out from the quadratic form. It is also evident that the preceding α_l will also not appear in the factor $F(\ldots k \ldots \alpha \ldots)$ multiplying the exponential.

In order to analyze the singularity we shall now decrease all the α_l by the same factor by setting

$$\alpha_i = \xi_i \lambda, \quad \sum \xi_i = 1, \quad \xi_i > 0, \quad \lambda \to 0,$$

and we shall determine the maximum effective order of the pole at $\lambda = 0$ in the resulting integral. It was established earlier that the effective order of the pole is equal to half the conventional rate of increase plus unity, and that the conventional rate of increase is not altered by the operation $\Delta(G_j)$. Consequently, in the present case the effective order of the pole is equal to

$$\frac{\omega(G)}{2} + 1.$$

In a completely analogous manner it may be concluded that the effective order of the pole is not changed by the operation $\Delta(G_1) \ldots \Delta(G_m)$.

26.5. *Choice of the Operation* $\Delta(G)$

Having established the above important property we now undertake the specific choice of the operation $\Delta(G)$. We shall first of all investigate the case when the masses m_i of the particles of all the fields under consideration are greater than zero. As we have just shown the effective order of the pole of the expression $\Delta(G_1) \ldots \Delta(G_m) J_M(k)$ is equal in the α-representation to $\omega(G)/2+1$.

On the other hand, it follows from (26.16) and (26.18) that each differentiation with respect to the components of the momenta k_a lowers the order of the pole by $\frac{1}{2}$. Therefore by taking the partial derivative of the Nth order with respect to the components k_a

$$\frac{\partial^N J_M(\ldots k \ldots)}{\partial^{N_1} k_1 \ldots \partial^{N_m} k_m} \quad (\sum N_i = N),$$

we obtain an expression in which the effective order of the pole will be decreased by $N/2$ and will turn out to be equal to $(\omega(G) - N + 2)/2$. On choosing $N = \omega(G) + 1$ we shall obtain in the integrand the factor $d\lambda \cdot \lambda^{-1/2}$. However, since all our functions are rational functions of the variables α they must also be rational with respect to λ. Therefore the factor $\lambda^{-1/2}$ is in fact absent.

We now note that if from the function $J(\ldots k \ldots)$ we subtract the sum of all the leading terms of its expansion into Maclaurin's series up to terms of order $\omega(G)$ inclusive then the remaining term

$$J(\ldots k \ldots) - \{J(\ldots k \ldots)\}_{\omega(G)}$$

may be expressed according to the well-known Schloemilch formula in the form of an integral over partial derivatives of order $\omega(G) + 1$. Thus in the remaining term the effective order of the pole at $\lambda = 0$ is equal to zero.

We now define the operation $\Delta(G)$ in the following way:

$$\Delta(G) = -M(G)\left\{1 + \sum_{\left(\substack{2 \leq m \leq n-1 \\ G = G_1 * G_2 * \ldots * G_n}\right)} \frac{1}{m!} \Delta(G_1) \ldots \Delta(G_m)\right\} \quad (26.24)$$

where the operation $M(G)$ is defined by the relation

$$M(G)[\delta(\sum k)\, F(k)] = \delta(\sum k)\{F(k)\}_{\omega(G)}. \quad (26.25)$$

In view of (26.9) we have:

$$R(G)\, J_M(k) = \{1 - M(G)\}\, J'_M(k),$$

where

$$J'_M(k) = \left(1 + \sum_{\left(\substack{2 \leq m \leq n-1 \\ G = G_1 * \ldots * G_n}\right)} \frac{1}{m!} \Delta(G_1) \ldots \Delta(G_m)\right) J_M(k),$$

and since the singularity with respect to λ in J'_M is not higher than in J_M, then $R(G)\, J_M$ will have no singularity at all at the point $\lambda = 0$.

We have thus shown that the application of the last operation $\Delta(G)$ removes the singularities when all α tend to zero at the same rate. Since at the same time the operations $\Delta(G_1) \ldots \Delta(G_M)$ compensate for the singularities in those regions in which only some of the α tend to zero it is clear that $R(G)\,J_M$ *contains no singularities at all.*

This last statement forms the content of an important theorem whose proof, together with all the required estimates, was recently given by Parasiuk (89), (90).[49] This theorem states that after the operation $R(G)$ has been performed the function $J_m(k)$ may be written in the form

$$R(G)\,J_M(k) = \delta(\sum k)\int_0^\infty d\alpha_1 \ldots$$

$$\ldots\int_0^\infty d\alpha_L \prod_{1 \leq l \leq L} \{I(\alpha_l)\} \exp\,(-i\sum_l \alpha_l m_l^2 - \varepsilon \sum_l \alpha_l) f(\ldots k \ldots \alpha \ldots), \quad (26.26)$$

where the function $f(\ldots k \ldots \alpha \ldots)$ is expressed as a sum of terms of the form

$$F(\ldots k \ldots \alpha \ldots)\,\exp i \sum A_{ab}(\ldots \alpha \ldots)\,k_a' k_b';$$

here the k_a' are equal either to k_a or to zero, while F satisfies the inequality [50]

$$|\,F(\ldots k \ldots \alpha \ldots)| \leq \frac{c}{\prod_l (\alpha_l^{1-1/2L})}, \quad (26.27)$$

where L is the number of all the internal lines of diagram G while c is polynomially bounded with respect to the variables k and α.

From this estimate, it follows directly that in formula (26.25) we can go to the limit $M \to \infty$ for a fixed $\varepsilon > 0$. Indeed, the

[49] See also Bogoliubov and Parasiuk (18)–(20).

[50] The right-hand side of the inequality (26.27) is, as always, in such cases, too high, and yet it is quite adequate for our purposes, since it guarantees the absolute integrability of the function in the neighborhood of the points $\alpha_l = 0$. The fact that in the inequality (26.27) we did not succeed in preventing α_l from appearing in the denominator is connected not only with the roughness of the estimate, but also with the fact that when the different α_l tend to zero without preserving a constant ratio, but with some approaching zero faster than others, the manner in which the function increases may change.

factor $\exp(-\varepsilon\Sigma\alpha_l)$ makes the integral (26.26) absolutely convergent for large α, while for $\alpha \to 0$ any possible singularities will be of an integrable nature in accordance with (26.27).

Thus if we make the factors $I(\alpha)$ tend to unity in the process of removing the regularization we find that $R(G)\,J_M$ tends in the ordinary sense to the expression

$$R(G)\,J(k)$$
$$=\delta(\sum k)\int^{\infty} d\alpha_1 \ldots \int_0^{\infty} d\alpha_L \exp\,(-i\sum_l \alpha_l m_l^2 - \varepsilon\sum_l \alpha_l)\,f(\ldots k \ldots \alpha \ldots). \tag{26.28}$$

Here it is necessary to emphasize the arbitrariness in the choice of the operation $R(G)$. Indeed, in accordance with (26.25) the operation $M(G)$ amounts to the subtraction from F of a Maclaurin polynomial of a degree equal to the conventional rate of increase which turns out to be sufficient for the removal of infinities. It is quite evident that if, for example, we were to define the operation $M(G)$ by the subtraction from F of a Maclaurin polynomial of degree $n > \omega(G)$, we would also arrive at expressions containing no divergences. It may be shown that the arbitrariness connected with the choice of n actually amounts to a change in the Lagrangian. The minimum values $n = \omega(G)$ which we have chosen before lead to counter terms which differ least of all in their operator structure from the terms of the initial Lagrangian. However, such a choice is not inevitable.

26.6. *Transition to the Limit* $\varepsilon \to 0$

We now consider the analytic properties of the expression obtained above and the possibility of going to the limit as $\varepsilon \to 0$. By rotating the coordinate axes of the variables α by 90° in the complex plane, i.e., by introducing the change of variables

$$\alpha_k = -\,i\beta_k, \tag{26.29}$$

we write the integral (26.27) in the form

$$\int_0^{\infty} d\beta_1 \ldots \int_0^{\infty} d\beta_L\, F(\ldots k \ldots \beta)$$
$$\exp\,(-\sum_l \beta_l m_l^2 + i\varepsilon \sum_l \beta_l + \sum A_{ab}(\ldots \beta \ldots)\, k_a' k_b'). \tag{26.30}$$

By writing the exponent in the following form:

$$A = \sum A_{ab}(\ldots\beta\ldots)k_a^0 k_b^0 - \sum A_{ab}(\ldots\beta\ldots)\mathbf{k}_a\mathbf{k}_b - \sum \beta_l m_l^2 + i\varepsilon \sum \beta_l,$$

we find with the aid of condition (26.20)

$$A < \sum_l \beta_l (\sum_a k_a^0)^2 - \sum_l \beta_l m_l^2 + i\varepsilon \sum_l \beta_l.$$

It is now evident that when the condition

$$(\sum_a k_a^0)^2 < \min m_l^2 \tag{26.31}$$

is satisfied the form A turns out to be negative, the integral (26.30) absolutely convergent, and the transformation (26.29) permissible. In the resultant expression one may go to the limit $\varepsilon \to 0$ and obtain a function which is analytic in the region defined by the inequality (26.31). This inequality may be written in a relativistically invariant form:

$$|\sum_a (k_a \xi)|^2 < \min m_l^2,$$

where ξ is a timelike unit vector directed towards the future:

$$\xi^2 = 1, \qquad \xi^0 > 0.$$

In the procedure described above we first made $M \to \infty$ and then carried out the limiting transition $\varepsilon \to 0$. However, the rotation operation (26.29) could have been carried out before going to the limit $M \to \infty$. We would have then obtained a linear combination of integrals of type (26.30), which contain the masses M_i. If the transitions to the limits $M \to \infty$ and $\varepsilon \to 0$ are made simultaneously, the terms containing the masses M_i tend to zero and we obtain the same results. Therefore, in the case under consideration the point $k_a = 0$ turns out to be a regular one and expansions into Maclaurin's series are permissible. This is due to the fact that we have assumed that all the masses m_l are real and positive and that

$$\min m_l^2 > 0.$$

In the case when some of the masses are equal to zero the point $k_a = 0$ need not be a regular one. In such a case it may turn out that it is not permissible in defining the operation $\Delta(G)$

to carry out the expansion about the point $k_a = 0$, and the point about which the expansion is made may have to be chosen at a certain point (k^0, k) with a purely imaginary time component $k^0 = i\omega$. However, since the choice of some one particular point in momentum space (with the exception of the point $k = 0$) is not invariant from the point of view of four-dimensional rotations, the corresponding polynominal must in addition be averaged over the sphere

$$\omega^2 + \mathbf{k}^2 = \mu^2, \quad \text{where} \quad \mu^2 = \text{const.}$$

With such a choice of the operation $\Delta(G)$ the conclusions which we have reached above with respect to the properties of the coefficient functions obtained as a result of the operation $R(G)$ will evidently remain valid, with the one difference that the function will be analytic only for points k with purely imaginary k^0.

We now assume that the momenta k are completely arbitrary. As long as the masses have finite purely imaginary negative additional terms $-i\varepsilon$ the integrals will contain cutoff factors $\exp(-\varepsilon \Sigma_l \alpha_l)$ and the functions will be regular. As ε tends to zero these functions are convergent only in the improper sense. The limiting expressions obtained in this process which represent the true coefficient functions of T'-products turn out to be improper ones and may contain singularities for certain ranges of values of their arguments.

However, in view of their integrability properties the operator integrals

$$\int T'(\mathscr{L}(x_1) \ldots \mathscr{L}(x_n))\, g(x_1) \ldots g(x_n)\, dx_1 \ldots dx_n$$

turn out to be convergent for sufficiently regular functions $g(x)$ which fall off sufficiently rapidly at infinity and difficulties arise in the case of the limiting transition $g(x) \to 1$: the corresponding matrix elements of $S(1)$ turn out to be divergent. In such cases it is customary to speak of divergences of the infrared catastrophe type or of resonance denominators.

Singularities of the former type arise, as is well known, due to the inapplicability of the method of perturbation theory to the description of processes involving quanta of very low energy, and may be eliminated from the results by the Bloch-Nordsieck (12) method or by introducing into the photon D_0^c-functions of a small constant which plays the role of a "photon mass."

Singularities of the latter type arise, for example, in the case when a higher order scattering process may be reduced for given values of the momenta to simpler independent lower order processes.

It should be noted that divergences of both these types manifest themselves also in ordinary quantum mechanics in those cases when it is not permissible to use perturbation theory. We take this occasion to emphasize that the condition of integrability of the operator functions $S_n'(x_1, \ldots, x_n)$ guarantees only the absence of divergences characteristic of quantum field theory, i.e., divergences "for large values of the momenta."

We have formulated above the prescription for constructing integrable coefficient functions for the operators $S_n(x_1, \ldots, x_n)$. We now note that the introduction of the regularized causal functions

$$\Delta^c \to \text{reg}\, \Delta^c$$

was of a purely auxiliary nature in our argument and was needed by us essentially only to show that the expressions obtained for S_n satisfy all the requirements imposed on the terms in the expansion of the scattering matrix. In practice, for example, in evaluating the above coefficient functions one could just as well make use of the "true" Δ^c-functions. Then in going to the α-representation one may apply the operation $R(G)$ by excluding from the region of integration over α only a small neighborhood of the point $\alpha = 0$.

26.7. *Generalization of the Prescription for the Construction of* $\Delta(G)$

The preceding method for the construction of the operation $\Delta(G)$ involves a certain degree of arbitrariness which consists of making the expansion about the point $k = 0$ (in the case when all $m_i \neq 0$) or of fixing the "radius" μ of the four-dimensional sphere over which an average is taken (in the case when some of the m_i are equal to zero). Therefore the operation $\Delta(G)$ must be somewhat generalized.

With this in mind, we consider a system of finite polynomials

$$Z'_G(\ldots k \ldots)$$

of degree not higher than $\omega(G)$ such that the expressions

$$Z'_G(\ldots k \ldots)\,\delta(\sum k)$$

are momentum representations of the coefficient functions of certain Hermitean, covariant, quasilocal operators $\Lambda'(\ldots x \ldots)$. The most general expression for the operation $\Delta(G)$ may now be obtained by defining it as the sum of the operation (26.24) introduced earlier and the operation of adding the polynomial Z'_G, i.e.,

$$\begin{aligned}\Delta(G)\,J_G(\ldots k \ldots) \\ = -M(G)\left\{1 + \sum_{\substack{2\leq m\leq n-1 \\ (G=G_1 * \ldots * G_m)}} \frac{1}{m!}\Delta(G_1)\ldots\Delta(G_m)\right\} J_G(\ldots k \ldots) \\ + Z'_G(\ldots k \ldots)\,\delta(\sum k).\end{aligned} \tag{26.32}$$

The most general expression for the operator S_n which corresponds to (26.32) differs from the one obtained earlier by the inclusion of the Hermitean covariant quasilocal operators Λ'_n. But, as we have already established earlier, the addition to S_n of certain Λ'_n may be taken into account by changing the effective interaction Lagrangian. Thus the change in the prescription for constructing integrable coefficient functions is equivalent to adding new finite counter terms to the effective Lagrangian. It is therefore possible to consider that the definition of the T'-product remains as before, but that the choice of the Lagrangian contains a degree of arbitrariness. This arbitrariness consists of the possibility of including in $\mathscr{L}(x)$ terms which correspond to quasilocal operators of type (18.37) associated with generalized strongly connected vertices G of nonnegative index $\omega(G)$.

Thus we have obtained the following *general prescription* for obtaining the operator functions $S_n(x_1, \ldots, x_n)$. One takes the coefficient function of the ordinary T-product for some G and transforms it into the "α-representation." By temporarily excluding an infinitesimal neighborhood of the points $\alpha_l = 0$ one applies the operation

$$R(G) = 1 + \sum_{\substack{2 \leqq m \leqq n-1 \\ G = G_1 * \ldots * G_m}} \frac{1}{m!} \Delta(G_1) \ldots \Delta(G_m) + \Delta(G),$$

in which $\Delta(G_j)$ contain the terms Z'_{G_j}, and after this the region in the neighborhood of the points $\alpha_l = 0$ is included in the integral. The improper transition to the limit $\varepsilon \to 0$ in the resulting expressions then gives the desired coefficient functions of the operators S_n.

§ 27. Analytic Properties of the Coefficient Functions in the Momentum Representation

27.1. *Analytic Properties of* S_n

In the preceding section it was established that the coefficient functions S_n of the scattering matrix in the momentum representation are analytic functions within the range of values of the momenta k_a for which

$$\sum_a k_a^0 < \min m_l \tag{27.1}$$

after carrying out the transition to the limit $\varepsilon \to 0$.

We may therefore consider that the functions S_n obtained after the divergences have been removed are defined as analytic functions of their arguments in the region determined by the inequality (27.1), while the values of the functions S_n outside this region may be obtained by means of analytic continuation which consists of adding to all the masses m_l which correspond to internal lines infinitesimal purely imaginary negative terms

$$m_l \to m_l - i\varepsilon_l. \tag{27.2}$$

We shall now show that by means of a different variant of analytic continuation it is possible to obtain from S_n the coefficient functions H_n (see 18.11) which, as will be shown in Chapter VI, are required for the construction of the special operator $H(x; g)$ which plays the role of the Hamiltonian in our theory.

27.2. *Structure of the Functions* H_n

We consider the functions $H_n(x, x_1, \ldots, x_n)$; according to (18.12) they may be simply expressed in terms of the coefficient functions of the scattering matrix $S_\nu(x_1, \ldots, x_\nu)$, i.e., the operator structure of H_n is completely determined by the operator structure of S_{n+1}. Indeed, it follows from (18.12) that among the coefficient functions H_n, there will appear first, the coefficient functions S_{n+1}, and second, terms which correspond to products of the type

$$S_{k+1}(x, x_1, \ldots, x_n)\, S^{\dagger}_{n-k}(x_{k+1}, \ldots, x_n). \tag{27.3}$$

By evaluating (27.3) and by bringing the product of the field operators to the normal form we shall obtain a sum of terms which agree with $S_{n+1}(x, x_1, \ldots, x_n)$ in their operator structure, but which differ from them by the various different replacements of the D^c functions by the $D^{(-)}$ functions for the internal lines connecting points from different sets $(x, x_1, \ldots, x_k)$ and $(x_{k+1}, \ldots, x_n)$. Thus the operator structure of H_n is in fact determined by the Feynman diagram for S_{n+1}.

Let us consider in somewhat greater detail the coefficient functions obtained above. First of all, let us show that the coefficient functions corresponding to unconnected diagrams are equal to zero. Let us assume that the parts of the diagram containing the points $(x, \ldots, x_a, \ldots,)$ and $(\ldots, x_b, \ldots)$ are not connected. The corresponding coefficient function of the operator H_n has the form

$$K^H(x, \ldots, x_a, \ldots, x_b, \ldots) = \sum_i Q_i(x, \ldots, x_a, \ldots)\, Q'_i(\ldots, x_b, \ldots),$$

where Q_i and Q'_i are invariant under translation. By displacing the arguments of Q_i by an amount ξ such that $x^0 + \xi^0 > x^0_b$ we obtain in virtue of the property (18.13)

$$K^H(x, \ldots, x_a, \ldots, x_b, \ldots) = K^H(x + \xi, \ldots, x_a + \xi, \ldots, x_b, \ldots) = 0.$$

Therefore we shall in future consider only connected diagrams.

We go over to the momentum representation

$$\int K(x, x_1, \ldots, x_n) \exp i(px + \sum_{j=1}^{n} p_j x_j)\, dx\, dx_1 \ldots dx_n$$
$$= \delta(p + \sum_j p_j) K(p_1, \ldots, p_n),$$

where

$$K(p_1, \ldots, p_n) = \int K(x, x_1, \ldots, x_n) \exp i\left(\sum_j p_j(x_j - x)\right) dx_1 \ldots dx_n \tag{27.4}$$

is a certain improper function of the momenta $p_1, \ldots, p_n$.

27.3. *Analytic Properties of the Functions H_n*

We consider the variables p_l to be complex and represent them in the form

$$p_l = \nu_l + i\Gamma_l,$$

where ν and Γ are real four-vectors. Then in place of (27.4) we may evidently write:

$$K(p_1, \ldots, p_n)$$
$$= \int K(x, x_1, \ldots, x_n) g'(x_1) \ldots g'(x_n) \exp i\left(\sum_l \nu_l(x_l - x)\right) dx_1 \ldots dx_n,$$

where

$$g'(x_l) = \exp\left[-\Gamma_l(x_l - x)\right].$$

It may now be seen that if one chooses for Γ_l a four-vector directed along the positive time-axis:

$$\Gamma = (\Gamma^0, 0, 0, 0), \qquad \Gamma^0 > 0,$$

then for $x_l^0 \to \infty$ the function g will tend to zero exponentially, and since the integration is carried out over the region $x_l^0 > x^0$ the integral (27.4) will turn out to be convergent and the function $K(p_1, \ldots, p_n)$ will turn out to be regular for $p_l = \nu_l + i\Gamma_l$. It is clear that the same will be true if for Γ_l we choose a timelike four-vector directed towards the future. In the preceding the function $K(p_1, \ldots, p_n)$ may be regarded for real values of p_l as the improper limit of a regular function for $\Gamma_l \to 0$. In other words the function $K(p_1, \ldots, p_n)$ turns out to be analytic in the region

$$p_l = \nu_l + i\varepsilon_l \Gamma,$$

where ν_l is a real four-vector, ε_l is a real positive parameter, while Γ is a timelike four-vector directed towards the future.

We shall now show that when condition (27.1) is satisfied

the coefficient functions of the operators H_n will also be analytic and will coincide with the coefficient functions of S_{n+1}. In § 26 it was shown that the function S_{n+1} is regular in the region defined by condition (27.1). Therefore it is sufficient to show that the products (27.3) will give no contribution to H_n in this region.[51] The corresponding coefficient functions have the form

$$\int Q(\ldots, k_a - \sum \lambda, \ldots)\,\delta(\sum k_a - \sum \lambda)\,Q'(\ldots, k_b + \sum \lambda, \ldots)$$
$$\times\,\delta(\sum k_b + \sum \lambda)\prod \{Z_{\alpha\beta}(\lambda_{\alpha\beta})\,\theta(-\lambda^0_{\alpha\beta})\,\delta(\lambda^2_{\alpha\beta} - m^2_{\alpha\beta})\,d\lambda_{\alpha\beta}\}.$$

From the conditions $\lambda^0_{\alpha\beta} < 0$ and $\lambda^0_{\alpha\beta} = m^2_{\alpha\beta}$ it follows that

$$-\sum \lambda^0_i \geqq m_i;$$

on the other hand we have

$$\sum |\,k\,| \leqq \min m,$$

therefore one of the two requirements:

$$\sum k^0_a - \sum \lambda^0 = 0, \qquad \sum k^0_b + \sum \lambda^0 = 0,$$

will always turn out not to be satisfied, the contribution of (27.3) will in fact turn out to be zero, and H_n will turn out to coincide with S_{n+1} which is analytic. Remembering that by means of adding to the masses small purely imaginary negative terms (27.2) we had obtained functions S_n analytic in the whole plane of the momentum variables, we obtain the following prescription for the construction of the coefficient functions of the operator H_n from the coefficient functions of the operator S_{n+1}.

We consider the operator S_{n+1} which corresponds to a certain (necessarily connected) diagram. The coefficient functions of this operator will be analytic for small momenta. Analytic continuation of these expressions for large momenta with the aid of the replacement (27.2) will again lead us to the coefficient functions of the operator S_{n+1}. In order to obtain the coefficient functions of the operator H_n one should carry out the analytic continuation for large momenta by making use of the substitution

[51] In the case when the minimum mass is equal to zero (the electromagnetic field), it may be taken equal to some small quantity κ for purposes of this section. Such an operation does not lead to any contradictions.

$$p_j^0 \to p_j^0 + i\Gamma^0. \tag{27.5}$$

We have considered the connection between the coefficient functions of the operators

$$S(g) \text{ and } H(x;\, g) = i\frac{\delta S(g)}{\delta g(x)} S^\dagger(g).$$

As was pointed out in § 17, in the case when the auxiliary functional argument is introduced not in the form of an "intensity of interaction" g but in the form of a classical external field u, the operator

$$i\frac{\delta S(u)}{\delta u(x)} S^\dagger(u)$$

will also possess the property of causality (17.31) in view of which its coefficient functions will be related in a similar manner to the coefficient functions of the matrix $S(u)$. It turns out that the analytic relationship between $S(u)$ and $i[\delta S(u)/\delta u(x)]\, S^\dagger(u)$ in the case of arbitrary introduction of the field u may be established for these operators as a whole without making use of their functional decomposition. This will be shown in Chapter IX.

§ 28. Classification of the Renormalizability of Different Theories

28.1. *Interactions of the First and Second Kinds*

As we have shown in the preceding section, the change in the effective interaction Lagrangian due to the introduction into it of counter terms depends on the presence of strongly connected diagrams G with a nonnegative index $\omega(G)$. Let us consider the relation between the structure of such diagrams and the structure of the corresponding counter terms in the x-representation.

If the above diagram unites n vertices and contains s external lines then the corresponding quasilocal operator will have the form

$$:u_{\alpha_1}(x_{i_1}) \ldots u_{\alpha_s}(x_{i_s}): Z\left(\ldots\frac{\partial}{\partial x}\ldots\right) \delta(x_1 - x_2) \ldots \delta(x_{n-1} - x_n),$$

with the degree of the polynomial Z being equal to the index of the diagram $\omega(G)$. Integrating this over all the variables x_i

except one we shall obtain the counter term of the Lagrangian. In carrying out these trivial integrations the derivatives will be transferred from the δ-functions to the field operators u and the result of the integration will take on the form of a normal product of a certain number of operator field functions and their derivatives. In the preceding the total order of all the derivatives turns out to be equal to the index of the diagram $\omega(G)$ while the "degree" of the whole expression with respect to the operator functions turns out to be equal to the number of external lines s.

Therefore if a given theory (completely determined by the fundamental ("initial") term of the interaction Lagrangian and by the structure of the causal functions) leads to strongly connected diagrams of nonnegative index for which the numbers $\omega(G)$ and s turn out to be bounded, then for the complete removal of all the divergences such a theory will require the introduction of counter terms of a finite number of types. In speaking of the counter term type we have in mind its operator type and the order of the derivatives of each field operator. In the opposite case the number of different types of counter terms turns out to be infinite.

We shall now analyze the dependence of the indices $\omega(G)$ on the number of external and internal lines of a diagram. In order to do this we introduce the concept of the index of a vertex by defining it by means of the equation

$$\omega_i = \frac{1}{2} \sum_{l_{\text{int}}} (r_l + 2) - 4, \tag{28.1}$$

where the summation is taken over all the internal lines entering the ith vertex. It may be easily seen that the index of the diagram is expressed in terms of the indices of the vertex parts of the diagram in the following way:

$$\omega(G) = \sum_{1 \leq i \leq n} \omega_i + 4, \tag{28.2}$$

since each internal line enters simultaneously into two different vertices. For a given vertex type the index ω_i will take on its maximum value $\omega_i^{\max}$ in the case when all the lines entering the vertex turn out to be internal lines. If

$$\omega_i^{\max} \leqq 0, \tag{28.3}$$

then it follows from (28.2) that

$$\omega(G) \leqq 4.$$

Conversely, if for some vertex types

$$\omega_i^{\max} > 0, \tag{28.4}$$

then it is always possible to construct such a diagram G containing a sufficiently large number of vertices of this type to make $\omega(G)$ larger than any number specified in advance. Thus the index of a diagram either does not exceed four, or it may be made arbitrarily large.

Taking into account the fact that

$$\omega_i = \omega_i^{\max} - \tfrac{1}{2} \sum_{l_{\text{ext}}} (r_l + 2),$$

where l_{ext} are the indices of the external lines entering a given vertex, the dependence of $\omega(G)$ on the number of external lines may be written in the form

$$\omega(G) = \sum_i \omega_i^{\max} + 4 - \tfrac{1}{2} \sum_{l_{\text{ext}}} (r_l + 2); \tag{28.5}$$

where the summation in the last term is taken over all the external lines of the given diagram.

Therefore in case (28.3) the number of external lines in a diagram with a positive index does not exceed four. In this case both quantities $\omega(G)$ and s are bounded by the number 4, the number of types of corresponding counter terms turns out to be finite and may be subjected to detailed classification. In case (28.4) holds both sums on the right-hand side of formula (28.5) may be made arbitrarily large for nonnegative $\omega(G)$. Both characteristics $\omega(G)$ and s turn out to be unbounded, and in order to compensate for the divergences of increasing order, it is necessary to introduce counter terms with an increasing degree of "linearity" and an increasing number of derivatives. It is not possible to obtain a closed expression for the total effective Lagrangian.

In accordance with the above properties the types of interaction may be divided into two classes: (a) interactions of the *first kind* (all $\omega_i \leqq 0$); and (b) interactions of *the second kind* (some $\omega_i > 0$). The corresponding theories are said to be *renormalizable* and *nonrenormalizable* respectively.

One essential qualification must be made with respect to the above definition. The point is that in certain cases individual vertex factors may mutually compensate one another and thereby lower the effective value of ω_i. Let us consider, for example, the interaction of the ordinary fermion field (spin $\frac{1}{2}$) with a neutral vector meson field of the type

$$\sum_n : \bar{\psi}(x)\,\gamma^n\,\psi(x)\,\varphi_n(x) : . \tag{28.6}$$

A direct calculation of ω_i, making use of the fact that the pairing of the vector field in the p-representation has the form

$$\frac{g^{mn} - (k^m k^n)/m^2}{k^2 - m^2}$$

and that consequently the r_l in this case are equal to 2, will evidently give us $\omega_i = 1$ and will lead us to classify the Lagrangian (28.6) as nonrenormalizable. However, it may be shown that in actual fact the Lagrangian (28.6) describes an interaction of the first type. In order to show this, following Stueckelberg (119), we shall decompose the vector field into a transverse and a longitudinal part:

$$\varphi_n(x) = \Phi_n(x) + \frac{1}{m}\frac{\partial B}{\partial x^n},$$

with the corresponding pairings

$$\overbrace{\Phi_n(x)\,\Phi_m(y)} \sim i g^{mn},$$

$$\overbrace{\frac{\partial B(x)}{\partial x^n}\,\frac{\partial B(y)}{\partial y^m}} \sim -\,k^m k^n.$$

We now recall that the scattering matrix S depends not on the Lagrangian density $\mathscr{L}(x)$ but on the integral $\int \mathscr{L}(x)dx$ as a whole. Substituting the above decomposition into this integral we obtain:

$$\int \mathscr{L}(x)dx = \sum_n \int : \bar{\psi}(x)\,\gamma^n\,\psi(x)\,\Phi_n(x) : dx + \frac{1}{m}\sum_n \int : \bar{\psi}(x)\,\gamma^n\,\psi(x)\,\frac{\partial B}{\partial x^n} : dx.$$

Making use of the law of conservation of spinor flux (or more accurately of the equation of continuity), which is not violated by the presence of neutral mesons,

$$\sum_n \frac{\partial}{\partial x^n} : j^n(x) : = \sum_n \frac{\partial}{\partial x^n} : \bar{\psi}(x)\, \gamma^n\, \psi(x) : = 0,$$

we find by integrating the second term by parts that it is equal to zero, i.e.,

$$\int \mathcal{L}(x)\, dx = \sum_n \int : \bar{\psi}(x)\, \gamma^n\, \psi(x)\, \Phi_n(x) : dx.$$

Therefore the longitudinal field $\partial B/\partial x^n$ in fact drops out from the S-matrix, the effective values of r_l and of the vertex index ω_i are reduced to zero and the Lagrangian (28.6) turns out to be renormalizable.

Similar questions of the "effective change of pairings" under canonical transformations of the gauge transformation type will be specially discussed below after we have examined the conditions of the conservation of charge and of gauge invariance which we have not touched so far.

Without at present going into details of these very special cases of compensation of singularities whose existence is due to a certain group of transformations we shall now give a general classification of the simplest Lagrangians similar to those which were introduced in § 8.

28.2. *List of Interactions of the First Kind*

In determining the corresponding indices $\omega_i^{\max}$ we shall take into account the fact that in accordance with the general structure of the commutation and causal functions, the degree of the polynomial r_l for the scalar field and for the vector field of zero mass (the electromagnetic field) with scalar coupling is equal to zero, for a spinor field of spin $\frac{1}{2}$ is equal to unity, for a vector field (with $m \neq 0$) with scalar coupling is equal to two. In the case of gradient coupling we find with the aid of formula (19.11) that r_l is equal to two for the scalar and for the electromagnetic field, and to four for the vector field.

As it was previously noted, the number of external lines in strongly connected diagrams with a nonnegative index cannot exceed four. Therefore the maximum degree of linearity of an interaction Lagrangian of the first kind is equal to four. From the formula

$$\omega_i^{\max} = \tfrac{1}{2} \sum_l (r_l + 2) - 4, \tag{28.7}$$

where the summation is taken over all the lines leaving a given vertex we find that all four lines must have the index $r_l = 0$, i.e., only a four-fold product of scalar fields and of electromagnetic fields

$$:\varphi_{\alpha_1}\varphi_{\alpha_2}\varphi_{\alpha_3}\varphi_{\alpha_4}:, \quad :\varphi_{\alpha_1}\varphi_{\alpha_2}A_k A_k:, \quad :A_k A_k A_l A_l: \tag{28.8}$$

describes an interaction of the first kind. All other four-fold interactions, for example, such as the four-fold Fermi interaction of spinor operator functions

$$(\bar{\psi}_{\alpha_1} O \psi_{\alpha_2})(\bar{\psi}_{\alpha_3} O \psi_{\alpha_4}) \qquad (\omega_i = 2),$$

the four-fold interactions including derivatives and vector field functions, for example,

$$:\varphi_{\alpha_1}\varphi_{\alpha_2}\frac{\partial \varphi_{\alpha_3}}{\partial x^k} A_k: \qquad (\omega_i = 1),$$

$$:\varphi_{\alpha_1}\varphi_{\alpha_2} U^k U^k: \qquad (\omega_i = 2),$$

represent interactions of the second kind.

Cubic terms in a Lagrangian of the first kind may evidently have the following structure: (a) a product of three scalar and electromagnetic functions without derivatives:

$$:\varphi_{\alpha_1}\varphi_{\alpha_2}\varphi_{\alpha_3}:, \quad :\varphi_{\alpha_1}A_k A_k: \quad (\omega_i = -1) \tag{28.9}$$

(the other combinations do not form a scalar); (b) a product of three scalar and electromagnetic functions with one first derivative:

$$:\varphi_{\alpha_1}\frac{\partial \varphi_{\alpha_2}}{\partial x^k} A_k: \qquad (\omega_i = 0); \tag{28.10}$$

the interaction of charged scalar mesons with the electromagnetic field (scalar electrodynamics) is of this type; (c) a product of one scalar, one vector, and one electromagnetic function:

$$\sum_{k} :\varphi_\alpha \varphi_\beta^k A_k: \qquad (\omega_i = 0); \tag{28.11}$$

(d) a product of two spinor functions and one scalar or electromagnetic function:

$$\sum_{\alpha,\beta} :\bar{\psi}_\alpha M_{\alpha\beta} \psi_\beta \varphi:, \quad \sum_{\alpha,\beta,k} :\bar{\psi}_\alpha \Gamma^k_{\alpha\beta} \psi_\beta A_k: \qquad (\omega_i = 0). \tag{28.12}$$

All the other cubic interactions, such as the interaction of a spinor field with the scalar field of the gradient coupling type

$$\sum_{\alpha,\beta,k} :\bar{\psi}_\alpha \Gamma^k_{\alpha\beta} \psi_\beta \frac{\partial \varphi}{\partial x^k}: \qquad (\omega_i = 1),$$

lead to nonrenormalizable theories.[52]

The nine Lagrangians (28.8)–(28.12) listed above exhaust all possible types of interactions of the first kind [53] since the quadratic forms which satisfy equation (28.3) correspond to vertices which are entered by two lines. Such forms do not describe processes of mutual transformation of particles and therefore represent only the possible types of counter terms.

The division of Lagrangians into interactions of the first and second kind which we have carried out above is in fact not sufficiently consistent. It was made from the point of view of the convergence of the individual terms of the expansion of the S-matrix into a series in powers of the coupling constant. It is quite possible that after the summation of such a series has been carried out the analytic nature of the functions under investigation will be altered and this will affect the above classification.

Therefore the following problem arises — without making use of perturbation theory to determine which interactions belong to the first kind and which to the second kind. In other words, the question arises as to what kind of Lagrangians of local type will enable us to construct a closed theory. The importance of this problem is due to the fact that, as we shall now show, there

[52] Not counting the Lagrangian (28.6).

[53] In fact their number is restricted even further by the charge and by the gauge invariance (see following).

is an essential physical difference between theories of the first kind and of the second kind.

28.3. *Nonlocal Nature of Interactions of the Second Kind*

We shall consider in greater detail the properties of the interactions of the second kind. As we have already seen, among the infinite number of types of counter terms arising in such theories there exist groups of terms of the same operator type but with infinitely increasing orders of derivatives. Such theories involving derivatives of infinitely increasing order in fact represent expansions of certain nonlocal expressions and therefore essentially represent nonlocal interactions.

For example, the Lagrangian for the pseudovector meson-nucleon coupling

$$:\bar{\psi}\gamma^5\gamma^k\psi\frac{\partial\varphi}{\partial x^k}:$$

requires the introduction into the effective Lagrangian of an infinite number of counter terms of the form

$$C_{\alpha_1,\ldots,\alpha_n}:\bar{\psi}\gamma^5\gamma^k\psi\frac{\partial^n}{(\partial x^\alpha)^n}\left(\frac{\partial\varphi}{\partial x^k}\right):,$$

whose sum may be regarded as the expansion of the nonlocal expression

$$\int:\bar{\psi}(x)\gamma^5\gamma^k\psi(x)\frac{\partial\varphi(y)}{\partial y^k}:K(x-y)\,dy$$

into a series involving derivatives of ever increasing order of the function φ.

Thus in the case of interactions of the second type the localizability of the effective Lagrangian in fact disappears and the Lagrangian begins to depend on the behavior of the field functions not only within an infinitesimal neighborhood of the point x. It turns out that independently of the smallness of the coupling constant higher-order terms become important for sufficiently large momenta. Indeed, it follows from dimensional considerations that the counter term containing n derivatives is proportional to the factor l^n where l is a small parameter of the dimensions of length ("universal length") polynomially related to the coupling constant. In the p-representation the derivatives $\partial/\partial x$ are changed into momenta and we obtain an expansion in powers of

$$pl = l/\lambda, \tag{28.13}$$

where

$$\lambda = 1/p$$

is the Compton wave length. For sufficiently large p the quantity λ becomes comparable with the universal length l and the parameter (28.13) of the expansion of the nonlocal Lagrangian into a series involving derivatives ceases to be small. In this case the universal length l is a characteristic of the physical "smearing-out" of the particle, and its appearance indicates the importance of the influence of the inner structure of the particle.

We conclude that the interaction Lagrangians of the second kind apparently represent "fragments" of nonlocalized interactions represented in localized form. For a consistent construction of such theories it is necessary from the outset to start with a nonlocal Lagrangian which takes into account the internal structure of the elementary particles. From this it follows that there is a deep physical difference between interactions of the first and the second kind.

The following question then becomes of interest: do all the interactions which occur in nature belong to the first kind? [54] We emphasize that a sufficiently well-founded answer to this question may be obtained only by comparing experimental results with calculations which are not based on perturbation theory.

At the present moment it is completely unclear, for example, whether the interactions which we have classified as belonging to the first kind on the basis of perturbation theory are in fact interactions of the first kind.

In the case that at least some of the actual interactions should turn out to belong to the second kind, the question of the internal

[54] In this connection see, for example, the article by Umezawa (128).

structure of elementary particles and of a consistent description of the interactions between them by means of nonlocal Lagrangians would become important. In view of the interrelationships between all the particles it will turn out in such a case that even if some of the interactions between them taken separately belong to the first kind, nevertheless the complete description of any kind of particles must necessarily turn out to be of a nonlocal character.

Since at the present moment there exist in fact no methods for the investigation of nonlocal interactions in quantum field theory, in accordance with the above remarks we shall not go at all into this second possibility, but we shall assume that all the actually occurring interactions belong to the first kind.

28.4. *Specification of a Theory of the First Kind by a Finite Number of Constants*

Let us now perform a more careful analysis of the various possibilities for constructing theories of the first kind. As we established earlier, the possible types of terms in the effective interaction Lagrangian are restricted to a finite number of terms of the fourth, third, and second order in the field operators. Therefore, in the theories of the first kind, the choice of the interaction Lagrangian is reduced to the choice of *a finite number* of "coupling constants." The number of independent constants among them is reduced as a result of taking into account the requirements of gauge invariance, conservation of charge and invariance with respect to charge conjugation. In order to specify a theory completely, it is naturally also necessary to specify the masses of the particles in the absence of interactions. Thus, any theory of the first kind is completely characterized by a finite set of numbers: the masses of the fictitious noninteracting particles, and the coupling constants. In our variant of the theory the fundamental quantity in addition to the Lagrangians of the free particles which fix the properties of the noninteracting field is the interaction Lagrangian $\mathscr{L}(x)$. As we have seen, by choosing $\mathscr{L}(x)$ in the usual way and by means of redefining the T-product it is possible to obtain integrable expressions for the terms of the S-matrix:

$$S_n(x_1, \ldots, x_n) = i^n T'(\mathscr{L}(x_1) \ldots \mathscr{L}(x_n)).$$

Although the set of prescriptions for the construction of the operator T' is not unique, the arbitrariness contained in it corresponds to a finite change in the coupling constants of the interaction Lagrangian, i.e., to the addition to the initial Lagrangian $\mathscr{L}(x)$ of finite counter terms of the same type as the terms occurring in a permissible effective Lagrangian of the first kind. Therefore, in order to make the calculations completely unambiguous, it is necessary to specify $\mathscr{L}(x)$ in a manner appropriate to the fixed set of prescriptions for the construction of the T'-product.

On the other hand, as we have seen, a completely equivalent result is obtained if instead of redefining the T-product one uses the usual T-product (with some form of auxiliary regularization in the intermediate stages of the argument), but instead of $\mathscr{L}(x)$ one employs a certain effective interaction Lagrangian $\mathscr{L}_{\text{eff}}$ which contains, in addition to the initial interaction Lagrangian, divergent counter terms which compensate for the divergences in the usual T-products. From the point of view of the S-matrix the situation is that as if, in place of the initial complete Lagrangian

$$\mathscr{L}_0(x) + \mathscr{L}(x)$$

we had the Lagrangian

$$\mathscr{L}_{\text{tot}} = \mathscr{L}_0 + \mathscr{L}_{\text{eff}}.$$

The "masses" and the "charges" occurring in it, i.e., the coefficients of the appropriate operator combinations, diverge; nevertheless the observable quantities calculated with their aid (including masses, charges, etc.) have finite values.

In this way we arrive at the so-called "renormalization" point of view, when in order to obtain finite values for the observables being calculated one introduces into the Lagrangian infinite "bare" masses, charges, etc. It is then said that the removal of infinities from the theory is attained by means of a "renormalization" of the fundamental constants. The renormalizing factors contain divergent expressions.

However, such a point of view is not carried through sufficiently consistently since one has to add to $\mathscr{L}_{\text{tot}}$ such counter terms the introduction of which does not reduce to a renormalization of the fundamental quantities (for example, in the case of spinor electrodynamics the obviously nongauge-invariant terms involving the photon mass[55] and the term $(\partial A_m/\partial x^m)^2$, the fourfold terms in meson theories, etc.). Moreover as we have seen in § 26, the structure of the counter terms changes when we investigate the generalized scattering matrix $S(g)$ and turns out to depend on the behavior of the function $g(x)$. As will be shown, it is the matrix $S(g)$ which determines the effective Hamiltonian of the system. Therefore it may be said that counter terms have to be introduced for the regularization of the Schrödinger equation which differ from those that are needed for the regularization of the S-matrix.

In view of all this we do not adhere to the "renormalization" terminology, but regard the procedure of introducing counter terms as a formal device which guarantees that the results of the calculations should be finite.

[55] When the nongauge-invariant method of regularization is used similar to the one employed in § 24.2.

CHAPTER V

Application of the General Theory of the Removal of Divergences to Special Cases

§ 29. Scalar Field with Nonlinear Interaction

29.1. *The Hurst-Thirring Field*

In the preceding chapter the general method of regularization used in the quantum theory of interaction was presented in detail. We now proceed to apply this method to various combinations of interacting wave fields.

In this section we shall examine the simplest case of a real scalar nonlinear field. We shall take the nonlinear term in the Lagrangian in the form due to Hurst (62) and Thirring (125)

$$\lambda\varphi^3(x).$$

This term in the total Lagrangian

$$\mathscr{L}_{\text{tot}}(x) = \tfrac{1}{2}\sum_n g^{nn} : \left(\frac{\partial\varphi}{\partial x^n}\right)^2 : -\frac{m}{2} : \varphi^2(x) : + \lambda : \varphi^3(x) : \qquad (29.1)$$

may be regarded as the interaction of the field φ with itself, i.e., as a "self-interaction"

$$\mathscr{L}_{\text{int}}(x) = \mathscr{L}(x) = \lambda : \varphi^3(x) :. \qquad (29.2)$$

Starting with expression (29.2) it is now possible to construct the S-matrix and the Schrödinger equation and to give a description of the Hurst-Thirring field along lines similar to the description of interacting fields.

Let us emphasize from the outset that the wave field defined by the Lagrangian (29.1) is of a purely fictitious nature, but its study is of definite methodological interest; since the Lagrangian (29.2) is the simplest one from the analytic point of view, and the description of the given field within the framework of the theory of interactions is based on the single simplest causal function of the scalar field

$$D^c(x) = \frac{1}{(2\pi)^4} \int \frac{e^{ikx}}{m^2 - k^2 - i\varepsilon} dk. \tag{29.3}$$

29.2. *Finiteness of the Number of Divergent Diagrams*

We shall now carry out a classification of the diagrams leading to divergent matrix elements in accordance with the general prescription of § 28. From the structure of the "interaction" Lagrangian (29.2) it follows that in the corresponding Feynman diagrams three identical lines meet at each vertex.

Since the degree of the polynomial in the numerator of the causal function (29.3) is equal to zero we find from (28.1) that the maximum vertex index is negative:

$$\omega_i^{\max} = -1 \tag{29.4}$$

and the Lagrangian (29.2) therefore belongs to the renormalizable type. Formula (28.5) now allows us to carry out a complete classification of the divergent diagrams.

We begin our discussion with the vacuum diagrams ($l_{\text{ext}} = 0$) which in the present case always contain an even number of vertices. It follows from (28.5) that the index of the vacuum diagrams is nonnegative only for $i = 2$ and $i = 4$. In the first case the situation corresponds to the diagram shown in Fig. 28

Fig. 28.

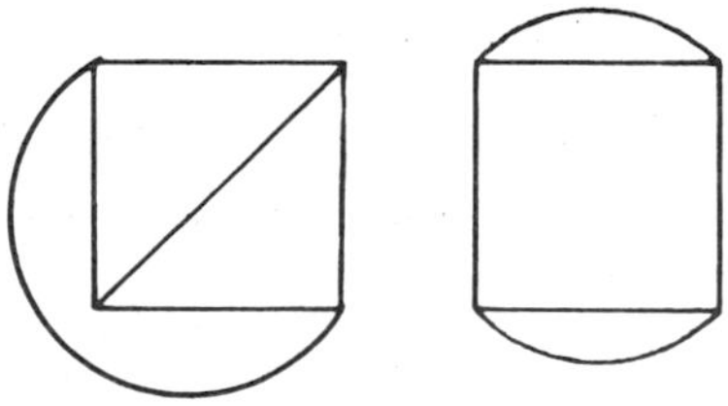

Fig. 29.

where $\omega(G) = 2$ and we obtain a quadratic divergence, in the second case (Fig. 29) $\omega(G) = 0$ and the divergence is of a logarithmic nature.

In the case when the diagram has one external line ($l_{\text{ext}} = 1$) the number of vertices in our case (29.2) is always odd. There are no diagrams with one vertex and one external line, while the diagram with three vertices ($i = 3$) shown in Fig. 30 already leads to a logarithmic divergence $(\omega(G) = 0)$. There are no other divergences in the case $l_{\text{ext}} = 1$.

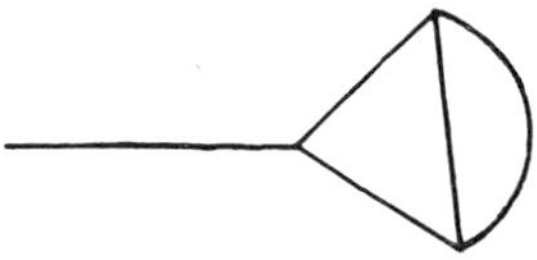

Fig. 30.

Fig. 31.

Finally, the only divergent diagram with two external lines is the two-vertex diagram (Fig. 31). Its index is equal to zero and the corresponding divergence is logarithmic.

The diagrams shown in Figs. 28–31 exhaust all the divergent diagrams of the Hurst-Thirring field. We note that the existence of a finite number of divergent diagrams is an important distinguishing characteristic of the Lagrangian (29.2). As we shall see later, in other theories divergent diagrams exist, as a rule, in arbitrarily high orders of the coupling constant and their total number turns out to be infinite. In the present case divergences exist only in the second, third, and fourth orders. Therefore the corresponding regularizing quasilocal operators have the form

$$\Lambda_2(x_1, x_2) = (A_1 + A_2 \Box_{x_1})\delta(x_1 - x_2) + A_3 :\varphi^2(x_1): \delta(x_1 - x_2), \quad (29.5)$$

$$\Lambda_3(x_1, x_2, x_3) = B\varphi(x_1)\delta(x_1 - x_2)\delta(x_1 - x_3), \quad (29.6)$$

$$\Lambda_4(x_1, x_2, x_3, x_4) = C\delta(x_1 - x_2)\delta(x_1 - x_3)\delta(x_1 - x_4) \quad (29.7)$$

and after the integrations have been carried out lead to the counter terms

$$\Delta\mathscr{L} = \frac{A_3}{2!} :\varphi^2(x): + \frac{B}{3!} :\varphi(x): + \frac{C}{4!} + A_{1,2}, \quad (29.8)$$

where the constants A_3, B, and C diverge logarithmically while $A_{1,2}$ diverge quadratically as $M \to \infty$.

From the renormalization point of view, the counter terms C and $A_{1,2}$ are unessential additive constants, the term $A_3 :\varphi^2(x):$ leads to mass renormalization, while the term $B\varphi$ produces an additive renormalization of the potential and an additional mass renormalization:

$$\begin{aligned}\mathscr{L} + \Delta\mathscr{L} &= \tfrac{1}{2}\sum_n g^{nn} : \left(\frac{\partial\varphi}{\partial x^n}\right)^2 : - \frac{m}{2} : \varphi^2 : + \lambda : \varphi^3(x) : \\ &\quad + A : \varphi^2(x) : + B : \varphi(x) : + C + A_{1,2} \\ &= \tfrac{1}{2}\sum_k g^{kk} : \left(\frac{\partial\varphi'}{\partial x^k}\right)^2 : - \frac{m'}{2} : \varphi'^2(x) : + \lambda : \varphi'^3(x) : + C', \qquad (29.9)\end{aligned}$$

where

$$\varphi'(x) = \varphi(x) + \varphi_0, \qquad (29.10)$$

while φ_0, m', C' are constants algebraically expressed in terms of m, λ, A. We also note that due to the absence of differential operators in the quasilocal operators which depend on the field operator $\varphi(x)$ the counter terms for the Schrödinger equation have the form

$$\Delta\mathscr{L}(x; g) = \frac{A_3}{2!} : \varphi^2(x) : g(x) + \frac{B}{3!} : \varphi(x) : g^2(x). \qquad (29.11)$$

This concludes our investigation of the nonlinear variant of the scalar Hurst-Thirring field.

§ 30. Spinor Electrodynamics. I. General Form of Counter Terms

30.1. *Types of Divergent Diagrams and Furry's Theorem*

As a second example of interacting quantized wave fields we shall examine in detail the practically important case of spinor electrodynamics, i.e., the system of the vector electromagnetic field interacting with the fermion spinor field with the interaction Lagrangian given by

$$\mathscr{L}(x) = e\sum_n : \bar{\psi}(x)\gamma^n\psi(x)A_n(x) : = e : \bar{\psi}(x)\hat{A}(x)\psi(x) :. \qquad (20.3)$$

We recall that in accordance with the structure of expression (20.3) two fermion lines and one photon line meet at each vertex of the Feynman diagrams, while the causal functions of the fields involved have the form

$$i\overline{A_m(x)A_n(y)} = -g^{mn} D_0^c(x-y) = g^{mn}\frac{1}{(2\pi)^4}\int \frac{dke^{ikx}}{k^2+i\varepsilon}, \tag{21.3}$$

$$i\overline{\psi(x)\bar{\psi}(y)} = S^c(x-y) = \frac{1}{(2\pi)^4}\int \frac{m+\hat{p}}{m^2-p^2-i\varepsilon} e^{-ipx}dp. \tag{21.4}$$

Therefore the degree of the polynomial P in the numerator of the causal function is equal to zero for the photon line, and is equal to unity for the fermion line. The maximum vertex index determined by the formula

$$\omega_i^{\max} = \tfrac{1}{2}\sum_l (r_l + 2) - 4, \tag{28.7}$$

turns out to be equal to zero, and therefore the Lagrangian (20.3) belongs to the renormalizable type.

We now carry out the classification of the divergent diagrams based on formula (28.5). We note first of all that since the maximum vertex index $\omega_i^{\max}$ is equal to zero the index of the diagram $\omega(G)$ does not depend on the number of vertices and turns out to depend only on the number and on the nature of the external lines:

$$\omega(G) = 4 - \tfrac{1}{2}\sum_{l_{\text{ext}}} (r_l + 2). \tag{30.1}$$

As was pointed out in § 28, the maximum number of external lines in divergent diagrams cannot exceed four. It follows from (30.1) that the only diagram of this nature in spinor electrodynamics is a diagram with four external photon lines. The index of this diagram $\omega(G)$ turns out to be equal to zero.

We now turn to diagrams with three external lines. Because the spinor lines are continuous (see § 20) the number of external spinor lines is always even. It is therefore sufficient to examine diagrams with three external photon lines and those with two external fermion lines and one photon line. The total contributions to the matrix elements from diagrams with an odd number of external photon lines in the absence of external spinor lines will be equal to zero on the basis of Furry's theorem given later in this section.

The diagram with two external spinor lines and one photon line has an index $\omega(G)$ equal to zero, the diagram with two external spinor lines has an index equal to unity, while that with two external photon lines has an index equal to two. Diagrams with one external fermion line do not occur because the fermion line must be continuous, while diagrams with one photon external line are forbidden by Furry's theorem.

This completes the enumeration of the divergent diagrams. Before turning to the investigation of the corresponding quasilocal operators we shall give a proof of Furry's theorem which was mentioned before. We note first of all that the general classification of divergent diagrams which we have made does not take into account the symmetry properties of the system and its invariance under different transformations. The possession by the system of these properties leads to considerable restrictions on the possible types of diagrams and, as we shall see later, establishes interrelationships between the structure of the regularizing quasilocal operators which correspond to the various divergent diagrams. For example, the continuity of spinor lines noted above is essentially a manifestation of the property of conservation of electric charge for the fermions (refer to § 8 for the corresponding transformation). An important restriction on the possible types of diagrams is imposed by the property of charge invariance, i.e., of invariance with respect to a change of the sign of the electric charge in those processes the initial and final states of which contain no electrically charged fermions. Such processes are described by diagrams the external lines of which are all photon lines. A change in the sign of the charge in the transformation of charge invariance obviously consists in this case of the change of the sign of the charge of the virtual fermions in the intermediate states. The motion of these virtual particles is described by means of closed spinor cycles in Feynman diagrams.

Furry's theorem (45) consists of the assertion that the matrix elements which correspond to diagrams containing at least one odd closed spinor cycle mutually cancel. Let us consider such a diagram G where L is an odd closed cycle (Fig. 32). It is evident that the matrix element corresponding to this diagram will consists of a sum of two terms, one of which corresponds to motion along L in the clockwise direction, while the other corresponds to the motion of the charge in the opposite direction. As we shall now show (the proof is due to Feynman (40)) the foregoing terms differ only in their signs and their sum is therefore zero.

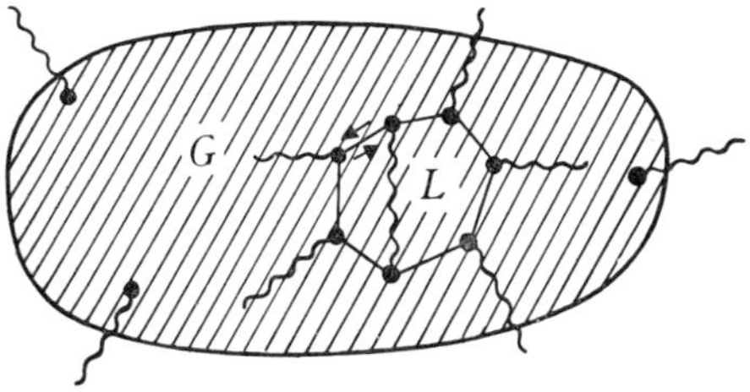

Fig. 32.

The factor in the matrix element which corresponds to the closed cycle L containing n vertices has, according to Feynman's rules, the form [56]

$$\mathrm{Sp}\,[\gamma S^c(1 \div 2)\gamma S^c(2 \div 3) \ldots \gamma S^c(n \div 1)]$$
$$= \sum_{\alpha, \ldots, \nu} \{\gamma_{\alpha\beta} S^c_{\beta\gamma}(1 \div 2)\, \gamma_{\gamma\delta} S^c_{\delta\varepsilon}(2 \div 3) \ldots \gamma_{\mu\nu} S^c_{\nu\alpha}(n \div 1)\}. \quad (30.2)$$

We now make use of the fact that the whole formalism of the spinor field and, in particular, the relation which defines the Dirac matrices:

$$\gamma^m \gamma^n + \gamma^n \gamma^m = 2g^{mn},$$

as well as the values of the traces of the products of any arbitrary number of matrices, are invariant under the following replacement

$$\gamma \rightarrow -\overset{T}{\gamma}, \text{ i.e., } \gamma_{\alpha\beta} \rightarrow -\gamma_{\beta\alpha}. \quad (30.3)$$

As a result of the transformation (30.3) the causal function

$$S^c_{\beta\gamma}(1 \div 2) = \frac{1}{(2\pi)^4} \int \frac{(m + \hat{p})_{\beta\gamma}}{m^2 - p^2 - i\varepsilon} e^{ip(2 \div 1)}\, dp$$

[56] Here for example, $S(n \div 1)$ is an abbreviated notation for $S(x_n - x_1)$, etc.

takes on the form

$$\frac{1}{(2\pi)^4}\int \frac{(m-\hat{p})_{\gamma\beta}}{m^2-p^2-i\varepsilon}\, e^{ip(2\div 1)}\,dp = S^c_{\gamma\beta}(2\div 1).$$

Therefore by subjecting the expression (30.2) to the transformation (30.3) we obtain:

$$\begin{aligned}\mathrm{Sp}\,[\gamma S^c(1\div 2)\gamma S^c(2\div 3)\,.\,.\,.\,\gamma S^c(n\div 1)] \\ &= (-1)^n \sum_{\alpha,\ldots,\nu} \{\gamma_{\beta\alpha} S^c_{\gamma\beta}(2\div 1)\gamma_{\delta\gamma} S^c_{\varepsilon\delta}(3\div 2)\,.\,.\,.\,\gamma_{\nu\mu} S^c_{\alpha\nu}(1\div n)\} \\ &= (-1)^n\,\mathrm{Sp}\,\{\gamma S^c(1\div n)\,.\,.\,.\,\gamma S^c(3\div 2)\gamma S^c(2\div 1)\}.\end{aligned}$$

From this we see that due to the invariance of the trace under the transformation (30.3) the factor (30.2) for even n coincides with the expression

$$\mathrm{Sp}\,\{\gamma S^c(1\div n)\,.\,.\,.\,\gamma S^c(3\div 2)\gamma S^c(2\div 1)\}, \qquad (30.4)$$

which corresponds to the contour L being described in the opposite direction, while for odd n it differs from it only by its sign. In this latter case the sum of the matrix elements which correspond to opposite directions of motion along an odd cycle becomes equal to zero, and the proof of Furry's theorem is complete.

We note that the above proof of Furry's theorem is of a formal nature since we are dealing with singular products of nonregularized causal functions. However, it may be easily seen that if S^c is replaced by reg S^c the proof remains valid, and the sum of the regularized matrix elements is zero. Therefore, by making such diagrams correspond to a quasilocal operator which is equal to zero

$$\Lambda_n(x_1, \ldots, x_n) = 0, \qquad (30.5)$$

we shall find that Furry's theorem holds for the complete coefficient functions $S_n(x_1, \ldots, x_n)$ after the divergences have been removed.

We emphasize that the condition (30.5) which guarantees the charge invariance of the theory after the removal of divergences is not, generally speaking, necessary. By replacing it by some other condition we could have obtained some kind of a noncharge-invariant theory.

We now return to the diagrams under consideration. Since the diagrams which contain an odd number of external photon lines have an odd number of vertices, they necessarily contain at least one odd spinor cycle, and therefore the matrix elements of the diagrams with an odd number of external photon lines are always equal to zero. We have made use of this fact earlier by excluding diagrams with three and with one external photon lines.

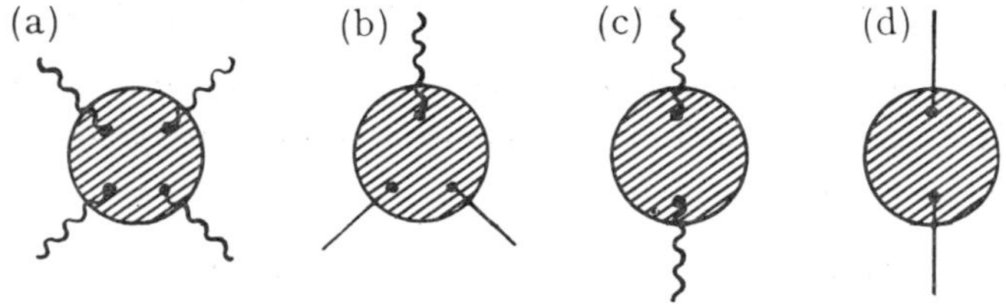

Fig. 33. (a), $\omega(G)=0$; (b), $\omega(G)=0$; (c), $\omega(G)=2$; (d), $\omega(G)=1$.

Thus, by taking Furry's theorem into account we obtain the following four types of divergent diagrams in spinor electrodynamics shown in Fig. 33. The shaded circles in these diagrams represent the internal parts of the diagrams containing an arbitrary number of vertices (even in a, c and d, and odd in b). We recall that the fact that in spinor electrodynamics the degree of divergence does not depend on the number of vertices is a consequence of the fact that the maximum vertex index is equal to zero.

We now investigate the form of the quasilocal operators which correspond to each of these divergent diagrams. For each even n, starting with $n = 4$, diagram a corresponds to the following term in $\Lambda_n (x_1, \ldots, x_n)$

$$A_n \sum_{k,l} g^{kk} g^{ll} : A_k(x_i) A_k(x_j) A_l(x_m) A_l(x_p) : \times \delta(x_1 - x_2)\delta(x_1 - x_3) \ldots \delta(x_1 - x_n). \quad (30.6)$$

The degree of the differential polynomial in this expression is equal to zero in accordance with the value of the index of diagram a. For each odd n, starting with $n = 3$, diagram b corresponds to the quasilocal operator

$$B_n : \bar{\psi}(x_i)\hat{A}(x_k)\psi(x_j) : \delta(x_1 - x_2)\delta(x_1 - x_3) \ldots \delta(x_1 - x_n)$$
$$(i \neq k,\ i \neq j,\ k \neq j). \tag{30.7}$$

For each even n, starting with $n = 2$, diagram c corresponds to the following term in $A_n(x_1, \ldots, x_n)$

$$\sum_{m,k} : A_m(x_i)\left\{\left(C_n g^{mk} + D_n g^{mm} g^{kk} \frac{\partial}{\partial x_i^m}\frac{\partial}{\partial x_j^k} + E_n g^{mk} \sum_l g^{ll} \frac{\partial}{\partial x_i^l}\frac{\partial}{\partial x_j^l}\right)\right.$$
$$\left.\times\ \delta(x_1 - x_2)\delta(x_1 - x_3) \ldots \delta(x_1 - x_n)\right\} A_k(x_j) : \quad (i \neq j). \tag{30.8}$$

The differential polynomial in the foregoing is of the second degree in accordance with the index of the corresponding diagram. The first degree term is absent from the polynomial, since it is impossible to construct an invariant combination involving it. Finally, for each even n, starting with $n=2$, diagram d corresponds to the operator

$$:\bar{\psi}(x_i)\left\{\left[F_n + G_n \frac{i}{2}\left(\frac{\hat{\partial}}{\partial x_i} - \frac{\hat{\partial}}{\partial x_j}\right)\right]\delta(x_1 - x_2)\delta(x_1 - x_3) \ldots \delta(x_1 - x_n)\right\}\psi(x_j):.$$
$$\tag{30.9}$$

From the preceding expressions, it may be seen that the quasilocal operators contain quite a large number of arbitrary constants.

30.2. *Gauge Invariance of the Scattering Matrix*

We note, however, that so far we have not taken into account the requirements of gauge invariance. In order to formulate this requirement let us first investigate the infinitesimal gauge transformation of the potentials of the electromagnetic field

$$A_m(x) \to A_m(x) + \frac{\partial f}{\partial x^m}, \tag{30.10}$$

where f is an arbitrary infinitesimal function. Under this transformation the nth-order term of the scattering matrix $S(1)$

$$\int S_n(x_1, \ldots, x_n)\, dx_1 \ldots dx_n, \tag{30.11}$$

acquires, if the linear dependence of S_n on the potentials $A(x_i)$ with different arguments is taken into account, the increment

$$\sum_{m,i} \int \frac{\partial S_n}{\partial A_m(x_i)} \frac{\partial f}{\partial x_i^m} dx_1 \ldots dx_n.$$

On integrating this expression by parts we find that it vanishes if the following identity holds

$$\operatorname{div}_i^{(4)} \frac{\partial S_n(x_1, \ldots, x_n)}{\partial A(x_i)} \equiv \sum_m \frac{\partial}{\partial x_i^m} \frac{\partial S^n(x_1, \ldots, x_n)}{\partial A_m(x_i)} = 0. \quad (30.12)$$

It may be easily seen that if this condition holds then the expression (30.11) also will not be changed by a finite gauge transformation. This is due to the fact that the coefficients of the leading powers of $\partial f/\partial x$ in the increment of the integrand may be expressed in terms of the derivatives of expression (30.12) with respect to $A(x_j)$.

Because of the aforementioned considerations, we shall adopt condition (30.12) as the *condition for the gauge invariance of the theory*. We shall see later (Chapter VI) that in addition to the invariance of $S(1)$ this condition also guarantees the validity of the differential conservation law for the electric current.

Let us now analyze the degree of arbitrariness in the choice of the coefficients $A_n, B_n, \ldots, F_n, G_n$ in expressions (30.6)–(30.9) which remains after the condition of gauge invariance has been imposed in the form (30.12). For example, let us consider the vertex part of the operator function

$$\sum_{\binom{i,j,k,m}{i \neq j \neq k}} :\bar{\psi}(x_i)\Gamma^m(x_1, \ldots, x_{k-1}, x_{k+1}, \ldots, x_n \,|\, x_k)\, \psi(x_j) A_m(x_k):. \quad (30.13)$$

In accordance with the condition of gauge invariance the vertex part must satisfy the condition

$$\operatorname{div}_k^{(4)} :\bar{\psi}(x_i)\Gamma^m(x_1, \ldots, x_{k-1}, x_{k+1}, \ldots, x_n \,|\, x_k)\, \psi(x_j): = 0.$$

Comparing this with (30.7) we see that the function Γ^m is determined up to the term

$$b_n \gamma^m \delta(x_1 - x_2)\, \delta(x_1 - x_3) \ldots \delta(x_1 - x_n). \quad (30.14)$$

It is evident that the introduction of b_n corresponds to a change in the coefficient B_n. However, it may be easily seen that if the vertex part (30.13) satisfies the condition (30.12), then the addition of the term (30.14) to Γ^m makes it lose this property since

$$\mathrm{div}_k^{(4)} :\bar{\psi}(x_i)\gamma\psi(x_j): \delta(x_1-x_2)\ldots\delta(x_1-x_n) \neq 0 \quad \text{when } k \neq i, j.$$

Therefore, if we choose the quasilocal operators (30.7) in such a way that the result of the subtraction procedure is gauge invariant then such a choice is quite unique and the ambiguity has been removed by the requirement of gauge invariance.

In a completely analogous manner, one can establish the uniqueness of the coefficients A_n in expressions (30.6) and of C_n in expressions (30.8). It is also evident that expressions (30.9) which do not contain the potentials of the electromagnetic field allow an arbitrariness in the choice of the coefficients F_n and G_n.

Let us also examine the ambiguity in the operator expressions of the type

$$\sum_{(m,k,i\neq j)} :A_m(x_i)\,\Pi^{mk}(x_1,\ldots,x_n)\,A_k(x_j):$$

with respect to terms of the same structure as the terms containing the coefficients D_n and E_n in expressions (30.8). On substituting such a term

$$\sum_{(m,k,i\neq j)} :A_m(x_i)\left\{\left(d_n g^{mm} g^{kk} \frac{\partial}{\partial x_i^m}\frac{\partial}{\partial x_j^m} + e_n g^{mk} \sum_l g^{ll} \frac{\partial}{\partial x_i^l}\frac{\partial}{\partial x_j^l}\right)\right.$$
$$\left.\times\, \delta(x_1-x_2)\,\delta(x_1-x_3)\ldots\delta(x_1-x_n)\right\} A_k(x_j):$$

into the condition (30.12) and on taking into account the properties of the derivative of the δ-function

$$\frac{\partial}{\partial x}\delta(x-y) = -\frac{\partial}{\partial y}\delta(x-y),$$

we find the relation between d_n and e_n:

$$d_n + e_n = 0, \tag{30.15}$$

which leaves one degree of arbitrariness in the choice of these coefficients.

Thus for each n there are only three nonunique constants F_n, G_n, and, for example, D_n. From the point of view of the counter terms of the Lagrangian only the following three numbers (compare (18.42)) turn out to be nonunique:

$$D = \sum_{n=2}^{\infty} \frac{1}{n!} D_n, \quad F = \sum_{n=2}^{\infty} \frac{1}{n!} F_n, \quad G = \sum_{n=2}^{\infty} \frac{1}{n!} G_n.$$

We shall see later that these three numbers appear in the results in only two combinations and that the ambiguity is completely eliminated by the choice of the mass and of the charge of the spinor particle.

We must now show that by means of choosing appropriate counter terms, we may actually obtain a gauge invariant theory. As is well known, the counter terms of the Lagrangian serve to describe the subtraction procedure used in our theory. We recall that the subtraction procedure adopted by us consists of subtracting from the divergent expression a sufficient number of terms of its expansion into a Maclaurin's series about the point $p = 0$ and of adding to the result an arbitrary finite polynomial of a definite degree. On the basis of the results just obtained, this arbitrariness is reduced to two constants in terms of type (30.9) and to one constant in terms of type (30.8). We shall show that a gauge invariant theory is obtained as a result of this method of removing the divergences.

In the course of our proof we shall make use of the following variant of regularization by means of auxiliary masses. We shall regularize the photon causal functions (21.3) in the usual way (see (24.9)), while the spinor causal functions will be regularized not individually, but by replacing their products which correspond to the closed cycles:

$$\mathrm{Sp}\,[\gamma S^c(x_1-x_2)\gamma S^c(x_2-x_3)\ldots\gamma S^c(x_{n-1}-x_n)\gamma S^c(x_n-x_1)], \quad (30.16)$$

by the expressions

$$\sum_M c_M \,\mathrm{Sp}\,[\gamma S^c_M(x_1-x_2)\gamma S^c_M(x_2-x_3)\ldots\gamma S^c_M(x_n-x_1)], \quad (30.17)$$

where $S^c_M(x)$ is the fermion causal function with mass M:

$$S_M^c(x) = \frac{1}{(2\pi)^4} \int \frac{M + \hat{p}}{M^2 - p^2 - i\varepsilon} e^{-ipx} dp. \tag{30.18}$$

The preceding method of regularizing spinor causal functions represents one of the variants of the Pauli-Villars (93) regularization.

We note in this connection that in accordance with the general properties of the above expressions undergoing regularization which were established in Chapter IV, a change in the method of the auxiliary regularization does not affect the structure of the final regularized expressions which are coefficient functions of the operators S_n' which determine the scattering matrix containing no infinities.

We shall now show that the regularization according to Pauli and Villars removes the divergences from the matrix elements which correspond to closed cycles. In order to do this we consider the result of integrating expression (30.16) written in the momentum representation:

$$\int dp \frac{\mathrm{Sp}[\gamma(m + \hat{p})\gamma(m + \hat{p} + \hat{k}_1) \ldots \gamma(m + \hat{p} + \hat{k}_{n-1})]}{(m^2 - p^2 - i\varepsilon)(m^2 - (p + k_1)^2 - i\varepsilon) \ldots (m^2 - (p + k_{n-1})^2 - i\varepsilon)}. \tag{30.19}$$

For large p the integrand behaves like p^{-n} and for n less than five the integral diverges like

$$\int^\infty \frac{p^3 dp}{p^n} \sim \int^\infty \frac{dp}{p^{n-3}}.$$

We note that for large p the integrand in (30.19)

$$\frac{P_n(p) + m^2 P_{n-2}(p) + \ldots + m^n}{P_{2n}(p) + m^2 P_{2n-2}(p) + \ldots + m^{2n}}$$
$$\cong \left\{ \frac{P_n(p)}{P_{2n}(p)} + \frac{P_n(p)}{P_{2n}(p)} \left[\frac{P_{n-2}(p)}{P_n(p)} - \frac{P_{2n-2}(p)}{P_{2n}(p)} \right] m^2 + \ldots \right\}$$

(where $P_i(p)$ is a polynomial of the ith degree in the components of p) may be represented in the form of a power series in m^2, where the rate at which the coefficient of the kth power of m^2 increases with p as $p \to \infty$ is equal to p^{-n-2k}. It is therefore clear that if the coefficients C_M in the sum (30.17) satisfy k relations of the type

$$\sum_M c_M = 0, \quad \sum_M c_M M^2 = 0, \ldots, \quad \sum_M c_M M^{2k-2} = 0,$$

then as $p \to \infty$ the integrand corresponding to (30.17) behaves like p^{-2k-n}, and the Pauli-Villars procedure regularizes the above expressions together with their $2k + n - 5$ first derivatives with respect to x_i. This property of the Pauli-Villars procedure could also have been established directly by going over to the "α-representation" of the causal functions.

Thus we shall introduce auxiliary masses only for photon lines and for closed spinor cycles. We shall in general not subject open spinor cycles to regularization. It may be easily seen that it is sufficient to regularize the photon functions by means of one auxiliary mass, and to regularize closed spinor cycles by two auxiliary masses. Indeed, the maximum degree of divergence of diagrams with closed spinor cycles is equal to two (diagrams of the type of Fig. 33c) ($n = 2$) while the introduction of two auxiliary masses lowers the degree by four. As a result of this procedure the integral now converges as $p \to \infty$ like

$$\int^{\infty} dp\, p^{-3}.$$

On the other hand, the maximum degree of divergence of diagrams with internal photon lines is equal to unity (diagrams of the type of Fig. 33d). The introduction of one auxiliary mass into the photon function lowers the degree of divergence by two and the integral now converges like

$$\int^{\infty} dp\, p^{-2}.$$

Therefore, there is no need to regularize open spinor cycles. We see from the foregoing that all the matrix elements turn out to be convergent for finite values of the auxiliary masses M_i. However, we recall that the regularization by means of auxiliary masses is only a technical auxiliary device employed at an intermediate stage of the argument, and that the actual removal of divergences is accomplished by means of a subtraction procedure. Therefore we shall now apply to the regularized expression for the scattering matrix obtained above the usual procedure of subtracting a Maclaurin's series in the momentum representation at the same time adding three arbitrary finite constants. In view of the invariance of the results of such a subtraction with respect to the method of introducing the auxiliary masses we have established earlier, it now remains only to establish the gauge invariance of the Pauli-Villars regularization and of the subtraction procedure which follows it.

We shall now demonstrate the gauge invariance of the regularized matrix $S(1)$ before the subtraction procedure has been applied to it. In doing so we shall make use of the fact that the set of diagrams of the nth order with k ($k \geqq 1$) external photon lines may be obtained from the diagram of the $(n-1)$th order with $(k-1)$ external photon lines by means of *inserting* an additional nth vertex ξ into any arbitrary external or internal spinor line. This process of insertion (which for the sake of brevity we shall refer to as the ξ *process*) at the same time establishes a graphical correspondence between the expressions

$$\sum_i \frac{\partial S_n(x_1, \ldots, x_n)}{\partial A(\xi)}\bigg|_{\xi = x_i} \quad \text{and} \quad S_{n-1}(x_1, \ldots, x_{n-1}).$$

We first examine the process of insertion into an internal spinor line. Inserting the ξ-vertex into the line x_1, x_2 we obtain

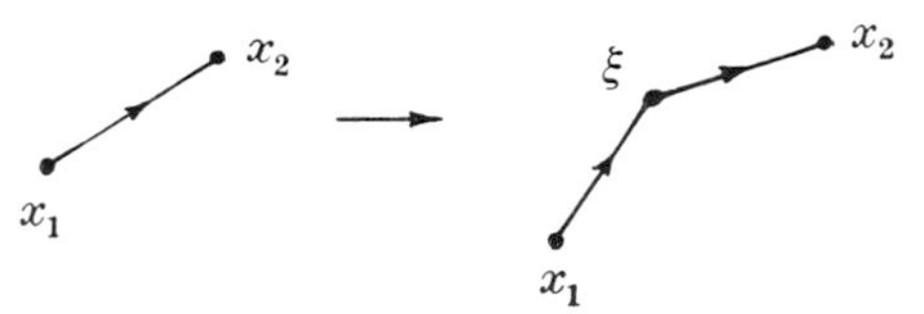

Fig. 34. The process of the insertion of a ξ-vertex into an internal fermion line.

Fig. 34. On calculating the divergence (30.12) with respect to ξ of the factor

$$S^c(x_2 - \xi)\gamma S^c(\xi - x_1),$$

we find, after making use of the equations for S^c,

$$\operatorname{div}_\xi^{(4)} [S^c(x_2 - \xi)\gamma S^c(\xi - x_1)] \equiv \sum_j \frac{\partial}{\partial \xi_j} S^c(x_2 - \xi)\gamma^j S^c(\xi - x_1)$$
$$= \frac{1}{i} (\delta(x_2 - \xi) - \delta(\xi - x_1))\, S^c(x_2 - x_1). \qquad (30.20)$$

The ξ-process for the internal lines of a complicated fermion cycle may be represented by the diagram of Fig. 35. By evaluating

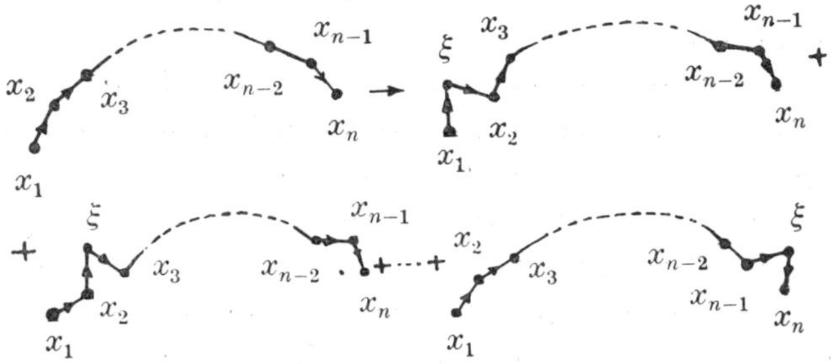

Fig. 35. ξ process for internal lines of a fermion cycle.

the divergence of the sum of the terms corresponding to the right-hand side of Fig. 35 we see without difficulty with the aid of (30.20) that it is proportional to the term which corresponds to the diagram on the left-hand side of Fig. 35, with the proportionality constant being equal to

$$\frac{1}{i} (\delta(x_n - \xi) - \delta(x_1 - \xi)). \qquad (30.21)$$

From this it follows that the preceding divergence vanishes for closed cycles (for $x_1 = x_n$).

By applying this argument to more complicated diagrams consisting of internal photon lines and of an arbitrary number of closed and open fermion cycles, we arrive at the relation

$$\operatorname{div}_\xi^{(4)} K_{n+1}(x_1, \ldots, x_n \mid \xi)$$
$$= i\,(\sum_a \delta(\xi - x_a) - \sum_b \delta(\xi - x_b))\, K_n(x_1, \ldots, x_n), \qquad (30.22)$$

where the summations Σ_a and Σ_b are taken over all the vertices of the diagram which are entered by (x_a), and from which there emerge (x_b) external fermion lines; here $K_n(x_1, \ldots, x_n)$ is the nth order coefficient function, while $K_{n+1}(x_1, \ldots, x_n \mid \xi)$ is the $(n+1)$th order coefficient function obtained from the preceding one by the ξ-process.

In order to complete the demonstration of the gauge invariance of the regularized matrix $S(1)$, we also consider the ξ-process for the external (entering and emerging) fermion lines

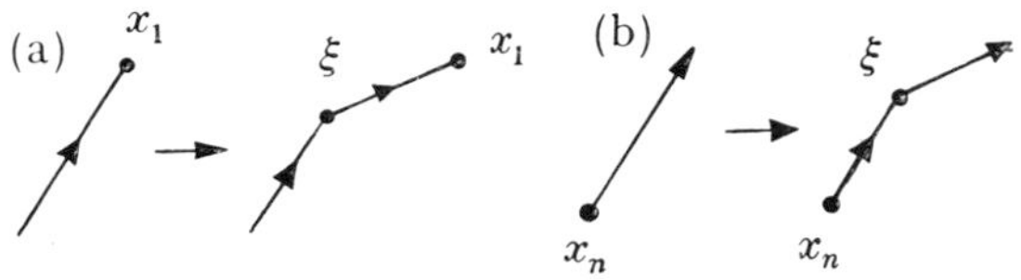

Fig. 36. ξ process for external fermion lines.

(Fig. 36). By calculating the appropriate divergences we find:

$$\operatorname{div}_\xi^{(4)} S^c(x_1 - \xi)\,\gamma\psi(\xi) = \frac{1}{i}\,\delta(x_1 - \xi)\,\psi(x_1), \tag{30.23}$$

$$\operatorname{div}_\xi^{(4)} \bar\psi(\xi)\,\gamma S^c(\xi - x_n) = -\frac{1}{i}\,\delta(\xi - x_n)\,\bar\psi(x_n). \tag{30.24}$$

By comparing these expressions with (30.21) we see that $S_n(x_1, \ldots, x_n)$ do in fact satisfy the condition of gauge invariance (30.12). Indeed, as we have just shown, the divergence of the factors which describe closed cycles is equal to zero. The divergence of the operator which corresponds to an open cycle is made up of the divergence of the sum of the ξ-insertions into the coefficient function and of insertions into the external lines and also vanishes because (30.24) compensates for the first term in (30.21), while (30.23) compensates for the second term.

This completes the formal demonstration of the gauge invariance of the matrix $S(1)$ prior to the process of regularization. However, we note that only the closed fermion cycles are subjected to the Pauli-Villars regularization with the mass having the same value in each of the additional terms in the expressions (30.17) for all the causal functions. Because of this the foregoing additional terms also have zero divergence after the ξ-process, and we conclude that the regularized matrix $S(1)$ satisfies the condition of gauge invariance also after the application of the Pauli-Villars procedure. We note here that the above property of retaining gauge invariance is an important advantage of the Pauli-Villars regularization method which we had in mind in departing from the method of introducing auxiliary masses adopted by us earlier.

We shall now show that the inclusion of the quasilocal operators Λ_n does not destroy the property of gauge invariance. In the course of the following arguments we shall find it convenient to make use of equation (30.22) which with the aid of the following formulas [57]

$$K_n(x_1, \ldots, x_n) = \frac{1}{(2\pi)^{4n}} \int e^{i\sum_1^n p_j x_j} \tilde{K}_n(p_1, \ldots, p_n)\, dp_1 \ldots dp_n, \quad (30.25)$$

$$K_{n+1}(x_1, \ldots, x_n \mid \xi)$$
$$= \frac{1}{(2\pi)^{4(n+1)}} \int e^{i\sum_1^n p_j x_j + i\pi\xi} \tilde{K}_{n+1}(p_1, \ldots, p_n \mid \pi)\, d\pi\, dp_1 \ldots dp_n, \quad (30.26)$$

$$\delta(\xi - x_a) = \frac{1}{(2\pi)^4} \int e^{i\pi(\xi - x_a)}\, d\pi \quad (30.27)$$

takes on in the momentum representation the form

$$\pi\tilde{K}_{n+1}(p_1, \ldots, p_n) \mid \pi) = \sum_b \tilde{K}(p_1, \ldots, p_b + \pi, \ldots, p_n)$$
$$- \sum_a K_n(p_1, \ldots, p_a + \pi, \ldots, p_n). \quad (30.28)$$

Because the coefficient functions K_n and K_{n+1} in the x-representation are invariant under translation all the quantities appearing in the last relation are proportional to the δ-function of the total momentum:

$$\tilde{K}_{n+1}(p_1, \ldots, p_n \mid \pi) = \delta(\sum p + \pi) K'_{n+1}(p_1, \ldots, p_n \mid \pi),$$
$$K_n(p_1, \ldots, p_i + \pi, \ldots, p_n) = \delta(\sum p + \pi) K'_n(p_1, \ldots, p_i + \pi, \ldots, p_n).$$

By separating out this δ-function we evidently obtain

[57] We hope that the use of the symbol π in (30.26), and (30.27) as a variable of integration simultaneously with its customary meaning will not lead to any confusion. (cf. Dirac (31), first footnote p. 157).

$$\pi K'_{n+1}(p_1, \ldots, p_n) \mid \pi) = \sum_b K'_n(p_1, \ldots, p_b + \pi, \ldots, p_n)$$
$$- \sum_a K'_n(p_1, \ldots, p_a + \pi, \ldots, p_n). \quad (30.29)$$

For illustration we note that a diagram of the type of Fig. 33b may be obtained from Fig. 33d by means of a ξ-process (see Fig. 37). The corresponding coefficient functions Σ and Γ

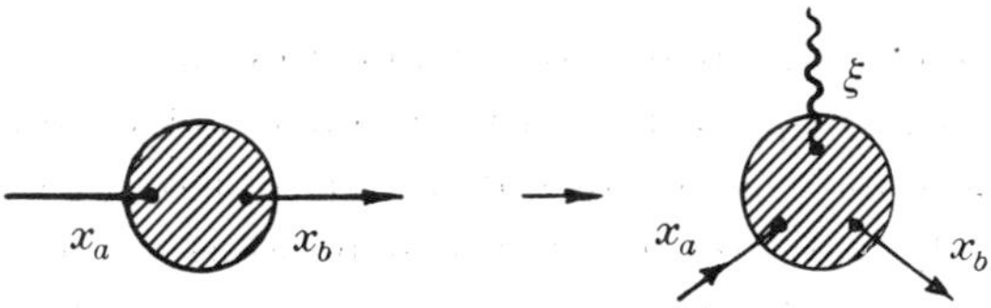

Fig. 37.

which appear in the operator expressions

$$:\bar{\psi}(x_b)\,\Sigma_n(x_1, \ldots, x_n)\,\psi(x_a):,$$
$$:\bar{\psi}(x_b)\,\Gamma_{n+1}(x_1, \ldots, x_n \mid \xi)\,\psi(x_a)\,A(\xi):,$$

according to (30.29) satisfy the relation

$$\pi\Gamma'_{n+1}(p_1, \ldots, p_n) \mid \pi)$$
$$= \Sigma'_n(p_1, \ldots, p_b+\pi, \ldots, p_n) - \Sigma'_n(p_1, \ldots, p_a+\pi, \ldots p_n). \quad (30.30)$$

By carrying out the integration over all the momenta except the external ones (π, p_a, p_b):

$$\int \Gamma'_{n+1}(p_1, \ldots, p_n \mid \pi)\, dp_1, \ldots dp_{a-1} dp_{a+1} \ldots dp_{b-1} dp_{b+1} \ldots dp_n = \Gamma_{n+1}(p_b, p_a \mid \pi),$$

$$\int \Sigma'_n(p_1, \ldots, p_a + \pi, \ldots p_n)\, dp_1 \ldots dp_{a-1} dp_{a+1} \ldots dp_{b-1} dp_{b+1} \ldots dp_n = \Sigma_n(p_b + \pi, p_a),$$

$$\int \Sigma'_n(p_1, \ldots, p_b + \pi, \ldots, p_n)\, dp_1 \ldots dp_{a-1} dp_{a+1} \ldots dp_{b-1} dp_{b+1} \ldots dp_n = \Sigma_n(p_b, p_a + \pi),$$

by differentiating with respect to π and setting $\pi = 0$ we obtain:

$$\Gamma_{n+1}(p_b, p_a \mid 0) = \frac{\partial \Sigma_n(p_b, p_a)}{\partial p_b} - \frac{\partial \Sigma_n(p_b, p_a)}{\partial p_a} \quad (30.31)$$

or

$$\Gamma_{n+1}(p, 0) = -\frac{\partial \Sigma_n(p)}{\partial p}, \tag{30.32}$$

where in accordance with (24.4) and (25.3) we have set:

$$\Gamma_{n+1}(p, k) = \Gamma_{n+1}(-p, p \mid k),$$
$$\Sigma_n(p) = \Sigma_n(-p, p).$$

Formula (30.32) establishes the connection between the coefficient function corresponding to the self-energy diagram in the nth approximation and the coefficient function of the vertex diagram of the $(n+1)$th approximation which holds both in the non-regularized theory (formally) and also after regularization according to Pauli-Villars.

We now turn to the proof of the gauge invariance of the subtraction procedure. Since condition (30.12) is satisfied prior to the subtraction process we must evidently demonstrate the gauge invariance of the quasilocal operators Λ_n that are being subtracted. If it should turn out that the operators being subtracted which correspond to the diagrams of Figs. 33a and c are individually gauge invariant, while the operators which correspond to the diagrams of Figs. 33b and d satisfy relation (30.29), then the gauge invariance of the subtraction procedure will have been established. We shall show that this is in fact the case.

Making use of the fact that we have already established (see § 25) the condition for the gauge invariance of the subtraction procedure in the second and third orders in e we shall carry out the proof by the method of induction. Let us suppose that the quasilocal operators Λ_n satisfy the above requirements up to a certain odd

$$n - 1 = 2\nu - 1.$$

We consider an element of the scattering matrix $S'_n(x_1, \ldots, x_n)$ before the quasilocal operator $\Lambda_n(x_1, \ldots, x_n)$ has been subtracted from it $(S'_n = S_n - i\Lambda_n)$. Since we have demonstrated the gauge invariance of the S-matrix before the subtraction process and since we have assumed the gauge invariance of the quasilocal operators of lower orders,

$$A_\nu(x_1, \ldots, x_\nu) \qquad (\nu = 1, \ldots n - 1),$$

the expression for S'_n will also be gauge invariant. The specific nth order divergences for even n correspond to the diagrams shown in Fig. 33a, c, d.

Since the expression for S'_n is itself gauge invariant its parts corresponding to the above three diagrams will also be gauge invariant: [58]

$$\left.\begin{aligned}
&\sum_{\binom{p,q,r,s}{a,b,c,d}} : A_p(x_a)A_q(x_b)A_r(x_c)A_s(x_d) : \square^{pqrs}(x_1, \ldots, x_n),\\
&\sum_{(p,q,a,b)} : A_p(x_a)A_q(x_b) : \Pi^{pq}(x_1, \ldots, x_n),\\
&\sum_{(a,b)} : \bar{\psi}(x_b)\Sigma(x_1, \ldots, x_n)\psi(x_a) :.
\end{aligned}\right\} \qquad (30.33)$$

The gauge invariance of the last expression is obvious, while the four- and the two-photon parts give:

$$\sum_p g^{pp} k_a^p \square^{pqrs}(k_1, \ldots, k_a, \ldots, k_n) = 0, \qquad (30.34)$$

$$\sum_p g^{pp} k_a^p \Pi^{pq}(k_1, \ldots, k_a, \ldots, k_n) = 0. \qquad (30.35)$$

Differentiating (30.34) with respect to k_a^p and setting $k_a = 0$ we find:

$$\square^{pqrs}(k_1, \ldots, k_{a-1}, 0, k_{a+1}, \ldots, k_n) = 0. \qquad (30.36)$$

The relation (30.36) is an important one. Because the diagram of Fig. 33a is only logarithmically divergent ($\omega(G) = 0$) the subtraction of Maclaurin's series reduces to the subtraction from $\square$ of its value for zero values of the momenta of external photons

$$\square^{pqrs}(k_1, \ldots, k_n)\,|_{k_a=k_b=k_c=k_d=0}\,. \qquad (30.37)$$

In view of (30.36), this quantity turns out to be equal to zero while $\square$ itself turns out to be convergent. Therefore one does not need to remove any divergences at all from the diagram of Fig. 33a.

[58] The symbol $\square$ is here used to denote the set of coefficient functions shown in Fig. 33a.

We now turn to the two-photon diagram. By differentiating the left-hand side of expression (30.35) once, twice, and three times with respect to the components of k_a and then setting $k_a = 0$ we find that the first, second, and third coefficients respectively of the Maclaurin series expansion of Π^{pq} multiplied by k_a^p (and summed over p) all vanish. We obtain the following result:

$$\left.\begin{aligned}\sum_p g^{pp} k_a^p \Pi^{pq}_{(0,k_a)}(k_1, \ldots, k_n) &= 0,\\ \sum_p g^{pp} k_a^p \Pi^{pq}_{(1,k_a)}(k_1, \ldots, k_n) &= 0,\\ \sum_p g^{pp} k_a^p \Pi^{pq}_{(2,k_a)}(k_1, \ldots, k_n) &= 0,\end{aligned}\right\} \tag{30.38}$$

where the symbol $\Pi_{(i,k_a)}$ denotes the ith term of the Maclaurin series expansion of the function Π with respect to the variable k_a. If we then expand the above expressions in Maclaurin series with respect to the variable k_b up to the second, first, and zero order respectively, we obtain the result

$$\sum_p k_a^p \{\Pi^{pq}(k_1, \ldots, k_n)\}_2^{k_a, k_b} = 0, \tag{30.39}$$

where the symbol $\{\ldots\}_i^{x,y,z,\ldots}$ denotes, as usual, the sum of terms of the Maclaurin series in the variables x, y, z, . . . up to the ith order inclusively. But the Maclaurin series which appears in (30.39) is just the coefficient function of the operator Λ_n being subtracted from S'_n and corresponding to the two-photon diagram. The relation (30.39) is an expression of its gauge invariance. The aforementioned operator Π is determined up to an arbitrary finite polynomial of the second degree in the components of $k = k_a = k_b$. From considerations of relativistic covariance, from the uniqueness of the coefficient C_n in expression (30.8) which was established earlier, and from relation (30.15), we obtain the result that this polynomial, which satisfies the requirement of gauge invariance, has the form

$$d_n(g^{pq}k^2 - k_p k_q). \tag{30.40}$$

The gauge invariance of the operator Λ_n which corresponds to the diagram of the proper mass of the electron (Fig. 33d) is obvious.

In accordance with the arbitrariness of the finite polynomial established above this operator is determined up to the expression

$$f_n m + g_n \hat{p}. \tag{30.41}$$

This concludes the investigation of the terms of Λ_n.

We now proceed to the next odd order $n + 1$. Since this order is odd the only diagram from which a divergence has to be removed is a diagram of the vertex type (see Fig. 33b). As we have established earlier we only need to verify the validity of relation (30.29) or of relation (30.30) which is equivalent to it. Since the coefficient functions of the quasilocal operator $\Sigma'^{\,\mathrm{subtr}}_n$ and $\Gamma'^{\,\mathrm{subtr}}_{n+1}$ are linear in the momenta, the relation (30.30) involving them takes on the form

$$\Gamma'^{\,\mathrm{subtr}}_{n+1}(p_1, \ldots, p_n \mid \pi) = \frac{\partial \Sigma'^{\,\mathrm{subtr}}_n(p_1, \ldots, p_b + \pi, \ldots, p_n)}{\partial p_b} - \frac{\partial \Sigma'^{\,\mathrm{subtr}}_n(p_1, \ldots, p_a + \pi, \ldots, p_n)}{\partial p_a}. \tag{30.42}$$

By carrying out the integration over all the variables with the exception of p_a and p_b we shall go over to the functions $\Gamma(p, k)$ and $\Sigma(p)$ (in analogy to the transition from (30.30) to (30.32)). By making use of the fact that the expressions being subtracted from Γ and Σ are up to finite polynomials equal to their Maclaurin series expansions:

$$\Gamma^{\mathrm{subtr}}_{n+1}(p, k) = \Gamma_{n+1}(p, k)\,|_{p=k=0} + b_{n+1}\gamma,$$

$$\Sigma^{\mathrm{subtr}}_n(p) = \{\Sigma_n(p)\}^p_2 + f_n - g_n \hat{p},$$

we verify by direct substitution that the condition (30.42), after taking (30.32) into account, reduces to the requirement

$$b_{n+1} = g_n. \tag{30.43}$$

Since we have previously established the uniqueness of the constant b_{n+1}, it is therefore determined by the above relation. The subtraction procedure in the $(n + 1)$th order also turns out to be gauge invariant if (30.43) holds. This completes the proof.

We also note that the set of the two relationships (30.32) and (30.43) establishes for each order in n the equality of the constants G_n and B_{n+1} in the operators (30.7) and (30.9), i.e., it is equivalent to the complete Ward's identity (see § 25).

30.3. *Counter Terms*

We now write down the counter terms of the Lagrangian which regularize the matrix $S(1)$. On substituting expressions (30.7)–(30.9) into (18.32) we obtain after integrating by parts and summing over ν the complete interaction Lagrangian in the form

$$\begin{aligned}\mathscr{L}(x) = \mathscr{L}(x;\,1) &= eZ_1 : \bar{\psi}(x)\hat{A}(x)\psi(x) : - \delta m : \bar{\psi}(x)\psi(x) : \\ &+ (Z_2 - 1)\left\{\frac{i}{2}\sum_k : \left(\bar{\psi}(x)\gamma^k\frac{\partial\psi}{\partial x^k} - \frac{\partial\bar{\psi}}{\partial x^k}\gamma^k\psi(x)\right) : - m : \bar{\psi}(x)\psi(x) :\right\} \\ &- (Z_3 - 1)\left\{\frac{1}{2}\sum_{m,n} g^{mm}g^{nn} : \frac{\partial A_n(x)}{\partial x^m}\frac{\partial A_n(x)}{\partial x^m} : - \frac{1}{2} : \left(\sum_n g^{nn}\frac{\partial A_n}{\partial x^n}\right)^2 : \right\},\end{aligned} \tag{30.44}$$

where the following notation has been used

$$Z_1 = 1 + \sum_{\nu=1}^{\infty}\frac{e^{2\nu}}{(2\nu)!}B_{2\nu+1}, \qquad Z_2 = 1 + \sum_{\nu=1}^{\infty}\frac{e^{2\nu}}{(2\nu)!}G_{2\nu},$$
$$Z_3 = 1 + \sum_{\nu=1}^{\infty}\frac{e^{2\nu}}{(2\nu)!}D_{2\nu}, \qquad \delta m = \sum_{\nu=1}^{\infty}\frac{e^{2\nu}}{(2\nu)!}(F_{2\nu} + G_{2\nu}). \tag{30.45}$$

In view of the relation

$$B_{2\nu+1} = G_{2\nu},$$

which was established earlier, Ward's identity in the present notation takes on the form

$$Z_1 = Z_2. \tag{30.46}$$

The constants Z_1, Z_2, Z_3, and δm, determined by the relations (30.45) depend on the auxiliary masses M_i with the coefficients in the expansions (30.45) diverging logarithmically as these masses are made to tend to infinity. However, the matrix elements of the matrix

$$S(1) = T(\exp i \int \mathscr{L}(x; 1) dx)$$

approach constant values in the limit $M_i \to \infty$.

Since the Pauli-Villars procedure is gauge invariant the Lagrangian (30.44), in contrast to the Lagrangian (24.45) which was obtained by means of a nongauge-invariant regularization, does not contain the term involving the photon mass

$$\delta m_\Phi \sum_n g^{nn} : A_n(x) A_n(x) :, \tag{30.47}$$

and is therefore manifestly gauge invariant.

We see from the above that the form and the properties of the counter terms depend in an essential way on the method of auxiliary regularization. Thus, by using the nongauge-invariant regularization of the photon and fermion pairings which we employed in Chapter IV for the removal of infinities from S_2 and S_3, we have arrived at the necessity for the introduction of nongauge-invariant counter terms of type (30.47). On the other hand, as we have just shown, by using the Pauli-Villars auxiliary regularization which does have the property of gauge invariance, we have arrived at expression (30.44) which does not contain any nongauge-invariant terms. Moreover, it may turn out that the counter terms will not have even the property of Lorentz invariance. As Stepanov (115) has shown, such a situation in fact arises when non-Lorentz-invariant auxiliary regularization is used. Of course in such a case after the auxiliary regularization has been removed, the scattering matrix turns out to be both gauge-invariant and Lorentz-invariant.

We now turn to the question of obtaining a finite matrix $S(g)$ for $g(x) \neq 1$. On substituting the expressions for the quasi-local operators into (18.39), we obtain counter terms which regularize the matrix $S(g)$ in the form:

$$\mathscr{L}(x;\,g) = eZ_1(g)\,g(x)\,:\bar{\psi}(x)\hat{A}(x)\psi(x): - \delta m(g)\,:\bar{\psi}(x)\psi(x):$$

$$+ (Z_2(g)-1)\left\{\frac{i}{2}\sum_k :\left(\bar{\psi}(x)\gamma^k\frac{\partial\psi}{\partial x^k} - \frac{\partial\bar{\psi}}{\partial x^k}\gamma^k\psi(x)\right): - m:\bar{\psi}(x)\psi(x):\right\}$$

$$- (Z_3(g)-1)\left\{\frac{1}{2}\sum_{m,n} g^{mm}g^{nn}:\frac{\partial A_n(x)}{\partial x^m}\,\frac{\partial A_n(x)}{\partial x^m}: - \frac{1}{2}:\left(\frac{\partial A}{\partial x}\right)^2:\right\}$$

$$- \frac{Z_3(g)-1}{g^2(x)}\,\frac{1}{2}\sum_{m,n} g^{mm}g^{nn}:\left\{A_m(x)A_m(x)\frac{\partial g(x)}{\partial x^n}\,\frac{\partial g(x)}{\partial x^n}\right.$$

$$+ 2\frac{\partial A_n(x)}{\partial x^m}A_n(x)g(x)\frac{\partial g(x)}{\partial x^m} - 2A_n(x)\frac{\partial A_m}{\partial x^m}\,\frac{\partial g}{\partial x^n}g(x)$$

$$\left. - A_n(x)A_m(x)\frac{\partial g}{\partial x^n}\,\frac{\partial g}{\partial x^m}\right\}:, \qquad (30.48)$$

where

$$\left.\begin{aligned} Z_1(g) &= 1 + \sum_{\nu=1}^{\infty}\frac{[eg(x)]^{2\nu}}{(2\nu)!}B_{2\nu+1}, \\ Z_2(g) &= 1 + \sum_{\nu=1}^{\infty}\frac{[eg(x)]^{2\nu}}{(2\nu)!}G_{2\nu}, \\ Z_3(g) &= 1 + \sum_{\nu=1}^{\infty}\frac{[eg(x)]^{2\nu}}{(2\nu)!}D_{2\nu}, \\ \delta m &= \sum_{\nu=1}^{\infty}\frac{[eg(x)]^{2\nu}}{(2\nu)!}(F_{2\nu}+G_{2\nu}). \end{aligned}\right\} \qquad (30.49)$$

The expression (30.48) is already nongauge-invariant, and so is the matrix $S(g)$.

§ 31. Spinor Electrodynamics. II. Mass and Charge Renormalization

31.1. *Gauge Transformation of the Pairing* $\overset{\frown}{AA}$

We now turn to a more detailed examination of the scattering matrix $S(1)$. Its gauge invariance was established in the preceding section. We first note that the property of gauge invariance allows one to add to the pairing of electromagnetic poetntials

$$\overline{A_m(k)A_n(k')},$$

which is used in the process of reducing the terms of the matrix $S(1)$ to the normal form, an expression of the type

$$k_m k_n f(k^2),$$

where $f(k^2)$ is an arbitrary function of k^2. In other words, the elements of the scattering matrix are not altered when

$$\overline{A_m(k)A_n(k')} \equiv \langle T(A_m(k)A_n(k')\rangle_0 = -\frac{ig^{mn}}{k^2+i\varepsilon}\delta(k+k') \quad (31.1)$$

is replaced by the expression

$$\frac{1}{i}\left(g^{mn}\frac{1}{k^2} + k_m k'_n f(k^2)\right)\delta(k+k').$$

In order to prove this we consider the gauge transformation

$$A_n \to A'_n = A_n + k_n F(k^2)\,(k\cdot A(k)). \quad (31.2)$$

We determine the chronological pairing of the new operators A':

$$\overline{A'_n(k)A'_m(k')} = \frac{1}{ik^2}\{g^{mn} + k_m k'_n(2F(k^2) + k^2F(k^2)F(k^2))\}\delta(k+k'). \quad (31.3)$$

Since it was shown in the preceding section that $S(1)$ is gauge invariant its matrix elements will not depend on the function

$$f(k^2) = 2F(k^2) + k^2F(k^2)F(k^2),$$

which is what we wanted to show. We also note that by setting

$$f(k^2) = \frac{1-d_l^0}{k^2}, \quad (31.4)$$

we may write expression (31.3) in the form

$$i\overline{A'_n(k)A'_m(k')} = \frac{1}{k^2}\left(g^{mn} - \frac{k_m k_n}{k^2}\right)\delta(k+k') + \frac{d_l^0}{k^2}\frac{k_m k_n}{k^2}\delta(k+k'). \quad (31.5)$$

Formula (31.5) is the most convenient one. In it we have carried out an explicit decomposition of the pairing $\overline{AA}$ into its transverse and longitudinal (in the four-dimensional sense) parts in which the arbitrariness of the gauge has been completely associated with the longitudinal part (the coefficient d_l^0). In the foregoing in accordance with (31.4) d_l^0 may, generally speaking, depend on k^2. However, for purposes of our future discussion it will be sufficient to take d_l^0 constant.

By setting $d_l^0 = 0$ we obtain from (31.5) the expression

$$i\overline{A_n^{\mathrm{tr}}(k)A_m^{\mathrm{tr}}}(k') = \frac{1}{k^2}\left(g^{mn} - \frac{k_m k_n}{k^2}\right)\delta(k+k), \tag{31.6}$$

which has the property of transversality

$$\sum_n k^n \overline{A_n^{\mathrm{tr}}(k)A_m^{\mathrm{tr}}}(k') = 0. \tag{31.7}$$

On the other hand, for $d_l^0 = 1$ we obtain the usual diagonal pairing. (31.1).

31.2. *Nonuniqueness of the Process of Removal of Infinities*

In § 30 it was shown that in the process of obtaining a gauge invariant matrix $S(1)$ which contains no infinities there is a certain arbitrariness connected with three finite constants which may be represented in the form of coefficients of operator expressions of the same type as the counter terms in the Lagrangian (30.44).

Thus, after we have completed the removal of infinities which may be accomplished either by means of introducing divergent counter terms (30.44) or by means of an appropriate redefinition of chronological products, the resulting expression for the S-matrix contains a certain degree of arbitrariness which is most conveniently recorded in the form of finite additive terms to the initial interaction Lagrangian:

$$\begin{aligned}\delta\mathscr{L} &= e(z_1 - 1) : \bar\psi(x)\hat{A}(x)\psi(x): - \delta m : \bar\psi(x)\psi(x) : \\ &+ (z_2 - 1)\left\{\frac{i}{2}\sum_n : \left(\bar\psi(x)\gamma^n\frac{\partial\psi}{\partial x^n} - \frac{\partial\bar\psi}{\partial x^n}\gamma^n\psi(x)\right): - m : \bar\psi(x)\psi(x):\right\} \\ &- (z_3 - 1)\left\{\frac{1}{2}\sum_{m,n} g^{mm}g^{nn} : \frac{\partial A_n(x)}{\partial x^m}\frac{\partial A_n(x)}{\partial x^m} : - \frac{1}{2}\left(\frac{\partial A}{\partial x}\right)^2\right\}.\end{aligned} \tag{31.8}$$

Here z_1, z_2, z_3 and δm are *finite* constants which in virtue of Ward's identity satisfy

$$z_1 = z_2. \tag{31.9}$$

We shall now examine the influence of the finite counter terms (31.8) on the scattering matrix and we shall show that it is equivalent to a certain finite renormalization of the mass and the charge of the fermion. With this end in view we shall write (31.8) in the momentum representation:[59]

$$\begin{aligned} \delta\mathscr{L}(p) = (z_1 - 1)e :\bar{\psi}\hat{A}\psi: \\ + (z_2 - 1) :\bar{\psi}(p)(\hat{p} - m)\psi(-p): - \delta m :\bar{\psi}(p)\psi(-p): \\ - (z_3 - 1)\tfrac{1}{2}\sum_{m,n} :A_m(p)(g^{mn}p^2 - p^m p^n)A_n(-p):. \end{aligned} \tag{31.10}$$

In contrast to the case of the usual "initial" interaction Lagrangian

$$\mathscr{L} = e\bar{\psi}\hat{A}\psi$$

vertices of three types will correspond to the Lagrangian $\mathscr{L} + \delta\mathscr{L}$ in Feynman diagrams. The term $(z_2 - 1)$ will correspond to vertices in which two fermion lines meet and to which we shall refer for the sake of brevity as z_2-vertices. The term $(z_3 - 1)$ will correspond to the z_3-vertices which join two photon lines. Finally, the term z_1 will correspond to a vertex of the usual type (z_1-vertex).

We now consider the structure of the "propagation factors" which correspond to the internal lines of the new more complicated diagrams. We begin our discussion with the internal fermion lines. By associating the factor $(z_2 - 1)(\hat{p} - m)$ with the z_2-vertex, and the factor ez_1 with the z_1-vertex, we shall find that the pairing[60]

$$\overbrace{\psi(-p)\bar{\psi}(p)} = \frac{i}{\hat{p} - m}$$

will correspond to internal fermion lines independently of the type

[59] Here we have used the symbolic notation
$$\bar{\psi}\hat{A}\psi = \frac{1}{(2\pi)^4}\int \bar{\psi}(p)\hat{A}(q)\psi(p')\delta(p + q + p')\,dq\,dp'.$$

[60] For the sake of brevity we have omitted here the delta function of the total momentum $\delta(p + p')$ and have set $p' = p$.

of vertices connected by the given internal line. We shall now evaluate the "complete propagation factor" which corresponds to the motion of the particle between two z_1-vertices. Evidently it will be represented by a sum of factors corresponding to open fermion cycles which have their beginning and end at vertices of type z_1 and which contain an arbitrary number of vertices of type z_2. By calculating these factors in succession, taking into account the appearance of the factor i^n in the nth order of the S-matrix and the cancellation of the factorial $n!$ in the denominator in the transition to the momentum representation, we find:

$$\frac{i}{\hat{p} - m};$$

$$\frac{i}{\hat{p} - m} i(z_2 - 1)(\hat{p} - m) \frac{i}{\hat{p} - m} = -(z_2 - 1) \frac{i}{\hat{p} - m},$$

i.e., the introduction of each new z_2-vertex corresponds to the appearance of the factor

$$y_2 = 1 - z_2.$$

Therefore by summing factors corresponding to different numbers of z_2-vertices from zero to infinity we obtain:

$$\frac{i}{\hat{p} - m}(1 + y_2 + y_2^2 + \ldots) = \frac{i}{\hat{p} - m} \frac{1}{1 - y_2} = \frac{1}{z_2} \frac{i}{\hat{p} - m}.$$

We conclude that the appearance in the interaction Lagrangian of the counter term $z_2 - 1$ is equivalent from the point of view of the internal fermion line to the following renormalization of the fermion causal function:

$$S^c(p) \rightarrow S'^c(p) = z_2^{-1} S^c(p). \tag{31.11}$$

By means of a completely analogous procedure we find that taking into account the counter term $z_2 - 1$ in the external fermion lines leads to the appearance of the factor z_2^{-1} multiplying the operators $\bar{\psi}$ and ψ which correspond to the free ends of the line:

$$\psi(p) \rightarrow z_2^{-1}\psi(p), \quad \bar{\psi}(p) \rightarrow z_2^{-1}\psi(p). \tag{31.12}$$

We now turn to the internal photon lines. We shall make the factor

$$\frac{1-z_3}{2}(g^{mn}p^2 - p^m p^n) = \frac{y_3}{2}(g^{mn}p^2 - p^m p^n),$$

correspond to the vertex z_3, while we shall set the internal photon lines in correspondence with the pairing in an arbitrary gauge

$$\overline{A_m(-p)A_n(p)} = \frac{1}{ip^2}\left(g^{mn} - \frac{p_m p_n}{p^2}\right) + \frac{d_l^0}{ip^2}\frac{p_m p_n}{p^2}. \quad (31.13)$$

We now investigate the structure of the expressions which correspond to the motion of the photon between two z_1-vertices. By considering the successive inclusions of the z_3-vertices and by taking into account the relations

$$\sum_{l,k}(g^{ml}p^2 - p^m p^l)\frac{\left(g^{lk} - \dfrac{p_l p_k}{p^2}\right)}{p^2}(g^{kn}p^2 - p^k p^n) = g^{mn}p^2 - p^m p^n$$

and

$$\sum_{l,k}(g^{ml}p^2 - p^m p^l)\frac{p_l p_n}{p^2} = 0,$$

we obtain a sum of terms of the form

$$\frac{1}{ip^2}\left(g^{mn} - \frac{p_m p_n}{p^2}\right) + \frac{d_l^0}{ip^2}\frac{p_m p_n}{p^2},$$

$$\sum_{k,l}\left\{\frac{1}{ip^2}\left(g^{mk} - \frac{p_m p_k}{p^2}\right) + \frac{d_l^0}{ip^2}\frac{p_m p_k}{p^2}\right\}\left\{2i\,\frac{y_3}{2}(g^{kl}p^2 - p^k p^l)\right\}$$
$$\times\left\{\frac{1}{ip^2}\left(g^{ln} - \frac{p_l p_n}{p^2}\right) + \frac{d_l^0}{ip^2}\frac{p_l p_n}{p^2}\right\} = \frac{y_3}{ip^2}\left(g^{mn} - \frac{p_m p_n}{p^2}\right),$$

$$\frac{y_3^2}{ip^2}\left(g^{mn} - \frac{p_m p_n}{p^2}\right),$$

. . . .

The appearance of the factor 2 in the expression which refers to the vertex z_3 is due to the two possible different ways of pairing the operators A appearing in the z_3 term in (31.10). By carrying out the summation over all the possible numbers of z_3-vertices:

$$(1 + y_3 + y_3^2 + y_3^3 + \ldots) = \frac{1}{1 - y_3} = \frac{1}{z_3},$$

we arrive at the expression

$$\frac{1}{z_3} \frac{1}{ip^2} \left(g^{mn} - \frac{p_m p_n}{p^2} \right) + \frac{d_l^0}{ip^2} \frac{p_m p_n}{p^2}.$$

Thus the term $(z_3 - 1)$ leads to the renormalization of only the transverse part of the photon Green's function while its longitudinal term does not undergo any changes. This term is usually neglected in the usual discussions of the scattering matrix (34), (86), by making use of the gauge invariance of the scattering matrix noted above. Therefore in the theory of the S-matrix the "incomplete renormalization" of the photon function turns out to be nonessential.

The situation is altered when we go over to the general theory of Green's functions of interacting fields which are sums of diagrams made up of internal lines only. In this case, the basic apparatus of the theory is formulated without any reference to matrix elements and to the Lorentz condition. In this case the longitudinal term may no longer be neglected. However, the difficulty which arises may be avoided if one chooses for the zero-order approximation to the Green's function the purely transverse expression

$$D_{mn}^{c,\,\mathrm{tr}}(p) = -\frac{1}{p^2} \left(g^{mn} - \frac{p_m p_n}{p^2} \right). \tag{31.14}$$

In this case, taking into account the counter term $(z_3 - 1)$ leads to a purely multiplicative renormalization:

$$D_{mn}^{c,\,\mathrm{tr}}(p) \to D_{mn}^{c,\,\mathrm{tr}}(p) = z_3^{-1} D_{mn}^{c,\,\mathrm{tr}}(p). \tag{31.15}$$

By considering further the process of the insertion of z_3-vertices into the external photon lines of the diagram, we find on taking into account the weakened Lorentz condition imposed on the allowed states that the terms quadratic in A lead to the transformation

$$A_m(p) \to z_3^{-1} A_m(p). \tag{31.16}$$

It is also clear that the effect of the term $(z_1 - 1)$ amounts to a change in the value of the charge

$$e \to e' = z_1 e. \tag{31.17}$$

In summarizing the results of the preceding discussion we conclude on the basis of (31.11), (31.12), (31.15)–(31.17) that the introduction into the interaction Lagrangian of the finite terms $(z_1 - 1)$, $(z_2 - 1)$, and $(z_3 - 1)$ is equivalent from the point of view of the structure of the S-matrix to the following transformation of propagation factors, of the field operators and of the electron charge:

$$S^c(p) \to z_2^{-1} S^c(p), \quad D^{c,\,\mathrm{tr}}(p) \to z_3^{-1} D^{c,\,\mathrm{tr}}(p), \quad e \to z_1 e, \tag{31.18}$$

$$\bar{\psi}(p) \to z_2^{-1} \bar{\psi}(p), \quad \psi(p) \to z_2^{-1} \psi(p), \quad A(p) \to z_3^{-1} A(p). \tag{31.19}$$

The formulas (31.18) may be generalized to the case $d_l^0 \neq 0$. Indeed the transition

$$D^c_{mn}(p) = -\frac{1}{p^2}\left(g^{mn} - \frac{p_m p_n}{p^2}\right) - \frac{d_l^0}{p^2}\frac{p_m p_n}{p^2}$$
$$\to -\frac{1}{z_3}\frac{1}{p^2}\left(g^{mn} - \frac{p_m p_n}{p^2}\right) - \frac{d_l^0}{p^2}\frac{p_m p_n}{p^2}$$

may be written in the form

$$D^c_{mn}(p \mid d_l^0) \to D'^c_{mn}(p \mid d_l'^0) = z_3^{-1} D^c_{mn}(p \mid d_l'^0),$$

where $d_l'^0 = z_3 d_l^0$ so that in place of (31.18) we obtain:

$$S^c \to z_2^{-1} S^c, \quad D^c \to z_3^{-1} D^c, \quad e \to z_1 e, \quad d_l^0 \to z_3 d_l^0. \tag{31.20}$$

We note here that in contrast to all the other quadratic counter terms the effect of the expression $\delta m \bar{\psi}\psi$ cannot be reduced to any sort of renormalization or to a replacement of the causal functions and the potentials and must therefore necessarily be retained in the interaction Lagrangian. Indeed, it may be easily shown that the inclusion of the vertices of type δm into the internal fermion lines leads us to a new fermion mass:

$$\frac{1}{\hat{p} - m} \to \frac{1}{\hat{p} - m'}, \qquad m' = m + \delta m. \tag{31.21}$$

The inclusion of the δm-vertices into the external fermion lines leads to the expression

$$\psi(p) \rightarrow \frac{\hat{p} - m}{\hat{p} - m'} \psi(p),$$

which gives zero when the matrix element is evaluated. Thus from the point of view of the S-matrix the introduction of the term $\delta m \bar{\psi} \psi$ cannot be described in a consistent way by changing the fermion mass.

31.3. *The Complete Green's Functions G, D, and the Vertex Part Γ*

It may also be shown that the set of transformations (31.19) and (31.20) which is equivalent to the terms (31.10) with respect to the internal lines of Feynman diagrams may be completely reduced to a change in the mass m and the charge e of the electron. In order to do this, we shall examine in more detail the structure of the factors which correspond to the internal elements of the diagram taking radiation corrections into account.

We begin this discussion with an internal fermion line. The radiation corrections for such a line are determined by diagrams of the self-energy type. We denote the sum of all such possible strongly connected diagrams of all orders by a circle with two fermion lines entering it (Fig. 38), and we denote the corresponding factor by Σ/i.[61]

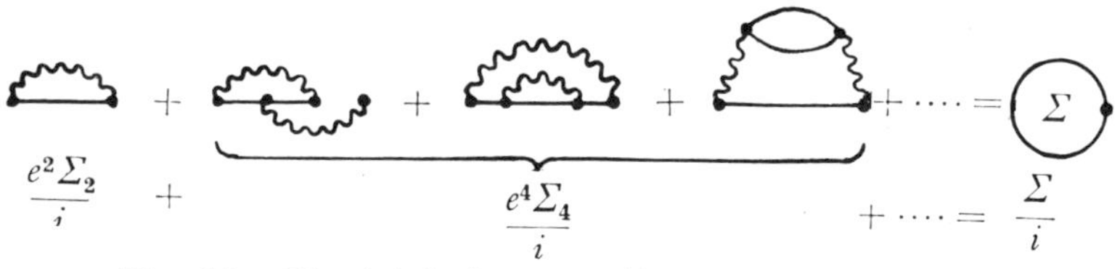

Fig. 38. The total electron self-energy operator Σ.

It is clear that Σ is a function of the momenta p_1 and p_2 which correspond to particles entering and leaving the diagram. But since $p_1 + p_2 = 0$ we have

$$\Sigma(p_1, p_2) = \Sigma(p),$$

[61] The Σ introduced in this way is the generalization of the fermion self-energy operator of order e^2 considered in § 24.

where in accordance with (24.4)

$$-p_1 = p_2 = p.$$

The complete fermion propagation factor G which contains all possible radiation insertions of the self-energy type corresponds to the set of diagrams shown in Fig. 39 and may be represented in the form

$$\frac{1}{i(m-\hat{p})}+\frac{1}{i(m-\hat{p})}\frac{\Sigma}{i}\frac{1}{i(m-\hat{p})}+\frac{1}{i(m-\hat{p})}\frac{\Sigma}{i}\frac{1}{i(m-\hat{p})}\frac{\Sigma}{i}\frac{1}{i(m-\hat{p})}+\dots$$
$$=\frac{i}{\hat{p}-m}\left(1+\Sigma\frac{1}{\hat{p}-m}+\Sigma\frac{1}{\hat{p}-m}\Sigma\frac{1}{\hat{p}-m}+\dots\right)$$
$$=\frac{i}{\hat{p}-m}\left(1-\frac{\Sigma}{\hat{p}-m}\right)^{-1}=\frac{i}{\hat{p}-m-\Sigma(p)},$$

i.e.,

$$G(p)=\frac{1}{m+\Sigma(p)-\hat{p}}. \qquad (31.22)$$

In a similar manner, it is possible to construct the complete photon Green's function and the generalized vertex part. Thus,

$$\frac{S^c}{i}+\frac{S^c}{i}\cdot\frac{\Sigma}{i}\cdot\frac{S^c}{i}+\frac{S^c}{i}\cdot\frac{\Sigma}{i}\cdot\frac{S^c}{i}\cdot\frac{\Sigma}{i}\cdot\frac{S^c}{i}+\dots=\frac{G}{i}$$

Fig. 39. The set of diagrams corresponding to the total electron Green's function.

by summing the contributions from the self-energy parts of the photon $\Pi(k)$:

$$\Pi^{mn}(k)=\pi(k)\left(g^{mn}-\frac{k^m k^n}{k^2}\right), \qquad (31.23)$$

we obtain the complete photon propagation factor

$$D_{mn}(k)=\frac{1}{\pi(k)-k^2}\left(g^{mn}-\frac{k_m k_n}{k^2}\right)-\frac{d_l^0}{k^2}\frac{k_m k_n}{k^2}. \qquad (31.24)$$

An important feature of formula (31.24) is the fact that due to the transverse nature of the operator Π the radiation corrections to the longitudinal term are equal to zero. In this connection we recall that the transverse form of Π is determined by the requirement of gauge invariance of the scattering matrix (see (24.39) and (30.35)). It may also be shown that $\Pi(k)$ is likewise a gauge-invariant quantity and does not depend on d_l^0.

Finally, in considering diagrams of the vertex type, i.e., connected diagrams with one fermion entering, one fermion emerging and one external photon entering, one may introduce their sum Γ which may sometimes be conveniently represented in the form

$$\Gamma^n(p, q, k) = \gamma^n + \Lambda^n(p, q, k). \tag{31.25}$$

Evidently here γ^n is the main term while Λ^n is the sum of all possible radiation corrections.

We now note that although relations (31.22), (31.24) and (31.25) may formally hold even before the removal of infinities we shall be principally interested in relations of this type between quantities not containing any divergences. We shall therefore consider that the foregoing relations have been formulated after the process of removing infinities has been completed.

Then the finite quantities G, D, and Γ introduced into the above relations contain an ambiguity related to the possibility of introducing the finite terms (31.10) into the interaction Lagrangian. Let us therefore establish the transformation properties of the quantities G, D, and Γ when expression (31.10) is added to the Lagrangian. We examine first of all the transformation of Σ and Π. It was shown that the functions S^c, $D^{c,\mathrm{tr}}$, and the charge e transform according to formulas (31.18) when the aforementioned terms are introduced. We now note that since two fermion and one photon lines meet at each vertex one may consider that the transformation (31.18) is equivalent to one in which the factors S^c and $D^{c,\mathrm{tr}}$ undergo no change while the charge e corresponding to each vertex internal with respect to Σ and Π undergoes a transformation of the type

$$e \to e' = z_1 z_2^{-1} z_3^{-1/2} e \tag{31.26}$$

(Fig. 40a). With respect to the two external vertices contained in Σ and in Π, i.e., those vertices which connect Σ and Π to the other parts of the diagrams, we note that for a complete renormalization of (31.26) each of these vertices will lack the square root of the corresponding z (see Fig. 40b). Therefore, the transformation law for Σ and Π may be represented in the form

$$\Sigma(p,\ e) \to z_2 \Sigma(p,\ e'), \tag{31.27}$$

$$\Pi(k,\ e) \to z_3 \Pi(k,\ e'), \tag{31.28}$$

where e' is given by (31.26).

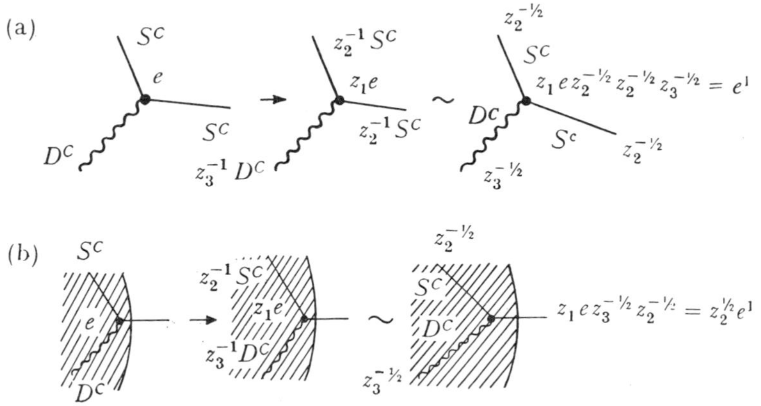

Fig. 40. (a) Transformation of a vertex internal with respect to Σ and Π. (b) Transformation of an internal vertex in Σ.

Turning to the transformation of the complete Green's functions G and D, we note that in the process of summation leading to (31.22) and (31.24) we need only make the replacements

$$\Sigma(p,\ e) \to z_2 \Sigma(p,\ e'),\quad \pi(k,\ e) \to z_3 \pi(k,\ e'),$$

$$\frac{1}{\hat{p} - m} \to \frac{1}{z_2} \frac{1}{(\hat{p} - m)},\quad \frac{1}{k^2} \to \frac{1}{z_3} \frac{1}{k^2},$$

which yield:

$$G(p,\ e) \to z_2^{-1} G(p,\ e'), \tag{31.29}$$

$$D^{\text{tr}}(k,\ e) \to z_3^{-1} D^{\text{tr}}(k,\ e'). \tag{31.30}$$

Finally, on taking into account the counter term δm in all the internal fermion lines we are led to the following mass renormalization:

$$m \to m' = m + \delta m. \tag{31.31}$$

It may be easily shown by analogous arguments that by taking into account the terms (31.10) in diagrams of the vertex type we obtain:

$$e\Gamma^n(p, k, q \mid e, m) \to z_2 z_3^{1/2} e' \Gamma^n(p, k, q \mid e', m') = z_1 e\Gamma^n(p, q, k \mid e', m'). \tag{31.32}$$

In summary, we have shown that the introduction of the terms (31.10) is equivalent to the following transformation of the factors G, D, Γ, e, and m:

$$\left.\begin{array}{l} G(p, e, m) \to z_2^{-1} G(p, e', m'),\ D^{\mathrm{tr}}(k, e) \to z_3^{-1} D^{\mathrm{tr}}(k, e', m'), \\ \qquad \Gamma(p, q, k \mid e, m) \to z_1 \Gamma(p, q, k \mid e', m'), \\ \text{where} \\ \qquad e' = z_1 z_2^{-1} z_3^{-1/2} e, \qquad m' = m + \delta m. \end{array}\right\} \tag{31.33}$$

We also note that with the aid of the factors G, D, and Γ calculations of arbitrarily high order for any process may be carried out on the basis of the so-called "skeleton" Feynman diagrams. The set of all the skeleton diagrams is obtained from the set of all the connected diagrams by excluding from them all those diagrams which contain elements of the type shown in Fig. 33. Therefore skeleton diagrams contain no self-energy parts and no vertex parts. However, for the calculation of the corresponding coefficient functions, we must employ not the ordinary propagation factors S^c and D^c but the complete propagation factors G and D, and we must make the vertices of the skeleton diagram correspond to Γ^n and not to γ^n. We emphasize that in this method of calculation utilizing the renormalized functions G, D, and Γ we need no longer make use of the subtraction procedure, since, as we have shown earlier, subtraction has to be applied only to the elements of a diagram of the type shown in Fig. 33.

Moreover, it follows from the above that the effect of the terms (31.10) on the coefficient functions of the S-matrix which correspond to more complicated irreducible diagrams is completely described by the renormalization (31.33) of the quantities

G, D^{tr}, Γ which correspond to elements of the appropriate skeleton diagram, and does not lead to any additional effects.

It is also clear that the factors z_2^{-1}, z_3^{-1} and z_1 which correspond to the factors G, D, and Γ of the skeleton diagram lead in the final result to the charge renormalization (31.26) at the internal vertices of the skeleton diagram.

Thus from the point of view of the internal parts of arbitrarily complicated diagrams of any arbitrary order, the introduction of the terms $(z_1 - 1)$, $(z_2 - 1)$, $(z_3 - 1)$ is equivalent to the renormalization of the quantities G, D, and Γ:

$$\Gamma \to z_1 \Gamma, \quad G \to z_2^{-1} G, \quad D^{\text{tr}} \to z_3^{-1} D^{\text{tr}}, \tag{31.34}$$

which in turn is equivalent to the charge renormalization (31.26) or, on taking Ward's identity into account, to

$$e \to e' = z^{-1/2} e. \tag{31.35}$$

Taken together with the nature of the effect produced by the term δm established above this means that the effect of the four terms (31.10) amounts to a renormalization of the two quantities — the mass m and the charge e as described by formulas (31.31) and (31.35).

Therefore, if simultaneously with the introduction of the terms (31.10) the mass m and the charge e in the initial equation are replaced by the quantities

$$\left.\begin{aligned} m'' &= m - \delta m, \\ e'' &= z_3^{1/2} e, \end{aligned}\right\} \tag{31.36}$$

then as a result of the transformations (31.31) and (31.35) we shall obtain the initial values of the mass m and the charge e. Conversely, instead of introducing the counter terms (31.10) it would have been sufficient to go over at the outset to the new mass and charge m' and e'.

Thus, the simultaneous introduction of the renormalizations (31.33) and (31.36) leads us to a theory which is equivalent to the initial one. These transformations evidently have the group property, and lead us to a group of transformations which leave invariant the observable values of m and e. We shall call this group the renormalization group. It will be discussed in greater detail in Chapter VIII. Equations (31.33) and (31.35) may be directly generalized to the case $d_l^0 \neq 0$:

$$\left.\begin{array}{lll} \Gamma_1 \to z_1 \Gamma, & G \to z_2^{-1} G, & D \to z_3^{-1} D, \\ m \to m + \delta m, & e \to z_3^{-1/2} e, & d_l^0 \to z_3 d_l^0. \end{array}\right\} \quad (31.37)$$

It is important to note that in order to preserve the physical meaning of the renormalized mass and charge the arbitrary constants must satisfy certain conditions. Thus, the requirements that the mass should be finite and positive, and that the charge should be finite and real, lead to the following restrictions on δm and z_3

$$0 < m + \delta m < \infty, \quad 0 < z_3 < \infty. \quad (31.38)$$

31.4. *The Formal Nature of Infinite Renormalizations*

In connection with the above we must make the following remarks.

1. By formally repeating arguments, similar to the ones given above, with respect to the nature of the effect of the infinite counter terms $(Z_1 - 1)$ $(Z_2 - 1)$, $(Z_3 - 1)$ and δm on the structure of the Green's functions G, D, and of the vertex part Γ one may obtain formulas for the charge and mass renormalization of type (31.35) which contain infinite δm and Z. Since the infinite counter terms indicated above remove all the divergences one may consider that formulas of the type (31.33) correspond to a process of the explicit segregation of the divergent factors from Γ, G, and D^{tr}

$$\begin{array}{l} \Gamma_{\text{sing}} \to \Gamma_{\text{reg}} = Z_1 \Gamma_{\text{sing}}, \; G_{\text{sing}} \to G_{\text{reg}} = Z_2^{-1} G_{\text{sing}} \\ D^{\text{tr}}_{\text{sing}} \to D^{\text{tr}}_{\text{reg}} = Z_3^{-1} D^{\text{tr}}_{\text{sing}} \end{array} \quad (31.39)$$

In particular, Dyson (34) first formulated by this method a prescription for the removal of infinities in quantum electrodynamics.

Then by turning to the mass and the charge one obtains instead of (31.31) and (31.35)

$$m_1 = m + \delta \bar{m}, \quad e_1 = Z_3^{-1/2} e, \quad (31.40)$$

where $\delta \bar{m}$ and Z_3 are expressed in the form of series in e^2 with divergent coefficients.

The quantities m_1 and e_1 appearing in (31.40) represent the mass and the charge initially ascribed to the electron. They may be regarded as characteristics of the "bare" noninteracting electron and are referred to the initial values. On the other hand, the quantities m and e correspond to the final formulas and are identified with the observable values of the mass and charge of the real electron. The formulas (31.40) establish the connection between the initial and the observable values of the mass and the charge.

However, it is clear that in view of the singular nature of Z_3 and $\delta\bar{m}$ the relations (31.40) are of a formal nature and their direct identification with some sort of graphic concepts, such as the concept of the observable charge being the result of the screening of the bare charge by virtual charges arising in the process of vacuum polarization, may lead to various paradoxes.

Let us consider the case when for purposes of auxiliary regularization a cutoff is used at large momenta of the virtual photons and the virtual electrons, which corresponds, as is well known, to abandoning the local character of the interaction. Let us consider, for example, the nonlocal interaction Lagrangian of the form (24)

$$\mathscr{L}(x) = e \int :\bar{\psi}(x)\,\hat{A}(z)\,\psi(x):\,K(x-z)\,dz, \tag{31.41}$$

where $K(x-z)$ represents a "smeared-out δ-function" characterized by some effective cutoff parameter in momentum space. For simplicity we may assume that $K(x-z)$ has the form

$$K(x-z) = \frac{1}{(2\pi)^4} \int \left[\frac{M_\Phi^2}{M_\Phi^2 - k^2}\right]^{1/2} e^{ik(x-z)}\,dk.$$

It may be easily seen that such a form of the function K corresponds to the regularization of photon pairings by means of the single auxiliary mass M_Φ:

$$\frac{1}{k^2} \to \frac{1}{k^2} - \frac{1}{k^2 - M_\Phi^2} = \frac{1}{k^2}\left(\frac{M_\Phi^2}{M_\Phi^2 - k^2}\right)$$

and that moreover

$$\lim_{M_\Phi \to \infty} K(x-z) = \delta(x-z).$$

By constructing the scattering matrix in the usual way in the form of the chronological exponential (18.43) we shall obtain a theory which contains divergences associated only with the second-order photon self-energy, since the corresponding diagram (Fig. 3) is the only diagram that does not contain internal photon lines and which consequently is not modified by the introduction of the cutoff factor $M_\Phi^2/(M_\Phi^2 - k^2)$. All the other divergences will vanish in the transition from $\delta(x-z)$ to $K(x-z)$ in view of their limiting logarithmic nature.

The only divergence of the theory obtained in this way may now be removed by redefining the T-product

$$T(:\bar{\psi}(x)\,\gamma^n\,\psi(x): \; :\bar{\psi}(y)\,\gamma^m\,\psi(y):),$$

which turns out to be equivalent to adding the single counter term $(Z_3 - 1)$

to the initial Lagrangian. For the determination of the explicit form of Z_3 we shall, as usual, carry out the intermediate regularization of electron pairings by means of a single auxiliary mass:

$$\frac{\hat{p} + m}{m^2 - p^2} \to (m + \hat{p}) \left(\frac{1}{m^2 - p^2} - \frac{1}{M_e^2 - p^2}\right).$$

By repeating without any changes the arguments of § 24 we shall obtain:

$$Z_3 = 1 - \frac{e^2}{12\pi^2} \ln \frac{M_e^2}{m^2} - e^2 G, \tag{31.42}$$

where G is a finite constant determined by the condition that e should coincide with the observable value of the charge and be independent of M_e in the limit of large M_e. By removing the auxiliary regularization with respect to $M_e (M_e \to \infty)$ and by going to the local limit $(M_\Phi \to \infty)$ we find that $Z_3 \to -\infty$. Substituting this result into the charge renormalization formula (31.40) we obtain for e_1 the meaningless value:

$$e_1 \to \frac{i}{\infty}. \tag{31.43}$$

We have obtained the paradoxical result of the purely imaginary vanishingly small value of the initial charge e_1 which contradicts the condition that the initial Lagrangian should be Hermitean.

Formulas of the type (31.42), (31.43) are sometimes even interpreted as evidence of the internal inconsistency of the present formulation of local theories.

Thus, for example, Pomeranchuk (97) on the basis of formulas of the type (31.42), (31.43) derived by him by means of the so-called "double limit cutoff technique" (which is essentially equivalent to the argument given above) arrived at the conclusion that quantum electrodynamics is a physically inconsistent theory. [62]

However, such deductions do not by any means have the status of proofs. Formulas (31.42), (31.43) are merely evidence of the fact that it is not permissible to operate with meaningless divergent expressions and formulas of the type (31.39) and (31.40). Naturally, the question of the existence or nonexistence of some sort of contradictions in the theory remains at the present time completely open, and requires the introduction of much deeper considerations for its investigation (in this connection see also § 43.2).

2. In connection with renormalization relations of the type (31.34), (31.35) we should take note of another attitude adopted by some investigators of quantum field theory. The investigators adopting this attitude [63] desiring to go beyond the framework of perturbation theory employ

[62] See also Landau and Pomeranchuk (79).

[63] Kallen (65), Lehman (81), and others.

so-called "renormalized" field operators, write down interaction Lagrangians containing meaningless divergent constants Z_1, Z_2, Z_3, δm, construct Heisenberg equations for renormalized operators, manipulate the latter formally and arrive in this way at a number of relationships. However, it is clear that such a method of procedure is quite without justification, and in order to give it some meaning (even in only a mathematical sense) it is necessary first of all to introduce some sort of auxiliary regularization. Naturally, the construction of an auxiliary regularization of such a nature is a very complicated matter, since its introduction corresponds to a departure from locality, while at the present time there exists no consistent nonlocal theory.

31.5. *Radiation Corrections to External Lines and the Choice of Finite Constants*

We shall now make the subtraction procedure more specific and shall remove entirely all arbitrariness of the polynomials being subtracted. In our general definition of the subtraction procedure (§ 28) we have agreed to subtract from the divergent expressions (in the present case Σ, Π, and Λ) the first terms of their expansions into Maclaurin series. However, for practical purposes, it turns out to be more convenient to expand the self-energy part of the fermion about the point $\hat{p} = m$. We therefore define the regular function Σ_{reg} as follows:

$$\Sigma_{\mathrm{reg}}(\hat{p}) = \Sigma(\hat{p}) - \Sigma(\hat{p})\Big|_{\hat{p}=m} - \frac{\partial \Sigma(\hat{p})}{\partial \hat{p}}\Big|_{\hat{p}=m} (\hat{p} - m). \qquad (31.44)$$

In the foregoing we have made use of the fact that Σ depends on p only through $\hat{p}$ and $p^2 = (\hat{p})^2$. In making the subtraction in this manner we obtain

$$\Sigma_{\mathrm{reg}}(\hat{p})\,|_{\hat{p}=m} = 0 \qquad (31.45)$$

and

$$\frac{\partial \Sigma_{\mathrm{reg}}(\hat{p})}{\partial \hat{p}}\Big|_{\hat{p}=m} = 0, \qquad (31.46)$$

from which it also follows that

$$\frac{1}{\hat{p} - m} \Sigma_{\mathrm{reg}}(\hat{p})\Big|_{\hat{p}=m} = \Sigma_{\mathrm{reg}}(\hat{p}) \frac{1}{\hat{p} - m}\Big|_{\hat{p}=m} = 0. \qquad (31.47)$$

It follows from (31.45) that the mass m turns out to be

equal to the experimental mass of the electron. This may be directly seen from the fact that the pole of the complete Green's function

$$G(p) = \frac{1}{m - \hat{p} + \Sigma_{\text{reg}}(\hat{p})}$$

coincides with the pole of the function

$$S^c(p) = \frac{1}{m - \hat{p}}.$$

Condition (31.46) leads to the result that the radiation corrections to the external fermion lines turn out to be equal to zero.

In connection with expanding the function Σ about the point $\hat{p} = m$ $(p^2 = m^2)$ it is also necessary to note that as we have shown in Chapter IV (§ 26.2, § 27.1), the region in which the regularized expressions are analytic in the limit $\varepsilon \to 0$ is restricted by the condition (27.1) which in our case assumes the form

$$p^0 < \min m_i.$$

Since in the present case the minimum mass is equal to zero (photon mass), the function $\Sigma(p)$ cannot be analytic at the point $p^2 = m^2$, which is in fact the case. The derivative $\partial\Sigma/\partial\hat{p}$ diverges at this point. However, this divergence is a manifestation of the well-known "infrared catastrophe" (see § 32), and for its removal it turns out to be sufficient to introduce in the intermediate stages of the argument an auxiliary quantity — the fictitious infinitesimal photon mass λ_0. Therefore, in the future we shall always assume that wherever necessary the photon will be assigned the small mass λ_0.

We now consider the subtraction process for the vertex part $\Gamma^n(p, q, k)$. As was shown in § 30, it follows from the requirement of gauge invariance that the subtraction procedure for Λ is completely determined by the subtraction procedure used for Σ. From (31.44) we obtain directly:

$$\left.\begin{aligned} \Lambda^n_{\text{reg}}(p, q, k) &= \Lambda^n(p, q, k) - \Lambda^n_1, \\ \Gamma^n_{\text{reg}}(p, q, k) &= \gamma^n + \Lambda^n(p, q, k) - \Lambda^n_1, \end{aligned}\right\} \tag{31.48}$$

where in accordance with (30.32)

$$\Lambda^n_{\text{reg}}(-p, p, 0) = -g^{nn}\frac{\partial \Sigma_{\text{reg}}(\hat{p})}{\partial p^n} \tag{31.49}$$

and consequently

$$\Lambda^n_1 = -\left.\frac{\partial \Sigma(\hat{p})}{\partial \hat{p}}\right|_{\hat{p}=m} \gamma^n.$$

It now remains for us to define the subtraction procedure for the self-energy part of the photon. Taking, as usual, the expansion about the point $k = 0$ we obtain:

$$\Pi^{mn}_{\text{reg}}(k) = \Pi^{mn}(k) - \Pi^{mn}(0)$$
$$- \sum_l \left.\frac{\partial \Pi^{mn}(k)}{\partial k^l}\right|_{k=0} k^l - \frac{1}{2}\sum_{l,s}\left.\frac{\partial^2 \Pi^{mn}(k)}{\partial k^l \partial k^s}\right|_{k=0} k^l k^s. \tag{31.50}$$

This expression, which satisfies the conditions

$$\Pi^{mn}_{\text{reg}}(0) = 0 \tag{31.51}$$

and

$$\left.\frac{1}{k^2}\Pi^{mn}_{\text{reg}}(k)\right|_{k=0} = 0, \tag{31.52}$$

in virtue of the property (31.51) does not change the pole of the photon function, and in accordance with (31.52) leads to the absence of radiation corrections to external photon lines.

Moreover, it may also be shown that expression (31.50) guarantees that the constant e in the interaction Lagrangian coincides with the observable value of the electron charge. Indeed, let us add to the right-hand side of equation (31.50) the expression

$$c(g^{mn}k^2 - k^m k^n), \tag{31.53}$$

which violates condition (31.52). This expression is equivalent to adding to the Lagrangian a finite term of the type $z_3 - 1 = c$ so that the constant c leads to the charge being altered by the factor $(1 + c)^{-1/2}$. We thus arrive at the possibility of determining the arbitrary finite constant c from the condition that e should coincide with the experimental value of the charge of the fermion. Assuming that the experimental value of the charge is determined by the scattering of a zero energy photon by the fermion, we obtain the result that such a process is described by the expression

$$e\bar{\psi}(p)\Gamma^{n}_{\text{reg}}(p,\ -p,\ 0)\psi(-p). \tag{31.54}$$

In evaluating (31.54) it turns out that the contribution of the difference

$$\Lambda_1^n - \Lambda^n(p,\ -p,\ 0) = g^{nn}\frac{\partial\Sigma(\hat{p})}{\partial p^n} - \gamma^n\frac{\partial\Sigma(\hat{p})}{\partial\hat{p}}\bigg|_{\hat{p}=m} \tag{31.55}$$

which appears in Γ^{n}_{reg} is equal to zero. In order to show this we note that $\Sigma(p)$ may be represented in the form

$$\Sigma(\hat{p}) = (\hat{p}-m)f(p^2) + m\varphi(p^2).$$

On evaluating (31.55) we find:

$$\Lambda_1^n - \Lambda^n(p,\ -p,\ 0) = (\hat{p}-m)\,2p^n\frac{\partial f}{\partial p^2} + 2p^n m\frac{\partial\varphi}{\partial p^2}$$
$$+\ \gamma^n[f(p^2) - f(m^2)] - 2\hat{p}\gamma^n m\frac{\partial\varphi}{\partial p^2}.$$

By evaluating the matrix element

$$\bar{\psi}(p)[\Lambda^n(p,\ -p,\ 0) - \Lambda_1^n]\psi(-p),$$

taking into account the field equations

$$\bar{\psi}(p)(\hat{p}-m) = 0, \quad (\hat{p}-m)\psi(-p) = 0$$

and making use of the relation

$$2(p^n - m\gamma^n) = (\hat{p}-m)\gamma^n + \gamma^n(\hat{p}-m)$$

we see that it is equal to zero.

Taking renormalization into account we obtain finally

$$e\bar{\psi}\Gamma^{n}_{\text{reg}}\psi = \frac{e}{\sqrt{1+c}}\bar{\psi}\gamma^n\psi,$$

from which it follows that the condition that e should coincide with the experimental value of the charge has the form

$$c = 0.$$

Thus the formula (31.50) does in fact guarantee both the absence of radiation corrections to external photon lines and also the equality of e to the experimental value of the electron charge.

§ 32. Spinor Electrodynamics. III. Radiation Corrections of the Second Order

We now turn to the application of the preceding results to the calculation of radiation corrections of lowest order to the different effects of spinor electrodynamics. With this end in view we shall first of all obtain expressions for the corrections to the propagation factors for the photon D, and for the electron G, and to the vertex function Γ.

32.1. *Correction to the Photon Function*

The photon Green's function D in zero approximation corresponding to the absence of interaction has in the case of arbitrary d_l^0 the form

$$D^c_{mn}(k) = -\frac{1}{k^2}\left(g^{mn} - \frac{k_m k_n}{k^2}\right) - \frac{d_l^0}{k^2}\,\frac{k_m k_n}{k^2}. \tag{32.1}$$

In order to calculate the radiation correction to (32.1) we must add a term corresponding to the photon line and containing

Fig. 41. Diagrams corresponding to the principal term of D_{mn} and to the first radiation correction.

the insertion of the second-order photon self-energy (Fig. 41). This term has the form

$$\sum_{k,\,l} D^c_{mk}\,\Pi^{kl}(k) D^c_{ln}(k). \tag{32.2}$$

Making use of the gauge invariant expression (24.40) for the polarization operator Π and determining the constant in it from the condition that the second-order partial derivatives at the point $k = 0$ should be equal to zero we find

$$\Pi^{kl}(k) = \frac{e^2}{4\pi^2}\,(g^{kl}k^2 - k^k k^l)\,I(k^2), \tag{32.3}$$

where

$$I(k^2) = 2\int_0^1 dx(1-x)x \ln\left|\frac{m^2 - x(1-x)k^2}{m^2}\right|. \tag{32.4}$$

Substituting (32.3) into (32.2) and adding to (32.1) we obtain:

$$D_{mn}(k) = -\frac{d(k^2)}{k^2}\left(g^{mn} - \frac{k_m k_n}{k^2}\right) - \frac{d_l^0}{k^2}\frac{k_m k_n}{k^2}, \qquad (32.5)$$

where

$$d(k^2) = 1 + \frac{e^2}{4\pi^2} I(k^2). \qquad (32.6)$$

From (32.4)–(32.6) it follows that, as should have been expected, on the one hand the longitudinal function d_l^0 has no influence on the radiation corrections to the transverse function $d(k^2)$, while on the other hand the radiation corrections make no contribution to d_l. Therefore we shall restrict ourselves to the examination of the purely transverse part of the photon Green's function writing it in the form

$$D^{\text{tr}}_{mn}(k) = -\frac{1}{k^2}\left(g^{mn} - \frac{k_m k_n}{k^2}\right) d(k^2). \qquad (32.7)$$

The integral I which appears in the definition of $d(k^2)$ may be put by means of a change of variables $z = 1 - 2x$ and by integration by parts in the form [64]

$$I(k^2) = \tfrac{1}{2}\int_0^1 dz(1-z^2)\ln\left|1 - \frac{1-z^2}{4}\frac{k^2}{m^2}\right| = -k^2\int_0^1 \frac{z^2 dz(1-z^2/3)}{4m^2 - k^2(1-z^2)}. \qquad (32.8)$$

For $k^2 > 4m$ the denominator of the integral (32.8) has zeros, which at first glance seems to lead to a nonintegrable singularity. However, we recall that in accordance with the general prescription one should in such cases regard the electron mass as having an infinitesimal imaginary additional part $(m^2 \to m^2 - i\varepsilon)$ so that the above singularities turn out to be integrable.

By introducing into (32.8) another change of variables $4m^2/(1 - z^2) = M^2$ and by taking into account the addition of the above imaginary term we obtain:

$$I(k^2) = -\frac{k^2}{3}\int_{4m^2}^{\infty} \frac{dM^2(1 + 2m^2/M^2)\sqrt{1 - 4m^2/M^2}}{M^2(M^2 - k^2 - i\varepsilon)}. \qquad (32.9)$$

[64] This agrees with the result of Karplus and Kroll (67).

Substituting (32.9) into (32.6) and (32.7) we obtain the well-known parametric representation of the photon Green's function [65]

$$D^{\mathrm{tr}}_{mn}(k) = -\left(g^{mn} - \frac{k_m k_n}{k^2}\right)$$
$$\times\left\{\frac{1}{k^2+i\varepsilon} - \frac{e^2}{12\pi^2}\int_{4m^2}^{\infty}\frac{dM^2}{M^2}\,\frac{(1+2m^2/M^2)\sqrt{1-4m^2/M^2}}{M^2-k^2-i\varepsilon}\right\}. \quad (32.10)$$

The integral (32.9) may be evaluated explicitly. In order to do this we write it in the form

$$I(k^2) = -\frac{5}{9} - \frac{4}{3}\frac{m^2}{k^2} - \left(1-\frac{4m^2}{k^2}\right)\frac{2}{3}\left(1+2\frac{m^2}{k^2}\right)J(k^2). \quad (32.11)$$

The quantity

$$J(k^2) = \frac{k^2}{2}\int_{4m^2}^{\infty}\frac{dM^2}{M^2}\,\frac{(1-4m^2/M^2)^{-1/2}}{M^2-k^2-i\varepsilon}$$

introduced above contains no singularities in the integrand for $k^2 < 4m^2$:

$$J(k^2) = \begin{cases} \left(\dfrac{4m^2}{k^2}-1\right)^{-1/2}\operatorname{arc\,tg}\left(\dfrac{4m^2}{k^2}-1\right)^{-1/2} & \text{for } 0<k^2<4m^2, \\ \left(1-\dfrac{4m^2}{k^2}\right)^{-1/2}\operatorname{arc\,th}\left(1-\dfrac{4m^2}{k^2}\right)^{-1/2} & \text{for } k^2<0. \end{cases} \quad (32.12)$$

For $k^2 > 4m^2$ a pole appears in the integrand, the rule for going around which is determined by the added term $-i\varepsilon$. For a direct calculation it is convenient to utilize the formula

$$\frac{1}{x-i\varepsilon} = \mathscr{P}\frac{1}{x} + i\pi\delta(x)$$

($\mathscr{P}$ denotes the principal value) which gives:

$$J(k^2) = \frac{i\pi}{2\sqrt{1-4m^2/k^2}} + \tfrac{1}{2}(1-4m^2/k^2)^{-1/2}\ln\frac{1-\sqrt{1-4m^2/k^2}}{1+\sqrt{1-4m^2/k^2}}. \quad (32.13)$$

[65] Compare Källen (65), and Gell-Mann and Low (48).

Combining (32.12), (32.13) and substituting into (32.11) [66] we obtain: [67]

$$I(k^2) = -\left(\frac{5}{9}+\frac{4}{3}\frac{m^2}{k^2}\right)-\frac{2}{3}\left(1+\frac{2m^2}{k^2}\right)\sqrt{1-\frac{4m^2}{k^2}}\,\text{arc th}\,\frac{1}{\sqrt{1-4m^2/k^2}}$$

$$-\,\theta(k^2-4m^2)\,\frac{i\pi}{3}\left(1+\frac{2m^2}{k^2}\right)\sqrt{1-\frac{4m^2}{k^2}}. \qquad (32.14)$$

For small k^2 we obtain from the above

$$I(k^2) = -\frac{1}{15}\frac{k^2}{m^2}+O\left(\frac{k^2}{m^2}\right)^2 \qquad (k^2 \ll m^2).$$

Comparing this result with (32.6) we obtain an important property [68] of the radiation correction to the function $d(k^2)$

$$d(k^2) = 1-\frac{e^2}{60\pi^2}\frac{k^2}{m^2}+\ldots \qquad (k^2 \ll m^2);$$

it vanishes in the limit $k^2 \to 0$.

For large $|k^2|$ we correspondingly obtain:

$$I(k^2) = \frac{1}{3}\ln\frac{|k^2|}{m^2}+O\left(\frac{m^2}{k^2}\right) \qquad (|k^2| \gg m^2).$$

This yields:

$$d(k^2) = 1+\frac{e^2}{12\pi^2}\ln\frac{|k^2|}{m^2}+\ldots \qquad (32.15)$$

32.2 *Corrections to the Electron Green's Function*

The second-order correction to the electron Green's function has the form

$$\frac{i}{\hat{p}-m}\,\frac{\Sigma^{(2)}(p)}{i}\,\frac{i}{\hat{p}-m}.$$

[66] Taking into account the relation

$$ix\,\text{arc th}\,\frac{1}{ix} = x\,\text{arc tg}\,\frac{1}{x}.$$

[67] Here θ is the well-known step function introduced in (3.18).

[68] Actually this property is a consequence of the vanishing of the second derivatives of the polarization operator for $k = 0$ (see 31.52).

For the determination of $\Sigma^{(2)}(p)$ we shall start with the photon causal function for arbitrary d_l^0. We shall determine the arbitrary constants in the expression for $\Sigma^{(2)}(p)$ (compare (24.30)) from the conditions

$$\Sigma^{(2)}(m) = 0, \qquad \left.\frac{\partial \Sigma^{(2)}(\hat{p})}{\partial \hat{p}}\right|_{\hat{p}=m} = 0. \tag{32.16}$$

It turns out that the derivative $\partial \Sigma^{(2)}(\hat{p})/\partial \hat{p}$ with respect to $\hat{p}$ contains a term of the form $\ln(1 - p^2/m^2)$ which diverges logarithmically as $\hat{p} \to m$. This divergence is a manifestation of the infrared catastrophe and is related to the fact that it is not permissible to make expansions in terms of the number of emitted photons in the investigation of processes in which photons with small momenta play a role. The nature of infrared divergences was investigated in its time by Bloch and Nordsieck (12). For a more detailed analysis of this difficulty we refer the reader to § 32.4 (see also § 43.3 and § 44.3 in Chapter VIII), and at present restrict ourselves to pointing out that the total transition probabilities in each order in e^2 are free of infrared divergences, while the actual regularization of the intermediate expressions is usually achieved by means of introducing a small fictitious photon mass λ_0.

By modifying the corresponding calculations of § 24 we obtain in place of (24.30)

$$\Sigma^{(2)}(p) = \frac{e^2}{16\pi^2}\left\{\frac{p^2-m^2}{m^2}\left(d_l^0\frac{p^2+m^2}{p^2}\hat{p} - (d_l^0+3)\,m\right)A(p^2) + d_l^0\hat{p}\,\frac{p^2-m^2}{p^2} + c_1(\hat{p}-m) + c_2 m\right\}, \tag{32.17}$$

where (omitting the imaginary part equal to $-\pi i(m^2/p^2)\theta(p^2-m^2)$)

$$A(p^2) = \int_0^1 \frac{dx\,(x-1)m^2}{(1-x)(m^2-xp^2)+x\lambda_0^2} = \begin{cases} \dfrac{m^2}{p^2}\ln\left|\dfrac{p^2-m^2}{m^2}\right| & \text{for } |p^2-m^2| \gg \lambda_0^2, \\[2ex] \dfrac{1}{2}\ln\dfrac{\lambda_0^2}{m^2} & \text{for } p^2 = m^2. \end{cases} \tag{32.18}$$

By determining the constants c_1 and c_2 from the conditions (32.16) we obtain in place of (32.17)

$$\Sigma^{(2)}(p) = \frac{e^2}{16\pi^2}\Big\{\frac{p^2-m^2}{m^2}\Big(d_l^0\frac{p^2+m^2}{p^2}\hat{p}-(d_l^0+3)m\Big)A(p^2)+d_l^0\hat{p}\frac{p^2-m^2}{p^2}$$

$$-2d_l^0(\hat{p}-m)+2(3-d_l^0)A(m^2)(\hat{p}-m)\Big\}$$

$$= \frac{e^2}{16\pi^2}(\hat{p}-m)\Big\{A(p^2)\Big(d_l^0\frac{p^2}{m^2}-3\Big)+A(m^2)(6-2d_l^0)$$

$$-d_l^0+\frac{\hat{p}}{m}\Big[A(p^2)\Big(d_l^0\frac{m^2}{p^2}-3\Big)+d_l^0\frac{m^2}{p^2}\Big]\Big\}. \quad (32.19)$$

Substituting (32.19) into the sum

$$G(p) = \frac{1}{m-\hat{p}}\Big(1+\Sigma(p)\frac{1}{\hat{p}-m}\Big),$$

we obtain:

$$G(p) = \frac{1}{m-\hat{p}}\Big\{1+\frac{e^2}{16\pi^2}\Big[A(p^2)\Big(d_l^0\frac{p^2}{m^2}-3\Big)+A(m^2)(6-2d_l^0)-d_l^0\Big]$$

$$+\frac{e^2}{16\pi^2}\frac{\hat{p}}{m}\Big[A(p^2)\Big(d_l^0\frac{m^2}{p^2}-3\Big)+d_l^0\frac{m^2}{p^2}\Big]\Big\}. \quad (32.20)$$

Sometimes it is also convenient to represent $G(p)$ in the form

$$G(p) = \frac{\hat{p}a(p^2)+mb(p^2)}{m^2-p^2}, \quad (32.21)$$

where in accordance with (32.20)

$$a(p^2) = 1+\frac{e^2}{16\pi^2}\Big\{\frac{(p^2-m^2)^2}{p^2m^2}d_l^0A(p^2)$$

$$+[A(p^2)-A(m^2)](2d_l^0-6)-d_l^0+d_l^0\frac{m^2}{p^2}\Big\}, \quad (32.22)$$

$$b(p^2) = 1+\frac{e^2}{16\pi^2}\Big\{\frac{p^2-m^2}{m^2}(d_l^0-3)A(p^2)+[A(p^2)-A(m^2)](2d_l^0-6)\Big\}. \quad (32.23)$$

For $p^2 \gg m^2$ we obtain:

$$G(p) = -\frac{1}{\hat{p}}\Big\{1+\frac{e^2d_l^0}{16\pi^2}\ln\frac{p^2}{m^2}\Big\}. \quad (32.24)$$

32.3. *Corrections to the Vertex Part*

We now turn to the vertex part

$$\Gamma^n(p, q, k) = \gamma^n + \Lambda^n(p, q, k),$$

where, as usual, p and q are respectively the four-moment of the emerging and the incident electron, while $k = p - q$ is the momentum of the incident photon (Fig. 42). It was shown in

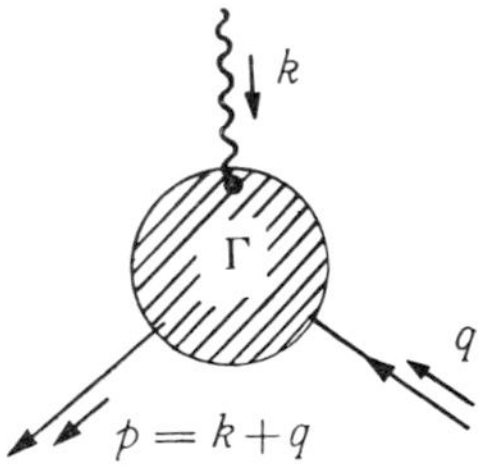

Fig. 42. Momentum variables for the vertex part.

§ 25 that the most general expression for Λ_3^n contains the term $C\gamma^n$ where the coefficient C is an arbitrary constant. In accordance with § 30 this coefficient must be determined by the condition of gauge invariance of the scattering matrix which has the form

$$\Lambda_3^n(p, p, 0) = -g^{nn}\frac{\partial \Sigma_2(p)}{\partial p^n}. \tag{32.25}$$

By generalizing the corresponding calculations of § 25 to the case $d_l^0 \neq 0$, $\lambda_0 \neq 0$, we obtain:

$$\Gamma^n_{\text{reg}}(p, q, k) = \gamma^n + \frac{e^2}{16\pi^2}\Bigg\{\gamma^n\Bigg[(1+d_l^0)\int_0^1 dx \ln\left|\frac{m^2}{m^2 - x(1-x)k^2}\right| - \tfrac{3}{2} - 2d_l^0 - C\Bigg]$$
$$+ \int_0^1 dx \int_0^{1-x} dy \, \frac{2A^n + A^n(1-x-y)(d_l^0 - 1) - 4\hat{Q}Q^n - 2R^n - (d_l^0 - 1)D^n}{Z}$$
$$+ (d_l^0 - 1)\int_0^1 dx \int_0^{1-x} dy \, \frac{(1-x-y)B^n}{Z^2} - 2\gamma^n \int_0^1 dx \int_0^{1-x} dy \ln\left|\frac{(x+y)m^2}{Z}\right|\Bigg\}, \tag{32.26}$$

where we have used the notation

$$\left.\begin{aligned}
A^n &= \gamma^n(\hat{q}+m)\hat{p}-(\hat{p}-m)(\hat{q}+m)\gamma^n-(\hat{p}-m)\gamma^n(\hat{q}-2m),\\
B^n &= \hat{Q}(\hat{p}+m)\gamma^n(\hat{q}+m)\hat{Q},\\
D^n &= \gamma^n(\hat{q}+m)\hat{Q}+\hat{Q}(\hat{p}+m)\gamma^n,\\
Q &= xq+yp,\\
R^n &= \hat{Q}\hat{k}\gamma^n-\gamma^n\hat{k}\hat{Q}-(\hat{p}-2m)\gamma^n\hat{Q}-\hat{Q}\gamma^n(\hat{q}-2m),\\
Z &= (1-x-y)yp^2+(1-x-y)xq^2+xyk^2\\
&\qquad -m^2(x+y)-(1-x-y)\lambda_0^2.
\end{aligned}\right\} \quad (32.27)$$

By determining the constant C from the condition (32.25) we find for it the value

$$C = 2d_l^0 + (3-d_l^0)\ln\frac{\lambda_0^2}{m^2} = 2[-d_l^0+(3-d_l^0)A(m^2)]. \quad (32.28)$$

32.4. *Outline of the Calculation of Corrections to the Klein-Nishina Formula*

Formulas (32.5), (32.6), (32.20), and (32.26) for D, G, and Γ which contain radiation corrections of order e^2 to the fundamental expressions allow us to calculate directly radiation corrections of order e^2 to the different effects in spinor electrodynamics. As an illustration of this we shall discuss *schematically* the procedure of calculating radiation corrections to the Klein-Nishina formula obtained by us in § 23. For this it is evidently necessary to take into account fourth-order diagrams containing two external photon lines and two external electron lines. Altogether there are eight such diagrams. Four of them differ from the basic Compton effect diagram by self-energy insertions into the external lines and in accordance with conditions (31.47) and (31.52) give no contributions to the matrix elements. Two other diagrams contain vertex parts of the second order (Fig. 43a, b), one diagram contains a self-energy insertion into the internal fermion line (Fig. 43c) and, finally, the last diagram corresponds to the emission of an additional virtual photon (Fig. 43d).

The structure of the matrix elements corresponding to the diagrams of Figs. 43a, b is analogous to the structure of the basic matrix elements of the second order (23.2) with the exception of the fact that the vertex parts contained in these diagrams correspond not to the matrix γ^n, but to the expression $\Gamma^n(p, q, k)$ determined by formula (32.26).

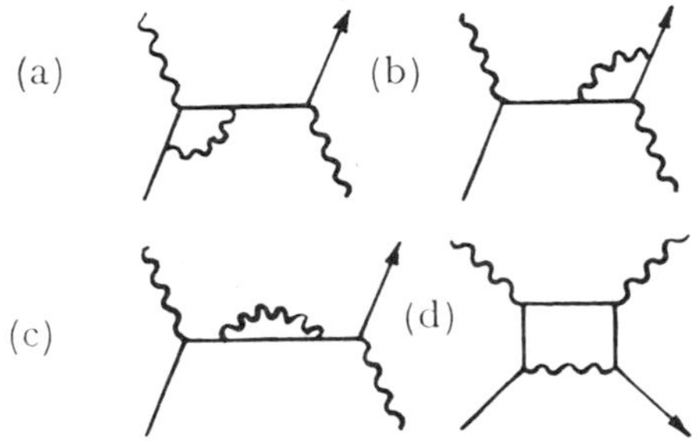

Fig. 43. Radiation corrections to the Compton effect which give matrix elements different from zero.

We note in this connection that the vertex factors $\Gamma^n(p, q, k)$ appearing in the above matrix elements correspond to one of the two groups of conditions:

$$1)\quad \hat{p} = m, \quad k^2 = 0, \quad \sum_n e_n k^n = 0,$$

$$2)\quad \hat{q} = m, \quad k^2 = 0, \quad \sum_n e_n k^n = 0.$$

In these two cases the integrations contained in (32.26) may be carried out almost completely and the vertex factor Γ^n may be expressed in terms of algebraic combinations of the Dirac matrices with the momenta, of logarithms, and of the function

$$w(z) = \frac{1}{z-1}\int_1^z \frac{dt}{t}(1-t)\ln(1-t). \qquad (32.29)$$

The matrix elements corresponding to the diagram of Fig. 43c may be constructed by means of using for the fermion propagation function in the intermediate state the expression (32.20) (which includes the radiation correction due to the self-energy loop contained in this diagram).

Thus the calculation of the matrix elements corresponding to all the fourth-order Compton scattering diagrams with the exception of the diagram of Fig. 43d may be carried out very simply with the aid of the explicit finite expressions for G and Γ obtained before. This calculation no longer contains any integrations over the four-momenta, and actually reduces to the evaluation of the trace of the square of the sum of matrix elements (cf. (23.3), (23.4)).

Finally, the evaluation of the matrix elements corresponding to the last diagram (Fig. 43d) requires the evaluation of integrals of the type

$$\sum_n g^{nn} \int \frac{dq}{q^2+i\varepsilon} \gamma^n \frac{1}{\hat{p}_2-\hat{q}-m} \gamma^m \frac{1}{\hat{p}_1+\hat{k}_1-\hat{q}-m} \gamma^l \frac{1}{\hat{p}_1-\hat{q}-m} \gamma^n, \quad (32.30)$$

where $p_1 + k_1 = p_2 + k_2$.

The integrals (32.30) do not contain ultraviolet divergences in an obvious manner. However, they diverge logarithmically for small q when $\hat{p}_1 = m$, $\hat{p}_2 = m$. Indeed, in this case a singularity of the form

$$\int \frac{dq}{q^2} \frac{1}{(p_2 q)(p_1 q)},$$

occurs which may be removed, as usual, by introducing the photon mass λ_0. The actual evaluation of the integrals (32.30) may be easily carried out by going over to the α-representation of the causal functions (of the type (24.12)). Because of the awkwardness of such calculations we do not carry out here the evaluation of integrals of type (32.30) and the calculation of traces, but instead we refer the reader who is interested in the final expression for the Klein-Nishina formula including radiation corrections of order e^4 to the article by Brown and Feynman (27).

We shall here say only a few additional words on the subject of compensation for the infrared divergences in the final expressions. As we have already seen, terms proportional to $\ln (\lambda_0^2/m^2)$ are contained in several fourth-order Compton scattering matrix elements. Such terms will also occur in the expressions for the transition probabilities. Thus, the expression for the probability of Compton scattering corresponding to the preceding eight fourth-order diagrams turns out to be *meaningless*.

The reason for this is that the problem has been incorrectly formulated physically.[69] As we have mentioned already, the infrared catastrophe is a consequence of the fact that it is not permissible to make expansions in the number of emitted photons for small energies of the latter. From the experimental point of view this situation corresponds to the physical indistinguishability of processes which differ from each other by the emission of a certain number of low energy photons. Indeed the fact that a photon of very low energy has been emitted may be established only by indirect methods by means of measuring the energy of all the other particles taking part in the process, and this may be carried out only with a certain finite accuracy. Therefore there always remains the possibility of emission of photons with a total energy smaller than a certain value E_{max} determined by the possible experimental error.

In the present case the first radiation corrections to the Klein-Nishina formula of order e^6, whose origin lies in the interference between second- and fourth-order terms, turn out to be physically indistinguishable from the phenomenon of the so-called *double* Compton scattering in which in addition to the usually observed Compton photon a second photon of very low energy is emitted, the probability of this being also of order e^6. If we take into account the probability of the double Compton effect integrated over the energies of the second photon from zero to E_{max}, we obtain an expression which is free of the infrared catastrophe, but which explicitly involves the quantity E_{max}.

§ 33. Pseudoscalar Meson Theory

33.1. *Isotopic Spin Formalism*

As a third example of the application of the general theory of the removal of divergences we shall examine the pseudoscalar meson theory, i.e., the theory of the pseudoscalar meson field and of the spinor nucleon field with pseudoscalar coupling. We shall consider the so-called symmetric variant of this theory which leads to nuclear forces symmetric with respect to the electric

[69] Brown and Feynman (27), Akhiezer and Berestetskii (2), Heitler (60).

charge (for example, to the same matrix elements for proton-proton and for neutron-neutron scattering). The mathematical description of the symmetric pseudoscalar theory is most simply given within the framework of the so-called isotopic spin formalism which consists of the following.

The nucleons are described by four-component spinor wave functions Ψ_N and Ψ_P where the indices N and P refer to the two charge states of the nucleon—the neutron and the proton. These functions may be combined into an eight-component nucleon function

$$\Psi = \begin{pmatrix} \Psi_P \\ \Psi_N \end{pmatrix}. \tag{33.1}$$

For the description of processes involving transitions between the proton and the neutron states it is customary to introduce the operators τ_+ and τ_- defined as follows:

$$\left.\begin{aligned} \tau_+ \Psi_N &= \Psi_P, & \tau_- \Psi_N &= 0, \\ \tau_+ \Psi_P &= 0, & \tau_- \Psi_P &= \Psi_N. \end{aligned}\right\} \tag{33.2}$$

In the representation (33.1) these operators have the matrix form

$$\tau_+ = \begin{pmatrix} 0 & 1 \\ 0 & 0 \end{pmatrix}, \qquad \tau_- = \begin{pmatrix} 0 & 0 \\ 1 & 0 \end{pmatrix}, \tag{33.3}$$

and possess the properties

$$\tau_+^2 = \tau_-^2 = 0, \qquad \tau_-\tau_+ + \tau_+\tau_- = 1. \tag{33.4}$$

Further, the following operators are introduced

$$\left.\begin{aligned} \tau_1 &= \tau_+ + \tau_- = \begin{pmatrix} 0 & 1 \\ 1 & 0 \end{pmatrix}, \\ \tau_2 &= -i(\tau_+ - \tau_-) = \begin{pmatrix} 0 & -i \\ i & 0 \end{pmatrix}, \\ \tau_3 &= \tau_+\tau_- - \tau_-\tau_+ = \begin{pmatrix} 1 & 0 \\ 0 & -1 \end{pmatrix}, \end{aligned}\right\} \tag{33.5}$$

which have algebraic properties similar to the properties of the Pauli spin matrices σ and which are called the isotopic spin matrices. The set of τ_1, τ_2, and τ_3 may be regarded as a vector in isotopic spin space.

Positively charged (π^+), negatively charged (π^-), and neutral (π^0) mesons are described respectively by complex (φ, φ^*) and by real (φ_0) wave functions which are taken to be pseudoscalar. The real combinations

$$\varphi_1 = \frac{\varphi + \varphi^*}{\sqrt{2}}, \quad \varphi_2 = i\,\frac{\varphi - \varphi^*}{\sqrt{2}}, \qquad \varphi_3 = \varphi_0 \tag{33.6}$$

are regarded as the components of a three-vector in isotopic spin space.

The interaction Lagrangian invariant with respect to "rotations in isotopic spin space" has the form

$$\mathscr{L}(x) = g \sum_{i=1,2,3} :\overline{\Psi}(x)\gamma^5\tau_i\Psi(x)\varphi_i(x):. \tag{33.7}$$

The constant g plays the role of the coupling constant and is called the mesonic charge.

We also note that for the sake of simplicity one sometimes considers the so-called "neutral model" of the pseudoscalar theory which has the Lagrangian

$$\mathscr{L}(x) = g :\bar{\psi}(x)\gamma^5\psi(x)\varphi(x):. \tag{33.8}$$

Here $\bar{\psi}$, ψ are four-component spinors, φ is a real one-component function. The neutral model differs from the symmetric model by the absence of the "isotopic spin algebra," but at the same time retains the principal elements of its structure. In the future we shall sometimes for the sake of brevity combine (33.7) and (33.8) in the form

$$\mathscr{L}(x) = g :\bar{\psi}(x)\Gamma\psi(x)\varphi(x):, \tag{33.9}$$

without specifying the structure of the vertex matrix Γ.

33.2. *Types of Divergent Diagrams and Counter Terms*

In turning to the analysis of divergent diagrams we note that the elementary pairings have the form

$$\overline{\Psi_\alpha(x)\,\overline{\Psi}_\beta(y)} = \frac{1}{i}\,\frac{1}{(2\pi)^4}\int dp\, e^{-ipx}\,\frac{(M+\hat{p})_{\alpha\beta}}{M^2-p^2-i\varepsilon}, \qquad (33.10)$$

$$\overline{\varphi_i(x)\,\varphi_j(y)} = \frac{\delta_{ij}}{i\,(2\pi)^4}\int\frac{dk\, e^{ikx}}{\mu^2-k^2-i\varepsilon}, \qquad (33.11)$$

where $M_{\alpha\beta} = MI_{\alpha\beta}$, $\hat{p}_{\alpha\beta} = \sum_n g^{nn} p^n \gamma^n_{\alpha\beta}$, $I_{\alpha\beta}$ is the unit matrix of the eighth rank, while $\gamma^n_{\alpha\beta}$ are matrices of the eighth rank related to the ordinary fourth-rank Dirac matrices by expressions of the form

$$\gamma^n_{\alpha\beta} = \begin{pmatrix} \gamma^n & 0 \\ 0 & \gamma^n \end{pmatrix}_{\alpha\beta}.$$

Finally, M and μ are the nucleon and the π-meson masses respectively.

It is essential for us in this case that in accordance with (33.10) and (33.11) the degree of the polynomial P in the numerator of the causal function is equal to zero for the meson line and to unity for the nucleon line. Therefore the maximum vertex index

$$\omega_i^{\max} = \tfrac{1}{2}\sum_l (r_l + 2) - 4$$

turns out to be equal to zero and the Lagrangian (33.9) belongs to the renormalizable type.

Turning to the classification of divergent diagrams we note that the situation in this case is strongly reminiscent of spinor electrodynamics and differs from it only in the following respects: (a) the meson mass is different from zero, which results in the absence of gauge invariance; (b) the meson functions form an isotopic three-vector, and not a four-vector as in the case of the electromagnetic field; (c) the structure of the vertex matrix Γ differs from the four-vector of the Dirac matrices γ^k.

In view of this, some of the results of the discussion given for the case of spinor electrodynamics in § 30 and § 31 may be directly carried over to the pseudoscalar meson theory.

Thus, taking Furry's theorem into account, we obtain the types of divergent diagrams shown in Fig. 44. In the foregoing, due to the absence of considerations of gauge invariance, the diagram with four external boson lines (Fig. 44a) leads, in contrast to spinor electrodynamics, to a divergence, to compensate which one must introduce a special "four-meson" counter term of the form $Z :\varphi^4:$, while for the subtraction of divergences connected with the meson self-energy diagram (Fig. 44c) one must introduce

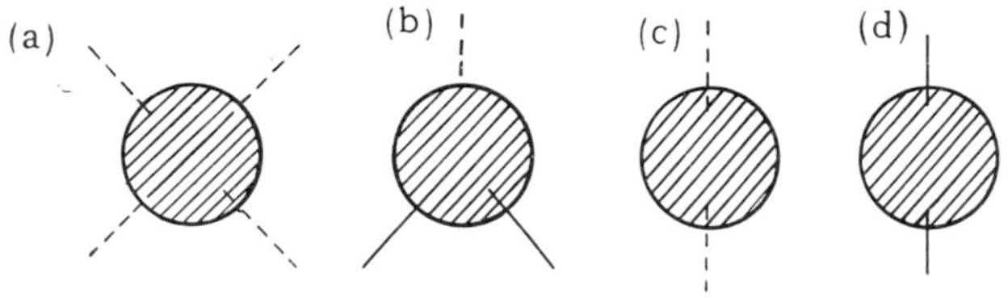

Fig. 44. Types of divergent diagrams in pseudoscalar meson theory. Solid lines refer to nucleons; dotted lines refer to mesons. (a), $\omega(G) = 0$; (b), $\omega(G = 0)$; (c), $\omega(G) = 2$; (d), $\omega(G) = 1$.

in addition to a counter term of the type $(Z_3 - 1)\varphi(p^2 - \mu^2)\varphi$ the counter term for the proper mass of the meson $- \delta\mu\varphi^2$. As a result we obtain the complete interaction Lagrangian in the form

$$\begin{aligned}\mathscr{L}_{\text{tot}} = \mathscr{L} + \Delta\mathscr{L} = g :\overline{\Psi}\Gamma\Psi\varphi: + (Z_1 - 1)g :\overline{\Psi}\Gamma\Psi\varphi: \\ + (Z_2 - 1) :\overline{\Psi}(\hat{p} - M)\Psi: - \delta M :\overline{\Psi}\Psi: \\ + (Z_3 - 1) :\varphi(p^2 - \mu^2)\varphi: - \delta\mu^2 :\varphi\varphi: + Z :\varphi^4:. \qquad (33.12)\end{aligned}$$

33.3. *Second Charge, Multiplicative Renormalizations, and External Lines*

It follows from the general theory that the introduction of the counter terms (33.12) into the interaction Lagrangian may be replaced by a redefinition of the corresponding chronological products. However, for us it is of importance that this introduces a degree of arbitrariness into the theory which is related to the possibility of introducting into the interaction Lagrangian finite terms with the six arbitrary coefficients

$$z_1, \; z_2, \; z_3, \; \delta M, \; \delta\mu^2 \text{ and } z, \qquad (33.13)$$

having the same operator structure as (33.12).

By analyzing the influence of these terms on the Green's functions G for the nucleon, Δ for the meson, on the vertex part Γ, on the masses and on the charge we conclude that the introduction of the constants z_1, z_2, and z_3 is equivalent to a renormalization of G, D, and Γ, and that consequently it corresponds to a change in the charge g, while δM and $\delta\mu^2$ lead to a change in the meson and nucleon masses in the internal lines of the diagrams.

However, the term $z\varphi^4$ does not amount to a change in g, M, and μ^2. This means that the theory in addition to the masses M, μ, and the mesonic charge g actually contains one other constant h which may be introduced into the interaction Lagrangian from the outset as the coefficient of φ^4. Thus $\mathscr{L}(x)$ takes on the form

$$\mathscr{L}(x) = g : \overline{\Psi}(x)\Gamma\Psi(x)\varphi(x) : + \, h : \varphi^2\varphi^2 : \tag{33.14}$$

(in the case of the symmetric theory $\varphi^2 = \sum_i \varphi_i\varphi_i$).

The constant introduced above in fact plays the role of a *second charge*. The magnitude of this second charge like the quantity g must be determined by experiment. The introduction of the term containing z which may be conveniently represented in the form

$$z = (z_4 - 1)h,$$

now amounts to a renormalization of the charge h. By means of arguments analogous to these given in § 31.2 we conclude that the introduction into the interaction Lagrangian of the finite terms

$$\begin{aligned}\delta\mathscr{L} = (z_1-1)g : \overline{\Psi}\Gamma\Psi\varphi : + (z_2-1) : \overline{\Psi}(\hat{p}-M)\Psi : -\delta M : \overline{\Psi}\Psi : \\ + (z_3-1) : \varphi(p^2-\mu^2)\varphi : - \delta\mu^2 : \varphi^2 : + (z_4-1)h : \varphi^2\varphi^2 :\end{aligned} \tag{33.15}$$

is equivalent to the following renormalization of the nucleon and meson Green's functions G, Δ and of the vertex functions Γ and $\Box$:

$$\left.\begin{aligned}G(m, M, g, h) &\to z_2^{-1} G(m', M', g', h'), \\ \Delta(m, M, g, h) &\to z_3^{-1} \Delta(m', M', g', h'), \\ \Gamma(m, M, g, h) &\to z_1 \Gamma(m', M', g', h'), \\ \Box(m, M, g, h) &\to z_4 \Box(m', M', g', h').\end{aligned}\right\} \tag{33.16}$$

Here

$$m' = m + \delta m, \quad M' = M + \delta M, \quad g' = z_1 z_2^{-1} z_3^{-1/2} g, \quad h' = z_4 z_3^{-2} h, \quad (33.17)$$

while $\square$ is a four-vertex function which may be represented by a sum of diagrams with four external meson lines (Fig. 45).

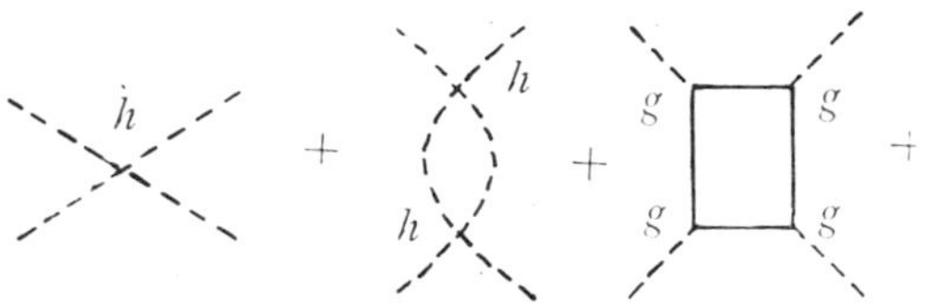

Fig. 45. Diagrams corresponding to the four-vertex function $\square$.

By continuing the arguments of § 31.2 we see that from the point of view of the internal parts of the diagram the introduction of the six terms (33.15) is equivalent to the following transformation of the two masses and the two charges:

$$\begin{aligned} \mu^2 \to \mu'^2 &= \mu^2 + \delta\mu^2, \qquad M \to M' = M + \delta M, \\ g \to g' &= z_1 z_2^{-1} z_3^{-1/2} g, \qquad h \to h' = z_4 z_3^{-2} h. \end{aligned} \quad (33.18)$$

We now turn to the external lines. By means of arguments similar to those given in § 31.5 we find that in order to eliminate the arbitrariness in the external lines it is particularly convenient to expand the self-energy parts of the meson and of the nucleon about the points $k^2 = \mu^2$ and $\hat{p} = M$ respectively. These conditions fix the constants $\delta\mu$, δM, z_2 and z_3.

The constants z_1 and z_4 may be uniquely determined by specifying an experimental method for the determination of the charges g and h, for example, by assuming that the experimental value of the charge g is determined from the scattering by a nucleon of a meson of zero velocity, while the value of h is determined from the mutual scattering of two mesons of zero velocity.

§ 34. Schwinger's Equations for Green's Functions[69a]

34.1. *Relation of the Complete Green's Functions to the Vacuum Expectation Values of T-Products*

In the preceding presentation of the theory we have repeatedly emphasized the fundamental role played by the chronological pairings of the free field operators Δ^c which are Green's functions of the corresponding field equations. From the point of view of the scattering matrix Green's functions $\Delta^c(x - y)$ are the propagation factors for particles moving between the points x and y without experiencing any interaction with other fields.

The influence of the interaction on the propagation processes, which is taken into account by means of the radiation corrections to the functions $\Delta^c(x - y)$, leads us, as was shown in § **31**, to the complete Green's functions $\Delta(x - y)$ which are the propagation factors for interacting particles moving between the points x and y. The complete Green's functions may therefore be regarded as generalizations for the case of interaction of the concepts of free field Green's functions.

It is therefore of interest to obtain in closed form equations for such generalized Green's functions similar to those which hold for the free-field Green's functions, because *Green's functions completely characterize the behavior of a dynamic system.* Having expressions for Green's functions we may easily calculate from them the matrix elements for the corresponding transitions. On the other hand, by considering the homogeneous equations for the "generalized wave functions" which correspond to the inhomogeneous equations for the complete Green's functions we are able to calculate radiation corrections to the energy eigenvalues for closed systems and to solve other similar problems.

One could try to set up such equations by a consideration of Feynman diagrams. For example, the fermion Green's function in spinor electrodynamics may be expressed in terms of the vertex part and of the photon Green's function. In turn, the vertex part may be expressed in terms of more complicated

[69a] The presentation of the material in this section follows the paper by Polivanov (95).

vertex parts and of the fermion and photon Green's functions, etc.

However, by proceeding in this manner we shall obtain a sequence of more and more complicated equations which will turn out to be excessively awkward. It is therefore natural to try to obtain the corresponding generating equations with the aid of functional derivatives. For this it is evidently necessary to introduce certain auxiliary classical fields which play the role of functional arguments with respect to which the operation of functional differentiation may be carried out.

We restrict ourselves to a discussion of spinor electrodynamics and following Schwinger (107),[70] we introduce the classical field of the external current. In other words we shall examine the system of the spinor field of the electrons interacting with the electromagnetic field of the photons in the presence of the field of the external current $J(x)$ produced by external charges which is taken into account by the addition to the interaction Lagrangian of the term

$$J(x)A(x) = \sum_n J^n(x)A_n(x). \tag{34.1}$$

In order to derive closed equations in terms of variational derivatives we give a definition of Green's functions in terms of the vacuum expectation values of the chronological products of the field operators and the scattering matrix. We recall that the free-field Green's functions may be defined as vacuum expectation values of chronological products of the corresponding operators. For example,

$$S^c_{\sigma\rho}(x-y) = i\langle T(\psi_\sigma(x)\bar{\psi}_\rho(y))\rangle_0 \equiv i(\Phi_0^* T(\psi(x)\bar{\psi}(y)), \Phi_0), \tag{34.2}$$

$$g^{mn} D_0^c(x-y) = \frac{1}{i}\langle T(A_m(x)A_n(y))\rangle_0 . \tag{34.3}$$

We further introduce expressions of the type

$$\langle T(\psi_\sigma(x)\bar{\psi}_\rho(y)S)\rangle_0, \qquad \langle T(A_m(x)A_n(y)S)\rangle_0, \tag{34.4}$$

[70] We differ from Schwinger by not introducing at the same time classical sources for the spinor field.

which contain within the T-product the scattering matrix

$$S \equiv S(1) = T\left(\exp i \int \mathscr{L}(x)\, dx\right), \tag{34.5}$$

and we examine their structure in various ascending orders in the coupling constant.

We shall make a preliminary remark with respect to the properties of expressions of type (34.4) which contain within the chronological product operator factors not explicitly dependent on the time (in this case the scattering matrix S). At first glance we might be tempted to take such a "time-independent" factor outside the T-product. However, as a result of this we shall obtain after evaluating the vacuum expectation value an expression in which certain chronological pairings will turn out to be replaced by ordinary ones, i.e., we shall obtain an incorrect result. It is necessary to keep in mind that the above operator factors are expressed in terms of integrals involving time-dependent field operators. Thus, for example, the first-order term in (34.4)

$$i\left\langle T\left(\psi_\sigma(x)\,\bar{\psi}_\rho(y) \int \mathscr{L}(z)\, dz\right)\right\rangle_0 \tag{34.6}$$

must be regarded as an integral over z of the expression

$$i\langle T(\psi_\sigma(x)\,\bar{\psi}_\rho(y)\,\mathscr{L}(z))\rangle_0 .$$

It is clear that the "factoring-out" of the expression $\int \mathscr{L}(z)dz$ is not permissible here.

We now turn to the structure of the different terms in expressions (34.4). It may be seen first of all that the zero terms in the expansion lead to the free field Green's functions (34.2) and (34.3) which correspond in Feynman diagrams to the simple lines

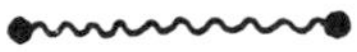 and 

By substituting the explicit expression for the interaction Lagrangian of spinor electrodynamics $\mathscr{L}(x)$ we then see that the first order terms in (34.3) give zero, while the second-order terms lead to expressions proportional to the following combinations of causal functions:

$$\int dz\,dt\,\psi_\sigma(x)\,\bar\psi_\eta(z)\,\gamma^n_{\eta\eta'}\,\psi_{\eta'}(z)\,\bar\psi_\tau(t)\,\gamma^m_{\tau\tau'}\,\psi_{\tau'}(t)\,\bar\psi_\rho(y)\,A_n(z)\,A_m(t),$$
$$\int dz\,dt\,A_m(x)\,A_k(z)\ \mathrm{Sp}\,\{\psi(z)\,\bar\psi(t)\,\gamma^l\,\psi(t)\,\bar\psi(z)\,\gamma^k\}\,A_l(t)\,A_n(y) \tag{34.7}$$

which evidently give second-order radiation corrections to the Green's functions S^c and D^c. These combinations are described by the diagrams of Fig. 46.

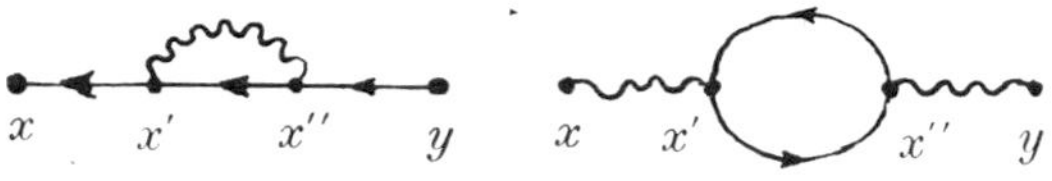

Fig. 46.

In a similar manner the higher-order terms in (34.4) contain all the radiation corrections of higher orders to S^c and D^c. However, expressions (34.4) are not yet the desired Green's functions of the interaction theory: they also contain terms which correspond to nonobservable vacuum transitions described by unconnected Feynman diagrams. Thus, for example, among the second-order terms the following ones appear in addition to expressions (34.7):

$$\psi_\sigma(x)\,\bar\psi_\rho(y)\int dz\,dt\,\mathrm{Sp}\,\{\psi(z)\,\bar\psi(t)\,\gamma^l\,\psi(t)\,\bar\psi(z)\,\gamma^k\}\,A_l(t)\,A_k(z),$$
$$A_m(x)A_n(y)\int dz\,dt\,\mathrm{Sp}\,\{\psi(z)\,\bar\psi(t)\,\gamma^l\,\psi(t)\,\bar\psi(z)\,\gamma^k\}A_l(t)\,A_k(z).$$

The corresponding diagrams are shown in Fig. 47. The above

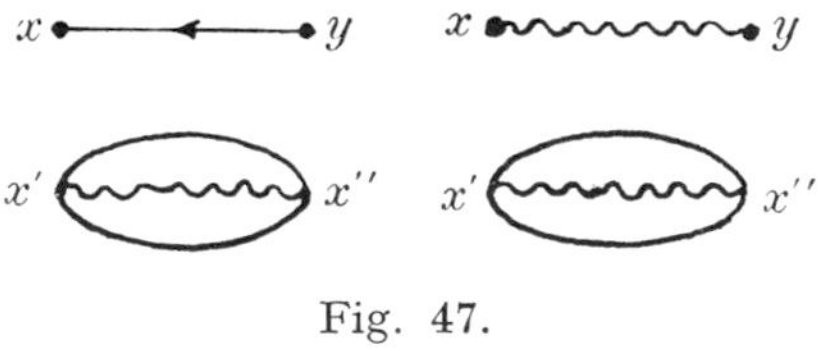

Fig. 47.

vacuum additions appear in expression (34.4) multiplicatively in the form of the vacuum expectation value of the S-matrix:

$$S_0 = \langle S\rangle_0 = (\Phi_0^* S\Phi_0). \tag{34.8}$$

In order to see this we shall examine those terms in (34.4) which contain some definite connected part of the diagram X.

In addition to the term which corresponds exactly to the part X other terms may be found in (34.4) which correspond to diagrams which in addition to the part X also contain various kinds of vacuum loops. By considering the sum of terms corresponding to such diagrams (Fig. 48) we find that it is equal

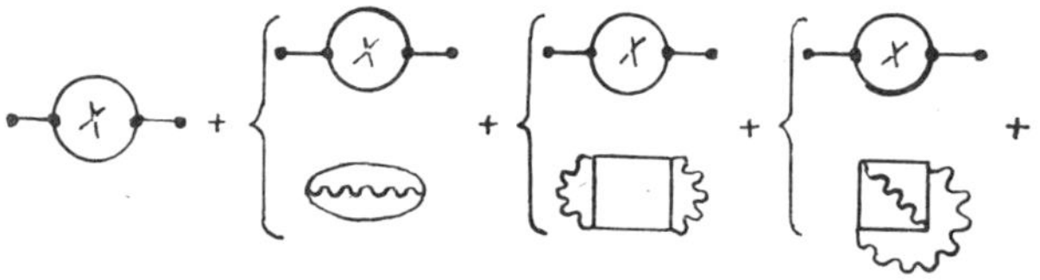

Fig. 48.

to the term corresponding to X multiplied by S_0. Therefore in order to obtain the desired Green's functions we must divide expressions (34.4) by S_0.

As a result of this we obtain Green's functions for real interacting particles which take into account all the radiation corrections and which in the limit of the interaction being switched off reduce to the free field Green's functions (34.2) and (34.3) in the form: [71]

$$G_{\sigma\rho}(x, y) = i\,\frac{\langle T(\psi_\sigma(x)\,\bar{\psi}_\rho(y)\,S)\rangle_0}{S_0}, \tag{34.9}$$

$$D_{mn}(x, y) = \frac{1}{i}\,\frac{\langle T(A_m(x)\,A_n(y)\,S)\rangle_0}{S_0}. \tag{34.10}$$

We note first of all that in the foregoing we everywhere use the value of the scattering matrix $S = S(1)$ which is obtained from $S(g)$ by making the function $g(x)$, which describes the region in which the interaction is switched on, tend to unity throughout all space-time. However, one should take into account the fact that even in this limiting case in accordance with the definition of the S-matrix the function $g(x)$ tends to zero adiabatically for positively and negatively infinite values of the time. From

[71] We denote here the newly introduced complete photon Green's function by the same letter D which earlier in Chapter II was used for the Pauli-Jordan commutation function. However, this will not lead to any difficulties.

this it follows that all integrals with infinite ranges of integration appearing in expressions (34.9) and (34.10) should be interpreted as the corresponding limits in the sense of the adiabatic switching-on and switching-off of the interaction at positively and negatively infinite values of the time.

We now turn to the classical external current density $J(x)$ introduced above and note that the Green's functions G and D depend on it through the Lagrangian function and the S-matrix. Therefore they are functionals of the current $J(x)$. We emphasize that the introduction of the external current density is an auxiliary mathematical device and does not at all presuppose the actual presence of external charges. $J(x)$ is an auxiliary function to some extent analogous to the function $g(x)$ which will enable us later to write the equations for the complete Green's functions in functional form. In the case when there are no real external charges $J(x)$ will be set equal to zero at the concluding stage of the argument or of the calculation.

34.2. *Generalized Wick's Theorem*

Before we begin to derive the equations for Green's functions, we shall consider one preliminary auxiliary proposition which may be called "the generalized Wick's theorem" and which asserts that the vacuum expectation value of the chronological product of $n + 1$ linear operators $A, B_1, \ldots, B_n$ is equal to the sum of n vacuum expectation values of the same chronological products with all possible pairings of one of these operators (for example A) with all the others, i.e.,

$$\langle T(AB_1 \ldots B_n)\rangle_0 = \sum_{1 \leq i \leq n} \langle T(\overbrace{AB_1 \ldots B_i} \ldots B_n)\rangle_0 . \quad (34.11)$$

It should be noted that in the right-hand side of equation (34.11), in contrast to the usual Wick's theorem (compare, for example, (16.17)), there are no expressions involving a number of pairings greater than one.

Nevertheless, the validity of the theorem (34.11) follows directly from the usual Wick's theorem. Since the vacuum expectation value of the normal product of any number other than zero of unpaired operators vanishes, the left-hand side of equation

(34.11) is equal to the sum over all the possible variants of the complete mutual pairings within the product of the operators

$$AB_1 \dots B_n, \tag{34.12}$$

i.e., over such pairings in which all the operators have been paired with one another. In a completely analogous manner any term of the sum appearing in the right-hand side of (34.11), for example the first one, may be represented in the form

$$\overbrace{AB_1}\langle T(B_2 \dots B_n)\rangle_0$$

and is equal to the product of the pairing $\overbrace{AB_1}$ and the sum of all possible complete pairings of the operators $B_2, \dots, B_n$.

On carrying out the summation over i in the right-hand side of (34.11) we obtain the sum over all possible pairings of the operators (34.12). This completes the proof of the generalized Wick's theorem.

Having in mind that the T-products in the vacuum expectation values defining the complete Green's functions also contain the S-matrix which is not a linear operator, we shall generalize theorem (34.11) also to that case. For this purpose we shall consider the process of the pairing of the linear operator A with the nth term in the expansion of the scattering matrix

$$\frac{i^n}{n!}\int T(\mathscr{L}(x_1) \dots \mathscr{L}(x_n))\, dx_1 \dots dx_n. \tag{34.13}$$

We introduce the operation of pairing the linear operator A with the Lagrangian $\mathscr{L}(x)$ which is also a nonlinear operator. It is natural to define the expression $\overbrace{A\mathscr{L}}(x)$ as the sum of products $A\mathscr{L}$ with all possible pairings of the operator A with the operators appearing in $\mathscr{L}$. For example, in the case of spinor electrodynamics when $\mathscr{L}(x)$ taking into account the external current term (34.1) has the form

$$\mathscr{L}(x) = e\sum_n :\bar{\psi}(x)\gamma^n\psi(x)A_n(x): + \sum_k J^k(x)A_k(x), \tag{34.14}$$

we obtain by definition

$$\overline{\psi(x)\mathscr{L}(y)} = e \sum_k \overline{\psi(x)\bar{\psi}(y)}\gamma^k : \psi(y) A_k(y) :, \tag{34.15}$$

$$\overline{\bar{\psi}(x)\mathscr{L}(y)} = e \sum_k : A_k(y)\bar{\psi}(y) : \gamma^k \overline{\psi(y)\bar{\psi}(x)}, \tag{34.16}$$

$$\overline{A_l(x)\mathscr{L}(y)} = e \sum_k : \bar{\psi}(y)\gamma^k \psi(y) : \overline{A_l(x) A_k(y)} + \sum_k J^k(y) \overline{A_l(x) A_k(y)}. \tag{34.17}$$

In this connection we note that the complete Green's functions defined above which are sums of contributions corresponding to the internal lines of Feynman diagrams naturally contain divergences of the same type as in the scattering matrix. For the removal of these divergences, one should from the outset introduce the usual counter terms into the interaction Lagrangian. However, for the sake of simplifying the presentation we shall first derive Schwinger's equations for Green's functions starting with the Lagrangian (34.14) and shall then also take the counter terms into account.

We now return to the pairing of (34.13) with the linear operator A; we obtain the sum of terms

$$\frac{i^n}{n!} \sum_j \int T(\overline{A\mathscr{L}(x_1) \ldots \mathscr{L}(x_j)} \ldots \mathscr{L}(x_n))\, dx_1 \ldots dx_n\,,$$

which in virtue of the symmetry of (34.13) with respect to the variables of integration $x_1, \ldots, x_n$ may be written in the following form:

$$\frac{i^n}{(n-1)!} \int d\tau \int dx_1 \ldots dx_{n-1} T(\overline{A\mathscr{L}(\tau)}\mathscr{L}(x_1) \ldots \mathscr{L}(x_{n-1})).$$

On summing over n we obtain the result of pairing the operator A with the matrix S in the form

$$\overline{AS} = i\int d\tau\, T\Big(\overline{A\mathscr{L}(\tau)} \exp i \int \mathscr{L}(x) dx\Big) = i \int d\tau\, T(\overline{A\mathscr{L}(\tau)} S). \tag{34.18}$$

Formulas (34.14)–(34.18) enable us to give a simple derivation of the equations for Green's functions.

34.3. *Schwinger's Equations*

Let us consider, for example, the fermion Green's function $G_{\sigma\rho}(x, y)$. The numerator of expression (34.9)

$$g_{\sigma\rho}(x, y) = i\langle T(\psi_\sigma(x)\,\bar{\psi}_\rho(y)\,S)\rangle_0, \tag{34.19}$$

can be written by using the generalized Wick's theorem and formula (34.18) in the form

$$\begin{aligned} g(x, y) &= i\langle T(\overbracket{\psi(x)\,\bar{\psi}(y)}S)\rangle_0 + i\langle T(\overbracket{\psi(x)\,\bar{\psi}(y)S})\rangle_0 \\ &= i\overbracket{\psi(x)\,\bar{\psi}(y)}S_0 + i^2\int d\tau\,\langle T(\overbracket{\psi(x)\mathscr{L}}(\tau)\,\bar{\psi}(y)\,S)\rangle_0. \end{aligned} \tag{34.20}$$

Further, by taking into account relation (34.15) and the definition

$$i\overbracket{\psi(x)\,\bar{\psi}(y)} = S^c(x-y),$$

we obtain:

$$\begin{aligned} g_{\sigma\rho}(x, y) &= S^c_{\sigma\rho}(x-y)\,S_0 \\ &\quad + ie\int d\tau \sum_{(\alpha,\beta,k)} S^c_{\sigma\alpha}(x-\tau)\,\gamma^k_{\alpha\beta}\langle T(\psi_\beta(\tau)\,\bar{\psi}_\rho(y)A_k(\tau)\,S)\rangle_0. \end{aligned} \tag{34.21}$$

Recalling that the function $S^c(x-y)$ satisfies the equation

$$\left(i\frac{\hat{\partial}}{\partial x} - m\right)S^c(x-y) = -\delta(x-y),$$

we apply the operation

$$\left(i\frac{\hat{\partial}}{\partial x} - m\right)$$

to both sides of equation (34.21). We obtain:

$$\begin{aligned} &\sum_\sigma \left(i\frac{\hat{\partial}}{\partial x} - m\right)_{\alpha\sigma} g_{\sigma\rho}(x, y) \\ &\quad = -\delta(x-y)\,S_0\,\delta_{\alpha\rho} - ie\sum_{(k,\beta)}\gamma^k_{\alpha\beta}\langle T(\psi_\beta(x)\,\bar{\psi}_\rho(y)A_k(x)S)\rangle_0. \end{aligned} \tag{34.22}$$

On the other hand, let us consider the expression

$$\frac{\delta}{\delta J^k(z)}\,g_{\sigma\rho}(x, y) = i\left\langle T\left(\psi_\sigma(x)\,\bar{\psi}_\rho(y)\,\frac{\delta S}{\delta J^k(z)}\right)\right\rangle_0.$$

By making a series expansion of the S-matrix and by carrying out term by term functional differentiation we find that

$$\frac{\delta S}{\delta J^k(z)} = iT(A_k(z)S). \tag{34.23}$$

Therefore

$$\frac{\delta}{\delta J^k(z)} g_{\sigma\rho}(x, y) = i^2 \langle T(\psi_\sigma(x)\bar{\psi}_\rho(y)A_k(z)S)\rangle_0.$$

On substituting (34.24) into (34.22), regrouping terms and omitting the matrix indices we obtain

$$\left\{i\sum_k \gamma^k \left(\frac{\partial}{\partial x^k} - e\frac{\delta}{\delta J^k(x)}\right) - m\right\} g(x, y) = -\delta(x-y)S_0. \tag{34.25}$$

By going over to the Green's function G itself:

$$g(x, y) = G(x, y)S_0,$$

we obtain after division by S_0:

$$\left\{i\sum_k \gamma^k \left(\frac{\partial}{\partial x^k} - e\frac{\delta}{\delta J^k(x)}\right) - m\right\} G(x, y)$$
$$= -\delta(x-y) + \frac{ie}{S_0}\sum_k \gamma^k \frac{\delta S_0}{\delta J^k(x)} G(x, y). \tag{34.26}$$

With the aid of (34.23) we find that the expression

$$\frac{1}{iS_0}\frac{\delta S_0}{\delta J^k(x)} = \frac{\langle T\{A_k(x)S\}\rangle_0}{S_0} = \mathfrak{A}_k(x) \tag{34.27}$$

has a structure of the type of Green's functions and may be interpreted as the average observable value of the electromagnetic field.

From (34.27) it also follows that the expression $\mathfrak{A}_k(x)$ may be represented in the form of the logarithmic derivative of S_0:

$$\mathfrak{A}_k(x) = \frac{1}{i}\frac{\delta \ln S_0}{\delta J^k(x)}. \tag{34.28}$$

From the formal point of view expression (34.28) is analogous to the well-known relations in statistical physics where the average values of dynamic variables are also expressed as logarithmic variational derivatives of the partition function Z. The analogy of the vacuum expectation value S_0 of the S-matrix with the partition function Z becomes even greater if we consider that by introducing auxiliary spinor sources we may express in terms of functional derivatives of S_0 the average values of ψ and $\bar{\psi}$ and also the complete Green's functions (see equation (34.34) below).

On substituting (34.27) into (34.26) we obtain the desired functional equation for the single-fermion Green's function:

$$\left\{i\sum_k \gamma^k\left(\frac{\partial}{\partial x^k} - e\frac{\delta}{\delta J^k(x)} - ie\mathfrak{A}_k(x)\right) - m\right\} G(x, y) = -\delta(x-y). \tag{34.29}$$

We shall now obtain the corresponding equations for $\mathfrak{A}_k(x)$. In order to do this we shall represent $\mathfrak{A}_k(x)$ with the aid of (34.11) and (34.18) in the form

$$\begin{aligned}\mathfrak{A}_k(x) &= \frac{1}{S_0}\langle T(A_k(x)S)\rangle_0 = \frac{1}{S_0}\langle T(\overline{A_k(x)S})\rangle_0 \\ &= \frac{i}{S_0}\int\langle T(\overline{A_k(x)\mathscr{L}}(\tau)S)\rangle_0 d\tau.\end{aligned} \tag{34.30}$$

Further, by using (34.17) and (34.2) we obtain:

$$\mathfrak{A}_k(x) = -\frac{1}{S_0}\sum_l g^{kl}\int D_0^c(x-\tau)[e\langle T(j^l(\tau)S)\rangle_0 + J^l(\tau)S_0]\,d\tau, \tag{34.31}$$

where we have introduced the notation

$$j^l(\tau) = :\bar{\psi}(\tau)\gamma^l\psi(\tau):.$$

Recalling that the function D_0^c satisfies the equation

$$\Box D_0^c(x-\tau) = -\delta(x-\tau),$$

we obtain after applying the operation $\Box$ to (34.31)

$$\Box\,\mathfrak{A}_k(x) = g^{kk}J^k(x) - g^{kk}e\frac{\langle T(j^k(x)S)\rangle_0}{S_0}.$$

By noting that

$$\langle T(j^k(x)S)\rangle_0 = \sum_{(\sigma,\sigma')} \langle T(\bar{\psi}_\sigma(x)\gamma^k_{\sigma\sigma'}\psi_{\sigma'}(x)S)\rangle_0$$
$$= -\sum_{(\sigma,\sigma')} \gamma^k_{\sigma\sigma'}\langle T(\psi_{\sigma'}(x)\bar{\psi}_\sigma(x)S)\rangle_0 = i \operatorname{Sp}(\gamma^k G(x, x)), \quad (34.32)$$

we obtain the final equation for $\mathfrak{A}_k(x)$ in the form

$$\Box \mathfrak{A}_k(x) = g^{kk}J^k(x) + ieg^{kk} \operatorname{Sp}(\gamma^k G(x, x)). \quad (34.33)$$

Equations (34.29) and (34.33) form a system which enables us to express the two unknown quantities G and $\mathfrak{A}$ in terms of the given function J. These equations were first obtained by Schwinger (107), (108) who based them on a quantum dynamical principle specially formulated by himself. Equations of the type (34.29), (34.33) are called Schwinger's equations.

It turns out to be more convenient to go over from J to the new argument $\mathfrak{A}$. In order to do this we note that the photon Green's function $D(x, y)$ and the average value of the electromagnetic potential are connected by the relation (in the limit $J \to 0$)

$$D_{kl}(x, y) = -\frac{\delta\mathfrak{A}_k(x)}{\delta J^l(y)}, \quad (34.34)$$

the validity of which may be verified by a direct substitution. Therefore the variational derivative with respect to J may be expressed in terms of the derivative with respect to $\mathfrak{A}$ by means of

$$\frac{\delta}{\delta J^l(y)} = \sum_k \int \frac{\delta\mathfrak{A}_k(\xi)}{\delta J^l(y)} \frac{\delta}{\delta\mathfrak{A}_k(\xi)} d\xi = -\sum_k \int D_{kl}(\xi, y)\frac{\delta}{\delta\mathfrak{A}_k(\xi)} d\xi, \quad (34.35)$$

which on substitution into (34.29) gives:

$$\left\{\sum_k \gamma^k \left(i\frac{\partial}{\partial x^k} + e\mathfrak{A}_k(x)\right) - m\right\} G(x, y)$$
$$+ ie\sum_k \gamma^k \int D_{kl}(\xi, x)\frac{\delta G(x, y)}{\delta\mathfrak{A}_l(\xi)} d\xi = -\delta(x-y). \quad (34.36)$$

On the other hand, on differentiating equation (34.33) with respect to $J^l(y)$ and on taking (34.34) and (34.35) into account we find:

$$\Box_x D_{kl}(x, y)$$
$$= -g^{kl}\delta(x-y) + ieg^{kk}\int d\xi \,\mathrm{Sp}\left\{\gamma^k \frac{\delta G(x, x)}{\delta \mathfrak{A}_m(\xi)}\right\} D_{ml}(\xi, y). \quad (34.37)$$

Equations (34.36) and (34.37) form a system from which the Green's functions G and D may be determined as functionals of the external field $\mathfrak{A}(x)$. The function J has been completely eliminated from these equations.

The variational derivatives of the function G contained in the latter system may be transformed into certain integral operators. To achieve this we introduce the inverse of the fermion Green's function G^{-1} defined by the equation

$$\int G(x, x')G^{-1}(x', y)\,dx' = \int G^{-1}(x, x')G(x', y)\,dx' = \delta(x-y). \quad (34.38)$$

We then have

$$\frac{\delta G(x, y)}{\delta \mathfrak{A}_k(\xi)} = \int \frac{\delta G(x, x')}{\delta \mathfrak{A}_k(\xi)} \delta(x'-y)\,dx'$$
$$= \int \frac{\delta G(x, x')}{\delta \mathfrak{A}_k(\xi)} G^{-1}(x', x'')G(x'', y)\,dx'\,dx''. \quad (34.39)$$

On the other hand, on differentiating (34.38) with respect to $\mathfrak{A}(x)$ we obtain the relation

$$\int \frac{\delta G(x, x')}{\delta \mathfrak{A}_k(\xi)} G^{-1}(x', y)dx' = -\int G(x, x') \frac{\delta G^{-1}(x', y)}{\delta \mathfrak{A}_k(\xi)}\,dx',$$

which on substitution into (34.39) yields:

$$\frac{\delta G(x, y)}{\delta \mathfrak{A}_k(\xi)} = e\int G(x, x')\Gamma^k(x', x'' \mid \xi)\,G(x'', y)\,dx'\,dx'', \quad (34.40)$$

where the function

$$\Gamma^k(x'x'' \mid \xi) = -\frac{\delta G^{-1}(x', x'')}{\delta e\mathfrak{A}_k(\xi)} \quad (34.41)$$

is called the vertex operator. The reason for this nomenclature will become apparent below.

On substituting (34.40) into equations (34.36) and (34.37) we find:

$$\sum_k \gamma^k \left(i \frac{\partial}{\partial x^k} + e\mathfrak{A}_k(x) \right) G(x, y) - \int M(x, x') G(x', y) dx' = -\delta(x-y) \tag{34.42}$$

and

$$\Box_x D_{kl}(x, y) = - g^{kl} \delta(x-y) + \sum_m \int P_k^m(x, \xi) D_{ml}(\xi, y) d\xi, \tag{34.43}$$

where the mass operator M and the polarization operator P introduced above are defined by the following relations

$$M(x, x') = m\delta(x-x') - ie^2 \sum_{k,l} \gamma^k \int G(x, x'') \Gamma^l(x'', x' \mid \xi) D_{kl}(\xi, x) d\xi\, dx'', \tag{34.44}$$

$$P_k^m(x, \xi) = ie^2 g^{kk} \operatorname{Sp} \left\{ \gamma^k \int G(x, x') \Gamma^m(x', x'' \mid \xi) G(x'', x) dx' dx'' \right\}. \tag{34.45}$$

We emphasize that the operators Γ, M, and P introduced above are functionals of $\mathfrak{A}$ similarly to Green's functions G and D.

In order to clarify the physical interpretation of the operators Γ, M, and P, it is convenient to go over from the integro-differential equations (34.42), (34.43) to purely integral equations by means of an operation which is inverse to applying the operators $\Box$ and $i(\hat{\partial}/\partial x) - m$. For this purpose it is sufficient to multiply equation (34.42) by $S^c(z-x)$ and equation (34.43) by $D_0^c(z-x)$ and to integrate over x. As a result of integrating by parts we obtain:

$$G(z, y) = S^c(z-y) - e \sum_k \gamma^k \int dx\, \mathfrak{A}_k(x) S^c(z-x) G(x, y) + \int S^c(z-x) M'(x, x') G(x', y)\, dx\, dx', \tag{34.46}$$

$$M'(x, x') = M(x, x') - m\delta(x-x'), \tag{34.47}$$

$$D_{kl}(z, y) = g^{kl} D_0^c(z-y) - \sum_m \int dx\, d\xi\, D_0^c(z-x) P_k^m(x, \xi) D_{ml}(\xi, y). \tag{34.48}$$

Equations (34.46)–(34.48) may be set in correspondence with

the graphical schemes shown in Fig. 49. The elements M' and P appearing in these diagrams may be interpreted by means of relations (34.44) and (34.45) (Fig. 50).

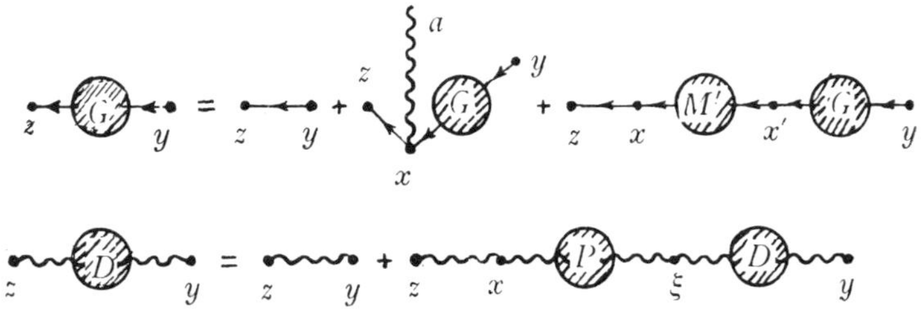

Fig. 49.

It may be seen from these diagrams that the operators M' and P contain all the radiation corrections to the motion of the fermion and the photon, while the operator Γ corresponds to the vertex part of the diagram which justifies its name.

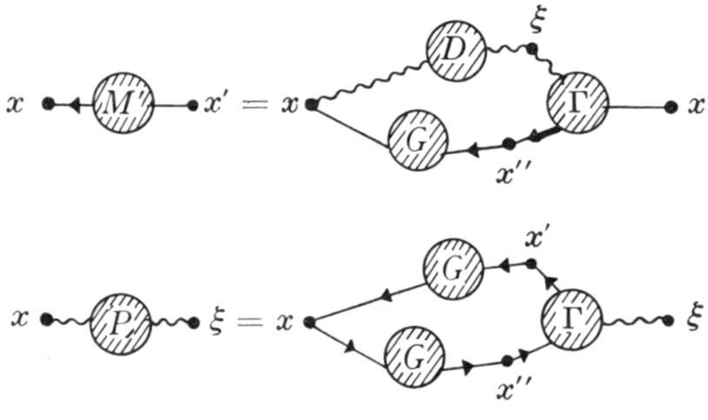

Fig. 50.

The method presented above may also be applied directly to obtain closed equations for more complicated expressions, for example, for Green's functions for two fermions, two photons, etc. By defining such functions in terms of the vacuum expectation values of the chronological product of the corresponding number of field operators one may, by using the generalized Wick's theorem, obtain for them corresponding equations similar to the equations obtained by Schwinger (108) for the two-fermion Green's function.

34.4. *Taking Counter Terms into Account*

As we have already noted, the "complete" Green's functions contain divergences of the same type as the scattering matrix. In order to compensate for these divergences it is necessary to introduce certain counter terms into the interaction Lagrangian, i.e., to go over from the Lagrangian (34.14) to (30.44).

We recall here that the counter terms (30.44) remove from the S-matrix all the divergences with the exception of the vacuum loops which by definition are compensated in Green's functions by the factor $(S_0)^{-1}$.

By repeating the preceding argument for the Lagrangian (30.44), i.e., by introducing into formulas (34.15)–(34.17), (34.21), (34.22), etc., the counter terms (30.44) we shall obtain Schwinger's equations for Green's functions without divergences in the form

$$Z_2\left(i\frac{\hat{\partial}}{\partial x}-m\right)G(x,y)-iZ_1e\sum_k\gamma^k\left(\frac{\delta}{\delta J^k(x)}+i\mathfrak{A}_k(x)\right)G(x,y)=-\delta(x-y), \tag{34.49}$$

$$\begin{aligned} Z_3\,\Box\,D_{kl}(x,y) = &-g^{kl}\,\delta(x-y)\\ &+iZ_1eg^{kk}\int d\xi\sum_m \mathrm{Sp}\left\{\gamma^k\frac{\delta G(x,x)}{\delta\mathfrak{A}_m(\xi)}\right\}D_{ml}(\xi,y)\\ &-(Z_3-1)\sum_n g^{nn}\frac{g^2}{\partial x^k\,\partial x^n}D_{nl}(x,y). \end{aligned} \tag{34.50}$$

In a completely analogous way one may go over to equations of the type (34.42), (34.43) which in place of variational derivatives contain the operators M and P.

An essential difference of equation (34.50) for the function D from equation (34.37) consists of the presence in it of the term

$$\frac{\partial^2}{\partial x^k\,\partial x^n}D_{nl}(x,y).$$

The origin of this expression is connected with the transverse form of the counter term (Z_3-1) which differs from the Lagrangian of the free electromagnetic field by the term $(\partial A/\partial x)^2$. Essentially we have here encountered the consequences of the "incomplete renormalization" of the function D which contains a longitudinal component. It may be shown that in order to obtain an equation with counter terms which has the same form as the equation without counter terms it is sufficient to utilize the purely transverse pairing instead of the diagonal pairing of the operators of the electromagnetic field.

It is also necessary to make the following remark with respect to equations of the type (34.49), (34.50). The direct motivation for the construction of Schwinger's equations lay in the hope of obtaining some information about the complete Green's functions which would not be based on the apparatus of perturbation theory. However, solutions of equations of type (34.36), (34.37) contain divergences while equations (34.49), (34.50) for the Green's functions free of infinities contain divergent constants and are therefore of a formal nature. Thus, attempts to obtain any sort of information about the complete Green's functions on the basis of Schwinger's equations encounter essential difficulties connected with carrying out the program of removing infinities.

Of course,if we regard these equations only as a source of obtaining formal expansions in powers of the coupling constant then the corresponding divergences will be compensated, but we shall obtain nothing new in comparison with perturbation theory. The problem of finding an effective method of solving these equations not based on perturbation theory is at present still far from any sort of satisfactory solution.

CHAPTER VI

Schrödinger Equation and Dynamic Variables

§ 35. Schrödinger Equation for the State Amplitude

35.1. *Equation for $\Phi(g)$ in Terms of Variational Derivatives*

In studying interactions between free fields we have up to now been considering such situations in which the interaction is effective over a finite space-time region. By means of an appropriate limiting transition in the course of which the "region of effectiveness" of the interaction is expanded indefinitely, we were able to determine the elements of the scattering matrix. The elements of the scattering matrix in turn permit us to calculate effective cross sections for scattering processes in those cases when particles which may be regarded as free appear at the beginning and at the end of the process. However, such processes do not exhaust all the problems which the theory has to solve. We have in mind problems of determining the energy and other characteristics of bound states, the lifetimes of excited states, effective cross sections for processes in cases when bound agglomerations of particles appear in the initial and final states, etc.

In order to be able to attack such problems it is not sufficient to have only the scattering matrix at one's disposal, but it turns out to be necessary to have an instrument for a more detailed description of the system, for example, an equation of the Schrödinger type. In order to approach the derivation of such an equation in a natural manner, we shall start in a purely formal way from the relation (17.13)

$$\Phi(g) = S(g)\,\Phi,$$

which we have established earlier, where Φ is a constant, $S(g)$ is the scattering matrix in the presence of an interaction switched on with an intensity g, while $\Phi(g)$ is the amplitude of the state describing the system which has been subjected to the interaction of the given intensity. By varying this relation with respect to the function $g(x)$ and by utilizing the condition that the matrix $S(g)$ is unitary we obtain:

$$\frac{\delta\Phi(g)}{\delta g(x)} = \frac{\delta S(g)}{\delta g(x)}\,\Phi = \frac{\delta S(g)}{\delta g(x)}\,S^{\dagger}(g)\,\Phi(g).$$

Therefore by introducing the operator (cf. § 18.2, § 27.2)

$$H(x;\ g) = i\,\frac{\delta S(g)}{\delta g(x)}\,S^{\dagger}(g), \tag{18.10}$$

we may write (cf. also (15), (16)):

$$i\,\frac{\delta\Phi(g)}{\delta g(x)} = H(x;\ g)\,\Phi(g) \tag{35.1}$$

or in integral form

$$i\,\delta\Phi(g) = \int H(x;\ g)\,\Phi(g)\,\delta g(x)\,dx. \tag{35.2}$$

In its form equation (35.2) is the variational analog of the Schrödinger equation, while the operator $H(x;\ g)$ plays the role of the generalized Hamiltonian (or, more accurately, of the generalized Hamiltonian density). Moreover, the analogy with the Schrödinger equation becomes greater and, as we shall see, reduces from the formal point of view to an identity, if the function $g(x)$ is made to approach the discontinuous function which is equal to unity for all those points of four-space which have a time coordinate smaller than a certain fixed

$$x^0 = \tau$$

and which is equal to zero for all points with $x^0 > \tau$. Such a $g(x)$ evidently describes the process of the instantaneous switching off of the interaction over the whole three-dimensional space at the instant of time $x^0 = \tau$. The state amplitude $\Phi(g)$ becomes in this case a function of the parameter τ and may be denoted by Φ_τ.

But in the usual theory such a concept as the wave function at a given time τ may also be defined by means of an instantaneous switching off of the interaction at time τ. After such a switching off of the interaction the wave function stops changing and we simply have

$$\Phi_\tau = \Phi_\infty$$

If the switching off of the interaction is carried out not over the four-plane $x^0 = \tau$ but over the spacelike four-plane σ:

$$x^0 = T_\sigma(\mathbf{x})$$

we shall obtain the well-known covariant equation in the Tomonaga-Schwinger form. Both in the ordinary Schrödinger equation and in the equation in the Tomonaga-Schwinger form the Hamiltonian density $H(x;\, \sigma)$ depends on the behavior of the fields in the infinitesimal neighborhood of the point x. Our point of view differs from the usual one by the fact that we employ the process of a continuous switching off of the interaction instead of a sudden one.

35.2. *Schrödinger Equation in the Interaction Representation and the Tomonaga-Schwinger Equation*

We shall investigate the behavior of the operator $H(x;\, g)$ in the process of letting the continuous function $g(x)$ tend to the discontinuous limit discussed above. We recall first of all that, as was shown in § 18.2, the generalized Hamiltonian $H(x;\, g)$ may be represented in the form of a functional expansion in powers of the interaction

$$H(x;g) = H_0(x) + \sum_{n\geq 1}\frac{1}{n!}\int H_n(x, x_1, \ldots, x_n)g(x_1)\ldots g(x_n)dx_1 \ldots dx_n, \tag{35.3}$$

where the H_n are expressed by the relations

$$H_0(x) = -\mathscr{L}(x), \tag{35.4}$$

$$H_n(x,\, x_1, \ldots, x_n)$$
$$= i \sum_{0\leq k\leq n} P\begin{pmatrix} x_1, \ldots, x_k \\ x_{k+1}, \ldots, x_n \end{pmatrix} S_{k+1}(x, x_1, \ldots, x_k)\, S^\dagger_{n-k}(x_{k+1}, \ldots, x_n)$$
$$(n = 1,\ 2, \ldots), \tag{18.12}$$

in terms of the expansion coefficients $S_k(x_1, \ldots, x_k)$ of the matrix $S(g)$, and in virtue of the condition of causality imposed on the matrix $S(g)$ have the property that

$$H_n(x, x_1, \ldots, x_n) = 0 \qquad n = 1, 2, \ldots$$

if for at least one x_j $(j = 1, \ldots, n)$

$$x^0 \gtrsim x_j^0 .$$

Therefore the integration over each of the x_j in the terms of the expansion (35.3) actually takes place over the light cone at the point x directed into the future. The convergence of the integrals appearing in (35.3) will be guaranteed if a sufficiently smooth weighting function $g(x)$ will fall off sufficiently rapidly (for example, exponentially) as x_j^0 tends to ∞. The function $g(x)$ will evidently satisfy this condition if it is defined as an approximation to the well-known step function $\theta(\tau - x_0)$ (see (3.18)) which vanishes for values of x^0 greater than a certain parameter τ. We can take, for example,

$$g(x) = f(\tau - x^0), \tag{35.5}$$

where

$$f(t) - \theta(t) = 0 \text{ for } |t| \geqq \Delta t,$$

if $f(t)$ is chosen to be a sufficiently smooth function. It is clear that the integrals (35.3) will converge with this choice of $g(x)$, since for $x_j^0 \to \infty$ $g(x_j)$ falls off sufficiently rapidly, while the integrals (35.3) in virtue of the property (18.13) do not depend on the behavior of $g(x_i)$ for infinite values of the spatial- and the negative-time variables.

Our choice of $g(x)$ corresponds to the situation when the interaction is switched on over the whole three-space and for times from $-\infty$ up to the instant $\tau - \Delta t$ and is gradually switched off between $\tau - \Delta t$ and $\tau + \Delta t$.

The state amplitude may now be regarded as a function of the parameter τ:

$$\Phi(g) = \Phi_\tau .$$

Determining the variation δg from (35.5):

$$\delta g(x) = f'(\tau - x^0)\,\delta\tau,$$

we find with the aid of (35.2)

$$i\,\delta_\tau \Phi_\tau = \int H(x; f)\, f'(\tau - x^0)\, dx\, \delta_\tau \Phi_\tau ,$$

from which it follows that:

$$i\frac{\partial \Phi_\tau}{\partial \tau} = \int H(x; f)\, f'(\tau - x^0)\, dx\, \Phi_\tau\,. \tag{35.6}$$

In virtue of the definition of the function f the integration here is taken over the time "slab" between $\tau - \Delta t$ and $\tau + \Delta t$. On the other hand, as was shown earlier, the integration in (35.3) is taken over the light cone of "height"

$$h = \tau + \Delta t - x^0.$$

Taking into account the fact that in (35.6) x^0 is in any case greater than $\tau - \Delta t$ we find (see Fig. 51) that $h \leqq 2\Delta t$. Thus

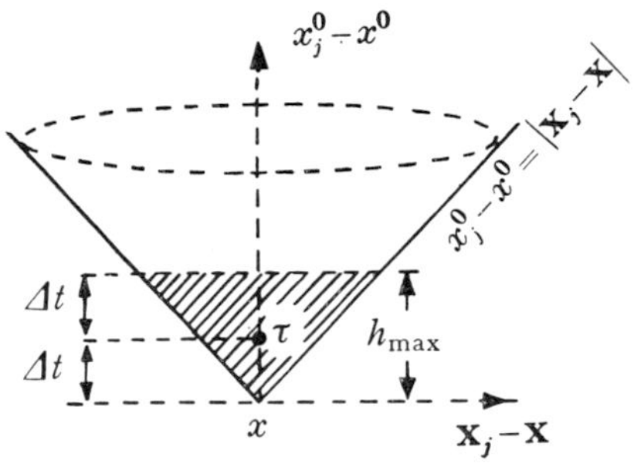

Fig. 51.

the integration in (35.3) is taken over the region which satisfies the condition

$$|\, x_j^0 - x^0 \,| \leqq 2\Delta t, \quad |\, \mathbf{x}_j - \mathbf{x} \,| \leqq 2\Delta t. \tag{35.7}$$

Therefore the "effective Hamiltonian" $H(x; f)$ appearing in (35.6) depends on the behavior of the field functions in the neighborhood of the point x of order $2\Delta t$. If it were possible to go to the limit $\Delta t \to 0$ in (35.6) and to deal with f in place of θ then we would obtain in its place the equation

$$i\frac{\partial \Phi_\tau}{\partial \tau} = \int H(x)\, d\mathbf{x}\, \Phi_\tau\,, \tag{35.8}$$

in which the Hamiltonian density $H(x)$ depends on the behavior of the fields within an infinitesimal neighborhood of the point x.

Equation (35.8) is essentially the Schrödinger equation in the interaction representation.

Until now we have considered only the special case of switching off the interaction along the plane $x^0 = \tau$. However, it is not difficult to generalize the argument. We consider the spacelike surface σ

$$x^0 = T_\sigma(\mathbf{x}),$$

for which the condition of being spacelike is fulfilled in the strong sense:

$$| T_\sigma(\mathbf{x}) - T_\sigma(\mathbf{y}) | < \lambda | \mathbf{x} - \mathbf{y} | \ (x \neq y),$$

with constant $\lambda < 1$. We introduce the step function $\theta_\sigma(x)$ such that

$$\begin{aligned} \theta_\sigma(x) &= 1 \text{ for } x^0 > T_\sigma(\mathbf{x}) \\ \theta_\sigma(x) &= 0 \text{ for } x^0 < T_\sigma(\mathbf{x}) \end{aligned} \tag{35.9}$$

i.e., $\theta_\sigma(x) = \theta(x^0 - T_\sigma(\mathbf{x}))$, and consider a sufficiently smooth function $g(x)$ which differs from $\theta_\sigma(-x)$ only within the time interval

$$| x^0 - T_\sigma(\mathbf{x}) | \leqq \Delta t$$

It is clear that in such a case the effective region of integration over each x_j in the expression

$$\int H_n(x, x_1, \ldots, x_n) g(x_1) \ldots g(x_n) \, dx_1 \ldots dx_n \tag{35.10}$$

is determined, similarly to the case considered earlier, by the intersection of the upper light cone at the point x with a "slab" of thickness $2\Delta t$ about the surface σ placed at an angle with respect to the cone axis not smaller than

$$\varphi = \text{arc ctg } \lambda. \tag{35.11}$$

From Fig. 52 it may be seen that the height of that part of the cone which contains the region of integration (shaded on the diagram) does not exceed the quantity $2\Delta t(1 - \lambda)^{-1}$.

Therefore the region of integration is restricted by the inequalities

$$x_j^0 - x^0 \leqq \frac{2\Delta t}{1 - \lambda}, \quad | \mathbf{x}_j - \mathbf{x} | \leqq \frac{2\Delta t}{1 - \lambda}. \tag{35.12}$$

We see that also in this case the time and the spatial dimensions of the effective region of integration in (35.10) do not exceed

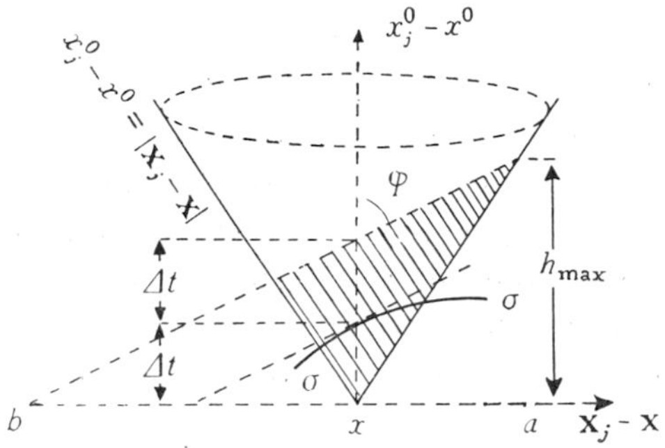

Fig. 52.

a quantity proportional to Δt. The operator $H(x; g)$ will therefore depend on the state of the fields only in the neighborhood of the point x with the dimensions of this neighborhood approaching zero as the "layer of smearing-out" defined by the function $g(x)$ is reduced in thickness. If we now carry out the formal transition to the limit in equation (35.2) which corresponds to making the layer over which $g(x)$ is smeared out infinitely thin, i.e.,

$$\Delta t \to 0, \quad g(x) \to \theta_\sigma(-x) = \sigma(x),$$

we shall obtain in the limit

$$i\delta_\sigma \Phi(\sigma) = \int H(x; \sigma)\, \delta\sigma(x)\, dx\, \Phi(\sigma)$$

or

$$i \frac{\delta \Phi(\sigma)}{\delta \sigma(x)} = H(x; \sigma)\, \Phi(\sigma), \tag{35.13}$$

where the operator $H(x; \sigma)$ depends on the behavior of the field only within an infinitesimal neighborhood of the point x. We have here obtained the well-known Tomonaga-Schwinger equation.

Therefore by reducing the size of the region in which the function $g(x)$ varies and by letting it approach a discontinuous limit we can in fact obtain from (35.1) both the usual Schrödinger equation (35.8) and also the Tomonaga-Schwinger equation

(35.13). In both cases the effective Hamiltonian $H(x;\ \sigma)$ or $H(x;\ f)$ is evidently given by the corresponding limit of expression (35.3)

35.3. *Singularities of the Generalized Hamiltonian*

However, it turns out that, generally speaking, the limit indicated above does not exist. In order to elucidate this situation we shall examine, for example, the Hurst-Thirring field which, as we have shown, contains the weakest divergences. It follows from formula (29.8) that already the second order term in the effective Hamiltonian which contains the factor

$$H(x) \sim \int H_1(x, x')\, g(x')\, dx' \sim \int A_2(x, x')\, g(x')\, dx'$$
$$\sim A_2 \frac{\partial^2}{\partial x^2} \int \delta(x - x')\, g(x')\, dx' = A_2 \frac{\partial^2 g(x)}{\partial x^2},$$

will give, when the limiting transition

$$g(x) = f(\tau - x^0) \to \theta_\sigma(-x)$$

is made, the following expression of nonintegrable type

$$\int f'(\tau - x^0)\, f''(\tau - x^0)\, dx$$

for the Hamiltonian. We make a special note of the fact that this difficulty is not connected with the divergence of the coefficient of the type A_2 when the auxiliary masses are made infinite.

Thus, the transition from equation (35.1) to the Schrödinger and the Tomonaga-Schwinger equations, even if it is carried out for regularized values of the causal functions ($M < \infty$), i.e., for finite values of the coefficient functions of the scattering matrix, leads to the appearance in the interaction Hamiltonian of meaningless divergent expressions.

Let us investigate in greater detail the structure of the limiting expression for the Hamiltonian density. We begin with the second-order term. Starting with equations (18.12) and (18.40) we find:

$$H_1(x, x') = -A_2(x, x') + i\mathscr{L}(x)\, \mathscr{L}(x') - iT(\mathscr{L}(x)\, \mathscr{L}(x')).$$

On carrying out the integration with respect to x' we shall obtain

$$\int H_1(x, x')\, g(x')\, dx' = -\int \Lambda_2(x, x')\, g(x')\, dx', \qquad (35.14)$$

since for finite values of the auxiliary masses the expression

$$\mathscr{L}(x)\,\mathscr{L}(x') - T(\mathscr{L}(x)\,\mathscr{L}(x'))$$

is regular while the region of integration over x' is restricted by inequalities of type (35.12) and shrinks to a point in the limit $\Delta t \to 0$. At the same time the quasilocal operator Λ_2 contains a δ-function and therefore the integral (35.14) differs from zero.

It may be shown by means of completely analogous arguments that in the more general case the following limiting equation holds

$$\int H_n(x, x_1, \ldots, x_n)\, g(x_1) \ldots g(x_n) dx_1 \ldots dx_n$$
$$= -\int \Lambda_{n+1}(x, x_1, \ldots, x_n)\, g(x_1) \ldots g(x_n)\, dx_1 \ldots dx_n.$$

In order to do this after writing H_n in the form of a sum of two terms

$$H_n(x, x_1, \ldots, x_n) = -\Lambda_{n+1}(x, x_1, \ldots, x_n) + \tilde{H}_n(x, x_1, \ldots, x_n),$$

we need only to show that the operator $\tilde{H}_n$ contains a number of δ-functions smaller than n and that therefore the n-fold integration of this operator over an infinitesimal region will also yield zero.

Thus, the limiting expression (as $\Delta t \to 0$) for the Hamiltonian density has the form

$$H(x;\, \sigma)$$
$$= \lim_{g \to \sigma} \left\{ -\mathscr{L}(x) - \sum_{n \geq 1} \frac{1}{n!} \int \Lambda_{n+1}(x, x_1, \ldots, x_n) g(x_1) \ldots g(x_n) dx_1 \ldots dx_n \right\}$$
$$= -\lim_{g \to \sigma} \int \frac{\delta \mathscr{L}(y;\, g)}{\delta g(x)}\, dy. \qquad (35.15)$$

It is evident that if the quasilocal operators Λ_{n+1} in the above contain derivatives of δ-functions then after carrying out the integration these derivatives will be transferred to the functions $g(x)$ and in the course of the transition to the limit $g \to \sigma$ we shall obtain terms which depend not only on the field functions at the point x but also on the differential characteristics of the surface σ at that point (through factors of the type $\partial\theta_\sigma(x)/\partial x$). It may be seen that such terms which depend on the surface may turn out to be divergent even before the main limiting transition $M \to \infty$ is made which removes the regularization.

We return to the Hurst-Thirring field. It may be seen from the structure of the quasi-local operators (29.8) that the derivatives of δ-functions are contained only in the second-order vacuum term, i.e., in the term which contains no operators. After all the integrations over $x_1, \ldots, x_n$ in (35.15) and over x in the equation (35.8) have been carried out the vacuum terms will give a contribution to the energy operator in the form of (divergent) constants. Such constants have no physical meaning in Schrödinger's equation and may be regarded formally as the energy of the vacuum. They may be eliminated from the equation by means of a unitary transformation (a shift of the time phase) and we may in general omit them from our consideration. On carrying out the integration in the remaining terms of (29.8) we obtain:

$$H(x;\sigma) = \lim_{g\to\sigma}\left\{-\lambda : \varphi^3(x) : - A_3^M : \varphi^2(x) : g(x) + \frac{B^M}{2} : \varphi(x) : g^2(x)\right\},$$

$$\int H(x;\sigma)dx = -\int d\mathbf{x}\mathscr{L}(\mathbf{x}, x^0)\,|_{x^0=T_\sigma(\mathbf{x})}$$

where

$$\mathscr{L}(x) = \lambda : \varphi^3(x) : + A_3^M : \varphi^2(x) : + \frac{B^M}{2} : \varphi(x) :$$

coincides with the operator part of the complete interaction Lagrangian of the Hurst-Thirring field (cf. (29.11)).

The constants A_3^M, B^M diverge logarithmically in the limit $M \to \infty$. It follows from this that in certain cases one may immediately write down the "real" Schrödinger equation (with instantaneous switching-off), but then divergent terms appear in it automatically.

We therefore see that a property of complementarity in the sense of appearance of infinities exists between the scattering matrix and the Schrödinger equation even in the absence of "surface" divergences. Thus in the usual theory the Hamiltonian (i.e., the Schrödinger equation) is regular, but the S-matrix contains infinite terms. On the other hand, we have just seen that if the scattering matrix is regularized then divergences automatically appear in the Schrödinger equation.

In this connection, one can make the following hypothesis with respect to the physical nature of the appeareance of such divergences. In the case of the instantaneous switching-off of the interaction the influence of the switching-off process on the system is so great that it is practically completely impossible to determine any characteristics of the system prior to the switching-off process. From the formal point of view, we have here a certain analogy to Heisenberg's uncertainty relations which, as is well known,[72] are related to very general properties of wave processes.

However, in the case of spinor electrodynamics it is no longer possible to include in the vacuum terms all the infinities of the surface type which appear. From the expression (30.48) for $\mathscr{L}(x; g)$ it follows that derivatives $\partial g/\partial x$ appear in those operator terms which in the transition to the Hamiltonian operator $H(x; \sigma)$ give rise in the limit $g \rightarrow \sigma$ to divergent operator expressions.[73] We note once again that the appearance of these divergences does not depend on a regularization of the Pauli-Villars type and can occur for finite values of the auxiliary masses.

We conclude that in the general case one can fairly simply write down the final equation for the amplitude $\Phi(g)$ where g is a sufficiently smooth function, but that it is impossible to go to the limit $g \rightarrow \sigma$ and obtain a meaningful amplitude $\Phi(\sigma)$. Thus, generally speaking, both the Schrödinger and the Tomonaga-Schwinger equations can have only purely formal significance in quantum field theory.

Thus, in order to avoid the appearance of infinities in the theory we must employ sufficiently smooth $g(x)$. We may note that for the convergence of the integrals under consideration it is not necessary to demand that $g(x) = 0$ everywhere outside a layer of thickness $2\Delta t$. It is sufficient to demand that $g(x)$

[72] See, for example, Blokhintsev (13).

[73] The existence of divergencies of this type was first noted by Stueckelberg (116).

should fall off sufficiently rapidly (for example, exponentially) outside such a layer and that it should be sufficiently smooth everywhere. It is quite evident that the class G of such functions will be relativistically invariant with respect to any Lorentz transformation L, i.e., if $g(x) \in G$ then also $g(Lx) \in G$.

35.4. *Fundamental Properties of the Generalized Hamiltonian*

We shall now establish a number of fundamental properties of the generalized Hamiltonian $H(x; g)$ introduced above. It is clear first of all that the operator $H(x; g)$ is Hermitean (as was already shown in § 18.2), i.e.,

$$H^\dagger(x; g) = H(x; g). \tag{35.16}$$

The transformation properties of $H(x; g)$ may be obtained from the condition of covariance of the matrix $S(g)$:

$$S(Lg) = U_L S(g) U_L^\dagger. \tag{17.21}$$

Recalling that $Lg(x) = g(L^{-1}x)$ we obtain from the above

$$H(x; Lg) = i\frac{\delta S(Lg)}{\delta g(L^{-1}x)} S^\dagger(Lg) = iU_L \frac{\delta S(g)}{\delta g(L^{-1}x)} U_L^\dagger U_L S^\dagger(g) U_L^\dagger,$$

i.e.,

$$H(x; Lg) = U_L H(L^{-1}x; g) U_L^\dagger$$

or

$$H(x; g) = U_L H(L^{-1}x; L^{-1}g) U_L^\dagger. \tag{35.17}$$

It may now be easily seen that the covariance of equation (35.1), as must be the case, is a consequence of the transformation laws of the state amplitude (17.18) and of the Hamiltonian (35.17). Indeed, by going over from g to $L^{-1}g$ in (35.2) and by using (17.18) we obtain in turn

$$i\delta\Phi'(g) = iU_L \delta\Phi(L^{-1}g) = U_L \int H(x; L^{-1}g)\, \delta g(Lx)\, dx\, \Phi(L^{-1}g)$$

$$\underset{Lx\to x}{=} U_L \int H(L^{-1}x; L^{-1}g) \delta g(x)\, dx\, U_L^\dagger U_L \Phi(L^{-1}g)$$

or after taking (35.17) into account,

$$i\delta\Phi'(g) = \int H(x; g)\, \delta g(x)\, dx\, \Phi'(g),$$

This completes the proof of covariance.

It may be easily seen that the definition of the Hamiltonian (18.10) taking the unitary property of the matrix $S(g)$ into account automatically guarantees the compatibility of equations (35.1). For this it is sufficient to calculate the second variation of the state amplitude

$$\frac{\delta^2 \Phi}{\delta g(x)\, \delta g(y)}$$

and to show that its value does not depend on the order of variation for $x \sim y$ (for greater detail see § 36).

We thus see that starting with the scattering matrix defined by the conditions of unitarity, causality, and covariance, one may uniquely obtain an equation of the Schrödinger type which satisfies the conditions of covariance, compatibility, and localizability of the Hamiltonian. One can also show that the converse procedure is likewise possible.

As has already been pointed out, both formalisms (i.e., the Schrödinger equation and the matrix $S(g)$), do not contain the usual divergences provided g belongs to the class G. Therefore, the question arises of the formulation of the whole theory for the case when the interaction is switched on with an intensity $g(x) \in G$. In other words, we must be able to define the principal physical quantities with the aid of the state amplitude $\Phi(g)$ in a manner similar to the way in which they are defined in the usual theory by means of the amplitude Φ_τ or Φ_σ. Since the particular form of the function g has no physical significance, it is necessary in the construction of the theory to guarantee that the observable values of physical quantities should not depend on the specific choice of $g(x)$.

§ 36. Dynamic Variables of a System of Interacting Fields

Let us now consider the problem of constructing dynamic characteristics of a system of interacting fields such as the energy-momentum four-vector, the angular-momentum tensor, and the current four-vector. In the theory of noninteracting fields, the corresponding expressions are obtained directly with the aid of Noether's theorem starting from the principle of extremal action.

In the case of interacting fields, we can not proceed in this way, since we do not have at our disposal exact solutions of the equations of the interacting fields which make the total action of the system as a whole an extremum. We have to employ the operator field functions for the three fields and to construct the various physical quantities from them.

It is not at all evident *a priori* that the problem just stated is soluble in all cases, i.e., that it is always possible to express the dynamic variables of an interacting system in terms of the free-field operators. In particular, the problem of constructing the energy-momentum tensor turns out to be insoluble (115).

36.1. *Energy, Momentum, and the Angular-Momentum Tensor* [73a]

In order to construct the energy-momentum four-vector and the angular-momentum tensor, we shall therefore have to modify the argument of E. Noether and to utilize in place of action, a unitary operator which defines the transformation of the state amplitude under infinitesimal translations and rotations

$$x \to x' = x + \delta x, \ \delta x^k = a^k + \sum_l g^{ll} x^l \omega^{kl} \quad (\omega^{kl} + \omega^{lk} = 0), \qquad (9.1)$$

$$\Phi(g) \to \Phi'(g) = U_L \Phi(L^{-1}g) = \Phi(g) + \delta_L \Phi(g), \qquad (36.1)$$

and which on the basis of (9.4) and (9.5) has the form

$$U_L = 1 + \delta U_L,$$

$$\delta U_L = i \sum_k g^{kk} P_0^k a^k + \frac{i}{2} \sum_{k,l} g^{kk} g^{ll} M_0^{kl} \omega^{kl}, \qquad (36.2)$$

where P_0 and M_0 are respectively the operators for the energy-momentum four-vector and the angular-momentum tensor for the dynamic system in the absence of interaction.

On the other hand,

$$g(Lx) - g(x) = \sum_i \frac{\partial g}{\partial x^i} a^i + \tfrac{1}{2} \sum_{k,l} \left(x^k g^{kk} \frac{\partial g}{\partial x^l} - x^l g^{ll} \frac{\partial g}{\partial x^k} \right) \omega^{lk}.$$

For the total variation of the state amplitude we therefore obtain on taking into account (35.2) and (17.17)

[73a] This subsection is based on the work of Bogoliubov (14).

$$\delta_L \Phi(g) = \delta U_L \Phi(g) + \int \frac{\delta \Phi(g)}{\delta g(x)} [g(Lx) - g(x)]\, dx$$
$$= i\{(P_0 \cdot a) + \tfrac{1}{2} \sum_{k,\, l} g^{kk} g^{ll} M_0^{kl} \omega^{kl}\} \Phi(g)$$
$$+ \int \frac{\delta \Phi(g)}{\delta g(x)} \left\{\left(a \cdot \frac{\partial g}{\partial x}\right) + \tfrac{1}{2} \sum_{k,\, l} \left(x^k g^{kk} \frac{\partial g}{\partial x^l} - x^l g^{ll} \frac{\partial g}{\partial x^k}\right) \omega^{lk}\right\} dx$$
$$= \{(P(g) \cdot a) + \tfrac{1}{2} \sum_{k,\, l} g^{kk} g^{ll} M^{kl}(g)\, \omega^{kl}\} \Phi(g), \tag{36.3}$$

where

$$P^k(g) = P_0^k - g^{kk} \int H(x;\, g) \frac{\partial g(x)}{\partial x^k}\, dx, \tag{36.4}$$

$$M^{ik}(g) = M_0^{ik} - \int H(x; g) \left(x^i g^{kk} \frac{\partial g}{\partial x^k} - x^k g^{ii} \frac{\partial g}{\partial x^i}\right) dx. \tag{36.5}$$

We have thus obtained the desired expressions for the components of the energy-momentum four-vector and of the angular-momentum tensor for the dynamic system in the presence of interaction. It is evident from the form of these expressions that these quantities have the correct transformation properties.

By taking

$$g(x) = f(\tau - x \cdot \xi),$$

where τ is the surface parameter while ξ is a certain four-vector which characterizes the geometry of the surface we obtain

$$\frac{\partial g}{\partial x^k} = -\, f'(\tau - x\xi) \frac{\partial (x\xi)}{\partial x^k} = -\, \xi_k f'(\tau - x\xi),$$

so that

$$P^k(\tau) = P_0^k + \xi^k \int f'(\tau - x\xi)\, H(x;\, f)\, dx. \tag{36.6}$$

In particular, if one chooses for ξ the unit vector along the time axis

$$\xi^k = \delta_{k0},$$

one obtains:

$$P^\alpha(\tau) = P_0^\alpha \quad (\alpha = 1,\ 2,\ 3), \tag{36.7}$$

$$P^0(\tau) = P_0^0 + \int f'(\tau - x^0)\, H(x;\, f)\, dx. \tag{36.8}$$

It may be seen that in this case the expression for the total momentum will be the same as in the absence of interaction, while the expression for the total energy is obtained as the sum of the "self-energy" of the particles P_0^0 and the interaction energy

$$\int f'(\tau - x^0)\, H(x; f)\, dx.$$

We have here a complete analogy with the usual formulation of quantum mechanics, and it is clear that to a degree of accuracy which depends on the extent of "smearing-out" of the function f, we may regard $H(x; f)$ as the interaction energy density.

We shall now show that the average values

$$\Phi^*(g)\, P^i(g)\, \Phi(g), \quad \Phi^*(g)\, M^{ik}(g)\, \Phi(g)$$

do not depend on the form of g when g is varied within the class of allowable functions under consideration.

To prove this we shall start from the property established earlier (see § 35.4) that the transformed state amplitude

$$\Phi'(g) = U_L \Phi(L^{-1} g)$$

also satisfies the Schrödinger equation in integral form. We therefore have

$$i\delta\{U_L \Phi(L^{-1} g) - \Phi(g)\} = \int H(x; g)\, \delta g(x)\, dx \{U_L \Phi(L^{-1} g) - \Phi(g)\},$$

This relation holds for any Lorentz transformation, in particular for an infinitesimal one. But as we have already shown for an infinitesimal Lorentz transformation

$$U_L \Phi(L^{-1} g) - \Phi(g) = J(g)\, \Phi(g),$$

where

$$J(g) = i(P(g) \cdot a) + \frac{i}{2} \sum_{k,\, l} g^{kk} g^{ll} M^{kl}(g)\, \omega^{kl}.$$

We therefore have

$$i\delta[J(g)\, \Phi(g)] = \int H(x; g)\, \delta g(x)\, dx\, J(g)\, \Phi(g),$$

from which on taking into account the fact that

$$i\delta\Phi^*(g) = -\, \Phi^*(g) \int H(x; g)\, \delta g(x)\, dx,$$

we obtain:

$$i\delta[\Phi^*(g)\,J(g)\,\Phi(g)] = i\delta\Phi^*(g)\,J(g)\,\Phi(g) + i\Phi^*(g)\,\delta[J(g)\,\Phi(g)] = 0,$$

i.e.,

$$\delta(\Phi^*(g)\,J(g)\,\Phi(g)) = 0.$$

Recalling that $J(g)$ is a linear combination of $P(g)$ and $M(g)$ with arbitrary coefficients a, ω we see that the following relations hold

$$\delta(\Phi^*(g)\,P^i(g)\,\Phi(g)) = 0 \text{ and } \delta(\Phi^*(g)\,M^{ik}(g)\,\Phi(g)) = 0, \qquad (36.9)$$

which is what we wanted to prove.

We shall now show that the eigenvalues of the operators $P^i(g)$ and $M^{ik}(g)$ also do not change as g is varied within the class G. We take, for example, the energy operator. We assume that for a certain acceptable $g = g_0$ the eigenfunction of this operator is Φ_E while the corresponding eigenvalue is E. Then

$$(P^0(g_0) - E)\,\Phi_E = 0.$$

Let $\Phi(g)$ be the state amplitude satisfying the fundamental equation which goes over into Φ_E for $g = g_0$, i.e.,

$$(P^0(g) - E)\,\Phi(g) = 0 \text{ for } g = g_0.$$

On the other hand, as we have already shown, if $\Phi(g)$ satisfies the Schrödinger equation (35.1) then $J(g)\Phi(g)$ also satisfies the same equation. But since $J(g)$ is a linear combination of the operators $P(g)$ and $M(g)$ with arbitrary coefficients, then each of them separately will have this property. Therefore $P^0(g)\Phi(g)$, and consequently also $\Psi(g) \equiv (P^0(g) - E)\Phi(g)$ satisfy (35.1). From this we conclude that since $\Psi(g)$ vanishes for $g = g_0$ in accordance with (36.10), then $\Psi(g)$ remains equal to zero everywhere within G. Thus everywhere within G

$$(P^0(g) - E)\,\Phi(g) = 0,$$

which proves the invariance of the eigenvalues. We also see that it is always possible to choose for the eigenfunction the state amplitude satisfying the fundamental equation.

The above properties of the invariance of the expectation values and of the eigenvalues of the operators under consideration, in our theory represent, at the same time, the laws of conservation, covariance, and the independence of the foregoing physical quantities on the extent of "smearing-out" of the allowable spacelike surfaces. Thus, invariance with respect to a change in g determined by a translation in time, evidently corresponds to the usual conservation laws. Invariance with respect to changes in g brought about by Lorentz rotations guarantees actual covariance. Finally, invariance with respect to changes in g due to changes in the process of smoothing out the function g expresses the independence of the physical quantities under consideration from the character of the process of switching off the interaction.

We note in this connection that in general if the relation

$$\delta_g(\Phi^*(g)\, O(g)\, \Phi(g)) = 0,$$

holds for some $O(g)$ then in our representation this means that the quantity $O(g)$ is an integral of the motion.

36.2. *Local Dynamic Quantities* [74]

In the preceding subsection we introduced the energy-momentum four-vector and the angular-momentum tensor which are characteristics of the system of quantized fields as a whole. However, certain other more detailed characteristics of the system of interacting fields, for example, the current density, which depend not only on the region in which the interaction g is switched on, but also on the point x, are also of interest. The Hamiltonian density $H(x;\, g)$ considered before is also a quantity of a similar local type.

We now turn to the general properties of local dynamic variables of the aforementioned type $B(x;\, g)$. We first of all formulate the physical requirements that they must satisfy by writing $B(x;\, g)$ in the form of a functional expansion in "powers" of g:

$$B\,(x;\, g) = B(x) + \sum_{n\geqq 1} \frac{1}{n\,!} \int B_n(x, x_1, \ldots, x_n) g(x_1) \ldots g(x_n) dx_1 \ldots dx_n. \tag{36.11}$$

[74] The presentation in this subsection is based on the work of Stepanov (115).

We begin with the property of locality. The property of locality of the dynamic quantity $B(x;\ g)$ corresponds to the fact that in the limit as the function $g(x)$ approaches the step function $\sigma(x)$ (see § 35) $B(x; g)$ turns out to depend on the behavior of the field only in an infinitesimal neighborhood of the point x. It may be easily shown that the corresponding condition imposed on the expansion coefficients B_n has the form

$$\left.\begin{array}{c} B_n(x,\ x_1, \ldots, x_n) = 0, \\ \text{if for at least one of the } x_j \ (j = 1, \ldots, n) \\ x \gtrsim x_j. \end{array}\right\} \tag{36.12}$$

Indeed, in § 35 the property of the locality of the Hamiltonian $H(x;\ g)$ was obtained directly from condition (36.12) in the form (35.7). Condition (36.12) may evidently also be written in the form

$$\frac{\delta B(x;\, g)}{\delta g(y)} = 0 \ \text{ for } x \gtrsim y. \tag{36.13}$$

An essential requirement is the condition that in the limit $g \to 0$ of the interaction being switched off $B(x;\ g)$ should coincide with the corresponding expression $B(x)$ taken from the theory of free fields

$$B(x;\ 0) = B(x). \tag{36.14}$$

Finally, an important requirement is the condition that the observable value

$$\Phi^*(g)\, B(x;\, g)\, \Phi(g) \tag{36.15}$$

should be independent of the behavior of the function g at times later than x:

$$\frac{\delta(\Phi^*(g)\, B(x;\, g)\, \Phi(g))}{\delta g(y)} = 0 \ \text{ for } y \gtrsim x \tag{36.16}$$

This condition is a consequence of the principle of causality and expresses the fact that the result of a measurement made at the time x and described by the quantity (36.15) cannot depend on the behavior of the system at later times.

By making use of the Schrödinger equation (35.1), we find from the foregoing the equation

$$i\,\frac{\delta B(x;\,g)}{\delta g(y)} = [H(y;\,g),\quad B(x;g)] \text{ for } y \gtrsim x, \qquad (36.16\text{a})$$

which in the special case $B(x;\ g) = H(x;\ g)$ assumes the form

$$i\,\frac{\delta H(x;\,g)}{\delta g(y)} - i\,\frac{\delta H(y;\,g)}{\delta g(x)} = [H(y;\,g),\ H(x;\,g)]. \qquad (36.17)$$

For $x \sim y$ relation (36.17) yields

$$\frac{\delta H(x;\,g)}{\delta g(y)} - \frac{\delta H(y;\,g)}{\delta g(x)} = 0,$$

which is the condition of compatibility for the Schrödinger equation (35.1).

We note that the definition of local dynamic variables which we gave is a natural generalization of the corresponding concepts occurring in the local theory of Schwinger (**104**). We shall investigate the behavior of the quadratic forms $(\Phi^*(g)B(x;\ g)\Phi(g)$ previously introduced by us as the function g approaches the step function σ passing through the point x. If this limiting transition turned out to be possible, we would have obtained an expression of just the type

$$\Phi^*(\sigma)\,B_\sigma(x)\,\Phi(\sigma), \qquad (36.18)$$

which was considered by Schwinger. Schwinger shows that the form (36.18) does not depend on the form of the surface σ which passes through the point x. In our case, the corresponding condition has the more general form (36.16).

We also note that in virtue of (36.16a) the following relation holds, which is more general than (36.16):

$$\frac{\delta(\Phi_1^*(g)B(x;\,g)\,\Phi_2(g))}{\delta g(y)} = 0 \qquad (y \gtrsim x), \qquad (36.19)$$

where Φ_1 and Φ_2 are two different solutions of Schrödinger's equation (35.1).

By starting with relations (36.11), (36.12), (36.14), and (36.16), we may determine all the coefficients B_n by an appropriate modification of the arguments by means of which we determined the expansion coefficients of the scattering matrix S_n. However, in view of the fact that such a procedure has already been employed in the case of the operator $H(x; g)$ of the type under consideration, we shall proceed differently, and shall reduce the present problem to the preceding one. For this purpose we introduce into the interaction Lagrangian the additional term

$$\mathscr{L}(x) \to \mathscr{L}(x) - B(x)\,b(x), \tag{36.20}$$

where $B(x)$ is the free field operator which corresponds to $B(x; g)$ while $b(x)$ is a certain classical function of the same tensor dimensionality as $B(x)$. The matrix $S(g)$, as well as the Hamiltonian $H(x; g)$ becomes a functional which depends on b:

$$S(g) \to S(g; b), \quad H(x; g) \to H(x; g; b) = i\frac{\delta S(g, b)}{\delta g(x)} S^\dagger(g; b).$$

We shall now show that the operator $B(x; g)$ may be represented in the form

$$B(x; g) = \left.\frac{\partial H(x; g; b)}{\partial b(x)}\right|_{b=0}. \tag{36.21}$$

Indeed, by carrying out the functional differentiation of expression (36.21) and by taking into account the fact that the operations of ordinary and of functional differentiation commute, we obtain

$$\frac{\delta B(x; g)}{\delta g(y)} = \frac{\partial}{\partial b(x)} \left[i\frac{\delta}{\delta g(y)} \left(\frac{\delta S(g, b)}{\delta g(x)} S^\dagger(g, b) \right) \right]_{b=0},$$

which on taking into account the condition of causality for the matrix $S(g, b)$, yields:

$$\frac{\delta B(x; g)}{\delta g(y)} = 0 \text{ for } x \gtrsim y.$$

From this it follows that the property of locality of the operator $B(x, g)$ is a direct consequence of the condition of causality for the scattering matrix. Further, recalling that

$$H(x; 0) = H(x) = -\mathscr{L}(x),$$

we find by means of differentiation with respect to b

$$B(x; 0) = B(x).$$

Finally, by differentiating (36.17) with respect to b for $b \neq 0$, and by setting $b = 0$ we obtain, on taking (36.20) into account, the condition of causality (36.16).

We also note that if $B(x)$ (and consequently also $b(x)$) in (36.20) are chosen to be Hermitean then $B(x;\ g)$ determined by formula (36.20) will also be Hermitean since $H(x; g)$ is Hermitean. It is evident that in the preceding, $B(x;\ g)$ will be covariant.

36.3. *The Current Vector*

For illustration we consider the expression for the current density in electrodynamics. By noting that the operator $j(x)$ always appears in the interaction Lagrangian in the combination

$$j(x)\,A(x),$$

where $A(x)$ is the potential of the electromagnetic field we see that the auxiliary classical field with respect to which $H(x;\ g)$ must be differentiated in order to obtain $j(x;\ g)$ is simply an addition to $A(x)$ and that therefore one may in general set

$$j^k(x;\,g) = -\frac{\partial H(x;\,g)}{\partial A_k(x)}. \tag{36.22}$$

As has just been shown, expression (36.22) will satisfy the conditions of locality and of causality, and when the interaction is switched off it will reduce to the current operator for the free field. We shall now show that it will also satisfy the equation of continuity

$$\operatorname{div}_x^{(4)} j(x;g) = 0. \tag{36.23}$$

By expressing condition (36.23) in terms of the coefficient functions H_n we obtain:

$$\operatorname{div}_4^{(x)} \frac{\partial H_n(x,\,x_1,\,\ldots,\,x_n)}{\partial A(x)} = 0. \tag{36.24}$$

By expressing H_n with the aid of relation (18.11) as a quadratic form in S_k in which the S_k depending on x appear linearly, we find that the condition of gauge invariance of the S-matrix in the form (30.12)

$$\operatorname{div}_{x_i}^{(4)} \frac{\partial S_n(x_1,\,\ldots,\,x_n)}{\partial A(x_i)} = 0$$

guarantees that the condition (36.24) is satisfied, and that consequently it also guarantees that the equation of continuity for the current defined by expression (36.22) is also satisfied.

We now turn to the problem of constructing an expression for the total charge of the system. In the usual theory this expression has the form

$$Q = \int d\mathbf{x} \cdot j^0(x), \tag{2.33}$$

where j^0 is the zero component of the current density. However, expression (2.33) is evidently noninvariant with respect to Lorentz transformations. By subjecting (2.33) to a transformation analogous to the transformation from (2.19) to (2.18) we obtain the Lorentz invariant expression

$$Q = \sum_k \int d\sigma_k j^k(x), \tag{36.25}$$

where $d\sigma_k$ is an element of the three-dimensional surface orthogonal to the x^k axis, while the integration is taken over the whole three-dimensional surface σ. This expression may evidently be rewritten in the following form:

$$\int d\sigma_k j^k = \int d\Sigma \cdot \cos(n \cdot x^k) \cdot j^k = \int \frac{\partial \theta_\sigma(x)}{dx^k} j^k(x)\, dx,$$

where $d\Sigma$ is an element of area of the surface σ, $\cos(n, x^k)$ is the cosine of the angle between the x^k axis and the normal n to the surface σ at the point x, while $\theta_\sigma(x)$ is the step function introduced in § 35

$$\theta_\sigma(x) = \begin{Bmatrix} 1 \text{ for } x^0 > T_\sigma(\mathbf{x}) \\ 0 \text{ for } x^0 < T_\sigma(\mathbf{x}) \end{Bmatrix} (\theta_\sigma(x) = \theta(x^0 - T_\sigma(\mathbf{x})). \tag{35.9}$$

The expression for the charge now assumes the form

$$Q = \sum_k \int dx\, j^k(x) \frac{\partial \theta_\sigma(x)}{\partial x^k}. \tag{36.26}$$

In our theory the natural generalization of this relation is the expression

$$Q(g) = -\sum_k \int dx\, j^k(x; g) \frac{\partial g(x)}{\partial x^k}, \tag{36.27}$$

which formally reduces to it in the course of the limiting transition $g(x) \to \theta_\sigma(-x)$. We shall now show that the expression (36.27) is an integral of the motion, i.e., that the observable value of Q does not depend on the form of the function $g(x)$ and that its variation

$$\delta_g \langle Q(g) \rangle = \delta_g (\Phi^*(g)\, Q(g)\, \Phi(g)) \tag{36.28}$$

vanishes for an arbitrary variation $\delta g(x)$.

In order to prove (36.28), we shall start with (36.17) differentiated with respect to $A(x)$:

$$-i\left(\frac{\delta j(x; g)}{\delta g(y)} + \frac{\partial}{\partial A(x)} \frac{\delta H(y; g)}{\delta g(x)}\right) = -[H(y; g), j(x; g)],$$

which may be written in the form

$$i\frac{\delta j(x; g)}{\delta g(y)} - [H(y; g), j(x; g)] = -i\frac{\partial}{\partial A(x)} \frac{\delta H(y; g)}{\delta g(x)}. \tag{36.29}$$

From (36.29) it also follows in virtue of (36.23) that

$$\operatorname{div}_x^{(4)} \frac{\partial}{\partial A(x)} \frac{\delta H(y; g)}{\delta g(x)} = 0. \tag{36.30}$$

By calculating the variation (36.28) taking into account Schrödinger's equation and relation (36.27) we obtain:

$$\begin{aligned}
\delta_{g(y)} \langle Q(g) \rangle &= \Phi^*(g)\left\{\frac{\delta Q(g)}{\delta g(y)} + i[H(y; g), Q(g)]\right\} \Phi(g)\, \delta g(y) \\
&= -\sum_k \int dx\, \Phi^*(g)\left[\left\{\frac{\delta j^k(x; g)}{\delta g(y)} + i[H(y; g), j^k(x; g)]\right\} \frac{\partial g(x)}{\partial x^k}\right. \\
&\qquad\left. + j^k(x; g) \frac{\partial}{\partial x^k} \frac{\delta g(x)}{\delta g(y)}\right] \Phi(g)\, \delta g(y) \\
&= -\sum_k \int dx\, \Phi^*(g)\left[-\frac{\partial}{\partial A_k(x)}\left(\frac{\delta H(y; g)}{\delta g(x)}\right) \frac{\partial g(x)}{\partial x^k}\right. \\
&\qquad\left. + j^k(x; g) \frac{\partial \delta(x-y)}{\partial x^k}\right] \Phi(g) \delta g(y).
\end{aligned}$$

By differentiating the second term by parts, we find that

$$-\sum_k \int dx\, j^k(x; g) \frac{\partial \delta(x-y)}{\partial x^k} = \sum_k \frac{\partial j^k(y; g)}{\partial x^k} = 0$$

in virtue of the equation of continuity (36.23), and also that

$$\sum_k \int dx \frac{\partial}{\partial A_k(x)} \frac{\delta H(y; g)}{\delta g(x)} \frac{\partial g(x)}{\partial x^k} = 0$$

in virtue of (36.30), of the vanishing of $g(x)$ for infinite values of the positive time variable, and of the vanishing of $\delta H(y; g)/\delta g(x)$ in accordance with the condition of localizability (36.13) for infinite values of the spatial and the negative time variables.

36.4. *The Lorentz Condition*

In conclusion, we shall also mention the problem of the subsidiary condition on the allowable states of the system of interacting fields. As is well known, in the theory of free fields this condition has the form

$$\left(\frac{\partial A^{(-)}(x)}{\partial x}\right) \Phi \equiv \sum_k g^{kk} \frac{\partial A_k^{(-)}(x)}{\partial x^k} \Phi = 0. \tag{13.8}$$

In the case of a system with interaction this condition must take on the form

$$\Omega^{(-)}(x; g)\, \Phi(g) = 0, \tag{36.31}$$

where the operator $\Omega^{(-)}(x; g)$ must, on the one hand, reduce to $\partial A^{(-)}(x)/\partial x$ for $g \to 0$, and on the other hand, must be an integral of the motion, since (36.31) is an equation with a time independent zero eigenvalue of the operator $\Omega^{(-)}$. The above requirement on the operator $\Omega^{(-)}$ is a condition of compatibility of equation (36.31) with the Schrödinger equation of motion.

We shall omit the corresponding calculations and shall merely state that the previous two conditions completely determine the operator $\Omega^{(-)}$ in the form

$$\Omega^{(-)}(x; g) = \left(\frac{\partial A^{(-)}(x)}{\partial x}\right) - \int D_0^{(-)}(x-y) \sum_k j^k(y; g) \frac{\partial g(y)}{\partial y^k} dy$$

and that the condition (36.31) assumes the form

$$\left\{\left(\frac{\partial A^{(-)}(x)}{\partial x}\right) - \int D_0^{(-)}(x - y) \sum_k j^k(y; g) \frac{\partial g(y)}{\partial y^k} dy\right\} \Phi(g) = 0. \tag{36.32}$$

Here $D_0^{(-)}(x)$ is the negative-frequency part of the Pauli-Jordan photon function

$$D_0^{(-)}(x) = \frac{i}{8\pi^3}\int dk\, \delta(k^2)\, \theta(-k^0)\, e^{ikx}.$$

36.5. *Wave Field Operators*

In a manner similar to that used for the definition of the operator $j(x;\, g)$, we may also introduce the operators

$$A(x;\, g), \quad \psi(x;\, g), \quad \bar{\psi}(x;\, g),$$

which are generalizations of the corresponding local quantities from the theory of free fields. For this purpose by following the general method of constructing local quantities in interaction theory we introduce into the interaction Lagrangian of spinor electrodynamics $\mathscr{L}$ the following additional terms:

$$\bar{\eta}(x)\,\psi(x) + \bar{\psi}(x)\,\eta(x) + J(x)\,A(x). \tag{36.33}$$

Here $J(x)$ is an unquantized function which may be identified with an external current, $\bar{\eta}(x)$ and $\eta(x)$ are unquantized spinor functions which anticommute with each other and with the fields $\bar{\psi}$, ψ. These "classical spinor fields" have no physical meaning, and their utilization (Schwinger (107)) is of a purely formal nature.

We introduce the expressions

$$\left.\begin{aligned} A(x;\, g) &= -\frac{\partial H(x;\, g)}{\partial J(x)} = -\frac{i}{g(x)}\left(\frac{\delta S}{\delta J(x)}\, S^\dagger\right), && (36.34)\\ \psi(x;\, g) &= -\frac{\partial H(x;\, g)}{\partial \bar{\eta}(x)} = -\frac{i}{g(x)}\left(\frac{\delta S}{\delta \bar{\eta}(x)}\, S^\dagger\right), && (36.35)\\ \bar{\psi}(x;\, g) &= -\frac{\partial H(x;\, g)}{\partial \eta(x)} = -\frac{i}{g(x)}\left(\frac{\delta S}{\delta \eta(x)}\, S^\dagger\right), && (36.36) \end{aligned}\right\}(J, \eta, \bar{\eta}=0).$$

We note that in contrast to η, $\bar{\eta}$, the auxiliary "field" $J(x)$ may have a physical meaning. Suppose, for example, that we wish to investigate the influence on the quantum system under consideration of some external sources of electric field that are characterized by an unquantized external current-density vector $J_0(x)$. In such a case it is evident that in place of (36.34) one should take

$$A(x; g) = -\frac{i}{g(x)}\left(\frac{\delta S(g)}{\delta J(x)} S^\dagger\right)\Bigg|_{\eta, \bar{\eta}=0, J=J_0} \tag{36.37}$$

The operators $A(x; g)$, $\psi(x; g)$ and $\bar{\psi}(x; g)$ introduced in this manner may be regarded as generalizations of the free field operators to the case of interaction switched on with an intensity g. In §§ 37 and 38 we shall investigate, with the aid of these operators, the problem of the anomalous magnetic moment of the electron and the shift of the electron levels in atoms.

§ 37. Vacuum Polarization and the Anomalous Magnetic Moment of the Electron

37.1. *Vacuum Polarization*

We now turn to an examination of some applications of the general formal theory presented above. We shall first of all consider the question of the change in the state of the vacuum under the action of an external unquantized current $J(x)$ or, the equivalent of this, under the action of the given external potential $A^{\text{ext}}(x)$ related to the current J by the expression

$$\Box A^{\text{ext}}(x) = -J(x). \tag{37.1}$$

It might seem that this problem is only of purely theoretical interest, since changes in the properties of the vacuum are not directly observable. However, the point is that a change in the properties of the vacuum under the action of an external electromagnetic field enters as a component into a number of observable effects (shift of the levels of atomic electrons, scattering of light by light, etc.).

For its solution it is convenient to investigate the average observable value of the operator for the electromagnetic potential. In accordance with the previously given general prescription (§ 36.5) we introduce into the Lagrangian the additional term

$$J(x) A(x). \tag{37.2}$$

Then on the basis of (36.37) the average observable value of the electromagnetic potential will be given by

$$A^{\text{eff}}(x) = -\Phi_0^*(g; J)\frac{i}{g(x)}\frac{\delta S(x; g; J)}{\delta J(x)} S^\dagger(g, J)\Phi_0(g; J). \tag{37.3}$$

Here $\Phi_0(g, J)$ is the state amplitude for the real vacuum altered by the action of the external current $J(x)$, while the function $g(y)$ is equal to unity for all $y \leqq x$. In accordance with the general theory A^{eff} does not depend on the particular choice of g. A physical meaning may evidently be ascribed only to the case when this external current may be considered to be independent of the time, since in the opposite case it would give rise to real processes of mutual transformation of particles. We shall therefore consider the case when

$$J(x) = J(\mathbf{x}). \tag{37.4}$$

Then $\Phi_0(g, J)$ may be defined as the lowest energy state of the dynamic system in the presence of $J(\mathbf{x})$.

We note first of all that

$$S^\dagger(g; J)\,\Phi_0(g; J) = \Phi_0, \tag{37.5}$$

where Φ_0 is the vacuum state amplitude in the case of free fields. By making use of the independence of expression (37.3) from the particular form of the function g, we make the usual transition to the limit $g(x) \to 1$. We then obtain:

$$A^{\mathrm{eff}}(x) = -\,i\,\Phi_0^*\,S^\dagger \frac{\delta S}{\delta J(x)}\,\Phi_0, \tag{37.6}$$

where the quantity

$$S = S(1; J)$$

represents the scattering matrix for the case when the interaction is equal to zero both in the remote past and in the remote future.

Since real processes of creation of particles cannot occur in the case of such an adiabatic switching-on and switching-off of the interaction, we also have

$$S\Phi_0 = a\Phi_0, \tag{37.7}$$

where evidently

$$a = \langle S\rangle_0 = S_0, \tag{37.8}$$

with

$$aa^* = 1.$$

and therefore

$$\Phi_0^*\,S_0^\dagger = \Phi_0^*\,a^* = \frac{\Phi_0^*}{S_0}. \tag{37.9}$$

Substituting (37.9) into (37.6), we obtain:

$$A^{\text{eff}}(x) = -i \frac{\Phi_0^* \dfrac{\delta S}{\delta J(x)} \Phi_0}{\Phi_0^* S \Phi_0} = -\frac{i}{S_0} \left\langle \frac{\delta S}{\delta J(x)} \right\rangle_0. \tag{37.10}$$

We shall further find it convenient to express the right-hand side of expression (37.10) in terms of the complete photon Green's function. In order to do this we consider the expression

$$\frac{\delta}{\delta J(y)} (S_0 \cdot A^{\text{eff}}(x)).$$

With the aid of (37.10) we obtain

$$\frac{\delta}{\delta J^m(y)} [S_0 \cdot A_n^{\text{eff}}(x)] = \frac{1}{i} \left\langle \frac{\delta^2 S}{\delta J^m(y) \delta J^n(x)} \right\rangle_0. \tag{37.11}$$

Let us point out the meaning of the operation of iterated variation with respect to the external current in the right-hand side of (37.11). The matrix $S(1, J)$ may be represented by a set of diagrams which in addition to the ordinary vertices also contain vertices corresponding to the term $J(x)A(x)$ in the Lagrangian from each of which one photon line emerges (we have already encountered vertices of this type in the course of considering the process of bremsstrahlung in § 23). As a result of variation with respect to J, the corresponding photon line acquires a free end and the operator $A(x)$ appears within the T-product. Therefore, by explicitly carrying out the operation of iterated variation in the right-hand side of (37.11) we find that the quantity

$$\bar{D}_{nm}(x, y; J) = i \left\langle \frac{\delta^2 S}{\delta J^m(y)\, \delta J^n(x)} \right\rangle_0 = \frac{1}{i} \langle T(A_m(y)\, A_n(x)\, S) \rangle_0 \tag{37.12}$$

represents a sum of coefficient functions which correspond to the internal lines of all possible diagrams with two free-photon line ends. Thus, up to the factor S_0^{-1}, the preceding expression for $\bar{D}$ represents Green's function $D(x, y; J)$ for a photon moving in the external field of the current J. We can now write:

$$\frac{\delta}{\delta J^m(y)}\left(S_0 \cdot A_n^{\text{eff}}(x)\right) = -\, S_0 D_{nm}(x, y; J). \tag{37.13}$$

The preceding formula allows us to write the functional expansion of A^{eff} "in powers" of J starting with the corresponding expansions for S_0 and $D(x, y; J)$. With later applications in mind, we shall now perform such an expansion explicitly treating the external current J as a small quantity and retaining only the leading terms in (37.13).

By letting $J \to 0$ in (37.13), we obtain:

$$S_0 \frac{\delta A_n^{\text{eff}}(x)}{\delta J^m(y)} = -\, S_0 D_{nm}(x, y). \tag{37.14}$$

Here we have made use of the fact that the expression

$$\frac{\delta S_0}{\delta J^m(y)} = i\langle A_m(y)\, S\rangle_0$$

in the limit $J \to 0$ corresponds to diagrams with one external photon line and is equal to zero. We also note that the expression

$$D_{nm}(x, y) = D_{nm}(x, y; J)\,|_{J=0}$$

represents the complete photon Green's function in the absence of external currents.

After cancelling out the factor S_0 in (37.14) and integrating over δJ, we obtain:

$$A_n^{\text{eff}}(x) = -\sum_m \int D_{nm}(x, y)\, J^m(y)\, dy. \tag{37.15}$$

By going over to the momentum representation

$$\left.\begin{aligned}
A_n^{\text{eff}}(x) &= \frac{1}{(2\pi)^2}\int e^{ikx}\, A_n^{\text{eff}}(k)\, dk,\\
J^m(y) &= \frac{1}{(2\pi)^2}\int e^{iqy}\, J^m(q)\, dq,\\
D_{nm}(x, y) &= -\frac{1}{(2\pi)^4}\int e^{ik(x-y)}\left\{\frac{d(k^2)}{k^2}\left(g^{nm} - \frac{k_n k_m}{k^2}\right) + \frac{d_l^0}{k^2}\frac{k_n k_m}{k^2}\right\} dk
\end{aligned}\right\} \tag{37.16}$$

and by taking into account the equation of continuity for the external current

$$\sum_m k_m J^m(k) = 0,$$

we obtain

$$A_n^{\text{eff}}(k) = \sum_m g^{nm} \frac{d\,(k^2)}{k^2} J^m(k) = \frac{d\,(k^2)}{k^2} J_n(k). \qquad (37.17)$$

In the particular case (37.4) under consideration when J does not depend on the time, we may set:

$$J_n(k) = 2\pi\delta(k^0) J_n(\mathbf{k}^2). \qquad (37.18)$$

Substituting this expression into (37.16) and (37.15) we obtain:

$$A_n^{\text{eff}}(\mathbf{x}) = \frac{1}{(2\pi)^3}\int e^{-i\mathbf{k}\cdot\mathbf{x}} \frac{d(-\mathbf{k}^2)}{-\mathbf{k}^2} J_n(\mathbf{k}^2)\, d\mathbf{k}. \qquad (37.19)$$

It follows from (37.19) that the "space part" $d(-\mathbf{k}^2)/(-\mathbf{k}^2)$ of the photon Green's function represents an effective potential produced by a unit charge as a result of its interaction with the electron-positron and photon vacuum (for this it is sufficient to set $J_m(y) = \delta_{m0}\delta(\mathbf{y})e_0$, i.e., $J(\mathbf{k}^2) = e_0$). By utilizing the fact that for a free field, when $d(-\mathbf{k}^2) = 1$, the potential (37.19) reduces to the Coulomb potential, we shall in the general case represent it in the form

$$V(r) = \frac{e_0}{(2\pi)^3}\int e^{-i\mathbf{k}\cdot\mathbf{r}} \frac{d\,(-\mathbf{k}^2)}{-\mathbf{k}^2}\, d\mathbf{k} = -\, e_0 \frac{\rho(r)}{4\pi r} \quad (r = |\,\mathbf{r}\,|). \qquad (37.20)$$

The deviations from unity of the function $\rho(r)$ introduced above correspond to the deviations of $V(r)$ from the Coulomb potential (the function d plays an analogous role in the momentum representation). This deviation of the effective potential from the Coulomb potential is a consequence of the polarization of the vacuum and may be visualized as the effect of the screening of the charge introduced into the vacuum by the creation in the vacuum of virtual electron-positron pairs. The function ρ describes the relative degree of screening. In order to obtain its specific form we must turn to the corresponding part of the photon propagation function.

At present the theory does not provide a complete expression for the photon propagation function. However, for our purposes we may use the expansion of d into a series in powers of e^2 whose first term was obtained in § 31.

We first consider the case of large r. By introducing the new variable $|\mathbf{k}|\, r = x$ in the integral (37.20) and by carrying out the integration over the angles we bring (37.20) into the form

$$\frac{\rho(r)}{r} = \frac{1}{\pi r}\int_0^\infty dx\, d\left(-\frac{x^2}{r^2}\right)\int_{-1}^{+1} d\mu e^{ix\mu} = \frac{2}{\pi r}\int_0^\infty dx \frac{\sin x}{x} d\left(-\frac{x^2}{r^2}\right). \tag{37.21}$$

From this it follows that in order to investigate the asymptotic behavior at large r it is necessary to know the behavior of the function d at small k^2. From (32.6) we find:

$$d(k^2)\,|_{k^2 \ll m^2} = 1 + e^2 O(k^2).$$

Substituting this expression into (37.21), we find that for large r (in comparison with $1/m$, or in ordinary units in comparison with $r_0 = \hbar/mc = 3.862 \times 10^{-11}$ cm) the function $\rho(r)$ tends to unity [75]

$$\rho(r) = 1 + O\left(\frac{1}{r^2}\right) \quad \left(r \gg \frac{1}{m}\right). \tag{37.22}$$

Therefore the constant e_0 should be identified with the value of the observable charge. The form of the function $\rho(r)$ at small r may be obtained in accordance with (37.21) by investigating the asymptotic form of $d(k^2)$ for large k^2. Making use of formula (32.15) we have:

$$d(k^2)\,|_{k^2 \gg m^2} = 1 + \frac{e^2}{12\pi^2} \ln \frac{k^2}{m^2} + \ldots$$

By a direct integration we obtain from the above the asymptotic behavior of $\rho(r)$ for small r in the form (Schwinger (105))

[75] This property remains unchanged when higher-order perturbation theory approximations are taken into account.

$$\rho(r) = 1 = + \frac{e^2}{6\pi^2}\left[\ln\left(\frac{1}{rm}\right) - \tfrac{5}{6} - \mathbf{C}\right] + \dots \qquad (37.23)$$

(Here $\mathbf{C} \simeq 0.5772$) is Euler's constant.)

Thus for small $r \ll m^{-1}$ the effective density $\rho(r)$ increases, and in the limit $r \to 0$ has a logarithmic singularity. However, it is important to emphasize that formula (37.23) has been obtained by means of perturbation theory and is consequently valid, roughly speaking, only in that region in which the second term in considerably smaller than the first one. Therefore any well-founded conclusions on the true behavior of $\rho(r)$ for $r \to 0$ may only be reached by means of arguments not connected with perturbation theory.

37.2. *Anomalous Magnetic Moment of the Electron*

As a second illustration of the application of the general theory to specific problems, we shall calculate the magnetic moment of the electron taking radiation corrections into account.

In order to do this we shall have to consider the problem of the interaction of a single electron with an external current and to find (taking radiation corrections into account) the energy due to this interaction. In doing this, we shall, of course, assume that the external field (the external current) is constant in time since the electron will have a definite energy only in this case.

We have considered above the problem of the change in the properties of the vacuum in the case when the constant external current

$$J(x) = J(\mathbf{x}),$$

is present, and we must now investigate the problem of the change in the properties of the one-electron state. By repeating the preceding arguments, we shall find with the aid of (36.37) that

$$\frac{\delta E(J)}{\delta J(x)} = -A_1^{\text{eff}}(x) = i\Phi_1^* \frac{\delta S(J)}{\delta J(x)} \Phi_1 \frac{1}{\langle S \rangle_0}, \qquad (37.24)$$

where

$$S(J) = S(1;\ J),$$

while the matrix element is taken between two single free-electron states normalized per unit volume

$$\Phi_1^* = (2\pi)^{3/2}\Phi_0^* a_\nu^-(\mathbf{k}'); \quad \Phi_1 = (2\pi)^{3/2} a_\nu^{*+}(\mathbf{k})\,\Phi_0. \tag{37.25}$$

with the same energy $(\mathbf{k}'^2 + m^2 = \mathbf{k}^2 + m^2)$.

Taking (37.25) into account and evaluating the variational derivative $\delta S/\delta J(x)$ we obtain

$$\frac{\delta E(J)}{\delta J^n(x)} = -\frac{(2\pi)^3}{S_0}\,\Phi_0^* a_{\nu'}^-(\mathbf{k}')\,T(A_n(x)S)\,a_\nu^{*+}(\mathbf{k})\,\Phi_0. \tag{37.26}$$

Keeping in mind that the term in the expression for the energy $E(J)$ corresponding to the magnetic moment is the one linear in the external field (current) we may set $J = 0$ in the right-hand side of (37.26).

We now note that if the operators a^- and a^+ in (37.26) were inside the T-product, then such an expression would correspond to the sum of connected diagrams of various orders with one external photon line and two external electron lines and could be represented in the form

$$G'\Gamma G D_{nk}\,. \tag{37.27}$$

Here the first electron Green's function G' corresponds to the external electron line k', the second Green's function G corresponds to the external electron line k, while D_{nk} is the photon Green's function which corresponds to the operator $A_k(x)$. Here, as usual, the vertex part Γ^n represents the sum of strongly connected diagrams with external ends corresponding to G', G, and D. In accordance with the foregoing remark, we may regard G', G, Γ, and D as corresponding to free particles (for $J = 0$).

However, in view of the fact that the operators a^- and a^+ in expression (37.26) are not inside the T-product, it differs from (37.27). The difference consists of the fact that the "last external" pairings in G' and G of (37.27) are replaced in expression (37.26) by ordinary pairings of the form

$$\underbrace{\psi(x)a_\nu^{*+}}(\mathbf{k}) = \frac{v^{\nu,-}(\mathbf{k})}{(2\pi)^{3/2}}\,e^{-ikx},$$

i.e.,

$$\frac{1}{\hat{k} - m} \to \frac{v^-(\mathbf{k})}{(2\pi)^{3/3}}, \quad \frac{1}{\hat{k}' - m} \to \frac{\bar{v}^+(\mathbf{k}')}{(2\pi)^{3/2}}$$

or

$$\left.\begin{aligned} G(k) &\to G(k)(\hat{k} - m)\frac{v^-(\mathbf{k})}{(2\pi)^{3/2}}, \\ G'(k') &\to \frac{\bar{v}^+(\mathbf{k}')}{(2\pi)^{3/2}}(\hat{k}' - m)G'(k'). \end{aligned}\right\} \tag{37.28}$$

The expressions appearing on the right-hand side of (37.28) may not be interpreted directly since $(\hat{k} - m)v^-(\mathbf{k}) = \bar{v}^+(\mathbf{k}')(\hat{k}'-m)=0$ while the function $G(k)$ has a pole at $\hat{k} = m$. In order to remove the ambiguity, we shall express the Green's function G in terms of the self-energy operator Σ:

$$G(k) = \frac{1}{m - \hat{k} + \Sigma(k)}$$

We shall consider that the infrared catastrophe has been removed from Σ by the introduction of a small photon mass λ_0 (as in § 32.2) and that $\Sigma(p)$ satisfies the condition

$$\left.\frac{\Sigma(k)}{\hat{k} - m}\right|_{k=m} = 0.$$

We then obtain

$$(m - \hat{k})G(k)\,|_{\hat{k}=m} = \left.\frac{m - \hat{k}}{m - \hat{k} - \Sigma(k)}\right|_{\hat{k}=m} = 1, \tag{37.29}$$

and consequently, taking conservation of energy into account $(k_0 = k_0')$,

$$(2\pi)^3 \Phi_0^* a_{\nu'}^-(\mathbf{k}')\, T\left\{A_k(x), \frac{S}{S_0}\right\} a_\nu^{*+}(\mathbf{k})\,\Phi_0$$

$$= \sum_n e \int \bar{v}^{\nu,-}(\mathbf{k}')\,\Gamma^n(k', k \mid q)\, v^{\nu,+}(\mathbf{k}) D_{nk}(q)\, e^{iqx}\, dq\, \delta(k' - k - q)$$

$$= e\bar{v}^{\nu,-}(\mathbf{k}')\,\Gamma^n(k', k \mid \mathbf{k}' - \mathbf{k}) v^{\nu,+}(\mathbf{k})\, D_{nk}(\mathbf{k}' - \mathbf{k})\, e^{i(\mathbf{k}-\mathbf{k}')\mathbf{x}}.$$

Substituting this expression into (37.24) and integrating over $J(x) = J(\mathbf{x})$, we obtain:

$$\sum_{k,n} e \int d\mathbf{x}\, J^k(\mathbf{x})\, e^{i\mathbf{x}(\mathbf{k}-\mathbf{k}')}\, \bar{v}^{\nu,-}(\mathbf{k}')\,\Gamma^n(k', k \mid \mathbf{k}' - \mathbf{k}) v^{\nu,+}(\mathbf{k})\, D_{nk}(\mathbf{k}' - \mathbf{k})$$

$$= e \sum_{k,n} \bar{v}^{\nu,-}(\mathbf{k}')\,\Gamma^n(k', k \mid \mathbf{k}' - \mathbf{k})\, v^{\nu,+}(\mathbf{k})\, D_{nk}(\mathbf{k}' - \mathbf{k})\, J^k(\mathbf{k} - \mathbf{k}').$$

By expressing in the foregoing the current J in terms of the external field A^{ext}, by taking into account the expression

$$D_{nk}(k) = -\frac{d\,(k^2)}{k^2}\left(g_{nk} - \frac{k_n k_k}{k^2}\right) - \frac{k_n k_k}{k^2}\frac{d_l^0}{k^2}$$

and the Lorentz condition for the external field

$$(k \cdot A^{\text{ext}}(k)) = 0,$$

we bring the foregoing expression into the form

$$e\bar{v}^{\nu,-}(\mathbf{k}')\,\Gamma^n(k', k \mid \mathbf{k}'-\mathbf{k})\,v^{\nu,+}(\mathbf{k})\,A_n^{\text{ext}}(\mathbf{k}-\mathbf{k}')\,d(-(\mathbf{k}-\mathbf{k}')^2). \quad (37.30)$$

In order to find the magnetic moment, we shall have to pick out from (37.30) the term that is proportional to the intensity of the magnetic field $\mathbf{H}$:

$$H_1 = H_{23}, \quad H_2 = H_{31}, \quad H_3 = H_{12},$$

$$H_{ik} = \frac{\partial A_k^{\text{ext}}}{\partial x_i} - \frac{\partial A_i^{\text{ext}}}{\partial x^k} \to i(q_i A_k^{\text{ext}}(q) - q_k A_i^{\text{ext}}(q)).$$

We shall first consider the main term in (37.30) when

$$\Gamma^n = \gamma^n \text{ and } d = 1.$$

The energy of interaction with the external field (37.30) assumes the form

$$E = -\sum_n j^n A_n^{\text{ext}}, \quad (37.31)$$

where

$$j^n = e\bar{v}^{\nu,-}(\mathbf{k}')\gamma^n v^{\nu,+}(\mathbf{k}). \quad (37.32)$$

In order to obtain the magnetic moment from the preceding expression, we have to go to the nonrelativistic limit. For $\mathbf{k} \to 0$, $k^0 > 0$ the positron components v_1 and v_2 are small in comparison with the electron components v_3 and v_4 (cf. (7.8)) and are of order $|\mathbf{k}|/2k^0$. We denote the electron components by v_{II} and the positron components by v_{I}, i.e.,

$$\left.\begin{aligned} v^+ &= (v_{\text{I}}, v_{\text{II}}), \\ v^{*-} &= (v_{\text{I}}^*, v_{\text{II}}^*), \end{aligned}\right\} \quad (37.33)$$

and note that in accordance with (6.19)

$$j^n = e(\bar{v}^{\nu,-}(\mathbf{k}')\gamma^n v^{\nu,+}(\mathbf{k})) = ev^{*\nu,-}(\mathbf{k}')\,\alpha_n v^{\nu,+}(\mathbf{k}) \text{ for } n = 1, 2, 3,$$

and that since in the "split-up" representation (37.33)

$$\alpha = \begin{pmatrix} 0 & \boldsymbol{\sigma} \\ \boldsymbol{\sigma} & 0 \end{pmatrix}, \tag{37.34}$$

where $\boldsymbol{\sigma} = (\sigma_1, \sigma_2, \sigma_3)$ are the two-rowed Pauli spin matrices, then

$$\mathbf{j} = e(v_{\mathrm{I}}^{*\nu}(\mathbf{k}')\boldsymbol{\sigma} v_{\mathrm{II}}^{\nu}(\mathbf{k})) + e(v_{\mathrm{II}}^{*\nu}(\mathbf{k}')\boldsymbol{\sigma} v_{\mathrm{I}}^{\nu}(\mathbf{k})). \tag{37.35}$$

Now noting that the relations

$$(k^0 + m)v_{\mathrm{I}} = (\boldsymbol{\sigma}\cdot\mathbf{k})\, v_{\mathrm{II}},$$
$$v_{\mathrm{I}}^*(k^0 + m) = v_{\mathrm{II}}^*(\boldsymbol{\sigma}\cdot\mathbf{k}),$$

follow from the Dirac equations, and taking into account the fact that in the limit of small $\mathbf{k}$

$$k_0 + m \simeq 2m,$$

we obtain:

$$j_\alpha = \frac{e}{2m} v_{\mathrm{II}}^{*\nu}[(\boldsymbol{\sigma}\cdot\mathbf{k}')\sigma_\alpha + \sigma_\alpha(\boldsymbol{\sigma}\cdot\mathbf{k})]\, v_{\mathrm{II}}^{\nu}. \tag{37.36}$$

Substituting (37.36) into (37.31) and taking into account the fact that because of the purely magnetic nature of the external field $A_0^{\mathrm{ext}} = 0$, and that in accordance with (6.19)

$$\sigma_1\sigma_2 = i\sigma_3, \quad \sigma_2\sigma_3 = i\sigma_1, \quad \sigma_3\sigma_1 = i\sigma_2,$$

we obtain:

$$E = \mathbf{j}\mathbf{A}^{\mathrm{ext}} = -\frac{e}{2m} v_{\mathrm{II}}^{*\nu}\, \boldsymbol{\sigma}\mathbf{H} v_{\mathrm{II}}^{\nu} - \frac{e}{m} v_{\mathrm{II}}^{\nu}(\mathbf{k}'\,\mathbf{A}^{\mathrm{ext}}(q))\, v_{\mathrm{II}}^{\nu}. \tag{37.37}$$

The second term contains the external potential and has no relation to the magnetic moment, while the first term corresponds to the magnetic moment of the electron

$$M = \mu_0\, v_{\mathrm{II}}^*\, \sigma v_{\mathrm{II}}, \tag{37.38}$$

where μ_0 is the Bohr magneton

$$\mu_0 = \frac{e}{2m}. \tag{37.39}$$

We now turn to the radiation corrections. In order to calculate the first radiation correction to μ_0 it is necessary to examine terms of order e^2 in the product $\Gamma^n d$ that appears in formula (37.30). However, it is clear that since we are interested in terms linear in the derivatives of A^{ext} while the expansion of $d(q)$ about $q = 0$ starts with quadratic terms, we actually need only to examine the correction to Γ^n.

According to (32.26), the expression

$$\bar{v}^{\nu,-}(\mathbf{k}')\,\Gamma(k', k \mid \mathbf{k}' - \mathbf{k})\,v^{\nu,+}(\mathbf{k})$$

in the limit of small $\mathbf{q} = \mathbf{k}' - \mathbf{k}$ may be represented up to terms of order e^2 in the form

$$\bar{v}^{\nu,-}(\mathbf{k}')\,\gamma^n v^{\nu,+}(\mathbf{k}) + \frac{e^2}{16\pi^2 m}\,\bar{v}^{\nu,-}(\mathbf{k})\,\gamma^n \hat{q} v^{\nu,+}(\mathbf{k}).$$

As we have just shown, the first term yields the Bohr magneton while the second one gives:

$$\Delta E = \frac{e}{2m}\,\frac{e^2}{8\pi^2}\,\bar{v}^{\nu,-}(\mathbf{k})\,\hat{A}^{\text{ext}}(q)\hat{q}v^{\nu,+}(\mathbf{k})$$

$$= -\,\mu_0\,\frac{e^2}{8\pi^2}\,\bar{v}^{\nu,-}(\mathbf{k})\,(\boldsymbol{\sigma}\mathbf{H}(q))\,v^{\nu,+}(\mathbf{k}).$$

In going to the nonrelativistic limit in the foregoing expression we shall make use of the fact that in the "split-up" representation (37.33) the four-rowed matrices $\boldsymbol{\sigma}$ are expressed diagonally in terms of the two-rowed Pauli matrices. As a result we obtain:

$$\Delta E = -\,\mu_0\,\frac{e^2}{8\pi^2}\,v^*_{\text{II}}(\boldsymbol{\sigma}\mathbf{H})\,v_{\text{II}} = -\,\mu_0\,\frac{e^2}{8\pi^2}\,(\mathbf{MH}).$$

According to this expression, the radiation correction of order e^2 gives an additional electron magnetic moment equal to

$$\Delta\mu = \mu_0\,\frac{e^2}{8\pi^2} = \mu_0\,\frac{\alpha}{2\pi} = 0.001161\,\mu_0.$$

This result was first obtained by Schwinger (105). Analogous calculations to the next order in e^2 were carried out by Karplus and Kroll (67). Their result

$$\mu = \mu_0\left(1 + \frac{\alpha}{2\pi} - 2.97\,\frac{\alpha^2}{\pi^2}\right) = 1.001145\,\mu_0$$

is in excellent agreement with the most accurate experimentally measured value (Koenig, Prodell, and Kusch (72))

$$\mu = (1.001146 \pm 0.000012)\,\mu_0.$$

§ 38. Dirac Equation with Radiation Corrections

38.1. *Generalization of the Electron Wave Function*

We now consider the problem of obtaining the equation which describes the motion of a single electron in a given external electromagnetic field $A^{\text{ext}}(x)$.

In classical theory, the equation for the unquantized spinor wave function $\psi(x)$ of the electron-positron field may be obtained with the aid of the variational principle from the complete Lagrangian of the system equal to the sum of the Lagrangian of the free electron-positron field and the interaction Lagrangian between the field $\psi(x)$ and the external field $A^{\text{ext}}(x)$:

$$\mathscr{L}(x) = \frac{i}{2}\sum_n \left(\overline{\psi}(x)\,\gamma^n \frac{\partial\psi(x)}{\partial x^n} - \frac{\partial\overline{\psi}(x)}{\partial x^n}\gamma^n\,\psi(x)\right) - m\overline{\psi}(x)\,\psi(x) + e\overline{\psi}(x)\,\hat{A}^{\text{ext}}(x)\,\psi(x). \quad (38.1)$$

For such a Lagrangian, the variational principle leads to the well-known Dirac equation

$$(i\hat{\partial} + e\hat{A}^{\text{ext}} - m)\,\psi(x) = 0, \quad (38.2)$$

on the basis of which quantum mechanics in its time achieved considerable success in the explanation of the magnetic properties of the electron, in the calculation of the fine structure of the levels of hydrogenlike atoms, etc.

However, this equation does not take into account such specifically quantum-field effects as polarization of the vacuum, creation of virtual pairs, etc., as a result of which it must be suitably generalized in quantum field theory. As a preliminary to the solution of the preceding problem, we shall examine the description in quantum theory of a free, noninteracting electron-positron field. Here the state with a single electron having a definite momentum $\mathbf{p}$ and a definite direction of spin will be described by the function

$$\Phi_1 = (2\pi)^{3/2}\,a_\nu^{*+}(\mathbf{p})\,\Phi_0. \quad (37.25)$$

The general single-electron state my be expressed by means of a superposition of such "pure" states:

$$\Phi_1 = (2\pi)^{3/2} \sum_\nu \int c_\nu(\mathbf{p})\, a_\nu^{*+}(\mathbf{p}) d\mathbf{p}\, \Phi_0. \tag{38.3}$$

We introduce the expression:

$$\Phi_0^* \psi(x)\, \Phi_1 = (2\pi)^{3/2} \sum_\nu \int c_\nu(\mathbf{p})\, \Phi_0^*\, \psi(x)\, a_\nu^{*+}(\mathbf{p})\, \Phi_0\, d\mathbf{p} \tag{38.4}$$

and note that in virtue of the commutation relations:

$$\psi(x)\, a_\nu^{*+}(\mathbf{p}) + a_\nu^{*+}(\mathbf{p})\, \psi(x) = \frac{1}{(2\pi)^{3/2}} v^{\nu,-}(\mathbf{p})\, e^{-ipx} (p_0 = \sqrt{\mathbf{p}^2 + m^2}).$$

Therefore,

$$\Phi_0^*\, \psi(x)\, \Phi_1 = \int e^{-ipx} \sum_\nu v^{\nu,-}(\mathbf{p}) c_\nu(\mathbf{p})\, d\mathbf{p}. \tag{38.5}$$

Since by definition,

$$(\hat{p} - m) v^{\nu,-}(\mathbf{p}) = 0,$$

we see that the unquantized spinor

$$\psi(x) = \Phi_0^*\, \psi(x)\, \Phi_1 \tag{38.6}$$

satisfies the Dirac equation for the free field $\psi(x)$

$$(i\hat{\partial} - m) \psi(x) = 0.$$

From the representation (38.5) it further follows that the spinor $\psi(x)$ completely determines the amplitudes $c_\nu(\mathbf{p})$ and thereby also the state Φ_1. In particular, when the electron in this state has a definite energy $E > 0$, then

$$c_\nu(\mathbf{p}) = f_\nu(\mathbf{p})\, \delta(\sqrt{\mathbf{p}^2 + m^2} - E)$$

and we obtain from (38.5):

$$\psi(x) = e^{-iEx^0} \chi(\mathbf{x}). \tag{38.7}$$

Having made these preliminary remarks, we now turn to the theory of the interaction of the electron-positron field with the electromagnetic field which is of interest to us, and in order to obtain an unquantized spinor characterizing the single electron states, we shall generalize (38.6). The state amplitudes Φ_0, Φ_1 must here be evidently replaced by $\Phi_0(g)$, $\Phi_1(g)$. We shall naturally take $\psi(x; g)$ as a local operator which is a generalization of $\psi(x)$. In order to eliminate the dependence on g we shall agree to deal only with such $g = g_x(y)$ for which

$$g_x(y) = 1 \text{ for } y \lesssim x. \tag{38.8}$$

Then, in virtue of the general results of § 36 the expression

$$\varphi(x) = \Phi_0^*(g)\, \psi(x; g)\, \Phi_1(g) \tag{38.9}$$

will be an unquantized spinor which does not depend on the particular choice of the function g satisfying condition (38.8).

We shall first consider the situation when there is no external electromagnetic field and when, consequently, invariance under translation holds. We consider a certain translation L,

$$x \to x + a,$$

and note that in accordance with the transformation law for the matrix $S(g)$ (17.21)

$$S(Lg) = U_L S(g)\, U_L^\dagger$$

and the transformation law for the operator $\psi(x)$ corresponding to a translation (see (9.9) and (2.7))

$$\psi(Lx) = U_L \psi(x)\, U_L^\dagger\,,$$

and in accordance with the definition (36.35), the following relation holds

$$\psi(Lx, Lg) = U_L \psi(x; g) U_L^\dagger$$

or

$$\psi(Lx, g) = U_L \psi(x, L^{-1} g)\, U_L^\dagger.$$

But for an infinitesimal translation $a = \delta a$

$$U_L = 1 + \delta U_L\,, \quad \delta U_L = i(P \cdot \delta a).$$

Therefore, in accordance with (9.12)

$$i g^{nn} \frac{\partial \psi(x; g)}{\partial x^n} = [\psi(x; g),\ P_0^n] + i g^{nn} \int \frac{\delta \psi(x; g)}{\delta g(y)} \frac{\partial g(y)}{\partial y^n}\, dy.$$

As a result of (38.8)

$$\frac{\partial g(y)}{\partial y^n} = 0 \text{ for } y \lesssim x,$$

and from (36.16)

$$i\frac{\delta\psi(x;g)}{\delta g(y)} = [H(x;g),\ \psi(x;g)] \text{ for } y \gtrsim x.$$

From this we have

$$ig^{nn}\frac{\partial\psi(x;g)}{\partial x^n} = \left[\psi(x;g),\ \left(P_0^n - g^{nn}\int H(y;g)\frac{\partial g(y)}{\partial y^n}dy\right)\right].$$

Consequently, in virtue of (36.4) we obtain:

$$ig^{nn}\frac{\partial\psi(x;g)}{\partial x^n} = [\psi(x;g),\ P^n(g)],$$

and therefore:

$$ig^{nn}\frac{\partial\varphi(x)}{\partial x^n} = \Phi_0^*(g)\,\psi(x;g)\,P^n(g)\,\Phi_1(g) - \Phi_0^*(g)\,P^n(g)\,\psi(x;g)\,\Phi_1(g).$$

We consider the case when the electron in the state $\Phi_1(g)$ has a definite energy-momentum four-vector p^n.

Then

$$P^n(g)\,\Phi_1(g) = p^n\,\Phi_1(g).$$

On the other hand, we always have for the vacuum state:

$$P^n(g)\,\Phi_0(g) = 0, \quad \Phi_0^*(g)\,P^n(g) = 0.$$

Therefore:

$$\frac{\partial\varphi(x)}{\partial x^n} = -\,ig^{nn}p^n\boldsymbol{\varphi}(x)$$

and

$$\boldsymbol{\varphi}(x) = Ce^{-ipx} \quad (C = \text{const},\quad p^0 = \sqrt{\mathbf{p}^2 + m^2}).$$

Since, moreover, $\boldsymbol{\varphi}(x)$ has the transformation properties of a spinor we see that

$$(i\hat{\partial} - m)\,\boldsymbol{\varphi}(x) = 0.$$

This equation is satisfied in the case when the single-electron state $\Phi_1(g)$ is characterized by a definite energy-momentum four-vector. Since any arbitrary single electron state may be obtained as a superposition of states of this type, we see that the Dirac equation is satisfied in general.

We finally turn to the investigation of the case when an external electromagnetic field is present. If this field does not depend on the time, we retain invariance under a translation with respect to time, and, therefore, by repeating the preceding argument, we see that if the single electron state is characterized by a definite energy E then

$$\varphi(x) = e^{-iEx_0}\chi(\mathbf{x}). \tag{38.10}$$

Thus the energy levels for stationary single electron states must be found by solving an eigenvalue problem.

38.2. *Generalization of the Dirac Equation*

We have obtained this solution by substituting (38.10) into the generalized Dirac equation. For the actual construction of this equation we return to formula (38.9). By substituting into it the representation (36.35) we obtain

$$\varphi(x) = \frac{1}{ig(x)} \Phi_0^* S^\dagger(g) \frac{\delta S(g)}{\delta\bar{\eta}(x)} \Phi_1,$$

where Φ_0 and Φ_1 are the vacuum and the single-electron states in the absence of interaction.

By carrying out the usual transition to the limit $g \to 1$ we obtain

$$\varphi(x) = \frac{1}{i} \Phi_0^* S^\dagger \frac{\delta S}{\delta\bar{\eta}(x)} \Phi_1. \tag{38.11}$$

But

$$\frac{\delta\mathscr{L}(x)}{\delta\bar{\eta}(x)} = i\psi(x),$$

from which it follows that

$$\frac{\delta S}{\delta\bar{\eta}(x)} = iT(\psi(x)S). \tag{38.12}$$

In order to exclude the usual divergences from the outset, we shall consider that the T-product in the foregoing is redefined in such a way that (38.12) does not contain any ultraviolet infinities. We consequently obtain,

$$\varphi(x) = \Phi_0^* S^\dagger T(\psi(x) S) \Phi_1 = \frac{\Phi_0^* T(\psi(x) S) \Phi_1}{S_0},$$

where Φ_1 is given by formula (38.3).

From this we see that the diagrams which determine $\varphi(x)$ are obtained directly from the corresponding diagrams for Green's function free of divergences

$$G(x, y \mid A^{\text{ext}}) = i \frac{\Phi_0^* T(\psi(x) \bar{\psi}(y) S) \Phi_0}{S_0}$$

by replacing the factor for the entering line

$$i\Phi_0^* T(\psi(x)\bar{\psi}(z)) \Phi_0 = S^c(x - z)$$

by the "external" factor

$$\Phi_0^* \psi(x) \Phi_1 = \int e^{-ipx} \sum_\nu v^{\nu,-}(\mathbf{p}) c_\nu(\mathbf{p}) \, d\mathbf{p} = \boldsymbol{\psi}(x).$$

Therefore, the relation between $\varphi(x)$ and G may be written in the following form:

$$\varphi(x) = \int \frac{\Phi_0^* T(\psi(x) \bar{\psi}(y) S) \Phi_0}{S_0} \frac{[S^c(y-\tau)]^{-1}}{i} \boldsymbol{\psi}(\tau) \, d\tau \, dy$$

$$= \int G(x, y \mid A^{\text{ext}}) S^{c-1}(y - \tau) \, \boldsymbol{\psi}(\tau) \, dy \, d\tau. \tag{38.13}$$

In § 34.3 on the basis of generalized Wick's theorem we obtained, for the electron Green's function, Schwinger's equation the integral form (34.46) of which may be symbolically written in the form

$$G = S^c - eS^c \hat{\mathfrak{A}} G + S^c M' G.$$

By substituting this expression into equation (38.13) written in the form

$$\varphi = G \frac{1}{S^c} \boldsymbol{\psi},$$

we shall obtain:

$$\varphi = (S^c - eS^c \hat{\mathfrak{A}} G + S^c M' G) \frac{1}{S^c} \boldsymbol{\psi} = \boldsymbol{\psi} - eS^c \hat{\mathfrak{A}} \varphi + S^c M' \varphi,$$

i.e.,

$$\varphi(x) = \boldsymbol{\psi}(x) - e\int S^c(x-y) \hat{\mathfrak{A}}(y) \varphi(y) dy + \int S^c(x-y) M'(y, z) \varphi(z) \, dy \, dz. \tag{38.14}$$

By applying the Dirac operator to (38.14) and by taking into account the fact that $\psi(x)$ satisfies the Dirac equation for the free field, we shall obtain for $\varphi(x)$ the equation

$$(i\hat{\partial}_x + e\hat{\mathfrak{A}}(x))\varphi(x) - \int M(x, y)\,\varphi(y)\,dy = 0, \tag{38.15}$$

which was first given by Schwinger (108). We recall that in the foregoing $M(x, y)$ is the mass operator introduced in § 34.3 which in accordance with (34.44) has the form

$$M(x, y) = m\delta(x - y) - ie^2 \sum_{k,\,l} \gamma^k \int G(x, z)\Gamma^l(z, y \mid \xi)D_{kl}(\xi, x)\,d\xi\,dz \tag{38.16}$$

and that, moreover,

$$\mathfrak{A}(x) = \frac{1}{S_0}\langle T[(A(x) + A^{\text{ext}}(x))S]\rangle_0. \tag{38.17}$$

It is now clear that in the limit when the interaction with the quantized electromagnetic field is switched off ($e \to 0$, eA^{ext} is finite) [76] we shall obtain from (38.15) the Dirac equation for the classical electron in an external field

$$(i\hat{\partial}_x + e\hat{A}^{\text{ext}}(x) - m)\varphi(x) = 0.$$

Thus (38.15) represents the Dirac equation with radiation corrections. It may be seen that these radiation corrections are of two different types. The term $\mathfrak{A}$ represents the potential of the external field A^{ext} added to the effective average potential of the field "induced" in the vacuum. This term contains corrections to A^{ext} associated with the polarization of the vacuum. The quantity $M(x, y)$ represents a mass operator which includes the self-energy effects. In the lowest order in e^2 these quantities may be written in the form (assuming that $e^2 \ll 1$, eA^{ext} is finite)

$$M(x, y) = m\delta(x - y) - ie^2 \sum_{k,l} \gamma^k \int S^c(x, z \mid A^{\text{ext}})\gamma^l \delta(z - y)\,\delta(z - \xi) \times D^c_{kl}(\xi - x)\,d\xi\,dz = m\delta(x - y) - ie^2 \sum_{k,l} \gamma^k S^c(x, y \mid A^{\text{ext}})\gamma^l D^c_{kl}(y - x) \tag{38.18}$$

[76] Here we have in mind the case when the interaction with the external electron field eA^{ext} is not small in spite of the smallness of the charge e. The simplest example of such a situation is the problem of the motion of an electron in the Coulomb field of a nucleus with a large value of Z in the case that

$$eA^{\text{ext}} \sim Ze^2 \sim 1 \quad \text{for} \quad Z \gg 1$$

and

$$\mathfrak{A}_k(x) = A_k^{\text{ext}}(x) - ie^2 \sum_{m,n} \int \text{Sp}[S^c(y-\tau)\gamma^m S^c(\tau - y)\gamma^n] \times D^c_{nk}(y-x) A_m^{\text{ext}}(\tau) dy d\tau. \quad (38.19)$$

Thus, after taking into account corrections of order e^2, the generalized Dirac equation (38.15) may be written in the form

$$\left(i\frac{\hat{\partial}}{\partial x} + e\hat{A}^{\text{ext}}(x) - m\right)\varphi(x) - ie^2 \sum_{k,m,n} \gamma^k \varphi(x) \int dy d\tau D^c_{kn}(x-y) \text{Sp}[S^c(y-\tau)\gamma^m S^c(\tau - y)\gamma^n] e A_m^{\text{ext}}(\tau) + ie^2 \sum_{k,l} \int dy \gamma^k S^c(x, y \mid A^{\text{ext}}) \gamma^l D^c_{lk}(y-x)\varphi(y) = 0. \quad (38.20)$$

Here $S^c(x, y \mid A^{\text{ext}})$ is Green's function for the classical electron moving in a given external field A^{ext}. This function by definition satisfies the equation

$$\left(i\frac{\hat{\partial}}{\partial x} + e\hat{A}^{\text{ext}} - m\right) S^c(x, y \mid A^{\text{ext}}) = -\delta(x-y) \quad (38.21)$$

and is represented by the sum of diagrams with two external electron lines and any number of external photon lines corresponding to the given field A^{ext} (Fig. 53). The corresponding expansion

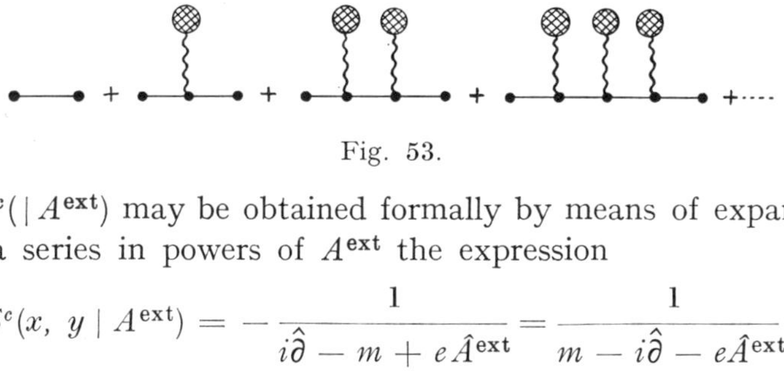

Fig. 53.

for $S^c(\mid A^{\text{ext}})$ may be obtained formally by means of expanding into a series in powers of A^{ext} the expression

$$S^c(x, y \mid A^{\text{ext}}) = -\frac{1}{i\hat{\partial} - m + e\hat{A}^{\text{ext}}} = \frac{1}{m - i\hat{\partial} - e\hat{A}^{\text{ext}}}$$

and has the form

$$S^c(x, y) \mid A^{\text{ext}}) = S^c(x-y) + e\int S^c(x-z)\hat{A}^{\text{ext}}(z) S^c(z-y) dz + e^2 \int S^c(x-z)\hat{A}^{\text{ext}}(z) S^c(z-t) \hat{A}^{\text{ext}}(t) S^c(t-y) dz dt + \ldots \quad (38.22)$$

Equation (38.20) enables us to calculate radiation corrections to the energy levels of bound states.

38.3. *Lamb Shift*

An important example of this type is the problem of calculating the radiation shift of the electron levels in a hydrogenlike atom — the so-called Lamb shift. For the calculation of the hyperfine structure of electron levels in a hydrogenlike atom, we shall consider the motion of an electron in the Coulomb field of a nucleus. In this case

$$\left.\begin{aligned} A_n^{\text{ext}}(x) &= \delta_{n0} A_0(\mathbf{x}), \\ A_0(\mathbf{x}) &= \frac{Ze}{4\pi \mid \mathbf{x} \mid} \end{aligned}\right\} \tag{38.23}$$

or in the momentum representation

$$A_0(\mathbf{x}) = \frac{1}{(2\pi)^{3/2}} \int e^{-i\mathbf{qx}} A_0(\mathbf{q})\, d\mathbf{q}, \tag{38.24}$$

$$A_0(\mathbf{q}) = \frac{Ze}{(2\pi)^{3/2} \mid \mathbf{q} \mid^2}. \tag{38.25}$$

In this case the function $\boldsymbol{\varphi}(x)$ has the form (38.10) where the energy E after substituting (38.10) into (38.15) may be determined from the equation

$$(E\gamma^0 - i\boldsymbol{\partial}\gamma + e\hat{\mathfrak{A}}(x))\boldsymbol{\chi}(\mathbf{x}) = \int e^{iE(x^0 - y^0)} M(x, y)\boldsymbol{\chi}(\mathbf{y}) dy, \tag{38.26}$$

where it is convenient to write the energy E in the form of a series in powers of $\alpha = e^2/4\pi$:

$$E = E_0 + \alpha E_1 + \ldots, \tag{38.27}$$

taking for the zero approximation the case when radiation corrections are absent. In this approximation, the equation

$$(E_0\gamma^0 - i\boldsymbol{\partial}\gamma + e\gamma^0 A_0(\mathbf{x}) - m)\boldsymbol{\chi}_0(\mathbf{x}) = 0 \tag{38.28}$$

is the usual Dirac equation for the motion of an electron in the Coulomb field of a nucleus, while the functions $\boldsymbol{\chi}_0$ and the eigenvalues E correspond to the fine structure of hydrogenlike levels. It is clear that the terms added to E_0 are just the desired Lamb shift of the levels due to the radiation corrections.

The calculation of the first correction E_1 may be carried out by means of equation (38.20). By substituting (38.25) and (38.27) into this equation, by taking (38.28) into account, by equating terms of order e^2, going over to momentum representation

$$\chi(\mathbf{x}) = \frac{1}{(2\pi)^{3/2}} \int e^{i\mathbf{px}} \chi(\mathbf{p}) d\mathbf{p},$$

and by multiplying $\chi(\mathbf{x})$ on the left by the adjoint spinor $\bar{\chi}(\mathbf{p})$ such that

$$\bar{\chi}(\mathbf{p})\gamma^0\chi(\mathbf{p}) = \chi^*(\mathbf{p})\chi(\mathbf{p}) = 1,$$

we find that E_1 may be expressed as a sum of two terms, one of which E_1' corresponds to the radiation correction to the mass operator, while the second E_1'' corresponds to polarization of the vacuum

$$\alpha E_1 = E_1' + E_1'', \tag{38.29}$$

where

$$\begin{aligned} E_1'' &= \frac{1}{(2\pi)^{3/2}} \bar{\chi}(\mathbf{p}) \int d\mathbf{x} e^{-i\mathbf{px}} \int M'(x, y) dy\, e^{iE(x^0-y^0)} \chi(\mathbf{y}) \\ &= \frac{e^2}{i(2\pi)^{3/2}} \bar{\chi}(\mathbf{p}) \int dy^0 e^{iE(x^0-y^0)} \int d\mathbf{x} d\mathbf{y} e^{-i\mathbf{px}} \\ &\quad \times \sum_{k,l} \gamma^k S^c(x, y \mid A^{\text{ext}}) \gamma^l D_{kl}(y-x) \chi(\mathbf{y}) \end{aligned} \tag{38.30}$$

and

$$\begin{aligned} E_1' = &- \frac{e}{(2\pi)^{3/2}} \bar{\chi}(\mathbf{p}) \int d\mathbf{x} e^{-i\mathbf{px}} \sum_{k,n,m} \gamma^k \chi(\mathbf{x}) \\ &\times \int D^c_{kn}(x-y) \Pi^{nm}(y-\tau) A^{\text{ext}}_m(\tau) dy\, d\tau. \end{aligned} \tag{38.31}$$

Here $\Pi^{nm}(y-\tau)$ is the second-order polarization operator that we have already considered in Chapter IV. In virtue of (32.3) and (32.8) this operator after the removal of divergences has the form

$$\Pi^{nm}(y) = \frac{1}{(2\pi)^4} \int e^{iky} \Pi^{nm}(k) dk, \tag{38.32}$$

where

$$\Pi^{nm}(k) = \frac{e^2}{4\pi^2}(g^{mn}k^2 - k^n k^m)I(k^2), \tag{38.33}$$

and

$$I(k^2) = -\frac{k^2}{4m^2}\int_0^1 \frac{z^2\left(1-\frac{z^2}{3}\right)dz}{1-\frac{k^2}{4m^2}(1-z^2)}. \tag{38.34}$$

Expression (38.30) gives the main contribution to the radiation shift of the levels. Substituting the expansion (38.22) for $S^c(x, y \mid A^{\text{ext}})$ into (38.30) we find that the first term leads to a divergent expression of the type of the electron self-energy which is completely compensated by a corresponding redefinition of the T-product (compare (38.12)). The second term leads to the expression

$$\begin{aligned} E_1'^{(2)} &= \frac{e^3}{i(2\pi)^{3/2}}\overline{\chi}(\mathbf{p})\int dy^0 e^{iE(x^0-y^0)}\int d\mathbf{x}d\mathbf{y}e^{-i\mathbf{px}} \\ &\times \sum_{k,l}\int dz\gamma^k S^c(x-z)\hat{A}^{\text{ext}}(z)S^c(z-y)\gamma^l D^c_{lk}(y-x)\chi(\mathbf{y}) \\ &= -\frac{e}{(2\pi)^{3/2}}\overline{\chi}(\mathbf{p})\int dy^0\, e^{iE(x^0-y^0)}\int d\mathbf{x}d\mathbf{y}e^{-i\mathbf{px}}\int dz \\ &\times \sum_n \Lambda^n(x, y \mid z)A_n^{\text{ext}}(z)\chi(\mathbf{y}), \end{aligned} \tag{38.35}$$

in which $\Lambda^n(x, y \mid z)$ is the vertex function introduced in § 25.1 which, after the removal of the ultraviolet divergence, may be represented in the form

$$\Lambda^n(x, y \mid z) = \frac{1}{(2\pi)^8}\int e^{ipx+iqz+iky}\Lambda^n(p, q \mid k)\delta(p+q+k)\,dp\,dq\,dk, \tag{38.36}$$

where $\Lambda^n(p, q \mid k)$ is determined by expression (32.28) which, as we have already shown, contains an infrared singularity. In order to remove this singularity, one has to examine the following terms of the mass operator. We refer the reader who is interested in the details of the calculation to the original papers [77] and merely note here that the principal contribution to E_1' is given by the nonrelativistic term corresponding to a small momentum $\mathbf{q}^2 \ll m^2$ of the external field $A_0(\mathbf{q})$ which was first calculated by Bethe (7).

An important feature of expression (38.35) is its explicit dependence on the form of the functions χ, $\overline{\chi}$ which leads to different values of the Lamb shift for different electron levels in a hydrogenlike atom. It is just this circumstance which leads to the experimentally observed splitting of the $2S_{1/2}$ and $2P_{1/2}$ levels which coincide exactly according to the one-electron theory of Dirac.

In contrast to the foregoing the term due to polarization of the vacuum (38.31) leads to a shift which does not depend on the wave functions χ, $\overline{\chi}$. Indeed, by substituting (38.23), (38.24), (38.32), and (38.33) into (38.31) we may easily show that

$$E_1'' = e\frac{\alpha}{\pi}\frac{1}{(2\pi)^{3/2}}\int I(-\mathbf{k}^2)A_0(\mathbf{k})\,d\mathbf{k}, \qquad (38.37)$$

where $I(-\mathbf{k}^2)$ is determined by expression (38.34) with $k^2 = -\mathbf{k}^2$.

Finally, we note that the theoretical value of the relative shift of the $2S_{1/2}$ and $2P_{1/2}$ levels of hydrogen calculated up to terms of order $Z\alpha^3$, taking into account the influence on the hyperfine structure of the interaction of the electron with the magnetic dipole field of the nucleus and also the influence of the structure and of the finite mass of the nucleus, turned out to be equal to 1057.8 Mc/sec which is in good agreement with the experimental value of $1057.77 + 0.1$ Mc/sec obtained by Triebwasser, Dayhoff, and Lamb (127).

38.4. *Concluding Remarks*

We note, finally, that the application of the method given in § 38.1 is, of course, not restricted to the examination of the Lamb shift of the levels in hydrogen. This method may be easily extended to systems containing an arbitrary number of electrons and positrons greater than unity.

[77] Karplus, Klein and Schwinger (66), Baranger, Bethe, and Feynman (6).

For example, the wave function describing a positron obviously has the form

$$\bar{\varphi}(x) = \frac{1}{i} \Phi_0^* S^\dagger \frac{\delta S}{\delta \eta(x)} \Phi_1 = \frac{\Phi_0^* T(\bar{\psi}(x) S) \Phi_1}{S_0}, \qquad (38.38)$$

where Φ_1 is the amplitude of the single-positron state. By noting that $\bar{\varphi}(x)$ differs from the single-electron Green's function by the replacement of the factor S^c for an emerging line by $\bar{\psi}(x)$, we may obtain, by means of arguments similar to the ones previously given, the Dirac equation with radiation corrections for the function $\bar{\varphi}$.

In a similar manner, we can introduce the wave function for two electrons or positrons. In considering positronium, it is convenient to introduce the quantity

$$\varphi(x, y) = \frac{1}{i^2} \Phi_0^* S^\dagger \frac{\delta^2 S}{\delta \bar{\eta}(x) \delta \eta(y)} \Phi_2 = \frac{\Phi_0^* T(\psi(x) \bar{\psi}(y) S) \Phi_2}{S_0}, \qquad (38.39)$$

where Φ_2 is the amplitude of the state containing one electron and one positron. The equation for $\varphi(x, y)$ may be obtained by appropriately modifying the equation for the two-electron Green's function

$$G(x, x', y, y') = \frac{\Phi_0^* T(\psi(x) \psi(x') \bar{\psi}(y) \bar{\psi}(y') S) \Phi_0}{S_0}.$$

It is obvious that by considering matrix elements of higher-order variational derivatives of the S-matrix, one may generalize the foregoing results to any arbitrary many-electron system.

CHAPTER VII

The Method of Functional Averaging

§ 39. Representation of Green's Functions in Terms of Continuous Integrals

39.1. *Introduction*

We now turn to an examination of various attempts to go beyond the framework of perturbation theory. Among these attempts, the method described in this chapter which is based on the use of the continuous integral first introduced by Feynman (39) is of considerable interest. We shall show that by using this method it is possible to obtain closed expressions for the complete Green's functions including all the radiation corrections. These expressions may be regarded as formulas for the averaging of the classical Green's functions for particles moving in a given external field over the quantum fluctuations of this field. It is just in the course of such averaging that continuous integrals over function space arise.

It should be noted that investigations relating to this problem are far from complete and contain a number of unsolved problems both with respect to technique and to principle.

Representations of Green's functions in the form of continuous integrals may be obtained in various ways. One of them [78] is based on the formal integration of the equations for Green's functions involving variational derivatives which we have considered in § 34. However, we shall present a different approach (Bogoliubov (16)) which in our opinion is simpler, and which starts by representing the Green's functions in terms of the vacuum expectation values of chronological products with

[78] Edwards and Peierls (37), Symanzik (122), Gel'fand and Minlos (46), Fradkin (44), Khalatnikov (70).

the operation of averaging over the boson vacuum being interpreted as a functional integral.

In considering the applications of the method of functional integration to problems of gauge transformations of electrodynamic Green's functions (§ 42) and to the investigation of the Bloch-Nordsieck model (§ 43), we shall follow the work of Svidzinskii (121).

Thus we shall start with the expressions obtained in § 34 for the complete Green's functions including radiation corrections in the form of vacuum expectation values of chronological products of corresponding operators and the S-matrix. We have in mind the expressions for the electron Green's function

$$G_{\alpha\beta}(x, y) = i\frac{\langle T(\psi_\alpha(x)\bar{\psi}_\beta(y)S)\rangle_0}{S_0} \tag{34.9}$$

and the photon Green's function

$$D_{mn}(x, y) = \frac{1}{i}\frac{\langle T(A_m(x)A_n(y)S)\rangle_0}{S_0}, \tag{34.10}$$

where

$$S = S(1) = T\left(\exp i\int \mathscr{L}(x)\,dx\right),$$

while the interaction Lagrangian $\mathscr{L}(x)$ for the case of spinor electrodynamics has the form

$$\mathscr{L}(x) = e:\bar{\psi}(x)\hat{A}(x)\psi(x):. \tag{20.3}$$

Corresponding expressions may also be written down for other theories. Thus, for example, in the case of the pseudoscalar meson theory considered in § 33 the nucleon Green's function G and the meson Green's function Δ have the form

$$G(x, y) = i\frac{\langle T(\Psi(x)\overline{\Psi}(y)S)\rangle_0}{S_0}, \tag{39.1}$$

$$\Delta(x, y) = i\frac{\langle T(\varphi(x)\varphi(y)S)\rangle_0}{S_0}, \tag{39.2}$$

where in accordance with (33.14)

$$\mathscr{L}(x) = g:\overline{\Psi}(x)\Gamma\Psi(x)\varphi(x): + M(x). \tag{39.3}$$

Here $M(x)$ is that part of the Lagrangian which does not depend on the spinor field Ψ, $\overline{\Psi}$.

In calculating vacuum expectation values of type (34.9), (34.10), (39.1), (39.2) the averaging over the boson and the fermion vacuum may be carried out independently, since the corresponding expressions are given by linear forms of products of vacuum expectation values over the boson and the fermion vacuum separately. Let us therefore first consider the procedure of calculating the vacuum expectation value of an expression which contains only Bose field operators.

We set ourselves the problem of determining the vacuum expectation value of an arbitrary functional F which depends on operator functions of a real field φ subjected to Bose-Einstein quantization $\langle T(F(\varphi))\rangle_0$. In doing so we shall assume that the chronological pairings of the operators φ are given and have the following form in the momentum representation

$$\overbrace{\varphi(p)\varphi(p')} = -i\delta(p+p')\Delta^c(p). \tag{39.4}$$

We shall first consider the special case when F is of exponential form and we shall evaluate the expression

$$I = \left\langle T\left(\exp i\int \nu(p)\varphi(p)\,dp\right)\right\rangle_0, \tag{39.5}$$

where $\nu(p)$ is an arbitrary function.

39.2. *Evaluation of* $\langle T\exp i\int\nu\varphi\,dp\rangle_0$

For the evaluation of I we note that the reduction to the normal form of any arbitrary operator T-functional F which depends on the Bose field φ may be carried out by means of the following procedure.[79] φ in F should be replaced by φ' which in the momentum representation has the form [80]

$$\varphi'(k) = \varphi(k) + \int \overbrace{\varphi(k)\varphi(k')}\frac{\delta}{\delta\varphi(k')}\,dk' = \varphi(k) - i\Delta^c(k)\frac{\delta}{\delta\varphi(-k)}. \tag{39.6}$$

[79] See, for example, Anderson (4).

[80] Correspondingly in the x-representation it has the form

$$\varphi'(x) \to \varphi(x) - i\int \Delta^c(x-x')\frac{\delta}{\delta\varphi(x')}\,dx'.$$

After the replacement (39.6) has been made, the resulting functional $F(\varphi')$ should be regarded as an ordinary c-functional of an unquantized function φ and its functional derivatives, and the necessary functional differentiations should be performed in it by considering that F is multiplied on the right by unity. The expression obtained as a result of this operation should be regarded as the functional F of operator functions φ written in normal form. For example,

$$T\left(\int \varphi(k)\, a(k)\, dk \int \varphi(k')\, b(k')\, dk'\right)$$

$$\to \int \left[\varphi(k) - i\Delta^c(k)\,\frac{\delta}{\delta\varphi(-k)}\right] a(k)\, dk \int \left[\varphi(k') - i\Delta^c(k')\,\frac{\delta}{\delta\varphi(-k')}\right] b(k')\, dk' \cdot 1$$

$$= \int \varphi(k)\, a(k)\, dk \int \varphi(k')\, b(k')\, dk' - i \int \Delta^c(k)\, b(-k)\, a(k)\, dk,$$

i.e.,

$$T\left\{\int \varphi(k)\, a(k)\, dk \int \varphi(k')\, b(k')\, dk'\right\}$$
$$= \int a(k) dk \int b(k') dk' : \varphi(k)\varphi(k') : - i \int a(k)\Delta^c(k)\, b(-k)\, dk$$

which may be checked by a direct substitution.

The validity of the prescription formulated above may also be directly checked in the case when F is of polynomial form, and from this its validity follows for all F which may be expanded in power series. Moreover, it is clear that for calculating vacuum expectation values it is sufficient to set $\varphi = 0$ in the result, i.e.,

$$\langle T(F(\varphi))\rangle_0 = \left\{F\left(\varphi - i\Delta^c \frac{\delta}{\delta\varphi}\right) \cdot 1\right\}_{\varphi=0}. \tag{39.7}$$

By applying the prescription (39.7) to the integral (39.5), we find that this integral may be represented in the form

$$I = \left[\left\{\exp i \int \nu(p) \left(\varphi(p) - i\Delta^c(p)\,\frac{\delta}{\delta\varphi(-p)}\right) dp\right\} \cdot 1\right]_{\varphi=0}. \tag{39.8}$$

In order to evaluate (39.8) we find the auxiliary quantity

$$U(\lambda \mid \varphi) = \exp\left(i\lambda \int \nu(p)\left(\varphi(p) - i\Delta^c(p)\frac{\delta}{\delta\varphi(-p)}\right)dp\right), \quad (39.9)$$

where evidently

$$I = U(1 \mid 0). \quad (39.10)$$

By differentiating (39.9) with respect to the parameter λ we obtain for U the differential equation

$$\frac{\partial U(\lambda)}{\partial\lambda} = i\int \nu(p)\left(\varphi(p) - i\Delta^c(p)\frac{\delta}{\delta\varphi(-p)}\right)dp\, U(\lambda), \quad (39.11)$$

the solution of which, satisfying the initial condition

$$U(\lambda \mid \varphi)\mid_{\lambda=0} = U(0 \mid \varphi) = 1, \quad (39.12)$$

we shall seek in the form

$$U(\lambda \mid \varphi) = e^{s(\lambda \mid \varphi)}. \quad (39.13)$$

On substituting (39.13) into (39.11) we obtain for s an equation in "partial derivatives":

$$\frac{\partial s}{\partial\lambda} = \int \nu(p)\left(i\varphi(p) + \Delta^c(p)\frac{\delta s}{\delta\varphi(-p)}\right)dp. \quad (39.14)$$

In order to solve it, we shall write s in the form

$$s(\lambda \mid \varphi) = i\lambda\int \nu(p)\varphi(p)\,dp + r(\lambda), \quad (39.15)$$

where r does not depend on φ and satisfies the equation

$$\frac{\partial r}{\partial\lambda} = i\lambda\int \nu(p)\Delta^c(p)\nu(-p)\,dp, \quad (39.16)$$

integration of which with the boundary condition taken into account gives:

$$r(\lambda) = \frac{i\lambda^2}{2}\int \nu(p)\Delta^c(p)\nu(-p)\,dp. \quad (39.17)$$

Thus

$$U(\lambda \mid \varphi) = \exp i\left(\lambda\int \nu(p)\varphi(p)dp + \frac{\lambda^2}{2}\int \nu(p)\Delta^c(p)\nu(-p)\,dp, \quad (39.18)\right.$$

and in accordance with (39.7), (39.8)

$$I = \left\langle T \left(\exp i \int \nu(p) \varphi(p) \, dp \right) \right\rangle_0 = \exp \left[\frac{i}{2} \int \nu(p) \Delta^c(p) \nu(-p) \, dp \right]. \tag{39.19}$$

39.3. *Continuous Integrals*

In order to go over from (39.19) to a functional integral we shall introduce a discrete "lattice" momentum representation based on a finite system of points p_j in momentum space symmetric with respect to the transformation

$$p \to -p.$$

Let Δp be the four-dimensional volume element of the lattice. Then by introducing the notation

$$\varphi(p_j) = \varphi_j, \quad \Delta^c(p_j) = \Delta_j^c, \quad \nu(p_j)\Delta p = \nu_j, \tag{39.20}$$

we obtain from (39.19), after taking into account the fact that Δ^c is even,

$$\langle T(\exp i \sum_j \nu_j \varphi_j) \rangle_0 = \exp \left(\frac{i}{2\Delta p} \sum_j \nu_j \Delta_j^c \nu_{-j} \right) = \prod_j \left(\exp \frac{i}{2\Delta p} \nu_j \Delta_j^c \nu_{-j} \right)$$

$$= \prod_{j>0} \left(\exp \frac{i}{\Delta p} \nu_j \Delta_j^c \nu_{-j} \right). \tag{39.21}$$

By noting that the condition that the field $\varphi(x)$ should be real has in the discrete momentum representation the form

$$\varphi^*(p_j) = \varphi(-p_j),$$

and by choosing our system of notation in such a way that

$$-p_j = p_{-j},$$

we shall write

$$\varphi_j = x_j + iy_j,$$

$$\varphi_{-j} = x_j - iy_j,$$

where $j > 0$ and all the x_j and y_j are real.

Then with the aid of the Gaussian quadrature

$$\int_{-\infty}^{+\infty} dx \int_{-\infty}^{+\infty} dy \, e^{i[-a(x^2+y^2)+\lambda x + i\mu y]} = \frac{\pi}{ia} e^{i\frac{\lambda^2-\mu^2}{4a}}$$

we may represent the factors in the right-hand side of (39.21) in the form

$$\exp\left(\frac{i}{\Delta p}\nu_j\Delta_j^c\nu_{-j}\right)=\frac{i\Delta p}{\pi\Delta_j^c}\int_{-\infty}^{+\infty}dx_j\int_{-\infty}^{+\infty}dy_j\exp i\left(\nu_j\varphi_j+\nu_{-j}\varphi_{-j}-\frac{\Delta p}{\Delta_j^c}\varphi_j\varphi_{-j}\right)$$

$$=\frac{\int_{-\infty}^{+\infty}dx_j\int_{-\infty}^{+\infty}dy_j\exp i\left(\nu_j\varphi_j+\nu_{-j}\varphi_{-j}-\frac{\Delta p}{\Delta_j^c}\varphi_j\varphi_{-j}\right)}{\int_{-\infty}^{+\infty}dx_j\int_{-\infty}^{+\infty}dy_j\exp\left(-\frac{i\Delta p}{\Delta_j^c}\varphi_j\varphi_{-j}\right)}$$

$$=\int\exp i\,(\nu_j\varphi_j+\nu_{-j}\varphi_{-j})\,d\varphi_j, \tag{39.22}$$

where the following notation has been introduced

$$\int d\varphi_j=\frac{i\Delta p}{\pi\Delta_j^c}\int_{-\infty}^{+\infty}dx_j\int_{-\infty}^{+\infty}dy_j\exp\left(-\frac{i\Delta p}{\Delta_j^c}\varphi_j\varphi_{-j}\right)$$

$$=\int_{-\infty}^{\infty}\int_{-\infty}^{\infty}\frac{dx_j\,dy_j}{\int_{-\infty}^{\infty}dx_j\int_{-\infty}^{\infty}dy_j\exp\left(-\frac{i\Delta p}{\Delta_j^c}\varphi_j\varphi_{-j}\right)}\exp\left(-\frac{i\Delta p}{\Delta_j^c}\varphi_j\varphi_{-j}\right). \tag{39.23}$$

Returning to (39.21) we obtain:

$$\langle T(\exp i\sum_j\nu_j\varphi_j)\rangle_0=\prod_{j>0}\left(\int\exp i\,(\nu_j\varphi_j+\nu_{-j}\varphi_{-j})\,d\varphi_j\right)$$

$$=\int\exp\,(i\sum_j\nu_j\varphi_j)\prod_{j>0}d\varphi_j, \tag{39.24}$$

where the $d\varphi_j$ are defined by relation (39.23).

The product $\prod_j d\varphi_j$ is the weighted volume element of integration in the discrete function space. Since it does not depend on ν_j we may, by introducing a Fourier transformation with respect to the variables ν_j, conclude that a relation of type (39.24) holds for any arbitrary function F of the variables $\ldots\varphi_j\ldots$, i.e.,

$$\langle T\,[F(\ldots\varphi_j\ldots)]\rangle_0=\int F(\ldots\varphi_j\ldots)\prod d\varphi_j. \tag{39.25}$$

Let us now make the inverse transition to continuous momentum space by diminishing the lattice element Δp and by increasing the region in four-dimensional momentum space occupied by this lattice. We shall define the *functional* (*continuous*) *integral* as the appropriate limit of the right-hand side of expressions (39.24), (39.25), and we shall denote it by the symbol

$$\int \ldots d\varphi,$$

i.e., by going to the limit in (39.21), (39.24), (39.25) we shall set

$$\left\langle T\left(\exp i\int \nu(p)\varphi(p)\,dp\right)\right\rangle_0 = \exp\left(\frac{i}{2}\int \nu(p)\Delta^c(p)\nu(-p)\right)dp$$
$$= \int \exp\left(i\int \nu(p)\varphi(p)\,dp\right)d\varphi, \qquad (39.26)$$

and

$$\langle T(F(\varphi))\rangle_0 = \int F(\varphi)\,d\varphi, \qquad (39.27)$$

where φ is an operator in the left-hand sides of (39.26) and (39.27) while in their right-hand sides φ is a c-function.

The last two relations may be regarded as definitions of the continuous integral. They may be interpreted as formulas which establish the relation between the vacuum T-expectation value $\langle T \ldots\rangle_0$ and the functional average of corresponding expressions dependent on classical c-fields over the quantum fluctuations of these fields.

Sometimes the functional integrals are also expressed in another form. Thus, by formally carrying out the transition to the limit in formula (39.22) we shall obtain on taking (39.26) into account

$$\int \exp\left(i\int \nu(p)\varphi(p)\,dp\right)d\varphi = \frac{\int \exp\,(i\int \nu(p)\varphi(p)\,dp + iA_0)\,\delta\varphi}{\int \exp\,(iA_0)\,\delta\varphi}, \qquad (39.28)$$

where $\delta\varphi$ denotes the limit of the product of the differentials dx_j, dy_j, while

$$A_0 = -\frac{1}{2}\int \varphi(p)\frac{1}{\Delta^c(p)}\varphi(-p)\,dp$$
$$= \frac{1}{2}\int \varphi(p)(p^2 - m^2)\varphi(-p)\,dp = \int \mathscr{L}_0(p)\,dp$$

turns out to be equal to the action of a free Bose field. Thus, formally

$$d\varphi = e^{iA_0}\delta\varphi \Big/ \int e^{iA_0}\delta\varphi. \tag{39.29}$$

It may be easily seen that (39.28) may be written in the form of a "Gaussian" quadrature with respect to $\delta\varphi$. By making use of relation (39.26) we obtain:

$$\int \exp\left\{ i \int \nu(p)\varphi(p)\,dp - \frac{i}{2}\int \varphi(p)\frac{1}{\Delta^c(p)}\varphi(-p)\,dp \right\}\delta\varphi$$
$$= C \exp\left\{ \frac{i}{2}\int \nu(p)\Delta^c(p)\nu(-p)\,dp \right\}, \tag{39.30}$$

where

$$C = \int \exp\left(-\frac{i}{2}\int \varphi(p)\frac{1}{\Delta^c(p)}\varphi(-p)\,dp \right)\delta\varphi. \tag{39.31}$$

We also note that formula (39.30) may be directly checked by means of the linear substitution

$$\varphi(p) = \varphi'(p) + \nu(-p)\Delta^c(p).$$

We emphasize once again that the limiting transition to the continuous function space has been carried out formally. The question of the restrictions that must be imposed on the class of functionals and on the space of the functions φ for the convergence of the transition to the limit must be investigated separately, and at the present moment it is still very far from being solved.

39.4. *Closed Expressions for Green's Functions*

With the aid of (39.28) it is easy to obtain expressions for Green's functions in the form of functional integrals. Let us consider, for example, a system of interacting fermion and boson fields whose interaction Lagrangian has the form

$$\mathscr{L}(x) = g : \bar{\psi}(x)\Gamma\psi(x)\varphi(x) : + M(x). \tag{39.3}$$

Here Γ is a vertex matrix (for example $\gamma^5\tau$ in the symmetric pseudoscalar meson theory) while $M(x)$ is a term in the Lagrangian which depends only on the boson field $\varphi(x)$. $M(x)$ may contain both a term with a "classical source" of the type $J(x)\varphi(x)$ and also nonlinear terms of the type $h\varphi^4$.

Let us further consider the fermion Green's function

$$G(x, y) = i\,\frac{\langle T(\psi(x)\bar{\psi}(y)S)\rangle_0}{\langle S\rangle_0}, \tag{34.9}$$

where

$$S = T\left(\exp i\int \mathscr{L}(x)\,dx\right), \tag{34.5}$$

and $\mathscr{L}(x)$ is defined by the relation (39.3). We note that in expression (34.9) we may set

$$\langle \ldots \rangle = \langle\langle \ldots \rangle_{F_0}\rangle_{B_0}, \tag{39.32}$$

i.e., we may first carry out the averaging over the fermion vacuum (F_0) and then average over the boson vacuum (B_0). Remembering that the operation of averaging over the boson vacuum reduces in accordance with (39.25) to functional quadrature, we obtain from (34.9) after taking into account (39.32), (34.5), and (39.3):

$$G(x, y) = i\,\frac{\int\langle T[\psi(x)\bar{\psi}(y)\exp(ig\int\bar{\psi}(z)\Gamma\psi(z)\varphi(z)\,dz]\rangle_{F_0}\exp(iM(x)\,dx)\,d\varphi}{\int\langle T[\exp(ig\int\bar{\psi}(z)\Gamma\psi(z)\varphi(z)\,dz)]\rangle_{F_0}\exp(i\int M(x)\,dx)\,d\varphi}. \tag{39.33}$$

On the other hand, the usual Green's function for a single fermion in a classical external field φ has the form

$$G(x, y\,|\,\varphi) = i\,\frac{\langle T[\psi(x)\bar{\psi}(y)\exp(ig\int\bar{\psi}(z)\Gamma\psi(z)\varphi(z)\,dz)]\rangle_{F_0}}{S_0(\varphi)}, \tag{39.34}$$

where

$$S_0(\varphi) = \left\langle T\left[\exp\left(ig\int\bar{\psi}(z)\,\Gamma\psi(z)\,\varphi(z)\,dz\right)\right]\right\rangle_0. \tag{39.35}$$

Thus

$$G(x, y) = \frac{\int G(x, y\,|\,\varphi)S_0(\varphi)\exp(i\int M(x)dx)d\varphi}{\int S_0(\varphi)\exp(i\int M(x)\,dx\,d\varphi)}. \tag{39.36}$$

Now only $S_0(\varphi)$ remains to be evaluated. In order to do this, we introduce the auxiliary numerical parameter λ multiplying φ in the argument of $S_0(\varphi)$. Then

$$\frac{\partial S_0(\lambda\varphi)}{\partial\lambda} = ig\int\left\langle T\left[\bar{\psi}(x)\Gamma\psi(x)\exp\left(i\lambda g\int\bar{\psi}(z)\Gamma\psi(z)\varphi(z)\,dz\right)\right]\right\rangle_{F_0}\varphi(x)dx$$
$$= -g\int \mathrm{SP}\,\{G(x, x\,|\,\lambda\varphi)\Gamma\varphi(x)\}\,dx S_0(\lambda\varphi),$$

where $S_0(0) = 1$, while the symbol SP denotes summation both over the spinor and the boson indices. On carrying out the integration, we obtain:

$$S_0(\varphi) = \exp\left(-g\int_0^1 d\lambda\int dx\,\mathrm{SP}\,\{G(x, x\,|\,\lambda\varphi)\Gamma\varphi(x)\}\right). \quad (39.37)$$

Substituting (39.37) into (39.36) we find:

$$G(x, y)$$
$$= \frac{\int G(x, y\,|\,\varphi)\exp\left(-g\int_0^1 d\lambda\int dx\,\mathrm{SP}\,\{G(x, x|\lambda\varphi)\Gamma\varphi(x)\} + i\int M(x)dx\right)d\varphi}{\int\exp\left(-g\int_0^1 d\lambda\int dx\,\mathrm{SP}\,\{G(x, x\,|\,\lambda\varphi)\Gamma\varphi(x)\} + i\int M(x)dx\right)d\varphi}. \quad (39.38)$$

Similar formulas may be easily obtained for Green's functions of a larger number of particles.

It may be seen that the fermion Green's functions which take into account radiation corrections may be obtained by averaging the usual Green's functions for particles moving in a classical field φ over the quantum fluctuations of this field.

Turning to the boson Green's function

$$\Delta(x, y) = i\,\frac{\langle T(\varphi(x)\varphi(y)S)\rangle_0}{S_0},$$

we obtain with the aid of (39.26), (39.29), (39.31), (39.32):

$$\Delta(x, y) = i\,\frac{\int S_0(\varphi)\,\varphi(x)\,\varphi(y)\,\exp\,(i\int M(x)\,dx)\,d\varphi}{\int S_0(\varphi)\,\exp\,(i\int M(x)\,dx)\,d\varphi},$$

which gives, after (39.37) has been taken into account:

$$\Delta(x, y) = i\,\frac{\int \varphi(x)\varphi(y) \exp\left(-g\int_0^1 d\lambda \int dx\, \mathrm{SP}\,\{G(x, x\,|\,\lambda\varphi)\Gamma\varphi(x)\} + i\int M(x)\,dx\right) d\varphi}{\int \exp\left(-g\int_0^1 d\lambda \int dx\, \mathrm{SP}\,\{G(x, x\,|\,\lambda\varphi)\,\Gamma\varphi(x)\} + i\int M(x)\,dx\right) d\varphi}. \tag{39.39}$$

Formulas (39.38), (39.39) give closed expressions for the fermion Green's function G and for the boson Green's function Δ which contain the Green's function for the fermion moving in the given classical external field $G(x, y \mid \varphi)$.

It might appear that the problem of determining G and Δ has been thereby reduced to finding $G(x, y \mid \varphi)$. However, it should be emphasized at this point that even if it were possible to obtain a closed expression for $G(x, y \mid \varphi)$ in some approximation, which in the general case is a very complicated problem, we still would have to carry out the functional integrations in (39.38), (39.39) which is also far from being trivial.

The point is that at the present time the technique for the evaluation of functional integrals is still practically nonexistent. The only type of continuous quadratures capable of being evaluated are Gaussian quadratures, or those which may be reduced to such by a change of functional argument, which may then be evaluated with the aid of formulas of type (39.26), (39.30). Therefore, the practical utility of the equations just obtained is as yet not very great. An important disadvantage of the continuous representations of Green's functions also consists of the fact that no connection has yet been established between these representations and the causal structure of the complete Green's functions. (For details on the causal structure of Green's functions see Chapter IX, §§ 48, 49.)

In view of the foregoing, we shall restrict ourselves to only two applications of the preceding formulas to the case of spinor electrodynamics. First of all we shall consider the transformation of the electron Green's function under a gauge transformation of the potentials of the electromagnetic field; for this we shall not need to calculate $G(x, y \mid A)$ explicitly. Secondly, we shall investigate the Bloch-Nordsieck model in spinor electrodynamics where it is possible to reduce the solution to a functional integral of Gaussian type and consequently to evaluate it explicitly.

§ 40. Gauge Transformation of the Electron Green's Function in Spinor Electrodynamics

40.1. *Transition to the Transverse Gauge and Transformation of the Function $G(x, y \mid A)$*

As we have shown in § 31, a gauge transformation of the potentials of the electromagnetic field allows us to go from one form of the elementary pairing $\overline{AA}$ to another by introducing an arbitrary change in the longitudinal part d_l of this pairing. Our immediate aim is to establish the transformation law for Green's functions of spinor electrodynamics corresponding to changes of d_l. We shall start with the potential A in an arbitrary gauge; in other words, we shall assume that the elementary pairing $\overline{AA}$ contains an arbitrary longitudinal part d_l^0:

$$\overline{A_n(k)A_m(k')} = \frac{\delta(k+k')}{ik^2}\left(g^{mn} - \frac{k_m k_n}{k^2}\right) + \frac{\delta(k+k')}{ik^2}\frac{k_m k_n}{k^2} d_l^0(k^2). \tag{40.1}$$

The potential A may be decomposed into longitudinal and transverse parts (in the four-dimensional sense), i.e., it may be written in the form

$$A_n(k) = A_n^{\text{tr}}(k) + \chi_n(k), \tag{40.2}$$

where $A_n^{\text{tr}}(k)$ is a purely transverse field satisfying the Lorentz condition

$$(k \cdot A^{\text{tr}}(k)) \equiv \sum k^n A_n^{\text{tr}}(k) = 0 \tag{40.3}$$

and containing a pairing of the transverse form

$$\overline{A_n^{\text{tr}}(k) A_m^{\text{tr}}(k')} = \frac{\delta(k+k')}{ik^2}\left(g^{mn} - \frac{k_m k_n}{k^2}\right). \tag{40.4}$$

The term $\chi_n(k)$ in (40.2) in turn corresponds to the longitudinal component and in accordance with (40.3) may be represented in the form

$$\chi_n(k) = k_n \frac{(k \cdot A(k))}{k^2}.$$

Thus χ has the structure of a gradient as a result of which the transformation (40.2) is in fact a gauge transformation of the four-potential of the electromagnetic field.

For us it will turn out to be essential that the mutual pairing of the longitudinal component χ and the transverse component A^{tr} is equal to zero

$$\overline{A_n^{\text{tr}}(k)\chi_m(k')} = 0, \tag{40.5}$$

and that the mutual pairing of the operators χ may be written in the form

$$\overline{\chi_n(k)\chi_m(k')} = \frac{i^2 k_n k'_m}{k^2 \cdot k'^2} \overline{(k \cdot A(k))\,(k' \cdot A(k'))} = i\delta(k+k')F(k^2)\,k_n k_m, \tag{40.6}$$

where

$$F(k^2) = \frac{d_l^0(k^2)}{k^2 \cdot k^2}. \tag{40.7}$$

We now turn to a consideration of the transformations of the Green's functions which correspond to the transition (40.2) from A to A^{tr}. As we have noted in § 32, the transverse part $d(k^2)$ of the complete photon Green's function

$$D(k^2) = -\frac{d(k^2)}{k^2}\left(g^{mn} - \frac{k_m k_n}{k^2}\right) - \frac{d_l}{k^2}\frac{k_m k_n}{k^2} \tag{32.5}$$

is gauge invariant, i.e., does not depend on d_l^0 while the longitudinal part $d_l(k^2)$ has no radiation corrections, and therefore

$$d_l(k^2) = d_l^0(k^2).$$

The elementary pairings of the operators of the electron-positron field $\overline{\psi\bar{\psi}}$ naturally do not depend on the gauge of the electromagnetic potential. However, the complete electron Green's function G is no longer a gauge invariant quantity since the form of the pairing $\overline{AA}$ affects the radiation corrections to G. The same applies to Green's function of an electron in a given external field, the transformation law for which may be easily found from the condition of gauge covariance of the equation which it satisfies:

$$\left(i\frac{\hat{\partial}}{\partial x} - m + e\hat{A}(x)\right)G(x, y \mid A) = -\delta(x - y). \tag{40.8}$$

By going over in this equation to the transverse potential

$$A_n(x) = A_n^{\text{tr}}(x) + \frac{\partial f(x)}{\partial x^n}\left(\frac{\partial f}{\partial x^n} = \chi_n\right) \tag{40.9}$$

(here naturally f is, like A and A^{tr}, an unquantized given function) we shall set

$$G(x, y \mid A) = G\left(x, y \mid A^{\text{tr}} + \frac{\partial f}{\partial x}\right) = R(x)R^{-1}(y)G(x, y \mid A^{\text{tr}}), \tag{40.10}$$

where R is a certain unknown function. On substituting (40.10) into (40.8) and multiplying by $R(y)$ we obtain:

$$R(x)\left(i\frac{\hat{\partial}}{\partial x} - m + e\hat{A}^{\text{tr}}(x)\right)G(x, y \mid A^{\text{tr}})$$

$$+\left[i\frac{\hat{\partial}}{\partial x}R(x) + eR(x)\frac{\hat{\partial}}{\partial x}f(x)\right]G(x, y \mid A^{\text{tr}}) = -R(x)\delta(x - y).$$

In order that the equation expressed in terms of the new variables A^{tr} shall have the form (40.8) it is only necessary to set

$$i\frac{\partial R(x)}{\partial x^n} + eR(x)\frac{\partial f(x)}{\partial x^n} = 0,$$

which yields:

$$R(x) = \exp\left[ief(x)\right].$$

We thus arrive at the following transformation law for Green's function of the electron in a given external field in the case of the gauge transformation (40.9):

$$G(x, y \mid A) = e^{ie[f(x) - f(y)]}G(x, y \mid A^{\text{tr}}). \tag{40.11}$$

On substituting this relation into the functional quadrature for the complete Green's function $G(x, y)$ of type (39.38) we shall be able to find its transformation law.

40.2. *The Functional Integral for $G(x, y)$ in the Case of Transverse Gauge*

In turning to the functional representation of type (39.38) for the electron Green's function in spinor electrodynamics, we note that formula (39.36) may be directly generalized for this case:

$$G(x, y) = \frac{\int G(x, y \mid A) S_0(A)\, dA}{\int S_0(A)\, dA}, \tag{40.12}$$

where

$$S_0(A) = \exp\left(-e \int_0^1 d\lambda \int dx \operatorname{Sp} G(x, x \mid \lambda A) \hat{A}(x)\right). \tag{40.13}$$

The functional integration in (40.12) is carried out over the four independent components of the potential A and the symbol dA should be interpreted as the product of differentials corresponding to the components, A_0, A_1, A_2, and A_3.

It is also clear that in the case of the diagonal gauge of the electromagnetic field when $d_l^0 = 1$ and the elementary pairing

$$D^0_{mn} = -g^{mn} \frac{1}{k^2}$$

is the inverse of the d'Alembertian operator, dA may be formally written as

$$dA = e^{iA_0} \delta A \Big/ \int e^{iA_0} \delta A,$$

where A_0 is the action of the free electromagnetic field

$$A_0 = \int \mathscr{L}_0(x)\, dx = \tfrac{1}{2} \sum_{m,n} \int A_m(k) k^2 A_n(-k)\, dk$$
$$= -\tfrac{1}{2} \sum_{m,n} g^{mm} g^{nn} \int \frac{\partial A_m}{\partial x^n} \frac{\partial A_m}{\partial x^n}\, dx.$$

We now consider the transition (40.2), (40.10) to the transverse potential. In this case in accordance with the Lorentz condition (40.3) only three components of the potential A^{tr} are independent and the functional integration must be carried out only over three functional arguments. In order to obtain the corresponding expression in a natural manner, the most convenient starting point is a relation of type (39.26):

$$\int \exp\left(i \sum_n \int \nu^n(k) A_n(k) dk\right) dA = \exp\left(-\frac{i}{2} \sum_{n,m} \int \nu^n(k) D^0_{nm}(k) \nu^m(-k) dk\right), \tag{40.14}$$

which, as we have pointed out, may be regarded as the definition of the functional integral over A. By introducing into (40.14) the substitution

$$A_n(k) = A^{tr}_n(k) + ik_n f(k),$$

and by taking into account the fact that in consequence of (40.5) the operations of integrating over A^{tr} and f may be separated, we shall obtain:

$$\int \exp\left(i \sum_n \nu^n(k) A^{tr}_n(k)\, dk\right) dA^{tr} \int \exp\left\{i \sum_n \int \nu^n(k) ik_n f(k^2)\, dk\right\} df$$
$$= \exp\left\{-\frac{i}{2} \sum_{n,m} \int \nu^n(k) D^{tr}_{nm}(k) \nu^m(-k)\, dk\right\}$$
$$\times \exp\left\{\frac{i}{2} \sum_{n,m} \nu^n(k) k_n F(k^2) k_m \nu^m(-k)\, dk\right\}.$$

Since the longitudinal and the transverse components are independent, two relations follow from the preceding equation:

$$\int \exp\left(i \sum_n \int \nu^n(k) A^{tr}_n(k)\, dk\right) dA^{tr}$$
$$= \exp\left(-\frac{i}{2} \sum_{n,m} \int \nu^n(k) D^{tr}_{nm}(k) \nu^m(-k)\, dk\right) \tag{40.15}$$

and

$$\int \exp\left(i \int \xi(k) f(k) dk\right) df = \exp\left(-\frac{i}{2} \int \xi(k) F(k^2) \xi(-k) dk\right) \tag{40.16}$$

(here the notation

$$i \sum_n k_n \nu^n(k) = \xi(k)$$

has been used).

Relation (40.15) may be regarded as the definition of the functional integral over the potential of the electromagnetic field A^{tr}, which satisfies the condition of transversality, while

(40.16), where $F(k^2)$ is defined by means of (40.7), may be regarded as the definition of the functional integral over the longitudinal component of the electromagnetic field.

40.3. *Gauge Transformation of the Function $G(x, y)$*

After the preceding auxiliary considerations, we now turn to the determination of the gauge transformation law for the complete electron Green's function. For our starting point we shall use its representation in the form of the functional integral (40.12). We shall obtain the desired form by then using the transformation law (40.11) for Green's function of the electron in a given external field and by carrying out separately the functional integrations over the longitudinal and the transverse components.

We first consider the integral

$$\int dx \,\mathrm{Sp}\, G(x, x \mid \lambda A)\hat{A}(x)$$

appearing in the expressions (40.13) for $S_0(A)$ and show that it is gauge invariant, i.e., that

$$\int dx \,\mathrm{Sp}\, G(x, x \mid \lambda A)\hat{A}(x) = \int dx \,\mathrm{Sp}\, G(x, x \mid \lambda A^{\mathrm{tr}})\hat{A}^{\mathrm{tr}}(x). \quad (40.17)$$

We note that in accordance with (40.11)

$$G(x, x \mid \lambda A) = G(x, x \mid \lambda A^{\mathrm{tr}}), \quad (40.18)$$

and we evaluate the difference

$$\int dx \,\mathrm{Sp}\, G(x, x \mid \lambda A^{\mathrm{tr}})\,(\hat{A}(x) - \hat{A}^{\mathrm{tr}}(x)) = \int dx \,\mathrm{Sp}\, G(x, x \mid \lambda A^{\mathrm{tr}})\,\frac{\hat{\partial}}{\partial x} f.$$

By carrying out integration by parts and by taking into account the fact that the fields vanish on the space-time boundaries of the region of integration we obtain

$$\int dx \,\mathrm{Sp}\, G(x, x \mid \lambda A^{\mathrm{tr}})\,\frac{\hat{\partial} f}{\partial x} = -\int dx \sum_n \frac{\partial}{\partial x^n}\,[\mathrm{Sp}\,\gamma^n G(x, x \mid \lambda A^{\mathrm{tr}})]\,f(x). \quad (40.19)$$

However, according to the definition of Green's functions G, the trace appearing above may be represented in the form

$$\mathrm{Sp}\,\gamma^n G(x, x|\lambda A^{\mathrm{tr}}) = i\,\mathrm{Sp}\,\gamma^n \frac{\langle T(\psi(x)\bar{\psi}(x)S)\rangle_0}{\langle S\rangle_0} = -i\frac{\langle T(\bar{\psi}(x)\gamma^n, \psi(x)S)\rangle_0}{\langle S\rangle_0}$$

$$= -\frac{1}{S_0}\frac{\delta S_0}{\delta e A_n(x)} = -\frac{1}{eS_0}\left\{\sum_m \frac{1}{(m-1)!}\int \frac{\partial S_m(x, x_2, \ldots, x_m)}{\partial A_n(x)} dx_2 \ldots dx_m\right\};$$

as a result of which and in view of the condition of gauge invariance of the scattering matrix (30.12) the right-hand side of (40.19) vanishes, i.e.,

$$\sum_n \frac{\partial}{\partial x^n}\,\mathrm{Sp}\,\gamma^n G(x, x\,|\,A) = 0.$$

This completes the proof of equation (40.17).

On separating in (40.12) the transverse and the longitudinal variables of integration and on taking into account (40.18) and (40.11) we obtain:

$$G(x, y) = \frac{\int (G(x, y\,|\,A^{\mathrm{tr}})\, e^{ie[f(x)-f(y)]} S_0(A)\, dA^{\mathrm{tr}} df}{\int S_0(A)\, dA^{\mathrm{tr}}\, df}, \tag{40.20}$$

where in accordance with the immediately preceding argument

$$S(A) = S_0(A^{\mathrm{tr}})$$

It is evident that the integrals over A^{tr} and over f may be separated. Remembering that for a purely transverse gauge the following relation holds

$$G^{\mathrm{tr}}(x, y) = \frac{\int G(x, y\,|\,A^{\mathrm{tr}})\, S_0(A)\, dA^{\mathrm{tr}}}{\int S_0(A^{\mathrm{tr}})\, dA^{\mathrm{tr}}},$$

we obtain

$$G(x, y) = \int e^{ie[f(x)-f(y)]}\, df \cdot G^{\mathrm{tr}}(x, y). \tag{40.21}$$

Formula (40.21) is the desired gauge transformation law for the electron Green's function.

The integration with respect to f in the first factor of the above transformation may be carried out with the aid of formula (40.16). In this way we obtain

$$\int \exp ie\,[f(x) - f(y)]\,df = \int \exp\left[\frac{ie}{(2\pi)^2}\int f(k)\,(e^{ikx} - e^{iky})\,dk\right] df$$

$$= \exp\left[-\frac{ie^2}{2(2\pi)^4}\int (e^{ikx} - e^{iky})(e^{-ikx} - e^{-iky})\,F(k^2)\,dk\right]$$

$$= \exp\{-\,ie^2[F(0) - F(x-y)]\}.$$

The constant

$$F(0) = \frac{1}{(2\pi)^4}\int F(k^2)\,dk = \frac{1}{(2\pi)^4}\int \frac{d_l^0}{k^2 \cdot k^2}\,dk \qquad (40.22)$$

in the foregoing expression diverges in the general case. Thus, as a result of the gauge transformation, the fermion Green's function acquires a singular factor. However, in accordance with the result of § 31, this factor may be removed by means of an appropriate change in the subtraction procedure. As a result we obtain the following formula for the gauge transformation of functions that do not contain infinities:

$$G^{\text{tr}}(x, y) \to G(x, y) = \exp\,[ie^2 F(x-y)]\,G^{\text{tr}}(x, y), \qquad (40.23)$$

where

$$F(x-y) = \frac{1}{(2\pi)^4}\int e^{ik(x-y)}\,\frac{d_l^0(k)}{k^2 \cdot k^2}\,dk. \qquad (40.24)$$

§ 41. Investigation of the Bloch-Nordsieck Model

41.1. *The Bloch-Nordsieck Model and the Determination of* $G(x, y \mid A)$

In this section we shall examine the application of the method of functional averaging to calculations based on the Bloch-Nordsieck model in spinor electrodynamics. As is well known, Bloch and Nordsieck (12), in order to remove the infrared catastrophe, developed a method for the approximate solution of the problem of the interaction of a fermion with the electromagnetic field in the region of low frequencies which is not based on perturbation theory. The first approximation in their method is equivalent to replacing the Dirac matrices by constant numbers

u. We shall refer to the equations of electrodynamics in which the above replacement has been made as the Bloch-Nordsieck model.

In addition to its importance for the analysis of the infrared catastrophe, the problem is also of methodological interest, since in the Bloch-Nordsieck model the functional integration may be carried out to the end without making any approximations, and this allows one to follow in great detail the procedure of obtaining closed expressions for Green's functions and of removing infinities from them. In discussing the problem we shall, as we have done already, employ the auxiliary Pauli-Villars regularization in the intermediate stages.

A characteristic feature of the Bloch-Nordsieck model is the fact that it does not include the polarization of the vacuum

$$G_0(A) = \langle G \rangle_{F_0} = 1, \qquad (41.1)$$

i.e., effects connected with the photon self-energy, as may be seen directly from the following simple considerations. Green's function for a free electron G_0 is in this case determined by the following first-order equation

$$\left(i \sum_n u^n \frac{\partial}{\partial x^n} - m\right) G_0(x-y) = -\delta(x-y), \qquad (41.2)$$

where

$$\sum_n g^{nn} u^n u^n = 1,$$

and in the momentum representation instead of having two poles, as in the usual electrodynamics, has only one:

$$G_0(p) = \frac{1}{m - up - i\varepsilon}. \qquad (41.3)$$

As a result

$$G_0(x-y) = 0 \text{ for } x^0 < y^0,$$

i.e., G_0 is a purely retarded function. Therefore the matrix element corresponding to a closed electron cycle (for example such as shown in the diagrams of Fig. 54) will contain at least one function G_0 which is equal to zero. Physically, this corresponds to the fact in the Bloch-Nordsieck model there are no antiparticles and that consequently no pairs can be created.

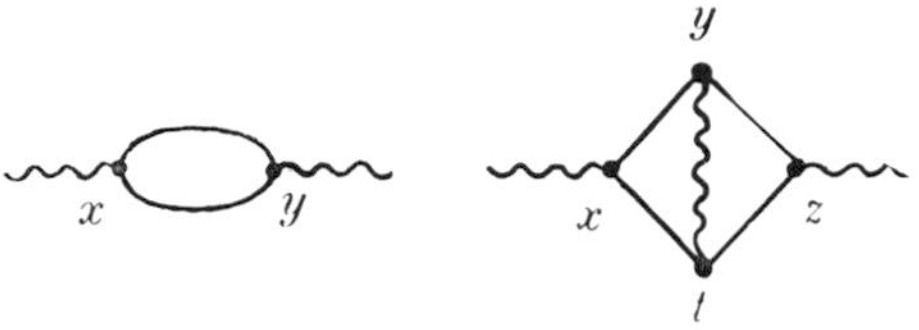

Fig. 54.

Thus in the Bloch-Nordsieck model there are no radiation corrections to the photon Green's function and we have to determine only the electron Green's function $G(x, y)$ which in accordance with (40.12) is determined by taking the functional average of the electron Green's function in a given external field $G(x, y \mid A)$.

In the present case, the latter function satisfies the equation

$$\left\{\sum_n u^n \left(i \frac{\partial}{\partial x^n} + eA_n(x) - m\right)\right\} G(x, y \mid A) = -\delta(x - y) \qquad (41.4)$$

which may be solved by quadratures. For this purpose we shall use the method of the fifth parameter due to Fock (43). This method is based on the symbolic representation of the inverse operator in the form of an exponential integral with respect to the fifth parameter:

$$H^{-1} = -i \int_0^\infty d\nu\, e^{i\nu H - \varepsilon\nu}. \qquad (41.5)$$

By using this representation and by setting

$$H = \left\{\sum_n u^n \left[i \frac{\partial}{\partial x^n} + eA_n(x)\right] - m\right\}, \qquad (41.6)$$

we may write the solution of equation (41.4) in the form

$$G(x, y \mid A) = i \int_0^\infty d\nu\, U(\nu), \qquad (41.7)$$

where the function $U(\nu)$ which is symbolically defined by the relation

$$U(\nu) = \exp i\nu \left\{ \sum_n u^n \left[i \frac{\partial}{\partial x^n} + eA_n(x) \right] - m + i\varepsilon \right\} \delta(x-y), \quad (41.8)$$

satisfies the homogeneous first-order differential equation in five variables:

$$-i \frac{\partial U(\nu)}{\partial \nu} = \left\{ \sum_n u^n \left[i \frac{\partial}{\partial x^n} + eA_n(x) \right] - m + i\varepsilon \right\} U(\nu) \quad (41.9)$$

with the initial condition

$$U(\nu)\,|_{\nu=0} = \delta(x-y). \quad (41.10)$$

We go over to the momentum representation for the δ-function

$$\delta(x-y) = \frac{1}{(2\pi)^4} \int e^{-ip(x-y)}\, dp, \quad (41.11)$$

and seek $U(\nu)$ in the form

$$U(\nu) = \frac{1}{(2\pi)^4} \int e^{i[K(x,\nu) - p(x-y) - (m-up-i\varepsilon)\nu]}\, dp. \quad (41.12)$$

The function K in the foregoing is determined by the equation

$$\frac{\partial K}{\partial \nu} = \sum_n u^n \frac{\partial K}{\partial x^n} + e \sum_n u^n A_n(x) \quad (41.13)$$

with the boundary condition

$$K(\nu)\,|_{\nu=0} = 0.$$

Equation (41.13) is a linear equation with constant coefficients. Solving it by means of a Fourier transformation we obtain:

$$K = \frac{e}{(2\pi)^2} \int dk (u \cdot A(k))\, e^{-ikx} \int_0^\nu d\nu'\, e^{i(uk)\nu'} \quad (41.14)$$

and consequently after taking (41.7), (41.12) into account

$$G(x, y\,|\,A) = i \frac{1}{(2\pi)^4} \int_0^\infty d\nu \int dp \exp\left[-ip(x-y) - i\nu(m-up-i\varepsilon) + iK(\nu\,|\,A)\right]. \quad (41.15)$$

Formula (41.15) gives a closed explicit expression for the electron Green's function in a given external field in the Bloch-Nordsieck model. Having obtained it, we can now turn to the determination of the complete electron Green's function.

41.2. *Evaluation of $G(x, y)$*

For the determination of the complete Green's function, we shall make use of formula (40.12), taking into account the fact that $\langle G\rangle_{F_0}$ is no longer determined by formula (40.13) but is equal to unity in accordance with (41.1). This gives:

$$G(x-y) = \frac{1}{(2\pi)^4}\int e^{-ip(x-y)}\, G(p)\, dp, \tag{41.16}$$

$$G(p) = i\int_0^\infty \exp\left[-i(m-up-i\varepsilon)\right] d\nu \int \exp\left[iK(\nu\,|\,A)\right] dA. \tag{41.17}$$

Thus in order to find G it is necessary to evaluate the functional integral of the following form:

$$\int \exp\left[iK(\nu\,|\,A)\right] dA = \int \exp\left[\frac{i}{(2\pi)^2}\int dk \sum_n R^n A_n(k)\right] dA, \tag{41.18}$$

where

$$R^n(k) = eu^n\, e^{-ikx}\int_0^\nu d\nu'\, e^{i(uk)\nu'}.$$

The integral (41.18) is of Gaussian type (with respect to δA) and may be evaluated by means of formula (40.14) yielding:

$$\int \exp\left[iK(\nu\,|\,A)\right] dA$$
$$= \exp\left\{-i\sum_{n,m}\frac{1}{2(2\pi)^4}R^n(k)\, D^0_{nm}(k)\, R^m(-k)\right\} = \exp\left[f(\nu)\right],$$

where

$$f(\nu) = -\frac{ie^2}{2(2\pi)^4}\int (uD^0(k)\,u)\int_0^\nu d\nu'\, e^{i(uk)\nu'}\int_0^\nu d\nu''\, e^{-i(uk)\nu''}\, dk. \tag{41.19}$$

We thus obtain:

$$G(p) = i\int_0^\infty d\nu \exp\left[-i\nu(m-up-i\varepsilon)+f(\nu)\right]. \tag{41.20}$$

On evaluating in (41.19) the integrals with respect to ν' and ν'' taking into account the fact that the function D is even we obtain:

$$f(\nu) = -\frac{ie^2}{(2\pi)^4}\int [uD^0(k)u]\frac{1-e^{i(uk)\nu}}{(uk)^2}\,dk. \tag{41.21}$$

We shall carry out further calculations in an arbitrary gauge for which

$$D^0_{mn}(k) = -\frac{1}{k^2}\left(g^{mn} - \frac{k_m k_n}{k^2}\right) - \frac{1}{k^2}\frac{k_m k_n}{k^2}d^0_l.$$

On taking into account the fact that $u^2 = 1$ it is then evident that

$$f(\nu) = \frac{ie^2}{(2\pi)^4}\int \frac{1-e^{i(uk)\nu}}{(uk)^2\cdot k^2}\left[1 + (d^0_l - 1)\frac{(uk)^2}{k^2}\right]dk. \tag{41.22}$$

We see that this integral diverges logarithmically for large $|k|$, but it is very important that for small k it contains no divergences at all. Thus the infrared catastrophe is absent from the complete solution (41.20).

For the explicit evaluation of the integral (41.22), it is convenient to make use of the Pauli-Villars auxiliary regularization. Omitting the fairly lengthy calculations [81] we merely state the final result for the case when only the factor

$$\frac{1}{k^2} \to \frac{1}{k^2} - \frac{1}{k^2 - M^2}$$

in (41.22) has been subjected to the auxiliary regularization.

In this case:

$$f(\nu) = \frac{e^2}{8\pi^2}(3 - d^0_l)\left(\ln\frac{M}{m} + \ln \nu m\right). \tag{41.23}$$

The first term in (41.23)

$$\frac{e^2}{8\pi^2}(3 - d^0_l)\ln\left(\frac{M}{m}\right)$$

[81] All the details of this calculation may be found in the work of Svidzinskii (121).

diverges logarithmically when the auxiliary regularization is removed ($M \to \infty$) and corresponds to a multiplicative renormalization of Green's function by the factor

$$Z = \exp\left[\frac{e^2}{8\pi^2}(3 - d_l^0)\ln\frac{M}{m}\right] = \left(\frac{M}{m}\right)^{\frac{e^2}{8\pi^2}(3-d_l^0)}, \qquad (41.24)$$

which may be eliminated by an appropriate subtraction procedure which, in accordance with the general theory of the removal of infinities (§ 31), reduces to a redefinition of chronological products.

After removing the ultraviolet divergence we obtain the final expression for Green's function

$$G'(p) = i\int_0^\infty d\nu \exp\left[-i\nu(m - up - i\varepsilon) + \frac{e^2}{8\pi^2}(3 - d_l^0)\ln \nu m\right]$$

$$= im^{\frac{e(3-d_l^0)}{8\pi^2}}\int_0^\infty d\nu \exp\left[-i(m - up - i\varepsilon)\nu\right]\nu^{\frac{e^2(3-d_l^0)}{8\pi^2}}. \qquad (41.25)$$

We now consider the case when $m - (up) > 0$. After introducing into (41.25) a new variable

$$[m - (up)]\nu = x,$$

we obtain

$$G'(p) = \frac{\left[1 - \frac{(up)}{m}\right]^{\frac{e^2(d_l^0-3)}{8\pi^2}}}{m - (up)} I, \qquad (41.26)$$

where

$$I = i\int_0^\infty dx\, x^{\frac{e^2(3-d_l^0)}{8\pi^2}} e^{-ix-\varepsilon x}.$$

The integral I may be evaluated approximately by making use of the fact that $e^2(3 - d_l^0)/8\pi^2 \ll 1$. We thus obtain

$$I = i\int_0^\infty dx\, e^{-ix-\varepsilon x} + O(e^2) = 1 + O(e^2).$$

Similarly in the case when

$$(up) - m > 0,$$

the change of variable

$$[(up) - m]\,v = y$$

leads to the expression

$$G'(p) = \frac{\left[\dfrac{(up)}{m} - 1\right]^{\frac{e^2(d_l^0-3)}{8\pi^2}}}{(up) - m} I' \qquad (41.27)$$

where

$$I' = i\int_0^\infty dy\, y^{\frac{e^2(3-d_l^0)}{8\pi^2}} e^{iy-\varepsilon y} = -1 + O'(e^2).$$

By combining expressions (41.26) and (41.27) we obtain the final expression for the electron Green's function in the Bloch-Nordsieck model:

$$G'(p) = \frac{1}{m - (up)} \left| 1 - \frac{(up)}{m} \right|^{\beta}, \qquad (41.28)$$

where

$$\beta = -\frac{e^2(3 - d_l^0)}{8\pi^2} = -\frac{\alpha}{2\pi}(3 - d_l^0) \qquad (41.29)$$

($\alpha = 1/137$ is the fine structure constant).

On comparing (41.28) with (41.3), we see that the total Green's function differs from the free-field Green's function by the factor

$$\left| 1 - \frac{(up)}{m} \right|^{\beta}.$$

If the complete function $G'(p)$ is expanded in a series in powers of α, then in each approximation we shall obtain logarithmic terms

$$\left| 1 - \frac{(up)}{m} \right|^{\beta} = e^{\beta \ln \left| 1 - \frac{up}{m} \right|} = 1 - \frac{\alpha}{2\pi}(3 - d_l^0) \ln \left| 1 - \frac{(up)}{m} \right| + \dots,$$

characteristic of the infrared catastrophe.

It will be shown in the next chapter (§ 43.3) that the infrared singularity of the electron Green's function in the usual spinor electrodynamics also has the nature (41.28).

CHAPTER VIII

The Renormalization Group

§ 42. The Group of Multiplicative Renormalizations in Spinor Electrodynamics

42.1. *Introduction*

We shall now turn to the investigation of a method of improving perturbation theory formulas which is based on the renormalization group occurring in field theory; this was already mentioned in Chapter V. The idea of this method is extremely simple, and is based on the fact that the individual terms of perturbation theory expansions for the Green's functions and for the vertex parts are not invariant with respect to the renormalization group, while the quantities themselves are invariant with respect to this group. Therefore, for example, in the ultraviolet region perturbation theory expansions turn out to be given not in terms of powers of the square of the charge e^2 but in terms of powers of the product $e^2 \ln (k^2/m^2)$.

Starting with these considerations, we shall try to transform the usual expansions into ones invariant with respect to the renormalization group. An important technical means of accomplishing this will be the Lie differential equations corresponding to the aforementioned renormalization group.

It should be noted that Stueckelberg and Peterman (118) already remarked on the existence of the renormalization group and on its role in quantum field theory. They also pointed out the possibility of introducing the corresponding infinitesimal operators and in this way indicated the possibility of constructing the Lie differential equations.

Essentially the same renormalization group, but from a different point of view, was utilized by Gell-Mann and Low (48) to obtain concrete information on the asymptotic behavior of electrodynamic Green's functions for large values of the momenta. However, the investigation of Gell-Mann and Low was not carried out sufficiently carefully, contained certain errors related to the fact that they did not take into account the transverse nature of the renormalized photon Green's function, and was therefore not completed.

These questions were investigated in a more consistent manner in the papers by Bogoliubov and Shirkov (22), (23), (25), (26), (112) which we follow in this presentation. In examining the questions related to the vertex operator, we have also made use of the results due to Blank and Shirkov (9), (10) while the generalization to the case $d_l \neq 0$ is treated by us according to Logunov (83).

42.2. *The Group Property of Multiplicative Renormalizations*

As was established in Chapter V, the introduction of a number of finite terms into the interaction Lagrangian of a theory being subjected to renormalization is, generally speaking, equivalent to a certain finite renormalization of the basic Green's functions and of the charges. One should, of course, keep in mind the fact that a term of the type of a proper mass does not lead to multiplicative renormalization, and that a purely multiplicative renormalization of the photon Green's function in quantum electrodynamics is achieved only in the case when this function is taken in the transverse form

$$D^{\text{tr}}_{mn} = -\frac{d(k^2)}{k^2}\left(g^{mn} - \frac{k_m k_n}{k^2}\right). \qquad (32.7)$$

To achieve this, it turns out to be sufficient in perturbation theory to choose in transverse form only its zero approximation — the chronological pairing of the operators of the electromagnetic field, and this is achieved by choosing an appropriate gauge.

It was also shown there that the introduction into the interaction Lagrangian of spinor electrodynamics of the three finite terms

$$(z_1-1)e\bar{\psi}\hat{A}\psi+(z_2-1)\bar{\psi}(\hat{p}-m)\psi+\frac{(z_3-1)}{2}\sum_{m,n}A_m(g^{mn}p^2-p^mp^n)A_n \tag{31.10}$$

turns out to be equivalent to the following multiplicative renormalization of the electron Green's function G, of the photon Green's function D, and of the vertex function Γ:

$$G\to z_2^{-1}G,\ \Gamma\to z_1\Gamma,\ D^{\text{tr}}\to z_3^{-1}D^{\text{tr}}, \tag{31.34}$$

which in turn leads to the following change in the effective value of the charge:

$$e^2\to z_1^2z_2^{-2}z_3^{-1}e^2. \tag{31.26}$$

It is now clear that if simultaneously with the introduction of the terms (31.10) we perform the compensating renormalization of the charge inverse to (31.26)

$$e^2\to z_1^{-2}z_2^2z_3e^2, \tag{42.1}$$

then as a result of these two operations we shall obtain a situation which corresponds to an unchanged value of e^2.

For future reference it will be convenient to write down formulas which are inverse to formulas (31.34) and (42.1). On doing this and taking into account Ward's identity

$$z_1=z_2=z,$$

we obtain:

$$\left.\begin{aligned}G_1\to G_2=zG_1,\ \Gamma_1\to\Gamma_2=z^{-1}\Gamma_1,\quad D_1\to D_2=z_3D_1,\\ e_1^2\to e_2^2=z_3^{-1}e_1^2.\end{aligned}\right\} \tag{42.2}$$

The significance of the transformation (42.2) consists of the fact that the use in the theory of the quantities G_1, Γ_1, D_1 and e_1 leads to the same results as the use of the quantities G_2, Γ_2, D_2, and e_2, i.e., to a description of the interaction between photons and electrons with the same coupling constant e which may be chosen equal to its experimental value.

The transformations of multiplicative renormalization (42.2) evidently possess the group property. We shall call this group the group of multiplicative renormalization or the renormalization group.

According to its definition, the renormalization group is the group of multiplicative transformations (42.2) contained in the theory of intermediate quantities of the type of the Green's functions and of the charges which do not lead to any changes in the expressions for observable effects. In particular, the matrix elements of the scattering matrix do not change their values under transformations belonging to this group (provided the factors corresponding to the external lines of Feynman diagrams are also suitably renormalized at the same time).

It is also clear that the existence of a group of multiplicative renormalizations is not peculiar to spinor electrodynamics and may be established for any renormalizable theory. In order to accomplish this, we must select from among all the allowable counter terms of a given theory only those which lead to multiplicative renormalization of the corresponding Green's functions and in this way optain transformation relations of type (42.2). We shall discuss in § 45 the renormalization group in the two-charge variant of pseudoscalar meson theory.

42.3. *Functional Equations of the Group*

The group of transformations (42.2) allows us to obtain simple functional equations for the Green's functions and also the Lie differential equations of the group.

In order to obtain the functional equations for the renormalization group in spinor electrodynamics, we shall consider the basic electrodynamic functions G, D, and Γ. For the sake of simplicity we shall at first restrict ourselves to the case when the photon Green's function D has the purely transverse form (32.7), while the transformations of the group have the form (42.2).[82]

The electron function $G(p)$ may be represented in the form

$$G(p) = \frac{a(p^2)\hat{p} + b(p^2)m}{m^2 - p^2}. \tag{42.3}$$

Thus with the aid of formulas (32.7) and (42.3) the functions D and G of the four-momenta k and p may be expressed in terms

[82] This restriction is not one of principle; the more general case when D also contains a longitudinal part will be considered in § 44.

of the functions d, a, and b each of which depends only on a single argument k^2 or p^2. In contrast to D and G the vertex function Γ depends on two independent four-momenta and therefore cannot be represented in such a simple way. Since the function Γ is relatively complicated, we shall discuss it separately later.

According to (42.2) the functions D and G contain finite multiplicative arbitrary constants. We shall fix these arbitrary constants by means of normalization conditions: thus, we shall transfer the arbitrary factor in front of the function $d(k^2)$ into its argument by assuming that the normalization of d is determined by the condition

$$d = 1 \text{ for } k^2 = \lambda^2, \tag{42.4}$$

where λ^2 thus plays the role of the square of the normalization momentum.

Normalization to unity is evidently possible only for such values of λ^2 for which the ordinary photon function d_0 (normalized at $k^2 = 0$) is both real and positive. This is associated with the fact that the renormalization of the function d is accomplished by means of the same quantity z_3 which renormalizes the square of the charge and which must therefore be both real and positive.

The condition that d_0 should be real for $k^2 = \lambda^2$ leads us to the condition

$$\lambda^2 < 4m^2 \tag{42.5}$$

in accordance with the second-order perturbation theory formulas (32.10). It may be shown that if higher orders of perturbation theory are taken into account this condition will be replaced by

$$\lambda^2 < 0. \tag{42.6}$$

Thus from the condition that the function d must be real, it follows that the normalization momentum is subject to the condition (42.6). However, in a number of cases, for example in the calculation of the infrared asymptotic behavior of the electron Green's function when it is sufficient to consider only the first term of the expansion of d in powers of e^2, one may use condition (42.5).

From considerations of homogenity in momentum space, it now follows that d may be represented by a function of the dimensionless momentum variables

$$d = d\left(\frac{k^2}{\lambda^2}, \frac{m^2}{\lambda^2}, e^2\right),$$

where $\lambda^2 < 0$ and

$$d\left(1, \frac{m^2}{\lambda^2}, e^2\right) = 1. \tag{42.7}$$

In a similar manner the constant z may be fixed by imposing the normalization condition on one of the functions a or b which, after taking into account the homogeneity in momentum space, may be written in the form

$$f\left(\frac{k^2}{\lambda^2}, \frac{m^2}{\lambda^2}, e^2\right),$$

where

$$a\left(1, \frac{m^2}{\lambda^2}, e^2\right) = a^0, \quad b\left(1, \frac{m^2}{\lambda^2}, e^2\right) = b^0 \tag{42.8}$$

We shall choose the normalization constants a^0, b^0, generally speaking, different from unity for the following reasons: (1) the points at which the functions a and b are normalized do not in the general case coincide, (2) in a small neighborhood of the point $k^2 = m^2$ in which a and b have an infrared singularity they can not be normalized at all, and (3) the normalization constants a^0, b^0 appear in the subsequent arguments only as unessential factors.

As may be seen from (42.7), the square of the normalization momentum λ^2 is functionally related to the charge e^2. Substituting (32.7) into equation

$$D_2 = z_3 D_1,$$

and taking into account the equation

$$e_2^2 = z_3^{-1} e_1^2$$

we obtain:

$$d\left(\frac{k^2}{\lambda_2^2}, \frac{m^2}{\lambda_2^2}, e_2^2\right) = z_3 d\left(\frac{k^2}{\lambda_1^2}, \frac{m^2}{\lambda_1^2}, e_1^2\right). \tag{42.9}$$

Setting $k^2 = \lambda_1^2$ in the foregoing and taking (42.7) into account, we obtain for z_3 the expression

$$z_3 = d\left(\frac{\lambda_1^2}{\lambda_2^2}, \frac{m^2}{\lambda_2^2}, e_2^2\right),$$

which on being substituted into (42.9) leads to the functional equation for d:

$$d\left(\frac{k^2}{\lambda_1^2}, \frac{m^2}{\lambda_1^2}, e_1^2\right) = d\left(\frac{k^2}{\lambda_2^2}, \frac{m^2}{\lambda_2^2}, e_2^2\right) \Big/ d\left(\frac{\lambda_1^2}{\lambda_2^2}, \frac{m^2}{\lambda_2^2}, e_2^2\right), \tag{42.10}$$

where

$$e_1^2 = e_2^2 d\left(\frac{\lambda_1^2}{\lambda_2^2}, \frac{m^2}{\lambda_2^2}, e_2^2\right). \tag{42.11}$$

Let us now relate the charge e^2 appearing in formulas (42.10), (42.11) to the observed value of the charge

$$\frac{e_0^2}{4\pi} = \alpha = \frac{1}{137}.$$

This value of the charge corresponds to the photon function d_0 which, as has been noted in Chapter V, is normalized to unity for $k^2 = 0$ and therefore has the form

$$d_0 = d_0\left(\frac{k^2}{m^2}, e_0^2\right). \tag{42.12}$$

It follows from (42.10) and (42.11) that the product $e^2 d$ does not depend on λ:

$$e_1^2 d\left(\frac{k^2}{\lambda_1^2}, \frac{m^2}{\lambda_1^2}, e_1^2\right) = e_2^2 d\left(\frac{k^2}{\lambda_2^2}, \frac{m^2}{\lambda_2^2}, e_2^2\right)$$

and is given by a certain universal function of k^2 which may be chosen in the form

$$e_\lambda^2 d\left(\frac{k^2}{\lambda^2}, \frac{m^2}{\lambda^2}, e_\lambda^2\right) = e_0^2 d_0\left(\frac{k^2}{m^2}, e_0^2\right). \tag{42.13}$$

We shall call the quantity $e^2 d$ which is an invariant of the renormalization group the invariant charge. Setting $k^2 = \lambda^2$ in (42.13), we shall obtain the explicit form of the dependence of e_λ^2 on λ^2:

$$e_\lambda^2 = e_0^2 d_0\left(\frac{\lambda^2}{m^2}, e_0^2\right). \tag{42.14}$$

We now turn to the electron Green's function. We shall carry through the argument simultaneously for the two functions a and b by introducing for them temporarily the common notation s. By writing for s an equation analogous to (42.9) and by determining the constant z, we shall obtain, after eliminating this constant, the functional equation for s:

$$s\left(\frac{k^2}{\lambda_2^2}, \frac{m^2}{\lambda_2^2}, e_2^2\right) s\left(\frac{\lambda_2^2}{\lambda_1^2}, \frac{m^2}{\lambda_1^2}, e_1^2\right) = s\left(1, \frac{m^2}{\lambda_2^2}, e_2^2\right) s\left(\frac{k^2}{\lambda_1^2}, \frac{m^2}{\lambda_1^2}, e_1^2\right). \tag{42.15}$$

42.4. *The Lie Differential Equations*

Equations (42.10), (42.11), (42.15) may be rewritten in a more compact form with the aid of the following auxiliary notation:

$$\frac{k^2}{\lambda_2^2} = x, \quad \frac{m^2}{\lambda_2^2} = y, \quad \frac{\lambda_1^2}{\lambda_2^2} = t. \tag{42.16}$$

We then obtain:

$$e^2 d(x, y, e^2) = e^2 d(t, y, e^2)\, d\left(\frac{x}{t}, \frac{y}{t}, e^2 d(t, y, e^2)\right) \tag{42.17}$$

and

$$s(x, y, e^2) s\left(1, \frac{y}{t}, e^2 d(t, y, e^2)\right) = s(t, y, e^2) s\left(\frac{x}{t}, \frac{y}{t}, e^2 d(t, y, e^2)\right). \tag{42.18}$$

Equations (42.17), (42.18) are functional equations of the renormalization group which describe the simultaneous transformation of all three arguments of the functions d, a, and b. Regarding these equations as equations in the unknown functions d and s, we can consider the problem of determining the functions d and s from them.

As Ovsiannikov (88) has shown, it turns out in the solution

of this problem that the general solutions of these equations are determined only up to arbitrary functions of two arguments. Therefore (42.17), (42.18) are not sufficient to determine the specific form of Green's function of quantum electrodynamics.

We shall consider the problem of finding solutions of the group equations (42.17), (42.18) which under certain definite conditions reduce to the already-known explicit expressions for Green's functions. As such conditions we shall choose the case of small e^2, and we shall require that for any arbitrary values of the arguments x and y in the limit of small e^2 the solutions d and s of these equations should have the form

$$d(x, y. e^2) = 1 + e^2 d_1(x, y) + e^4 d_2(x, y) + \ldots, \tag{42.19}$$

$$s(x, y, e^2) = 1 + e^2 s_1(x, y) + e^4 s_2(x, y) + \ldots, \tag{42.20}$$

where the functions d_1, $d_2, \ldots, s_1$, $s_2, \ldots$ are determined by perturbation theory and in accordance with the formulas of § 32 have for $d_l = 0$ the form

$$d_1(x, y) = \frac{1}{2\pi^2}\int_0^1 \alpha(1-\alpha)\ln\left|\frac{y-\alpha(1-\alpha)x}{y-\alpha(1-\alpha)}\right| d\alpha, \tag{42.21}$$

$$a_1(x, y) = \frac{1}{8\pi^2}\left\{-3\frac{y}{x}\ln\left|\frac{x-y}{y}\right| + c(y)\right\}, \tag{42.22}$$

$$b_1(x, y) = \frac{1}{8\pi^2}\left\{-\frac{3(x+y)}{2x}\ln\left|\frac{x-y}{y}\right| + c(y)\right\}. \tag{42.23}$$

In these formulas we have retained the arbitrary constant $c(y)$ which may be used to normalize one of the functions a or b.

In order to find the desired solutions, we shall pass from (42.17), (42.18) over to the Lie differential equations, since a group of continuous transformations, such as the renormalization group, may be completely characterized by the form of an infinitesimal transformation. The equations that describe the infinitesimal transformations of the group — the Lie differential equations — may be obtained in the present case in the following manner. By taking the derivative of (42.17) and the logarithmic derivative of (42.18) with respect to x, and then by setting $t = x$ we obtain:

$$\frac{\partial e^2 d(x, y, e^2)}{\partial x} = \frac{e^2 d(x, y, e^2)}{x} \varphi\left(\frac{y}{x}, e^2 d(x, y, e^2)\right) \tag{42.24}$$

and

$$\frac{\partial \ln s(x, y, e^2)}{\partial x} = \frac{1}{x} \psi\left(\frac{y}{x}, e^2 d(x, y, e^2)\right), \tag{42.25}$$

where

$$\varphi(y, e^2) = \left[\frac{\partial}{\partial \xi} d(\xi, y, e^2)\right]_{\xi=1} \tag{42.26}$$

and

$$\psi(y, e^2) = \left[\frac{\partial}{\partial \xi} \ln s(\xi, y, e^2)\right]_{\xi=1}. \tag{42.27}$$

Equations (42.24) and (42.25) are the Lie equations for the renormalization group in quantum electrodynamics. From these equations it follows that in order to determine the functions d and s for all values of their arguments it is sufficient to determine the behavior of $d(x, y, e^2)$ and $s(x, y, e^2)$ only in the infinitesimal neighborhood of the point $x = 1$.

For this we shall make use of ordinary perturbation theory which will automatically guarantee for us that the requirement of correspondence for $e^2 \to 0$ will be satisfied. We also note that the use in (42.26), (42.27) of the expansions for d and s valid for $e^2 \ll 1$ will have as a consequence the fact that expressions φ and ψ which are expansions in powers of the "invariant charge" $e^2 d$ will appear in the Lie equations. Therefore, the domain of applicability of the solutions of the Lie equations will be limited by the condition that the "invariant charge" should be small

$$e^2 d \ll 1. \tag{42.28}$$

We also note that actually only equations (42.24) will have to be solved since for a given d the functions s may be obtained from (42.25) by means of a simple quadrature

$$\ln \frac{s(x, y, e^2)}{s(x_0, y, e^2)} = \int_{x_0}^{x} \frac{dz}{z} \psi\left(\frac{y}{z}, e^2 d(z, y, e^2)\right). \tag{42.29}$$

42.5. *The Vertex Part*

We now turn to the vertex part $\Gamma^n_{\alpha\beta}$. In contrast to Green's functions, $\Gamma^n_{\alpha\beta}$ is a four-vector, has a complicated matrix structure, and depends on two independent four-momenta. In the general case the vertex part $\Gamma^n_{\alpha\beta}(p, q)$ may be expanded in terms of products of different numbers of Dirac matrices by the components of the four-momentum arguments. In this way it is possible to explicitly separate out the matrix and the vector structure (with respect to the indices α, β and n) of the vertex part $\Gamma^n_{\alpha\beta}$ by expressing it in terms of scalar functions of the three invariant arguments p^2, q^2, $k^2 (k = p - q)$, for example, in the following way:

$$\Gamma^n_{\alpha\beta}(p, q) = \sum_{\begin{pmatrix} \nu, \nu', \mu', \mu = 0, 1 \\ \nu + \nu' + \mu' + \mu \leqq 2 \end{pmatrix}} [(\hat{p})^{\nu} (\hat{q})^{\nu'} \gamma^n (\hat{q})^{\mu'} (\hat{p})^{\mu}]_{\alpha\beta} \Gamma_{\nu\nu' \mu' \mu}(p^2, q^2, k^2).$$

Let us now consider one of the scalar functions $\Gamma_{\nu\nu' \mu\mu'}$ with fixed values of the indices ν, ν', μ, μ' after denoting it by Γ. In accordance with (42.2) the multiplicative renormalization of this function reduces to the transformation

$$\Gamma \to z^{-1}\Gamma. \tag{42.30}$$

From this it follows that the function Γ is determined up to an arbitrary constant z. As usual, we shall "transfer" this arbitrariness into the arguments of the function Γ by introducing the square of an auxiliary momentum λ^2 and by going over to dimensionless arguments:

$$\Gamma \to \Gamma\left(\frac{p^2}{\lambda^2}, \frac{q^2}{\lambda^2}, \frac{k^2}{\lambda^2}, \frac{m^2}{\lambda^2}, e^2\right).$$

Then in place of (42.30) we may write:

$$\Gamma\left(\frac{p^2}{\lambda^2}, \frac{q^2}{\lambda^2}, \frac{k^2}{\lambda^2}, \frac{m^2}{\lambda^2}, e^2\right) = z\Gamma\left(\frac{p^2}{\lambda_1^2}, \frac{q^2}{\lambda_1^2}, \frac{k^2}{\lambda_1^2}, \frac{m^2}{\lambda_1^2}, e_1^2\right), \tag{42.31}$$

where $e = e_2$ satisfies (42.11).

We now write Γ as a function of p^2 having temporarily fixed the values of the other momentum variables. By introducing the notation

$$\frac{p^2}{\lambda^2} = x, \quad \frac{q^2}{\lambda^2} = y, \quad \frac{k^2}{\lambda^2} = z, \quad \frac{m^2}{\lambda^2} = u, \quad \frac{\lambda_1^2}{\lambda^2} = t \tag{42.32}$$

and by eliminating the constant z from (42.31) we obtain the functional equation

$$\frac{\Gamma(x, y, z, u, e^2)}{\Gamma(t, y, z, u, e^2)} = \frac{\Gamma\left(\frac{x}{t}, \frac{y}{t}, \frac{z}{t}, \frac{u}{t}, e^2 d(t, u, e^2)\right)}{\Gamma\left(1, \frac{y}{t}, \frac{z}{t}, \frac{u}{t}, e^2 d(t, u, e^2)\right)}. \quad (42.33)$$

By differentiating (42.33) with respect to x and by then setting $t = x$ we obtain the Lie differential equation. In the equation obtained in this manner, the variable x plays a distinctive role. However, it is quite clear that similar arguments may be given with respect to any one of the other momentum arguments y or z. As a result of this we shall obtain a system of three differential equations the successive solution of which taking correspondence considerations into account enables us to improve effectively the formulas of the usual perturbation theory (see § 44.3).

§ 43. Asymptotic Properties of the Electrodynamic Green's Functions

43.1. *Formulation of the Problem*

The principal relations of multiplicative renormalizations (31.34) have been obtained by means of the formalism of perturbation theory. There are some reasons for supposing that these equations are also valid in the more general case not associated with the limitations of perturbation theory. However, we do not have at our disposal any more or less rigorous arguments in support of this hypothesis, nor do we have any information on Green's functions which does not come from perturbation theory.

Therefore, we shall restrict ourselves to the problem of improving the results of ordinary perturbation theory by making use of the solutions of the group differential equations which satisfy the requirement of correspondence with perturbation theory.

The solution of equation (42.24) may be obtained particularly simply in the case when the function φ is obtained by second-order perturbation theory. In such a case, (42.24) may be completely integrated explicitly. Indeed, since in this case in accordance with (42.19) and (42.21)

$$d(x, y, e^2) = 1 + \frac{e^2}{2\pi^2}\int_0^1 t(1-t)\ln\left|\frac{y - t(1-t)x}{y - t(1-t)}\right| dt + \dots$$
$$= 1 + e^2\left[f\left(\frac{x}{y}\right) - f\left(\frac{1}{y}\right)\right] + \dots, \tag{43.1}$$

then

$$\varphi(y, e^2) = e^2\left[\frac{\partial}{\partial\xi} f\left(\frac{\xi}{y}\right)\right]_{\xi=1}$$

and consequently

$$\frac{\partial e^2 d(x, y, e^2)}{\partial x} = \frac{[e^2 d]^2}{x}\left[\frac{\partial}{\partial\xi} f\left(\frac{x\xi}{y}\right)\right]_{\xi=1} = [e^2 d]^2\left[\frac{\partial}{\partial x} f\left(\frac{x}{y}\right)\right],$$

which leads to

$$d^{-1}(x, y, e^2) = 1 - e^2\int_1^x dx\frac{\partial}{\partial x} f\left(\frac{x}{y}\right) = 1 - e^2\left[f\left(\frac{x}{y}\right) - f\left(\frac{1}{y}\right)\right]. \tag{43.2}$$

In the more general case, when φ is determined up to terms of higher order, equation (42.24) as well as equation (43.2) can be integrated only for certain special values of the arguments x and y. We have in mind here the practically important domains of the "ultraviolet catastrophe" and the "infrared catastrophe."

This occurs because due to the smallness of the expansion parameter

$$\alpha = \frac{e_0^2}{4\pi} = \frac{1}{137}$$

the successive terms in the power series expansions for the Green's functions of quantum electrodynamics decrease, generally speaking, quite rapidly. This does not happen only in the cases $p^2 \sim m^2$ and $|p^2| \gg m^2$ when logarithmic terms appear in the above expansions (see in particular (42.21)—(42.23)), for example, of the type

$$\left(\alpha \ln \left|\frac{p^2}{m^2}\right|\right)^n$$

in the "ultraviolet" region for $|p^2| \gg m^2$. One may say that in such cases the actual expansion no longer occurs in powers of the small parameter α, but rather in powers of the product of α by the corresponding logarithm.

Therefore the problem arises of "improving" the convergence of perturbation theory series in the domains of the "ultraviolet catastrophe" and the "infrared catastrophe." We now investigate this problem with the aid of the equation of the renormalization group.

43.2. *Asymptotic Behavior in the Ultraviolet*

We shall first consider the asymptotic region of large momenta when $|p^2| \gg m^2$. In this case the individual terms of the perturbation theory series become functions of $\ln x = \ln (|p^2|/\lambda^2)$ and cease to depend on the variable y.

By omitting y in formulas (42.24), (42.29) we obtain:

$$\frac{\partial e^2 d(x, e^2)}{\partial x} = \frac{e^2 d}{x} \varphi(e^2 d), \tag{43.3}$$

$$\ln \frac{s(x, e^2)}{s(x_0, e^2)} = \int_{x_0}^{x} \frac{dz}{z} \psi(e^2 d(z, e^2)), \tag{43.4}$$

where $d(x, e^2)$, $s(x, e^2)$, $\varphi(e^2)$ and $\psi(e^2)$ are limiting expressions for the functions $d(x, y, e^2)$, $s(x, y, e^2)$, $\varphi(y/x, e^2)$, and $\psi(y/x, e^2)$ for $x \gg y$ which depend only on $\ln x$.

In order to determine the form of the dependence of e^2 (appearing in the foregoing expressions) on the square of the observed value of the charge e_0^2 in the region $x \gg y$ under consideration we note that this relation is equivalent to the condition

$$|p^2| \gg \lambda^2 \sim m^2, \tag{43.5}$$

the substitution of which into (42.13) with the logarithmic character of the dependence of $d_0(x, e_0^2)$ on its first argument being taken into account gives us with logarithmic accuracy

$$e^2 d(x, e^2) = e_0^2 d_0^{\text{as}}(x, e^2)$$

and consequently

$$e^2 = e_0^2 d_0^{\text{as}}(1, e_0^2), \tag{43.6}$$

where $d_0^{\text{as}}(x, e^2)$ denotes the asymptotic form of the function $d_0(x, e^2)$ for large values of x.

On integrating (43.3) and taking into account the normalization of the function d we obtain the equation

$$\int_{e^2}^{e^2 d(x, e^2)} \frac{dz}{z\varphi(z)} = \ln x, \tag{43.7}$$

while by changing the variable of integration, we bring (43.4) into the form

$$\ln \frac{s(x, e^2)}{s(x_0, e^2)} = \int_{e^2 d(x_0, e^2)}^{e^2 d(x, e^2)} \frac{dz}{z\varphi(z)} \psi(z). \tag{43.8}$$

In order to determine the function $d(x, e^2)$ from equation (43.7), we first obtain the function φ defined by formula (42.28) in the limiting case $x \gg y$. The first term of the expansion of d_0 into a series in z we obtain from (42.21), while in order to obtain the second term, we make use of the calculations of Jost and Luttinger (64). In this way we obtain

$$d_0(x, e^2) = 1 + \frac{e^2}{12\pi^2} \ln x + \frac{e^4}{16\pi^2}\left(\frac{1}{4\pi^2} \ln x + \frac{1}{9\pi^2} \ln^2 x\right) + \ldots, \tag{43.9}$$

from which, with the aid of (42.26), and taking into account the smallness of z, we find:

$$\frac{1}{\varphi(z)} \approx \left(\frac{z}{12\pi^2} + \frac{z^2}{64\pi^4}\right)^{-1} \approx \frac{12\pi^2}{z}\left(1 - \frac{3z}{16\pi^2} + z^2 c_1 + \ldots\right). \tag{43.10}$$

From this it follows directly that the quantity $e^2 d$ can not remain small for all x. Indeed, as long as $e^2 d$ (and therefore also z) is small the following relation holds

$$\frac{1}{\varphi(z)} < \frac{12\pi^2}{z}(1 + c) \qquad (c > 0),$$

and consequently

$$\ln x < 12\pi^2 \int_{e^2}^{e^2 d} \frac{dx}{x} (1 + c) < \frac{12\pi^2}{e^2} (1 + c).$$

It should be noted that the argument of the function φ is the square of the charge, and therefore in order to determine the behavior of Green's function for very high momenta when $e^2 d$ becomes of the order of unity or more, it is necessary to investigate the domain of large values of e^2 (strong coupling). In doing this, it should be kept in mind that the structure of $\varphi(z)$ can in this case no longer be determined on the basis of an analysis of a finite number of terms of an expansion of the type (43.8).

Substituting (43.10) into (43.7) we obtain:

$$1 - d^{-1} - \frac{3e^2}{16\pi^2} \ln d + c_1 e^4 (d - 1) + \ldots = \frac{e^2}{12\pi^2} \ln x, \qquad (43.11)$$

from which we directly find [83] that:

$$d^{-1}(x, e^2) = 1 - \frac{e^2}{12\pi^2} \ln x + \frac{3e^2}{16\pi^2} \ln \left(1 - \frac{e^2}{12\pi^2} \ln x\right) + \ldots \qquad (43.12)$$

In a quite analogous manner by means of the quadrature (43.8) one may improve the expansions of the usual perturbation theory for the coefficients a and b of the electron Green's function. Thus, perturbation theory gives us:

$$a_0(x, e^2) = 1 - \frac{1}{2(4\pi)^4} e^4 \ln x + \ldots, \qquad (43.13)$$

$$b_0(x, e^2) = b_0 \left[1 - \frac{3e^2}{16\pi^2} \ln x + \frac{e^4}{(4\pi^2)^2} (\alpha_1 \ln^2 x + \alpha_2 \ln x) + \ldots\right]. \qquad (43.14)$$

In these expansions the terms of order e^2 are obtained from formulas (42.22), (42.23) in the limit $x \gg y$, while in order to obtain the term of order e^4 in (43.13) we have made use of the calculations of Gor'kov (54).

It follows from (43.13), (43.14) that

[83] By restricting ourselves to the first two terms we have the formula which was first obtained by Landau, Abrikosov, and Khalatnikov (77).

$$\psi_a(z) = -\frac{1}{2(4\pi)^4}z^2 + \ldots \quad \psi_b(z) = -\frac{3z}{16\pi^4} + \frac{\alpha_2}{16\pi^4}z^2 + \ldots.$$

Substituting these expressions into (43.8), taking (43.10) into account and setting $a(1, e^2) = 1$ we find

$$\ln a(x, e^2) = -\frac{3}{8(4\pi)^2}e^2(d(x, e^2) - 1) + \ldots \qquad (43.15)$$

$$\ln\frac{b(x, e^2)}{b(1, e^2)} = \frac{9}{4}\ln d^{-1} + \frac{3}{4\pi^2}\left(\alpha_2 + \frac{9}{16}\right)e^2(d - 1) + \ldots \qquad (43.16)$$

The expansion (43.12) should be substituted in place of d into (43.15), (43.16).

It may be seen from these three expressions that we have obtained for the Green's functions under consideration expansions of the type

$$f(e^2 \ln x) + e^2 f_1(e^2 \ln x) + \ldots \qquad (43.17)$$

From the comparison of these expressions with formulas (43.9), (43.13), (43.14) it follows that the analytic structure of the functions $f, f_1, \ldots$ is completely determined by the differential equations of the group up to numerical coefficients, while if the set of functions $f, f_1, \ldots, f_{n-1}$ is given then, in order to determine the explicit form of the next function f_n, it is sufficient to find by means of the usual perturbation theory the first term of the expansion of f_n into a series in $e^2 \ln x$ of the form $c_n e^{2n+2} \ln x$.

A second noteworthy feature of the resulting expressions (43.12), (43.15), (43.16) consists of the fact that for sufficiently large values of x, such that the product $(e^2/12\pi^2) \ln x$ approaches unity, the function $e^2 d(x, e^2)$ ceases to be a small quantity of order e^2 and, formally speaking, increases indefinitely in accordance with (43.12).

Thus, by restricting ourselves in formula (43.12) to the first term following unity, we obtain an expression for d of the form

$$\frac{1}{1 - \dfrac{e^2}{12\pi^2}\ln\left|\dfrac{p^2}{m^2}\right|}, \qquad (43.18)$$

which has a pole at

$$1 = \frac{e^2}{12\pi^2} \ln \left| \frac{p^2}{m^2} \right| . \tag{43.19}$$

On the basis of the foregoing results some investigators (for example, Landau and Pomeranchuk (79)) have even arrived at the conclusion that modern quantum electrodynamics is logically incomplete.

However, it is clear that the expression (43.18) represents only the first term in the expansion of the function d into a series of the type (43.17) for the derivation of which the expansion of the function φ (involving d_0) into a series in powers of the "invariant charge" e^2d was used, i.e., it was assumed that $e^2d \ll 1$. Therefore the region of applicability of expression (43.18) is limited by the condition

$$1 - \frac{e^2}{12\pi^2} \ln \left| \frac{p^2}{m^2} \right| \gg e^2, \tag{43.20}$$

and the question of the true behavior of the photon Green's function in the region of the supposed pole (43.19) where e^2d no longer satisfies condition (42.28) cannot be answered on the basis of results of perturbation theory.

In accordance with the foregoing, the region of applicability of expressions (43.15) and (43.16) for the electron Green's function is also limited to the region

$$1 - \frac{e^2}{12\pi^2} \ln x \gg e^2.$$

In this connection it should be noted that equation (43.7) has an interesting property. Let us suppose that the function $\varphi(z)$ is positive definite over the whole range of values of its argument $0 < z < \infty$, and also that

$$\int_{e^2}^{\infty} \frac{dz}{z\varphi(z)} = \infty.$$

We thereby assume that the true function $d(x, e^2)$ has its only singularity at $x \to \infty$, and the theory does not contain any unpleasant features of the type of a "logarithmic pole" (43.18).

We further suppose that we shall calculate the true function $\varphi(z)$ by means of a certain limiting transition starting from the function $\varphi_\Lambda(z)$

which has the property

$$\lim_{\Lambda\to\infty} \varphi_\Lambda(z) = \varphi(z) \text{ for any arbitrary value of } z$$

where, however, for any fixed Λ

$$\varphi_\Lambda(z) > z \cdot \tau_\Lambda > 0. \tag{A}$$

Substituting φ_Λ into (43.7) we obtain

$$\int_{e_\Lambda^2}^{e_\Lambda^2 d_\Lambda} \frac{dz}{z\varphi_\Lambda(z)} = \ln x, \tag{B}$$

from which on the basis of (A) we obtain:

$$\ln x < \int_{e_\Lambda^2}^{\infty} \frac{dz}{z^2 \tau_\Lambda} = \frac{1}{\tau_\Lambda e_\Lambda^2}.$$

It is now clear that in order for formula (B) to be applicable over the entire range of variation of $\ln x$ (from 0 to ∞) we must set

$$e_\Lambda^2 = 0.$$

It may be easily seen that an approximation of this type for $\varphi(z)$ is just the one obtained by using an auxiliary regularization by means of introducing a nonlocal interaction as was done by Landau and Pomeranchuk (79).

The above argument shows that it is dangerous to make on the basis of approximations any sort of conclusions with respect to the state of affairs in the exact problem.

43.3. *Asymptotic Behavior in the Infrared*

We now turn to the region $p^2 \sim m^2$ where the electron Green's function has a singularity. Since the photon Green's function is regular in this region we shall examine only the functions $s = a, b$. It will be convenient to write them in the form

$$s\left(\frac{k^2}{\lambda^2}, \frac{m^2}{\lambda^2}, e^2\right) = S\left(\frac{k^2 - m^2}{\lambda^2 - m^2}, \frac{\lambda^2 - m^2}{m^2}, e^2\right). \tag{43.21}$$

We now return to equation (42.25) and set $y = 1$ in it. Then, making use of the representation (43.21), we obtain:

$$\ln \frac{s(x, e^2)}{s(x_0, e^2)} = \int_{x_0}^{x} \frac{dz}{z-1} \left[\frac{\partial}{\partial \xi} \ln S(\xi, z-1, e^2 d(z, 1, e^2))\right], \tag{43.22}$$

where we have introduced the following notation

$$s(x, 1, e^2) = s(x, e^2). \tag{43.23}$$

We also recall that the momentum λ is the point at which only the function d is normalized, and need not be related to the normalization of s. Therefore, by setting $y = 1$ (i.e., $\lambda^2 = m^2$) we do not restrict ourselves by any assumptions with respect to the normalization of s at the point $x = 1$ where the electron Green's function has singularities, and we merely guarantee that the "invariant charge" $e^2 d$ is close to e^2 in the region under consideration $x \sim 1$.

The limits of integration in (43.22) should be so chosen as to avoid the pole at $x = 1$. We therefore assume that

$$x_0 > 1 \quad \text{for} \quad x > 1$$

and

$$x_0 < 1 \quad \text{for} \quad x < 1.$$

For the determination of s from (43.22) we have to know the function $S(\xi, z - 1, e^2)$ only in the infinitesimal neighborhood of the point

$$\xi = \frac{k^2 - m^2}{\lambda^2 - m^2} = 1.$$

For this purpose we can utilize the formulas of the usual perturbation theory. Taking its second approximation (42.22) and (42.23)

$$A(\xi, z - 1, e^2) = a\left(\frac{1-\xi}{z} + \xi, \frac{1}{z}, e^2\right)$$

$$= 1 - \frac{e^2}{8\pi^2}\left\{\frac{\xi}{1 + \xi(z-1)} \ln\left[\xi(z-1)\right] + c\right\} + \ldots, \tag{43.24}$$

$$B(\xi, z - 1, e^2) = b\left(\frac{1-\xi}{z} + \xi, \frac{1}{z}, e^2\right)$$

$$= 1 - \frac{e^2}{8\pi^2}\left\{\frac{\xi}{2}\,\frac{2 + \xi(z-1)}{1 + \xi(z-1)} \ln\left[\xi(z-1)\right] + c\right\} + \ldots, \tag{43.25}$$

$$e^2 d(x, 1, e^2) = e_0^2 + \ldots, \tag{43.26}$$

we shall obtain in the neighborhood of the point $z = 1$ up to terms of order e_0^4

$$\left[\frac{\partial}{\partial \xi} \ln A(\xi, z - 1, e^2 d)\right]_{\xi=1} = -\frac{3e_0^2}{8\pi^2} = -\frac{3\alpha}{2\pi},$$

$$\left[\frac{\partial}{\partial \xi} \ln B(\xi, z - 1, e^2 d)\right]_{\xi=1} = -\frac{3e_0^2}{8\pi^2} = -\frac{3\alpha}{2\pi}.$$

By substituting these expressions into (43.22), we shall obtain:

$$\frac{a(x, e^2)}{a(x_0, e^2)} \sim \left|\frac{x-1}{x_0-1}\right|^{-\frac{3\alpha}{2\pi}},$$

$$\frac{b(x, e^2)}{b(x_0, e^2)} \sim \left|\frac{x-1}{x_0-1}\right|^{-\frac{3\alpha}{2\pi}}.$$

From this it may be seen that the functions a, b will have at $k^2 \sim m^2$ the well-known infrared singularity

$$a, b \sim \left|1 - \frac{k^2}{m^2}\right|^{-\frac{3\alpha}{2\pi}}. \tag{43.27}$$

Such a behavior of these functions essentially follows directly from (43.23). Indeed, the principal part of the integral in the right-hand side of this relation will be given in the region under consideration by

$$\beta(e_0^2) \ln \left|1 - \frac{k^2}{m^2}\right|,$$

and therefore the corresponding principal part of the function s will be given by

$$c_1 \left|1 - \frac{k^2}{m^2}\right|^{\beta(e_0^2)} \quad (c_1 = \text{const}).$$

It may be seen that the second approximation of perturbation theory will give for the index $\beta(e_0^2)$ the value $-3e_0^2/8\pi^2$.

§ 44. The Renormalization Group in Electrodynamics for $d_l \neq 0$

44.1. *Generalization of the Group Equations*

The whole presentation of the renormalization group in

quantum electrodynamics just given was restricted to the case when the chronological pairing of the potentials of the electromagnetic field had the purely transverse form (32.7). However, the group of multiplicative renormalizations may also be formulated for the more general case when the photon Green's function

$$D_{mn}(k) = -\frac{d(k^2)}{k^2}\left(g^{mn} - \frac{k_m k_n}{k^2}\right) - \frac{d_l(k^2)}{k^2}\frac{k_m k_n}{k^2} \qquad (32.5)$$

contains the longitudinal part d_l.

As we have shown in § 31, the introduction of the counter term $(z_3 - 1)$ (see (31.10)) leads to a multiplicative renormalization only of the first term in (31.1) while the second, i.e., the longitudinal, term undergoes no change.

It is convenient to formulate the corresponding modification of the renormalization group by writing out separately the transformation law for d_l. The equations of the renormalization group may in this case be written in the following form (cf. (31.37)):

$$\left.\begin{aligned} G_1 \to G_2 = zG_1,\ D_1 \to D_2 = z_3 D_1;\ \Gamma_1 \to \Gamma_2 = z^{-1}\Gamma_1, \\ e_1^2 \to e_2^2 = z_3^{-1} e_1^2,\ (d_l)_1 \to (d_l)_2 = z_3 (d_l)_1. \end{aligned}\right\} \qquad (44.1)$$

These equations are a direct generalization of the transformations (42.2) to the case when the photon pairing contains an arbitrary longitudinal part.

The significance of the transformations (44.1), similarly to the case considered earlier, consists of the fact that the sets of quantities G_1, D_1, Γ_1, e_1, $(d_l)_1$ and G_2, D_2, Γ_2, e_2, $(d_l)_2$ are completely equivalent for the description of the interaction between electrons, positrons, and photons.

In going over from the functions G and D to the functions a, b, d, and d_l which depend on the square of the corresponding four-momentum p^2 or k^2 in accordance with formulas (42.3) and (32.5) it is necessary to note the following.

First of all, the presence in (32.5) of the longitudinal term d_l is related to the particular choice of the gauge for the potentials of the electromagnetic field. As we have shown, it follows from the requirement of gauge invariance of the polarization operator

Π that the term d_l does not depend on e^2 and is equal to the longitudinal term of the unperturbed photon Green's function, i.e., to the longitudinal term of the chronological pairing of the operators of the electromagnetic field. In the future for the sake of simplicity we shall consider that this longitudinal term of the chronological pairing, which does not depend on the charge e, is also independent of k^2, and we shall denote it by d_l^0 (similar to the way it was done in § 32).

Second, a change in the gauge of the potentials alters the form of the electron Green's function G and does not affect the transverse part of the photon Green's function $d(k^2)$. Therefore in the present case the functions a and b turn out to depend on d_l, while d does not depend on d_l.

If we then introduce the normalization momentum and go over to dimensionless variables by means of formulas (42.16), then, after eliminating the constants z and z_3, we obtain the functional equations

$$e^2 d(x, y, e^2) = e^2 d(t, y, e^2)\, d\left(\frac{x}{t}, \frac{y}{t}, e^2 d(t, y, e^2)\right) \tag{44.2}$$

and

$$\frac{s(x, y, e^2, e^2 d_l^0)}{s(t, y, e^2, e^2 d_l^0)} = \frac{s\left(\frac{x}{t}, \frac{y}{t}, e^2 d(t, y, e^2), e^2 d_l^0\right)}{s\left(1, \frac{y}{t}, e^2 d(t, y, e^2), e^2 d_l^0\right)}. \tag{44.3}$$

Equation (44.2) coincides with (42.17) while (44.3) is a generalization of (42.18).

By going over to the Lie differential equations and by integrating the second equation we shall find that the first equation coincides with (42.24) and in place of (42.29) we shall obtain:

$$\ln \frac{s(x, y, e^2, e^2 d_l^0)}{s(x_0, y, e^2, e^2 d_l^0)} = \int_{x_0}^{x} \frac{dz}{z}\, \psi\left(\frac{y}{z}, e^2 d(z, y, e^2), e^2 d_l^0\right), \tag{44.4}$$

where

$$\psi(y, e^2, e^2 d_l^0) = \left[\frac{\partial}{\partial \xi} \ln s_0(\xi, y, e^2, e^2 d_l^0)\right]_{\xi=1}. \tag{44.5}$$

The function $s_0(x, y, e^2, e^2 d_l^0)$ which appears in (44.4) has the form (42.20) where the individual terms a, b, etc. have been calculated by using the electromagnetic pairing of the form

$$i\overline{A_m A_n} = \frac{1}{k^2}\left(g^{mn} - \frac{k_m k_n}{k^2}\right) + \frac{1}{k^2}\frac{k_m k_n}{k^2} d_l^0. \tag{44.6}$$

Thus, for example,

$$a_1(x, y, d_l^0) = \frac{1}{8\pi^2}\left\{-3\frac{y}{x}\ln\left|\frac{x-y}{y}\right| + d_l^0\frac{x^2+y^2}{2x^2}\ln\left|\frac{x-y}{y}\right| + d_l^0\frac{y}{2x} + c(y, d_l^0)\right\}, \tag{44.7}$$

$$b_1(x, y, d_l^0) = \frac{1}{8\pi^2}\left\{-\frac{3(x+y)}{2x}\ln\left|\frac{x-y}{y}\right| + d_l^0\frac{x+y}{2x}\ln\left|\frac{x-y}{y}\right| + c(y, d_l^0)\right\}. \tag{44.8}$$

44.2. *Determination of the Asymptotic Behavior in the Ultraviolet and in the Infrared*

We now turn to the determination of the asymptotic behavior of the electron Green's function in the ultraviolet and in the infrared. By setting $x \gg y$ in (44.7) and (44.8) we obtain:

$$a_1(x, d_l^0) = \frac{d_l^0}{16\pi^2}\ln x,$$

$$b_1(x, d_l^0) = \frac{d_l^0 - 3}{16\pi^2}\ln x.$$

By substituting these expressions first into (44.5) and then into (44.4) we obtain respectively

$$\ln\frac{a(x, e^2, e^2 d_l^0)}{a(1, e^2, e^2 d_l^0)} = \int_1^x \frac{dz}{z}\frac{e^2 d_l^0}{16\pi^2} = \frac{e^2 d_l^0}{16\pi^2}\ln x,$$

$$\ln\frac{b(x, e^2, e^2 d_l^0)}{b(1, e^2, e^2 d_l^0)} = \int_1^x \frac{dz}{z}\left(\frac{e^2 d_l^0}{16\pi^2} - \frac{3e^2}{16\pi^2}d(z, e^2)\right)$$

$$= \frac{e^2 d_l^0}{16\pi^2}\ln x - \frac{3e^2}{16\pi^2}\int_1^x \frac{dz}{z}d(z, e^2).$$

By substituting into the foregoing for $d(z, e^2)$ the expression (43.18)

$$d(z, e^2) = \frac{1}{1 - \frac{e^2}{12\pi^2} \ln z},$$

we obtain:

$$\ln \frac{b(x, e^2, e^2 d_l^0)}{b(1, e^2, e^2 d_l^0)} = \frac{e^2 d_l^0}{16\pi^2} \ln x - \tfrac{9}{4} \ln d(x, e^2).$$

We have thus obtained [84]

$$a(x, e^2, e^2 d_l^0) = a(1, e^2, e^2 d_l^0)\, x^{\frac{e^2 d_l^0}{16\pi^2}}, \tag{44.9}$$

$$b(x, e^2, e^2 d_l^0) = b(1, e^2, e^2 d_l^0)\, x^{\frac{e^2 d_l^0}{16\pi^2}} [d(x, e^2)]^{-\frac{9}{4}}. \tag{44.10}$$

Formulas (44.9), (44.10) are generalizations of the corresponding formulas of § 43 and for $d_l^0 = 0$ reduce to the first approximations of formulas (43.15) and (43.16).

In the infrared region by introducing new variables in formulas (44.4), (44.5)

$$\ln \frac{s(x, 1, e^2, e^2 d_l^0)}{s(x_0, 1, e^2, e^2 d_l^0)} = \int_{x_0}^{x} \frac{dt}{t-1} \left[\frac{\partial}{\partial \xi} \ln S(\xi, t-1, e^2 d(t, 1, e^2), e^2 d_l^0)\right]_{\xi=1}$$

and by utilizing for A and B their values in the limit $z \to 1$ and in the first order in e^2:

$$A(\xi, z-1, e^2, e^2 d_l^0)\Big|_{z\to 1} = a\left(\frac{1-\xi}{z} + \xi, \frac{1}{z}, e^2\right)\Big|_{z\to 1}$$
$$\approx 1 + \frac{e^2}{8\pi^2}\{(d_l^0 - 3)\ln[\xi(z-1)] + c\},$$

$$B(\xi, z-1, e^2, e^2 d_l^0)\Big|_{z\to 1} = b\left(\frac{1-\xi}{z} + \xi, \frac{1}{z}, e^2\right)\Big|_{z\to 1}$$
$$\approx 1 + \frac{e^2}{8\pi^2}\{(d_l^0 - 3)\ln[\xi(z-1)] + c\},$$

[84] These formulas were first obtained by Landau, Abrikosov, and Khalatnikov (76), (78), by means of solving approximate integral equations for Green's functions.

we obtain for $s = a,\ b$:

$$\ln\frac{s(x,\,1,\,e^2,\,e^2 d_l^0)}{s(x_0,\,1,\,e^2,\,e^2 d_l^0)}$$

$$=\int_{x_0}^{x}\frac{dt}{t-1}\,\frac{(e^2 d_l^0 - 3e^2 d(t,\,1,\,e^2))}{8\pi^2} = \frac{(d_l^0-3)\,e^2}{8\pi^2}\ln\left|\frac{x-1}{x_0-1}\right|. \quad (44.11)$$

We have thus found that the index β of the singularity

$$\left|1-\frac{k^2}{m^2}\right|^{\beta}$$

of the electron Green's function for $d_l^0 \neq 0$ and in the first order in e^2 has the form

$$\beta = \frac{(d_l^0-3)e_0^2}{8\pi^2} = \frac{\alpha(d_l^0-3)}{2\pi}. \quad (44.12)$$

44.3. *Asymptotic Behavior of the Vertex Part*

In conclusion, we shall consider the asymptotic expressions for the vertex part in the ultraviolet and in the infrared regions. They may be obtained from the functional equation (42.33) by a procedure analogous to the one which was used for the investigation of the function G.

In the case when $d_l^0 \neq 0$ equation (42.33) may be written in the form

$$\frac{\Gamma(x,\,y,\,z,\,u,\,e^2,\,e^2 d_l^0)}{\Gamma(t,\,y,\,z,\,u,\,e^2,\,e^2 d_l^0)} = \frac{\Gamma\left(\frac{x}{t},\,\frac{y}{t},\,\frac{z}{t},\,\frac{u}{t},\,e^2 d(t,\,u,\,e^2),\,e^2 d_l^0\right)}{\Gamma\left(1,\,\frac{y}{t},\,\frac{z}{t},\,\frac{u}{t},\,e^2 d(t,\,u,\,e^2),\,e^2 d_l^0\right)}. \quad (44.13)$$

With the foregoing aim in view, we shall from the outset restrict ourselves to the term in $\Gamma_{\alpha\beta}^n$ which is proportional to the Dirac matrix γ^n:

$$\Gamma_{\alpha\beta}^n \sim \gamma_{\alpha\beta}^n\,\Gamma, \quad (44.14)$$

i.e., in equation (44.13) and in the following we shall take Γ to denote a quite definite function whose contribution to the vertex part of Γ^n is proportional to γ^n. As we shall see, this will turn out to be quite sufficient.

By taking the logarithmic derivative of equation (44.13) with respect to x and by then setting $t = x$ we obtain:

$$\frac{\partial}{\partial x} \ln \Gamma(x, y, z, u, e^2, e^2 d_l^0) = \frac{1}{x}\left[\frac{\partial}{\partial \xi} \ln \Gamma\left(\xi, \frac{y}{x}, \frac{z}{x}, \frac{u}{x}, e^2 d(x, u, e^2), e^2 d_l^0\right)\right]_{\xi=1}. \quad (44.15)$$

The solution of equation (44.15) has the form

$$\ln \frac{\Gamma(x, y, z, u, e^2, e^2 d_l^0)}{\Gamma(x_0, y, z, u, e^2, e^2 d_l^0)} = \int_{x_0}^{x} \frac{dx'}{x'}\left[\frac{\partial}{\partial \xi} \ln \Gamma\left(\xi, \frac{y}{x'}, \frac{z}{x'}, \frac{u}{x'}, e^2 d(x', u, e^2), e^2 d_l^0\right)\right]_{\xi=1}. \quad (44.16)$$

If we now regard $\Gamma(x_0, y, z, \ldots)$, as a function of y and then regard $\Gamma(x_0, y_0, z, \ldots)$ as a function of z we shall obtain the final formula:

$$\ln \frac{\Gamma(x, y, z, u, e^2, e^2 d_l^0)}{\Gamma(x_0, y_0, z_0, u, e^2, e^2 d_l^0)} = \int_{x_0}^{x} \frac{dx'}{x'}\left[\frac{\partial}{\partial \xi} \ln \Gamma\left(\xi, \frac{y}{x'}, \frac{z}{x'}, \frac{u}{x'}, e^2 d(x', u, e^2), e^2 d_l^0\right)\right]_{\xi=1}$$
$$+ \int_{y_0}^{y} \frac{dy'}{y'}\left[\frac{\partial}{\partial \eta} \ln \Gamma\left(\frac{x_0}{y'}, \eta, \frac{z}{y'}, \frac{u}{y'}, e^2 d(y', u, e^2), e^2 d_l^0\right)\right]_{\eta=1}$$
$$+ \int_{z_0}^{z} \frac{dz'}{z'}\left[\frac{\partial}{\partial \zeta} \ln \Gamma\left(\frac{x_0}{z'}, \frac{y_0}{z'}, \zeta, \frac{u}{z'}, e^2 d(z', u, e^2), e^2 d_l^0\right)\right]_{\zeta=1}. \quad (44.17)$$

Of course the order of integration in (44.17) may also be different. As we shall see, in each specific case this order is uniquely determined by considerations of correspondence with perturbation theory.

The right-hand side of (44.17) may be considerably simplified if for the determination of Γ appearing in it we make use of second-order perturbation theory:

$$\Gamma(x, y, z, e^2, e^2 d_l^0) = 1 + e^2\left[\Lambda_t\left(\frac{x}{u}, \frac{y}{u}, \frac{z}{u}\right) - \tilde{\Lambda}_t(u)\right] + e^2 d_l^0\left[\Lambda_l\left(\frac{x}{u}, \frac{y}{u}, \frac{z}{u}\right) - \tilde{\Lambda}_l(u)\right], \quad (44.18)$$

since in this case the integrals in (44.17) containing Λ_l may be evaluated completely. The use of (44.18) is, of course, justified only in the case when

$$\left.\begin{aligned} e^2\Lambda_t\left(\frac{x}{u}, \frac{y}{u}, \frac{z}{u}\right) \ll 1, \\ e^2\Lambda_l\left(\frac{x}{u}, \frac{y}{u}, \frac{z}{u}\right) \ll 1, \end{aligned}\right\} \tag{44.19}$$

which imposes certain restrictions on the arguments of the functions Λ_t and Λ_l. These restrictions should be taken into account in evaluating Γ in the right-hand side of (44.17).

We consider the specific case of the asymptotic behavior in the ultraviolet

$$|k^2| \gg |p^2|, \ |q^2| \gg m^2$$

or

$$|z| \gg |x|, \ |y| \gg |u|.$$

The corresponding calculations using second order perturbation theory have been carried out by Abrikosov (1) and by Sudakov (120). They obtained

$$\Lambda_l = 0, \quad \Lambda_t\left(\frac{x}{u}, \frac{y}{u}, \frac{z}{u}\right) = -\frac{1}{8\pi^2}\ln\left|\frac{z}{x}\right|\ln\left|\frac{z}{y}\right|. \tag{44.20}$$

Here, as in previous analogous cases, the "mass" variable u has dropped out.

In order to find the asymptotic behavior of Γ we change the order of integration in formla (44.17) and write it in the form

$$\ln\frac{\Gamma(x, y, z, e^2)}{\Gamma(x_0, y_0, z_0, e^2)} = I_1(x, y, z, e^2 \mid z_0) + I_2(x, y, z_0, e^2 \mid x_0) + I_3(x_0, y, z_0, e^2 \mid y_0), \tag{44.21}$$

$$I_1 = \int_{z_0}^{z} \frac{dz'}{z'}\left[\frac{\partial}{\partial\xi}\ln\Gamma\left(\frac{x}{z'}, \frac{y}{z'}, \xi, e^2 d(z', e^2)\right)\right]_{\xi=1}, \tag{44.22}$$

$$I_2 = \int_{x_0}^{x} \frac{dx'}{x'}\left[\frac{\partial}{\partial\eta}\ln\Gamma\left(\eta, \frac{y}{x'}, \frac{z_0}{x'}, e^2 d(x', e^2)\right)\right]_{\eta=1}, \tag{44.23}$$

$$I_3 = \int_{y_0}^{y} \frac{dy'}{y'}\left[\frac{\partial}{\partial\zeta}\ln\Gamma\left(\frac{x_0}{y'}, \zeta, \frac{z_0}{y'}, e^2 d(y', e^2)\right)\right]_{\zeta=1}. \tag{44.24}$$

By assuming that x_0, y_0, z_0 are quantities of the same order of magnitude we may use ordinary perturbation theory for the calculation of I_3. This gives:

$$I_3 = \frac{e^2}{8\pi^2} \ln \frac{z_0}{x_0} \int_{y_0}^{y} \frac{dy'}{y'} d(y', e^2) = \frac{3}{2} \ln \frac{z_0}{x_0} \ln \frac{d(y, e^2)}{d(y_0, e^2)}. \quad (44.25)$$

As usual, the applicability of this formula is restricted by the condition of applicability of invariant perturbation theory

$$e^2 d(y, e^2) \ll 1$$

or

$$1 - \frac{e^2}{12\pi^2} \ln y \gg e^2. \quad (44.26)$$

We now turn to the evaluation of I_2. The second argument of the function Γ in the right-hand side of (44.23) may turn out to be much larger than unity for $x' \sim x_0$, which is not possible for the first and the third arguments. Therefore, for the determination of Γ appearing in I_2 we shall utilize the equation of type (44.16) obtained by integrating with respect to the variable y:

$$\ln \frac{\Gamma(\bar{x}, y, \bar{z}, e^2)}{\Gamma(\bar{x}, y_0, \bar{z}, e^2)} = I_3(\bar{x}, y, \bar{z}, e^2 \mid y_0). \quad (44.27)$$

Here $\bar{x}$ and $\bar{z}$ cannot be much greater than unity while the range of values of y is restricted only by the condition (44.26). By substituting (44.27) into (44.23) and by taking (44.20) into account we find:

$$I_2(x, y, z_0, e^2 \mid x_0)$$

$$= \frac{e^2}{8\pi^2} \ln \frac{z_0}{y_0} \int_{x_0}^{x} \frac{dx'}{x'} d(x', e^2) - \frac{3}{2} \int_{x_0}^{x} \frac{dx'}{x'} \ln \frac{d\left(\frac{y}{x'}, e^2 d(x', e^2)\right)}{d\left(\frac{y_0}{x'}, e^2 d(x', e^2)\right)}$$

$$= \frac{3}{2} \ln \frac{z_0}{y_0} \ln \frac{d(x, e^2)}{d(x_0, e^2)} - \frac{3}{2} \ln \frac{x}{x_0} \ln \frac{d(y, e^2)}{d(y_0, e^2)}. \quad (44.28)$$

This formula is valid when the condition (44.26) on the variables y and x is satisfied.

We finally turn to the evaluation of I_1. By considering the arguments of the function Γ in the right-hand side of (44.22) we find that in order to determine it we should utilize an equation of type (44.27) the right-hand side of which contains the sum I_2+I_3. An appropriate calculation leads us to the expression

$$I_1(x, y, z, e^2 \mid z_0)$$
$$= 3\left(\ln\frac{z}{z_0} - \frac{12\pi^2}{e^2}\ln\frac{d(z, e^2)}{d(z_0, e^2)}\right) + \frac{3}{2}\ln\frac{z}{z_0}\left[\ln\frac{d(x, e^2)}{d(x_0, e^2)} + \ln\frac{d(y, e^2)}{d(y_0, e^2)}\right]$$
$$+ \frac{3}{2}\ln x_0 y_0 \cdot \ln\frac{d(z, e^2)}{d(z_0, e^2)}. \qquad (44.29)$$

Before we write down the final form for the right-hand side of (44.21), we must make the following remark. While expression (44.29) is symmetric in x and y, the sum of (44.25) and (44.28) does not have this property, since in the evaluation of I_3 and I_2 assumptions were made which were not symmetric with respect to x and y. However, since the initial formulas are symmetric, we perform the appropriate symmetrization. This yields:

$$\ln\frac{\Gamma(x, y, z, e^2)}{\Gamma(x_0, y_0, z_0, e^2)} = 3\left[\ln\frac{z}{z_0} - \frac{12\pi^2}{e^2}\ln\frac{d(z, e^2)}{d(z_0, e^2)}\right]$$
$$+ \frac{3}{2}\ln x_0 y_0 \cdot \ln\frac{d(z, e^2)}{d(z_0, e^2)} + \frac{3}{2}\left[\ln\frac{z}{x_0}\ln\frac{d(y, e^2)}{d(y_0, e^2)} + \ln\frac{z}{y_0}\ln\frac{d(x, e^2)}{d(x_0, e^2)}\right]$$
$$+ \frac{3}{4}\left[\ln\frac{x_0}{x}\ln\frac{d(y, e^2)}{d(y_0, e^2)} + \ln\frac{y_0}{y}\ln\frac{d(x, e^2)}{d(x_0, e^2)}\right]. \qquad (44.30)$$

The preceding formula holds when the following conditions are satisfied:

$$\left.\begin{array}{c} 1 - \dfrac{e^2}{12\pi^2}\ln z \gg e^2; \\ \ln z > \ln x;\ \ln y \geqq \ln x_0,\ \ln y_0,\ \ln z_0; \\ z_0,\ y_0,\ x_0 \gg 1. \end{array}\right\} \qquad (44.31)$$

In the above $\ln x_0 \sim \ln y_0$, while $\ln z_0$ cannot be much greater than $\ln x_0$, $\ln y_0$.

We also note that for $e^2 \ln z \ll 1$ we obtain the formula [85]

$$\ln \frac{\Gamma(x, y, z, e^2)}{\Gamma(x_0, y_0, z_0, e^2)} = \frac{e^2}{8\pi^2}\left[\ln\frac{z}{x}\ln\frac{z}{y} - \ln\frac{z_0}{x_0}\ln\frac{z_0}{y_0}\right]. \quad (44.32)$$

In another case of asymptotic behavior in the ultraviolet

$$p^2 = q^2 \gg k^2, m^2$$

perturbation theory gives:

$$\Lambda_t = 0, \quad \Lambda_l\left(\frac{x}{u}, \frac{x}{u}, \frac{z}{u}\right) = -\frac{1}{16\pi^2}\ln\frac{x}{u}, \quad (44.33)$$

from which we obtain:

$$\frac{\Gamma(x, x, e^2, e^2 d_l^0)}{\Gamma(x_0, x_0, e^2, e^2 d_l^0)} = \left(\frac{x}{x_0}\right)^{-\frac{e^2 d_l^0}{16\pi^2}}. \quad (44.34)$$

We now turn to the asymptotic behavior in the infrared. We consider the case when

$$p^2 = q^2 \to m^2, \quad k^2 < 0.$$

The corresponding calculations in second order perturbation theory were carried out by Abrikosov (1). He found:

$$\Lambda_l\left(\frac{x}{u}, \frac{z}{u}\right) = \frac{1}{8\pi^2}\ln\left|\frac{u}{x-u}\right|, \quad (44.35)$$

$$\Lambda_t\left(\frac{x}{u}, \frac{z}{u}\right) = \varphi\left(\frac{z}{u}\right) + \psi\left(\frac{z}{u}\right)\ln\left|\frac{u}{x-u}\right|, \quad (44.36)$$

where

$$\varphi\left(\frac{z}{u}\right) = \frac{1-(2u/z)}{\sqrt{1-(4u/z)}}\left[\ln\left|1-\frac{z}{2u}\right|\right]^2, \quad (44.37)$$

$$\psi\left(\frac{z}{u}\right) = 2\frac{(2u/z)-1}{\sqrt{1-(4u/z)}}\ln\left(1-\frac{4u}{z}+\frac{|z|}{2u}\sqrt{1+\frac{4u}{|z|}}\right) - 1. \quad (44.38)$$

[85] This formula was first obtained by Sudakov (120) by means of summing a number of "essential" Feynman diagrams, and later by Blank (8) by means of an approximate solution of Schwinger's equation by the method of proper time.

By carrying out the appropriate integrations we obtain:

$$\ln \frac{\Gamma(x, z, u, e^2, e^2 d_l^0)}{\Gamma(x_0, z_0, u, e^2, e^2 d_l^0)}$$
$$= \frac{e^2}{8\pi^2} \ln \left| \frac{x_0 - u}{x - u} \right| \Phi\left(\frac{z}{u}, \frac{z_0}{u}, u\right) + \frac{e^2}{8\pi^2} \Psi\left(\frac{z}{u}, \frac{z_0}{u}, \frac{x_0}{u}, u\right). \tag{44.39}$$

$$\Psi\left(\frac{z}{u}, \frac{z_0}{u}, \frac{x_0}{u}, u\right)$$
$$= \int_{z_0}^{z} d(z', u, e^2) \left[\frac{\partial \varphi(z'/u)}{\partial z'} + \ln \left| \frac{u}{x_0 - u} \right| \frac{\partial \psi(z'/u)}{\partial z'}\right] dz', \tag{44.40}$$

$$\Phi\left(\frac{z}{u}, \frac{z_0}{u}, u\right) = \int_{z_0}^{z} d(z', u, e^2) + \frac{\partial \psi(z'/u)}{\partial z'} dz' + f\left(\frac{z_0}{u}\right) - 1 + d_l^0. \tag{44.41}$$

Let us examine in greater detail the index of the infrared singularity

$$\Phi\left(\frac{z}{u}, \frac{z_0}{u}, u\right).$$

In order to evaluate the integral (44.41), we note that the function d has, in the present case, the form (43.2), while the function $f(t)$ appearing in (43.2) is proportional to $\psi(t)$ for large t. Because of this, one may set to small terms of order e^2:

$$\int_{z_0}^{z} \frac{dz'}{1 - e^2[f(z'/u) - f(1/u)]} \frac{\partial \psi(z'/u)}{\partial z}$$
$$\approx \int_{z_0}^{z} \frac{dz'}{1 - (e^2/24\pi^2)\psi(z'/u)} \frac{\partial \psi(z'/u)}{\partial z'} = \frac{24\pi^2}{e^2} \ln \frac{1 - (e^2/24\pi^2)\,\psi(z_0/u)}{1 - (e^2/24\pi^2)\,\psi(z/u)}. \tag{44.42}$$

By substituting this expression into (44.41) and taking into account the smallness of the quantity $(e^2/24\pi^2)\psi(z_0/u)$, we obtain for the index of the infrared singularity

$$\Gamma(p^2, p^2, k^2, m^2, e^2, e^2 d_l^0) \approx \left| \frac{m^2}{p^2 - m^2} \right|^{\beta\left(\frac{k^2}{m^2}\right)}$$

the following expression

$$\beta\left(\frac{k^2}{m^2}\right) = \frac{e^2 d_l^0}{8\pi^2} - 3 \ln \left[1 - \frac{e^2}{24\pi^2} \psi\left(\frac{k^2}{m^2}\right)\right]. \tag{44.43}$$

In the limiting case of large k^2 when

$$\frac{e^2}{12\pi^2} \ln \frac{k^2}{m^2} \sim 1,$$

we obtain from the foregoing:

$$\beta\left(\frac{k^2}{m^2}\right) = \frac{e^2 d_l^0}{8\pi^2} + 3 \ln d \left(\frac{k^2}{m^2}, e^2\right).$$

On the other hand, for

$$\frac{e^2}{12\pi^2} \ln \frac{k^2}{m^2} \ll 1,$$

when

$$\frac{e^2}{24\pi^2} \psi \left(\frac{k^2}{m^2}\right) \ll 1,$$

we obtain: [86]

$$\beta\left(\frac{k^2}{m^2}\right) = \frac{e^2}{8\pi^2} \left[d_l^0 + \psi\left(\frac{k^2}{m^2}\right)\right]. \tag{44.44}$$

By going to the limit $k^2 \to 0$ in (44.44) we obtain the formula

$$\beta(0) = \frac{e^2}{8\pi^2} (d_l^0 - 3), \tag{44.45}$$

which in virtue of Ward's identity agrees with (44.12).

We have examined above the main asymptotic expressions for the vertex function when Γ^n is proportional to the matrix γ^n.

In going to higher orders in e^2 it may turn out to be necessary to examine terms of Γ^n having a different matrix structure. However, from the preceding discussion it follows that corresponding arguments may be extended to such cases as well.

[86] This formula was first obtained by Abrikosov (1) by summing a number of fundamental diagrams.

44.4. *Various Possibilities*

The existence of the renormalization group in quantum electrodynamics allows us to improve the perturbation theory formulas not only for the Green's functions and for the vertex parts, but also for diagrams having more than three external lines. These diagrams are not themselves divergent. Divergences may appear in them only as a result of divergences being present in their component parts (Green's functions and the vertex part). Therefore, their transformation formulas under multiplicative renormalization may be directly obtained from a consideration of the specific structure of the diagrams.

Let us, for example, consider the diagram for the scattering of an electron in an external field with the emission of a photon (or the scattering of a photon by an electron). In this case we have in mind not the diagram of second-order perturbation theory but the sum of all possible diagrams of the scattering matrix with two photon and two electron external lines. We denote by M the operator which corresponds to such a generalized diagram. From the structure of the diagram it is clear that the multiplicative renormalization of the operator M reduces to the transformation

$$M_1 \rightarrow M_2 = z_1^{-1} z_2 z_1^{-1} M_1$$

or, by taking Ward's identity into account, to

$$M_2 = z_1^{-1} M_1, \tag{44.46}$$

i.e., M transforms like the vertex part.

By making use of (44.46) one may in the usual manner first write the functional and then the differential equation for the matrix element of this operator. The differential equation may be integrated. A particularly simple result is obtained for $d = 1$:

$$M_{\alpha\beta} = \exp \{\ln M^0_{\alpha\beta}\}; \tag{44.47}$$

whose significance consists of the fact that in the improved perturbation theory one must make a series expansion not of the matrix element itself, but of its logarithm which appears in the index of the exponential.

The diagram with three photon and two electron free ends

(double Compton effect) and, in general, the diagram for any arbitrary process may be treated in a similar manner. The result is usually considerably simplified by setting $d = 1$, i.e., by neglecting the electron-positron loops.

Expression (44.47) may be directly used to investigate the "infrared catastrophe" arising in the calculation of the radiation corrections to scattering. As is well known, in order to remove the "infrared catastrophe" it is necessary to consider not the purely elastic scattering, but scattering with a certain energy loss not exceeding $\Delta\varepsilon$. The usual perturbation theory leads to incorrect dependence of the differential effective cross section on $\Delta\varepsilon$: viz., for $\Delta\varepsilon \to 0$, i.e., for purely elastic scattering, $d\sigma \to \infty$. A discussion making use of the improved perturbation theory yields the physically correct result: $d\sigma \to 0$ as $\Delta\varepsilon \to 0$. In order to show this, it is necessary to utilize (44.47) and the corresponding expression for the vertex part. When $\Delta\varepsilon$ is considerably different from zero the results of the usual and of the improved perturbation theory coincide. The "infrared catastrophe" which arises in calculating the radiation correction to the Compton effect may be treated in a completely analogous manner.

§ 45. The Renormalization Group in the Two-Charge Pseudoscalar Meson Theory

45.1. *The Second Charge in Meson Theory*

The method of the renormalization group may also be carried over to any renormalizable meson theory. Let us consider, for example, pseudoscalar meson theory with pseudoscalar coupling. As we have shown in § 33, the essential difference between this case and that of spinor electrodynamics is the existence of two charges in this theory, following from the fact that in the subtraction of divergences one must introduce the "four-meson" counter term $h\varphi^4$ in addition to the counter terms which correspond to the ones used in quantum electrodynamics. The divergent part of the coefficient h is uniquely determined by the subtraction procedure, while there is some arbitrariness in the finite part. Thus the theory, in addition to the meson charge g, in fact contains another finite constant h and the initial interaction Lagrangian should be written in the form

$$\mathscr{L} = g : \bar{\psi}\Gamma\psi\varphi : + h : \varphi^4 :. \qquad (33.14)$$

Here, ψ, $\bar{\psi}$ are spinor functions of the nucleon field of mass M, φ is the pseudoscalar function for the meson field of mass μ, and Γ is the vertex matrix.

After writing the finite multiplicative additions to the Lagrangian in the form

$$(z_1 - 1)g : \bar{\psi}\Gamma\psi\varphi : - (z_2 - 1) : \bar{\psi}(\hat{p} - M)\psi : \\ + (z_3 - 1) : \varphi(p^2 - \mu^2)\varphi : + (z_4 - 1)h : \varphi^4 :, \qquad (45.1)$$

we introduce the nucleon Green's function G, the meson Green's function Δ, the three-vertex function Γ^5 and the fourmeson function $\square$. Here, just as in the earlier case, Γ^5 is a sum of terms corresponding to the internal lines of diagrams of the type shown in Fig. 55a with one external meson line and two external nucleon lines, while $\square$ corresponds to diagrams with four external meson lines (Fig. 55b).

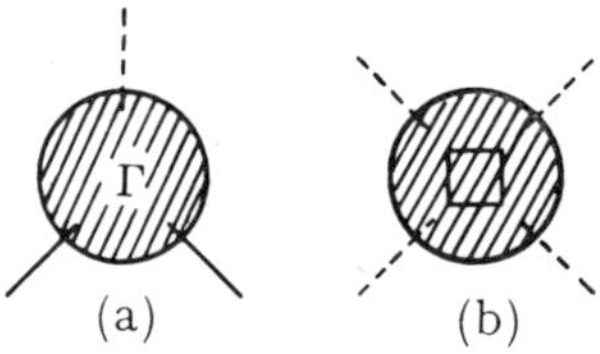

Fig. 55.

By investigating the effect of the terms (45.1) on G, Δ, Γ^5, and $\square$ we easily obtain the following equations (see also (33.16) and (33.18))

$$\left.\begin{aligned} &G_1 \to G_2 = z_2 G_1, \ \Gamma^5_1 \to \Gamma^5_2 = z_1^{-1}\Gamma^5_1, \ \Delta_1 \to \Delta_2 = z_3\Delta_1, \\ &\square_1 \to \square_2 = z_4^{-1}\square_1, g_1^2 \to g_2^2 = z_1^2 z_2^{-2} z_3^{-1} g_1^2, h_1 \to h_2 = z_4 z_3^{-2} h_1, \end{aligned}\right\} \qquad (45.2)$$

which define the two-charge renormalization group in meson theory.

45.2. *Transition to Functional Equations of the Group*

In the momentum representation the functions G and Δ may be expressed by means of relations

$$G(p) = \frac{\hat{p}s_1(p^2) + Ms_2(p^2)}{M^2 - p^2}, \tag{45.3}$$

$$\Delta(k) = \frac{d(k^2)}{\mu^2 - k^2} \tag{45.4}$$

in terms of the scalar functions s_1, s_2, and d which depend only on the squares of the corresponding four-momenta.

The vertex functions $\Gamma^5_{\alpha\beta}$ and $\Box_{ijkl}$ depend on a larger number of scalar arguments and may be written in the form

$$\Gamma^5_{\alpha\beta}(p, q) = \tilde{\Gamma}_{\alpha\beta}\Gamma(p^2, q^2, (p+q)^2), \tag{45.5}$$

$$\Box_{ijkl}(p, q, k) = \tilde{\Box}_{ijkl}\Box(p^2, q^2, k^2, (p+q)^2, (p+k)^2, (p+q+k)^2), \tag{45.6}$$

where Γ and $\Box$ are scalar functions of scalar arguments. Thus, in the general case, the group equations contain functions of three and even of six momentum variables.

By going over to dimensionless arguments by means of the normalizing momentum λ such that

$$s\left(\frac{p^2}{\lambda^2}, \frac{\mu^2}{\lambda^2}, \frac{M^2}{\lambda^2}, g^2, h\right)\Bigg|_{p^2=\lambda^2} = 1, \quad d\left(\frac{k^2}{\lambda^2}, \frac{\mu^2}{\lambda^2}, \frac{M^2}{\lambda^2}, g^2, h\right)\Bigg|_{k^2=\lambda^2} = 1$$

$$\Gamma\left(\frac{p^2}{\lambda^2}, \frac{q^2}{\lambda^2}, \frac{k^2}{\lambda^2}, \frac{\mu^2}{\lambda^2}, \frac{M^2}{\lambda^2}, g^2, h\right)\Bigg|_{p^2=q^2=k^2=\lambda^2} = 1, \tag{45.7}$$

$$\Box\left(\frac{p_1^2}{\lambda^2}, \ldots, \frac{p_6^2}{\lambda^2}, \frac{\mu^2}{\lambda^2}, \frac{M^2}{\lambda^2}, g^2, h\right)\Bigg|_{p_1^2=\ldots=p_6^2=\lambda^2} = 1$$

we are able to determine and to eliminate the contants $z_1, \ldots, z_4$ from equations (45.2). In this way we obtain

$$g_2^2 = g_1^2\psi\left(\frac{\lambda_2^2}{\lambda_1^2}, \frac{\mu^2}{\lambda_1^2}, \frac{M^2}{\lambda_1^2}, g_1^2, h_1\right), \quad h_2 = h_1\varphi\left(\frac{\lambda_2^2}{\lambda_1^2}, \frac{\mu^2}{\lambda_1^2}, \frac{M^2}{\lambda_1^2}, g_1^2, h_1\right) \tag{45.8}$$

where

$$\psi(x, y, Y, g^2, h)$$
$$= s^2(x, y, Y, g^2, h)\,\Gamma^2(x, x, x, y, Y, g^2, h)\,d(x, y, Y, g^2, h) \tag{45.9}$$

and

$$\varphi(x, y, Y, g^2, h) = d^2(x, y, Y, g^2, h)\square(x, \ldots, x, y, Y, g^2, h) \quad (45.10)$$

From (45.8) it follows that for functions ψ and φ the transformation law has the form

$$g_1^2\psi_1 = g_2^2\psi_2\,,\; h_1\varphi_1 = h_2\varphi_2\,. \quad (45.11)$$

We note that (this may be easily seen from an examination of the corresponding Feynman diagrams) the function ψ plays the role of an effective interaction between two nucleons, while the function φ describes the interaction between two mesons.

It follows from (45.11) that the products $g^2\psi$ and $h\varphi$ are invariants of the two-charge renormalization group and may be called the invariant nuclear charge and the invariant meson charge respectively.

We note that in accordance with (45.9) and (45.10) the invariant charges are defined by products of symmetric asymptotic expressions for Green's functions.

By noting that in accordance with (45.7) the normalization conditions for ψ and φ have the form

$$\psi\left(1, \frac{\mu^2}{\lambda^2}, \frac{M^2}{\lambda^2}, g^2, h\right) = 1 \quad (45.12)$$

$$\varphi\left(1, \frac{\mu^2}{\lambda^2}, \frac{M^2}{\lambda^2}, g^2, h\right) = 1, \quad (45.13)$$

we arrive at the following system of equations:

$$\psi(x, y, Y, g^2, h) = \psi(t, y, Y, g^2, h)\,\psi\left(\frac{x}{t}, \frac{y}{t}, \frac{Y}{t}, g_1^2, h_1\right), \quad (45.14)$$

$$\varphi(x, y, Y, g^2, h) = \varphi(t, y, Y, g^2, h)\,\varphi\left(\frac{x}{t}, \frac{y}{t}, \frac{Y}{t}, g_1^2, h_1\right), \quad (45.15)$$

$$\frac{a(x, y, Y, g^2, h)}{a(t, y, Y, g^2, h)} = \frac{a\left(\frac{x}{t}, \frac{y}{t}, \frac{Y}{t}, g_1^2, h_1\right)}{a\left(1, \frac{y}{t}, \frac{Y}{t}, g_1^2, h_1\right)}, \quad (45.16)$$

where

$$x = \frac{k^2}{\lambda_2^2}, \; y = \frac{\mu^2}{\lambda_2^2}, \; Y = \frac{M^2}{\lambda_2^2}, \; t = \frac{\lambda_1^2}{\lambda_2^2} \quad (45.17)$$

and

$$g_1^2 = g^2 \psi(t, y, Y, g^2, h), \tag{45.18}$$

$$h_1 = h\varphi(t, y, Y, g^2, h), \tag{45.19}$$

while a denotes any one of the functions s, $\tilde{\Gamma}$, d, and $\tilde{\square}$.

Equations (45.14)–(45.19) express the fact that due to the existence of the renormalization group it is possible to change the scale of the masses and of the momenta by simultaneously changing the charges g and h.

By taking the derivatives of equations (45.14), (45.15) and the logarithmic derivative of equation (45.16) with respect to x and by then setting $t = x$ we obtain the Lie differential equations for the two-charge meson theory:

$$\frac{\partial\psi(x, y, Y, g^2, h)}{\partial x} = \frac{\psi(x, y, Y, g^2, h)}{x}\, \Psi\left(\frac{y}{x}, \frac{Y}{x}, g^2\psi, h\varphi\right), \tag{45.20}$$

$$\frac{\partial\varphi(x, y, Y, g^2, h)}{\partial x} = \frac{\varphi(x, y, Y, g^2, h)}{x}\, \Phi\left(\frac{y}{x}, \frac{Y}{x}, g^2\psi, h\varphi\right), \tag{45.21}$$

$$\frac{\partial \ln a(x, y, Y, g^2, h)}{\partial x} = \frac{1}{x}\left[\frac{\partial}{\partial \xi} \ln a\left(\xi, \frac{y}{x}, \frac{Y}{x}, g^2\psi, h\varphi\right)\right]_{\xi=1}, \tag{45.22}$$

where

$$\Psi(y, Y, g^2, h) = \left[\frac{\partial}{\partial\xi}\psi(\xi, y, Y, g^2, h)\right]_{\xi=1}, \tag{45.23}$$

$$\Phi(y, Y, g^2, h) = \left[\frac{\partial}{\partial\xi}\varphi(\xi, y, Y, g^2, h)\right]_{\xi=1}. \tag{45.24}$$

The problem has thus been reduced to the system of two equations (44.20), (44.21), since when ψ and φ are known, all the other functions a may be determined from (44.22) by means of the quadrature:

$$\ln\frac{a(x, y, Y, g^2, h)}{a(x_0, y, Y, g^2, h)}$$
$$= \int_{x_0}^{x}\frac{dz}{z}\left[\frac{\partial}{\partial\xi}\ln a\left(\xi, \frac{y}{z}, \frac{Y}{z}, g^2\psi(z, y, Y, g^2, h), h\varphi(z, y, Y, g^2, h)\right)\right]_{\xi=1}. \tag{45.25}$$

If we agree to obtain the functions appearing in the right-hand side of equations (45.20)–(45.22) by means of perturbation theory, we shall be able to find the functions ψ, φ, S, $\tilde{\Gamma}$, Δ and $\tilde{\Box}$ which satisfy the requirement of correspondence with ordinary perturbation theory.[87]

45.3. *Asymptotic Behavior in the Ultraviolet*

We shall now apply the group equations just obtained to the region of large momenta when

$$|k^2| \gg M^2 > \mu^2.$$

In this case the individual terms of the perturbation theory series reduce to functions of $\ln x$ and cease to depend on the variables y and Y. Therefore the corresponding transition in equations (45.20)–(45.25) may be performed by omitting y and Y in them. We further introduce the notation

$$g^2\psi(x, g^2, h) = \sigma(z, g^2, h), \tag{45.26}$$

$$h\varphi(x, g^2, h) = \rho(z, g^2, h), \tag{45.27}$$

where

$$z = \ln x,$$

and σ and ρ are nothing other than invariant charges. In place of (45.21), (45.22), we obtain the system

$$\frac{d\sigma}{dz} = \sigma\Psi(\sigma, \rho), \tag{45.28}$$

$$\frac{d\rho}{dz} = \rho\Phi(\sigma, \rho), \tag{45.29}$$

where

$$\Psi(\sigma, \rho) = \left[\frac{\partial}{\partial\xi}\psi(\xi, \sigma, \rho)\right]_{\xi=1}, \tag{45.30}$$

[87] In the foregoing, one should of course, bear in mind that in mesodynamics because of the large observed value of the coupling constant ($g^2/4\pi \sim 15$) the improvement of perturbation theory given here does not have any direct application to experiment and is of the nature of a model calculation only.

$$\Phi(\sigma, \rho) = \left[\frac{\partial}{\partial \xi} \varphi(\xi, \sigma, \rho)\right]_{\xi=1} \tag{45.31}$$

and, moreover,

$$\ln \frac{a(x, g^2, h)}{a(x_0, g^2, h)} = \int_{lnx_0}^{lnx} dz \left[\frac{\partial}{\partial \xi} \ln a(\xi, \sigma(z, g^2, h), \rho(z, g^2, h))\right]_{\xi=1}. \tag{45.32}$$

By dividing (45.29) by (45.28) we eliminate the variable z:

$$\frac{d\rho}{d\sigma} = \frac{\rho\Phi(\sigma, \rho)}{\sigma\Psi(\sigma, \rho)}. \tag{45.33}$$

Equation (45.33) may be easily analyzed in the case of weak coupling when the constants g^2, $h \ll 1$, and the power series expansions of the functions Ψ and Φ may be obtained from the usual perturbation theory. By considering diagrams of lowest order, we find that the first few terms in the expansion of these functions have the form

$$\Psi(\sigma, \rho) = \psi_1 \sigma + \psi_2 \sigma^2 + \psi_3 \sigma\rho + \psi_4 \rho^2 + \ldots, \tag{45.34}$$

$$\rho\Phi(\sigma, \rho) = \varphi_1 \sigma^2 + \varphi_2 \sigma\rho + \varphi_3 \rho^2 + \varphi_4 \sigma\rho^2 + \ldots, \tag{45.35}$$

where $\psi_1, \psi_2, \ldots, \varphi_1, \varphi_2, \ldots$ are certain numerical coefficients.

From these expansions, it follows immediately that in the neighborhood of the point $\sigma = 0$ (45.33) has two particular solutions of the form

$$\rho(\sigma) = a_1 \sigma + a_2 \sigma^2 + \ldots, \tag{45.36}$$

where the first coefficients a_1 are roots of the quadratic equation

$$\varphi_3 a_1^2 + (\varphi_2 - \psi_1) a_1 + \varphi_1 = 0. \tag{45.37}$$

By substituting the expansion (45.36) into (45.33) and into equation (45.29) we see that, in this case, the main approximation to the equation for σ has the same form as in the absence of the charge h:

$$\frac{d\sigma}{dz} = \psi_1 \sigma^2 + \ldots \tag{45.38}$$

For purposes of illustration we shall solve equation (45.37) and obtain the asymptotic expressions for the functions s, $\tilde{\Gamma}$, d, and $\tilde{\Box}$ for the symmetric pseudoscalar theory when $\psi_1 = 5/16\pi^2$.

By integrating (45.38), we obtain

$$\sigma(z, g^2, h) = g^2 \psi(x, g^2, h) = g^2 \left(1 - \frac{5}{16\pi^2} g^2 \ln x\right)^{-1}. \quad (45.39)$$

By utilizing expression (45.39) for the determination of s, d, $\tilde{\Gamma}$, and $\tilde{\Box}$, we shall also find by means of calculations involving the lowest orders of perturbation theory:

$$\left.\begin{aligned} S(x, g^2) &= \left(1 - \frac{5}{16\pi^2} g^2 \ln x\right)^{-3/10}, \quad d(x, g^2) = \left(1 - \frac{5}{16\pi^2} g^2 \ln x\right)^{-4/5}, \\ \tilde{\Gamma}(x, g^2) &= \left(1 - \frac{5}{16\pi^2} g^2 \ln x\right)^{1/5}, \quad \tilde{\Box}(x, g^2) = \left(1 - \frac{5}{16\pi^2} g^2 \ln x\right)^{3/5}, \\ h &= a_1 g^2. \end{aligned}\right\} \quad (45.40)$$

From formula (45.39) it follows that in a manner analogous to the case of electrodynamics the function $\sigma = g^2\psi$ for sufficiently large momenta attains even for small g^2 values of the order of magnitude of unity, and we therefore step beyond the framework of weak coupling.

It is also not difficult to integrate equation (45.33) in the more general case

$$\sigma \sim \rho \ll 1,$$

when it has the form

$$\psi_1 \frac{d\rho}{d\sigma} = \varphi_1 + \varphi_2 \left(\frac{\rho}{\sigma}\right) + \varphi_3 \left(\frac{\rho}{\sigma}\right)^2.$$

The solution of this equation and also the detailed investigation of the behavior of the integral curves in the phase plane (σ, ρ) were recently given by Ginzburg (49).

We refer the reader who is interested in the details of this investigation to the original article, and note that it follows from this investigation that for sufficiently large momenta the functions σ and ρ in the general case also leave the neighborhood of the origin of coordinates even for small values of the constants g^2 and h. Therefore with an arbitrary ratio between the small constants g^2 and h, we unavoidably find ourselves in the domain of strong coupling.

CHAPTER IX

Dispersion Relations

§ 46. General Remarks on the Method

46.1. *Introduction*

Up to this point of our presentation, the method of perturbation theory has served as the principal tool of investigation. By using it we have carried out a general analysis of the structure of the scattering matrix taking into account the physical requirements of causality, unitarity, and covariance; we have also formulated methods for the removal of infinities and for obtaining power series expansions for the fundamental quantities of the theory.

As we have already pointed out, these methods turn out to be unsuitable in the domain of meson theory where the expansion parameter $g^2/4\pi\hbar c$ is not small (according to the most recent investigations this parameter is approximately equal to 15). Because of this, the successive terms in the power series expansions increase rapidly, and finite sums of such terms are not in quantitative agreement with experiment. Moreover, as we have noted in the preceding chapter, within the domain of quantum electrodynamics where $e^2/4\pi\hbar c = 1/137$, perturbation theory is also of limited applicability, and, as a result of this, is not internally consistent.

Therefore, all attempts of a radical departure from the framework of perturbation theory are of considerable interest. At present all investigations of this kind may be classified into four different groups: (1) the method of functional integration, (2) the strong coupling method, (3) the method of investigation of various model theories, and finally, (4) the method of dispersion relations.

We have already considered the first of these methods in Chapter VII. As we have pointed out there, this method encounters considerable mathematical difficulties and as a result has not led to any significant results up to the present time.

The second and the third of the approaches enumerated above are fundamentally approximate ones, and therefore can be expected to yield only limited results. Nevertheless, neither the strong coupling method (92), (110), (94) which is an attempt to construct a field theory on the basis of expansions in inverse powers of the coupling parameter nor the method of investigation of model theories (80), (99) which consists of investigating various models of the interaction capable of yielding exact solutions, have led to any significant results so far.

The fourth approach to which this chapter is devoted appears to be particularly important. In the investigations utilizing this approach (for detailed bibliography refer to § 46.3) exact relationships have been obtained between individual matrix elements of the scattering matrix. It is of particular importance that these relationships are from the outset not tied to any form of power series expansions, but are based on the investigation of the analytic properties of the matrix elements of the S-matrix as a whole.

46.2. *The Mathematical and the Physical Bases of the Dispersion Relations*

The mathematical basis of the dispersion relations is the Cauchy integral formula. As is well known, this formula allows one to represent an analytic function f of the complex variable z as an integral over a closed contour Γ bounding the region G within which $f(z)$ is analytic. According to this formula

$$\frac{1}{2\pi i}\int_{\Gamma}\frac{f(z')}{z'-z}\,dz' = \begin{cases} f(z) \text{ if } z \text{ lies inside } \Gamma & (46.1\text{a}) \\ 0 \quad \text{ if } z \text{ lies outside } \Gamma. & (46.1\text{b}) \end{cases}$$

In the intermediate case when the point z lies on the contour of integration the interpretation of the Cauchy integral in the sense of the principal value leads to the formula [88]

$$f(z) = \frac{1}{\pi i} \mathscr{P} \int_{\Gamma} \frac{f(z')}{z' - z} \, dz'. \tag{46.2}$$

Taking separately the real and the imaginary parts of equation (46.2), we obtain relations between Re f and Im f. The dispersion relations are relations of just this type between the real and the imaginary parts of the matrix elements of the scattering matrix.

It is therefore clear that in order to obtain the dispersion relations, it is very important to carry out an investigation of the analytic properties of the matrix elements. For this purpose it is customary to investigate the analytic nature of the elements of the scattering matrix considered as functions of energy, and the possibility of analytic continuation of these matrix elements into the upper half plane.

We now turn to the case when as a result of such analytic continuation we obtain a function $g(E)$ which falls off not slower than const/$|E|$ as $|E| \to \infty$ in the upper half plane, i.e.,

$$|g(E)| \leqq \frac{A}{|E|} \quad \text{for} \quad |E| \to \infty. \tag{46.4}$$

Then by choosing for the contour of integration in (46.2) the real axis and the upper semicircle of infinitely large radius, we can neglect the integral over the semicircle and obtain a formula of the following type

$$g(E) = \frac{1}{\pi i} \mathscr{P} \int_{-\infty}^{\infty} \frac{g(E')}{E' - E} \, dE'. \tag{46.5}$$

Taking the real part of (46.5), we obtain a relation between the real and the imaginary parts of the function g:

$$\operatorname{Re} g(E) = \frac{1}{\pi} \mathscr{P} \int_{-\infty}^{\infty} \frac{\operatorname{Im} g(E')}{E' - E} \, dE'. \tag{46.6}$$

[88] This formula may be obtained from (46.1a) with the aid of the symbolic indentity

$$\frac{1}{z' - z \mp i\varepsilon} = \mathscr{P} \frac{1}{z' - z} \pm i\pi\delta(z' - z) \quad (\varepsilon \to + 0). \tag{46.3}$$

It should be noted that for physical applications the condition (46.4) turns out to be somewhat restrictive. However, it is not difficult to extend the arguments given above also to the case of functions $g(E)$ which for large $|E|$ increase polynomially. For example, let $g(E)$ have at infinity a pole of the nth order, i.e.,

$$g(E) \leqq A\,|E|^n \quad \text{for} \quad |E| \to \infty. \tag{46.7}$$

Then the quantity

$$\frac{g(E)}{(E - E_0)^{n+1}} \tag{46.8}$$

will be an analytic function in the upper half plane and will satisfy condition (46.4) for all E_0 that have a negative imaginary part. Substituting (46.8) into (46.2), in which the contour Γ has been chosen in the same way as was done earlier in (46.1), we shall obtain after going to the limit[89] $\operatorname{Im} E_0 \to 0$ a relation whose real part has the form

$$\operatorname{Re} g(E) = \frac{(E - E_0)^{n+1}}{\pi} \mathscr{P} \int_{-\infty}^{\infty} \frac{\operatorname{Im} g(E')\,dE'}{(E' - E)(E' - E_0)^{n+1}}$$
$$+ \operatorname{Re} g(E_0) + \ldots + \frac{\operatorname{Re} g^{(n)}(E_0)}{n!}(E - E_0)^n \quad (-\infty < E,\ E_0 < \infty). \tag{46.10}$$

A relation of this type is, for example, the dispersion relation in the domain of classical electrodynamics between the real and the imaginary parts of the index of refraction[90] which was obtained in the twenties by Kronig (75) and by Kramers (73)

$$\operatorname{Re}\,[n(\omega) - n(0)] = \frac{2}{\pi} \mathscr{P} \int_0^{\infty} \frac{\omega^2 \operatorname{Im} n(\omega')}{\omega'(\omega'^2 - \omega^2)}\,d\omega'. \tag{46.11}$$

[89] This transition to the limit may be carried out with the aid of the formula

$$\frac{1}{(E' - E + i\varepsilon)^{n+1}} = \mathscr{P}\frac{1}{(E' - E)^{n+1}} - \frac{i\pi(-1)^n}{n!}\delta^{(n)}(E' - E), \tag{46.9}$$

which is obtained from (46.3) by differentiating n times.

[90] The Kramers-Kronig formula may be obtained from (46.10) by setting

$$n = 0, \quad E_0 = 0 \text{ and } \operatorname{Im} g(E') = -\operatorname{Im} g(-E').$$

Relations of the type (46.10) are called dispersion relations in order to indicate their kinship to the Kramers–Kronig formula.

We emphasize that the possibility of analytic continuation into the upper half plane of the energy variable, and consequently the possibility of obtaining formulas of type (46.10), rests on considerations of causality which form the physical basis of the dispersion relations.

In order to clarify the connection just indicated, let us suppose, by somewhat simplifying the actual state of affairs, that

$$f(E) = \int_{-\infty}^{\infty} F(t)\, e^{iEt}\, dt, \tag{46.12}$$

where as a result of the "condition of causality" the function F, which depends on the time t, has the property

$$F(t) = 0 \quad \text{for} \quad t < 0.$$

In passing into the upper half plane when $+ i \mid \operatorname{Im} E \mid$ is added to E and the integral (46.12) acquires the factor $\exp(-t \mid \operatorname{Im} E \mid)$ this factor will play the role of a cutoff factor which guarantees the convergence of the integral since for $t<0$, when $\exp(-t \mid \operatorname{Im} E \mid)$ increases, the function $F(t)$ is equal to zero as a result of the condition of causality.

It may also be shown that even if $F(t)$ is a singular function, as long as it is integrable in the sense of the definition given in § 16, the integral (46.6) converges and defines a function without essential singularities at infinity.

A different situation will exist when $F(t)$ vanishes only for $t < -a$ where a is some "elementary length." Then by replacing t by $t - a$ in the integrand of (46.12) we shall find that

$$f(E) = e^{-iaE} f_1(E), \tag{46.13}$$

where the function $f_1(E)$ will have no essential singularity at infinity (the factor $\exp(-iaE)$ will have such a singularity). Therefore in order to obtain in this case a function for which the dispersion relation holds it is necessary to multiply $F(E)$ by $\exp i\alpha E$ with $\alpha \geqq a$.

In the actual case, the situation will of course, be considerably more complicated because in any event the formulas replacing (46.12) will contain a larger number of variables of integration.

Nevertheless, in spite of the necessity of an essential technical improvement of the preceding argument, its fundamentals will remain unchanged.

46.3. *A Review of the Work on the Dispersion Relations*

In order to make use of the mathematical dispersion relations for the study of any process of collision between particles, it is necessary, as we have seen, to satisfy oneself beforehand that the appropriate scattering characteristic which is a function of energy may be suitably continued into the upper half plane.

In quantum mechanics the so-called scattering amplitude f is usually taken as such a characteristic; we shall introduce this characteristic in the present case of quantum field theory, after restricting ourselves for the sake of definiteness to elastic scattering of a meson by a nucleon, in the following manner:

$$\langle \mathbf{p}'s',\ \mathbf{q}'\rho' \,|\, S \,|\, \mathbf{p}s,\ \mathbf{q}\rho\rangle = \delta(\mathbf{p}-\mathbf{p}')\,\delta_{ss'}\,\delta(\mathbf{q}-\mathbf{q}')\,\delta_{\rho\rho'} + \frac{i}{2\pi\sqrt{q^0 q'^0}}\,\delta(p'+q'-p-q)\,f_{s'\rho',\,s\rho}(\mathbf{p}',\mathbf{q}',\mathbf{p},\mathbf{q}). \quad (46.14)$$

Here $\mathbf{p}(\mathbf{p}')$ is the nucleon momentum before (after) scattering, $s(s')$ is the set of its discrete spin and isotopic spin indices before (after) scattering, $\mathbf{q}$, ρ, $\mathbf{q}'$, ρ' are the corresponding characteristics of the meson:

$$|\,\mathbf{p}s,\ \mathbf{q}\rho\rangle = a_s^{(+)}(\mathbf{p})\,a_\rho^{(+)}(\mathbf{q})\,\Phi_0, \quad (46.15)$$

$$\langle \mathbf{p}'s',\ \mathbf{q}'\rho'\,| = \Phi_0^*\,a_{s'}^{(-)}(\mathbf{p}')\,a_{\rho'}^{(-)}(\mathbf{q}') \quad (46.16)$$

and f is the scattering amplitude. It may be seen that the scattering amplitude introduced in this manner differs from the function F utilized earlier (see (21.35)) only by the factor $i\,[2\pi\sqrt{q^0 q'^0}]^{-1}$.

Many papers have been devoted to problems of analytic continuation of the scattering amplitude. We may mention, for example, the papers by Heisenberg (57)–(59), Hu Ning (61), Akhiezer and Pomeranchuk (3), van Kampen (130), (131), and Krein (74). These papers discuss from the point of view of ordinary quantum mechanics the process of the elastic collision of two particles which may be reduced to the problem of the scattering of a single particle by a fixed center of force. For the function $g(E)$ the above papers utilize the component of the scattering amplitude which corresponds to the partial wave with a definite angular momentum, principally the *s*-wave component.

An important result obtained by this approach is the theorems on the possibility of analytic continuation into the upper half plane of the *s*-scattering amplitude $f_s(E)$ in the case when the interaction practically vanishes at distances greater than the radius of a certain "sphere of interaction." However, it turns out that at infinity $f_s(E)$ may have an essential singularity. But this singularity may be removed by means of multiplying by the cutoff factor $\exp iaE$ (in accordance with (46.13)) so that the function $f_s(E)e^{iaE}$ will be regular in the upper half plane and the dispersion relation (46.3) will be applicable to it. A dispersion relation of this type was applied by Goebel, Karplus, and Ruderman (50) to the study of the elastic scattering of π-mesons (pions) by nucleons. By utilizing available experimental data on *s*-scattering, these authors obtained, in particular, the result that the radius of the meson-nucleon interaction must be greater than 0.1 of a meson Compton wavelength. However, it should be emphasized that the investigations following this approach are based on ordinary quantum mechanics which does not take into account specific features of field theory, in particular, the possibility of processes of particle creation and annihilation.

Dispersion relations for the scattering of bosons in quantum field theory were the subject of investigations utilizing a different approach exemplified by the work of Gell-Mann, Goldberger, and Thirring (47), Goldberger (51), (52), Karplus and Ruderman (68), Goldberger, Miyazawa, and Oehme (53), Oehme (87), Salam (101), Salam and Gilbert (102), Polkinghorne (96), and others. In these papers the forward scattering amplitude is taken as the function $g(E)$ (E is the meson energy) with experimental data providing convincing grounds for assuming that the singularity of $g(E)$ at infinity will be of order not higher than the first. It is particularly convenient to investigate the forward scattering amplitude f since in accordance with the so-called "optical theorem" its imaginary part is proportional to the total effective cross section for the process.

In order to show this, we consider the matrix element of $SS^\dagger = 1$ between the state amplitudes $\langle \mathbf{p}'s', \mathbf{q}'\rho' |$ and $|\mathbf{p}s, \mathbf{q}\rho\rangle$ which contain a nucleon of momentum $\mathbf{p}'(\mathbf{p})$ and discrete index $s'(s)$, and a meson of momentum $\mathbf{q}'(\mathbf{q})$ and discrete index $\rho'(\rho)$:

$$\langle \mathbf{p}'s', \mathbf{q}'\rho' | SS^\dagger | \mathbf{p}s, \mathbf{q}\rho\rangle = \langle \mathbf{p}'s', \mathbf{q}'\rho' || \mathbf{p}, s, \mathbf{q}\rho\rangle = \delta(\mathbf{p}-\mathbf{p}')\delta_{ss'}\delta(\mathbf{q}-\mathbf{q}')\delta_{\rho\rho'}. \tag{46.17}$$

By writing the left-hand side of this expression in the form of a sum over the complete system of state amplitudes $| n\rangle$ we obtain:

$$\langle \mathbf{p}'s', \mathbf{q}'\rho' | SS^\dagger | \mathbf{p}s, \mathbf{q}\rho\rangle = \sum_n \langle \mathbf{p}'s', \mathbf{q}'\rho' | S | n\rangle \langle n | S^\dagger | \mathbf{p}s, \mathbf{q}\rho\rangle. \tag{46.18}$$

The summation over n includes both summation over the discrete characteristics of the states $| n\rangle$ and also integration over their continuous characteristics.

By restricting the summation in the right-hand side of (46.18) to states containing one nucleon $(\mathbf{p}'', s'')$ and one meson $(\mathbf{q}'', \rho'')$, and by going over to the scattering amplitude with the aid of (14) we obtain:

$$\begin{aligned}\langle \mathbf{p}'s', \mathbf{q}'\rho' | SS^\dagger | \mathbf{p}s, \mathbf{q}\rho\rangle &= \delta(\mathbf{p}-\mathbf{p}')\delta_{ss'}\delta(\mathbf{q}-\mathbf{q}')\delta_{\rho\rho'}\\ &+ \frac{i\delta(p'+q'-p-q)}{2\pi\sqrt{q^0 q'^0}}\left(f_{s'\rho', s\rho}(\mathbf{p}', \mathbf{q}', \mathbf{p}, \mathbf{q}) - f^*_{s'\rho', s\rho}(\mathbf{p}', \mathbf{q}', \mathbf{p}, \mathbf{q})\right)\\ &+ \frac{\delta(p'+q'-p-q)}{(2\pi)^2\sqrt{q^0 q'^0}} \sum_{s'', \rho''} \int \frac{d\mathbf{p}''\, d\mathbf{q}''}{q''^0} f_{s'\rho', s''\rho''}(\mathbf{p}', \mathbf{q}', \mathbf{p}'', \mathbf{q}'') f^*_{s''\rho'', s\rho}(\mathbf{p}'', \mathbf{q}'', \mathbf{p}, \mathbf{q})\\ &\times \delta(p''+q''-p-q).\end{aligned}$$

By taking (46.18) into account, we obtain from the foregoing in the case of forward scattering when $\mathbf{p}' = \mathbf{p}$, $\mathbf{q}' = \mathbf{q}$, $s' = s$, $\rho' = \rho$:

$$\begin{aligned}&i\left(f_{s\rho, s\rho}(\mathbf{p}, \mathbf{q}, \mathbf{p}, \mathbf{q}) - f^*_{s\rho, s\rho}(\mathbf{p}, \mathbf{q}, \mathbf{p}, \mathbf{q})\right)\\ &= -\sum_{s'', \rho''} \int \frac{d\mathbf{p}''\, d\mathbf{q}''}{2\pi q''^0} \delta(p''+q''-p-q) \, | f_{s\rho, s''\rho''}(\mathbf{p}, \mathbf{q}, \mathbf{p}'', \mathbf{q}'') |^2\\ &= -\int \frac{d\mathbf{q}''}{2\pi q''^0} \delta(p''^0+q''^0-p^0-q^0) \sum_{s'', \rho''} | f_{s\rho, s''\rho''}(\mathbf{p}, \mathbf{q}, \mathbf{p}'', \mathbf{q}'') |^2 \big|_{\mathbf{p}''=\mathbf{p}+\mathbf{q}-\mathbf{q}''}.\end{aligned} \tag{46.19}$$

By comparing this expression with the formulas of § 22, we obtain:

$$\operatorname{Im} f = \frac{|\mathbf{q}|}{4\pi}\sigma, \tag{46.20}$$

$$\frac{d\sigma}{d\Omega} = |f|^2. \tag{46.21}$$

Here σ and $d\sigma/d\boldsymbol{\Omega}$ are respectively the total and the differential effective cross sections for the elastic scattering of a meson by a nucleon, while f is the forward scattering amplitude:

$$f = f_{sp,\, sp}(\mathbf{p},\, \mathbf{q},\, \mathbf{p},\, \mathbf{q}).$$

It may be shown that if we take into account in the summation in the right-hand side of (46.19) terms which correspond to states containing a larger number of particles, we shall be led to the situation that in (46.20) σ will denote the total effective cross section for all the possible processes.

We now give the result of the previously cited paper (68), which refers to the case of neutral mesons. If, in accordance with their argument, we assume that the scattering amplitude $f(E)$ is analytic in the upper half plane and that its pole at infinity is of an order not higher than the first, then we shall be able to use formula (46.10) with $n = 1$. If we note that because the scalar meson field is real the passage from positive to negative energies is equivalent to complex conjugation, i.e.,

$$f^*(E) = f(-E)$$

and that consequently

$$\operatorname{Im} f(-E) = -\operatorname{Im} f(E), \quad \operatorname{Re} f(-E) = \operatorname{Re} f(E),$$

we obtain from (46.9), after eliminating the term containing the derivative of $\operatorname{Re} f$ and the integral over the negative region:

$$\operatorname{Re}\,[f(E) - f(E_0)] = \frac{2}{\pi}\int_0^\infty \operatorname{Im} f(E')\, E' dE' \left\{\frac{1}{E'^2 - E^2} - \frac{1}{E'^2 - E_0^2}\right\}. \tag{46.22}$$

If we now pass from $\operatorname{Im} f(E)$ to the total cross section by means of formula (46.20) and from the energy variable E to the momentum variable $p = (E^2 - \mu^2)^{1/2}$ we obtain (after excluding the non-observable region $0 \leqq E' \leqq \mu$) the final form of the dispersion relation for the scattering of neutral mesons by nucleons:

$$\operatorname{Re}\,[f(k) - f(k_0)] = \frac{1}{2\pi^2}\int_0^\infty \sigma(k')\, dk' \left\{\frac{k^2}{k'^2 - k^2} - \frac{k_0^2}{k'^2 - k_0^2}\right\}. \tag{46.23}$$

Similar dispersion relations for the scattering of charged

mesons by nucleons were investigated by Goldberger (51) and by Goldberger, Miyazawa, and Oehme (53). Oehme (87) obtained the corresponding equations for the amplitude of such scattering of a meson by a nucleon as a result of which the nucleon spin changes its direction (spin-flip scattering). More accurately, the dispersion relation was obtained for the derivative of the spin-flip amplitude taken at zero angle.[91] In a later paper Oehme (87a) obtained the dispersion relation for higher derivatives at zero angle for scattering without spin-flip. The same problem was solved simultaneously by Salam and Gilbert (101), (102). Finally, a number of papers has appeared recently devoted to obtaining dispersion relations for processes of photoproduction of π-mesons on nucleons.[92]

All these dispersion relations have in their right-hand sides integrals of type (46.22) over the energy range from 0 to ∞. However, it is clear that Im $f(E)$ (or $\sigma(E)$) may be experimentally determined only for meson energies greater than the rest energy: $E > \mu$, and thus the above integrals always contain a "non-observable part" which corresponds to the interval $0 < E < \mu$.

However, it fortunately turns out that in a number of important cases (for example, for the amplitude of meson-nucleon forward scattering) the integral over this energy range may be evaluated explicitly since $f(E)$ turns out to be proportional to $\delta(E - E_p)$ where E_p is the energy of a certain bound state.

We shall not dwell on this important point now since it will be investigated in detail later (§ 50–52). We shall merely point out two basic possibilities for applying the dispersion relations.

For the reduction of experimental data on meson-nucleon scattering, one often uses phase analysis which is based only on the covariance and unitarity of the scattering matrix. As is well known, phase analysis in practice does not lead to a unique

[91] The spin-flip amplitude itself is equal to zero for forward scattering.

[92] Reports by B. L. Ioffe, A. A. Logunov, B. M. Stepanov, and A. N. Tavkhelidze at the All-Union Conference on the Physics of High Energies (Moscow, May 1956), and also reports by Goldberger, Low, Chew, and Nambu at the International Congress on Theoretical Physics (Seattle, September 1956).

determination of the phase angles, but yields a number of possible sets of these angles. The dispersion relations based on properties of a different type, in particular on the properties of causality, yield a number of additional equations which enable one to discriminate between these sets and to choose the correct system of phase angles (see, for example, the paper by Anderson, Davidon, and Kruse (5)).

Moreover, and this is particularly important from the fundamental point of view, the dispersion relations provide a possibility for an experimental test of the existence of an elementary length. The connection between the condition of microscopic causality and the property of analytic continuation of the scattering amplitude has been already examined in outline earlier. It was established (formula (46.13)) that in the case of deviations from the condition of causality at small distances of order a, it is necessary to multiply $f(E)$ by $\exp i\alpha E$ $(\alpha \geqq a)$ in order to obtain a function for which dispersion relations hold.

The actual situation will, of course, be more complicated, but the fact will remain that the dispersion relations will require a definite modification if an elementary length should be found to exist, and, as a result of this, an experimental observation of a deviation from the usual dispersion relations will provide evidence of the necessity to introduce a nonlocal modification of the theory.

46.4. *The Problem of the Foundations of the Dispersion Relations*

During the last two years dispersion relations have been obtained for a number of the more interesting problems. However, it should be noted that correct mathematical derivations of these relations were lacking until very recently. This was connected primarily with the difficulties of proving that the scattering amplitude is analytic.

The first derivation of dispersion relations within the formalism of quantum field theory was proposed by Gell-Mann, Goldberger, and Thirring (47) who made use of Cauchy's theorem having established beforehand the necessary analytic properties of the forward scattering amplitude. However, this proof (in any case for particles with rest mass different from zero) is not free from objections whose seriousness was later admitted by the authors themselves (see Goldberger (52)).

Karplus and Ruderman (68) have established the dispersion relation (46.23) for the scattering of neutral mesons by nucleons basing it on the analytic nature of the scattering amplitude introduced as a preliminary assumption.

Goldberger (52) tried to avoid entirely the question of the analytic continuation of the scattering amplitude into the complex plane by regarding the dispersion relations simply as identities following purely algebraically from the representation of the Hermitean and the anti-Hermitean parts of the scattering amplitude in terms of a sum over the complete system of intermediate states. However, the arguments used by him are not correct, since the corresponding expressions diverge for $E < \mu$.

This was apparently noticed by Oehme (87) who returned to the use of theorems from the theory of functions of a complex variable. However, he succeeded in carrying out the analytic continuation of the scattering amplitude into the upper half plane only on the assumption of its quadratic integrability. Such an assumption turns out to be too restrictive for real physical processes, since it excludes the possibility of using generalized functions (for example δ-functions).

Finally, quite recently, two proofs of dispersion relations have been given (one of them [93] for forward scattering, and the other [94] for an arbitrary angle of scattering) which are free from objections.

Thus, it may now be considered as established that the dispersion relations do actually follow from the fundamental assumptions of modern quantum field theory, and that the condition of microscopic causality is essential for their derivation.

This chapter contains a derivation of dispersion relations for

[93] Symanzik, report at the International Congress on Theoretical Physics (Seattle, September 1956).

[94] N. N. Bogoliubov, report at the International Congress on Theoretical Physics (Seattle, September 1956); see also the paper by Bogoliubov, Medvedev, and Polivanov (17).

the amplitude of scattering of π-mesons (pions) by nucleons. Our presentation essentially follows that of Bogoliubov, Medvedev, and Polivanov (17), and is based on the condition of causality for the scattering matrix in the form (17.30), (17.31). The following § 47 is devoted to the analysis and the selection of the fundamental assumptions of modern quantum field theory required for obtaining the dispersion relations. In § 48 and 49 the so-called spectral (parametric) representations for single-particle Green's functions are established. The inclusion of material on parametric representations in this chapter is explained by the fact that from the methodological point of view the derivation of the parametric representations is very similar to the derivation of the dispersion relations. This derivation is also carried out by means of analytic continuation into the complex plane, but at the same time it is much simpler; § 48 and 49 play the role of a methodological introduction to the material which follows.

§ 50 and 51 contain the derivation of the dispersion relations. Finally, in § 52 explicit formulas are given for specific scattering processes.

§ 47. Fundamental Properties of the S-Matrix in Local Field Theory

47.1. *Introductory Remarks*

In the majority of the papers referred to in the preceding section, the dispersion relations are obtained by using the formalism of the usual symmetric pseudoscalar meson theory, although it is noted that the essential role is played not by specific models of the interaction but by some very general physical assumptions the primary one among which is the condition of causality.

In view of the great significance from a fundamental point of view of the question of the applicability of the dispersion relations and of the possibility of their generalization, it is useful to give an explicit formulation of those basic physical assumptions which are really necessary for their derivation.

In the present monograph, we have attempted to carry out a program of this kind in constructing a theory of the scattering matrix, having adopted for our basic assumptions some explicitly formulated conditions imposed on the S-matrix (the conditions of unitarity, covariance, and causality). Our construction of such a theory was limited by the framework of perturbation theory.

Moreover, our method of procedure had another serious defect related to the use of the auxiliary function $g(x)$. With the aid of this function we formulated the generally accepted "pseudo-physical" concept of the adiabatic switching-on and switching-off of the interaction, and we were also able to investigate the local characteristics of the theory. Technically this possibility was associated with the operation of functional differentiation of the S-matrix with respect to $g(x)$.

It therefore appears desirable to undertake at this point a reexamination of the system of our basic assumptions in order to eliminate the introduction of the function $g(x)$ which is needed essentially only to obtain expansions in powers of the small interaction parameter. Indeed, it was pointed out in § 17.6 that in the description of the local structure of the theory connected with the variational derivatives of the S-matrix classical external fields may play the role of the functional argument in place of $g(x)$. This enables us to introduce formally the corresponding functional derivatives of the S-matrix with respect to quantized fields by defining them as limits in the case $\eta(x) = 0$ of the corresponding functional derivatives with respect to the additive classical terms $\eta(x)$ to the quantized $u(x)$, i.e.,

$$\frac{\delta^k S}{\delta u_{a_1}(x_1) \ldots \delta u_{a_k}(x_k)} = \left\{ \frac{\delta^k}{\delta \eta_{a_1}(x_1) \ldots \delta \eta_{a_k}(x_k)} S(\eta) \right\}_{\eta=0}, \quad (47.1)$$

where $S(\eta)$ is obtained from S by the replacement operation

$$u_i(x) \rightarrow u_i(x) + \eta_i(x). \quad (47.2)$$

In order that the variational derivatives with respect to the Fermi-fields ψ obtained in this way should have the required properties of anticommutativity, it is necessary to distinguish between right derivatives and left derivatives and to regard the auxiliary classical spinors η as strictly anticommuting among themselves and with all the ψ.

The variational "left derivative" $\delta C/'\delta\psi(x)$ will then in virtue of its definition

$$\delta C(\psi+\eta) = \int \delta\eta_i(x)' A_i(x; \psi+\eta)\, dx = \int A_i'(x; \psi+\eta)\, \delta\eta_i(x)\, dx,$$

$$\frac{\delta C}{'\delta\psi_i(x)} = \lim_{\eta\to 0} {}' A_i(x;\ \psi+\eta),$$

differ in sign from the "right derivative" $\delta C/\delta'\psi(x)$

$$\frac{\delta C}{\delta'\psi_i(x)} = \lim_{\eta\to 0} A_i'(x;\ \psi+\eta),$$

in those cases when C is a function of an even number of Fermi-operators ψ and will coincide with it if C depends on an odd number of ψ.

Let us consider, for example,

$$C = A = \int \mathscr{L}(x)\, dx = g \int :\bar\psi(x)\, O\varphi(x)\, \psi(x) :\, dx.$$

It is clear that

$$\frac{\delta A}{\delta'\bar\psi(x)} = -\frac{\delta A}{'\delta\bar\psi(x)} = -\, gO :\varphi(x)\, \psi(x):$$

On the other hand,

$$\frac{\delta}{\delta'\psi(y)}\left(\frac{\delta A}{\delta'\bar\psi(x)}\right) = \frac{\delta}{'\delta\bar\psi(y)}\left(\frac{\delta A}{\delta'\psi(x)}\right) = -\, gO\varphi(x)\, \delta(x-y).$$

In future we shall find it convenient always to take the "right" derivatives with respect to the nucleon spinor ψ and "left" derivatives with respect to the conjugate spinor $\bar\psi$. We shall therefore use the notation

$$\frac{\delta}{\delta'\psi} \equiv \frac{\delta}{\delta\psi} \text{ and } \frac{\delta}{'\delta\bar\psi} \equiv \frac{\delta}{\delta\bar\psi}. \tag{47.3}$$

We shall also drop the method of introducing the S-matrix by means of the generally accepted idea of the adiabatic switching-on and switching-off of the interaction, and shall return to its original definition given by Heisenberg as a matrix whose elements are the probability amplitudes for the transition from one state at $t = -\infty$ to another state at $t = \infty$. Each of these states may describe a system of elementary particles "infinitely" separated from each other or of their combinations in bound states. Such a formulation of the method of introducing the S-matrix is a more realistic one than the one which we have used earlier since it does not assume that interaction with virtual fields is absent in reai states at $t = \pm \infty$ (see § 17.1).

Problems now arise of describing the initial and final states of spatially separated real particles and their bound states. However, we shall not go into these complicated questions and shall now proceed to the formulation of the fundamental necessary physical assumptions of modern field theory which are of interest to us.

The problem of the description of spatially separated particles and of bound combinations of such particles was recently investigated in the usual theory by Klein (71) who solved the problem of separating out the self-interaction term by the following ingenious method.

If for a system described by the total Hamiltonian H we denote by R_0 the vacuum state, by R_1 the space of all the single particle eigenstates (containing a single real elementary particle) and (if the Hamiltonian allows bound states) by R_2, R_3, ... the spaces of all the states which contain one bound combination of 2, 3, ... real particles (we note that such states may also be regarded as "single particle" states, if we keep in mind two of their properties: (a) a certain degree of localizability from the point of view of observing them, and (b) their stability), then the space whose vectors will describe the initial (or the final) states of interest to us containing any number of particles or bound combinations may now be obtained in the form of the direct product of R_0 by the spaces R_1, R_2, R_3, ... with each of the factors appearing in this product an arbitrary number of times in accordance with the existence of an arbitrary number of particles of a given kind:

$$R = R_0 \times R_1 \times R_1 \times \ldots \times R_2 \times R_2 \times \ldots \times R_k \times R_k \times \ldots$$

In order to construct the "free" Hamiltonian whose eigenfunctions are the amplitudes of states containing an arbitrary number of real particles and of bound combinations which do not interact with each other we introduce the projection operators P_0, P_1, ... projecting the Hamiltonian H onto the spaces R_0, R_1, R_2, ..., and we define the "free" Hamiltonian H_0 in the following form:

$$H_0 = P_0 H + P_1 H + P_1 H + \ldots + P_2 H + P_2 H + \ldots + P_k H + \ldots \quad (47.4)$$

The total Hamiltonian H may now be written in the form

$$H = H_0 + V = H_0 + (H - H_0). \tag{47.5}$$

The interaction Hamiltonian V here describes only the interactions between different particles and combinations, but not the self-interaction which is completely contained in H_0. More accurately, V refers only to that part of the interaction which is responsible only for processes of scattering and of mutual transformation of particles and combinations of particles, since the interaction which "holds" the particles inside the combinations is likewise included in H_0. Therefore in going over to the initial or the final state ($t \to \pm \infty$) we may, for example, utilize the adiabatic switching-off of V and this shall lead neither to the disappearance of the self-interaction, nor to the break-up of bound states.

47.2. *General Properties*

We emphasize that all the assumptions to be formulated do not represent anything new and are known in the usual modern theory.[95] On the other hand, we also do not consider that these assumptions completely exhaust the content of the modern theory, nor that they form a system of independent axioms which is to any extent complete. Leaving aside all these interesting questions, we shall regard the system of assumptions given below only as a set of hypotheses sufficient to obtain the dispersion relations.

All these hypotheses may be conveniently divided into two groups: (a) general properties which characterize a very broad class of possible theories, and (b) special local properties which are related, in particular, to the condition of microscopic causality.

General Properties[96]

A. The asymptotic states of the system contain infinitely separated real particles and bound combinations of such particles. The interaction between such particles and their combinations is equal to zero and therefore the fundamental dynamic characteristics of the system (such as energy, momentum, and angular momentum) are additive. Such states are described by amplitudes $|\ldots\rangle$ which are elements of a certain linear space.

[95] In this connection see, for example, the papers by Haag (56), and by Lehmann, Symanzik, and Zimmerman (82).

[96] The following statements will be later referred to as 47.2A, 47.2B, etc.

B. There exists a group G of transformations L which includes the group of Lorentz transformations of space-time (G may also include other elements, for example, transformations in isotopic spin space). When subjected to transformations L belonging to G the state amplitudes $|\ldots\rangle$ transform according to a certain unitary representation U_L of the group.

C. If in the state $|p\rangle$ there exists a definite energy-momentum four-vector p then

$$U_{L_a}|p\rangle = e^{-ipa}|p\rangle, \tag{47.6}$$

where L_a is the translation $x \to x + a$. There exists a vacuum state $|0\rangle$ for which

$$U_{L_a}|0\rangle = |0\rangle. \tag{47.7}$$

D. There exists a set of amplitudes $|n, \mathbf{k}\rangle$ which together with the amplitude $|0\rangle$ forms a complete set so that

$$\langle\alpha|AB|\beta\rangle = \langle\alpha|A|0\rangle\langle 0|B|\beta\rangle + \sum_n \int d\mathbf{k}\,\langle\alpha|A|n, \mathbf{k}\rangle\langle n, \mathbf{k}|B|\beta\rangle, \tag{47.8}$$

and such that the state $|n, \mathbf{k}\rangle$ corresponds to a definite momentum $\mathbf{k}$ and energy $E_n(\mathbf{k}) > 0$. The index n denotes the set of discrete and continuous quantum numbers which together with $\mathbf{k}$ completely characterize the state of the given closed system. Analogous properties may be formulated for the irreducible representations of other subgroups of G, in particular, for the representations corresponding to the angular momentum.

E. The probability amplitude for the transition from the state $|\alpha\rangle$ to the state $|\beta\rangle$ is given by the matrix element $\langle\beta|S|\alpha\rangle$ of the operator S (the scattering matrix) which satisfies the condition of unitarity

$$SS^{\dagger} = 1. \tag{47.9}$$

F. Under the action of the transformation L belonging to the group G the scattering matrix S transforms by means of the unitary representation U_L.

G. If $|\alpha\rangle$ is the amplitude of the vacuum state or of a state containing one real particle or one stable combination, then the condition for the stability of such states has the form

$$S \mid \alpha\rangle = \mid \alpha\rangle. \tag{47.10}$$

Condition (47.10) represents the determination of the unitary phase factor up to which the scattering matrix is usually defined. Thus from the point of view of the usual theory presented in Chapters III and IV (47.10) reduces to the condition of stability of the vacuum state and of the single particle states.

Such a condition could have been obtained there by replacing the usual scattering matrix S by the operator S' obtained from S by subtracting from the interaction Lagrangian the vacuum and the single-particle counter terms. For example, in the case of spinor electrodynamics

$$S' = T\Big[\exp i \int dp\, \{\mathscr{L}(p) - (Z_2 - 1)\,\bar{\psi}(\hat{p} - m)\,\psi - \delta m\bar{\psi}\psi\} - (Z_3 - 1)\sum_{n,m} A_n(g^{mn}p^2 - p^m p^n)\,A_m - R_{\text{vac}}\Big],$$

so that

$$\langle 0 \mid S' \mid 0\rangle = 1,$$

and also

$$\langle 1 \text{ photon} \mid S' \mid 1 \text{ photon}\rangle = 1$$
$$\langle 1 \text{ electron} \mid S' \mid 1 \text{ electron}\rangle = 1,$$

which is equivalent to (47.10).

Assumptions 47.2A–47.2G are so general that, apparently, they will be preserved even in the event of possible future modifications of the theory of elementary particles.

47.3. *Local Properties*

Before we begin the formulation of the local properties of the theory which we require, we recall the corresponding points of the usual formulation. We begin with the fact that the representation of the S-matrix in terms of the T-exponential

$$S = T\left(\exp i \int \mathscr{L}(z)\,dz\right)$$

allows us (by means of a procedure of the type (47.1), (47.2)) to obtain at once its variational derivatives. For example,

$$\frac{\delta S}{\delta u_a(x)} = iT\left(\frac{\partial \mathscr{L}(x)}{\partial u_a(x)} \exp i \int \mathscr{L}(z)\,dz\right).$$

Expressions of the same type will be obtained also for the higher variational derivatives.

We may now write the condition of causality in a form analogous to (17.31):

$$\frac{\delta}{\delta u_a(x)}\left[\frac{\delta S}{\delta u_\beta(y)} S^\dagger\right] = 0 \quad \text{for} \quad x \lesssim y. \tag{47.11}$$

We note further that the probability amplitude for processes of scattering of free particles (i.e., for such processes in which bound combinations are not present initially nor appear in the course of the process) may be expressed in terms of the vacuum expectation values of the variational derivatives of the S-matrix with respect to the free fields. Indeed, such a matrix element is

$$\frac{(2\pi)^{\frac{3(r+s)}{2}}}{S_0} \langle 0 \mid a^{(-)}_{\beta_1}(\mathbf{p}'_1) \ldots a^{(-)}_{\beta_s}(\mathbf{p}'_s)\, S a^{(+)}_{\alpha_1}(\mathbf{p}_1) \ldots a^{(+)}_{\alpha_r}(\mathbf{p}_r) \mid 0\rangle \tag{47.12}$$

for a process at the beginning of which we have particles with momenta $\mathbf{p}_1, \ldots, \mathbf{p}_r$ and with other quantum numbers $\alpha_1, \ldots, \alpha_r$, and at the end of which we have particles with momenta $\mathbf{p}'_1, \ldots, \mathbf{p}'_s$ and other quantum numbers $\beta_1, \ldots, \beta_s$ (in the foregoing it is assumed, as usual, that there are no identical pairs among the pairs $\mathbf{p}_i \alpha_i$, $\mathbf{p}'_j \beta_j$). We now make use of the usual commutation relations of type (21.11), (21.12)

$$\left.\begin{aligned} \{a^{(-)}_\beta(\mathbf{p}'),\ u_\gamma(x)\}_\pm &= \frac{1}{(2\pi)^{3/2}}\, e^{ip'x} v^{\beta,+}_\gamma(\mathbf{p}'), \\ \{u_\gamma(x),\ a^{(+)}_\alpha(\mathbf{p})\}_\pm &= \frac{1}{(2\pi)^{3/2}}\, e^{-ipx} v^{\alpha,-}_\gamma(\mathbf{p}) \end{aligned}\right\} \tag{47.13}$$

and we take into account the fact that $\mathscr{L}(x)$ must be an even function of the Fermi fields. This gives:

$$\left.\begin{aligned} [a^{(-)}_\beta(\mathbf{p}'),\ S]_- &= \frac{1}{(2\pi)^{3/2}} \sum_\sigma v^{\beta,+}_\sigma(\mathbf{p}') \int dx e^{ip'x} \frac{\delta S}{\delta u_\sigma(x)}, \\ [S,\ a^{(+)}_\alpha(\mathbf{p})]_- &= \frac{1}{(2\pi)^{3/2}} \sum_\sigma v^{\alpha,-}_\sigma(\mathbf{p}) \int dx e^{-ipx} \frac{\delta S}{\delta u_\sigma(x)}. \end{aligned}\right\} \tag{47.14}$$

We now transfer all the annihilation operators in (47.12) to the right until they yield zero by acting on $\mid 0\rangle$, and we move all the creation operators to the left. Then with the aid of (47.14) we shall be able to express the matrix element (47.12) in the form of a sum of terms proportional to the integrals

$$\int \left\langle 0 \left| \frac{\delta^{r+s} S}{\delta u_{\beta_1}(x_1') \ldots \delta u_{\alpha_r}(x_r)} \right| 0 \right\rangle \exp i \left(\sum_{\beta} p'x' - \sum_{\alpha} px \right) dx_1' \ldots dx_r. \tag{47.15}$$

After eliminating the vacuum loops we shall obtain in the integrands matrix elements of the form

$$\frac{1}{S_0} \left\langle 0 \left| \frac{\delta^n S}{\delta u_1(x_1) \ldots \delta u_n(x_n)} \right| 0 \right\rangle = \left\langle 0 \left| \frac{\delta^n S}{\delta u_1(x_1) \ldots \delta u_n(x_n)} S^\dagger \right| 0 \right\rangle. \tag{47.16}$$

We can easily verify the preceding relation if we take into account the fact that the amplitude $S^\dagger \mid 0\rangle$ may differ from $\mid 0\rangle$ only by a phase factor which is exactly equal to $(S_0)^{-1}$.

We have thus arrived at the important concept of the radiation operator of the nth order

$$H_n(x_1, \ldots, x_n) = \frac{\delta^n S}{\delta u_1(x_1) \ldots \delta u_n(x_n)} S^\dagger. \tag{47.17}$$

It is seen that the order of the operator in the foregoing is taken to mean the total order of the variational derivatives. The matrix elements may be reduced to the vacuum expectation values of such radiation operators (47.12).

Doubts may arise as to the admissibility of the transition to the variational derivatives with respect to the quantized fields of type (47.1), since the property of the quantized functions of satisfying the field equations is not in any way apparent from the definition (47.1). However, it may be easily shown that there are no foundations whatever for doubts of this nature. Indeed in the S-matrix the foregoing property is in fact related to the procedure of calculating the matrix elements and becomes apparent only for those field operators which from the point of view of Feynman diagrams correspond to external lines. In such a case the above property turns out to be a trivial consequence of the commutation relations (47.13) between the operator $u(x)$ from the matrix S and the creation (or annihilation) operator for a free particle $a^{\pm}(k)$ in the expression for the state amplitude. Therefore, in the investigation of the S-matrix and of its variational derivatives we may completely ignore the above property (and consider that we are here dealing with a formal extension of the functional S to a class of functions which do not have to satisfy any equations). Of course, at the final stage in going over to the matrix elements we have to consider the projection of S on the set of the classes of operators which satisfy the free-field equations (here we have in mind only operators corresponding to the *external* lines of Feynman diagrams!).

For subsequent presentation we shall need neither the representation of the S-matrix in terms of the T-exponential, nor even the concept of the interaction Lagrangian. It will be sufficient to retain only the possibility of carrying out the variational differentiation of the S-matrix, the condition of causality in the form (47.11) and the possibility of expressing the amplitude for the transition (47.12) in terms of integrals of the type (47.15). Therefore we arrive at the possibility of formulating the following local properties.

Local Properties [97]

A. Real elementary particles (but not their combinations!) are characterized by boson and fermion fields $u(x)$ which have the same transformation and commutation properties as in the theory of free fields. The operator S has variational derivatives of arbitrary order with respect to these fields. The variational derivatives in this case have all their usual properties. Thus, their transformation properties are determined by the transformation properties of the fields. The derivatives with respect to the boson fields commute, and those with respect to the fermion fields anticommute among themselves.

The radiation operators (47.17) and products of such operators with independent arguments are integrable (in the sense of the definition given in § 16), i.e., all the matrix elements

$$\langle\beta \mid H(x_1, \ldots, x_n) \ldots H(z_1, \ldots, z_k) \mid \alpha\rangle$$

are generalized functions integrable over one of the classes $C(q, r, n)$.

B. The condition of causality holds in the form (47.11).

[97] These properties are referred to later as 47.3A, 47.3B, etc.

C. Let

$$|\alpha_1, \mathbf{p}_1, \ldots, \alpha_r, \mathbf{p}_r\rangle = |\omega\rangle$$

denote the state amplitude for a system of infinitely separated elementary particles with momenta $\mathbf{p}_1, \ldots, \mathbf{p}_r$ and with other quantum numbers $\alpha_1, \ldots, \alpha_r$. Then the matrix element

$$S_{\omega'\omega} = \langle\omega' | S | \omega\rangle$$

may be expressed in terms of vacuum expectation values of radiation operators (47.11) by means of the following formal procedure. We write

$$S_{\omega'\omega} = \langle 0 | a^{(-)}_{\alpha_1'}(p_1') \ldots a^{(-)}_{\alpha_s'}(p_s')\, S a^{(+)}_{\alpha_1}(p_1) \ldots a^{(+)}_{\alpha_r}(p_r) | 0\rangle$$

and transfer the annihilation operators $a^{(-)}$ to the right, and $a^{(+)}$ to the left until we obtain terms in which $a^{(-)}$ acts on $|0\rangle$ and $a^{(+)}$ acts on $\langle 0|$ and which therefore vanish. In doing this we shall make use of the usual commutation relations for $a^{(+)}$, $a^{(-)}$ from the theory of noninteracting fields, and of the relations of type (47.14) for the commutation of $a^{(+)}$, $a^{(-)}$, and S.

Having thus expressed $S_{\omega'\omega}$ in terms of the vacuum expectation values of the variational derivatives of the S-matrix, and having then made use of the condition 47.2G we can reduce them to the vacuum expectation values of the radiation operators.

§ 48. Spectral Representation of the Pion Green's Function

In this and the following sections we shall obtain the so-called spectral representations for the pion and the nucleon Green's functions. Representations of this type were first obtained by Källen (65) in quantum electrodynamics and by Lehmann (81) in meson theory. However, the method by which the investigation of these functions was carried out in the references cited above cannot be considered to be satisfactory, since it manipulates formally with infinitely large renormalization constants etc. (for a criticism of investigations using this approach refer to § 31.4).

Below we shall obtain the Källen-Lehmann spectral representations for the Green's functions in the pseudoscalar meson theory by starting from the general properties of a local field theory which were formulated in § 47 and by using the method of analytic continuation into the complex plane. As we have mentioned already the material contained in § 48 and 49 does not have any direct connection to the derivation of the dispersion relations which follows later, and may be regarded as a methodological introduction to the latter.

48.1. *Radiation Operators of the First and Second Order and Their Vacuum Expectation Values*

Having in mind later applications to processes of meson-nucleon scattering we shall restrict ourselves to the investigation of the eight-component spinor nucleon field and the three-component meson field which interact with each other in a charge-symmetric manner and we shall not take into account the existence of the electromagnetic field and of weak interactions with light particles.

As we have done earlier (§ 33.1), we shall take for the meson field a field with three real pseudoscalar components $\varphi_i(x)$ which form a vector in isotopic spin space (isovector). The particles π^+, π^-, and π^0 (of mass μ) are made to correspond to the fields

$$\varphi_+ = \frac{\varphi_1 + i\varphi_2}{\sqrt{2}}, \qquad \varphi_- = \frac{\varphi_1 - i\varphi_2}{\sqrt{2}}, \qquad \varphi_0 = \varphi_3. \tag{48.1}$$

The nucleon field (of mass M) is characterized by the spinor

$$\psi(x) = \begin{vmatrix} \Psi_P(x) \\ \Psi_N(x) \end{vmatrix}. \tag{48.2}$$

In addition to isotopic invariance, i.e., invariance under transformations of rotation in three-dimensional isotopic spin space, we shall make use of the concept of invariance under gauge transformations of the first kind

$$\psi(x) \to e^{i\alpha}\psi(x), \quad \bar{\psi}(x) \to e^{-i\alpha}\bar{\psi}(x), \tag{48.3}$$

i.e., we shall consider that both of these transformations are included in the group G of assumption 47.2B.

We shall now investigate the vacuum expectation values of the radiation operators of the first and second kinds within the framework of the theory formulated above.

It is not difficult to show that due to considerations of covariance with respect to rotations in ordinary and in isotopic spin space the vacuum expectation values of the radiation operators of the first order are equal to zero, and so are the vacuum expectation values of those operators of the second order in which one differentiation is carried out with respect to the boson field and the other with respect to the fermion field. From consideration of invariance under the gauge transformation (48.3) it follows that the vacuum expectation values of $\delta^2 S/\delta\psi\,\delta\psi$ and $\delta^2 S/\delta\bar{\psi}\,\delta\bar{\psi}$ also vanish. Thus only the vacuum expectation values of the radiation operators $\delta^2 S/\delta\varphi(x)\,\delta\varphi(y)$ and $\delta^2 S/\delta\bar{\psi}\,\delta\psi(y)$ turn out to be different from zero. On the basis of considerations of invariance under translation these expectation values can depend only on the difference $x - y$; we shall therefore write them in the form

$$i\left\langle 0 \left| \frac{\delta^2 S}{\delta\varphi_\sigma(x)\,\delta\varphi_\rho(y)} S^\dagger \right| 0 \right\rangle = Q_{\sigma\rho}(x - y), \tag{48.4}$$

$$i\left\langle 0 \left| \frac{\delta^2 S}{\delta\bar{\psi}_\alpha(x)\,\delta\psi_\beta(y)} S^\dagger \right| 0 \right\rangle = R_{\alpha\beta}(x - y). \tag{48.5}$$

We note that in virtue of property 47.2G $S^\dagger \mid 0\rangle = \mid 0\rangle$ as a result of which the factor $S^\dagger$ may be omitted in formulas (48.4) and (48.5).

In order to interpret expressions (48.4) and (48.5) within the framework of the usual theory we note that they may be very simply related to the complete Green's functions by means of the following argument based on the "generalized Wick's theorem" formulated in § 34.2.

By applying this theorem to the complete meson Green's function

$$\Delta_{\sigma\rho}(x - y) = i\,\frac{\langle T(\varphi_\sigma(x)\varphi_\rho(y)S)\rangle_0}{S_0},$$

we obtain:

$$\Delta_{\sigma\rho}(x - y) = i\,\overbrace{\varphi_\sigma(x)\varphi_\rho}(y) + \frac{i}{S_0}\sum_\alpha \int \left\langle \overbrace{\varphi_\sigma(x)\varphi_\rho(y)\varphi_\alpha}(z)\,\frac{\delta S}{\delta\varphi_\alpha(z)}\right\rangle_0 dz.$$

Then by applying this theorem once again to the second term we obtain:

$$\Delta_{\sigma\rho}(x- y) = \Delta^0_{\sigma\rho}(x-y) - \sum_{\alpha,\beta}\int \Delta^0_{\sigma\alpha}(x-z)\,Q_{\alpha\beta}(z-\tau)\,\Delta^0_{\beta\rho}(\tau-y)\,dz\,d\tau, \tag{48.6}$$

where

$$\Delta^0_{\sigma\rho}(x-y) = i\overline{\varphi_\sigma(x)\varphi_\rho}(y).$$

By changing (48.6) with the aid of formulas of the type

$$Q_{\alpha\beta}(z-\tau) = \frac{1}{(2\pi)^4}\int e^{-ip(z-\tau)}\, q_{\alpha\beta}(p)\, dp \tag{48.7}$$

to the momentum representation we obtain:

$$\Delta_{\sigma\rho}(p) = \frac{1}{\mu^2-p^2} - \frac{1}{\mu^2-p^2}\, q_{\sigma\rho}(p)\, \frac{1}{\mu^2-p^2}. \tag{48.8}$$

In a similar way we may obtain for the nucleon Green's function G

$$G(p) = (M-\hat{p})^{-1} - (M-\hat{p})^{-1}\gamma(p)(M-\hat{p})^{-1}. \tag{48.9}$$

We emphasize that relations (48.8) and (48.9) have been given for purposes of illustration only.

48.2. *Vacuum Expectation Value of* $\delta^2 S/\delta\varphi_\sigma(x)\delta\varphi_\rho(y)$

We shall now examine $Q(x-y)$ in greater detail. In order to do this we shall introduce the radiation Bose-operator of the first order

$$j_\sigma(x) = i\,\frac{\delta S}{\delta\varphi_\sigma(x)}\, S^\dagger, \tag{48.10}$$

which we shall call the current operator (in order to establish a correspondence with the usual pseudoscalar meson theory). The operator j is Hermitean:

$$j^\dagger_\rho(x) = j_\rho(x), \tag{48.11}$$

which is a consequence of the fact that φ is real and S is unitary; this may be shown by means of an elementary calculation (similar to the one used in § 18.2 to prove that the generalized Hamiltonian is Hermitean).

We may now express the radiation operator appearing in (48.4) in terms of j and of its variational derivative. By varying (48.10) and by taking into account the fact that the S-matrix is unitary and the current (48.11) is Hermitean we obtain

$$\begin{aligned}\frac{\delta j_\sigma(x)}{\delta\varphi_\rho(y)} &= i\,\frac{\delta^2 S}{\delta\varphi_\sigma(x)\,\delta\varphi_\rho(y)}\, S^\dagger + i\,\frac{\delta S}{\delta\varphi_\sigma(x)}\,\frac{\delta S^\dagger}{\delta\varphi_\rho(y)}\\ &= i\,\frac{\delta^2 S}{\delta\varphi_\sigma(x)\delta\varphi_\rho(y)}\, S^\dagger + i j_\sigma(x)\, j_\rho(y).\end{aligned} \tag{48.12}$$

Now taking into account the fact that in accordance with condition 47.3B

$$\frac{\delta j_\sigma(x)}{\delta \varphi_\rho(y)} = 0 \text{ for } y \lesssim x,$$

we obtain

$$i \frac{\delta^2 S}{\delta \varphi_\sigma(x)\, \delta \varphi_\rho(y)} S^\dagger = -\, i j_\sigma(x)\, j_\rho(y) \text{ for } y \lesssim x. \tag{48.13}$$

Since the left-hand side of this relation is symmetric with respect to an interchange of (x, σ) and (y, ρ) we also have:

$$i \frac{\delta^2 S}{\delta \varphi_\sigma(x) \delta \varphi_\rho(y)} S^\dagger = -\, i j_\rho(y)\, j_\sigma(x) \text{ for } x \lesssim y. \tag{48.14}$$

We thus obtain

$$i \frac{\delta^2 S}{\delta \varphi_\sigma(x)\, \delta \varphi_\rho(y)} S^\dagger = -\, i T(j_\sigma(x)\, j_\rho(y)). \tag{48.15}$$

It also follows from (48.13) and (48.14) that

$$[j_\sigma(x),\; j_\rho(y)]_- = 0 \text{ for } x \sim y.$$

For $Q(x - y)$ we obtain from (48.15):

$$Q_{\sigma\rho}(x-y) = -i\langle T(j_\sigma(x) j_\rho(y))\rangle_0 = \begin{cases} -\, i\langle j_\sigma(x)\, j_\rho(y)\rangle_0 \text{ for } x \gtrsim y, \\ -\, i\langle j_\rho(y)\, j_\sigma(x)\rangle_0 \text{ for } y \gtrsim x. \end{cases} \tag{48.16}$$

48.3. *Vacuum Expectation Value of the Product of Two Currents*

We have expressed Q in terms of the vacuum expectation value of the product of two currents $\langle j_\sigma(x) j_\rho(y)\rangle_0$.

Let us investigate in greater detail the structure of this expression making use of condition 47.2D for its transformation. By noting that, as has been recently established (§ 48.1), the vacuum expectation value of the current is equal to zero we may now write:

$$\langle j_\sigma(x)\, j_\rho(y)\rangle_0 = \sum_n \int d\mathbf{k} \,\langle 0 \mid j_\sigma(x) \mid n, \mathbf{k}\rangle\, \langle n, \mathbf{k} \mid j_\rho(y) \mid 0\rangle. \tag{48.17}$$

Further, by making use of properties 42.2B and 42.2C we have:

$$\langle n, \mathbf{k} \mid j_\rho(y) \mid 0\rangle = \langle n, \mathbf{k} \mid U^\dagger_{L_y} j_\rho(0) U_{L_y} \mid 0\rangle$$
$$= \langle n, \mathbf{k} \mid j_\rho(0) \mid 0\rangle e^{i[E_n(\mathbf{k})y^0 - \mathbf{k}\mathbf{y}]}. \qquad (48.18)$$

By making use of an analogous representation for $\langle 0 \mid j_\sigma(x) \mid n, \mathbf{k}\rangle$ we obtain instead of (48.17)

$$\langle j_\sigma(x) j_\rho(y)\rangle_0$$
$$= \sum_n \int d\mathbf{k}\, e^{-i[E_n(\mathbf{k})(x^0-y^0)-\mathbf{k}(\mathbf{x}-\mathbf{y})]} \langle 0 | j_\sigma(0) | n, \mathbf{k}\rangle \langle n, \mathbf{k} | j_\rho(0) | 0\rangle. \quad (48.19)$$

We now assume that in the sum (48.19) the states of lowest energy above the vacuum state are states with one, two, and three mesons. (This corresponds to assuming the nonexistence of bound combinations of mesons and nucleons of mass smaller than 3μ, which apparently is not in contradiction with experiment, and also to assuming the absence of an interaction with particles lighter than a π-meson.) We shall show that for single meson states $\mid n, \mathbf{k}\rangle$ the matrix elements

$$\langle n, \mathbf{k} \mid j_\sigma(0) \mid 0\rangle \qquad (48.20)$$

vanish. For this purpose we introduce the meson annihilation operators $a_\rho^{(-)}(\mathbf{p})$ with the usual commutation relations (compare (11.12) and (3.36))

$$[a_\rho^{(\mp)}(\mathbf{p}), \varphi_\sigma(x)] = \pm \frac{\delta_{\rho\sigma}}{(2\pi)^{3/2}\sqrt{2p^0}} e^{\pm ipx} (p^0 = \sqrt{\mu^2 + \mathbf{p}^2} > 0)$$

and we make use of condition 47.3C. This yields:

$$a_\sigma^{(\mp)}(\mathbf{p})S - S a_\sigma^{(\mp)}(\mathbf{p}) = \pm \frac{1}{(2\pi)^{3/2}\sqrt{2p^0}} \int e^{\pm ipx} \frac{\delta S}{\delta\varphi_\sigma(x)} dx. \qquad (48.21)$$

With the aid of this relationship and condition 47.2G (47.10) for the vacuum and the single meson states we obtain:

$$\int e^{-ipx} \langle n, \mathbf{k} \mid j_\sigma(x) \mid 0\rangle dx = i \int e^{ipx} \left\langle n, \mathbf{k} \left| \frac{\delta S}{\delta\varphi_\sigma(x)} S^\dagger \right| 0 \right\rangle dx$$
$$= i(2\pi)^{3/2}\sqrt{2p^0}\{\langle n, \mathbf{k} \mid S a_\sigma^{(+)}(\mathbf{p}) S^\dagger \mid 0\rangle - \langle n, \mathbf{k} \mid a_\sigma^{(+)}(\mathbf{p}) \mid 0\rangle\} = 0,$$

and therefore in virtue of (48.18)

$$\delta(p - k)\langle n, \mathbf{k} \mid j_\sigma(0) \mid 0\rangle = \frac{1}{(2\pi)^4}\int e^{-ipx}\langle n, \mathbf{k} \mid j_\sigma(x) \mid 0\rangle\, dx = 0,$$

which completes the proof of the statement made above. We also note that the vanishing of expressions (48.20) for the two-meson states follows directly from the fact that the mesons are pseudoscalar.

Thus in the expansion (48.19) the states $\mid n, \mathbf{k}\rangle$ include at least three mesons, and for them

$$E_n^2(\mathbf{k}) - \mathbf{k}^2 \geqq (3\mu)^2. \tag{48.22}$$

We now take into account the fact that because of translational and isotopic invariance

$$\langle j_\sigma(x)\, j_\rho(y)\rangle_0 = \delta_{\sigma\rho}\, u(x - y).$$

The function u may be represented in the form

$$u(x) = \frac{1}{(2\pi)^3}\int e^{-ikx}\, v(k)\, dk,$$

where in accordance with (48.19) the function $v(k)$ has the form

$$v(k) = (2\pi)^3 \sum_n \mid\langle 0 \mid j_\sigma(0) \mid n, \mathbf{k}\rangle\mid^2 \delta(k^0 - E_n(\mathbf{k})). \tag{48.23}$$

On the basis of (48.22) and (48.23) and taking into account considerations of Lorentz covariance one can conclude that

$$v(k) = \theta(k^0) J(k^2), \tag{48.24}$$

where the function J has the properties

$$J(k^2) \geqq 0 \tag{48.25}$$

and

$$J(k^2) = 0 \text{ for } k^2 < (3\mu)^2. \tag{48.26}$$

We have thus obtained:

$$\langle j_\sigma(x)\, j_\rho(y)\rangle_0 = \frac{\delta_{\sigma\rho}}{(2\pi)^3}\int e^{-ik(x-y)}\,\theta(k^0)\, J(k^2)\, dk. \tag{48.27}$$

This formula in fact provides the spectral representation for $\langle j_\sigma(x) j_\rho(y)\rangle_0$.

From (48.16) and (48.27) it follows that the function $Q(x-y)$ has the "property of causality" similar to the causal Green's functions; for $x^0 > y^0$ it has only negative frequencies with respect to the argument $x^0 - y^0$, and for $x^0 < y^0$ it has only positive frequencies. We shall therefore denote this function in the following by Q^c:

$$Q_{\sigma\rho}(x-y) = \delta_{\sigma\rho} Q^c(x-y). \tag{48.28}$$

48.4. *Analytic Properties of Q^r and Q^a*

However, relations (48.16) and (48.27) are still insufficient to allow us to draw conclusions with respect to the analytic properties of the function Q^c. The point is that the relation (48.16) defines Q^c only for $x \neq y$. In order to obtain the information which is lacking we shall have to introduce two more functions:

$$\delta_{\sigma\rho} Q^r(x-y) = \left\langle \frac{\delta j_\rho(y)}{\delta \varphi_\sigma(x)} \right\rangle_0, \tag{48.29}$$

$$\delta_{\sigma\rho} Q^a(x-y) = \left\langle \frac{\delta j_\sigma(x)}{\delta \varphi_\rho(y)} \right\rangle_0. \tag{48.30}$$

In writing the left-hand sides of these relations we have made use of considerations of translational and isotopic invariance. The indices r and a correspond to the properties

$$Q^r(x-y) = Q^a(y-x) = 0 \text{ for } x \lesssim y.$$

It is also clear that in general

$$Q^r(x-y) = Q^a(y-x). \tag{48.31}$$

By going over to the momentum representation

$$Q(x) = \frac{1}{(2\pi)^4} \int e^{-ikx} q(k)\, dk,$$

we obtain on the basis of formulas (48.12) and (48.27) that

$$q^c(k) = -i 2\pi\theta(k^0) J(k^2) + q^a(k) = i 2\pi\theta(-k^0) J(k^2) + q^r(k) \tag{48.32}$$

and that, therefore, in particular

$$q^c(k) = q^a(k) = q^r(k) \text{ for } k^2 < (3\mu)^2. \tag{48.33}$$

We shall now investigate the analytic properties of the function

$$q^r(k) = \int Q^r(x)\, e^{ikx}\, dx, \tag{48.34}$$

taking into account the fact that in consequence of the condition of causality

$$Q^r(x) = 0 \text{ for } x \lesssim 0. \tag{48.35}$$

The relation (48.34) defines $q^r(k)$ for real values of the components of k. From (48.35) it follows that $q^r(k)$ may be continued in a definite way into the region of complex k. We assume that k has an imaginary part different from zero, i.e.,

$$\left.\begin{array}{c} k = p + i\Gamma, \\ p = \operatorname{Re} k, \quad \Gamma = \operatorname{Im} k, \quad \Gamma^2 > 0, \quad \Gamma^0 > 0. \end{array}\right\} \tag{48.36}$$

We then obtain:

$$q^r(p + i\Gamma) = \int Q^r(x)\, e^{ipx}\, e^{-\Gamma x}\, dx. \tag{48.37}$$

The factor exp $(-\Gamma x)$ will play the role of a cutoff factor which guarantees the convergence of the integral. Indeed, in accordance with (48.35) the integral (48.37) is actually taken over the region for which

$$x^0 \geqq 0, \qquad \mathbf{x}^2 \leqq (x^0)^2,$$

and in this region according to the roughest estimate

$$\Gamma x = \Gamma^0 x^0 - \boldsymbol{\Gamma}\mathbf{x} > (\Gamma^0 - |\boldsymbol{\Gamma}|)\, x^0 > \tfrac{1}{2}(\Gamma^0 - |\boldsymbol{\Gamma}|)\,(|x^0| + |\mathbf{x}|),$$

so that

$$e^{-\Gamma x} \leqq e^{-\alpha(|x^0| + |\mathbf{x}|)}, \tag{48.38}$$

where in accordance with (48.36) $\alpha = (\frac{1}{2})(\Gamma^0 - |\boldsymbol{\Gamma}|) > 0$.

At the same time in virtue of condition 47.3A the function $Q_r(x)$ is integrable and therefore the integral

$$\int Q^r(x)\, h(x)\, dx,$$

which is a linear functional in the space of the functions $h(x)$ belonging to the class $C(q, n, 1)$ which satisfy the condition that the quantities

$$h_{mn} = \sup \left\{ |x|^m \frac{\partial^n h(x)}{(\partial x^0)^{\alpha_0} \ldots (\partial x^3)^{\alpha_3}} \right\} \begin{matrix} m = 0, 1, \ldots, r; \\ n = \alpha_0 + \ldots + \alpha_3 = 0, 1, \ldots, q, \end{matrix}$$

are bounded, exists and is bounded in absolute value by a linear combination of the quantities h_{mn}.

In virtue of the estimate (48.38) the function $\exp\{ipx - \Gamma x\}$ belongs in any case to the class $C(q, r, 1)$ with arbitrary finite values of q, r as a result of which the integral (48.37) and its derivatives with respect to k

$$\int Q^r(x)\,(x^0)^{\beta_0} \ldots (x^3)^{\beta_3}\, e^{-ikx}\, dx \tag{48.39}$$

will converge. Thus $q^r(k)$ is an analytic function of k in the region (48.36). Since the derivatives of $\exp ikx$ with respect to the components of x are proportional to powers of k the function $q^r(k)$ bounded by a combination of the quantities h_{mn} will increase at infinity not faster than a polynomial in k of degree not higher than n (of course we are here dealing with values of k for which the inequality (48.38) is not relaxed).

The transition to a real k is accomplished by means of the improper limiting transition

$$q^r(p + i\Gamma) \to q^r(p); \quad \Gamma^2 \to +0, \quad \Gamma^0 \to +0. \tag{48.40}$$

By similar arguments it may be shown that the function $q_a(k)$ may be continued into the complex region

$$k \to p - i\Gamma; \quad \Gamma^2 > 0, \quad \Gamma^0 > 0 \tag{48.41}$$

with the same analytic properties as the function $q^r(k)$.

But since in virtue of (48.33) both these functions coincide for real k in the region in which $k^2 < (3\mu)^2$ they should be regarded as a single analytic function f defined in the regions (48.38) and (48.41). As a result of the fact that in the foregoing regions these functions also coincide with $q^c(k)$, which in virtue of considerations of covariance and of invariance of $Q^c(x)$ with respect to time reversal depends only on k^2, the function f also depends only on k^2.

The function $f(k^2)$ is consequently analytic in that range of values of its argument which corresponds to complex components of k such that

$$\Gamma^2 = (\text{Im } k)^2 > 0. \tag{48.42}$$

We now introduce the notation

$$\text{Re } k^2 = \xi, \quad \text{Im } k^2 = \eta, \quad \text{i.e.,} \quad k^2 = \zeta = \xi + i\eta,$$

so that

$$\xi = p^2 - \Gamma^2, \quad \eta = 2(p\Gamma). \tag{48.43}$$

It is now clear that the condition (48.42) reduces to the exclusion from the complex ζ plane of the real positive axis [98]

$$\eta = 0, \quad 0 < \xi < \infty. \tag{48.44}$$

Thus the function $f(\zeta)$ is an analytic function with a cut (48.44), and at infinity it increases not faster than a polynomial.

We shall now define the boundary values of the function f along the upper and the lower edges of the cut as the corresponding improper limits:

$$f_\pm(p^2) = \lim_{\eta\to\pm 0} f(k^2). \tag{48.45}$$

It now follows from (48.4), (48.31), (48.36), (48.41), and (48.43) that

$$q^r(k) = q^a(-k) = \begin{Bmatrix} f_+(k^2) & \text{for} & k^0 > 0, \\ f_-(k^2) & \text{for} & k^0 < 0. \end{Bmatrix} \tag{48.46}$$

Taking (48.32) into account we also obtain:

$$f_+(k^2) - f_-(k^2) = 2\pi i J(k^2). \tag{48.47}$$

Now by noting that in virtue of (48.33) the difference (48.47) vanishes for $k^2 < (3\mu)^2$ we find that the cut is given not by the whole positive real axis, but only by its segment

$$\eta = 0, \quad (3\mu)^2 \leqq \xi < \infty. \tag{48.48}$$

On taking (48.43) into account, these limiting relations may

[98] Indeed, if $\xi > 0$, then also $p^2 > \Gamma^2 + \xi > 0$. But since also $\Gamma > 0$, then $\eta = 2p\Gamma \neq 0$.

also be written in the more compact form

$$q^r(k) = \lim_{\varepsilon \to +0} f(k^2 + i\varepsilon k^0), \tag{48.49}$$

$$q^a(k) = \lim_{\varepsilon \to +0} f(k^2 - i\varepsilon k^0). \tag{48.50}$$

By combining these expressions with (48.32), we also obtain:

$$q^c(k) = \lim_{\varepsilon \to +0} f(k^2 + i\varepsilon). \tag{48.51}$$

48.5. *Spectral Representation for q^r, q^a, and q^c*

The conclusions just reached with respect to the analytic function $f(\zeta)$ now enable us to obtain spectral representations of the type (48.27) for q^r, q^a, and q^c. For this purpose we shall now make use of the Cauchy integral theorem in a manner similar to the way it was used in § 46.2. We introduce the auxiliary function

$$h(\zeta) = \frac{f(\zeta)}{(\zeta - \mu^2)^{n+1}}$$

with an appropriate n and we choose for the closed contour the

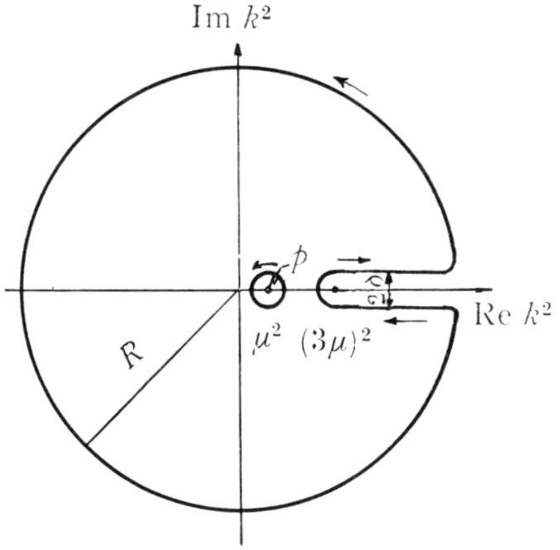

Fig. 56. Contour of integration to obtain spectral representations.

contour shown in Fig. 56. By going to the limit $R \to \infty$ and subsequently setting $\rho \to 0$, $\delta \to 0$, we obtain:

$$f(z) = \frac{(z-\mu^2)^{n+1}}{2\pi i}\int_{(3\mu)^2}^{\infty}\frac{f_+(z')-f_-(z')}{(z'-\mu^2)^{n+1}(z'-z)}\,dz' + \frac{(z-\mu^2)^{n+1}}{2\pi i}\oint_{\rho}\frac{dz'}{(z'-\mu^2)^{n+1}}\,\frac{f(z')}{z'-z}.$$

By evaluating the integral along the small circle of radius ρ about the point μ^2 and by utilizing (48.47) we find:

$$f(k^2) = (k^2-\mu^2)^{n+1}\int_{(3\mu)^2}^{\infty}\frac{J(z)\,dz}{(z-\mu^2)^{n+1}(z-k^2)} + i\sum_{0\leqq m\leqq n}\frac{(k^2-\mu^2)^m}{m!}f^{(m)}(\mu^2),$$

$$f^{(m)}(\mu^2) = \left[\frac{\partial^m f(z)}{\partial z^m}\right]_{z=\mu^2}. \tag{48.52}$$

Relations (48.49)–(48.51) enable us at once to go over in (48.52) to any one of the functions q^a, q^r, q^c. Thus, for example, we obtain for q^c:

$$q^c(k^2) = (k^2-\mu^2)^{n+1}\int_{(3\mu)^2}^{\infty}\frac{J(z)\,dz}{(z-\mu^2)^{n+1}(z-k^2-i\varepsilon)} + i\sum_{0\leqq m\leqq n}\frac{(k^2-\mu^2)^m}{m!}f^{(m)}(\mu^2). \tag{48.53}$$

Similar relations which differ from (48.53) by the replacement of $i\varepsilon$ by $\pm i\varepsilon k^0$ may be written for q^a and q^r.

We note here that the spectral representation (48.53) could have been obtained formally directly from formulas (48.16), (48.27) with the aid of the "subtraction formalism." Indeed, from the relations referred to above we have:

$$Q(x) = \frac{i}{(2\pi)^3}\int e^{-ikx}\theta(k^0)J(k^2)\,dk = \int_{(3\mu)^2}^{\infty}dz'J(z')\frac{i}{(2\pi)^3}\int e^{-ikx}\theta(k^0)\delta(k^2-z')\,dk$$
$$= \int_{(3\mu)^2}^{\infty}dz'\,J(z')\,D_{z'}^{(-)}(x)\,dz' \quad \text{for } x \gtrsim 0. \tag{48.54}$$

Here $D_{z'}^{(-)}$ is the negative-frequency part of the Pauli-Villars function corresponding to the mass $\sqrt{z'}$:

$$D_{z'}^{(-)}(x) = \frac{i}{(2\pi)^3}\int e^{-ikx}\,\theta(k^0)\,\delta(k^2-z')\,dk.$$

Combining (48.54) with the corresponding representation for $Q(x)$ in the region $x \lesssim 0$ we obtain:

$$Q(x) - \int_{(3\mu)^2}^{\infty} J(z') D^c_{z'}(x)\, dz' = 0 \quad \text{for } x \neq 0,$$

from which it follows that:

$$q^c(k) = \int_{(3\mu)^2}^{\infty} \frac{J(z)dz}{z - k^2 - i\varepsilon} + P(k^2), \tag{48.55}$$

where $P(k^2)$ is a certain polynomial in k^2.

If the function $J(z)$ does not fall off sufficiently rapidly at infinity the integral in (48.55) will diverge. However, it may be made to converge by means of a subtraction procedure and in this way a definite meaning may be given to formula (48.55). We shall utilize the formula

$$\frac{1}{z - k^2} = \frac{1}{z - \mu^2 - (k^2 - \mu^2)}$$

$$= \frac{1}{z - \mu^2} \left\{ 1 + \frac{k^2 - \mu^2}{z - \mu^2} + \ldots + \left(\frac{k^2 - \mu^2}{z - \mu^2}\right)^n \right\} + \frac{(k^2 - \mu^2)^{n+1}}{(z - k^2)(z - \mu^2)^{n+1}},$$

with the aid of which we can represent (48.55) in the form

$$q^c(k) = (k^2 - \mu^2)^{n+1} \int_{(3\mu)^2}^{\infty} \frac{J(z)dz}{(z - k^2 - i\varepsilon)(z - \mu^2)^{n+1}}$$

$$+ \sum_{0 \leqq m \leqq n} (k^2 - \mu^2)^m \int_{(3\mu)^2}^{\infty} \frac{J(z)\, dz}{(z - \mu^2)^{m+1}} + P(k^2). \tag{48.56}$$

We choose the number n sufficiently large so that the first integral in (48.56) will turn out to be convergent. The divergent terms in the sum involving the powers of $(k^2 - \mu^2)$ may be compensated by means of the polynomial $P(k^2)$. As a result of such a "compensation of divergences" typical for the usual subtraction procedure we shall obtain formula (48.53).

We shall now show that in virtue of our conditions, the zero term is absent in the sum in (48.53), i.e.,

$$f(\mu^2) = 0. \tag{48.57}$$

In order to do this, we note that in virtue of property 47.3C the matrix element of S between two single-meson states $\langle \mathbf{p}'\sigma |$ and $| \mathbf{p}\rho \rangle$ may be represented with the aid of (48.21) in the form

$$\langle \mathbf{p}'\sigma | S | \mathbf{p}\rho \rangle = \langle 0 | S a_\sigma^{(-)}(\mathbf{p}')\, a_\rho^{(+)}(\mathbf{p}) | 0 \rangle$$

$$+ \frac{1}{(2\pi)^{3/2}\sqrt{2p'^0}} \int \left\langle 0 \left| \frac{\delta S}{\delta \varphi_\sigma(x)}\, a_\rho^{(+)}(\mathbf{p}) \right| 0 \right\rangle e^{ip'x} dx \quad \text{for } p^2 = p'^2 = \mu^2.$$

By commuting $a^{(+)}$ with $\delta S/\delta\varphi$ under the integral in the right-hand side and by taking into account 47.2G and (48.4), we obtain:

$$\langle \mathbf{p}'\sigma \mid S \mid \mathbf{p}\rho\rangle = \langle a_\sigma^{(-)}(\mathbf{p}')\, a_\rho^{(+)}(\mathbf{p})\rangle_0 + \frac{1}{(2\pi)^3\, 2\sqrt{p^0 p'^0}} \int Q_{\sigma\rho}(x, y)\, e^{i(p'x - py)}\, dx\, dy$$

$$= \langle \mathbf{p}'\sigma \mid \mathbf{p}\rho\rangle + \delta_{\sigma\rho}\frac{\pi}{p^0}\,\delta(p - p')\, q^c(p) \text{ for } p^2 = \mu^2.$$

On the other hand, in virtue of the same condition we may directly write:

$$\langle \mathbf{p}'\sigma \mid S \mid \mathbf{p}\rho\rangle = \langle \mathbf{p}'\sigma \mid \mathbf{p}\rho\rangle,$$

from which (48.57) follows after (48.33) and (48.51) have been taken into account.

We shall also show that the constants $f^m(\mu^2)$ are purely imaginary. Indeed, in virtue of the definition (48.4) and the fact that φ is real the function O is Hermitean as a result of which, and taking into account the fact that $q^c(k)$ is even, we obtain:

$$q^{*c}(k^2) = -\, q^c(k^2).$$

But since according to (48.33) and (48.51) the function q^c coincides with f in the neighborhood of the point μ^2 this gives:

$$f^{*(m)}(\mu^2) = -\, f^{(m)}(\mu^2).$$

We have thus proved that the functions q^r, q^a, and q^c possess spectral representations of the type (48.52) in which

$$f^{(0)}(\mu^2) = f(\mu^2) = 0 \tag{48.58}$$

and

$$f^{*(m)}(\mu^2) = -\, f^{(m)}(\mu^2). \tag{48.59}$$

The well-known result of Källen and Lehmann for the boson Green's function may be obtained from formulas (48.53), (48.58), (48.59), with the aid of (48.8) if the additional assumption is made that the "rate of increase" n is equal to unity. On substituting (48.53) into (48.8) we then obtain:

$$\Delta(p) = -\frac{1 + if^{(1)}(\mu^2)}{\mu^2 - p^2} + \int_{(3\mu)^2}^{\infty} \frac{I(z)\, dz}{z - p^2}, \quad I(z) = \frac{J(z)}{(z - \mu^2)^2}. \tag{48.60}$$

§ 49. Spectral Representation of the Fermion Green's Function

49.1. *Spectral Representation of the Vacuum Expectation Value of* $\delta^2 S/\delta\bar{\psi}\delta\psi$

We now proceed to construct the spectral representation for the vacuum expectation value of the Fermi radiation operator of the second order

$$R^c_{\alpha\beta}(x-y) = i\left\langle \frac{\delta^2 S}{\delta\bar{\psi}_\alpha(x)\,\delta\psi(y)}\, S^\dagger \right\rangle_0, \tag{48.5}$$

which, as was shown in § 48.1, is the only radiation operator of the second order containing a second variational derivative and having a vacuum expectation value different from zero. Since the following arguments differ from the material in § 48 only by the difference in the transformation properties of R and Q we shall present them in a more abbreviated form.

For auxiliary purposes we introduce the radiation Fermi-operators of the first order [99]

$$\vartheta(x) = iS\,\frac{\delta S^\dagger}{\delta\bar{\psi}(x)} \tag{49.1}$$

and

$$\bar{\vartheta}(x) = -\,i\,\frac{\delta S}{\delta\psi(x)}\,S^\dagger. \tag{49.2}$$

By investigating the relation between the variational Fermi-derivatives $\delta\vartheta(x)/\delta\psi$, $\delta\vartheta(x)/\delta\bar{\psi}$ and $\delta^2 S/\delta\bar{\psi}\delta\psi$ in a manner similar to the way this was done in § 48.2 for Bose derivatives, and by taking the condition of unitarity into account, we obtain the formulas [100]

[99] With the aid of (47.3) it may be easily seen that $\bar{\vartheta}(x) = [\vartheta(x)]^*\gamma^0$.

[100] By making use of the formula for differentiating a product

$$\frac{\delta(AB)}{\delta\psi} = \frac{\delta A}{\delta\psi}\,B + (-1)^{\eta_A}\,A\,\frac{\delta B}{\delta\psi}, \tag{49.3}$$

where η_A is the "degree of linearity" of A with respect to the Fermi operators.

$$\frac{\delta\vartheta(x)}{\delta\psi(y)} = i\,\frac{\delta^2 S}{\delta\bar{\psi}(x)\,\delta\psi(y)}\,S^\dagger + i\vartheta(x)\,\bar{\vartheta}(y), \tag{49.4}$$

$$\frac{\delta\bar{\vartheta}(y)}{\delta\bar{\psi}(x)} = -\,i\,\frac{\delta^2 S}{\delta\bar{\psi}(x)\,\delta\psi(y)}\,S^\dagger + i\bar{\vartheta}(y)\,\vartheta(x), \tag{49.5}$$

from which we obtain with the aid of the condition of causality

$$\left\{\frac{\delta}{\delta\bar{\psi}(x)}\,\frac{\delta}{\delta\psi(y)}\,S\right\}S^\dagger = -\,T(\vartheta(x)\,\bar{\vartheta}(y)),$$

$$i\left(\frac{\delta\vartheta(x)}{\delta\psi(y)} + \frac{\delta\bar{\vartheta}(y)}{\delta\bar{\psi}(x)}\right) + [\vartheta(x),\ \bar{\vartheta}(y)]_+ = 0 \ \text{for}\ x \sim y.$$

We now introduce the vacuum expectation values

$$R^r(x-y) = -\left\langle\frac{\delta}{\delta\bar{\psi}(x)}\,\bar{\vartheta}(y)\right\rangle_0, \tag{49.6}$$

$$R^a(x-y) = \left\langle\frac{\delta}{\delta\psi(y)}\,\vartheta(x)\right\rangle_0, \tag{49.7}$$

$$R^{(-)}(x-y) = i\langle\vartheta(x)\bar{\vartheta}(y)\rangle_0, \tag{49.8}$$

$$R^{(+)}(x-y) = -\,i\langle\bar{\vartheta}(x)\vartheta(y)\rangle_0, \tag{49.9}$$

which on the basis of (49.4) and (49.5) are related to R^c by the following equations

$$\left.\begin{aligned} R^a(x) &= R^c(x) + R^{(-)}(x),\\ R^r(x) &= R^c(x) + R^{(+)}(x). \end{aligned}\right\} \tag{49.10}$$

In virtue of the condition of causality we have

$$\left.\begin{aligned} R^r(x) &= 0 \ \text{for}\ x \lesssim 0,\\ R^a(x) &= 0 \ \text{for}\ x \gtrsim 0. \end{aligned}\right\}$$

In view of considerations of isotopic and Lorentz invariance all these functions have the following structure:

$$R(x) = \delta_{st}(i\hat{\partial}u_1(x) + u_2(x)), \tag{49.11}$$

where u_1 and u_2 are invariant scalar functions, s and t are isotopic (proton-neutron) indices, while the components $\hat{\partial}$ contain the usual Dirac matrices of the fourth rank.

By taking into account the fact that expressions (49.6)–(49.9) are invariant under the transformation of charge conjugation (see § 12.3) we find that the functions $u(x)$ are interrelated by the equations

$$\left.\begin{aligned} u_1^{(+)}(x) &= -u_1^{(-)}(-x), \; u_2^{(+)}(x) = u_2^{(-)}(-x), \\ u_1^{r}(x) &= -u_1^{a}(-x), \; u_2^{r}(x) = u_2^{a}(-x). \end{aligned}\right\} \tag{49.12}$$

We now examine the function $R^{(-)}$. In accordance with condition 47.2C we may write it in the form

$$R^{(-)}(x-y) = \sum_n \int d\mathbf{k} \langle 0 \mid \vartheta(0) \mid n, \mathbf{k}\rangle \langle n, \mathbf{k} \mid \bar{\vartheta}(0) \mid 0\rangle e^{-ik(x-y)}. \tag{49.13}$$

In this sum, as was also the case previously in § 48.2, a number of the initial terms vanishes. Thus, due to considerations of covariance

$$\langle 0 \mid \vartheta(0) \mid n, \mathbf{k}) = 0 \tag{49.14}$$

for the states $| n, \mathbf{k}\rangle$ containing no nucleons. Moreover, by using arguments similar to those of § 48.3, we see that (49.14) also holds for a single-nucleon state; therefore the integral (49.13) is in fact taken over the region in which $k^2 \geqq (M+\mu)^2$. It is now clear that $R^{(-)}$ may be written in the form

$$R^{(-)}(x) = \frac{\delta_{\rho\sigma}}{(2\pi)^3 i} \int e^{-ikx} \theta(k^0) [\hat{k}\rho_1(k^2) + \rho_2(k^2)]\, dk, \tag{49.15}$$

$$\rho_{1,2}(k^2) = 0 \text{ for } k^2 < (M+\mu)^2.$$

By introducing for R^a, R^r, and R^c similar momentum representations in terms of the scalar functions φ_1 and φ_2:

$$R(x) = \frac{\delta_{\rho\sigma}}{(2\pi)^4} \int e^{-ikx} [\hat{k}\varphi_1(k) + \varphi_2(k)]\, dk, \tag{49.16}$$

we obtain with the aid of (49.10) and (49.12) the relations

$$\varphi_i^c(k) = \varphi_i^r(k) - 2\pi i \theta(k^0) \rho_i(k^2) = \varphi_i^a(k) + 2\pi i \theta(-k^0) \rho_i(k^2) \quad (i=1, 2). \tag{49.17}$$

By using (49.16) in the above we also obtain

$$\varphi_i^c(k) = \varphi_i^r(k) = \varphi_i^a(k) \text{ for } k^2 < (M+\mu)^2. \tag{49.18}$$

Since relations (49.17) and (49.18) are completely analogous to formulas (48.32) and (48.33), we may now repeat word for word in the case of the functions u_i the arguments given in § 48.4 in the case of the functions q.

In this way we obtain:

$$\left.\begin{aligned} \varphi_i^r(k) &= \lim_{\varepsilon\to+0} f_i(k^2 + i\varepsilon k^0), \\ \varphi_i^a(k) &= \lim_{\varepsilon\to+0} f_i(k^2 - i\varepsilon k^0), \\ \varphi_i^c(k) &= \lim_{\varepsilon\to+0} f_i(k^2 + i\varepsilon), \end{aligned}\right\} \tag{49.19}$$

where the functions f_i are analytic over the whole complex plane of their argument with the exception of the cut

$$\operatorname{Im} k^2 = 0, \quad \operatorname{Re} k^2 > (M+\mu)^2,$$

and at infinity increase not faster than a polynomial of the nth degree, as a result of which they may be represented in a form similar to (48.52):

$$f_i(k^2) = (k^2 - M^2)^{n+1} \int_{(M+\mu)^2}^{\infty} \frac{\rho_i(z)\, dz}{(z - M^2)^{n+1}(z - k^2)} + i \sum_{0\leq m\leq n} \frac{(k^2 - M^2)^m}{m!} f_i^{(m)}(M^2). \tag{49.20}$$

We shall now establish certain inequalities which must be satisfied by the functions ρ_i. In order to do this we note that on the basis of (49.11), (49.13) and (49.18) we may write the relation

$$\hat{k}_{\alpha\beta}\,\rho_1(k^2) + \delta_{\alpha\beta}\,\rho_2(k^2) = \sum_{n,\,\omega} \langle 0 \mid \vartheta_\alpha(0) \mid n, \mathbf{k}\rangle \langle n, \mathbf{k} \mid \vartheta^*_\omega(0) \mid 0\rangle\, \gamma^0_{\omega\beta}, \tag{49.21}$$

which is valid for all $k^2 = M_n^2$, $k^0 > 0$. In it we set [101]

$$\mathbf{k} = 0, \; k^0 = \nu > 0, \; k^2 = \nu^2, \; \alpha = \beta$$

and make use of the fact [102] that in the usual representation

[101] i.e., we choose k to be purely timelike and denote by ν the set of M_n for which the right-hand side of (49.21) is different from zero.

[102] It is not necessary to introduce a special representation of the Dirac matrices at this point. We have introduced it only in order to simplify the presentation.

$$\gamma^0 = \begin{pmatrix} 1 & 0 & 0 & 0 \\ 0 & 1 & 0 & 0 \\ 0 & 0 & -1 & 0 \\ 0 & 0 & 0 & -1 \end{pmatrix}.$$

We then obtain:

$$\left.\begin{aligned} \nu\rho_1(\nu^2)+\rho_2(\nu^2) &= \sum_n |\langle 0 \mid \vartheta_\alpha(0) \mid n, 0\rangle|^2 > 0, \text{for } \alpha = 1, 2 \\ -\nu\rho_1(\nu^2)+\rho_2(\nu^2) &= -\sum_n |\langle 0 \mid \vartheta_\alpha(0) \mid n, 0\rangle|^2 < 0, \text{for } \alpha = 3, 4 \end{aligned}\right\}. \quad (49.22)$$

We now introduce the functions

$$J_1(\nu) = \frac{\rho_1(\nu^2) - \dfrac{\rho_2(\nu^2)}{\nu}}{2}, \quad J_2(\nu) = \frac{\rho_1(\nu^2) + \dfrac{\rho_2(\nu^2)}{\nu}}{2},$$

which in virtue of (49.22) are nonnegative:

$$J_1(\nu) \geqq 0, \ J_2(\nu) \geqq 0, \quad (49.23)$$

and we note that

$$\hat{k}\rho_1(\nu^2) + \rho_2(\nu^2) = (\hat{k} - \nu)J_1(\nu^2) + (\hat{k} + \nu)\, J_2(\nu^2). \quad (49.24)$$

On the basis of (49.20) and (49.24) we can now conclude that the combinations

$$R(\hat{k}) = \hat{k}f_1(k^2) + f_2(k^2) \quad (49.25)$$

have a spectral representation of the form

$$R(\hat{k}) = (k^2 - M^2)^{n+1} \int_{\nu > M+\mu}^{\infty} \frac{(\hat{k} - \nu)\, J_1(\nu) + (\hat{k} + \nu) J_2(\nu)}{(\nu^2 - M^2)^{n+1}} \frac{d\nu^2}{\nu^2 - k^2}$$

$$+ \, i \sum_{0 \leqq m \leqq n} \frac{(k^2 - M^2)^m}{m!} (\hat{k}f_1^{(m)}(M^2) + f_2^{(m)}(M^2)). \quad (49.26)$$

It is clear that because of (49.16) and (49.19) we can take for $R(\hat{k})$ in (49.26) the momentum representation of R^r, E^a, or R^c choosing in accordance with (49.19) the appropriate method of going around the pole $\nu^2 = k^2$.

The spectral representation (49.26) may be brought into a somewhat different form. In order to do this we note that the differences

$$\left(\frac{k^2 - M^2}{\nu^2 - M^2}\right)^{n+1} \frac{1}{\nu \pm \hat{k}} - \left(\frac{\hat{k} - M}{\nu \pm M}\right)^{2n+2} \frac{1}{\nu \pm \hat{k}}$$

are polynomials of degree $2n + 1$ with respect to $\hat{k}$. In view of this formula (49.26) may be written in the form

$$R(\hat{k}) = (\hat{k} - M)^{2n+2} \int_{(\nu \geqq M+\mu)} \left(\frac{I_1(\nu)}{\nu + \hat{k}} + \frac{I_2(k)}{\nu - \hat{k}}\right) d\nu + \sum_{0 \leqq m \leqq 2n+1} B_m (\hat{k} - M)^m, \tag{49.27}$$

where

$$\left.\begin{aligned} I_1(\nu) &= \frac{2\nu J_1(\nu)}{(\nu + M)^{2n+2}} \geqq 0, \\ I_2(\nu) &= \frac{2\nu J_2(\nu)}{(\nu - M)^{2n+2}} \geqq 0, \end{aligned}\right\} \tag{49.28}$$

and B_m are scalar constants.

Just as in the case of the boson function q it may be shown that $B_0 = 0$ since in virtue of (48.9) only in this case does the corresponding Green's function have a pole of the first order at the point $\hat{k} = M$. The corresponding proof may be carried out by investigating the matrix element of S between two single nucleon states just as in the boson case.

Finally, by making use of the rule for taking conjugates

$$\bar{R}^r(x - y) \equiv (R^r(x - y))^* \gamma^0 = R^a(y - x),$$

which follows from the definitions (49.5) and (49.7), and from which it also follows that

$$\gamma^0 R^{*r}(k) \gamma^0 = R^a(k),$$

we find that all the B_m are real.

The Källen-Lehmann representation for the fermion Green's function may be obtained from the foregoing with the aid of (48.9) and with the additional assumption that $n = 0$.

We are here again (as in § 48.5) confronted by the interesting fact that under our system of conditions (§§ 47.2, 3) a specification of the "rate of increase" is equivalent to specifying the form of the Lagrangian.

49.2. *Proximity to a Contradiction*

In conclusion we shall say a few words with respect to condition 47.3A in accordance with which the vacuum expectation values of the radiation operators must be "integrable functions" in the generalized sense.

Let us consider what would happen if we would impose on these vacuum expectation values $h(x_1, \ldots, x_n)$ a more restrictive condition by requiring that they should be ordinary functions for which integrals of the form

$$\int | h(x_1, \ldots, x_n) | \rho(x_1, \ldots, x_n) dx_1 \ldots dx_n \qquad (49.29)$$

exist with weighting functions ρ falling off at infinity as

$$\left(\frac{1}{| x_1 |^2 + \ldots + | x_n |^2}\right)^m \qquad (| x | = | x^0 | + | \mathbf{x} |)$$

with a sufficiently high value of m.

Since we are not relaxing our system of conditions, but, on the contrary, are making it stricter, all the theorems which have been proven above continue to hold. In particular, formulas (48.52), (48.26), (48.27) remain valid.

Let us go over to the x-representation, for example, in (48.53). We obtain:

$$Q_{\sigma\rho}(x - y) = \delta_{\rho\sigma}(\Box_x - \mu^2)^{n+1} \int_{(3\mu)^2}^{\infty} I(z) D_z^c(x - y) dz + \sum_{1 \leq m \leq n} c_m (\mu^2 - \Box_x)^m \delta(x - y), \qquad (49.30)$$

where

$$\Box_x = \Delta_x - \frac{\partial^2}{(\partial x^0)^2}, \quad I(z) = \frac{J(z)}{(z - \mu^2)^{n+1}} \geq 0,$$

and D_z^c is a causal function for a field of mass $\sqrt{z}$.

But, as is well known, (see § 15.2) the function $D_z^c(x - y)$ has on the light cone a singularity of the type $1/(x - y)^2$. Because the weighting function I in the integral (49.30) is positive all these singularities add instead of compensating each other. The action of the operator $(\Box - \mu^2)^m$ still further intensifies the singularities on the light cone. As a result of this integrals of the type (49.29) diverge for the functions Q which belong to the class of functions under investigation—the class of vacuum expectation values of radiation operators.

Thus it has turned out to be sufficient to restrict somewhat one of the conditions of the system (47.2), (47.3) in order to arrive at an internal contradiction. Of course we cannot draw any conclusions from the above with respect to the compatibility of the "undeformed" system of conditions (47.2), (47.3). We merely wish to note that the question of the absence of internal contradictions in the whole local theory is not entirely clear.

We shall also note another interesting point. Thus the opinion is sometimes expressed that the application of the subtraction formalism in field theory depends on the use of perturbation theory. This opinion seems to us to be incorrect.

Indeed, as we have just seen, the complete Green's function has a singularity on the light cone which is in any case not weaker than the function D^c for the free field. Let us suppose that we must perform the operation of multiplication

$$D^c_\alpha(x-y)\,D^c_\beta(x-y).$$

In order to ascribe meaning to it, it is necessary to employ the subtraction procedure since if we use the trivial interpretation we immediately find that a divergence arises of the type of the ultraviolet catastrophe. It therefore seems to us that the subtraction formalism is an inevitable attribute of any local theory.

§ 50. Amplitude for Meson-Nucleon Scattering

This section contains auxiliary material on the basis of which we shall give in § 51 a derivation of the dispersion relations for the process of the scattering of mesons by nucleons. Here we introduce all the fundamental and auxiliary quantities and outline a mathematically simpler derivation of the dispersion relations for the case of forward scattering.

50.1. *Connection Between the Scattering Amplitude and the "Retarded" and "Advanced" Matrix Elements*

We consider the case when before scattering the nucleon is in a state characterized by momentum **p** and by discrete spin and isotopic spin indices which are together denoted by the letter s, and the meson (pion) is in the state of momentum $\mathbf{q}$ and discrete indices ρ. The corresponding quantities for the nucleon and for the pion in the state after scattering will be denoted by primed letters ($\mathbf{p}'$, s' for the nucleon, $\mathbf{q}'$, ρ' for the pion). For the following discussion we shall find it convenient to separate out the pion momenta $\mathbf{q}$ and $\mathbf{q}'$ and to denote the remaining quantities characterizing the initial and the final states by a single symbol:

$$\alpha = (\mathbf{p}, s, \rho), \qquad \omega = (\mathbf{p}', s', \rho').$$

In accordance with (46.14) the scattering amplitude for the above process may be expressed in terms of the matrix element

$$\langle \mathbf{p}'s', \ \mathbf{q}'\rho' \mid S \mid \mathbf{p}s, \ \mathbf{q}\rho\rangle.$$

After picking out the pion operators $a_{\rho'}^{(-)}(q')$ and $a_{\rho}^{(+)}(q)$ in the amplitudes of the initial and final states, we commute $a^{(+)}$ with the S-matrix:

$$\begin{aligned}\langle \mathbf{p}'s', \mathbf{q}\rho' \mid S \mid \mathbf{p}s, \mathbf{q}\rho\rangle &= \langle \mathbf{p}'s' \mid a_{\rho'}^{(-)}(\mathbf{q}')\, Sa_{\rho}^{(+)}(\mathbf{q}) \mid \mathbf{p}s\rangle \\ &= \langle \mathbf{p}'s' \mid a_{\rho'}^{(-)}(\mathbf{q}')\, a_{\rho}^{(+)}(\mathbf{q})S \mid \mathbf{p}s\rangle \\ + \frac{1}{(2\pi)^{3/2}\sqrt{2q^0}} \int dy e^{iqy} &\left\langle \mathbf{p}'s' \left| a_{\rho'}^{(-)}(\mathbf{q}')\, \frac{\delta S}{\delta\varphi^{\rho}(y)} \right| \mathbf{p}s \right\rangle. \qquad (50.1)\end{aligned}$$

In order to evaluate the first term, we make use of the condition of stability of the single-nucleon state. Then by commuting the operators we find that this term is equal to a product of δ-functions. In the second term it is also necessary to commute $a^{(-)}$ with $\delta S/\delta\varphi$. By taking (46.14) into account we obtain from this the following expression for the scattering amplitude:

$$\begin{aligned}&\delta(p + q - q' - p')f(\alpha\mathbf{q}, \omega\mathbf{q}') \\ &= \frac{\pi}{(2\pi)^3 i} \int dx\,dy e^{i(q'x - qy)} \left\langle \mathbf{p}'s' \left| \frac{\delta^2 S}{\delta\varphi_{\rho'}(x)\,\delta\varphi_{\rho}(y)} S^{\dagger} \right| \mathbf{p}s \right\rangle, \qquad (50.2)\end{aligned}$$

$$p'^0 = \sqrt{\mathbf{p}^2 + M^2}, \ldots, q^0 = \sqrt{\mathbf{q}^2 + \mu^2}.$$

By analogy with the vacuum expectation values and the Green's functions considered in § 48, 49 it is appropriate to refer to the matrix element appearing under the integral sign as the "causal matrix element" and to denote it by F^c:

$$F^c(x, y) = \frac{2\pi^2}{i}\left\langle \mathbf{p}' s' \left| \frac{\delta^2 S}{\delta\varphi_{\rho'}(x)\,\delta\varphi_\rho(y)} S^\dagger \right| \mathbf{p}s \right\rangle. \qquad (50.3)$$

In future we shall find it convenient to employ the quantities

$$F^{\text{ret}}(x, y) = \frac{2\pi^2}{i}\left\langle \mathbf{p}' s' \left| \frac{\delta}{\delta\varphi_{\rho'}(x)}\left(\frac{\delta S}{\delta\varphi_\rho(y)} S^\dagger\right) \right| \mathbf{p}s \right\rangle, \qquad (50.4)$$

$$F^{\text{adv}}(x, y) = \frac{2\pi^2}{i}\left\langle \mathbf{p}' s' \left| \frac{\delta}{\delta\varphi_\rho(y)}\left(\frac{\delta S}{\delta\varphi_{\rho'}(x)} S^\dagger\right) \right| \mathbf{p}s \right\rangle, \qquad (50.5)$$

which have the properties

$$F^{\text{ret}}(x, y) = 0 \text{ for } x \lesssim y, \qquad (50.6)$$

$$F^{\text{adv}}(x, y) = 0 \text{ for } y \lesssim x, \qquad (50.7)$$

and also the expressions

$$F^{(-)}(x, y) = \frac{2\pi^2}{i}\left\langle \mathbf{p}' s' \left| \frac{\delta S}{\delta\varphi_{\rho'}(x)} \frac{\delta S^\dagger}{\delta\varphi_\rho(y)} \right| \mathbf{p}s \right\rangle$$

$$= \frac{2\pi^2}{i}\langle \mathbf{p}' s' \mid j_{\rho'}(x)\, j_\rho(y) \mid \mathbf{p}s\rangle, \qquad (50.8)$$

$$F^{(+)}(x, y) = \frac{2\pi^2}{i}\langle \mathbf{p}' s' \mid j_\rho(y)\, j_{\rho'}(x) \mid \mathbf{p}s\rangle, \qquad (50.9)$$

related to F^{ret}, F^{adv} and F^c by the equations

$$F^c = F^{\text{ret}} - F^{(+)} = F^{\text{adv}} - F^{(-)}. \qquad (50.10)$$

In virtue of conditions 47.2C, 47.2F, and (47.6) we find that under a transformation of translation by $a = (x + y)/2$ the matrix elements F^c, F^{ret}, F^{adv}, $F^{(+)}$, and $F^{(-)}$ may be represented in the form

$$F(x,y) = e^{i(p'-p)a}\, F(x - a, y - a) = e^{i\frac{(p'-p)}{2}(x+y)}\, F(x - y), \qquad (50.11)$$

where

$$F(x - y) = F\left(\frac{x - y}{2}, \frac{y - x}{2}\right).$$

We shall find it convenient to introduce the Fourier representations for the functions $F(x)$:

$$T_{\alpha\omega}(k) = \int dx e^{ikx} F(x). \tag{50.12}$$

From the definitions (50.4)–(50.9) the following relations follow for T ($P_{\rho\rho'}$ denotes an interchange of indices ρ and ρ'):

$$\left.\begin{aligned} T^{\mathrm{ret}}_{\alpha\omega}(k) &= P_{\rho\rho'} T^{\mathrm{adv}}_{\alpha\omega}(-k), \\ T^{(-)}_{\alpha\omega}(k) &= P_{\rho\rho'} T^{(+)}_{\alpha\omega}(-k), \end{aligned}\right\} \tag{50.13}$$

from which after taking (50.10) into account we also obtain:

$$T^{c}_{\alpha\omega}(k) = T^{\mathrm{ret}}_{\alpha\omega}(k) - T^{(+)}_{\alpha\omega}(k) = T^{\mathrm{adv}}_{\alpha\omega}(k) - T^{(-)}_{\alpha\omega}(k) \tag{50.14}$$

and

$$T^{\mathrm{ret}}_{\alpha\omega}(k) - T^{\mathrm{adv}}_{\alpha\omega}(k) = T^{(+)}_{\alpha\omega}(k) - P_{\rho\rho'} T^{(+)}_{\alpha\omega}(-k). \tag{50.15}$$

We note that the scattering amplitude is related to T^c by the equation

$$f(\alpha\mathbf{q}, \omega\mathbf{q}') = T^{c}_{\alpha\omega}\left(\frac{q+q'}{2}\right). \tag{50.16}$$

In a manner similar to the one in which this was done previously we now reduce the causal function T^c (or F^c) to the retarded or the advanced one, having in mind the fact that in virtue of properties (50.6) and (50.7) the functions F^{ret} and F^{adv} are more convenient for analytic continuation. With this in view we examine in greater detail the quantity $T^{(+)}$:

$$T^{(+)}_{\alpha\omega}\left(\frac{q+q'}{2}\right) = \frac{2\pi^2}{i}\int dx e^{i\frac{q+q'}{2}x}\left\langle \mathbf{p}' s' \left| j_\rho\left(\frac{y-x}{2}\right) j_{\rho'}\left(\frac{x-y}{2}\right)\right| \mathbf{p} s\right\rangle.$$

We make use of the fact that the system of functions (47.21) is complete. By making replacements of the type

$$j(z) = U^{\dagger}_{Lz}\, j(0)\, U_{Lz}$$

and making use of property (47.6) we obtain after integrating over x:

$$T^{(+)}_{\alpha\omega}\left(\frac{q+q'}{2}\right)=\frac{2\pi^2}{i}\int dx e^{i\frac{q+q'}{2}x}\sum_n\int d\mathbf{k}\left\langle \mathbf{p}'s'\left|j_{\rho'}\left(-\frac{x}{2}\right)\right|\mathbf{k}n\right\rangle$$

$$\times\left\langle \mathbf{k}n\left|j_{\rho'}\left(\frac{x}{2}\right)\right|\mathbf{p}s\right\rangle=\frac{(2\pi)^5\pi}{i}\sum_n\delta\left(\sqrt{\mathbf{k}^2+M_n^2}+\frac{q^0+q'^0-p^0-p'^0}{2}\right)$$

$$\times\langle \mathbf{p}'s'|j_\rho(0)|\mathbf{k}n\rangle\langle \mathbf{k}n|j_\rho(0)|\mathbf{p}s\rangle|\,;\ \mathbf{k}=\frac{\mathbf{p}+\mathbf{p}'-\mathbf{q}-\mathbf{q}'}{2}. \qquad (50.17)$$

Since in virtue of (50.16) we are interested in the region in which

$$p+q-p'-q'=0,$$

we see that the argument of the δ-function in the sum (50.17) may be represented in the form

$$\sqrt{(\mathbf{p}-\mathbf{q}')^2+M_n^2}+q'^0-p^0$$
$$=\sqrt{(\mathbf{p}-\mathbf{q}')^2+M_n^2}+\sqrt{\mu^2+\mathbf{q}'^2}-\sqrt{M^2+\mathbf{p}^2}. \qquad (50.18)$$

Since (50.18) appears inside the δ-function we must have:

$$\sqrt{M_n^2+(\mathbf{p}-\mathbf{q}')^2}+\sqrt{\mu^2+\mathbf{q}^2}=\sqrt{M^2+\mathbf{p}^2}.$$

This relation corresponds to the transformation of a particle of mass M into two particles of masses μ and M_n. But since in any case

$$M_n \geqq M, \qquad (50.19)$$

the foregoing is impossible in view of conservation of energy and momentum. From this it follows that the expression (50.18) is essentially positive, as a result of which $T^{(+)}$ vanishes.

Thus in the case when the matrix elements are taken between states involving real particles having a positive energy:

$$p^0=\sqrt{\mathbf{p}^2+M^2}>0 \text{ etc.},$$

with the four-momentum being conserved, the causal matrix element coincides with the retarded one:

$$\left.\begin{aligned}T^c_{\alpha\omega}(k)&=T^{\text{ret}}_{\alpha\omega}(k),\\ k^0&=\frac{q^0+q'^0}{2}>\mu.\end{aligned}\right\} \qquad (50.20)$$

In a completely analogous manner it may be shown that

$$T^{c}_{\alpha\omega}(k) = T^{\mathrm{adv}}_{\alpha\omega}(k) \text{ for } k^0 < -\mu. \tag{50.21}$$

50.2. *Transition to a Fixed Frame of Reference. The Difficulties of Analytic Continuation*

As was already pointed out in § 46, in order to obtain the dispersion relations it is necessary to establish the existence of analytic properties in the complex plane of the energy variable. Such properties for the retarded function of a single argument in the example of § 46 were directly obtained from a property analogous to (50.6).

In the present case we are dealing with functions of a large number of independent arguments (momenta of different particles) with these arguments, in contrast to the case discussed in § 48, 49, not being reducible to a single scalar (of the type of the square of the four-momentum k^2). This makes the problem considerably more complicated.

In order to be able to write individual independent energy and momentum variables in explicit form we now fix our frame of reference. It is most convenient to employ the generally accepted frame of reference in which the sum of the nucleon momenta before and after scattering is equal to zero:

$$\mathbf{p} + \mathbf{p}' = 0 \tag{50.22}$$

(this system reduces to the laboratory system in the case of forward scattering for which $\mathbf{p} = \mathbf{p}' = 0$). In such a system $\mathbf{p}^2 = \mathbf{p}'^2$, and also in virtue of the law of conservation of energy $\mathbf{q}^2 = \mathbf{q}'^2$. The law of conservation of momentum in turn leads to the relations

$$\mathbf{p} = \frac{\mathbf{q}' - \mathbf{q}}{2} \text{ and } (\mathbf{q}' + \mathbf{q})\,\mathbf{p} = 0. \tag{50.23}$$

As a result of this we can set:

$$\frac{\mathbf{q}' + \mathbf{q}}{2} = \lambda \mathbf{e}, \tag{50.24}$$

where $\mathbf{e}$ is a unit vector orthogonal to $\mathbf{p}$:

$$\mathbf{e}^2 = 1, \ \mathbf{ep} = 0.$$

It follows from (50.23) and (50.24) that

$$\mathbf{q} = -\mathbf{p} + \lambda\mathbf{e}, \quad \mathbf{q}' = \mathbf{p} + \lambda\mathbf{e}$$

and, consequently, that

$$\mathbf{q}^2 = \mathbf{q}'^2 = \mathbf{p}^2 + \lambda^2, \quad q^0 = q'^0 = \sqrt{\mu^2 + \mathbf{p}^2 + \lambda^2},$$

i.e., the four-vector argument $(q + q')/2$ may be replaced by the quantities λ and $\mathbf{e}$. In doing this it is convenient in addition to λ to make use of the meson energy

$$\frac{q^0 + q'^0}{2} = q^0 = E = \sqrt{\mu^2 + \mathbf{p}^2 + \lambda^2}. \tag{50.25}$$

For a fixed $\mathbf{p}$ the quantities E and λ are related to each other in an unambiguous way.

Thus in the frame of reference (50.22) the quantities T^{ret} which are of interest to us may be represented with the aid of (50.12) in the following way:

$$T^{\text{ret}}_{\alpha\omega}(E, \mathbf{e}) = \int dx e^{i(Ex^0 - \mathbf{ex}\sqrt{E^2 - \mu^2 - \mathbf{p}^2})} F^{\text{ret}}_{\alpha\omega}(x). \tag{50.26}$$

In accordance with (50.6) the integral in (50.26) is actually taken over the upper light cone $x^0 > |\mathbf{x}|$.

Let us investigate the possibility of analytic continuation of expression (50.26) into the upper half of the complex plane of the variable E. We note, first of all, that for real positive a we always have [103]

$$\operatorname{Im} \sqrt{E^2 - a} > \operatorname{Im} E. \tag{50.27}$$

Because of this if a purely imaginary quantity $i\Gamma$ is added to the real E:

$$E \to E + i\Gamma \quad (\Gamma > 0),$$

[103] A direct algebraic proof of inequality (50.27) is rather awkward. Its validity may be verified in a simpler manner by means of graphical constructions in the complex plane.

then for each value of x^0 there will always exist a region of $\mathbf{x}$ for which

$$x^0\Gamma + \mathbf{ex}\,\mathrm{Im}\,\sqrt{E^2 - \mu^2 - \mathbf{p}^2} > 0,$$

as a result of which expression (50.26) will not be analytic in the upper half plane of the variable E.

We see that this difficulty completely precludes the possibility of a direct analytic continuation of the expression (50.26) into the domain of complex values of the variable E. Moreover, expression (50.26) is meaningful for real E only if $E^2 > \mu^2 + \mathbf{p}^2$, since after going through the branch point $E_0 = \pm\sqrt{\mu^2 + \mathbf{p}^2}$ the integrand acquires an increasing factor $\exp\left\{\mathbf{ex}\sqrt{\mu^2+\mathbf{p}^2-E^2}\right\}$ and loses its meaning.

Thus, formula (50.26) represents the function T only along the two segments of the real axis

$$-\infty < E < -\sqrt{\mu^2 + \mathbf{p}^2}, \quad \sqrt{\mu^2 + \mathbf{p}^2} < E < \infty$$

and cannot be directly continued beyond the bounds of these segments.

It is also clear that completely analogous difficulties will arise if we attempt the analytic continuation of the advanced function $T^{\mathrm{adv}}(E, \mathbf{e})$. As a result of this it is necessary to adopt complicated artificial devices for the analytic continuation of the expressions T^{ret} and T^{adv}. The analytic continuation in the case of forward scattering may be regarded as a relatively simpler procedure, and we now proceed to investigate it.

50.3. *Outline of the Method of Obtaining Dispersion Relations for Forward Scattering*

In the case of forward scattering when $\mathbf{p} = 0$,

$$T(E, \mathbf{e}) = \int dx e^{i(Ex^0 - \mathbf{ex}\sqrt{E^2-\mu^2})} F(x), \tag{50.28}$$

and also [104]

[104] Here it is again essential to assume that there is no interaction with particles lighter than π-mesons.

$$T^{(\pm)}\left(\frac{q+q'}{2}\right) = T^{(\pm)}(q)$$

$$= \frac{(2\pi)^5\pi}{i}\,\delta(\sqrt{M^2+\mathbf{q}^2}-M\pm E)\sum_{s''}\langle 0\,s'|\,j_\rho(0)\,|\,\mathbf{q}s''\rangle\langle\mathbf{q}s''\,|\,j_{\rho'}(0)|0s\rangle$$

$$+\frac{(2\pi)^5\pi}{i}\sum_{(M_n>M+\mu)}\delta(\sqrt{M_n^2+\mathbf{q}^2}-M\pm E)$$

$$\times\langle 0\,s'\,|\,j_\rho(0)\,|\,\mathbf{q}n\rangle\langle\mathbf{q}n\,|\,j_{\rho''}(0)\,|\,0\,s\rangle. \quad (50.29)$$

We shall investigate the structure of the terms in (50.29) for arbitrary real values of E. In doing this we naturally shall not assume that E is restricted by conditions of the type

$$E^2 = \mu^2 + \mathbf{q}^2, \quad E > \mu,$$

but shall regard E as a variable which is independent of $\mathbf{q}$.

The first term in (50.29) gives a contribution different from zero for

$$E = \pm(\sqrt{M^2+\mathbf{q}^2} - M),$$

or, which is equivalent to it, for

$$E = \pm\frac{E^2 - \mathbf{q}^2}{2M} = \pm\frac{q^2}{2M}. \quad (50.30)$$

The contribution of the second term differs from zero for

$$|E| = \sqrt{M_n^2+\mathbf{q}^2}-M > \sqrt{(M+\mu)^2+\mathbf{q}^2}-M > (M+\mu)-M=\mu. \quad (50.31)$$

Thus, along the segment of the real axis $-\mu<E<\mu$ a contribution to T is given only by the intermediate single nucleon state for two values of the energy which are related to the square of the four-momentum by equation (50.30). Therefore, if instead of the function F we consider the expression

$$\tilde{F}(x) = -\left[\left(\frac{\partial}{\partial x^0}\right)^2 + \left(\frac{\Box}{2M}\right)^2\right]F(x), \quad (50.32)$$

which in the momentum representation is equivalent to multiplication by the polynomial

$$\tilde{T}(q) = \left[(q^0)^2 - \left(\frac{q^2}{2M}\right)^2\right]T(q), \quad (50.33)$$

then for values $-\mu < q^0 < \mu$ the functions $\tilde{T}^{(+)}$ and $\tilde{T}^{(-)}$ will vanish,[105] as a result of which [106]

$$\tilde{T}(q) = \tilde{T}^{\text{ret}}(q) = \tilde{T}^{\text{adv}}(q) \text{ for } -\mu < q^0 < \mu. \qquad (50.34)$$

From (50.28) it follows that the points $k^0 = \pm\mu$ are, generally speaking, branch points of the functions $\tilde{T}$. In order to eliminate the double sign in front of the square root $\pm\sqrt{E^2 - \mu^2}$ it is simplest of all to consider in place of the functions $T(E, \mathbf{e})$ their symmetrized and antisymmetrized combinations

$$\left.\begin{aligned} S_+ T(E, \mathbf{e}) &= \frac{T(E, \mathbf{e}) + T(E, -\mathbf{e})}{2}, \\ S_- T(E, \mathbf{e}) &= \frac{T(E, \mathbf{e}) - T(E, -\mathbf{e})}{2\lambda}, \end{aligned}\right\} \qquad (50.35)$$

the set of which we shall in future denote by ST. The functions ST^{ret} and ST^{adv} may be continued into the domain of complex values of E in the following manner. We introduce the expressions

$$S\int \tilde{F}^{\text{ret}}(x)\, e^{i(Ex^0 - \mathbf{ex}\sqrt{E^2-\mu^2}) - \varepsilon\mathbf{x}^2}\, dx^0\, d\mathbf{x} = \Phi^r(E, \mathbf{e}; \varepsilon), \quad (50.36)$$

$$S\int \tilde{F}^{\text{adv}}(x) e^{i(Ex^0 - \mathbf{ex}\sqrt{E^2-\mu^2}) - \varepsilon\mathbf{x}^2}\, dx^0\, d\mathbf{x} = \Phi^a(E, \mathbf{e}; \varepsilon), \quad (50.37)$$

where in accordance with (50.35)

$$S_+ e^{-i\mathbf{ex}\sqrt{E^2-\mu^2}} = \cos(\lambda\mathbf{ex}), \qquad (50.38)$$

$$S_- e^{-i\mathbf{ex}\lambda} = \frac{\sin(\lambda\mathbf{ex})}{i\lambda}. \qquad (50.39)$$

It is clear, first of all, that because of the presence of the factor $\exp(-\varepsilon\mathbf{x}^2)$ the function $\Phi^r(E, \mathbf{e}; \varepsilon)$ will be analytic in the upper half of the complex plane of E, while $\Phi^a(E, \mathbf{e}; \varepsilon)$ will be analytic in the lower half. Secondly, in virtue of (50.34)

$$\Phi^r(E, \mathbf{e}; \varepsilon) - \Phi^a(E, \mathbf{e}; \varepsilon) = 0 \text{ for } -\mu \leqq \operatorname{Re} E < \mu, \quad \operatorname{Im} E = 0.$$

[105] In virtue of relations of type $x\delta(x) = 0$.

[106] In virtue of the assumption $\mathbf{p} = 0$, since in the case $\mathbf{p} \neq 0$ the inequality (50.31) ceases to hold.

Thus the set of functions Φ^r and Φ^a represents the function

$$\Phi(E, \mathbf{e}; \varepsilon) = \begin{cases} \Phi^r(E, \mathbf{e}; \varepsilon) & \text{for } \operatorname{Im} E > 0, \\ \Phi^a(E, \mathbf{e}; \varepsilon) & \text{for } \operatorname{Im} E < 0, \end{cases} \tag{50.40}$$

which is analytic in the whole complex plane of its argument with the exception of the cuts

$$\left.\begin{array}{ll} -\infty < \operatorname{Re} E < -\mu, & \operatorname{Im} E = 0 \\ \mu < \operatorname{Re} E < \infty, & \operatorname{Im} E = 0. \end{array}\right\} \quad \text{and} \tag{50.41}$$

In the above the values of Φ along the upper edges of the cuts are equal to the values of Φ^r, while along the lower edges of the cuts they are equal to the values of Φ^a.

If we denote by n the rate of increase of the function Φ for large values of E we may apply Cauchy's integral theorem to the expression

$$\frac{\Phi(E, \mathbf{e}; \varepsilon)}{(E - E_0)^{n+1}},$$

where E_0 is a certain real parameter lying in the interval $(-\mu, +\mu)$.

We choose the contour of integration consisting of a circle of small radius δ about the point E_0, of two semicircles of large radius R, and of two contours connecting the aforementioned semicircles along the edges of the cuts and separated from these cuts by a distance δ (Fig. 57).
By letting R tend to infinity we make the integrals along the large semicircles vanish. Then by going to the limit $\delta \to 0$ we obtain:

$$\Phi(E, \mathbf{e}; \varepsilon) = \frac{(E - E_0)^{n+1}}{2\pi i} \int_{-\infty}^{-\mu} \frac{\Phi(E'+i0, \mathbf{e}; \varepsilon) - \Phi(E'-i0, \mathbf{e}; \varepsilon)}{(E' - E)(E' - E_0)^{n+1}} dE'$$

$$+ \frac{(E - E_0)^{n+1}}{2\pi i} \int_{\mu}^{\infty} \frac{\Phi(E'+i0, \mathbf{e}; \varepsilon) - \Phi(E'-i0, \mathbf{e}; \varepsilon)}{(E' - E)(E' - E_0)^{n+1}} dE' + P_n(E), \tag{50.42}$$

where $P_n(E)$ is a polynomial of the nth degree in E. We go to the limit $\varepsilon \to 0$ in the integrals in (50.42). Since the integration is taken over the observable region $E'^2 > \mu^2$ the numerators in the integrand in accordance with (50.36) and (50.37) will assume the form

$$\Phi^r(E', \mathbf{e}; 0) - \Phi^a(E' \mathbf{e}; 0) = S\tilde{T}^{\text{ret}}(E', \mathbf{e}) - S\tilde{T}^{\text{adv}}(E', \mathbf{e}).$$

The integrals themselves, multiplied by $(E - E_0)^{n+1}$, will for $\varepsilon = 0$ represent functions analytic over the whole complex plane of the variable E with the exception of the cuts (50.41). It

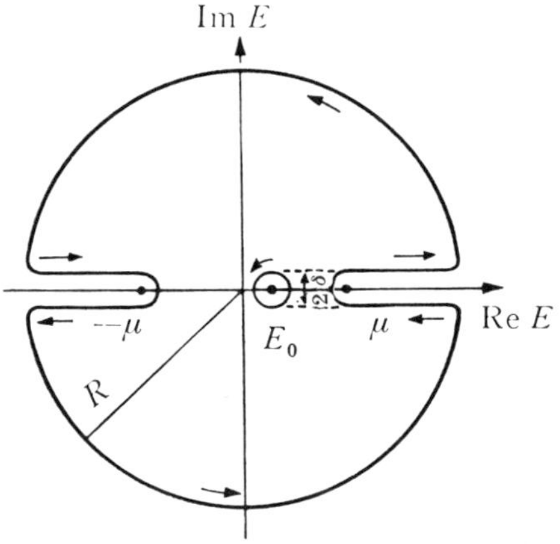

Fig. 57.

therefore follows from (50.42) that for $\varepsilon = 0$ the right-hand side defines a function $\Phi(E, \mathbf{e}; 0)$ which is analytic over the whole plane of E with the exception of the two cuts referred to above. But it follows from (50.30), (50.36), (50.37), and (50.40), that $\Phi(E, \mathbf{e}; 0)$ differs from the function

$$S\tilde{T}(E, \mathbf{e}) = \begin{cases} ST^{\text{ret}}(E, \mathbf{e}) & \text{for } \operatorname{Im} E > 0, \\ ST^{\text{adv}}(E, \mathbf{e}) & \text{for } \operatorname{Im} E < 0 \end{cases}$$

only by the factor (for $\mathbf{q}^2 = E^2 - \mu^2$)

$$E^2 - (\mu^2/2M)^2 = \left(E - \frac{\mu^2}{2M}\right)\left(E + \frac{\mu^2}{2M}\right) \tag{50.43}$$

It is therefore clear that the function $S\tilde{T}(E, \mathbf{e})$ will also be an analytic function over the whole complex domain of the variable E with the exception of the two cuts (50.41) and those points for which the factor (50.43) becomes equal to zero. At such points lying outside the cuts the function $S\tilde{T}(E, \mathbf{e})$ will have poles of the first order. Moreover, the function $S\tilde{T}$ will increase at infinity not faster than a polynomial of the $(n-2)$nd degree.

Consequently the Cauchy integral formula may be applied to the function $S\tilde{T}(E, \mathbf{e})/(E - E_0)^{n-1}$ with the contour of integration being chosen in such a way as to take into account the existence of additional poles associated with the factor (50.43) which appear at the points

$$E_1 = \mu^2/2M < \mu$$

$$E_2 = -E_1 = -\mu^2/2M > -\mu$$

and the contour of integration must include two additional circles around these poles as shown in Fig. 58.

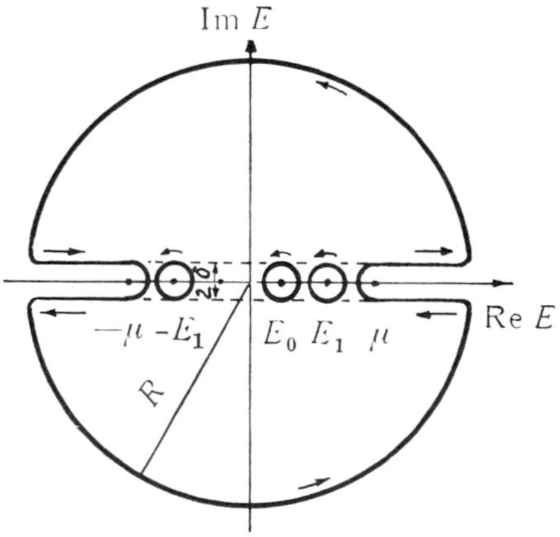

Fig. 58.

Then by going to the limit $R \to \infty$, $\delta \to 0$ we reduce the integral term to integrals over the observable region $(-\infty < E < -\mu)$, $(\mu < E < \infty)$, (analogous to 50.42)) and to residues at the poles $\pm E_1$. Then by letting the argument of the function $S\tilde{T}(E, \mathbf{e})$

which appears outside the integral tend towards the observable region we shall obtain the dispersion relations for the observable quantity $ST^c(E, \mathbf{e})$.

However, we shall not carry out the calculations now, having in mind that later (§ 51) we shall obtain the dispersion relations for the more general case $\mathbf{p} \neq 0$. These relations will be discussed in detail in § 52.

§ 51. Problems of Analytic Continuation of the Scattering Amplitude for $\mathbf{p} \neq 0$

We now proceed to derive the dispersion relations for the general case $\mathbf{p} \neq 0$. In the preceding section the scattering amplitude was represented by the integral

$$T^c(E, \mathbf{e}) = \int e^{i(Ex^0 - \lambda \mathbf{ex})} F^c(x) dx,$$

which we investigated in the case

$$\lambda^2 = E^2 - \mathbf{p}^2 - \mu^2. \tag{51.1}$$

As was shown in this case, all the difficulties presented by the analytic continuation into the domain of the complex values of E were associated with the fact that $\lambda^2 < E^2$. Therefore we shall first consider the fictitious case when $\lambda^2 > E^2$ and the operation of analytic continuation to complex values of E presents no difficulties, we shall construct the dispersion relations for this case, and we shall then carry out the analytic continuation into the region $\lambda^2 < E^2$ and obtain the dispersion relations for the actual case.

51.1. *Analytic Properties in the Fictitious Region* $\tau < -\mathbf{p}^2$

In place of (51.1) we set

$$\lambda^2 = E^2 - \mathbf{p}^2 - \tau, \tag{51.2}$$

where τ is a new auxiliary variable for the time being limited by the condition

$$\tau < -\mathbf{p}^2. \tag{51.3}$$

We now introduce the expressions

$$\left.\begin{aligned} ST^r(E, \mathbf{e}; \tau) &= S \int e^{i(Ex^0 - \mathbf{ex}\sqrt{E^2 - \mathbf{p}^2 - \tau})} F^{\text{ret}}(x)dx, \\ ST^a(E, \mathbf{e}; \tau) &= S \int e^{i(Ex^0 - \mathbf{ex}\sqrt{E^2 - \mathbf{p}^2 - \tau})} F^{\text{adv}}(x)dx, \end{aligned}\right\} \tag{51.4}$$

which in the actual case $\tau = \mu^2$ reduce to $ST^{\text{ret}}(E, \mathbf{e})$ and $ST^{\text{adv}}(E, \mathbf{e})$ which were discussed earlier (§ 50):

$$\left.\begin{aligned} ST^r(E, \mathbf{e}; \mu^2) &= ST^{\text{ret}}(E, \mathbf{e}), \\ ST^a(E, \mathbf{e}; \mu^2) &= ST^{\text{adv}}(E, \mathbf{e}). \end{aligned}\right\} \tag{51.5}$$

It is now clear that since in the region (51.3) we always have

$$\operatorname{Im} E > \operatorname{Im} \sqrt{E^2 - \mathbf{p}^2 - \tau} = \operatorname{Im} \lambda, \tag{51.6}$$

then $ST^r(E, \mathbf{e}; \tau)$ will be an analytic function in the region $\operatorname{Im} E > 0$ while $ST^a(E, \mathbf{e}; \tau)$ will be an analytic function in the region $\operatorname{Im} E < 0$.

In order to show that the function

$$\tilde{ST}(E, \mathbf{e}; \tau) = \left\{\begin{array}{ll} ST^r(E, \mathbf{e}; \tau) & \text{for } \operatorname{Im} E > 0, \\ ST^a(E, \mathbf{e}; \tau) & \text{for } \operatorname{Im} E < 0 \end{array}\right\} \tag{51.7}$$

will be analytic over the whole complex plane of E (with the exception, perhaps, of a certain number of points and cuts on the real axis) we consider the difference of the functions ST^r and ST^a for real values of E. In accordance with (51.4), (50.10), and (50.13) we have:

$$\begin{aligned} ST(E, \mathbf{e}; \tau) &\equiv ST^r(E, \mathbf{e}; \tau) - ST^a(E, \mathbf{e}; \tau) \\ &= S \int dx\, e^{i(Ex^0 - \lambda \mathbf{ex})} \{F^{(+)}(x) - P_{\rho\rho'} F^{(+)}(-x)\}. \end{aligned} \tag{51.8}$$

After substituting with the aid of (50.12) and (50.17) into the right-hand side of this expression an expression for $F^{(+)}$ in terms of sums over the complete system of states, we shall obtain after carrying out the integration (in the frame of reference in which $\mathbf{p} + \mathbf{p}' = 0$):

$$ST(E, \mathbf{e}; \tau) = (2\pi)^5 \pi i \sum_n \delta(E - \sqrt{\lambda^2 + M_n^2} + \sqrt{\mathbf{p}^2 + M^2})$$
$$\times\, S\langle \mathbf{p}' s' \mid j_{\rho'}(0) \mid \lambda\mathbf{e},\, n\rangle \langle \lambda\mathbf{e},\, n \mid j_\rho(0) \mid \mathbf{p}s\rangle$$
$$-\, (2\pi)^5 \pi i \sum_n \delta(E + \sqrt{\lambda^2 + M_n^2} - \sqrt{\mathbf{p}^2 + M^2})$$
$$\times\, S\langle \mathbf{p}' s' \mid j_\rho(0) \mid -\lambda\mathbf{e},\, n\rangle \langle -\lambda\mathbf{e},\, n \mid j_{\rho'}(0) \mid \mathbf{p}s\rangle. \qquad (51.9)$$

We now restrict ourselves to the domain of those momenta $\mathbf{p}$ for which

$$\mathbf{p}^2 < \frac{\mu M + \frac{\mu^2}{2} - \tau}{2}. \qquad (51.10)$$

We introduce the notation

$$E_1 = \frac{2M\mu + \mu^2 - 2\mathbf{p}^2 - \tau}{2\sqrt{M^2 + \mathbf{p}^2}} > 0. \qquad (51.11)$$

It is not difficult to show that the single nucleon terms in the sum (51.9) differ from zero only when

$$E = \pm E_p, \qquad E_p = \frac{2\mathbf{p}^2 + \tau}{2\sqrt{M^2 + \mathbf{p}^2}}. \qquad (51.12)$$

In the above we have in virtue of (51.11)

$$-E_1 < -E_p,\; E_p < E_1. \qquad (51.13)$$

On the other hand, in accordance with the assumption made earlier we have in the sums of (51.9) for all n, with the exception of the single nucleon term, $M_n > M + \mu$. From this it follows that the sums of all the terms in (51.9) with the exception of the single-nucleon term differ from zero only when

$$|E| = \frac{|M_n^2 - M^2 - 2\mathbf{p}^2 - \tau|}{2\sqrt{M^2 + \mathbf{p}^2}} > E_1. \qquad (51.14)$$

From this it follows that for $|E| < E_1$ only those single nucleon terms differ from zero in formula (51.9) which may be written in the form

$$ST(E,\ \mathbf{e};\ \tau)$$
$$= (2\pi)^5 \pi i \frac{2M^2 - \tau}{2(M^2 + \mathbf{p}^2)} \delta(E + E_p)\, S \sum_{s''} \langle \mathbf{p}'s' | j_{\rho'}(0) | \lambda\mathbf{e}, s'' \rangle \langle \lambda\mathbf{e}, s'' | j_\rho(0) | \mathbf{p}s \rangle$$
$$- (2\pi)^5 \pi i \frac{2M^2 - \tau}{2(M^2 + \mathbf{p}^2)} \delta(E - E_p)\, S \sum_{s''} \langle \mathbf{p}'s' | j_\rho(0) | -\lambda\mathbf{e}, s'' \rangle \langle -\lambda\mathbf{e}, s'' | j_{\rho'}(0) | \mathbf{p}s \rangle. \tag{51.15}$$

It is now clear that ST^r and ST^a represent the same analytic function $S\tilde{T}$ (see (51.7)) which is regular in the region $\operatorname{Im} E \neq 0$ with cuts along the real axis given by

$$-\infty < E < -E_1 \text{ and } E_1 < E < \infty \tag{51.16}$$

and with poles of the first order at the points E_p and $-E_p$.

We can formulate Cauchy's integral theorem for $S\tilde{T}$. We denote the rate of increase of the function $S\tilde{T}$ at infinity by n and introduce the function

$$\frac{S\tilde{T}(E,\ \mathbf{e};\ \tau)}{(E - E_0)^{n+1}}, \tag{51.17}$$

where E_0 is a certain real parameter lying within the interval

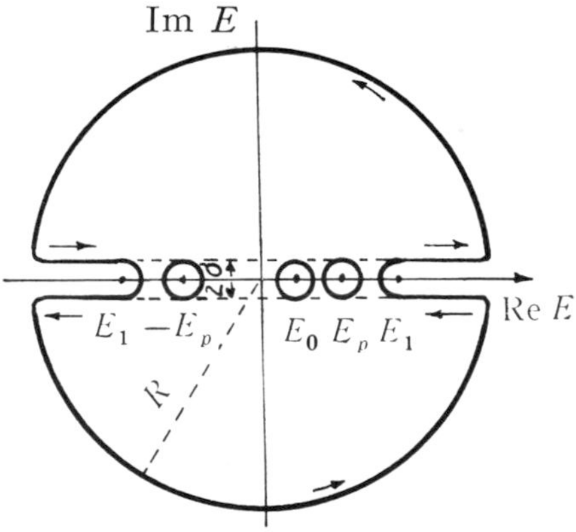

Fig. 59.

$(-E_1,\ E_1)$ and not coinciding with $\pm E_p$. By choosing the contour of integration as shown in Fig. 59 we can easily obtain after carrying out transitions to the limits $R \to \infty$, $\delta \to 0$:

$$S\tilde{T}(E, \mathbf{e}; \tau) = \frac{(E-E_0)^{n+1}}{2\pi i}\int_{-\infty}^{\infty} \frac{ST(E', \mathbf{e}; \tau)dE'}{(E'-E_0)^{n+1}(E'-E)} + \sum_{0\leqq k\leqq n} c_k(\tau)E^k$$

$$= \frac{(E-E_0)^{n+1}}{2\pi i}\int_{|E'|>E_1} \frac{ST(E', \mathbf{e}; \tau)\,dE'}{(E'-E_0)^{n+1}(E'-E)} + \left(\frac{E_0-E}{E_0-E_p}\right)^{n+1} \frac{A_{\rho\rho'}(-\lambda\mathbf{e}, \tau)}{E-E_p}$$

$$- \left(\frac{E_0 - E}{E_0 + E_p}\right)^{n+1} \frac{A_{\rho'\rho}(\lambda\mathbf{e}, \tau)}{E + E_p} + \sum_{0\leqq k\leqq n} c_k(\tau)E^k, \qquad (51.18)$$

where $C_k(\tau)$ are constants depending on τ, and

$$A_{\rho'\rho}(\lambda\mathbf{e}, \tau)$$

$$= (2\pi)^4\pi\frac{2M^2 - \tau}{2(M^2+\mathbf{p}^2)} S\sum_{s''}\langle\mathbf{p}'s'\,|\,j_{\rho'}(0)\,|\,\lambda\mathbf{e}, s''\rangle\langle\lambda\mathbf{e}, s''\,|\,j_\rho(0)\,|\,\mathbf{p}s\rangle. \quad (51.19)$$

We reiterate that so far the dispersion relation (51.18) has been obtained by us only for the fictitious nonobservable region (51.3) in which $\lambda^2 > E^2$, and that we must still carry out its analytic continuation to the point $\lambda^2 = E^2 - \mathbf{p}^2 - \mu^2$. However, before we undertake this we shall examine in greater detail the structure of the coefficients (51.19) which represent the contribution to ST of the single nucleon state.

51.2. *Structure of the Single Nucleon Term*

In order to put expression (51.19) into a simpler and more direct form we shall investigate a typical matrix element of the current evaluated between two single nucleon states $\langle\mathbf{p}''s''\,|\,j_\rho(0)\,|\,\mathbf{p}s\rangle$ which appears in it. After noting that in our fictitious case for any real value of E

$$\lambda^2 = E^2 + a, \quad a = -\tau - \mathbf{p}^2 > 0 \text{ and } \lambda^2 > 0,$$

we assume that both single nucleon states $\langle\,\mathbf{p}''s''\,|$ and $|\,\mathbf{p}s\rangle$ have real momenta. In virtue of invariance under translation we have after taking into account conditions 47.2C and 47.2F

$$\langle\mathbf{p}''s''\,|\,j_\rho(0)\,|\,\mathbf{p}s\rangle = ie^{i(p-p'')x}\left\langle\mathbf{p}''s''\left|\frac{\delta S}{\delta\varphi_\rho(x)}\right|\mathbf{p}s\right\rangle. \quad (51.20)$$

By going over in the right-hand side from variation with respect to $\varphi_\rho(x)$ to variation with respect to $\varphi_\rho(q)$ in accordance with the formula

$$\frac{\delta}{\delta\varphi_\rho(x)} = \frac{1}{(2\pi)^{5/2}} \int e^{iqx} \frac{\delta}{\delta\varphi_\rho(q)}\, dq,$$

we obtain:

$$\delta(q + p - p'')\langle \mathbf{p}''s'' \mid j_\rho(0) \mid \mathbf{p}s\rangle = \frac{i}{(2\pi)^{5/2}} \left\langle \mathbf{p}''\, s'' \left| \frac{\delta S}{\delta\varphi_\rho(q)} \right| \mathbf{p}s \right\rangle . \tag{51.21}$$

The matrix element which appears in the right-hand side of the above expression may be transformed by means of condition 47.3C. By commuting the nucleon creation and annihilation operators from the amplitudes $\langle \mathbf{p}''s'' \mid$ and $\mid \mathbf{p}s\rangle$ with $\delta S/\delta\varphi(q)$ (after taking into account in an appropriate way the anticommutativity of variational derivatives with respect to spinor fields) we obtain successively:

$$i\left\langle \mathbf{p}''\, s'' \left| \frac{\delta S}{\delta\varphi_\rho(q)} \right| \mathbf{p}s \right\rangle$$

$$= i \sum_{\alpha,\beta} \int dx\, dy [a_{s''}^{-}(\mathbf{p}''), \bar{\psi}_\alpha(y)]_+ [\psi_\beta(x), a_s^{*+}(\mathbf{p})]_+ \left\langle \frac{\delta^3 S}{\delta\bar{\psi}_\alpha(y)\delta\varphi_\rho(q)\delta\psi_\beta(x)} \right\rangle_0$$

$$= i \left(\bar{v}^{s'',+}(\mathbf{p}'') \left\langle \frac{\delta^3 S}{\delta\bar{\psi}(p'')\,\delta\varphi_\rho(q)\,\delta\psi(p)} \right\rangle_0 v^{s,-}(\mathbf{p}) \right),$$

$$(p^0 = \sqrt{\mathbf{p}^2 + M^2}, \quad p''^0 = \sqrt{\mathbf{p}''^2 + M^2}).$$

We now investigate the vacuum expectation value of the third variational derivative appearing in the above expression. From considerations of invariance with respect to transformations from the extended Lorentz group and with respect to transformations of rotation in isotopic spin space it follows that

$$i\left\langle \frac{\delta^3 S}{\delta\bar{\psi}_\alpha(p'')\delta\varphi_\rho(q)\delta\psi_\beta(p)} \right\rangle_0$$

$$= \delta(p'' - q - p)\, \tau_\rho \sum_{\nu,\,\omega=0,\,1} \{[\hat{p}'']^\omega \gamma^5 [\hat{p}]^\nu\}_{\alpha\beta} h_{\omega\nu}(p''^2, p^2; q^2), \tag{51.22}$$

where $h_{\omega\nu}$ are scalar functions of three scalar arguments. Now, by taking into account the fact that only such p'' and p appear in (51.21) for which $p''^2 = p^2 = M^2$ and that the spinor functions $\bar{v}$ and v satisfy the Dirac equations, we obtain:

$$\langle \mathbf{p}'' s'' \mid j_\rho(0) \mid \mathbf{p}s \rangle = -\frac{g(k^2)}{(2\pi)^3} (\bar{v}^{s'', +}(\mathbf{p}'') \gamma^5 \tau_\rho v^{s, -}(\mathbf{p})), \quad (51.23)$$

where

$$g(k^2) = -\sqrt{2\pi} \sum_{\omega, \nu} M^{\omega+\nu} h_{\omega\nu}(M^2, M^2, k^2), \quad (51.24)$$

and

$$\mathbf{k} = \mathbf{p}'' - \mathbf{p}, \quad k^0 = \sqrt{\mathbf{p}''^2 + M^2} - \sqrt{\mathbf{p}^2 + M^2}. \quad (51.25)$$

It follows from (51.23) that the function $g(k^2)$ introduced in (51.24) is real:

$$g^*(k^2) = g(k^2). \quad (51.26)$$

We now return to expression (51.20) which is of interest to us. With the aid of (51.23) we transform the product of the matrix elements of the current which appears in it:

$$\sum_{s''} \langle \mathbf{p}' s' \mid j_{\rho'}(0) \mid \lambda \mathbf{e}, s'' \rangle \langle \lambda \mathbf{e}, s'' \mid j_\rho(0) \mid \mathbf{p}s \rangle$$

$$= \frac{g^2(k^2)}{(2\pi)^6} \sum_{s''} (\bar{v}^{s', +}(\mathbf{p}') \gamma^5 \tau_{\rho'} v^{s'', -}(\lambda \mathbf{e})) (\bar{v}^{s'', +}(\lambda \mathbf{e}) \gamma^5 \tau_\rho v^{s, -}(\mathbf{p})), \quad (51.27)$$

where in accordance with (51.25) and (50.25)

$$k^2 = (\sqrt{M^2 + \mathbf{p}'^2} - \sqrt{\lambda^2 + M^2})^2 - (\mathbf{p}' - \lambda \mathbf{e})^2$$
$$= (\sqrt{\lambda^2 + M^2} - \sqrt{M^2 + \mathbf{p}^2})^2 - (\lambda \mathbf{e} - \mathbf{p})^2 = 2M^2 - 2\sqrt{M^2 + \mathbf{p}^2}\sqrt{M^2 + \lambda^2}.$$

By substituting (51.2) and (51.12) into the above:

$$\lambda^2 = E_p^2 - \mathbf{p}^2 - \tau = \frac{(2\mathbf{p}^2 + \tau)^2}{4(M^2 + \mathbf{p}^2)} - \mathbf{p}^2 - \tau,$$

we obtain after an elementary calculation

$$k^2 = \tau. \quad (51.28)$$

The summation has been reduced in this case to a summation

over the spin and the isotopic spin indices of the nucleon. By utilizing the formula for the summation over the spin index from § 7.2

$$\sum_{\sigma} v^{\sigma, -}_{t', \alpha}(k)\, \bar{v}^{\sigma, +}_{t, \beta}(k) = \frac{(\hat{k} + M)_{\alpha\beta}}{2k^0}\, \delta_{t' t} \tag{51.29}$$

(here α, β are the usual four-valued Dirac indices, while t', t are two-valued isotopic spin indices) we obtain finally, after substituting (51.27) into (51.20) and combining the matrices γ^5,

$$\begin{aligned} A_{\rho'\rho}(\lambda\mathbf{e}, \tau) &= \frac{g^2(\tau)}{4\pi} \frac{2M^2 - \tau}{2(M^2 + \mathbf{p}^2)} \left(\bar{v}^{s', +}(\mathbf{p}')\, \tau_{\rho'} \tau_{\rho} S \frac{\hat{\lambda} - M}{2\lambda^0} v^{s, -}(\mathbf{p}) \right) \\ &= \frac{g^2(\tau)}{4\pi} \frac{\bar{v}^{s', +}(\mathbf{p}')\, \tau_{\rho'} \tau_{\rho} S(\hat{\lambda} - M) v^{s, -}(\mathbf{p})}{2\sqrt{M^2 + \mathbf{p}^2}}, \end{aligned} \tag{51.30}$$

since

$$\lambda^0 = \sqrt{\boldsymbol{\lambda}^2 + M^2} = \frac{2M^2 - \tau}{2\sqrt{M^2 + \mathbf{p}^2}} \quad \text{and } \boldsymbol{\lambda} = \lambda\mathbf{e}. \tag{51.31}$$

51.3. *An Auxiliary Theorem*

We have derived above formula (51.18) from which we can obtain the dispersion relation. However, it was obtained for the fictitious case $\tau < -\mathbf{p}^2$ and we must still make the transition to the real case $\tau = \mu^2$ which we shall carry out by the method of analytic continuation with respect to the auxiliary variable τ.

We note that in § 50.3 in the course of deriving the dispersion relations for forward scattering, we have in fact made use only of the general properties of the functions F^{ret} and F^{adv} of being advanced, or retarded, or equal to one another within a certain domain of their momentum representations. The arguments to be given will also consist of an analysis of the general properties of matrix elements of the type of F^{ret} and F^{adv}, but they will be essentially more complicated due to the necessity of taking into account the additional variable $\mathbf{p} = -\mathbf{p}'$.

In order to carry out the analytic continuation of the relations obtained above right up to the value $\tau = \mu^2$ we shall have to obtain more detailed information on the behavior of the function

ST, and in particular on the nature of its dependence on the nucleon momentum $\mathbf{p}$. With this in mind, we shall examine the expression

$$\langle \mathbf{p}'s' \mid j_{\rho'}(x) j_\rho(y) - j_\rho(y) j_{\rho'}(x) \mid \mathbf{p}s\rangle = \frac{1}{2\pi^2 i} e^{i\frac{p'-p}{2}(x+y)} F_{\alpha\omega}(x-y), \tag{51.32}$$

which in accordance with (50.8)–(50.11) is equal to the difference between the retarded and the advanced matrix elements. By going over to the momentum representation by means of a formula of the type of (50.12) we obtain:

$$\delta(p' - p + p_3 + p_4)\, T_{\alpha\omega}\left(\frac{p'-p}{2} + p_3\right)$$
$$= \frac{\pi i}{(2\pi)^3} \int \langle \mathbf{p}'s' \mid j_{\rho'}(x) j_\rho(y) - j_\rho(y) j_{\rho'}(x) \mid \mathbf{p}s\rangle e^{i(p_3 x + i p_4 y)}\, dx\, dy. \tag{51.33}$$

We now express the matrix element between single nucleon states which appears on the right-hand side of the foregoing expression in terms of vacuum expectation values with the aid of property 47.3C; by commuting the nucleon creation and annihilation operators from $\langle \mathbf{p}'s'|$ and $|\,\mathbf{p}s\rangle$ with $j(x)$ and $j(y)$ with the aid of formulas of type (47.14) we obtain:

$$\delta(p'-p+p_3+p_4) T_{\alpha\omega}\left(\frac{p'-p}{2}+p_3\right) = \frac{\pi i}{(2\pi)^6} \Big(\bar{v}^{s',+}(\mathbf{p}') \int e^{i(p'x_1 - px_2 + p_3x_3 + p_4x_4)}$$
$$\times \left\langle \frac{\delta^2}{\delta\bar{\psi}(x_1)\delta\psi(x_2)} [j_{\rho'}(x_3) j_\rho(x_4) - j_\rho(x_4) j_{\rho'}(x_3)] \right\rangle_0 v^{s,-}(\mathbf{p})\Big)\, dx_1\, dx_2\, dx_3\, dx_4. \tag{51.34}$$

By utilizing the fact that the integrand is invariant under translation we can now write:

$$T_{\alpha\omega}(q) = \frac{\pi i}{(2\pi)^6} \bar{v}^{s',+}(\mathbf{p})\, \tilde{D}(p', -p, p_3, p_4)\, v^{s,-}(\mathbf{p}), \tag{51.35}$$

$$\delta(p_1 + p_2 + p_3 + p_4)\, \tilde{D}(p_1, \ldots, p_4)$$
$$= \int D(x_1, x_2, x_3, x_4)\, e^{i(p_1x_1 + \ldots + p_4x_4)}\, dx_1 \ldots dx_4, \tag{51.36}$$

$$D(x_1, x_2, x_3, x_q) = \left\langle \frac{\delta^2}{\delta\bar{\psi}(x_1)\,\delta\psi(x_2)} [j_{\rho'}(x_3), j_\rho(x_4)]_- \right\rangle_0 \quad (51.37)$$

and

$$q = \frac{p' - p}{2} + p_3, \quad p' - p + p_3 + p_4 = 0. \quad (51.38)$$

It is clear that in the case of interest to us

$$T(E, \mathbf{e}; \tau) = \frac{\pi i}{(2\pi)^6} \bar{v}^{s',+}(\mathbf{p}')\,\tilde{D}(p', -p, p_3, p_4)\, v^{s,-}(\mathbf{p}), \quad (51.39)$$

where in accordance with (50.22)

$$\mathbf{p} + \mathbf{p}' = 0, \; p'^0 = p^0 = \sqrt{\mathbf{p}^2 + M^2}, \; p_3^0 + p_4^0 = 0, \quad (51.40)$$

$$\mathbf{p}_3 = \mathbf{p} + \lambda\mathbf{e}, \; \mathbf{p}_4 = \mathbf{p} - \lambda\mathbf{e}, \; \lambda^2 = E^2 - \mathbf{p}^2 - \tau. \quad (51.41)$$

We now make use of the following theorem.[107]

Suppose that we are given four groups of generalized functions invariant under translations

$$D_{ij}^{(\alpha)}(x_1, \ldots, x_4) \quad (\alpha = 1, 2, 3, 4; \; i, j = a, r) \quad (51.42)$$

which transform according to linear finite-dimensional representations of the Lorentz group and which have the properties

$$\begin{aligned}
D_{rr}^{(\alpha)}(x_1, \ldots, x_4) &= 0 \quad \text{for} \quad x_1 \lesssim x_3 \quad \text{or} \quad x_2 \lesssim x_4; \\
D_{ra}^{(\alpha)}(x_1, \ldots, x_4) &= 0 \quad \text{for} \quad x_1 \lesssim x_3 \quad \text{or} \quad x_2 \gtrsim x_4; \\
D_{ar}^{(\alpha)}(x_1, \ldots, x_4) &= 0 \quad \text{for} \quad x_1 \gtrsim x_3 \quad \text{or} \quad x_2 \lesssim x_4; \\
D_{aa}^{(\alpha)}(x_1, \ldots, x_4) &= 0 \quad \text{for} \quad x_1 \gtrsim x_3 \quad \text{or} \quad x_2 \gtrsim x_4.
\end{aligned} \quad (51.43)$$

Suppose that, moreover, these functions satisfy the conditions

$$\begin{aligned}
\tilde{D}_{rj}^{(\alpha)}(p_1, \ldots, p_4) - D_{aj}^{(\alpha)}(p_1, \ldots, p_4) &= 0 \text{ for } p_1^2 < (M + \mu)^2, \; p_3^2 < (3\mu)^2; \\
\tilde{D}_{ir}^{(\alpha)}(p_1, \ldots, p_4) - D_{ia}^{(\alpha)}(p_1, \ldots, p_4) &= 0 \text{ for } p_2^2 < (M + \mu)^2, \; p_4^2 < (3\mu)^2
\end{aligned} \quad (51.44)$$

and

$$[(p_1 + p_3)^2 - M^2]\,\tilde{D}_{ij}^{(\alpha)}(p_1, \ldots, p_4) = 0 \quad (51.45)$$

[107] The proof of this theorem is given in the Mathematical Appendix.

if

$$(p_1 + p_3)^2 < (M + \mu)^2 \quad \text{or} \quad p_1^0 + p_3^0 < 0$$

Then it is possible to construct generalized functions $\Phi_\omega(z_1, \ldots, z_5; z_6)$ of the real variable z_6 which are analytic functions of the complex variables $z_1, \ldots, z_5$, and which have the following properties:

1. The functions Φ_ω are regular in the region

$$| z_1 - M^2 | < \rho\mu^2; \quad | z_2 - M^2 | < \rho\mu^2; \quad | z_3 - \tau^* | < \rho\mu^2;$$

$$| z_4 - \tau^* | < \rho\mu^2; \quad -4 \frac{M}{M + \mu} \mu^2 < \operatorname{Re} z_5 \leqq 0; \; | \operatorname{Im} z_5 | \leqq \rho\mu^2 \frac{M^2}{| z_6 |} \tag{51.46}$$

where ρ is a sufficiently small positive number, and the real τ^* satisfies the inequalities:

$$-V \leqq \tau^* \leqq \mu^2 \tag{51.47}$$

where V is some arbitrary, but fixed, positive number.

2. The functions Φ_ω satisfy

$$\Phi_\omega(z_1, \ldots, z_5; z_6) = 0 \quad \text{if} \quad z_6 < (M + \mu)^2 \tag{51.48}$$

3. For real $p_1, \ldots, p_4$ such that

$$p_1 + p_2 + p_3 + p_4 = 0$$

while the quantities

$$\begin{gathered} z_1 = p_1^2; \quad z_2 = p_2^2; \quad z_3 = p_3^2; \quad z_4 = p_4^2 \\ z_5 = (p_1 + p_2)^2; \; z_6 = (p_1 + p_3)^2 \end{gathered} \tag{51.49}$$

satisfy the inequalities (51.46), the functions $\tilde{F}_{ij}^{(\nu)}$ may be represented in the form of a sum with a finite number of terms

$$\left.\begin{aligned} &\tilde{D}_{ij}^{(\alpha)}(p_1, \ldots, p_4) = \sum_\omega p_{i_1}^{\alpha_1} \ldots p_{i_s}^{\alpha_s} \Phi(z_1, \ldots, z_5; z_6) \\ &\text{if} \\ &p_1^0 + p_3^0 > 0. \end{aligned}\right\} \tag{51.49a}$$

In order to apply the theorem we shall first have to check that the functions (51.37) and (51.39) under discussion can be represented in the form of a linear combination of functions satisfying the conditions of the theorem (51.43)–(51.45).

By carrying out in (51.39) the functional differentiation with respect to the spinor fields we obtain:

$$D(x_1, x_2, x_3, x_4) = (1 - P_{\rho\rho'} P_{34})\, d(x_1, x_2, x_3, x_4), \qquad (51.50)$$

where

$$d(x_1, x_2, x_3, x_4) = \left\langle \frac{\delta^2}{\delta\bar{\psi}(x_1)\delta\psi(x_2)} j_{\rho'}(x_3) j_\rho(x_4) \right\rangle_0 = \sum_{1 \leqq i \leqq 4} d^i(x_1, x_2, x_3, x_4),$$

and

$$\left.\begin{aligned}
d^1(x_1, x_2, x_3, x_4) &= \left\langle \frac{\delta j_{\rho'}(x_3)\, \delta j_\rho(x_4)}{\delta\bar{\psi}(x_1)\delta\psi(x_2)} \right\rangle_0, \\
d^2(x_1, x_2, x_3, x_4) &= -\left\langle \frac{\delta j_{\rho'}(x_3)\, \delta j_\rho(x_4)}{\delta\psi(x_2)\, \delta\bar{\psi}(x_1)} \right\rangle_0, \\
d^3(x_1, x_2, x_3, x_4) &= \left\langle \left\{ \frac{\delta^2}{\delta\bar{\psi}(x_1)\, \delta\psi(x_2)} j_{\rho'}(x_3) \right\} j_\rho(x_4) \right\rangle_0, \\
d^4(x_1, x_2, x_3, x_4) &= \left\langle j_{\rho'}(x_3) \left\{ \frac{\delta^2}{\delta\bar{\psi}(x_1)\, \delta\psi(x_2)} j_\rho(x_4) \right\} \right\rangle_0.
\end{aligned}\right\} \qquad (51.51)$$

Let us consider the expression for d^3. By applying to it condition 47.2D we obtain:

$$d^3(x_1, x_2, x_3, x_4) = \left\langle \frac{\delta^2 j_{\rho'}(x_3)}{\delta\bar{\psi}(x_1)\, \delta\psi(x_2)} \right\rangle_0 \langle j_\rho(x_4) \rangle_0$$

$$+ \sum_n \int d\mathbf{k} \left\langle 0 \left| \frac{\delta^2 j_{\rho'}(x_3)}{\delta\bar{\psi}(x_1)\, \delta\psi(x_2)} \right| n\mathbf{k} \right\rangle \langle n\mathbf{k} \mid j_\rho(x_4) \mid 0 \rangle. \qquad (51.52)$$

As we have already noted earlier (§ 48.3) the vacuum expectation value of the current and the matrix elements of the current between the vacuum state and the one-meson and the two-meson states are equal to zero:

$$\langle j_\rho(x) \rangle_0 = \langle n\mathbf{k} \mid j_\rho(x) \mid 0 \rangle = 0,$$

while for

$$E_n^2(\mathbf{k}) - \mathbf{k}^2 \geqq (3\mu)^2$$

we have in virtue of conditions 47.2C and 47.2F:

$$\langle n\mathbf{k} \mid j_\rho(x_4) \mid 0 \rangle = \langle n\mathbf{k} \mid j_\rho(0) \mid 0 \rangle\, e^{i(E_n(\mathbf{k}) x_4^0 - \mathbf{k}\mathbf{x}_4)}. \qquad (51.53)$$

Thus, the function d^3 regarded as a function of x_4 is represented by a superposition of exponentials $\exp(ip_4 x_4)$ with p_4 restricted by the conditions $p_4^2 \geqq (3\mu)^2$ and $p_4^0 > 0$. Therefore

$$\tilde{d}^3(p_1, p_2, p_3, p_4) = 0, \text{ if } p_4^2 < (3\mu)^2. \tag{51.54}$$

In a quite analogous manner we find that

$$\tilde{d}^4(p_1, p_2, p_3, p_4) = 0, \text{ if } p_3^2 < (3\mu)^2. \tag{51.55}$$

If we also note that in virtue of the condition of causality

$$d^1(x_1, x_2, x_3, x_4) = 0 \qquad \text{if } x_1 \lesssim x_3 \text{ or if } x_2 \lesssim x_4 \tag{51.56}$$

and also

$$d^2(x_1, x_2, x_3, x_4) = 0 \qquad \text{if } x_2 \lesssim x_3 \text{ or if } x_1 \lesssim x_4 \tag{51.57}$$

then on taking into account (51.49), (51.50), (51.54) and (51.55) we see that the function $\tilde{D}$ satisfies condition (51.42).

We now proceed to the construction of the functions (51.43) and to conditions (51.44), (51.45). It is clear, first of all, that in virtue of (51.56) the function d^1 defined by (51.51) may be denoted by d^1_{rr} in the sense of (51.43). We then introduce the expressions

$$\left.\begin{aligned}
d^1_{ar}(x_1, x_2, x_3, x_4) &= -\left\langle \frac{\delta\vartheta(x_1)}{\delta\varphi_{\rho'}(x_3)} \frac{\delta j_\rho(x_4)}{\delta\psi(x_2)} \right\rangle_0, \\
d^1_{ra}(x_1, x_2, x_3, x_4) &= -\left\langle \frac{\delta j_{\rho'}(x_3)}{\delta\bar{\psi}(x_1)} \frac{\delta\bar{\vartheta}(x_2)}{\delta\varphi_\rho(x_4)} \right\rangle_0, \\
d^1_{aa}(x_1, x_2, x_3, x_4) &= \left\langle \frac{\delta\vartheta(x_1)}{\delta\varphi_{\rho'}(x_3)} \frac{\delta\bar{\vartheta}(x_2)}{\delta\varphi_\rho(x_4)} \right\rangle_0
\end{aligned}\right\} \tag{51.58}$$

(here $\vartheta + \bar{\vartheta}$ are defined by (49.1) and (49.2))

which are invariant under translation and transform in accordance with the spinor representations of the Lorentz group. In accordance with condition 47.2B these expressions also satisfy (51.43). We shall show that they also satisfy (51.44). As a starting point for our proof we take the identities

$$\frac{\delta j(x_3)}{\delta\bar{\psi}(x_1)} - \frac{\delta\vartheta(x_1)}{\delta\varphi(x_3)} = i[\theta(x_1), j(x_3)], \tag{51.59}$$

$$\frac{\delta j(x_4)}{\delta\psi(x_2)} - \frac{\delta\bar{\vartheta}(x_2)}{\delta\varphi(x_4)} = i[\bar{\theta}(x_2), j(x_4)]. \tag{51.60}$$

By forming the difference $d^1_{rr} - d^1_{ar}$ and taking (51.59) into account we obtain:

$$d^1_{rr}(x_1, x_2, x_3, x_4) - d^1_{ar}(x_1, x_2, x_3, x_4)$$
$$= i\left\langle \theta(x_1)\, j(x_3)\, \frac{\delta j_\rho(x_4)}{\delta\psi(x_2)} \right\rangle_0 - i\left\langle j(x_3)\, \theta(x_1)\, \frac{\delta j_\rho(x_4)}{\delta\psi(x_2)} \right\rangle_0 .$$

By making use of condition 47.2D for the first term in the above expression we find that its Fourier-transform vanishes for $p_3^2 < (3\mu)^2$. In an analogous manner we can see that the Fourier transform of the second term vanishes for $p_1^2 < (M + \mu)^2$. In this way we have obtained the first of conditions (51.44). In the same way we can verify without difficulty the remaining conditions (51.44) for the functions d^1_{ij}.

We finally proceed to the last condition (51.45). We have for d^1_{ij}

$$\left\{\left(\frac{\partial}{\partial x_1} + \frac{\partial}{\partial x_3}\right)^2 + M^2\right\} d^1_{rr}(x_1, x_2, x_3, x_4)$$
$$= \sum_n \int d\mathbf{k} \langle 0 \mid A(x_1, x_3) \mid n\mathbf{k}\rangle \langle n\mathbf{k} \mid B(x_2, x_4) \mid 0\rangle, \qquad (51.61)$$

where

$$A(x_1, x_3) = \left\{\left(\frac{\partial}{\partial x_1} + \frac{\partial}{\partial x_3}\right)^2 + M^2\right\} C(x_1, x_2),$$

$$B(x_2, x_4) = \frac{\delta j(x_4)}{\delta\psi(x_2)}, \qquad C(x_1, x_3) = \frac{\delta j(x_3)}{\delta\bar{\psi}(x_1)}.$$

But according to the property of translational invariance

$$\langle n\mathbf{k} \mid B(x_2, x_4) \mid 0\rangle = \langle n\mathbf{k} \mid B(0, x_4 - x_2) \mid 0\rangle\, e^{i\{E_n(\mathbf{k})x_2^0 - \mathbf{k}\mathbf{x}_2\}}, \qquad (51.62)$$

$$\langle 0 \mid C(x_1, x_3) \mid n\mathbf{k}\rangle = \langle 0 \mid C(x_1 - x_3, 0) \mid n\mathbf{k}\rangle\, e^{-i\{E_n(\mathbf{k})x_3^0 - \mathbf{k}\mathbf{x}_3\}}. \qquad (51.63)$$

On the other hand, the expression

$$\langle n\mathbf{k} \mid B(x_2, x_4) \mid 0\rangle = \langle n\mathbf{k} \left| \frac{\delta j(x_4)}{\delta\psi(x_2)} \right| 0\rangle$$

is equal to zero for states not containing nucleons due to the law of conservation of nucleon charge. With respect to the state containing one nucleon for which

$$E_n^2(\mathbf{k}) - \mathbf{k}^2 = M^2,$$

we can see that its contribution is nullified by the differential operator which appears in $A(x_1, x_3)$ as a result of which

$$\langle 0 \,|\, A(x_1, x_3) \,|\, n\mathbf{k} \rangle = 0$$

both for states containing no nucleons and one nucleon.

Therefore the sum (51.61) must be taken only over states for which

$$E_n^2(\mathbf{k}) - \mathbf{k}^2 \geqq (M + \mu)^2. \tag{51.64}$$

From (51.62)–(51.64) it follows that the function which appears in the left-hand side of (51.61) is given by a superposition of exponentials

$$\exp i\{q_1(x_1 - x_3) + q_2(x_4 - x_2) + k(x_2 - x_3)\}$$

such that

$$k^2 \geqq (M + \mu)^2, \quad k^0 > 0.$$

By introducing in accordance with (51.38) the notation

$$p_1 = -q_1, \quad p_2 = q_2 - k, \quad p_3 = q_1 + k, \quad p_4 = -q_2,$$

we see that

$$(p_1 + p_3)^2 = k^2 \geqq (M + \mu)^2 \text{ and } p_1^0 + p_3^0 > 0.$$

From this it follows that the Fourier transform of the left-hand side of (51.61) vanishes when $(p_1 + p_3)^2 < (M + \mu)^2$ or when $p_1^0 + p_3^0 < 0$ as a result of which the function d_{rr}^1 satisfies the condition (51.45). In exactly the same way we can check condition (51.45) for the functions d_{ra}^1, d_{ar}^1, d_{aa}^1.

It is clear that conditions (51.43)–(51.45) may be easily extended also to the functions d_{ij}^2 which differ from d_{ij}^1 by an interchange of the operators

$$\delta/\delta\bar{\psi}(x_1) \text{ and } \delta/\delta\psi(x_2).$$

51.4. *Special Representation of the Function ST*

We shall now show that having established the correspondence between formulas (51.49) and (51.40), (51.41) we may obtain on the basis of our theorem a special representation for the function ST in the region

$$|E| < E_1 \tag{51.64a}$$

(With the aid of this representation we shall then carry out the analytic continuation of the dispersion relation (51.18) up to the point $\tau = \mu^2$.)

In order to do this we shall substitute for the variables $p_1, \ldots, p_4$ the values (51.40), (51.41) which are of interest to us. We shall then obtain:

$$\begin{aligned} &p_1^2 = p'^2 = M^2; \quad p_2^2 = p^2 = M^2; \quad p_3^2 = q'^2 = \tau = \tau^*; \\ &p_4^2 = q^2 = \tau = \tau^*; \quad (p_1 + p_2)^2 = (p' - p)^2 = -4\mathbf{p}^2; \\ &(p_1 + p_3)^2 = (p' + q')^2 = \tau + 2E\sqrt{M^2 + \mathbf{p}^2} + M^2 + 2\mathbf{p}^2; \\ &(p_1^0 + p_3^0) \;= \sqrt{M^2 + \mathbf{p}^2} + E; \\ &(p_1 + p_4)^2 = (p' - q)^2 = \tau - 2E\sqrt{M^2 + \mathbf{p}^2} + M^2 + 2\mathbf{p}^2; \\ &(p_1^0 + p_4^0) \;= p'^0 - q^0 = \sqrt{M^2 + \mathbf{p}^2} - E. \end{aligned} \tag{51.65}$$

We first consider the inequalities appearing in (51.45). On substituting into them the values (51.65) and taking into account (51.14) we obtain

$$\begin{aligned} &E < E_1(\tau) \text{ instead of } (p_1 + p_3)^2 < (M + \mu)^2; \\ &E < -\sqrt{M^2 + \mathbf{p}^2} \text{ instead of } p_1^0 + p_3^0 < 0 \end{aligned} \tag{51.66}$$

and

$$\begin{aligned} &E > -E_1(\tau) \text{ instead of } (p_1 + p_4)^2 < (M + \mu)^2; \\ &E > \sqrt{M^2 + \mathbf{p}^2} \text{ instead of } p_1^0 + p_4^0 < 0. \end{aligned} \tag{51.67}$$

By taking this into account and by utilizing (51.65) we obtain the following expression for the Fourier transform $\tilde{D}(p_1, \ldots, p_4)$ of the function $D(x_1, \ldots, x_4)$:

$$\tilde{D}(p_1, \ldots, p_4)$$
$$= \sum_{\omega} P_{\omega} \Phi_{\omega}(M^2, M^2, \tau, \tau, -4\mathbf{p}^2; \tau + 2E\sqrt{M^2+\mathbf{p}^2} + M^2 + 2\mathbf{p}^2)$$
$$+ \sum_{\omega} P'_{\omega} \Phi'_{\omega}(M^2, M^2, \tau, \tau, -4\mathbf{p}^2; \tau - 2E\sqrt{M^2+\mathbf{p}^2} + M^2 + 2\mathbf{p}^2) \tag{51.68}$$

where

$$\Phi_{\omega}(\ldots) = 0 \text{ for } E < E_1(\tau); \quad \Phi'_{\omega}(\ldots) = 0 \text{ for } E > E_1(\tau) \tag{51.69}$$

while P_{ω} and P'_{ω} are polynomials in the components of the momenta. In accordance with (51.46) and (51.47) the expression (51.68) is valid if

$$-V \leqq \tau \leqq (1+\rho)\mu^2; \quad (\mathrm{Im}\,\tau = 0) \text{ and } \mathbf{p}^2 < \frac{M}{M+\mu}\mu^2. \tag{51.70}$$

The quantities Φ_{ω} and Φ'_{ω} appearing in (51.68) are analytic functions of the first five arguments regular in the following region

$$\mathbf{p}^2 < \frac{M}{M+\mu}\mu^2; \; -V \leqq \mathrm{Re}\,\tau \leqq (1+\rho)\mu^2; \quad |\mathrm{Im}\,\tau| < \rho\mu^2 \tag{51.71}$$

and are generalized functions of the sixth argument.

We now note that the set of conditions (51.69) leads to the function $\tilde{D}(p_1, \ldots, p_4)$ vanishing in the region (51.64a). Because of this the function ST obtained by means of the operation[108] S from the expression (51.39) has, provided conditions (51.70) are satisfied in the region (51.64a), the special representation

$$ST(E, \tau) = F_1(2E\sqrt{M^2+\mathbf{p}^2} + \tau; \tau) + F_2(-2E\sqrt{M^2+\mathbf{p}^2} + \tau; \tau) \tag{51.72}$$

where $F_i(\xi, \tau)$ are analytic functions of the variable τ in the region (51.71) and are generalized functions of the real variable ξ with the property

[108] The operation S is needed here because the polynomials P_{ω} and P'_{ω} may contain the first power of λ which depends on τ nonanalytically.

$$F_i(\xi, \tau) = 0 \text{ for } \xi < 2M\mu + \mu^2 - 2\mathbf{p}^2 \tag{51.73}$$

and differing from the terms in the sum of formula (51.68) by spinor factors and by the factor $\pi i S/(2\pi)^6$.

51.5. *Analytic Continuation Towards* $\tau = \mu^2$

Thus the verification of the conditions of the theorem is complete and we can now proceed to prove that it follows from the representation (51.72) that the relation (51.18) is valid at the point

$$\tau = \mu^2$$

of interest to us provided $\mathbf{p}^2$ is sufficiently small and satisfies condition (51.71).

In order to prove the last assertion we shall first take a negative τ satisfying condition (51.3). For such τ both the relation (51.18) established above and (in accordance with our theorem) the representation (51.72) are valid.

Substituting (51.72) into (51.18) we have:

$$\begin{aligned} S\tilde{T}(E, \mathbf{e}; \tau) &= \Phi_1(E, \tau) + \Phi_2(E, \tau) \\ &+ \left(\frac{E_0 - E}{E_0 - E_p}\right)^{n+1} \frac{A_{\rho\rho'}(-\lambda\mathbf{e}, \tau)}{E - E_p} \\ &- \left(\frac{E_0 - E}{E_0 + E_p}\right)^{n+1} \frac{A_{\rho'\rho}(\lambda\mathbf{e}, \tau)}{E + E_p} + \sum_{0 \leqq k \leqq n} c_k(\tau) E^k, \end{aligned} \tag{51.73a}$$

where

$$\Phi_{1,2}(E, \tau) = \frac{(E - E_0)^{n+1}}{2\pi i} \times \int_{-\infty}^{\infty} \frac{F_{1,2}(2E'\sqrt{M^2 + \mathbf{p}^2}; \tau)\, dE'}{\left(\pm E' \mp \frac{\tau}{2\sqrt{M^2+\mathbf{p}^2}} - E_0\right)^{n+1} \left(\pm E' \mp \frac{\tau}{2\sqrt{M^2+\mathbf{p}^2}} - E\right)}. \tag{51.74}$$

Let us take an arbitrary E_0 in the interval

$$|E_0| < \frac{M\mu - (\rho + 2\sigma)\mu^2}{\sqrt{M^2 + \mathbf{p}^2}}. \tag{51.75}$$

Then, in accordance with the properties (51.73) of the functions F_1 and F_2 and conditions (51.71) we see that the formulas (51.74) will define analytic functions of the variables E and τ in the region restricted by the conditions (51.71) and by the inequality

$$|\text{Im}\,\tau| < 2\sqrt{M^2 + \mathbf{p}^2}\,|\text{Im}\,E|.$$

On the other hand, as has been shown previously, the function $S\tilde{T}(E, \tau)$ is analytic in the region (51.6). Therefore the function

$$\{S\tilde{T}(E, \tau) - \Phi_1(E, \tau) - \Phi_2(E, \tau)\}\{E^2 - E_p^2(\tau)\} \quad (51.76)$$

will be analytic for the range of arguments defined by the set of conditions

$$\left.\begin{aligned} \text{Re}\,\tau &< (1 + \rho)\,\mu^2, \\ |\text{Im}\,\tau| &< \rho\mu^2, \\ \text{Im}\,\tau &< 2\sqrt{M^2 + \mathbf{p}^2}\,|\text{Im}\,E|, \\ |\text{Im}\,E| &> |\text{Im}\sqrt{E^2 - \mathbf{p}^2 - \tau}|. \end{aligned}\right\} \quad (51.77)$$

But in virtue of (51.73a) the function (51.76) must coincide with the polynomial in E

$$\begin{aligned} &\left(\frac{E_0 - E}{E_0 - E_p}\right)^{n+1} (E + E_p)\, A_{\rho\rho'}(\tau, -\mathbf{e}) \\ &\qquad - \left(\frac{E_0 - E}{E_0 + E_p}\right)^{n+1} (E - E_p)\, A_{\rho'\rho}(\tau, \mathbf{e}) \quad (51.78) \\ &\qquad + (E^2 - E_p^2(\tau)) \sum_{0 \leq k \leq n} c_k(\tau) E^k \end{aligned}$$

in the region of negative τ restricted by the condition (51.3). Therefore its $(n + 3)$th derivative with respect to E which is an analytic function in the region (51.77) vanishes in the region (51.3). In accordance with the theorem on the uniqueness of analytic functions we conclude that this derivative vanishes over the whole region (51.77). From this it follows that the function (51.76) is itself a polynomial in E of degree $(n + 1)$ in the region (51.77). Taking into account the fact that the function $E_p(\tau)$ is according to its definition (51.12) an analytic function in the region under consideration we obtain from the above that the functions $c_k(\tau)$ and $A_{\rho\rho'}(\tau)$ must be capable of being continued analytically into the region (51.77).

We shall now show that $c_k(\tau)$ and $A_{\rho\rho'}(\tau)$ are analytic functions in the broader region (51.71). In order to do this let us take any arbitrary value $\tau = \tau^*$ from the region (51.71) which does not lie on the real axis ($\text{Im}\,\tau^* \neq 0$) and let us construct the corresponding E^* by setting

$$E^* = E_r + iE_i,$$

where

$$2E_rE_i = \text{Im}\,\tau^*, \quad E_r < M, \quad E_r^2 - E_i^2 - \text{Re}\,\tau^* - \mathbf{p}^2 > 0.$$

It is clear that the "point" (E^*, τ^*) belongs to the region (51.77) as a result of which τ^* must lie in the region in which the functions $c_k(\tau)$ and $A(\tau)$ are analytic. From this it follows that these functions are analytic in the region (51.71) with a possible cut lying on the real axis ($\text{Im}\,\tau = 0$).

We shall now show that in fact there is no such cut and that the above functions are regular over the whole region (51.71). In order to do this, let us consider a real $\tau_r < (1 + \rho)\mu^2$ and let us introduce the points (E_+, τ_+) and (E_-, τ_-):

$$\tau_{\pm} = \tau_r \pm i\eta \quad (\eta > 0),$$

$$E_{\pm} = E_r \pm \frac{i\eta}{2E_r} \ (E_r > 0),$$

$$\mathbf{p}^2 + (1 + \rho)\,\mu^2 < E_r^2 < M^2.$$

For sufficiently small $\eta < \rho\mu^2$ the points (E_+, τ_+) and (E_-, τ_-) will satisfy conditions (51.77). We now note that in virtue of (51.74) the following limiting relations hold

$$\lim_{\eta\to 0} \Phi_i(E_{\pm}, \tau_{\pm}) = \lim_{\varepsilon\to 0} \Phi_i(E_r \pm i\varepsilon, \tau_r), \tag{51.79}$$

since the points $(E_r \pm i\varepsilon, \tau_r)$ as well as the points $(E_{\pm}, \tau_{\pm})$ satisfy the conditions

$$\begin{aligned} &\text{Re}\,\tau < (1 + \rho)\mu^2, \quad |\text{Im}\,\tau| < \rho\mu^2, \\ &\text{Im}\,\tau < 2\sqrt{M^2 + \mathbf{p}^2}\,|\text{Im}\,E|, \end{aligned} \tag{51.80}$$

which restrict the region in which the formulas (51.74) define the analytic functions Φ_1 and Φ_2. Then by going over in (51.74) to real E with the aid of formula (46.3) we obtain:[109]

$$\Phi_1(E_+, \tau_+) - \Phi_1(E_-, \tau_-) \to F_1(\tau + 2E\sqrt{M^2 + \mathbf{p}^2}),$$
$$\Phi_2(E_+, \tau_+) - \Phi_2(E_-, \tau_-) \to F_2(\tau - 2E\sqrt{M^2 + \mathbf{p}^2}).$$

On taking (51.72) into account this gives:

$$\Phi_1(E_+, \tau_+) + \Phi_2(E_+, \tau_+) - \Phi_1(E_-, \tau_-) - \Phi_2(E_-, \tau_-) \to ST(E_r, \mathbf{e}, \tau_r). \tag{51.81}$$

On the other hand, in virtue of (51.4) and (51.7)

$$S\tilde{T}(E_+, \tau_+) = \int e^{-\frac{\eta x^0}{2E_r}} F^{\text{ret}}(x)\, S \exp i[E_r x^0 - \mathbf{ex}\sqrt{E_r^2 - \tau_r - \mathbf{p}^2 - (\eta/2E_r)^2}]\, dx,$$

and therefore

$$S\tilde{T}(E_+, \tau_+) \to ST^r(E_r, \tau_r). \tag{51.82}$$

In an exactly analogous manner we can show that

$$S\tilde{T}(E_-, \tau_-) \to ST^a(E_r, \tau_r). \tag{51.83}$$

By combining (51.81)–(51.83) we obtain:

$$\lim\{S\tilde{T}(E_+, \tau_+) - \Phi_1(E_+, \tau_+) - \Phi_2(E_+, \tau_+)\} = \lim\{S\tilde{T}(E_-, \tau_-) - \Phi_1(E_-, \tau_-) - \Phi_2(E_-, \tau_-)\}. \tag{51.84}$$

But since at the points $(E_\pm, \tau_\pm)$ the function (51.76) is equal to the polynomial (51.78) a limiting relation of the type (51.84) will also hold for the latter. From this it follows that the expressions $A(\tau_r + i\eta)$, $c_k(\tau_r + i\eta)$ tend to the same limits as expressions $A(\tau_r - i\eta)$, $c_k(\tau_r - i\eta)$, as a result of which $A(\tau)$

[109] A direct use of formula (46.3) in the integrand of (51.74) gives rise to a product of two generalized functions. However, a more detailed examination shows that by introducing a "convolution" of these generalized functions one can justify this calculation.

and $c_k(\tau)$ have no cuts and are regular in the whole region (51.71).[110]

We now return to relation (51.73a); as we can now see, it holds at the points (E, τ) of the region (51.77). But the analytic function of the variables E and τ in the right-hand side of (51.73a) is regular in the broader region (51.80). Because of this we can carry out the analytic continuation of the function $S\tilde{T}(E, \tau)$ in such a way as to make it equal to the right-hand side of (51.73a) over the whole region (51.80).

We emphasize that for the analytic function $S\tilde{T}$ continued in the manner just indicated the usual relations with improper limits are valid:

$$S\tilde{T}(E + i\varepsilon, \tau) \to ST^r(E, \tau), \tag{51.85}$$

$$S\tilde{T}(E - i\varepsilon, \tau) \to ST^a(E, \tau), \tag{51.86}$$

provided only that E, τ, and $\lambda = (E^2 - \mathbf{p}^2 - \tau)^{1/2}$ are real and $\tau < (1 + \rho)\mu^2$.

Indeed, in virtue of (51.73a) we see that

$$\lim_{\delta \to +0} S\tilde{T}(E + i\delta, \tau) = \lim_{\delta \to +0} S\tilde{T}(E + i\delta, \tau + i2\alpha E\delta),$$

where

$$|\alpha| < -\frac{\sqrt{M^2 + \mathbf{p}^2}}{E}.$$

But, on the other hand, for sufficiently small δ the point

$$E_+ = E + i\delta, \quad \tau_+ = \tau + i2\alpha E\delta$$

lies in the region (51.77) within which we can use formulas (51.4) and (51.7) and write

[110] From here it follows, in particular, that the function $g^2(\tau)$ may be continued analytically to $\tau = \mu^2$. On the basis of definitions (51.22) and (51.24) and of Theorem IV from the Mathematical Appendix it may be easily shown that $g(\tau)$ may also be analytically continued to $\tau = \mu^2$. Since $g(\tau)$ is real for $\tau < -\mathbf{p}^2$ we have

$$\operatorname{Im} g(\tau) = 0 \text{ for } \tau < -\mathbf{p}^2$$

from which it follows that this relation will hold for $\tau = \mu^2$. This means that $g(\mu^2)$ is real and $g(\mu^2) > 0$.

$$S\tilde{T}(E + i\delta, \tau + i2\alpha E\delta) = S\int \exp\{-\delta x^0 + \mathbf{ex}\,\mathrm{Im}\sqrt{E_+^2 - \tau_+ - \mathbf{p}^2}\}$$
$$\times \exp i\{Ex^0 - \mathbf{ex}\,\mathrm{Re}\sqrt{E_+^2 - \tau_+ - \mathbf{p}^2}\}\,F^{\mathrm{ret}}(x)\,dx, \quad (51.87)$$

with

$$|\mathrm{Im}\sqrt{E_+^2 - \tau_+ - \mathbf{p}^2}| < \delta;$$

so that consequently

$$\lim_{\delta\to+0} S\tilde{T}(E + i\delta, \tau + i2\alpha E\delta) = ST^{\mathrm{ret}}(E, \tau).$$

In an analogous manner we can also verify the property (51.82).

We have thus established the validity of the relation (51.73a) over the whole region (51.77). But $\tau = \mu^2$ lies in this region for an arbitrary value of E which does not lie on the real axis. Therefore (51.73a) always holds provided

$$\mathrm{Im}\,E \neq 0, \quad \tau = \mu^2.$$

If we now introduce a change of variables of integration inverse to the one employed in going from (51.18) to (51.73a), we shall bring (51.73a) into the form (51.18) in which $ST(E', \mathbf{e}, \mu^2)$ will be replaced by the expression

$$F_1(\mu^2 + 2E'\sqrt{M^2 + \mathbf{p}^2};\, \mu^2) + F_2(\mu^2 - 2E'\sqrt{M^2 + \mathbf{p}^2};\, \mu^2), \quad (51.88)$$

which coincides with the preceding function in the observable region when

$$E'^2 > \mu^2 + \mathbf{p}^2.$$

Expression (51.88) vanishes when

$$|E'| < \frac{M\mu - \mathbf{p}^2}{\sqrt{M^2 + \mathbf{p}^2}},$$

while in the interval

$$\frac{M\mu - \mathbf{p}^2}{\sqrt{M^2 + \mathbf{p}^2}} < |E'| < \sqrt{\mu^2 + \mathbf{p}^2} \quad (51.89)$$

the direct definition of the function $ST(E', \mathbf{e}, \mu^2)$ in terms of the integral (51.4) has no meaning; the expression (51.88) may be regarded as the appropriate analytic continuation of this function into the interval (51.89).

Thus, we have proved the validity of relation (51.18) involving the extended function (51.87) for the value $\tau = \mu^2$ of interest to us. To accomplish the transition to real values of E we can make use of formulas (51.85)–(51.87). We shall carry out this transition as well as the derivation of the actual dispersion relations between the real and the imaginary parts of the scattering amplitude in § 52.

§ 52. Dispersion Relations for the Scattering of Pions by Nucleons

52.1. *Transition to Real Quantities*

In § 51 it was shown that for any arbitrary E not lying on the real axis ($\operatorname{Im} E \neq 0$) the following relation holds [111]

$$S\tilde{T}(E) = \frac{(E-E_0)^{n+1}}{2\pi i}\int_{-\infty}^{\infty}\frac{ST(E')\,dE'}{(E'-E_0)^{n+1}(E'-E)} + P_n(E), \tag{52.1}$$

where

$$ST(E') = ST^{\text{ret}}(E') - ST^{\text{adv}}(E') \quad (\operatorname{Im} E' = 0), \tag{52.2}$$

while the functions $S\tilde{T}$ has, in accordance with (51.85) and (51.86), the properties

$$\left.\begin{aligned} \lim_{\varepsilon\to+0} S\tilde{T}(E+i\varepsilon) &= ST^{\text{ret}}(E), & (52.3)\\ \lim_{\varepsilon\to+0} S\tilde{T}(E-i\varepsilon) &= ST^{\text{adv}}(E) & (52.4)\end{aligned}\right\}\quad (\operatorname{Im} E = 0).$$

We now choose some real value E^* from the observable region $E^* > (\mathbf{p}^2+\mu^2)^{1/2}$, set $E = E^* + i\varepsilon$ in (52.1), and carry out the transition to the limit $\varepsilon \to 0$. By using formula (52.3) in the left-hand side of equation (52.1) and formula (46.3) in the right-hand side of this equation, we obtain as a result

$$ST^{\text{ret}}(E) + ST^{\text{adv}}(E) = \frac{(E-E_0)^{n+1}}{\pi i}\int_{-\infty}^{\infty}\frac{ST^{\text{ret}}(E')-ST^{\text{adv}}(E')}{(E'-E_0)^{n+1}}\mathscr{P}\frac{dE'}{E'-E} + 2P_n(E). \tag{52.5}$$

[111] Here we omit the argument $\tau = \mu^2$.

We now note that in accordance with the results of § 51.1 and 51.2 the difference $ST^{\text{ret}}(E') - ST^{\text{adv}}(E')$ may be represented within the interval $|E'| < E_1$ in the form of a sum of two δ-like terms:

$$ST(E) = iSf(E) = \frac{ig^2}{2}\,\delta(E+E_p)\,B_{\rho'\rho}(\mathbf{e}) - \frac{ig^2}{2}\,\delta(E-E_p)\,B_{\rho\rho'}(-\mathbf{e}); \tag{52.6}$$

this allows us to carry out explicitly the integration over the interval $(-E_1, E_1)$. Here

$$B_{\rho'\rho}(\mathbf{e}) = \frac{4\pi}{g^2(\mu^2)}\,A_{\rho'\rho}(\mathbf{e}, \mu^2) = \frac{\bar{v}^{s',+}(\mathbf{p}')\tau_{\rho'}\tau_\rho S(\hat{\lambda} - M)\,v^{s,-}(\mathbf{p})}{2\sqrt{M^2+\mathbf{p}^2}} \tag{52.7}$$

and

$$g = g(\mu^2). \tag{52.8}$$

We shall call the constant g defined by relation (52.8) the mesonic charge.

It should be noted here that, as is well known, the procedure of introducing the mesonic charge it not unique also in the usual theory (cf. (65)). The point is that due to the meson mass μ being different from zero the range of the nuclear forces is finite. This leads to the impossibility (in contrast to electrodynamics) of constructing a classical macroscopic mesodynamics, and of relating the procedure of determining the mesonic charge to macroscopic experiments of the type of Millikan's experiment or of the experiment on the deflection of pith balls. In view of this the mesonic charge g has to be introduced in some way in terms of the fundamental quantities of the theory, and its numerical value has then to be determined by means of a comparison of the predictions of the theory with the data of microscopic experiments. It is clear that the method of introducing the mesonic charge is not in itself essential, however, some specific method of determining the numerical value of g has to be agreed on.

In accordance with (51.22) and (51.24) the formula (52.8) corresponds from the point of view of the usual theory to the definition

$$g\gamma^5\tau_\rho = g_0\Gamma^5_\rho(M^2, M^2; \mu^2), \tag{52.9}$$

where g_0 is the "bare" charge which appears in the interaction Lagrangian (33.7), while Γ^5_ρ is the vertex operator. By fixing the procedure of completing the definition of chronological products in such a way that

$$\Gamma^5_\rho(M^2, M^2; \mu^2) = \gamma^5\tau_\rho, \tag{52.10}$$

we are able to identify g_0 with g.

We also note that the function $\Gamma^5_\rho(M^2, M^2; \mu^2)$ has no direct relation to real processes, since the emission (or absorption) of a real meson ($q^2 = \mu^2$) by a real nucleon ($p^2 = M^2$, $(p \pm q)^2 = M^2$) is forbidden by the energy-momentum conservation law.

The next step in the transformation of equation (52.6) is associated with the separation of the Hermitean and the anti-Hermitean parts of the scattering amplitude. With this aim in view we shall examine the Hermitean properties of the functions ST^{ret} and ST^{adv}. We note, first of all, that it follows directly from the definition (50.4) that

$$F^{*\mathrm{ret}}_{\alpha\omega}(x) = P_{\rho\rho'} F^{\mathrm{ret}}_{\omega\alpha}(x). \tag{52.11}$$

From this in turn follows the relation expressing the Hermitean property in the momentum representation

$$T^{*\mathrm{ret}}_{\alpha\omega}(k) = P_{\rho\rho'} T^{\mathrm{ret}}_{\omega\alpha}(-k). \tag{52.12}$$

On the other hand we have in virtue of (50.13):

$$T^{\mathrm{adv}}_{\alpha\omega}(k) = P_{\rho\rho'} T^{\mathrm{ret}}_{\alpha\omega}(-k). \tag{52.13}$$

By combining (52.12) and (52.13) we obtain:

$$T^{\dagger\mathrm{adv}}_{\alpha\omega}(k) = T^{\mathrm{ret}}_{\alpha\omega}(k). \tag{52.14}$$

We have here introduced the notation

$$T^{\dagger}_{\alpha\omega}(k) \equiv T^{*}_{\omega\alpha}(k). \tag{52.15}$$

By going over in (52.14) to the arguments E and $\mathbf{e}$ we also obtain:

$$ST^{\dagger\mathrm{adv}}_{\alpha\omega}(E) = ST^{\mathrm{ret}}_{\alpha\omega}(E). \tag{52.16}$$

The relation (52.16) is a very important one since from it it follows directly that the linear combinations

$$\frac{ST^{\mathrm{ret}}_{\alpha\omega}(E) + ST^{\mathrm{adv}}_{\alpha\omega}(E)}{2} = D_{\alpha\omega}(E) \tag{52.17}$$

and

$$\frac{ST^{\mathrm{ret}}_{\alpha\omega}(E) - ST^{\mathrm{adv}}_{\alpha\omega}(E)}{2i} = A_{\alpha\omega}(E) \tag{52.18}$$

are Hermitean:

$$D^{\dagger}_{\alpha\omega}(E) = D_{\alpha\omega}(E), \quad A^{\dagger}_{\alpha\omega}(E) = A_{\alpha\omega}(E), \tag{52.19}$$

and represent the Hermitean and the anti-Hermitean parts of the function ST^{ret}, i.e.,

$$ST^{\text{ret}}(E) = D(E) + iA(E). \tag{52.20}$$

We shall now make an important assumption with respect to the value of the rate of increase n. We shall assume that $n = 1$, i.e., that for large values of E the scattering amplitude increases not faster than E (such an assumption agrees with experiment). It is interesting to note that, as was also the case earlier in § 48, 49, instead of having to specify the form of the interaction Lagrangian it turns out to be sufficient to fix the rate of increase.

On substituting formulas (52.17) and (52.18) into (52.5) and on making the above assumption we obtain

$$D_{\alpha\omega}(E) = \frac{(E - E_0)^2}{\pi} \int_{|E'| > E_1} \frac{A_{\alpha\omega}(E')}{(E' - E_0)^2} \mathscr{P} \frac{dE'}{E' - E}$$
$$+ \frac{(E - E_0)^2}{2\pi} \int_{|E'| < E_1} \frac{Sf(E')dE'}{(E' - E_0)^2(E' - E)} + P_1(E). \tag{52.21}$$

52.2. *Taking into Account the Symmetry Properties with Respect to E*

We shall now eliminate the integral over negative energies (from $-\infty$ to $-E_1$). For this purpose we shall take into account the symmetry properties with respect to the replacement $E \to -E$ in the individual terms of formula (52.21). On combining (52.13), (52.14), (52.17), and (52.18) we obtain:

$$(1 \pm P_{\rho\rho'}) D_{\alpha\omega}(q) = (P_{\rho\rho'} \pm 1) D_{\alpha\omega}(-q),$$
$$(1 \pm P_{\rho\rho'}) A_{\alpha\omega}(q) = -(P_{\rho\rho'} \pm 1) A_{\alpha\omega}(-q).$$

By noting that in accordance with their definition

$$S_+ f(E) = \frac{f(E, \mathbf{e}) + f(E, -\mathbf{e})}{2},$$

$$S_- f(E) = \frac{f(E, \mathbf{e}) - f(E, -\mathbf{e})}{2\lambda},$$

we can draw conclusions with respect to the parity properties of expressions of the type $(1 \pm P_{\rho\rho'})S_{\pm}A$ and $(1 \pm P_{\rho\rho'})S_{\pm}D$. In this way we obtain even functions of the energy

$$D_{\text{even}}(E) = \{(1 + P_{\rho\rho'})\,S_{+}D(E);\ (1 - P_{\rho\rho'})\,S_{-}D(E)\}, \tag{52.22}$$

$$A_{\text{even}}(E) = \{(1 - P_{\rho\rho'})\,S_{+}A(E);\ (1 + P_{\rho\rho'})\,S_{-}A(E)\}, \tag{52.23}$$

and odd functions of the energy

$$D_{\text{odd}}(E) = \{(1 - P_{\rho\rho'})\,S_{+}D(E);\ (1 + P_{\rho\rho'})\,S_{-}D(E)\}, \tag{52.24}$$

$$A_{\text{odd}}(E) = \{(1 + P_{\rho\rho'})\,S_{+}A(E);\ (1 - P_{\rho\rho'})\,S_{-}A(E)\}. \tag{52.25}$$

By turning to the parity properties of the function $Sf(E)$ we can easily show starting from (52.6) and (52.7) that the operations $(1 - P_{\rho\rho'})S_{+}$ and $(1 + P_{\rho\rho'})S_{-}$ lead to even expressions, while the operations $(1 - P_{\rho\rho'})S_{-}$ and $(1 + P_{\rho\rho'})S_{+}$ lead to odd expressions. We therefore have

$$f_{\text{even}}(E) = \{(1 - P_{\rho\rho'})\,S_{+}f(E);\ (1 + P_{\rho\rho'})\,S_{-}f(E)\},$$

$$f_{\text{odd}}(E) = \{(1 + P_{\rho\rho'})\,S_{+}f(E);\ (1 - P_{\rho\rho'})\,S_{-}f(E)\}.$$

By taking into account the symmetry properties of (52.21) and by carrying out explicitly the integration over the interval $|E| < E_1$ we obtain:

$$D_{\text{even}}(E) - D_{\text{even}}(E_0) = \frac{2(E^2 - E_0^2)}{\pi}\,\mathscr{P}\int_{E'}^{\infty} \frac{E'A_{\text{odd}}(E')dE'}{(E'^2 - E_0^2)(E'^2 - E^2)} - \frac{g^2}{2\pi}\left(\frac{E^2 - E_0^2}{E_p^2 - E_0^2}\right)\frac{E_p}{E_p^2 - E^2}\,B_{\text{odd}}(\mathbf{e}, \mathbf{p}) \tag{52.26}$$

and

$$D_{\text{odd}}(E) - \frac{E}{E_0}D_{\text{odd}}(E_0) = \frac{2E(E^2 - E_0^2)}{\pi}\,\mathscr{P}\int_{E_1}^{\infty} \frac{A_{\text{even}}(E')dE'}{(E'^2 - E_0^2)(E'^2 - E^2)} + \frac{g^2}{2\pi}\left(\frac{E^2 - E_0^2}{E_p^2 - E_0^2}\right)\frac{E}{E_p^2 - E^2}\,B_{\text{even}}(\mathbf{e}, \mathbf{p}). \tag{52.27}$$

Here

$$B_{\text{even}}(\mathbf{e}, \mathbf{p}) = \{-(1 - P_{\rho\rho'})\,S_{+}B_{\rho'\rho}(-\mathbf{e});\ (1 + P_{\rho\rho'})\,S_{-}B_{\rho'\rho}(-\mathbf{e})\}, \tag{52.28}$$

$$B_{\text{odd}}(\mathbf{e}, \mathbf{p}) = \{(1+P_{\rho\rho'})\, S_+ B_{\rho'\rho}(-\mathbf{e});\; -(1-P_{\rho\rho'})\, S_- B_{\rho'\rho}(-\mathbf{e})\}. \tag{52.29}$$

52.3 *Isotopic Spin and Spin Structure*

The dispersion relations just obtained actually do not yet refer to definite physical processes since the meson field φ describes pions of three different charges (1, 0, -1), while the nucleon field ψ describes four kinds of particles (proton, neutron, antiproton, and antineutron) with different values of the projection of their spins on a fixed axis. In order to obtain from (52.26), (52.27) dispersion relations for specific scattering processes, one must take into account the isotopic spin and the spin structure of the scattering amplitude.

We first consider the isotopic spin structure of the amplitude $T^{\text{ret}}_{\alpha\omega}$. From considerations of invariance in isotopic spin space it follows that $T^{\text{ret}}_{\alpha\omega}$ must have the form

$$T^{\text{ret}}_{\alpha\omega} = \delta_{t't}\delta_{\rho'\rho} T^{(1)} + \tfrac{1}{2}[\tau_{\rho'}\tau_{\rho} - \tau_{\rho}\tau_{\rho'}]_{t't} T^{(2)}. \tag{52.30}$$

This formula may be rewritten in a different form:

$$T^{\text{ret}}_{\alpha\omega} = \delta_{t't}\delta_{\rho'\rho} T^{(1)} - \boldsymbol{\omega}_{\rho'\rho}\boldsymbol{\tau}_{t't} T^{(2)}, \tag{52.31}$$

where

$$\omega^{\alpha}_{\rho'\rho} = -ie_{\rho'\rho\alpha}, \tag{52.32}$$

and $e_{\alpha\beta\gamma}$ is the completely antisymmetric unit tensor of the third rank ($e_{\alpha\beta\gamma} = -e_{\alpha\gamma\beta} = -e_{\beta\alpha\gamma}$ and $e_{123} = 1$). The matrix vector $\boldsymbol{\omega}$ introduced above is the isotopic spin operator for the pions. Indeed, it follows directly from (52.32) that

$$[\omega^{\alpha}, \omega^{\beta}]_- = ie_{\alpha\beta\gamma}\omega^{\gamma} \text{ and } \omega^2 = 2 = 1(1+1),$$

i.e., $\boldsymbol{\omega}$ is an angular momentum operator with the eigenvalues 1, 0, -1.

If we denote the operator of the total isotopic spin of the nucleon-pion system by $\boldsymbol{\Omega}$:

$$\boldsymbol{\Omega} = \boldsymbol{\omega} + \frac{\boldsymbol{\tau}}{2}, \quad \boldsymbol{\Omega}^2 = T(T+1),$$

we obtain:

$$\boldsymbol{\omega\tau} = \boldsymbol{\Omega}^2 - \boldsymbol{\omega}^2 - \left(\frac{\boldsymbol{\tau}}{2}\right)^2 = T(T+1) - 2 - \tfrac{1}{2}(1+\tfrac{1}{2}) = T(T+1) - \tfrac{11}{4}.$$

From this it follows that the eigenvalue of the operator $\boldsymbol{\omega\tau}$ in the state with the total isotopic spin $T = 3/2$ is equal to

$$\tfrac{3}{2}(\tfrac{3}{2} + 1) - \tfrac{11}{4} = 1,$$

while in the state with the total isotopic spin $T = 1/2$ it is equal to

$$\tfrac{1}{2}(\tfrac{1}{2} + 1) - \tfrac{11}{4} = -2.$$

Therefore if we introduce the amplitudes $T_{3/2}$ and $T_{1/2}$ which refer to states with definite values of total isotopic spin equal to 3/2 and 1/2 respectively, then it follows from (52.31) that

$$T_{3/2} = T^{(1)} - T^{(2)} \text{ and } T_{1/2} = T^{(1)} + 2T^{(2)},$$

i.e.,

$$T^{(1)} = \frac{T_{1/2} + 2T_{3/2}}{3}, \quad T^{(2)} = \frac{T_{1/2} - T_{3/2}}{3}. \tag{52.33}$$

Further, by going over to the consideration of specific physical scattering processes (i.e., by fixing not only the total isotopic spin T, but also its component T_3) one can express the quantities $T^{(1)}$ and $T^{(2)}$ in terms of the amplitudes of concrete physical processes. However, we shall not undertake this, and after referring the reader to the available literature [112] on the subject we shall proceed to discuss the spin structure of T^{ret}.

From considerations of invariance in ordinary three-dimensional space it follows that similarly to formula (52.31) $T^{\text{ret}}_{\sigma\sigma'}$ may be represented as a sum of a term independent of $\boldsymbol{\sigma}$ and a term linear in $\boldsymbol{\sigma}$. The linear term must contain the scalar product of $\boldsymbol{\sigma}$ and some axial vector. But from the available vectors $\mathbf{p}$ and $\mathbf{e}$ we can form only the one axial vector $[\mathbf{p} \times \lambda\mathbf{e}] = [\mathbf{q}' \times \mathbf{q}]$. We thus obtain:

$$T^{\text{ret}}_{\alpha\omega} = \delta_{\sigma\sigma'} T_{(1)} + i(\boldsymbol{\sigma}[\mathbf{p} \times \lambda\mathbf{e}])_{\sigma\sigma'} T_{(2)}. \tag{52.34}$$

By combining the results of our analysis in the spin and the isotopic spin spaces (formulas (52.30) and (52.34)), we obtain:

[112] See, for example, Goldberger, Miyazawa, and Oehme (53), and Fermi (38).

$$T^{\text{ret}}_{\alpha\omega} = \delta_{\sigma\sigma'}\delta_{\rho\rho'}\delta_{tt'}T^{(1)}_{(1)} + i(\boldsymbol{\sigma}[\mathbf{p}\times\lambda\mathbf{e}])_{\sigma\sigma'}\delta_{\rho\rho'}\delta_{tt'}T^{(1)}_{(2)}$$
$$+ \tfrac{1}{2}[\tau_{\rho'}, \tau_\rho]_{t't}\delta_{\sigma\sigma'}T^{(2)}_{(1)} + \frac{i}{2}[\tau_{\rho'}, \tau_\rho]_{tt'}(\boldsymbol{\sigma}[\mathbf{p}\times\lambda\mathbf{e}])_{\sigma\sigma'}T^{(2)}_{(2)}. \quad (52.35)$$

Expression (52.35) is somewhat awkward. However, in the dispersion relations T^{ret} does not appear itself but only the even and the odd components of its Hermitean and anti-Hermitean parts. By noting that in accordance with (52.15) the operation of taking the Hermitean conjugate consists in our case of taking the complex conjugate and replacing α by ω, i.e.,

$$\mathbf{p} \rightleftarrows \mathbf{p}' = -\mathbf{p}, \quad \rho' \rightleftarrows \rho, \quad \sigma' \rightleftarrows \sigma, \quad t' \rightleftarrows t,$$

we find that the operation of symmetrization with respect to ρ, ρ' and $\mathbf{e}$, $-\mathbf{e}$ commutes with the operation of taking the Hermitean conjugate, and that all the matrix factors in (52.35) are transformed into themselves as a result of taking the Hermitean conjugate. Therefore, by breaking up the functions $T^{(i)}_{(k)}$ in (52.35) into their real and imaginary parts:

$$T^{(i)}_{(k)} = D^{(i)}_{(k)} + iA^{(i)}_{(k)} \quad (i, k = 1, 2),$$

we obtain, after carrying out the operations $(1 \pm P_{\rho\rho'})S_\pm$, in place of (52.22)–(52.25):

$$D_{\text{even}}(E) = \{2\delta_{\sigma\sigma'}\delta_{\rho'\rho}\delta_{t't}D^{(1)}_{(1)}(E);\ i[\tau_{\rho'}, \tau_\rho]_{t't}(\boldsymbol{\sigma}[\mathbf{p}\times\mathbf{e}])_{\sigma'\sigma}D^{(2)}_{(2)}(E)\}, \quad (52.36)$$

$$A_{\text{even}}(E) = \{[\tau_{\rho'}, \tau_\rho]_{t't}\delta_{\sigma\sigma'}A^{(2)}_{(1)}(E);\ 2i\delta_{\rho'\rho}\delta_{t't}(\boldsymbol{\sigma}[\mathbf{p}\times\mathbf{e}])_{\sigma'\sigma}A^{(1)}_{(2)}(E)\} \quad (52.37)$$

and

$$D_{\text{odd}}(E) = \{[\tau_{\rho'}, \tau_\rho]_{t't}\delta_{\sigma\sigma'}D^{(2)}_{(1)}(E);\ 2i\delta_{\rho'\rho}\delta_{t't}(\boldsymbol{\sigma}[\mathbf{p}\times\mathbf{e}])_{\sigma'\sigma}D^{(1)}_{(2)}(E)\}, \quad (52.38)$$

$$A_{\text{odd}}(E) = \{2\delta_{\sigma\sigma'}\delta_{\rho'\rho}\delta_{t't}A^{(1)}_{(1)}(E);\ i[\tau_{\rho'}, \tau_\rho]_{t't}(\boldsymbol{\sigma}[\mathbf{p}\times\mathbf{e}])_{\sigma'\sigma}A^{(2)}_{(2)}(E)\}. \quad (52.39)$$

The function $B_{\rho\rho'}(\mathbf{e})$ which appears in formulas (52.28) and (52.29) should be subjected to a similar analysis. In order to do this we must write the spin and the isotopic spin structure of $B_{\rho\rho'}(\mathbf{e})$ in explicit form by going over from the eight-component spinors $\bar{v}$ and v to the four-component proton and neutron spinors by means of formulas of the type

$$v^s \equiv v_t^\sigma = \delta_t^P v_P^\sigma + \delta_t^N v_N^\sigma .$$

In this way in place of (52.28) and (52.29) we obtain

$$B_{\text{even}}(\mathbf{e}, \mathbf{p}) = \{2\delta_{t't}\delta_{\rho'\rho}\delta_{\sigma'\sigma}B_1(\mathbf{p});\ i[\tau_{\rho'}, \tau_\rho]_{t't}(\boldsymbol{\sigma}[\mathbf{p}\times\mathbf{e}])_{\sigma'\sigma}B_2(\mathbf{p})\}, \tag{52.40}$$

$$B_{\text{odd}}(\mathbf{e}, \mathbf{p}) = \{[\tau_{\rho'}, \tau_\rho]_{t't}\delta_{\sigma'\sigma}B_1(\mathbf{p});\ 2i\delta_{t't}\delta_{\rho'\rho}(\boldsymbol{\sigma}[\mathbf{p}\times\mathbf{e}])_{\sigma'\sigma}B_2(\mathbf{p})\}, \tag{52.41}$$

where

$$B_1(\mathbf{p}) = \frac{\bar{v}^{\sigma,+}(-\mathbf{p})(\gamma^0\lambda_0 - M)v^{\sigma,-}(\mathbf{p})}{4\sqrt{M^2+\mathbf{p}^2}}, \tag{52.42}$$

$$i(\boldsymbol{\sigma}[\mathbf{p}\times\mathbf{e}])_{\sigma'\sigma}B_2(\mathbf{p}) = \frac{\bar{v}^{\sigma',+}(-\mathbf{p})\,\mathbf{e}\gamma v^{\sigma,-}(\mathbf{p})}{4\sqrt{M^2+\mathbf{p}^2}} \tag{52.43}$$

In formulas (52.42) and (52.43) we have omitted the isotopic spin indices (N, P) of the four-component spinors since in virtue of the condition of isotopic spin symmetry the neutron and the proton spinors must be chosen in the same representation.

Expressions (52.42) and (52.43) may be evaluated explicitly to the end. For this purpose one can utilize the explicit form of the spinors $\bar{v}$ and v (for example, formula (7.41) with a subsequent generalization of the result to the case $p_2 \neq 0$, $p_1 \neq 0$ based on considerations of invariance under rotations in three-dimensional space). In this way we obtain

$$B_1(\mathbf{p}) = -\frac{M(\mu^2+2\mathbf{p}^2)}{4(M^2+\mathbf{p}^2)^{3/2}}, \tag{52.44}$$

$$B_2(\mathbf{p}) = \frac{1}{4(M^2+\mathbf{p}^2)}. \tag{52.45}$$

Collecting together the results of formulas (52.36)–(52.45), we write the dispersion relations (52.26), (52.27) in the form

$$D_{(i)}^{(i)}(E) - D_{(i)}^{(i)}(E_0) = \frac{2(E^2-E_0^2)}{\pi}\mathscr{P}\int_{E_1}^{\infty}\frac{E'A_{(i)}^{(i)}(E')dE'}{(E'^2-E_0^2)(E'^2-E^2)}$$
$$-\frac{g^2}{2\pi}B_i(\mathbf{p})\frac{E_p(E^2-E_0^2)}{(E_0^2-E_p^2)(E^2-E_p^2)} \quad (i = 1, 2), \tag{52.46}$$

$$D^{(i)}_{(k)}(E) - \frac{E}{E_0} D^{(i)}_{(k)}(E_0) = \frac{2E(E^2 - E_0^2)}{\pi} \mathscr{P} \int_{E_1}^{\infty} \frac{A^{(i)}_{(k)}(E')dE'}{(E'^2 - E_0^2)(E'^2 - E^2)}$$

$$- \frac{g^2}{2\pi} B_k(\mathbf{p}) \frac{E(E^2 - E_0^2)}{(E_0^2 - E_p^2)(E^2 - E_p^2)} \quad (i, k = 1, 2; \ i \neq k). \quad (52.47)$$

52.4. *The Nonobservable Region and Transition to the Case of Forward Scattering*

In order to make the transition to observable quantities in formulas (52.46) and (52.47) it is necessary to make use of the connection (46.20) between the imaginary part of the scattering amplitude and the total effective cross section. However, total effective cross sections are observable only for real values of the momenta when $E > (\mu^2 + \mathbf{p}^2)^{1/2}$ (cf. (50.24), (50.25)). Therefore the range of integration in (52.46) and (52.47) includes a non-observable interval

$$E_1 = \frac{M\mu - \mathbf{p}^2}{\sqrt{M^2 + \mathbf{p}^2}} < E' < \sqrt{\mu^2 + \mathbf{p}^2}. \quad (52.48)$$

From this we see that relations (52.46) and (52.47), generally speaking, contain nonobservable quantities.

An exception to this is the case of forward scattering when $\mathbf{p}^2 = 0$ and the region (52.48) reduces to a point. By utilizing (46.20) we obtain, after taking into account (52.44) and (52.45)

$$D^{(1)}_{(1)}(k) - D^{(1)}_{(1)}(k_0) = \frac{k^2 - k_0^2}{2\pi^2} \mathscr{P} \int_0^{\infty} \frac{k'^2 \sigma_1^1(k')dk'}{(k'^2 - k_0^2)(k'^2 - k^2)}$$

$$+ f^2 \frac{\mu^2}{M} \frac{k^2 - k_0^2}{[E^2 - (\mu^2/2M)^2][E_0^2 - (\mu^2/2M)^2]}, \quad (52.49)$$

$$D^{(2)}_{(2)}(k) - D^{(2)}_{(2)}(k_0) = \frac{k^2 - k_0^2}{2\pi^2} \mathscr{P} \int_0^{\infty} \frac{k'^2 \sigma_2^2(k')dk'}{(k'^2 - k_0^2)(k'^2 - k^2)}$$

$$- f^2 \frac{1}{M} \frac{k^2 - k_0^2}{[E^2 - (\mu^2/2M)^2][E_0^2 - (\mu^2/2M)^2]}, \quad (52.50)$$

$$D^{(2)}_{(1)}(k) - \frac{E}{E_0} D^{(2)}_{(1)}(k_0) = \frac{E\,(k^2 - k_0^2)}{2\pi^2} \mathscr{P}\int_0^\infty \frac{k'^2}{E'} \frac{\sigma_1^2(k')dk'}{(k'^2 - k_0^2)(k'^2 - k^2)}$$
$$+ 2f^2 \frac{E\,(k^2 - k_0^2)}{[E^2 - (\mu^2/2M)^2]\,[E_0^2 - (\mu^2/2M)^2]}, \qquad (52.51)$$

$$D^{(1)}_{(2)}(k) - \frac{E}{E_0} D^{(1)}_{(2)}(k_0) = \frac{E\,(k^2 - k_0^2)}{2\pi^2} \mathscr{P}\int_0^\infty \frac{k'^2}{E'} \frac{\sigma_2^1(k')\,dk'}{(k'^2 - k_0^2)(k'^2 - k^2)}$$
$$- f^2 \frac{2}{\mu^2} \frac{E\,(k^2 - k_0^2)}{[E^2 - (\mu^2/2M)^2]\,[E_0^2 - (\mu^2/2M)^2]}. \qquad (52.52)$$

We have here introduced the following notation for the magnitude of the meson momentum

$$k = \sqrt{E^2 - \mu^2} = \sqrt{\mathbf{q}^2},$$

and also

$$f^2 = \frac{1}{4\pi}\left(\frac{g\mu}{2M}\right)^2.$$

The formulas (52.49)–(52.52) considered in the region $0 < k < \infty$ represent the dispersion relations for forward scattering in their final form and contain no unobservable quantities. Of these formulas (52.49) and (52.51) correspond to scattering without a change in the direction of spin, while formulas (52.49) and (52.52) correspond to scattering without charge exchange for the nucleon.

§ 53. Conclusion

The main part of this book (Chapters III, IV, V) is taken up with a systematic and consistent development of perturbation theory. In its structure the presentation of this book differs considerably from the usual one. We did not adopt the Hamiltonian formalism and we have determined the scattering matrix directly from a number of physical conditions among which, in addition to the well-known conditions of unitarity and relativistic covariance, we have utilized the condition of causality in a new form. With the aid of these conditions, we have obtained a system of relations for the coefficients S_n in the expansion of the S-matrix in powers of the small interaction constant. Although the question of the properties of this expansion as a whole is as yet inaccessible to rigorous mathematical analysis, nevertheless, the problem of determining the coefficients S_n from the aforementioned conditions has turned out to be formulated quite correctly. Its complete solution has been accomplished by means of utilizing the Sobolev-Schwartz theory of generalized functions and a number of theorems of this theory established by Parasiuk.

A method has thus been developed for the actual construction of the operator functions S_n free of divergences. It has turned out that this method is equivalent to the usual subtraction procedure. In this way the latter, which until now had the nature purely of a set of prescriptions, has been given a rigorous mathematical foundation within the framework of perturbation theory.

A further utilization of the ideas upon which the construction of the scattering matrix is based, has enabled us to obtain the equation for the state amplitude (Chapter VI) from which it is possible, by means of an appropriate limiting transition, to obtain the Tomonaga-Schwinger equation. In the course of this transition the nature of additional divergences of "surface type" arising therein, and not removed by the usual counter terms, has become quite clear.

Although the problem of the removal of divergences from the individual terms of perturbation theory expansions may thus be considered solved, the question of the properties of the perturbation theory series as a whole remains for the time being open. In this connection the method of functional integration discussed in Chapter VII, which allows us to obtain closed expressions for the principal functions of quantum field theory, is of particular interest. However, these closed functions which have the appearance of "quadratures" are in the form of continuous integrals, the technique for the evaluation of which is at present only in a rudimentary stage. Because of this, no essentially new results in quantum field theory have as yet been obtained by the method of functional integration.

The method of the renormalization group (Chapter VIII) also

represents an attempt to go beyond the framework of the usual perturbation theory. The essence of this method consists of a regrouping of the perturbation theory series, the sum of any finite number of terms of which is not invariant with respect to the group of multiplicative renormalizations, in such a way as to put it into invariant form. Here it was possible to obtain an improvement of the approximation properties of the expansions for the principal Green's functions of quantum electrodynamics. Proceeding in this direction, in contrast, for example, to the method of Schwinger's integral functional equations, one automatically establishes the domain within the limits of which one may obtain improved formulas by starting with the usual perturbation theory.

However, the existence of such a limit in the ultraviolet region of the momentum variables allows one to reach a conclusion with respect to the logical inconsistency of the weak coupling method in quantum electrodynamics. As regards the question of the possible logical inconsistency of quantum electrodynamics itself which has been widely discussed recently, an investigation by means of the method of the renormalization group allows one to conclude that this problem cannot be solved by using weak coupling methods, and requires for its solution the introduction of methods of intermediate and, possibly, of strong coupling.

But whereas in quantum electrodynamics, in view of the smallness of the square of the charge e^2, perturbation theory ceases to be applicable only at energies unattainable in practice, in pseudoscalar meson theory the method of weak coupling is not applicable at all, since the square of the corresponding charge $g^2/4\pi = 15$ and one may consider expansions in powers of this quantity only when one is "in a state of utter desperation."

In view of the circumstances just enumerated, the question arises of a radical departure from the weak coupling formulation of the theory of quantized fields. In our opinion at the present time there are two possible approaches, neither of which is in principle tied down to any form of perturbation theory, which offer definite promise of leading to significant results within the framework of the present local theory. The first such approach is the method of continuous integration which was already mentioned earlier. Here one might expect some progress to be made as a result of studying mathematical problems of the theory of functional integration. At the present time, in particular, a number of interesting results have already been obtained from numerical evaluation of such integrals which are, it is true, connected not with quantum field theory, but with simpler problems, such as, for example, the problem of the motion of an electron in a crystal.[113] However, the extension of these results to quantum field theory will require considerable difficulties to be overcome which are connected, in particular, with the removal of divergences.

Therefore, it seems to us that in the immediate future the second approach connected with the investigation of different kinds of dispersion relations (Chapter IX) is the more promising one. Using this approach it is apparently possible to obtain approximate equations (in models of the "single-meson approximation" type) which characterize in a sufficiently satisfactory manner the processes of meson-nucleon scattering, photoproduction, etc., at not too high energies ($\leqq 300$ Mev). However, it is hardly to be expected that such agreement will be preserved in going to higher energies since the situation will become considerably more complicated both because of the necessity of taking into account a large number of virtual π-mesons, and also because of the existence of heavier particles. Definite hopes are also engendered by the possibility of using dispersion relations for the experimental discovery of an "elementary length" of the order of the "nucleon radius" in scattering processes.

If the existence of such an elementary length will be established experimentally then, quite independently of the solution of the mathematical problem of the internal consistency or inconsistency of the present field theory and of the problem of the construction of a theory for intermediate and strong coupling, the problem will arise of creating a nonlocal field theory.

Conversely, if experiments will not demonstrate the existence

[113] Gel'fand, I. M., Minlos, R. A., and Yaglom, A. M. — report presented at the third All-Union Mathematical Congress (Moscow, July 1956).

of an elementary length of the order of 10^{-13} to 10^{-14} cm, then, independently of whether an elementary length of a smaller order of magnitude will be discovered in future, this will mean that a description of the processes of scattering, photoproduction, etc. up to energies of the order of several billion electron volts may be given on the basis of present local concepts.

Moreover, independently of the nature of possible changes in the mathematical methods and in the fundamental assumptions of local field theory, because of the singular nature of local commutation and causal functions the principal quantities in terms of which the theory will be formulated will have to be generalized functions, i.e., some modification of the subtraction formalism associated with the operation of multiplication of generalized functions will be an unavoidable attribute of any future local theory. The question of the existence of divergences in a possible future nonlocal theory of course remains open for the time being.

A List of Singular Functions

A. Auxiliary Singular Functions

The one-dimensional Dirac δ-function:

$$\delta(\alpha) = \frac{1}{2\pi}\int_{-\infty}^{+\infty} e^{i\alpha\tau}\, d\tau.$$

The four-dimensional Dirac δ-function:

$$\delta(x) = \frac{1}{(2\pi)^4}\int_{-\infty}^{+\infty} e^{ikx}\, dk$$

$$(kx \equiv k^0x^0 - \mathbf{kx}, \quad dk = dk^0 d\mathbf{k}),$$

$$\delta(x) = \delta(x^0)\,\delta(\mathbf{x}) = \delta(x^0)\,\delta(x^1)\,\delta(x^2)\,\delta(x^3)\,.$$

The step functions $\theta(\alpha)$ and $\varepsilon(\alpha)$:

$$\theta(\alpha) = \frac{1}{2\pi i}\int_{-\infty}^{+\infty} \frac{e^{i\alpha\tau}}{\tau - i\varepsilon}\, d\tau = \begin{cases} 1 & \text{for } \alpha > 0, \\ 0 & \text{for } \alpha < 0, \end{cases}$$

$$\varepsilon(\alpha) = \frac{1}{\pi i}\mathscr{P}\int_{-\infty}^{+\infty} e^{i\alpha\tau}\,\frac{d\tau}{\tau} = \theta(\alpha) - \theta(-\alpha) = \begin{cases} 1 & \text{for } \alpha > 0, \\ -1 & \text{for } \alpha < 0 \end{cases}$$

($\mathscr{P}$ denotes the principal value).

The positive- and negative-frequency parts of the δ-function:

$$\delta_{\pm}(\alpha) = \frac{1}{2\pi}\int_{0}^{\infty} e^{\pm i\alpha\tau}\, d\tau = \frac{1}{2}\left(\delta(\alpha) \pm \frac{i}{\pi}\mathscr{P}\frac{1}{\alpha}\right).$$

Some useful relations:

$$\frac{1}{\alpha + i\varepsilon} = \frac{2\pi}{i}\,\delta_+(\alpha) = \frac{\pi}{i}\delta(\alpha) + \mathscr{P}\frac{1}{\alpha},$$

$$\frac{1}{\alpha - i\varepsilon} = 2\pi i\delta_-(\alpha) = \pi i\delta(\alpha) + \mathscr{P}\,\frac{1}{\alpha}$$

$$\left(\mathscr{P}\,\frac{1}{\tau} = \frac{1}{2i}\int_{-\infty}^{+\infty} \varepsilon(\alpha)\, e^{i\alpha\tau}\, d\alpha\right).$$

B. Scalar Field Functions

The Pauli-Jordan commutation function $D(x)$:

$$[\varphi(x), \varphi(y)]_- = \frac{1}{i}D(x-y);$$

$$(\Box - m^2)D(x) = 0;$$

$$D(x) = \frac{1}{(2\pi)^3 i}\int e^{ikx}\,\varepsilon(k^0)\,\delta(k^2 - m^2)\,dk,$$

$$D(x) = \frac{1}{2\pi}\,\varepsilon(x^0)\,\delta(\lambda) - \frac{m}{4\pi\sqrt{\lambda}}\,\varepsilon(x^0)\,\theta(\lambda)\,J_1(m\sqrt{\lambda})$$

$$(\lambda = x^2 \equiv (x^0)^2 - \mathbf{x}^2).$$

In the neighbourhood of the light cone $D(x)$ has the form

$$D(x) \approx \frac{1}{2\pi}\varepsilon(x^0)\,\delta(\lambda) - \frac{m^2}{8\pi}\,\varepsilon(x^0)\,\theta(\lambda).$$

The positive- and negative-frequency parts of the Pauli-Jordan function $D^{(+)}(x)$ *and* $D^{(-)}(x)$:

$$[\varphi^{(-)}(x), \varphi^{(+)}(y)]_- = \langle\varphi(x)\,\varphi(y)\rangle_0 = \frac{1}{i}\,D^{(-)}(x-y),$$

$$[\varphi^{(+)}(x), \varphi^{(-)}(y)]_- = \frac{1}{i}\,D^{(+)}(x-y) = iD^{(-)}(y-x);$$

$$(\Box - m^2)\,D^{(-)}(x) = 0, \quad (\Box - m^2)\,D^{(+)}(x) = 0\,;$$

$$D^{(-)}(x) = \frac{i}{(2\pi)^3}\int e^{ikx}\,\theta(-k^0)\,\delta(k^2 - m^2)\,dk,$$

$$D^{(+)}(x) = \frac{1}{(2\pi)^3 i}\int e^{ikx}\,\theta(k^0)\,\delta(k^2 - m^2)\,dk;$$

$$D^{(+)}(x) = \frac{1}{4\pi}\,\varepsilon(x^0)\,\delta(\lambda) - \frac{mi}{8\pi\sqrt{\lambda}}\theta(\lambda)[N_1(m\sqrt{\lambda}) - i\varepsilon(x^0)\,J_1(m\sqrt{\lambda})]$$
$$+ \frac{mi}{4\pi^2\sqrt{-\lambda}}\theta(-\lambda)K_1(m\sqrt{-\lambda}),$$

$$D^{(-)}(x) = \frac{1}{4\pi}\,\varepsilon(x^0)\,\delta(\lambda) + \frac{mi}{8\pi\sqrt{\lambda}}\,\theta(\lambda)[N_1(m\sqrt{\lambda}) + i\varepsilon(x^0)J_1(m\sqrt{\lambda})]$$
$$- \frac{mi}{4\pi^2\sqrt{-\lambda}}\theta(-\lambda)\,K_1(m\sqrt{-\lambda}).$$

In the neighborhood of the light cone, $D^{(+)}$ and $D^{(-)}$ have the form

$$D^{(+)}(x) \approx \frac{1}{4\pi}\,\varepsilon(x^0)\delta(\lambda) + \frac{i}{4\pi^2\lambda} - \frac{im^2}{8\pi^2}\ln\frac{m\,|\,\lambda\,|^{1/2}}{2} - \frac{m^2}{16\pi}\,\varepsilon(x^0)\,\theta(\lambda),$$

$$D^{(-)}(x) \approx \frac{1}{4\pi}\,\varepsilon(x^0)\,\delta(\lambda) - \frac{i}{4\pi^2\lambda} + \frac{im^2}{8\pi^2}\ln\frac{m\,|\,\lambda\,|^{1/2}}{2} - \frac{m^2}{16\pi}\,\varepsilon(x^0)\,\theta(\lambda).$$

The causal Green's functions $D^c(x)$:

$$\langle T(\varphi(x)\,\varphi(y))\rangle_0 = \frac{1}{i}D^c(x-y);$$

$$(\Box - m^2)\,D^c(x) = -\,\delta(x);$$

$$D^c(x) = \frac{1}{(2\pi)^4}\int e^{ikx}\,D^c(k)\,dk, \quad D^c(k) = \frac{1}{m^2 - k^2 - i\varepsilon};$$

$$D^c(x) = \frac{1}{4\pi}\,\delta(\lambda) - \frac{m}{8\pi\sqrt{\lambda}}\,\theta(\lambda)[J_1(m\sqrt{\lambda}) - iN_1(m\sqrt{\lambda})]$$
$$+ \frac{mi}{4\pi^2\sqrt{-\lambda}}\,\theta(-\lambda)\,K_1(m\sqrt{-\lambda}).$$

The behavior of $D^c(x)$ in the neighborhood of the light cone:

$$D^c(x) \approx \frac{1}{4\pi}\,\delta(\lambda) + \frac{1}{4\pi^2 i\lambda} + \frac{im^2}{8\pi^2}\ln\frac{m\,|\,\lambda\,|^{1/2}}{2} - \frac{m^2}{16\pi}\,\theta(\lambda).$$

The retarded and the advanced Green's functions D^{ret} *and* D^{adv} :

$$D^{\text{ret}}(x) = 0 \text{ for } x^0 < 0; \quad D^{\text{adv}}(x) = 0 \text{ for } x^0 > 0;$$

$$(\Box - m^2)\, D^{\text{ret}}(x) = -\,\delta(x); \quad (\Box - m^2)\, D^{\text{adv}}(x) = -\,\delta(x);$$

$$D^{\text{ret}}(x) = \frac{1}{(2\pi)^4}\int \frac{e^{ikx}}{m^2 - k^2 + i\varepsilon k^0}\, dk; \; D^{\text{adv}}(x) = \frac{1}{(2\pi)^4}\int \frac{e^{ikx}}{m^2 - k^2 - i\varepsilon k^0}\, dk;$$

$$D^{\text{ret}}(x) = \frac{1}{2\pi}\,\theta(x^0)\left\{\delta(\lambda) - \theta(\lambda)\frac{m}{2\sqrt{\lambda}}\,J_1(m\sqrt{\lambda})\right\};$$

$$D^{\text{adv}}(x) = \frac{1}{2\pi}\,\theta(-\,x^0)\left\{\delta(\lambda) - \theta(\lambda)\,\frac{m}{2\sqrt{\lambda}}\,J_1(m\sqrt{\lambda})\right\}.$$

Relations between the functions D, $D^{(+)}$, $D^{(-)}$, D^c, D^{adv}, D^{ret} :

$$D(x) = D^{(+)}(x) + D^{(-)}(x),$$

$$D^c(x) = \theta(x^0)\, D^{(-)}(x) - \theta(-\,x^0)\, D^{(+)}(x),$$

$$D^{\text{ret}}(x) = \theta(x^0)\, D(x) = D^c(x) + D^{(+)}(x),$$

$$D^{\text{adv}}(x) = -\,\theta(-\,x^0)\, D(x) = D^c(x) - D^{(-)}(x),$$

$$D(x) = D^{\text{ret}}(x) - D^{\text{adv}}(x).$$

C. Singular Functions of the Electromagnetic, Vector and Spinor Fields

The electromagnetic field:

$$[A_m(x), A_n(y)]_- = ig^{mn}\, D_0(x - y);$$

$$\langle A_m(x) A_n(y)\rangle_0 = ig^{mn}\, D_0^{(-)}(x - y);$$

$$\langle T(A_m(x)\, A_n(y))\rangle_0 = ig^{mn}\, D_0^c(x - y)$$

$$(g^{mn} = 0 \text{ for } m \neq n; \quad g^{00} = -\,g^{11} = -\,g^{22} = -\,g^{33} = 1).$$

The functions D_0, $D_0^{(-)}$, D_0^c, etc. are obtained from the functions D, $D^{(-)}$, D^c of the scalar field for $m = 0$, for example:

$$D_0^c(x) = D^c(x)|_{m=0} = -\frac{1}{(2\pi)^4}\int \frac{e^{ikx}}{k^2 + i\varepsilon}\, dk = \frac{1}{4\pi}\left(\delta(\lambda) - \frac{i}{\pi\lambda}\right) = \frac{1}{2\pi}\,\delta_+(-\lambda).$$

The vector field:

$$[U_m(x), U_n(y)]_- = \frac{1}{i} D_{mn}(x-y);$$

$$\langle U_m(x)\, U_n(y)\rangle_0 = \frac{1}{i} D_{mn}^{(-)}(x-y);$$

$$\langle T(U_m(x) U_n(y))\rangle_0 = \frac{1}{i} D_{mn}^{c}(x-y).$$

The functions D_{mn}, $D_{mn}^{(-)}$, D_{mn}^{c}, etc. may be obtained from the corresponding functions of the scalar field by applying the differential operator

$$g^{mn} + \frac{1}{m^2} \frac{\partial^2}{\partial x^n\, \partial x^m},$$

for example:

$$D_{nl}(x) = \left(g^{nl} + \frac{1}{m^2} \frac{\partial^2}{\partial x^n\, \partial x^l}\right) D(x)$$

$$= \frac{1}{(2\pi)^3 i} \int \left(g^{nl} - \frac{k_n\, k_l}{m^2}\right) e^{ikx}\, \delta(k^2 - m^2)\, \varepsilon(k^0)\, dk,$$

$$D_{nl}^{c}(x) = \frac{1}{(2\pi)^4} \int \left(g^{nl} - \frac{k_n k_l}{m^2}\right) \frac{e^{ikx}}{m^2 - k^2 - i\varepsilon}\, dk.$$

The spinor field:

$$[\psi_\alpha(x), \bar{\psi}_\beta(y)]_+ = \frac{1}{i} S_{\alpha\beta}(x-y);$$

$$\langle \psi_\alpha(x)\, \bar{\psi}_\beta(y)\rangle_0 = \frac{1}{i} S_{\alpha\beta}^{(-)}(x-y);$$

$$\langle T(\psi_\alpha(x) \bar{\psi}_\beta(y))\rangle_0 = \frac{1}{i} S_{\alpha\beta}^{c}(x-y).$$

The functions $S_{\alpha\beta}$, $S_{\alpha\beta}^{(-)}$, $S_{\alpha\beta}^{c}$, etc. may be obtained from the corresponding functions for the scalar field by applying the operator

$$(i\hat{\partial} + m)_{\alpha\beta} \equiv i \sum_n \gamma_{\alpha\beta}^{n} \frac{\partial}{\partial x^n} + m I_{\alpha\beta}$$

the Dirac matrices γ are here defined by the relations $\gamma^n\gamma^m + \gamma^m\gamma^n = 2g^{mn}$, for example:

$$S^c(x) = \frac{1}{(2\pi)^4}\int \frac{m - \hat{p}}{m^2 - p^2 - i\varepsilon}\, e^{ipx}\, dp.$$

D. The Connection Between the Notation for the Singular Functions Used in This Book with the Notations of Stueckelberg-Rivier and of Schwinger

Our notation	Schwinger's notation	Stueckelberg–Rivier notation
$D(x)$	$-\Delta(x)$	$D^0(x)$
$D^{(-)}(x)$	$-\Delta^{(+)}(x)$	$\frac{i}{2}\, D^+(x)$
$D^{(+)}(x)$	$-\Delta^{(-)}(x)$	$\frac{1}{2i}\, D^-(x)$
$D^c(x)$	$\Delta_+(x)$	$D^c(x)$

The special functions $\Delta^1(D^1)$, $\bar{\Delta}(D^s)$ and D^a used by Schwinger and by Stueckelberg-Rivier:

$$\Delta^1(x) = D^1(x) = \frac{1}{(2\pi)^3}\int e^{ikx}\,\delta(k^2 - m^2)\, dk,$$

$$\bar{\Delta}(x) = D^s(x) = \frac{1}{(2\pi)^4}\,\mathscr{P}\int \frac{e^{ikx}}{m^2 - k^2}\, dk,$$

$$D^a(x) = \frac{1}{(2\pi)^4}\int \frac{e^{ikx}}{m^2 - k^2 + i\varepsilon}\, dk,$$

may be expressed in terms of the functions D, $D^{(-)}$, $D^{(+)}$, D^c, D^{ret}, and D^{adv} used in this book in the following manner:

$$\Delta^1(x) = D^1(x) = i(D^{(+)}(x) - D^{(-)}(x)),$$

$$\bar{\Delta}(x) = D^s(x) = \tfrac{1}{2}\varepsilon(x^0)\, D(x),$$

$$D^a(x) = \theta(x^0)\, D^{(+)}(x) - \theta(-\, x^0)\, D^{(-)}(x).$$

Mathematical Appendix [113a]

We introduce a number of definitions. We shall say that a certain function $h(x_1, \ldots, x_n; \theta_1, \ldots, \theta_q) = h(x; \theta_1, \ldots, \theta_q)$ continuous in $E_n \times \Omega_q$, where E_n is the real Euclidean space of the points $x = (x_1, \ldots, x_n)$ while Ω_q is a q-dimensional torus whose points are characterized by the angle variables $\theta_1, \ldots, \theta_q$, belongs to the class $C(r, s; n \mid \nu; \Omega_q)$ if all the expressions of the form

$$x_{\gamma_1} \ldots x_{\gamma_l} \frac{\partial^{p+\mu} h(x; \theta_1, \ldots, \theta_q)}{\partial x_{\alpha_1} \ldots \partial x_{\alpha_p} \partial \theta_{\beta_1} \ldots \partial \theta_{\beta_\mu}}, \quad \begin{array}{l} 0 \leqq l \leqq r,\ 0 \leqq p \leqq s,\ 0 \leqq \mu \leqq \nu, \\ 1 \leqq (\alpha_i, \gamma_i) \leqq n, \quad 1 \leqq \beta_i \leqq q \end{array}$$

exist and are bounded for all $(x_1, x_2, \ldots, x_n; \theta_1, \theta_2, \ldots, \theta_q) \in E_n \times \Omega_q$. If for such a function h some of the indices r, s, ν may take on arbitrarily large values we shall agree to insert ∞ in the appropriate places in specifying the class C. In the case when the functions under consideration do not depend on $x_1, \ldots, x_n$ or on $\theta_1, \ldots, \theta_q$ we shall speak of the class $C(\nu; \Omega_q)$ or $C(r, s; n)$ respectively.

For the class $C(r, s; n)$ we shall introduce the norm by means of the formula

$$||h|| = \sup_{\substack{x \\ 0 \leqq l \leqq r,\ 0 \leqq p \leqq s}} \left| x_{\gamma_1} \ldots x_{\gamma_l} \frac{\partial^p h(x)}{\partial x_{\alpha_1} \ldots \partial x_{\alpha_p}} \right| .$$

By this means, $C(r, s; n)$ is converted into a linear normalized space.

We shall refer to linear (bounded) functionals $f(h)$ in the spaces $C(r, s; n)$, where r, s are arbitrary nonnegative numbers, as generalized functions integrable over the class $C(r, s; n)$ and we shall use the symbols

$$f(x), \quad \int f(x)\, h(x)\, dx.$$

[113a] This Appendix was written by N. N. Bogoliubov.

Thus if f is a generalized function then numbers r and s can always be found such that f will be integrable over the class $C(r, s; n)$. We shall say that the generalized functions f_1 and f_2 are equal if sufficiently large r and s can be found such that the functional $f_1 - f_2$ is equal to zero over $C(r, s; n)$.

We shall say that the sequence of generalized functions $f_n(x)$ converges weakly (in the improper sense) to the generalized function $f(x)$ over the class $C(r, s; n)$ if $f_n(x)$ and $f(x)$ are integrable over the class $C(r, s; n)$ and if for any arbitrary $h(x) \in C(r, s; n)$ the following relation holds:

$$\int f_n(x) h(x) \, dx \to \int f(x) h(x) \, dx \text{ as } n \to \infty.$$

We shall say that the sequence of the generalized functions $f_n(x)$ converges weakly (in the improper sense) to the generalized function $f(x)$ if sufficiently large numbers r and s can be found such that the sequence $f_n(x)$ converges weakly to $f(x)$ over the class $C(r, s; n)$.

Let G be an open set of the n-dimensional Euclidean space E_n and let Γ be its boundary. We shall say that the boundary Γ is regular if for any arbitrary point $x \in \Gamma$ an arbitrary sphere with its center at the point x contains another sphere which has no points in common with G.

We shall say that the generalized function $f(x)$ is equal to zero on the open set G with the regular boundary Γ if there exist sufficiently large numbers r and s such that

$$\int f(x) h(x) \, dx = 0$$

for all $h(x)$ from $C(r, s; n)$ which vanish in $E_n - G$.

We shall agree to say that a certain expression

$$f(k, t), \quad k = (k_1, \ldots, k_m), \quad t = (t_1, \ldots, t_n)$$

is a generalized function of the (real) variables t which is integrable over the class $C(r, s; n)$ and is an analytic function of the complex variables k regular in the region D if for any arbitrary function $h(t)$ from the class $C(r, s; n)$ the integral

$$\int f(k, t) h(t) \, dt$$

is an analytic function of k regular in the region D.

If in a similar formulation we do not specifically mention integrability over a certain concrete class $C(r, s; n)$ and speak simply about a generalized function, we shall thereby tacitly imply that such a class exists for sufficiently large r and s.

Let us adopt a specific notation for the case $n = 4$. We define the Fourier transform $\tilde{f}(p)$ of the generalized function $f(x)$ by means of the formula

$$\tilde{f}(p_0, \mathbf{p}) = \int f(x_0, \mathbf{x}) \exp i(x_0 p_0 - \mathbf{x} \cdot \mathbf{p})\, dx$$

where we adopt the following notation which will also be used later:

$$x = (x_0, \mathbf{x}) = (x_0, x_1, x_2, x_3), \quad p = (p_0, \mathbf{p}) = (p_0, p_1, p_2, p_3)$$

$$xp = x_0 p_0 - \mathbf{x} \cdot \mathbf{p}, \quad \mathbf{x} \cdot \mathbf{p} = \sum_{1 \leqq \alpha \leqq 3} x_\alpha p_\alpha, \quad |\mathbf{k}| = \sqrt{\sum_{\alpha=1}^{3} |k_\alpha|^2}.$$

§ 1.

LEMMA I. We consider the analytic function $\phi(k_0, \ldots, k_\alpha, \ldots)$ of the four complex variables k_0, k_α ($\alpha = 1, 2, 3$) regular in the region:

$$|k_0| < w. \tag{1.1}$$

Let r_0, R be positive numbers satisfying the inequality:

$$r_0 < R < w. \tag{1.2}$$

Further, let r_α be positive numbers, and N a positive integer.

Then, in the region:

$$|k_0| < r_0, \quad |k_\alpha| < r_\alpha \tag{1.3}$$

the following integral representation holds:

$$\phi(k_0, \ldots, k_3) = \left(\frac{1}{2\pi}\right)^4 \int_0^{2\pi} \cdots \int_0^{2\pi} \frac{\phi(r_0 e^{i\theta_0}, \ldots, r_3 e^{i\theta_3})\, d\theta_0, \ldots, d\theta_3}{\left(1 - \dfrac{k_0}{r_0} e^{-i\theta_0}\right) \prod\limits_\alpha \left(1 - \dfrac{k_\alpha}{r_\alpha} e^{-i\theta_\alpha}\right)} \tag{1.4}$$

Moreover, here

$$\Phi(r_0 e^{i\theta_0}, \ldots, r_3 e^{i\theta_3})$$
$$= \frac{1}{2\pi}\int_0^{2\pi} \frac{\Phi(R e^{i\theta}, \ldots, u_\alpha(\theta, \theta_0, \ldots, \theta_3) \ldots)}{1 - \frac{r_0}{R} e^{i(\theta_0-\theta)}} \frac{(1 - e^{2i\theta})^N}{\left(1 - \frac{r_0^2}{R^2} e^{2i\theta_0}\right)^N} d\theta \qquad (1.5)$$

where

$$u_\alpha(\theta, \theta_0, \ldots, \theta_3) = \frac{ia_\alpha}{2} R(1 - e^{2i\theta}) + b_\alpha$$

$$a_\alpha = a_\alpha(\theta_0, \ldots, \theta_3) = \frac{2r_\alpha \sin\theta_\alpha}{R\left(1 - \frac{r_0^2}{R^2}\cos 2\theta_0\right)}$$

$$b_\alpha = b_\alpha(\theta_0, \ldots, \theta_3) = r_\alpha \cos\theta_\alpha - \frac{a_\alpha}{2}\frac{r_0^2}{R}\sin 2\theta_0.$$

PROOF. We note first of all that because of the inequality (1.2) the circles:

$$|z_0| \leqq r_0, \ldots, |z_\alpha| \leqq r_\alpha$$

lie entirely within the region in which the function $\phi(k_0, \ldots, k_3)$ is regular.

We can, therefore, in the present case apply Cauchy's theorem to each of the four complex variables $k_0, \ldots, k_3$ and thereby establish the validity of the relations (1.4).

In order to prove the validity of the representation (1.5) we shall consider the analytic function of a single complex variable:

$$f(z) = \Phi\left(z, \ldots, \frac{ia_\alpha R}{2}\left(1 - \frac{z^2}{R^2}\right) + b_\alpha, \ldots\right)(R^2 - z^2)^N. \qquad (1.6)$$

Since this function is regular in the region

$$|z| \leqq R < w$$

we can use Cauchy's theorem and write:

$$f(r_0 e^{i\theta_0}) = \frac{1}{2\pi}\int_0^{2\pi} \frac{f(Re^{i\theta})}{1 - \frac{r_0}{R} e^{i(\theta_0-\theta)}} d\theta. \qquad (1.7)$$

On the other hand, because of (1.6) we have:

$$f(r_0 e^{i\theta_0}) = \phi(r_0 e^{i\theta_0}, \ldots, r_\alpha e^{i\theta_\alpha}, \ldots)\left(1 - \frac{r_0^2}{R^2} e^{2i\theta_0}\right)^N R^{2N}$$

$$f(Re^{i\theta}) = \phi(Re^{i\theta}, \ldots, u_\alpha(\theta, \theta_0, \ldots, \theta_3), \ldots)(1 - e^{2i\theta})^N R^{2N}.$$

Substituting these expressions into both sides of the equality (1.7) we obtain the representation (1.5) in question.

§ 2.

LEMMA II. Let us suppose that the functions $a_\alpha(\theta_0, \ldots, \theta_3)$ introduced in the preceding section satisfy the inequality:

$$|\mathbf{a}| \leqq 1 - \sigma \tag{2.1}$$

where σ is some positive number.

Then if $\varphi(t)$, $g(t)$ are functions from the class $C(0, \infty; 1)$ such that

$$\begin{aligned} \varphi(t) &= 0, \quad t \leqq -\delta; \qquad g(t) = 0, \quad t \leqq -\delta \\ \varphi(t) &= 1, \quad t \geqq 0; \qquad g(t) = 1, \quad t \geqq 0 \end{aligned} \tag{2.2}$$

then the expression

$$\varphi(x_0)\, g(x_0^2 - \mathbf{x}^2) \int_0^\pi d\theta \frac{(1 - e^{2i\theta})^N}{\left(1 - \frac{r_0^2}{R^2} e^{2i\theta_0}\right)^N \left(1 - \frac{r_0}{R} e^{i(\theta_0 - \theta)}\right)}$$

$$\times \exp i\{x_0 Re^{i\theta} - \mathbf{xu}(\theta, \theta_0, \ldots, \theta_3)\} \tag{2.3}$$

regarded as a function $f(x_0, \ldots, x_3;\ \theta_0, \ldots, \theta_3)$ belongs to any class $C(r, s;\ 4 \mid \nu;\ \Omega_4)$ for which

$$r + s + \nu \leqq N + 1 \tag{2.4}$$

PROOF. We note first of all that

$$i\{x_0 Re^{i\theta} - \mathbf{xu}(\theta, \theta_0, \ldots, \theta_3)\} = -x_0 R \sin\theta + \mathbf{xa} R \sin^2\theta$$

$$+ ix_0 R \cos\theta - i\mathbf{x}\left(\frac{\mathbf{a}}{2} R \sin 2\theta + \mathbf{b}\right)$$

$$\frac{1 - e^{2i\theta}}{2} = \sin\theta(\sin\theta - i\cos\theta).$$

We further note that the functions

$$\frac{(\sin\theta - i\cos\theta)^N}{\left(1 - \frac{r_0^2}{R^2}e^{2i\theta_0}\right)^N \left(1 - \frac{r_0}{R}e^{i(\theta_0-\theta)}\right)}; \qquad \frac{\mathbf{a}}{2}R\sin 2\theta + \mathbf{b}$$

belong to classes $C(\infty, \Omega_2)$ and $C(\infty, \Omega_5)$ respectively. Therefore the lemma just formulated above will be proved if we succeed in establishing the following more general assertion.

If

$$f(\theta, \theta_0, \ldots, \theta_3) \in C(\infty; \Omega_5)$$
$$\mathbf{A}(\theta, \theta_0, \ldots, \theta_3) \in C(\infty; \Omega_5)$$

and if the values of A_α are real then the function

$$F = \varphi(x_0)\, g(x_0^2 - \mathbf{x}^2) \int_0^\pi d\theta \sin^N \theta f(\theta, \theta_0, \ldots, \theta_3)$$
$$\times \exp\{-x_0 R\sin\theta + \mathbf{xa}R\sin^2\theta + ix_0 R\cos\theta - i\mathbf{xA}\} \quad (2.5)$$

belongs to the class $C(r, s; 4 \mid \nu; \Omega_4)$ where $r + s + \nu \leqq N + 1$.

We shall now prove this assertion. First of all it is clear that because of condition (2.2) expression (2.5) can differ from zero only in the region for which:

$$x_0 > -\delta \qquad \mathbf{x}^2 < x_0^2 + \delta \quad (2.6)$$

We note further that

$$\frac{\partial^{r+\mu} F}{\partial x_{\alpha_1} \ldots \partial x_{\alpha_r} \partial\theta_{\beta_1} \ldots \partial\theta_{\beta_\mu}}$$

can be represented in the form of a finite sum of expressions of the type

$$\varphi_\lambda(x_0, \ldots, x_3)\mathscr{P}_\lambda(x_0, \ldots, x_3) \int_0^\pi d\theta \sin^N\theta\, f_\lambda(\theta, \ldots, \theta_3)$$
$$\times \exp\{-x_0 R\sin\theta + \mathbf{xa}R\sin^2\theta + ix_0 R\cos\theta - i\mathbf{xA}\}$$

in which

$$\left.\begin{array}{l}\varphi_\lambda \in C(0, 0; 4)\\ f_\lambda \in C(\infty, \Omega_5)\end{array}\right.; \ \varphi_\lambda = 0 \text{ outside the region (2.6)}$$

and $\mathscr{P}_\lambda(x_0, \ldots, x_3)$ are polynomials of degree not higher than $r + \mu$.

Finally we have:

$$\left| \int_0^\pi d\theta \sin^N\theta\, f_\lambda \exp\{-x_0 R \sin\theta + \mathbf{xa}\, R \sin^2\theta + i x_0 R \cos\theta - i\mathbf{xA}\} \right|$$

$$\leqq \max_{(0\leqq\theta\leqq\pi)} |f_\lambda(\theta, \theta_0, \ldots, \theta_3)| \int_0^\pi d\theta \sin^N\theta \exp\{-x_0 R \sin\theta + \mathbf{xa} R \sin^2\theta\}.$$

In view of all the foregoing we see that our proof will be completed as soon as we have shown that for sufficiently large x_0 the following inequality holds in the region (2.6):

$$\int_0^\pi e^{-R(x_0 \sin\theta - \mathbf{xa}\sin^2\theta)} \sin^N\theta\, d\theta \leqq \frac{\text{const.}}{|x_0|^{N+1}}.$$

We now proceed to establish this inequality. We take into account the fact that in the region under consideration:

$$x_0 \sin\theta - \mathbf{ax}\sin^2\theta \geqq x_0\sin\theta - |\mathbf{a}|\sqrt{x_0^2+\delta}\,\sin^2\theta$$

and therefore in virtue of (2.1)

$$x_0\sin\theta - \mathbf{ax}\sin^2\theta \geqq x_0\sin\theta - (1-\sigma)\sqrt{x_0^2+\delta}\,\sin^2\theta.$$

We choose a positive X such that

$$(1-\sigma)\sqrt{X^2+\delta} = \left(1-\frac{\sigma}{2}\right)X$$

and consider $x_0 \geqq X$. Then

$$x_0\sin\theta - \mathbf{ax}\sin^2\theta \geqq \frac{\sigma}{2}x_0\sin\theta;$$

from which it follows that

$$\int_0^\pi e^{-R(x_0\sin\theta - \mathbf{xa}\sin^2\theta)}\sin^N\theta\, d\theta \leqq \int_0^\pi e^{-R\frac{\sigma}{2}x_0\sin\theta}\sin^N\theta\, d\theta$$

$$< \sqrt{2}\int_0^{\frac{\pi}{4}} e^{-R\frac{\sigma}{2}x_0 t}\sin^N\theta\cos\theta\, d\theta + \frac{\pi}{2}e^{-R\frac{\sigma x_0}{2\sqrt{2}}}$$

$$+\sqrt{2}\int_{\frac{3\pi}{4}}^{\pi} e^{-R\frac{\sigma}{2}x_0\sin\theta}\sin^N\theta(-\cos\theta)d\theta = 2\sqrt{2}\int_0^{1/\sqrt{2}} e^{-R\frac{\sigma}{2}x_0 t}\,t^N\, dt$$

$$+\frac{\pi}{2}e^{-R\frac{\sigma x_0}{2\sqrt{2}}} < 2\sqrt{2}\left(\frac{2}{R\sigma x_0}\right)^{N+1}\int_0^\infty e^{-t}t^N\, dt + \frac{\pi}{2}e^{-R\frac{\sigma x_0}{2\sqrt{2}}}$$

and our proof is complete.

§ 3.

We now proceed to apply Lemmas I and II.

We consider two generalized functions $F_r(x)$, $F_a(x)$ $(x = (x_0, \mathbf{x}))$ one of which is retarded and the other advanced:

$$\begin{aligned} F_r(x) &= 0, \quad x \lesssim 0 \\ F_a(x) &= 0, \quad x \gtrsim 0 \end{aligned} \tag{3.1}$$

We construct their "smoothed-out Fourier transforms":

$$\begin{aligned} \tilde{F}_r(k, \varepsilon) &= \int F_r(x) \exp \{-\varepsilon(x_0^2+\mathbf{x}^2)+i(k_0x_0-\mathbf{kx})\}\, dx, \\ \tilde{F}_a(k, \varepsilon) &= \int F_a(x) \exp \{-\varepsilon(x_0^2+\mathbf{x}^2)+i(k_0x_0-\mathbf{kx})\}\, dx, \end{aligned} \quad \varepsilon > 0 \tag{3.2}$$

and note that they are analytic functions of the complex variables $k(k_0, k_1, \ldots, k_3)$ having no singularities at finite distances.

We introduce the function $\tilde{F}(k, \varepsilon)$ of the same complex variables by setting:

$$\begin{aligned} \tilde{F}(k, \varepsilon) &= \tilde{F}_r(k, \varepsilon) - T(k, \varepsilon), \qquad \operatorname{Im} k_0 > 0; \\ \tilde{F}(k, \varepsilon) &= \tilde{F}_a(k, \varepsilon) - T(k, \varepsilon), \qquad \operatorname{Im} k_0 < 0, \end{aligned} \tag{3.3}$$

where

$$T(k, \varepsilon) = \frac{1}{2\pi i} \int_{-\omega}^{\omega} \frac{\tilde{F}_r(t, \mathbf{k}, \varepsilon) - \tilde{F}_a(t, \mathbf{k}, \varepsilon)}{t - k_0}\, dt \tag{3.4}$$

in which ω is some positive number.

From this we see that $\tilde{F}(k, \varepsilon)$, $T(k, \varepsilon)$ have no singularities at finite distances other than the "cut":

$$\operatorname{Im} k_0 = 0.$$

We take k_0 on this line, and obtain:

$$\begin{aligned} &\tilde{F}(k_0 + i0, \mathbf{k}, \varepsilon) - \tilde{F}(k_0 - i0, \mathbf{k}, \varepsilon) \\ &= \tilde{F}_r(k_0, \mathbf{k}, \varepsilon) - \tilde{F}_a(k_0, \mathbf{k}, \varepsilon) - \{T(k_0 + i0, \mathbf{k}, \varepsilon) - T(k_0 - i0, \mathbf{k}, \varepsilon)\}. \end{aligned}$$

But in the case when $-\omega < k_0 < \omega$ we can write:

$$\begin{aligned} &T(k_0 + i0, \mathbf{k}, \varepsilon) - T(k_0 - i0, \mathbf{k}, \varepsilon) \\ &= \frac{1}{2\pi i} \int_{-\omega}^{\omega} \{\tilde{F}_r(t, \mathbf{k}, \varepsilon) - \tilde{F}_a(t, \mathbf{k}, \varepsilon)\} \left\{\frac{1}{t - k_0 - i0} - \frac{1}{t - k_0 + i0}\right\} dt \\ &= \tilde{F}_r(k_0, \mathbf{k}, \varepsilon) - \tilde{F}_a(k_0, \mathbf{k}, \varepsilon). \end{aligned}$$

Consequently,

$$\tilde{F}(k_0 + i0, \mathbf{k}, \varepsilon) - \tilde{F}(k_0 - i0, \mathbf{k}, \varepsilon) = 0 \qquad -\omega < k_0 < \omega. \quad (3.5)$$

From this we see that the analytic function $\tilde{F}(k, \varepsilon)$ is regular in the region

$$|k_0| < \omega \qquad (3.6)$$

(has no singularities in it at finite distances)and we can therefore apply Lemma I to it.

We thus arrive at the integral representation:

$$\tilde{F}(k, \varepsilon) = \frac{1}{(2\pi)^4} \int_0^{2\pi} \cdots \int_0^{2\pi} \frac{\phi_1(\theta_0, \ldots, \theta_3, \varepsilon) - \phi_2(\theta_0, \ldots, \theta_3, \varepsilon)}{\left(1 - \frac{k_0}{r_0} e^{-i\theta_0}\right) \prod_\alpha \left(1 - \frac{k_\alpha}{r_\alpha} e^{-i\theta_\alpha}\right)} d\theta_0 \ldots d\theta_3 \qquad (3.7)$$

$$|k_0| < r_0, \quad |k_\alpha| < r_\alpha$$

in which

$$\begin{aligned} \phi_1(\theta_0, \ldots, \theta_3; \varepsilon) &= \frac{1}{2\pi} \int_0^{\pi} \frac{\tilde{F}_r\{R\, e^{i\theta}, \ldots, u_\alpha(\theta, \theta_0, \ldots, \theta_3) \ldots; \varepsilon)}{1 - \frac{r_0}{R} e^{i(\theta_0 - \theta)}} \frac{(1 - e^{2i\theta})^N}{\left(1 - \frac{r_0^2}{R^2} e^{2i\theta_0}\right)^N} d\theta \\ &+ \frac{1}{2\pi} \int_\pi^{2\pi} \frac{\tilde{F}_a\{R\, e^{i\theta}, \ldots, u_\alpha(\theta, \theta_0, \ldots, \theta_3) \ldots; \varepsilon)}{1 - \frac{r_0}{R} e^{i(\theta_0 - \theta)}} \left(\frac{1 - e^{2i\theta}}{1 - \frac{r_0^2}{R^2} e^{2i\theta_0}}\right)^N d\theta \end{aligned} \qquad (3.8)$$

$$\phi_2(\theta_0, \ldots, \theta_3; \varepsilon) = \frac{1}{2\pi} \int_0^{2\pi} \frac{T\{R\, e^{i\theta}, \ldots, u_\alpha(\theta, \theta_0, \ldots, \theta_3) \ldots; \varepsilon)\}}{1 - \frac{r_0}{R} e^{i(\theta_0 - \theta)}} \left(\frac{1 - e^{2i\theta}}{1 - \frac{r_0^2}{R^2} e^{2i\theta_0}}\right)^N d\theta. \qquad (3.9)$$

In order to be able to utilize Lemma II, it is necessary to guarantee that the inequality (2.1) is satisfied. For this we require that the foregoing r_α should satisfy the inequality:

$$\frac{2|\mathbf{r}|}{R\left(1 - \frac{r_0^2}{R^2}\right)} < 1. \qquad (3.10)$$

Then, indeed, as may be seen from (1.6), the requirement (2.1) is satisfied, for example, for

$$\sigma = 1 - \frac{2|\mathbf{r}|}{R\left(1 - \frac{r_0^2}{R^2}\right)}.$$

We first turn to the first term in the right-hand side of (3.8). Substituting (3.2) into it we find:

$$\frac{1}{2\pi}\int_0^{\pi} \frac{\tilde{F}_r(R\,e^{i\theta}, \ldots, u_\alpha(\theta, \theta_0, \ldots, \theta_3) \ldots; \varepsilon\}}{1 - \frac{r_0}{R}\,e^{i(\theta_0-\theta)}} \left(\frac{1 - e^{2i\theta}}{1 - \frac{r_0^2}{R^2}\,e^{2i\theta_0}}\right)^N d\theta$$

$$= \frac{1}{2\pi}\int F_r(x)\,e^{-\varepsilon(x_0^2+\mathbf{x}^2)}\,I(x; \theta_0, \ldots, \theta_3)\,dx \tag{3.11}$$

$$I(x; \theta_0, \ldots, \theta_3) = \int_0^{\pi} d\theta\, \frac{(1 - e^{2i\theta})^N \exp i\,\{x_0\,R\,e^{i\theta} - \mathbf{xu}\}}{\left(1 - \frac{r_0^2}{R^2}\,e^{2i\theta_0}\right)^N \left(1 - \frac{r_0}{R}\,e^{i(\theta_0-\theta)}\right)}.$$

We now note that because of the presence of the exponential cutoff factor, the functions

$$e^{-\varepsilon(x_0^2+\mathbf{x}^2)}\,I(x; \theta_0, \ldots, \theta_3), \quad \varphi(x_0)\,g(x_0^2 - \mathbf{x}^2)\,I(x; \theta_0, \ldots, \theta_3)\,e^{-\varepsilon(x_0^2+\mathbf{x}^2)}$$

belong to the class $C(\infty, \infty; 4 \mid \infty; \Omega_4)$. On the other hand, their difference is equal to zero if

$$x_0 \geqq 0, \qquad x_0^2 - \mathbf{x}^2 \geqq 0.$$

But in the region where $x_0 < 0$, or $x_0^2 - \mathbf{x}^2 < 0$ the function $F_r(x)$ itself vanishes (see (3.1)). We thus have:

$$\int F_r(x)\,e^{-\varepsilon(x_0^2+\mathbf{x}^2)}\,I(x; \theta_0, \ldots, \theta_3)\,dx$$
$$= \int F_r(x)\,e^{-\varepsilon(x_0^2+\mathbf{x}^2)}\,\varphi(x_0)\,g(x_0^2 - \mathbf{x}^2)\,I(x; \theta_0, \ldots, \theta_3)\,dx.$$

Consequently expression (3.11) is equal to:

$$\frac{1}{2\pi}\int F_r(x)\,e^{-\varepsilon(x_0^2+\mathbf{x}^2)}\,h_+(x, \theta_0, \ldots, \theta_3)\,dx$$

where

$$h_+(x; \theta_0, \ldots, \theta_3)$$
$$= \varphi(x_0)\, g(x_0^2 - \mathbf{x}^2) \int_0^{\pi} d\theta \frac{(1 - e^{2i\theta})^N \exp i\{x_0 R e^{i\theta} - \mathbf{xu}\}}{\left(1 - \frac{r_0^2}{R^2} e^{2i\theta_0}\right)^N \left(1 - \frac{r_0}{R} e^{i(\theta_0 - \theta)}\right)}. \quad (3.12)$$

In a completely analogous manner we see that the second term in the right-hand side of relation (3.8) is equal to:

$$\frac{1}{2\pi} \int F_a(x)\, e^{-\varepsilon(x_0^2 + \mathbf{x}^2)}\, h_-(x; \theta_0, \ldots, \theta_3)\, dx$$

with

$$h_-(x, \theta_0, \ldots, \theta_3)$$
$$= \varphi(-x_0)\, g(x_0^2 - \mathbf{x}^2) \int_{\pi}^{2\pi} d\theta \frac{(1 - e^{2i\theta})^N \exp i\{x_0 R e^{i\theta} - \mathbf{xu}\}}{\left(1 - \frac{r_0^2}{R^2} e^{2i\theta_0}\right)^N \left(1 - \frac{r_0}{R} e^{i(\theta_0 - \theta)}\right)}. \quad (3.13)$$

We now select arbitrarily large indices r, s, ν and take $N = r + s + \nu - 1$. Then, in accordance with Lemma II, we can assert that both functions h_+ and h_- belong to the class $C(r, s; 4 \mid \nu; \Omega_4)$.

Thus, by the above method we can construct within the class $C(r, s; 4 \mid \nu\Omega_4)$ with arbitrarily high indices two functions h_+ and h_- such that

$$\Phi_1(\theta_0, \ldots, \theta_3; \varepsilon) = \frac{1}{2\pi} \int F_r(x)\, e^{-\varepsilon(x_0^2 + \mathbf{x}^2)}\, h_+(x; \theta_0, \ldots, \theta_3)\, dx$$
$$+ \frac{1}{2\pi} \int F_a(x)\, e^{-\varepsilon(x_0^2 + \mathbf{x}^2)}\, h_-(x; \theta_0, \ldots, \theta_3)\, dx. \quad (3.14)$$

We shall say that the functions h_+ and h_- are universal in the sense that they depend only on the indices r, s, ν and not on the form of the functions $F_r(x)$, $F_a(x)$.

§ 4.

In order to carry out the transition to the limit $\varepsilon \to +0$ in relation (3.7), we formulate and prove the following lemma.

LEMMA III. We consider a certain generalized function $f(x)$ and suppose that there exists such a positive η that

$$\int f(x)\, e^{ipx}\, dx = 0 \tag{4.1}$$

in the region

$$p_0^2 + \mathbf{p}^2 < \eta^2. \tag{4.2}$$

We select positive R, ω, δ satisfying the inequalities

$$R^2 + \delta^2 < \omega^2 + \delta^2 < \frac{\eta^2}{2} \tag{4.3}$$

and construct a function of the complex variables $k = (k_0, \mathbf{k}) = (k_0, k_1, k_2, k_3)$:

$$T(k, \varepsilon) = \frac{1}{2\pi i} \int_{-\omega}^{\omega} \frac{\tilde{f}(t, \mathbf{k}, \varepsilon)}{t - k_0}\, dt \tag{4.4}$$

where

$$\tilde{f}(k, \varepsilon) = \int f(x) \exp\{-\varepsilon(x_0^2 + \mathbf{x}^2) + ikx\}\, dx. \tag{4.5}$$

We can then assert that

$$T(k; \varepsilon) \underset{\varepsilon \to +0}{\to} 0 \tag{4.6}$$

uniformly within the closed region of complex variables given by

$$|k_0| \leqq R, \qquad |\mathbf{k}| \leqq \delta. \tag{4.7}$$

PROOF. We consider expression (4.5) and substitute into it the Fourier representation:

$$f(x) = \left(\frac{1}{2\pi}\right)^4 \int \tilde{f}(p)\, e^{-ipx}\, dp.$$

We then obtain:

$$\begin{aligned} \tilde{f}(k, \varepsilon) &= \frac{1}{(2\pi)^4} \int \tilde{f}(p) \left\{ \int \exp\left[-\varepsilon(x_0^2 + \mathbf{x}^2) + i(k - p)x\right] dx \right\} dp \\ &= \frac{1}{2^4 \pi^2 \varepsilon^2} \int \tilde{f}(p) \exp\left\{ -\frac{(k_0 - p_0)^2 + (\mathbf{k} - \mathbf{p})^2}{4\varepsilon} \right\} dp. \end{aligned} \tag{4.8}$$

We now select a positive $\bar{\eta}$ such that:

$$\omega^2 + \delta^2 < \frac{\bar{\eta}^2}{2} < \frac{\eta^2}{2} \tag{4.9}$$

and construct within the class $C(0, \infty; 1)$ the function $v(t)$ for which

$$v(t) = 1, \qquad t \geqq \eta^2$$
$$v(t) = 0, \qquad t \leqq \bar{\eta}^2.$$

We note that the functions (k is fixed):

$$\exp\left\{-\frac{(k_0-p_0)^2+(\mathbf{k}-\mathbf{p})^2}{4\varepsilon}\right\}, \quad v(p_0^2+\mathbf{p}^2)\exp\left\{-\frac{(k_0-p_0)^2+(\mathbf{k}-\mathbf{p})^2}{4\varepsilon}\right\}$$

belong to the class $C(\infty, \infty; 4)$. Their difference is equal to zero for

$$p_0^2 + \mathbf{p}^2 \geqq \eta^2.$$

On the other hand, in accordance with the statement of the lemma $\tilde{f}(p)$ is equal to zero when

$$p_0^2 + \mathbf{p}^2 < \eta^2.$$

We see therefore that the relation (4.8) may be represented in the form

$$f(k, \varepsilon) = \int \tilde{f}(p)\, H_k(p, \varepsilon)\, dp \tag{4.10}$$

$$H_k(p, \varepsilon) = \frac{1}{2^4\pi^2\varepsilon^2} v(p_0^2 + \mathbf{p}^2) \exp\left\{-\frac{(k_0-p_0)^2 + (\mathbf{k}-\mathbf{p})^2}{4\varepsilon}\right\}. \tag{4.11}$$

We shall present our subsequent arguments after fixing k to have an arbitrary value in the closed region:

$$|k_0| \leqq \omega, \qquad |\mathbf{k}| \leqq \delta. \tag{4.12}$$

We now analyze the manner in which the sequence $H_k(p, \varepsilon)$ tends to zero as $\varepsilon \to +0$.

Since in accordance with the definition of v:

$$v(p_0^2 + \mathbf{p}^2) = 0 \quad \text{for } p_0^2 + \mathbf{p}^2 \leqq \bar{\eta}^2 \tag{4.13}$$

we can restrict ourselves to the region:

$$p_0^2 + \mathbf{p}^2 > \bar{\eta}^2. \tag{4.14}$$

We have here:

$$
\begin{aligned}
\operatorname{Re}\{(p_0 - k_0)^2 + (\mathbf{p} - \mathbf{k})^2\}
&= (p_0 - \operatorname{Re} k_0)^2 + (\mathbf{p} - \operatorname{Re}\mathbf{k})^2 - (\operatorname{Im} k_0)^2 - (\operatorname{Im}\mathbf{k})^2 \\
&= p_0^2 + \mathbf{p}^2 + (\operatorname{Re} k_0)^2 + (\operatorname{Re}\mathbf{k})^2 - 2p_0 \operatorname{Re} k_0 - 2\mathbf{p}\operatorname{Re}\mathbf{k} \\
&\qquad - (\operatorname{Im} k_0)^2 - (\operatorname{Im}\mathbf{k})^2.
\end{aligned}
$$

But

$$p_0 \operatorname{Re} k_0 + \mathbf{p}\operatorname{Re}\mathbf{k} \leqq \sqrt{p_0^2 + \mathbf{p}^2}\,\sqrt{(\operatorname{Re} k_0)^2 + (\operatorname{Re}\mathbf{k})^2}$$

and therefore:

$$
\begin{aligned}
&\operatorname{Re}\{(p_0 - k_0)^2 + (\mathbf{p} - \mathbf{k})^2\} \\
&\quad \geqq 2\left\{\frac{\sqrt{p_0^2 + \mathbf{p}^2}}{2} - \sqrt{(\operatorname{Re} k_0)^2 + (\operatorname{Re}\mathbf{k})^2}\right\}^2 - (\operatorname{Im} k_0)^2 - (\operatorname{Im}\mathbf{k})^2 \\
&\quad - (\operatorname{Re} k_0)^2 - (\operatorname{Re}\mathbf{k})^2 + \frac{p_0^2 + \mathbf{p}^2}{2} \geqq \frac{p_0^2 + \mathbf{p}^2}{2} - (|k_0|^2 + |\mathbf{k}|^2).
\end{aligned}
$$

Therefore in view of (4.9), (4.12), (4.14)

$$\operatorname{Re}\{(p_0 - k_0)^2 - (\mathbf{p} - \mathbf{k})^2\} > \zeta^2 + \frac{p_0^2 + \mathbf{p}^2}{2} - \frac{\bar{\eta}^2}{2}$$

where

$$\zeta^2 = \frac{\bar{\eta}^2}{2} - (\omega^2 + \delta^2).$$

Thus

$$\left|\exp\left\{-\frac{(k_0 - p_0)^2 + (\mathbf{k} - \mathbf{p})^2}{4\varepsilon}\right\}\right| < e^{-\frac{\zeta^2}{4\varepsilon} - \frac{1}{8\varepsilon}(p_0^2 + \mathbf{p}^2 - \bar{\eta}^2)}. \tag{4.15}$$

From here it follows in virtue of (4.11) that

$$(p_0^2 + \mathbf{p}^2)^s H_k(p, \varepsilon) \underset{\varepsilon \to +0}{\longrightarrow} 0 \tag{4.16}$$

uniformly for all p and for all k in (4.12) for arbitrarily large values of s.

Moreover, since the cutoff exponential remains unchanged on differentiation and can only be multiplied by polynomial expressions, we also obtain the result that all the partial derivatives tend uniformly to zero:

$$(p_0^2 + \mathbf{p}^2)^s \frac{\partial^{\nu+\mu} H_k(p, \varepsilon)}{\partial k_{\alpha_1} \ldots \partial k_{\alpha_\nu} \partial p_{\beta_1} \ldots \partial p_{\beta_\mu}} \underset{\varepsilon \to +0}{\to} 0. \tag{4.17}$$

Taking (4.10) into account we see from the foregoing that as $\varepsilon \to +0$ $\tilde{f}(k, \varepsilon)$ together with all its partial derivatives with respect to $k_0, \ldots, k_3$ tends uniformly to zero within the region (4.12).

We now make use of this result to investigate expression (4.4). We have:

$$T(k, \varepsilon) = \frac{1}{2\pi i} \int_{-\omega}^{\omega} \frac{\tilde{f}(t, \mathbf{k}, \varepsilon) - \tilde{f}(k_0, \mathbf{k}, \varepsilon)}{t - k_0} dt + \tilde{f}(k_0, \mathbf{k}, \varepsilon) \frac{1}{2\pi i} \int_{-\omega}^{\omega} \frac{dt}{t - k_0}$$

from which it follows that:

$$|T(k, \varepsilon)| < \frac{\omega}{\pi} \max_{|t| \leqq \omega} \left| \frac{\tilde{f}(t, \mathbf{k}, \varepsilon) - \tilde{f}(k_0, \mathbf{k}, \varepsilon)}{t - k_0} \right| + |\tilde{f}(k_0, \mathbf{k}; \varepsilon)| \left| \frac{1}{2\pi i} \int_{-\omega}^{\omega} \frac{dt}{t - k_0} \right|.$$

But in virtue of the result obtained

$$\max_{|t| \leqq \omega} \left| \frac{\tilde{f}(t, \mathbf{k}, \varepsilon) - \tilde{f}(k_0, \mathbf{k}, \varepsilon)}{t - k_0} \right| \underset{\varepsilon \to +0}{\to} 0, \quad |\tilde{f}(k_0, \mathbf{k}; \varepsilon)| \underset{\varepsilon \to +0}{\to} 0$$

uniformly in the region (4.12). On the other hand, if

$$|k_0| \leqq R < \omega$$

then the integral

$$\left| \frac{1}{2\pi i} \int_{-\omega}^{\omega} \frac{dt}{t - k_0} \right| < \frac{1}{2\pi} \ln \left| \frac{\omega + R}{\omega - R} \right| + \tfrac{1}{2}$$

is bounded.

Thus, within the region (4.7) we have in the sense of uniform convergence:

$$T(k, \varepsilon) \to 0$$
$$\text{as } \varepsilon \to +0$$

and the proof of our lemma is complete.

§ 5.

We now examine the transition to the limit $\varepsilon \to 0$ in the integral representation (3.7)–(3.9), (3.14).

We make the fundamental assumption that

$$\tilde{F}_r(p) - \tilde{F}_a(p) = 0 \tag{5.1}$$

for

$$p_0^2 + \mathbf{p}^2 < \eta^2 . \tag{5.2}$$

Then in order to be able to utilize Lemma III, we must guarantee that the arguments k appearing in the expression for T which occurs in the right-hand side of the integral representation (3.9) satisfy the inequalities (4.3) and (4.7).

In other words, we must guarantee that

$$R^2 + \mathbf{r}^2 < \frac{\eta^2}{2} \qquad R^2 + \mathbf{u}^2 < \frac{\eta^2}{2} . \tag{5.3}$$

Moreover, in order to be able to apply Lemma II, we must also take into account the inequality

$$\frac{2\,|\,\mathbf{r}\,|}{1 - \dfrac{r_0^2}{R^2}} < R. \tag{5.4}$$

But, in consequence of (1.6):

$$|\,u_\alpha\,| < |\,a_\alpha\,|\,R + |\,b_\alpha\,| < |\,a_\alpha\,|\,R\left(1 + \frac{r_0^2}{2R^2}\right) + r_\alpha\,|\cos\theta_\alpha\,|$$

$$< \frac{2r_\alpha}{1 - \dfrac{r_0^2}{R^2}}\,|\sin\theta_\alpha\,|\left(1 + \frac{r_0^2}{2R^2}\right) + r_\alpha\,|\cos\theta_\alpha\,| ,$$

from which it follows that

$$\mathbf{u}^2 < \mathbf{r}^2 \left\{ 4 \left(\frac{1 + \dfrac{r_0^2}{2R^2}}{1 - \dfrac{r_0^2}{R^2}} \right)^2 + 1 \right\} .$$

We consequently see that all the required conditions (5.3), (5.4) will be satisfied if we choose r_0, r_α, R so that

$$2\,|\,\mathbf{r}\,| < R\left(1 - \frac{r_0^2}{R^2}\right), \quad R^2 + R^2\left(1 + \frac{r_0^2}{2R^2}\right)^2 + \mathbf{r}^2 < \frac{\eta^2}{2}. \quad (5.5)$$

We shall adopt this choice for our future considerations.

We now return to the examination of expression (3.9) and note that in consequence of Lemma III, we have uniformly over the torus Ω_5

$$T\{\mathrm{Re}^{i\theta}, \ldots, u_\alpha(\theta, \theta_0, \ldots, \theta_3), \ldots;\ \varepsilon\} \underset{\varepsilon\to+0}{\to} 0.$$

Therefore, we have also in the sense of uniform convergence

$$\Phi_2(\theta_0, \ldots \theta_3,\ \varepsilon) \underset{\varepsilon\to+0}{\to} 0. \quad (5.6)$$

We now turn to formula (3.14). Let the generalized functions $F_r(x)$ and $F_a(x)$ be integrable over the class $C(r,\ s;\ 4)$. We take $N \geqq r + s + \nu - 1$. In accordance with Lemma II, h_+ and h_- belong to the class $C(r,\ s;\ 4)$.

Then, by going to the limit, we shall obtain in the sense of uniform convergence:

$$\phi_1(\theta_0, \ldots, \theta_3,\ \varepsilon) \to \frac{1}{2\pi}\int F_r(x) h_+(x;\ \theta_0, \ldots, \theta_3)\, dx$$

$$+ \frac{1}{2\pi}\int F_a(x)\, h_-(x;\ \theta_0, \ldots, \theta_3)\, dx. \quad (5.7)$$

Taking into account the integral representation (3.7) and the limiting relations (5.6), (5.7) just obtained, we see that in any closed region contained within the complex variable region (1.3) under consideration the functions $\tilde{F}(k, \varepsilon)$ converge uniformly to the limit:

$$\tilde{F}(k) = \left(\frac{1}{2\pi}\right)^4 \int_0^{2\pi} \cdots \int_0^{2\pi} \frac{\phi(\theta_0, \ldots, \theta_3)\, d\theta_0 \ldots d\theta_3}{\left(1 - \dfrac{k_0}{r_0} e^{-i\theta_0}\right) \prod\limits_\alpha \left(1 - \dfrac{k_\alpha}{r_\alpha} e^{-i\theta_\alpha}\right)} \quad (5.8)$$

$$\phi(\theta_0, \ldots, \theta_3) = \frac{1}{2\pi} \int F_r(x)\, h_+(x; \theta_0, \ldots, \theta_3)\, dx$$
$$+ \frac{1}{2\pi} \int F_a(x)\, h_-(x; \theta_0, \ldots, \theta_3)\, dx$$

which is an analytic function of k regular in the region (1.3).

We now transform the integral representation obtained above to momentum variables. We denote, as always, the Fourier transforms of the functions h_+, h_- by $\tilde{h}_+, \tilde{h}_-$ and note that for any values of the indices r_1, s_1 we can always choose such r, s for which the relations:

$$h_+ \in C(r, s; 4 \mid \nu; \Omega_4); \quad h_- \in C(r, s; 4 \mid \nu; \Omega_4)$$

always lead to the relations:

$$\tilde{h}_+ \in C(r_1, s_1; 4 \mid \nu; \Omega_4); \quad \tilde{h}_- \in C(r_1, s_1; 4 \mid \nu, \Omega_4).$$

We choose r_1, s_1 in such a way that $\tilde{F}_r(p)$, $\tilde{F}_a(p)$ are integrable over the class $C(r_1, s_1; \nu)$. Then:

$$\phi(\theta_0, \ldots, \theta_3) = \left(\frac{1}{2\pi}\right)^5 \int \tilde{F}_r(p)\, \tilde{h}_+(-p; \theta_0, \ldots, \theta_3)\, dp$$
$$+ \frac{1}{(2\pi)^5} \int \tilde{F}_a(p) \tilde{h}_-(-p; \theta_0, \ldots, \theta_3)\, dp.$$

We set:

$$H_\pm(p; k) = \left(\frac{1}{2\pi}\right)^9 \int_0^{2\pi} \cdots \int_0^{2\pi} \frac{\tilde{h}_\pm(-p; \theta_0, \ldots \theta_3)\, d\theta_0 \ldots d\theta_3}{\left(1 - \frac{k_0}{r_0} e^{-i\theta_0}\right) \prod_\alpha \left(1 - \frac{k_\alpha}{r_\alpha} e^{-i\theta_\alpha}\right)}. \quad (5.9)$$

By introducing such functions we shall be able to write relation (5.8) in the form:

$$\tilde{F}(k) = \int \tilde{F}_r(p)\, H_+(p, k)\, dp + \int \tilde{F}_a(p)\, H_-(p, k)\, dp. \quad (5.10)$$

The functions $H_\pm$ defined by formula (5.9) evidently have the common property that for any arbitrary generalized function $f(p)$ integrable over the class $C(r_1, s_1; 4)$ the expressions

$$\int f(p)\, H_{\pm}(p;\ k)\, dp$$

are analytic functions of k regular in the region (1.3).

For the sake of brevity we shall agree to have this particular property in mind when we say that $H_{\pm}(p; k)$ regarded as functions of p belong to the class $C(r_1, s_1; 4)$, while regarded as functions of k, they are analytic functions regular in the region (1.3). We shall call these functions universal since their form depends only on the indices of the class C, on the number η, etc., but not on the special choice of F_r, F_a within the given class.

We now consider real[114] $k = p$ lying in the region (1.3). In virtue of Lemma III, we have the uniform convergence

$$T(p_0 \pm i\,0,\ \mathbf{p},\ \varepsilon) \to 0 \qquad \varepsilon \to +0,$$

and therefore we conclude from (3.3) that in the region under consideration we have also in the sense of uniform convergence:

$$\tilde{F}_r(p,\ \varepsilon) \to \tilde{F}(p), \quad \tilde{F}_a(p,\ \varepsilon) \to \tilde{F}(p), \quad \varepsilon \to +0.$$

On the other hand, in the whole space of real p the following improper (generalized) limiting relation holds

$$\tilde{F}_r(p,\ \varepsilon) \to \tilde{F}_r(p), \quad \tilde{F}_a(p,\ \varepsilon) \to \tilde{F}_a(p), \quad \varepsilon \to 0.$$

Consequently

$$\tilde{F}_r(p) = \tilde{F}_a(p) = \tilde{F}(p)$$

in the region

$$|\, p_\alpha \,| < r_\alpha, \qquad \alpha = 0,\ 1,\ 2,\ 3.$$

The results just obtained may be summarized in the following theorem.

Theorem I. (i) Given the generalized functions $F_r(x)$, $F_a(x)$ of which the first is retarded and the second advanced.

(ii) Suppose that such a positive η exists for which

$$\tilde{F}_r(p) = \tilde{F}_a(p)$$

[114] In general we shall denote real momenta by the letters p, and complex momenta by the letters k.

in the region

$$p_0^2 + \mathbf{p}^2 < \eta^2.$$

(iii) Choose positive numbers r_0, r_α, R which satisfy the inequalities:

$$2\,|\,\mathbf{r}\,| < R\left(1 - \frac{r_0^2}{R^2}\right), \quad R^2 + R^2\left(1 + \frac{r_0^2}{2R^2}\right)^2 + \mathbf{r}^2 < \frac{\eta^2}{2}. \tag{5.11}$$

It is then possible to construct an analytic function $\tilde{F}(k)$ of the complex variables $k(k_0, k_1, k_2, k_3)$ regular within the region

$$|\,k_\alpha\,| < r_\alpha, \qquad \alpha = 0, 1, 2, 3 \tag{5.12}$$

in such a way that

$$\tilde{F}(p) = \tilde{F}_a(p) = \tilde{F}_r(p)$$

within the region of the real variables $p(p_0, \ldots, p_3)$ defined by the inequalities (5.12).

Moreover, by taking sufficiently high indices r, s we can construct "universal" functions $H_\pm(p;\,k)$ with the properties: (a) regarded as functions of p $H_\pm(p;\,k)$ belong to the class $C(r, s;\,4)$, while regarded as functions of k, they are analytic and regular within the region (5.12); (b) within the region (5.12) the following integral representation holds:

$$\tilde{F}(k) = \int \tilde{F}_r(p)\, H_+(p;\,k)\, dp + \int \tilde{F}_a(p)\, H_-(p;\,k)\, dp.$$

§ 6.

We now proceed to generalize Theorem I. We consider the generalized functions

$$\begin{matrix} F_{r,r}(x_1, x_2), & F_{r,a}(x_1, x_2) \\ F_{a,r}(x_1, x_2), & F_{a,a}(x_1, x_2) \end{matrix}$$

for which

$$\begin{aligned} F_{r,r}(x_1, x_2) &= 0 \quad \text{if} \quad x_1 \lesssim 0 \quad \text{or} \quad x_2 \lesssim 0 \\ F_{r,a}(x_1, x_2) &= 0 \quad \text{if} \quad x_1 \lesssim 0 \quad \text{or} \quad x_2 \gtrsim 0 \\ F_{a,r}(x_1, x_2) &= 0 \quad \text{if} \quad x_1 \gtrsim 0 \quad \text{or} \quad x_2 \lesssim 0 \\ F_{a,a}(x_1, x_2) &= 0 \quad \text{if} \quad x_1 \gtrsim 0 \quad \text{or} \quad x_2 \gtrsim 0. \end{aligned} \tag{6.1}$$

We assume that for some positive η:

$$\begin{aligned}\tilde{F}_{r,j}(p_1, p_2) - \tilde{F}_{a,j}(p_1, p_2) &= 0 \text{ if } p_1^{0^2} + \mathbf{p}_1^2 < \eta^2 \quad j = r, a \\ \tilde{F}_{j,r}(p_1, p_2) - \tilde{F}_{j,a}(p_1, p_2) &= 0 \text{ if } p_2^{0^2} + \mathbf{p}_2^2 < \eta^2\end{aligned} \tag{6.2}$$

We apply Theorem I to the expressions:

$$\tilde{F}_{r,j}(p_1, p_2), \quad \tilde{F}_{a,j}(p_1, p_2)$$

regarding them as functions of p_1. We obtain the functions

$$\tilde{F}_j(k_1, p_2)$$

to which we again apply Theorem I, but this time with respect to the variables p_2.

In this way we demonstrate the validity of the following assertion.

Let $r_0, \ldots, r_3$ be arbitrary positive numbers satisfying the inequalities (5.11).

Then there exists an analytic function $\tilde{F}(k_1, k_2)$ of the complex variables $k_1(k_{10}, \ldots, k_{13})$, $k_2(k_{20}, \ldots, k_{23})$ regular in the region:

$$|k_{1\alpha}| < r_\alpha, \quad |k_{2\alpha}| < r_\alpha, \qquad \alpha = 0, \ldots, 3. \tag{6.3}$$

For real $p_1(p_{10}, \ldots, p_{13})$, $p_2(p_{20}, \ldots, p_{23})$ from this region:

$$\tilde{F}(p_1, p_2) = \tilde{F}_{i,j}(p_1, p_2); \quad i = r, a; \quad j = r, a.$$

Moreover, the following integral representation holds in the region (6.3) under consideration:

$$\tilde{F}(k_1, k_2) = \sum_{(i,\, j=r,\, a)} \int \tilde{F}_{i,j}(p_1, p_2) H_{i,j}(p_1, p_2; k_1, k_2)\, dp_1 dp_2 \tag{6.4}$$

$$H_{ij}(p_1, p_2; k_1, k_2) = H_i(p_1, k_1) H_j(p_2, k_2); \quad H_r = H_+, H_a = H_-;$$

provided that the indices of the class $C(r, s; 4)$, to which $H_\pm$ (regarded as functions of p) should belong, are chosen to be sufficiently large.

We consider the generalized functions

$$F_{i,j}(x_1, x_2, t), \quad i, j = r, a \qquad t = \text{a real number}$$

which have the properties (6.1); (6.2) independently of the value of t.

We note that in accordance with the definition of generalized functions there exists such a class $C(r, s; 9)$ over which the $F_{i,j}$ are integrable.

We take an arbitrary function $h(t)$ from the class $C(r, s; 1)$ and consider the integral

$$F_{i,j}(x_1, x_2) = \int F_{i,j}(x_1, x_2, t)\, h(t)\, dt$$

It may be easily shown that these $F_{i,j}(x_1, x_2)$ will be generalized functions integrable over the class $C(r, s; 8)$ and that they satisfy conditions (6.1), (6.2). We can therefore make use of the assertion formulated earlier and thus arrive at the following lemma.

LEMMA IV. Given the generalized functions

$$F_{i,j}(x_1, x_2, t), \quad i, j = r, a$$

satisfying the conditions:

$$\begin{aligned} F_{r,r}(x_1, x_2, t) &= 0 \quad \text{if} \quad x_1 \lesssim 0 \quad \text{or} \quad x_2 \lesssim 0 \\ F_{r,a}(x_1, x_2, t) &= 0 \quad \text{if} \quad x_1 \lesssim 0 \quad \text{or} \quad x_2 \gtrsim 0 \\ F_{a,r}(x_1, x_2, t) &= 0 \quad \text{if} \quad x_1 \gtrsim 0 \quad \text{or} \quad x_2 \lesssim 0 \\ F_{a,a}(x_1, x_2, t) &= 0 \quad \text{if} \quad x_1 \gtrsim 0 \quad \text{or} \quad x_2 \gtrsim 0 \end{aligned} \tag{6.5}$$

$$\begin{aligned} \tilde{F}_{r,j}(p, p_2, t) - \tilde{F}_{a,j}(p_1, p_2, t) = 0, \text{ if } p_{10}^2 + \mathbf{p}_1^2 < \eta^2, \ j = r, a \\ \tilde{F}_{i,r}(p_1, p_2, t) - \tilde{F}_{i,a}(p_1, p_2, t) = 0, \text{ if } p_{20}^2 + \mathbf{p}_2^2 < \eta^2, \ i = r, a. \end{aligned} \tag{6.6}$$

Let $r_0, \ldots, r_3$ be any positive numbers satisfying the inequalities (5.11).

Then there exists a generalized function of t which is an analytic function $\tilde{F}(k_1, k_2, t)$ of the complex variables k_1, k_2 which is regular within the region:

$$| k_{1\alpha} | < r_\alpha, \quad | k_{2\alpha} | < r_\alpha \qquad \alpha = 0, 1, 2, 3 \tag{6.7}$$

with the relation

$$\tilde{F}(p_1, p_2, t) = \tilde{F}_{i,j}(p_1, p_2, t)$$

holding within the domain of real p_1, p_2 which satisfy the inequalities (6.7).

We now consider the generalized functions

$$f_{i,j}(x_1, x_2, t), \qquad i, j = r, a$$

which satisfy conditions (6.5). We assume that instead of conditions (6.6) the following conditions are satisfied:

$$\begin{aligned}&\tilde{f}_{r,j}(p_1, p_2, t) - \tilde{f}_{a,j}(p_1, p_2, t) = 0\\ \text{if} \quad &| p_{10} - \lambda_{10}(t) |^2 + | \mathbf{p}_1 - \boldsymbol{\lambda}_1(t)|^2 < \eta^2 \varepsilon_1^2(t)\end{aligned} \tag{6.8}$$

$$\begin{aligned}&\tilde{f}_{i,r}(p_1, p_2, t) - f_{i,a}(p_1, p_2, t) = 0,\\ \text{if} \quad &| p_{20} - \lambda_{20}(t)|^2 + | \mathbf{p}_2 - \boldsymbol{\lambda}_2(t)^2 < \eta^2 \varepsilon_2^2(t)\\ &\tilde{f}_{i,j}(p_1, p_2, t) = 0, \text{ if } t < N.\end{aligned} \tag{6.9}$$

We further assume that the functions $\lambda(t)$, $\varepsilon(t)$ appearing in the foregoing possess the following common properties:

(*1*) $\lambda_{j\alpha}(t)$, $\varepsilon_j(t)$ are continuous and differentiable an infinite number of times in the interval $N \leqq t < \infty$; (*2*) $\lambda_{j\alpha}(t)$, $\varepsilon_j(t)$ are polynomially bounded; (*3*) $\varepsilon_j(t)$ are essentially positive and satisfy the inequality

$$\varepsilon_j(t) > \frac{\nu}{| t |^m} \qquad \nu > 0 \qquad m > 0;$$

(*4*) all derivatives (of arbitrarily high order) of the functions $\lambda_{j\alpha}(t)$, $\varepsilon_j(t)$ are uniformly bounded in the interval $N \leqq t < \infty$. We now continue these functions $\lambda(t)$, $\varepsilon(t)$ in some manner to the whole real axis retaining all the properties enumerated above.

It may then be easily shown that for any values of the indices r, s of the class C, it is always possible to find indices r_1, s_1 in such a way that from

$$h(x_1, x_2, t) \in C(r_1, s_1; 9)$$

it follows that

$$e^{i\{\lambda_1(t)x_1+\lambda_2(t)x_2\}} h\{\varepsilon_1(t)\, x_1, \varepsilon_2(t)\, x_2, t\} \in C(r, s; 9).$$

Consequently for any generalized function $f(x_1, x_2, t)$ we can choose such r_1, s_1 that the integral

$$\int f(x_1, x_2, t)\, e^{i\{\lambda_1(t)x_1+\lambda_2(t)x_2\}} h\{\varepsilon_1(t)x_1, \varepsilon_2(t)x_2, t\}\, dx_1\, dx_2\, dt$$

will be defined as a linear functional of

$$h\{\varepsilon_1(t)\,x_1,\ \varepsilon_2(t)x_2,\ t\} \in C(r,\ s;\ 9).$$

But this linear functional may be transformed into the form:

$$\int f\left(\frac{x_1}{\varepsilon_1(t)},\ \frac{x_2}{\varepsilon_2(t)},\ t\right) e^{i\left\{\frac{\lambda_1(t)}{\varepsilon_1(t)}x_1+\frac{\lambda_2(t)}{\varepsilon_2(t)}x_2\right\}} \frac{1}{(\varepsilon_1\,\varepsilon_2)^4} h(x_1,\ x_2,\ t)\,dx_1\,dx_2\,dt$$

which defines the generalized function

$$\frac{1}{(\varepsilon_1\,\varepsilon_2)^4} f\left(\frac{x_1}{\varepsilon_1(t)},\ \frac{x_2}{\varepsilon_2(t)},\ t\right) e^{i\left\{\frac{\lambda_1(t)}{\varepsilon_1(t)}x_1+\frac{\lambda_2(t)}{\varepsilon_2(t)}x_2\right\}}.$$

Thus, since $f_{ij}(x_1,\ x_2,\ t)$ are generalized functions the expressions

$$F_{ij}(x_1,\ x_2,\ t) = \frac{1}{(\varepsilon_1\,\varepsilon_2)^4} f_{ij}\left(\frac{x_1}{\varepsilon_1(t)},\ \frac{x_2}{\varepsilon_2(t)},\ t\right) e^{i\left\{\frac{\lambda_1(t)}{\varepsilon_1(t)}x_1+\frac{\lambda_2(t)}{\varepsilon_2(t)}x_2\right\}} \tag{6.10}$$

will also be generalized functions.

Moreover, in view of the fact that the $f_{i,j}$ satisfy conditions (6.5), the functions F_{ij} just introduced also satisfy these conditions.

We also note that

$$\tilde{F}_{ij}(p_1,\ p_2,\ t) = \tilde{f}_{ij}(\lambda_1(t) + \varepsilon_1(t)p_1,\ \lambda_2(t) + \varepsilon_2(t)p_2,\ t\}.$$

Therefore, it follows from (6.8) that $\tilde{F}_{ij}$ satisfy conditions (6.6).

Thus we can apply Lemma IV to the functions $\tilde{F}_{ij}(x_1,\ x_2,\ t)$ as a result of which we see that the following assertion is valid.

LEMMA V. Given the generalized functions

$$f_{i,j}(x_1,\ x_2,\ t),\quad i,\ j = r,\ a$$

satisfying conditions (6.5), (6.8), (6.9). It is assumed that the functions $\lambda_{j\alpha}(t)$, $\varepsilon_j(t)$ possess the properties *(1)*, *(2)*, *(3)*, *(4)*. We choose the numbers r_α, $\alpha = 0, 1, 2, 3$ in the same way as in Theorem I. Then there exists a generalized function

$$\tilde{f}\,(\lambda_1(t) + \varepsilon_1(t)\,k_1,\quad \lambda_2(t) + \varepsilon_2(t)\,k_2,\ t\}$$

which is an analytic function of the complex variables k_1, k_2 regular in the region

$$|\,k_{1\alpha}\,| < r_\alpha,\quad |\,k_{2\alpha}\,| < r_\alpha;\quad \alpha = 0, \ldots, 3 \tag{6.11}$$

and such that within the domain of real p_1, p_2 satisfying the inequalities (6.11) the following relation holds:

$$f(\lambda_1(t) + \varepsilon_1(t)p_1, \quad \lambda_2(t) + \varepsilon_2(t)p_2, t)$$
$$= \tilde{f}_{i,j}(\lambda_1(t) + \varepsilon_1(t)p_1, \quad \lambda_2(t) + \varepsilon_2(t)p_2, t).$$

Moreover,

$$\tilde{f}\{\lambda_1(t) + \varepsilon_1(t)k_1, \quad \lambda_2(t) + \varepsilon_2(t)k_2, t\} = 0 \qquad \text{for} \quad t < N.$$

§ 7.

THEOREM II. For given constant

$$M \geqq \mu > 0, \quad \delta \geqq 0, \quad 1 \geqq \omega \geqq 0, \quad V \geqq 0$$

it is possible to find such $\rho > 0$ that the following assertion will hold.

Let

$$f_{i,j}(x_1, x_2, t), \quad i, j = r, a$$

be generalized functions invariant under spatial rotations and reflections (of the vectors $\mathbf{x}$), satisfying conditions (6.5) and in addition to that conditions:

$$\tilde{f}_{r,j}(p_1, p_2, t) - \tilde{f}_{a,j}(p_1, p_2, t) = 0, \quad \text{if} \quad \begin{array}{l}(p_{10} + t)^2 - \mathbf{p}_1^2 < (M + \mu)^2 \\ (p_{10} - t)^2 - \mathbf{p}_1^2 < 9\mu^2\end{array} \tag{7.1}$$

$$\tilde{f}_{i,r}(p_1, p_2, t) - \tilde{f}_{i,a}(p_1, p_2, t) = 0, \quad \text{if} \quad \begin{array}{l}(p_{20} + t)^2 - \mathbf{p}_2^2 < (M + \mu)^2 \\ (p_{20} - t)^2 - \mathbf{p}_2^2 < 9\mu^2\end{array} \tag{7.2}$$

$$\tilde{f}_{i,j}(p_1, p_2, t) = 0, \quad \text{if} \quad t < \tfrac{1}{2}[M + \mu(1 + \delta)]. \tag{7.3}$$

Then there exists a generalized function of t which is an analytic function of the complex variables $z_1, \ldots, z_5$

$$\phi(z_1, \ldots, z_5, t)$$

which is regular in the region

$$| z_1 - M^2 | < \rho\mu^2, \; | z_2 - \mu^2 | < \rho\mu^2, \; | z_3 - \tau | < \rho\mu^2, \; | z_4 - \tau | < \rho\mu^2$$
$$| z_5 + 4a^2 | < \rho\mu^2 \left(\frac{M}{t}\right)^2, \; - V \leqq \tau < \mu^2(1 - \omega), \; 4a^2 \leqq u^2 \tag{7.4}$$

where

$$u^2 = \left[M + \mu(1+\delta) + \frac{M^2 - \mu^2(1-\omega)}{M + \mu(1+\delta)}\right]^2 - 4M^2 \qquad (7.5)$$

and which has the properties: (*1*) $\phi(z_1, \ldots, z_5, t) = 0$ if $t < \frac{1}{2}[M + \mu(1+\delta)]$ (*2*) Within the domain of the real four-vectors p_1, p_2 for which the quantities:

$$z_1 = (p_{10} + t)^2 - \mathbf{p}_1^2,\ z_2 = (p_{20} + t)^2 - \mathbf{p}_2^2;\ z_3 = (p_{10} - t)^2 - \mathbf{p}_1^2,$$
$$z_4 = (p_{20} - t)^2 - \mathbf{p}_2^2,\ z_5 = (p_{10} - p_{20})^2 - (\mathbf{p}_1 - \mathbf{p}_2)^2 \qquad (7.6)$$

satisfy the inequalities

$$| z_1 - M^2 | < \rho\mu^2,\ | z_2 - M^2 | < \rho\mu^2,\ | z_3 - \tau | < \rho\mu^2,\ | z_4 - \tau | < \rho\mu^2,$$
$$| z_5 + 4a^2 | < \rho\mu^2 \left(\frac{M}{t}\right)^2,\ -V \leqq \tau < \mu^2(1-\omega),\ 4a^2 \leqq u^2 \qquad (7.7)$$

we have:

$$\tilde{f}_{ij}(p_1, p_2, t) = \phi(z_1, \ldots, z_5, t). \qquad (7.8)$$

PROOF. The proof is based on Lemma V. We set

$$\lambda_{10}(t) = \lambda_{20}(t) = \frac{M^2 - \tau}{4t}$$
$$\boldsymbol{\lambda}_1(t) = \mathbf{e}_1 \varphi_1(t) + \mathbf{e}_2 a,\quad \boldsymbol{\lambda}_2(t) = \mathbf{e}_1 \varphi(t) - \mathbf{e}_2 a \qquad (7.9)$$
$$\varphi(t) = \sqrt{\left[t + \frac{M^2 - \tau}{4t}\right]^2 - M^2 - a^2}.$$

Here $\mathbf{e}_1$, $\mathbf{e}_2$ are two arbitrary mutually perpendicular unit vectors; a, τ are arbitrary real numbers satisfying the inequalities:

$$-V \leqq \tau < \mu^2(1-\omega),\quad 4a^2 \leqq u^2. \qquad (7.10)$$

We also introduce

$$\varepsilon_1(t) = \varepsilon_2(t) = \frac{1}{t + \dfrac{M^2 - \tau}{4t}}. \qquad (7.11)$$

We note that in the interval of interest to us

$$t \geqq \frac{M + \mu(1+\delta)}{2}$$

the following relation holds:

$$\left(t + \frac{M^2 - \tau}{4t}\right)^2 - M^2 - a^2 > 0.$$

Therefore the functions $\varepsilon_j(t)$, $\lambda_j(t)$ satisfy conditions *(1)*–*(4)* of Lemma V.

We further choose the number ζ in such a way that

$$\sup_{2t \geqq M+\mu(1+\delta)} \left\{ \frac{\zeta}{\mu} \frac{2\sqrt{-M^2+2\left(t+\dfrac{M^2-\tau}{4t}\right)^2}}{t+\dfrac{M^2-\tau}{4t}} + \zeta^2 \frac{1}{\left(t+\dfrac{M^2-\tau}{4t}\right)^2} \right\} < \begin{cases} 2\dfrac{M}{\mu}+1 \\ 8 \end{cases} \tag{7.12}$$

It is then evident that

$$2\sqrt{[\lambda_{j0}(t) \pm t]^2 + \boldsymbol{\lambda}_j^2(t)}\, \varepsilon_j(t)\zeta\mu + \varepsilon_j^2(t)\zeta^2\mu^2 < \begin{cases} 2M\mu + \mu^2 \\ 8\mu^2 \end{cases}. \tag{7.13}$$

We now take

$$|\, p_{10} - \lambda_{10}(t)\,|^2 + |\mathbf{p}_1 - \boldsymbol{\lambda}_1(t)\,|^2 < \zeta^2\mu^2\varepsilon^2(t).$$

We then have

$$\begin{aligned}(p_{10} \pm t)^2 - \mathbf{p}_1^2 &= [\lambda_{10}(t) \pm t]^2 - \boldsymbol{\lambda}_1^2(t) + 2[\lambda_{10}(t) \pm t]\cdot[p_{10} - \lambda_{10}(t)] \\ &\quad - 2\boldsymbol{\lambda}_1(t)[\mathbf{p}_1 - \boldsymbol{\lambda}_1(t)] + [p_{10} - \lambda_{10}(t)]^2 + [\mathbf{p}_1 - \boldsymbol{\lambda}_1(t)]^2 \\ &< [\lambda_{10}(t) \pm t]^2 - \boldsymbol{\lambda}_1^2(t) + 2\sqrt{[\lambda_{10}(t) \pm t]^2 + \boldsymbol{\lambda}_1^2(t)}\,\varepsilon(t)\zeta\mu + \varepsilon^2(t)\zeta^2\mu^2.\end{aligned} \tag{7.14}$$

But evidently

$$[\lambda_{10}(t) + t]^2 - \boldsymbol{\lambda}_1^2(t) = M^2, \quad [\lambda_{10}(t) - t]^2 - \boldsymbol{\lambda}_1^2(t) = \tau$$

and therefore on the basis of (7.13) and (7.14)

$$(p_{10} + t)^2 - \mathbf{p}_1^2 < M^2 + 2M\mu + \mu^2 = (M + \mu)^2$$
$$(p_{10} - t)^2 - \mathbf{p}_1^2 < \tau + 8\mu^2 \leqq 9\mu^2.$$

In a quite analogous manner from the inequality

$$|\, p_{20} - \lambda_{20}(t)\,|^2 + |\,\mathbf{p}_2 - \boldsymbol{\lambda}_2(t)\,|^2 < \zeta^2\mu^2\varepsilon^2(t)$$

it will follow that

$$(p_{20} + t)^2 - \mathbf{p}_2^2 < (M + \mu)^2$$
$$(p_{20} - t)^2 - \mathbf{p}_2^2 < 9\mu^2.$$

We shall thus obtain from (7.1), (7.2):

$$\tilde{f}_{r,j}(p_1, p_2, t) - \tilde{f}_{a,j}(p_1, p_2, t) = 0,$$
$$\text{if } |p_{10} - \lambda_{10}(t)|^2 + |\mathbf{p}_1 - \boldsymbol{\lambda}_1(t)|^2 < \zeta^2\mu^2\varepsilon^2(t)$$

and

$$f_{i,r}(p_1, p_2, t) - \tilde{f}_{i,a}(p_1, p_2, t) = 0,$$
$$\text{if } |p_{20} - \lambda_{20}(t)|^2 + |\mathbf{p}_2 - \boldsymbol{\lambda}_2(t)|^2 < \zeta^2\mu^2\varepsilon^2(t).$$

We can therefore apply Lemma V setting in it

$$\eta = \zeta\mu, \quad N = \frac{M + \mu(1 + \delta)}{2}.$$

In order to satisfy the inequalities (5.11) of Theorem I, we set

$$r_0 = \frac{1}{2\sqrt{6}}\zeta\mu, \quad |\mathbf{r}| = \frac{3}{8\sqrt{6}}\zeta\mu.$$

Now in virtue of the preceding lemma we can see that the following assertion holds.

There exists a generalized function of t

$$\tilde{f}(k_1, k_2, t) \tag{7.15}$$

which is an analytic function of the complex four-vectors k_1, k_2 regular in the region:

$$\begin{aligned} |k_{10} - \lambda_{10}(t)| &< \frac{\zeta}{2\sqrt{6}}\mu\varepsilon(t), \quad |\mathbf{k}_1 - \boldsymbol{\lambda}_1(t)| < \frac{3}{8\sqrt{6}}\zeta\mu\varepsilon(t) \\ |k_{20} - \lambda_{20}(t)| &< \frac{\zeta}{2\sqrt{6}}\mu\varepsilon(t), \quad |\mathbf{k}_2 - \boldsymbol{\lambda}_2(t)| < \frac{3}{8\sqrt{6}}\zeta\mu\varepsilon(t) \end{aligned} \tag{7.16}$$

and possessing the following properties: (*1*) Within the domain of real p_1, p_2 which satisfy the inequalities (7.16):

$$\tilde{f}_{i,j}(p_1, p_2, t) = \tilde{f}(p_1, p_2, t);$$

$$(2) \qquad \tilde{f}(p_1, p_2, t) = 0 \quad \text{if} \quad t < \frac{M + \mu(1+\delta)}{2}.$$

We now make use of the condition of invariance under spatial rotations and reflections. Because of this condition the function (7.15) depends on k_1, k_2 only through the five variables:

$$k_{10}, \quad k_{20}, \quad \mathbf{k}_1^2, \quad \mathbf{k}_2^2, \quad \mathbf{k}_1 \cdot \mathbf{k}_2.$$

Instead of them we can introduce the completely equivalent system of variables:

$$\begin{gathered} z_1 = (k_{10}+t)^2 - \mathbf{k}_1^2, \; z_2 = (k_{20}+t)^2 - \mathbf{k}_2^2, \; z_3 = (k_{10}-t)^2 - \mathbf{k}_1^2 \\ z_4 = (k_{20}-t)^2 - \mathbf{k}_2^2, \; z_5 = (k_{10}-k_{20})^2 - (\mathbf{k}_1 - \mathbf{k}_2)^2 \end{gathered} \tag{7.17}$$

so that

$$\tilde{f}(k_1, k_2, t) = \Phi(z_1, z_2, z_3, z_4, z_5, t). \tag{7.18}$$

Consequently, in order to complete the proof of our theorem we need only to show that (with a suitable choice of the number ρ) we can find complex four-vectors satisfying the inequalities (7.16) for arbitrary complex $z_1, \ldots, z_5$ which satisfy the inequalities:

$$\begin{gathered} |z_1 - M^2| < \rho\mu^2, \; |z_2 - M^2| < \rho\mu^2, \; |z_3 - \tau| < \rho\mu^2, \\ |z_4 - \tau| < \rho\mu^2, \; |z_5 + 4a^2| < \rho\mu^2 \left(\frac{M}{t}\right)^2, \\ 4a^2 \leqq u^2, \quad -V \leqq \tau \leqq \mu^2(1-\omega). \end{gathered} \tag{7.19}$$

We therefore turn to the question of constructing k_1, k_2 from given $z_1, \ldots, z_5, t$.

From (7.17) we find:

$$k_{10} = \frac{z_1 - z_3}{4t}, \quad k_{20} = \frac{z_2 - z_4}{4t} \tag{7.20}$$

and also $$\mathbf{k}_1^2 = t^2 - \frac{z_1 + z_3}{2} + \left(\frac{z_1 - z_3}{4t}\right)^2,$$

$$\mathbf{k}_2^2 = t^2 - \frac{z_2 + z_4}{2} + \left(\frac{z_2 - z_4}{4t}\right)^2,$$

$$(\mathbf{k}_1 - \mathbf{k}_2)^2 = -z_5 + \left(\frac{z_1 - z_2 - z_3 + z_4}{4t}\right)^2. \tag{7.21}$$

In order to select $\mathbf{k}_1$, $\mathbf{k}_2$ satisfying relations (7.16) we set:

$$\mathbf{k}_1 = A\mathbf{e}_1 + C\mathbf{e}_2, \quad \mathbf{k}_2 = B\mathbf{e}_1 - C\mathbf{e}_2$$

where $\mathbf{e}_1$, $\mathbf{e}_2$ are two mutually perpendicular unit vectors. Then in order to determine A, B, C we obtain from (7.21) the equations:

$$A^2 + C^2 = t^2 - \frac{z_1 + z_3}{2} + \left(\frac{z_1 - z_3}{4t}\right)^2,$$

$$B^2 + C^2 = t^2 - \frac{z_2 + z_4}{2} + \left(\frac{z_2 - z_4}{4t}\right)^2,$$

$$(A - B)^2 + 4C^2 = -z_5 + \left(\frac{z_1 - z_2 - z_3 + z_4}{4t}\right)^2,$$

from which we obtain:

$$\left.\begin{aligned} A &= A(t, z_1, \ldots, z_5) \\ B &= B(t, z_1, \ldots, z_5) \end{aligned}\right\} =$$

$$= \frac{1}{2}\sqrt{4t^2 - (z_1+z_2+z_3+z_4-z_5) + 2\left(\frac{z_1-z_3}{4t}\right)^2 + 2\left(\frac{z_2-z_4}{4t}\right)^2 - \left(\frac{z_1-z_2-z_3+z_4}{4t}\right)^2}$$

$$\pm \frac{1}{2}\,\frac{\frac{1}{2}(z_2 + z_4 - z_1 - z_3) + \left(\frac{z_1 - z_3}{4t}\right)^2 - \left(\frac{z_2 - z_4}{4t}\right)^2}{\sqrt{4t^2 - (z_1+z_2+z_3+z_4-z_5) + 2\left(\frac{z_1-z_3}{4t}\right)^2 + 2\left(\frac{z_2-z_4}{4t}\right)^2 - \left(\frac{z_1-z_2-z_3+z_4}{4t}\right)^2}};$$

$$C(t, z_1, \ldots, z_5) = \frac{1}{2}\left\{ -z_5 + \left(\frac{z_1 - z_2 - z_3 + z_4}{4t}\right)^2 - \frac{\left[\frac{z_2 + z_4 - z_1 - z_3}{2} + \left(\frac{z_1 - z_3}{4t}\right)^2 - \left(\frac{z_2 - z_4}{4t}\right)^2\right]^2}{4t^2 - (z_1+z_2+z_3+z_4-z_5) + 2\left(\frac{z_1-z_3}{4t}\right)^2 + 2\left(\frac{z_2-z_4}{4t}\right)^2 - \left(\frac{z_1-z_2-z_3+z_4}{4t}\right)^2} \right\}^{1/2} \tag{7.22}$$

Obviously

$$A(t,\ M^2,\ M^2,\ \tau,\ \tau,\ -\ 4a^2) = \varphi(t),$$
$$B(t,\ M^2,\ M^2,\ \tau,\ \tau,\ -\ 4a^2) = \varphi(t),$$
$$C(t,\ M^2,\ M^2,\ \tau,\ \tau,\ -\ 4a^2) = a.$$

Thus, our theorem will be proved as soon as we show that

$$\left|\frac{\xi_1 - \xi_3}{4t}\right| < \frac{\zeta}{2\sqrt{6}} \frac{\mu}{t + \dfrac{M^2 - \tau}{4t}}, \quad \left|\frac{\xi_2 - \xi_4}{4t}\right| < \frac{\zeta}{2\sqrt{6}} \frac{\mu}{t + \dfrac{M^2 - \tau}{4t}}$$

$$\left| A\left(t,\ M^2 + \xi_1,\ M^2 + \xi_2,\ \tau + \xi_3,\ \tau + \xi_4,\ -\ 4a^2 + \xi_5 \frac{M^2}{t^2}\right) - A(t,\ M^2,\ M^2,\ \tau,\ \tau,\ -\ 4a^2)\right| < \frac{3}{8\sqrt{12}} \frac{\mu}{t + \dfrac{M^2 - \tau}{4t}}$$

$$\left| B\left(t,\ M^2 + \xi_1,\ M^2 + \xi_2,\ \tau + \xi_3,\ \tau + \xi_4,\ -\ 4a^2 + \xi_5 \frac{M^2}{t^2}\right) - B(t,\ M^2,\ M^2,\ \tau,\ \tau,\ -\ 4a^2)\right| < \frac{3}{8\sqrt{12}} \frac{\mu}{t + \dfrac{M^2 - \tau}{4t}} \tag{7.23}$$

$$\left| C\left(t,\ M^2 + \xi_1,\ M^2 + \xi_2,\ \tau + \xi_3,\ \tau + \xi_4,\ -\ 4a^2 + \xi_5 \frac{M^2}{t^2}\right) - C(\tau,\ M^2,\ M^2,\ \tau,\ \tau,\ -\ 4a^2)\right| < \frac{3}{8\sqrt{12}} \frac{\mu}{t + \dfrac{M^2 - \tau}{4t}}$$

for

$$t \geqq \frac{M + \mu(1 + \delta)}{2}, \quad -V \leqq \tau \leqq \mu(1 - \omega), \quad 4a^2 \leqq u^2$$

$$|\xi_j| < \rho\mu^2 \qquad j = 1, \ldots, 5.$$

But the possibility of choosing a sufficiently small value of

ρ follows directly from an examination[115] of expressions (7.22).

NOTE. We consider a special case of Theorem II when $\delta = \omega = 0$. In this case $u = 0$ and, consequently, $a = 0$. Thus the domain of those values of z_5 which belong to the region in which the function $\phi(z_1, \ldots, z_5, t)$ is regular will be restricted by the inequality:

$$|z_5| < \rho\mu^2 \left(\frac{M}{t}\right)^2.$$

However, by means of completely elementary considerations, it is easy to extend the limits of possible variation of $\operatorname{Re} z_5$.

Indeed, we choose the function $h(t)$ in the class $C(0, \infty; 1)$ in such a way that

$$h(t) = 0, \qquad t < M + \mu/2$$
$$h(t) = 1, \qquad t > M + \mu.$$

We set

$$f_{i,j}(x_1, x_2, t) = f_{i,j}^{(1)}(x_1, x_2, t) + f_{i,j}^{(2)}(x_1, x_2, t),$$

$$f_{i,j}^{(1)}(x_1, x_2, t) = [1-h(t)]f_{i,j}(x_1, x_2, t);\ f_{i,j}^{(2)}(x_1, x_2, t) = h(t)f_{i,j}(x_1, x_2, t).$$

The functions $f_{i,j}^{(1)}, f_{i,j}^{(2)}$ satisfy the conditions of our theorem. The former does so for $\omega = 0$, $\delta = 0$, while the latter does so for $\omega = 0$, $\delta = M/\mu$.

Let us examine the regions in which the functions $\phi^{(1)}, \phi^{(2)}$ are regular, and in doing so let us write out explicitly the appropriate inequalities only for the argument z_5.

For the first of them we have

$$|z_5| < \rho\mu^2 \left(\frac{M}{t}\right)^2.$$

[115] The inequalities (7.23) involving the functions A, B, would hold even without multiplying ξ_5 by M^2/t^2. Such multiplication is necessary only to guarantee the validity of the inequality containing the function C, since only when the argument is given by $\xi_5(M^2/t^2)$ will its left-hand side be proportional to $1/t$ for large t.

This inequality will be satisfied if

$$\left|\operatorname{Re} z_5\right| < \frac{\rho\mu^2}{\sqrt{2}}\left(\frac{M}{t}\right)^2, \qquad \left|\operatorname{Im} z_5\right| < \frac{\rho\mu^2}{\sqrt{2}}\left(\frac{M}{t}\right)^2.$$

But, obviously,

$$\phi^{(1)} = 0 \quad \text{for} \quad t > M + \mu.$$

Therefore $\phi^{(1)}$ is regular for

$$\operatorname{Re} z_5 < \frac{\rho\mu^2}{\sqrt{2}}\left(\frac{M}{M+\mu}\right)^2, \quad |\operatorname{Im} z_5| < \frac{\rho\mu^2}{\sqrt{2}}\left(\frac{M}{t}\right)^2.$$

Further, for $\phi^{(2)}$

$$u^2 = \left(2M + \mu + \frac{M^2 - \mu^2}{2M + \mu}\right)^2 - 4M^2 > 0.$$

Therefore $\phi^{(2)}$ will be regular for

$$-u^2 \leqq \operatorname{Re} z_5 \leqq 0 \quad |\operatorname{Im} z_5| < \rho\mu^2\left(\frac{M}{t}\right)^2.$$

Let ρ_1 be the smaller of the two numbers

$$\frac{\rho}{\sqrt{2}}\left(\frac{M}{M+\mu}\right)^2, \quad \left(\frac{u}{\mu}\right)^2.$$

We then see that both functions $\phi^{(1)}$, $\phi^{(2)}$ and, consequently, also their sum $\phi = \phi^{(1)} + \phi^{(2)}$, will be regular for

$$-\rho_1\mu^2 \leqq \operatorname{Re} z_5 \leqq 0, \quad |\operatorname{Im} z_5| < \frac{\rho\mu^2}{\sqrt{2}}\left(\frac{M}{t}\right)^2.$$

We have thus demonstrated the validity of the following assertion.

THEOREM III. If the conditions of Theorem II are satisfied for $\omega = \delta = 0$, then it is possible to choose a sufficiently small $\rho > 0$ such that

$$\phi(z_1, \ldots, z_5, t)$$

will be regular in the region

$$| z_1 - M^2 | < \rho\mu^2, \ | z_2 - M^2 | < \rho\mu^2, \ | z_3 - \tau | < \rho\mu^2, \ | z_4 - \tau | < \rho\mu^2,$$

$$- \rho\mu^2 \leqq \operatorname{Re} z_5 \leqq 0, \quad | \operatorname{Im} z_5 | < \rho\mu^2 \left(\frac{M}{t}\right)^2; \quad - V \leqq \tau \leqq \mu^2.$$

We note that the lower limit on the variation in $\operatorname{Re} z_5$ may be significantly reduced, but this will require deeper considerations.

§ 8.

THEOREM IV. We consider the generalized functions $F_r(x)$ and $F_a(x)$ of the four-vector x one of which is retarded and the other advanced.

We assume that the Fourier transform $\tilde{f}(p)$ of their difference

$$f(x) = F_r(x) - F_a(x)$$

vanishes:

$$\tilde{f}(p) = 0$$

for

$$| p_0 | < m.$$

Then there exists an analytic function $\tilde{F}(k)$ of the complex four-vector k regular in the region:

$$| \operatorname{Im} \mathbf{k} | < | \operatorname{Im} \sqrt{k_0^2 - m^2} | \tag{8.1}$$

such that for real $k = p$ from this region

$$\tilde{F}(p) = \tilde{F}_r(p) = \tilde{F}_a(p).$$

PROOF. Within the class $C(0, \infty; 1)$ we choose a function $\varphi(t)$ such that

$$\varphi(t) = 1, \qquad x_0 \geqq 0$$

$$\varphi(t) = 0, \qquad x_0 \leqq - \delta$$

where δ is some positive number.

We take an arbitrarily small fixed positive ρ and note that the function

$$\varphi(x_0)\, e^{-\rho \mathbf{x}^2 + ikx}$$

belongs to the class $C(\infty, \infty; 4)$, provided that $\operatorname{Im} k_0 > 0$ (k_0 is complex). Therefore we can define the integral

$$\tilde{F}_r(k; \rho) \equiv \tilde{F}_r(k^0, \mathbf{k}; \rho) = \int F_r(x)\, \varphi(x_0)\, e^{-\rho \mathbf{x}^2 + ikx}\, dx \qquad (8.2)$$

which is an analytic function of k regular in the domain in which $\operatorname{Im} k_0 > 0$.

It may be easily seen that this integral does not depend on the particular choice of the function $\varphi(t)$. Indeed, if φ_1 and φ_2 represent two possible particular forms of the function φ we have:

$$\varphi_1(x_0) - \varphi_2(x_0) = 0 \quad \text{for} \quad x_0 \geqq 0$$

from which we see that in virtue of the property of retardation we have over the whole four-dimensional space

$$\int F_r(x)[\varphi_1(x_0) - \varphi_2(x_0)]\, e^{-\rho \mathbf{x}^2 + ikx}\, dx = 0.$$

Therefore we shall write (8.2) in the form

$$\tilde{F}_r(k; \rho) = \int F_r(x)\, e^{-\rho \mathbf{x}^2 + ikx}\, dx, \qquad (8.3)$$

taking the right-hand side of (8.2) to be the definition of such an integral. In a completely analogous manner we define the function

$$\tilde{F}_a(k; \rho) = \int F_a(x) e^{-\rho \mathbf{x}^2 + ikx}\, dx \qquad (8.4)$$

which is analytic and regular in the region in which $\operatorname{Im} k_0 < 0$.

We note that expressions (8.3), (8.4) also have meaning for real k_0. Indeed, they may then be regarded as Fourier transforms of a generalized function of the one variable x_0:

$$\int F_j(x)\, e^{-\rho \mathbf{x}^2 - i\mathbf{k}\cdot\mathbf{x}}\, d\mathbf{x} \qquad j = r,\ a.$$

Thus for real k_0 $\tilde{F}_r(k_0, \mathbf{k}, \rho)$, $\tilde{F}_a(k_0, \mathbf{k}, \rho)$ will be generalized functions of k_0 which are analytic functions of $\mathbf{k}$.

It is also not difficult to show that in the generalized sense (with respect to the real variable p_0):

$$\lim_{\varepsilon \to +0} \tilde{F}_r(p_0 + i\varepsilon, \mathbf{k}; \rho) = \tilde{F}_r(p_0, \mathbf{k}; \rho),$$
$$\lim_{\varepsilon \to +0} \tilde{F}_a(p_0 - i\varepsilon, \mathbf{k}; \rho) = \tilde{F}_a(p_0, \mathbf{k}; \rho). \tag{8.5}$$

Finally, in the generalized sense with respect to the real four-vector p

$$\lim_{\rho \to +0} \tilde{F}_r(p; \rho) = \tilde{F}_r(p),$$
$$\lim_{\rho \to +0} \tilde{F}_a(p; \rho) = \tilde{F}_a(p), \tag{8.6}$$

where $\tilde{F}_r$, $\tilde{F}_a$ are the usual Fourier transforms of the functions $F_r(x)$, $F_a(x)$.

We consider the difference:

$$\lim_{\varepsilon \to +0} \{\tilde{F}_r(p_0+i\varepsilon, \mathbf{k}; \rho) - \tilde{F}_a(p_0-i\varepsilon, \mathbf{k}; \rho)\} = \tilde{F}_r(p_0, \mathbf{k}; \rho) - \tilde{F}_a(p_0, \mathbf{k}; \rho)$$
$$= \int f(x)\, e^{ip_0 x_0}\, e^{-\rho \mathbf{x}^2 - i\mathbf{k}\mathbf{x}}\, dx_0\, d\mathbf{x}.$$

But in accordance with the conditions of the theorem

$$\int f(x)\, e^{ip_0 x_0}\, dx_0 = 0 \qquad \text{for} \quad |p_0| < m.$$

Consequently

$$\lim_{\varepsilon \to +0} \{\tilde{F}_r(p_0 + i\varepsilon, \mathbf{k}; \rho) - \tilde{F}_a(p_0 - i\varepsilon, \mathbf{k}; \rho)\} = 0 \quad \text{for} \quad |p_0| < m \tag{8.7}$$

and therefore $\tilde{F}_a(k; \rho)$, $\tilde{F}_r(k; \rho)$ represent the same analytic function $\tilde{F}(k; \rho)$ in the regions $\operatorname{Im} k_0 > 0$ and $\operatorname{Im} k_0 < 0$ respectively. The region in which $\tilde{F}(k; \rho)$ is defined includes all the positions of the complex vector $\mathbf{k}$; with respect to the complex variable k_0 this function has the cuts

$$-\infty < k_0 \leqq -m \qquad m \leqq k_0 < \infty. \tag{8.8}$$

Having noted this we fix the numbers λ, m_1,

$$0 \leqq \lambda \leqq 1 \qquad 0 \leqq m_1 < m \tag{8.9}$$

and construct the expression

$$\Phi(k_0) = \tilde{F}(k_0, \lambda \mathbf{e} \sqrt{k_0^2 - m_1^2} + \mathbf{f}; \rho) \tag{8.10}$$

in which $\mathbf{f}$ is a real vector, $\mathbf{e}$ is a real unit vector.

We form the "symmetrized" and the "antisymmetrized" functions invariant with respect to the change in sign of the square root appearing in them:

$$\phi_a(k_0) = \frac{1}{2\sqrt{k_0^2 - m_1^2}} \{\tilde{F}(k_0, \lambda\mathbf{e}\sqrt{k_0^2 - m_1^2} + \mathbf{f}; \rho) - \tilde{F}(k_0, -\lambda\mathbf{e}\sqrt{k_0^2 - m_1^2} + \mathbf{f}; \rho)\} \tag{8.11}$$

$$\phi_s(k_0) = \tfrac{1}{2}\tilde{F}(k_0, \lambda\mathbf{e}\sqrt{k_0^2 - m_1^2} + \mathbf{f}; \rho) + \tfrac{1}{2}\tilde{F}(k_0, -\lambda\mathbf{e}\sqrt{k_0^2 - m_1^2} + \mathbf{f}; \rho).$$

In view of (8.7) we shall have the following expression:

$$\lim_{\varepsilon\to+0} \{\phi_s(p_0 + i\varepsilon) - \phi_s(p_0 - i\varepsilon)\}$$
$$= \tfrac{1}{2}\tilde{F}_r(p_0, \lambda\mathbf{e}\sqrt{p_0^2 - m_1^2} + \mathbf{f}; \rho) - \tfrac{1}{2}\tilde{F}_a(p_0, \lambda\mathbf{e}\sqrt{p_0^2 - m_1^2} + \mathbf{f}; \rho)$$
$$+ \tfrac{1}{2}\tilde{F}_r(p_0, -\lambda\mathbf{e}\sqrt{p_0^2 - m_1^2} + \mathbf{f}; \rho)$$
$$- \tfrac{1}{2}\tilde{F}_a(p_0, -\lambda\mathbf{e}\sqrt{p_0^2 - m_1^2} + \mathbf{f}; \rho) = 0 \quad \text{for } |p_0| < m. \tag{8.12}$$

In a completely analogous manner we shall also find:

$$\lim_{\varepsilon\to+0} \{\phi_a(p_0 + i\varepsilon) - \phi_a(p_0 - i\varepsilon)\} = 0 \quad \text{for } |p_0| < m. \tag{8.13}$$

Thus, we can regard $\phi_s(k_0)$, $\phi_a(k_0)$ as analytic functions of the complex variable k_0, regular in the whole complex plane with the exception of the cut (8.8).

We shall now discuss the question of the nature of the possible rate of increase of these functions at infinity.

From an examination of the cutoff factor

$$\exp\{-\rho\mathbf{x}^2 - x_0 \operatorname{Im} k_0 \pm \lambda\mathbf{e}\cdot\mathbf{x} \operatorname{Im}\sqrt{k_0^2 - m_1^2}\}$$

we can establish the following property.

There exists such a positive integral n_0 that for arbitrarily small $\sigma > 0$ the expressions

$$|\phi_s(k_0)|, \quad |\phi_a(k_0)|$$

are bounded for

$$|\operatorname{Im} k_0| \geqq \sigma$$

by a certain polynomial of degree n_0. In order to make use of Cauchy's theorem we choose an appropriate multiplier $h(k_0)$ which guarantees a sufficiently rapid rate of falling off of the products

$$\phi_s(k_0)\, h(k_0), \quad \phi_a(k_0)\, h(k_0) \tag{8.14}$$

at infinity.

In order to do this we take a function $g(\tau)$ of the real variable τ which has continuous derivatives of all orders in the interval

$$a \leqq \tau \leqq b \qquad (a > m^2)$$

and such that it vanishes together with all its derivatives at the end points of this interval.

We form the following function of a complex variable

$$h^{(n)}(k_0) = \int_a^b \frac{g(\tau)}{(k_0^2 - \tau)^n}\, d\tau \tag{8.15}$$

and note that it is an analytic function regular over the whole complex plane with the exception of the cut

$$\operatorname{Im} k_0 = 0, \qquad a \leqq k_0^2 \leqq b.$$

At infinity $h^{(n)}(k_0)$ and its derivatives of all orders fall off not slower than

$$\frac{\text{const}}{|\, k_0^2\, |^n}.$$

Moreover, when

$$\operatorname{Im} k_0 \to +0, \qquad \operatorname{Re} k_0 = p_0$$

we have uniformly[116] with respect to $p_0 (-\infty < p_0 < \infty)$

$$h^{(n)}(k_0) \to h_+^{(n)}(p_0), \quad \frac{d^q h^{(n)}(k_0)}{dk_0^q} \to \frac{d^q h_+^{(n)}(p_0)}{dp_0^q} \qquad q = 1, 2, \ldots.$$

However, if

$$\operatorname{Im} k_0 \to -0, \qquad \operatorname{Re} k_0 = p_0$$

[116] Here we have in mind the usual uniform convergence.

then we have again uniformly with respect to $p_0(-\infty < p_0 < \infty)$

$$h^{(n)}(k_0) \to h_-^{(n)}(p_0); \quad \frac{d^q h^{(n)}(k_0)}{dk_0^q} \to \frac{d^q h_-^{(n)}(p_0)}{dp_0^q}; \qquad q = 1, 2, \ldots.$$

The limiting functions

$$h_+^{(n)}(p_0), \; h_-^{(n)}(p_0)$$

of the real variable p_0 are continuous together with all their derivatives of arbitrary order along the whole real axis; when $p_0 \to \pm\infty$ these functions and their derivatives tend to zero not slower than

$$\frac{\text{const}}{|p_0^2|^n}.$$

Finally, it is clear that $h_+^{(n)}(p_0) = h_-^{(n)}(p_0)$ if $p_0^2 < a$, or $p_0^2 > b$, i.e., in any case if $p_0^2 \leqq m^2$.

Therefore $(j = s, a)$

$$\phi_j(p_0 + i0)\, h_+^{(n)}(p_0) - \phi_j(p_0 - i0)\, h_-^{(n)}(p_0) = 0 \text{ if } |p_0| \leqq m \tag{8.16}$$

where

$$\phi_j(p_0 \pm i0) = \lim_{\varepsilon \to 0} \phi_j(p_0 \pm i\varepsilon).$$

We now take $2n \geqq n_0 + 1$. Then for arbitrarily small $\sigma > 0$

$$|h(k_0)\,\phi_j(k_0)| < \frac{C_\sigma}{|k_0|}; \quad |\operatorname{Im} k_0| \geqq \sigma.$$

Further, since the sequences $\phi_j(p_0 \pm i\varepsilon)$ converge in the generalized sense we may in virtue of the definition of such convergence find the class $C(r, s; 1)$ over which this convergence takes place. We take $2n \geqq r - 1$. Then the sequences $h(p_0 \pm i\varepsilon)\,\phi_j(p_0 \pm i\varepsilon)$ will converge in the generalized sense over the class $C(1, s; 1)$. Having chosen the number n we can apply Cauchy's theorem, taking for the contour of integration the contour of Fig. 60 surrounding the cuts. After making the limiting transition $\delta \to 0$ we obtain

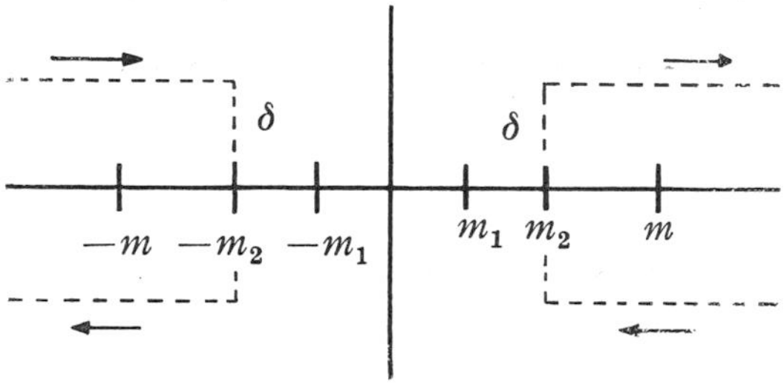

Fig. 60.

$$h(k_0)\,\phi_j(k_0)=\frac{1}{2\pi i}\int_{m_2}^{\infty}\frac{\phi_j(\tau+i0)\,h_+(\tau)-\phi_j(\tau-i0)\,h_-(\tau)}{\tau-k_0}\,d\tau$$
$$+\frac{1}{2\pi i}\int_{-\infty}^{-m_2}\frac{\phi_j(\tau+i0)\,h_+(\tau)-\phi_j(\tau-i0)\,h_-(\tau)}{\tau-k_0}\,d\tau;\ (j=s,a)$$

for any k_0 not lying on one of the cuts (8.8).

But in accordance with the definition of ϕ_s, ϕ_a we have

$$\phi(k_0)=\phi_s(k_0)+\sqrt{k_0^2-m_1^2}\,\phi_a(k_0).$$

Consequently

$$h(k_0)\,\phi(k_0)=\frac{1}{2\pi i}\int_{m_2}^{\infty}\frac{\phi_s(\tau+i0)\,h_+(\tau)-\phi_s(\tau-i0)\,h_-(\tau)}{-k_0+\tau}\,d\tau$$
$$+\frac{\sqrt{k_0^2-m_1^2}}{2\pi i}\int_{m_2}^{\infty}\frac{\phi_a(\tau+i0)\,h_+(\tau)-\phi_a(\tau-i0)\,h_-(\tau)}{-k_0+\tau}\,d\tau$$
$$+\frac{1}{2\pi i}\int_{-\infty}^{-m_2}\frac{\phi_s(\tau+i0)\,h_+(\tau)-\phi_s(\tau-i0)\,h_-(\tau)}{-k_0+\tau}\,d\tau \qquad (8.17)$$
$$+\frac{\sqrt{k_0^2-m_1^2}}{2\pi i}\int_{-\infty}^{-m_2}\frac{\phi_a(\tau+i0)\,h_+(\tau)-\phi_a(\tau-i0)\,h_-(\tau)}{-k_0+\tau}\,d\tau.$$

We now consider an arbitrary complex four-vector k for which the inequality (8.1) holds. It is clear that we can find for it such $m_1^2 < m^2$ that

$$|\,\mathrm{Im}\,\mathbf{k}\,| < |\,\mathrm{Im}\sqrt{k_0^2-m^2}\,|\,. \qquad (8.18)$$

We shall utilize these values of m_1^2 in our arguments. Further, for a given k we shall form $\lambda(k)$, $\mathbf{e}(k)$ by setting:

$$\lambda(k) = \frac{|\operatorname{Im} \mathbf{k}|}{|\operatorname{Im} \sqrt{k_0^2 - m_1^2}|}, \quad \mathbf{e}(k) = \frac{\operatorname{Im} \mathbf{k}}{|\operatorname{Im} \mathbf{k}|} \cdot \frac{\operatorname{Im} \sqrt{k_0^2 - m_1^2}}{|\operatorname{Im} \sqrt{k_0^2 - m_1^2}|} \tag{8.19}$$

Then

$$\operatorname{Im} \mathbf{k} = \lambda(k)\, \mathbf{e}(k) \operatorname{Im} \sqrt{k_0^2 - m_1^2}. \tag{8.20}$$

We also take

$$\mathbf{f} = \operatorname{Re} \mathbf{k} - \lambda(k)\, \mathbf{e}(k) \operatorname{Re} \sqrt{k_0^2 - m_1^2} + \mathbf{q}$$

where $\mathbf{q}$ is an arbitrary real vector. From (8.17) we then obtain

$$\begin{aligned} & h(k_0)\, \tilde{F}(k_0, \mathbf{k}+\mathbf{q};\ \rho) \\ &= \frac{1}{2\pi i} \int_{m_2}^{\infty} \frac{A_s(\tau, \mathbf{q};\ k, \rho)}{-k_0+\tau}\, d\tau + \frac{\sqrt{k_0^2-m_1^2}}{2\pi i} \int_{m_2}^{\infty} \frac{A_a(\tau, \mathbf{q};\ k, \rho)}{-k_0+\tau}\, d\tau \\ &+ \frac{1}{2\pi i} \int_{-\infty}^{-m_2} \frac{A_s(\tau, \mathbf{q};\ k, \rho)}{-k_0+\tau}\, d\tau + \frac{\sqrt{k_0^2-m_1^2}}{2\pi i} \int_{-\infty}^{-m_2} \frac{A_a(\tau, \mathbf{q};\ k, \rho)}{-k_0+\tau}\, d\tau, \end{aligned} \tag{8.21}$$

where

$$\begin{aligned} & A_s(\tau, \mathbf{q};\ k, \rho) \\ &= \tfrac{1}{2} \tilde{F}_r\{\tau, \lambda(k)\, \mathbf{e}(k) (\sqrt{\tau^2-m_1^2} - \operatorname{Re}\sqrt{k_0^2-m_1^2}) + \operatorname{Re} \mathbf{k}+\mathbf{q};\ \rho\}\, h_+(\tau) \\ &- \tfrac{1}{2} \tilde{F}_a\{\tau, \lambda(k)\, \mathbf{e}(k) (\sqrt{\tau^2-m_1^2} - \operatorname{Re}\sqrt{k_0^2-m_1^2}) + \operatorname{Re} \mathbf{k}+\mathbf{q};\ \rho\}\, h_-(\tau) \\ &+ \tfrac{1}{2} \tilde{F}_r\{\tau, -\lambda(k)\mathbf{e}(k) (\sqrt{\tau^2-m_1^2} + \operatorname{Re}\sqrt{k_0^2-m_1^2}) + \operatorname{Re} \mathbf{k}+\mathbf{q};\ \rho\}\, h_+(\tau) \\ &- \tfrac{1}{2} \tilde{F}_a\{\tau, -\lambda(k)\mathbf{e}(k) (\sqrt{\tau^2-m_1^2} + \operatorname{Re}\sqrt{k_0^2-m_1^2}) + \operatorname{Re} \mathbf{k}+\mathbf{q};\ \rho\}\, h_-(\tau); \end{aligned} \tag{8.22}$$

$$\begin{aligned} & A_a(\tau, \mathbf{q};\ k, \rho) \\ &= (2\sqrt{\tau^2-m_1^2})^{-1} \tilde{F}_r\{\tau, \lambda(k)\, \mathbf{e}(k) (\sqrt{\tau^2-m_1^2} - \operatorname{Re}\sqrt{k_0^2-m_1^2}) + \operatorname{Re} \mathbf{k}+\mathbf{q};\ \rho\}\, h_+(\tau) \\ &- (2\sqrt{\tau^2-m_1^2})^{-1} \tilde{F}_a\{\tau, \lambda(k)\, \mathbf{e}(k) (\sqrt{\tau^2-m_1^2} - \operatorname{Re}\sqrt{k_0^2-m_1^2}) + \operatorname{Re} \mathbf{k}+\mathbf{q};\ \rho\}\, h_-(\tau) \\ &- (2\sqrt{\tau^2-m_1^2})^{-1} \tilde{F}_r\{\tau, -\lambda(k)\, \mathbf{e}(k) (\sqrt{\tau^2-m_1^2} + \operatorname{Re}\sqrt{k_0^2-m_1^2}) + \operatorname{Re} \mathbf{k}+\mathbf{q};\ \rho\}\, h_+(\tau) \\ &+ (2\sqrt{\tau^2-m_1^2})^{-1} \tilde{F}_a\{\tau, -\lambda(k)\, \mathbf{e}(k) (\sqrt{\tau^2-m_1^2} + \operatorname{Re}\sqrt{k_0^2-m_1^2}) + \operatorname{Re} \mathbf{k}+\mathbf{q};\ \rho\}\, h_-(\tau). \end{aligned}$$

We emphasize here that

$$\left.\begin{aligned} A_s(\tau, \mathbf{q};\ k, \rho) = 0 \\ A_a(\tau, \mathbf{q};\ k, \rho) = 0 \end{aligned}\right\}, \quad \text{if} \quad |\tau| < m. \tag{8.23}$$

We now consider the transition $\rho \to 0$. We shall show, for example, that for $\tau > m_2$ the expression

$$\tilde{F}_r\{\tau,\ \lambda(k)\,\mathbf{e}(k)(\sqrt{\tau^2 - m_1^2} - \operatorname{Re}\sqrt{k_0^2 - m_1^2}) + \operatorname{Re}\mathbf{k} + \mathbf{q};\ \rho\}$$

regarded as a function of the variables τ, $\mathbf{q}$ converges in the generalized sense to

$$\tilde{F}_r\{\tau,\ \lambda(k)\,\mathbf{e}(k)(\sqrt{\tau^2 - m_1^2} - \operatorname{Re}\sqrt{k_0^2 - m_1^2}) + \operatorname{Re}\mathbf{k} + \mathbf{q}\}.$$

Indeed, let us consider the integral

$$\int \tilde{F}_r\{\tau, \lambda(k)\,\mathbf{e}(k)(\sqrt{\tau^2 - m_1^2} - \operatorname{Re}\sqrt{k_0^2 - m_1^2}) + \operatorname{Re}\mathbf{k} + \mathbf{q};\rho\}H(\tau, \mathbf{q})\,d\tau\,d\mathbf{q},$$

in which the function $H(\tau, \mathbf{q})$ belongs to a certain class $C(r, s; 4)$ with sufficiently high indices r, s and vanishes for $\tau < m_2$.

We have

$$\int \tilde{F}_r\{\tau, \lambda(k)\,\mathbf{e}(k)(\sqrt{\tau^2 - m_1^2} - \operatorname{Re}\sqrt{k_0^2 - m_1^2}) + \operatorname{Re}\mathbf{k} + \mathbf{q};\rho\}H(\tau, \mathbf{q})\,d\tau\,d\mathbf{q}$$
$$= \int \tilde{F}_r(p_0, \mathbf{p};\rho)H\{p_0, \mathbf{p} + \lambda(k)\mathbf{e}(k)(\operatorname{Re}\sqrt{k_0^2 - m_1^2} - \sqrt{p_0^2 - m_1^2}) - \operatorname{Re}\mathbf{k}\}\,dp_0\,d\mathbf{p}.$$

Taking into account the fact that $m_2 > m_1$ we may note that $(p_0^2 - m_1^2)^{1/2}$ is regular for $p_0 > m_2 > m_1$ and that therefore the expression

$$H\{p_0, \mathbf{p} + \lambda(k)\,\mathbf{e}(k)(\operatorname{Re}\sqrt{k_0^2 - m_1^2} - \sqrt{p_0^2 - m_1^2}) - \operatorname{Re}\mathbf{k}\},$$

regarded as a function of the variables p_0, p also belongs to $C(r, s; 4)$. But in virtue of (8.6)

$$\tilde{F}_r(p_0,\ \mathbf{p};\ \rho) \to \tilde{F}_r(p_0,\ \mathbf{p}), \qquad \rho \to +0.$$

We have, therefore,

$$\int \tilde{F}_r(p_0, \mathbf{p};\rho)\,H\{p_0, \mathbf{p} + \lambda(k)\mathbf{e}(k)(\operatorname{Re}\sqrt{k_0^2 - m_1^2} - \sqrt{p_0^2 - m_1^2}) - \operatorname{Re}\mathbf{k}\}\,dp_0\,d\mathbf{p}$$
$$\to \int \tilde{F}_r(p_0, \mathbf{p})H\{p_0, \mathbf{p} + \lambda(k)\,\mathbf{e}(k)(\operatorname{Re}\sqrt{k_0^2 - m_1^2} - \sqrt{p_0^2 - m_1^2}) - \operatorname{Re}\mathbf{k}\}\,dp_0\,d\mathbf{p},$$

i.e.,

$$\left.\begin{aligned}&\int \tilde{F}_r\{\tau, \lambda(k)\,\mathbf{e}(k)(\sqrt{\tau^2 - m_1^2} - \operatorname{Re}\sqrt{k_0^2 - m_1^2}) + \operatorname{Re}\mathbf{k} + \mathbf{q};\ \rho\}H(\tau,\ \mathbf{q})\,d\tau\,d\mathbf{q}\\ \to &\int \tilde{F}_r\{\tau, \lambda(k)\,\mathbf{e}(k)(\sqrt{\tau^2 - m_1^2} - \operatorname{Re}\sqrt{k_0^2 - m_1^2}) + \operatorname{Re}\mathbf{k} + \mathbf{q}\}\,H(\tau,\ \mathbf{q})\,d\tau\,d\mathbf{q}.\end{aligned}\right\} \tag{8.24}$$

Since the approach to the limit in (8.24) is uniform with respect to k (in every sufficiently small neighborhood of a point of the region (8.18) under consideration) we may say that the relation:

$$\begin{aligned}&\tilde{F}_r\{\tau, \lambda(k)\,\mathbf{e}(k)(\sqrt{\tau^2-m_1^2}-\mathrm{Re}\sqrt{k_0^2-m_1^2})+\mathrm{Re}\,\mathbf{k}+\mathbf{q};\,\rho\}\\ \rightarrow\ &\tilde{F}_r\{\tau, \lambda(k)\,\mathbf{e}(k)(\sqrt{\tau^2-m_1^2}-\mathrm{Re}\sqrt{k_0^2-m_1^2})+\mathrm{Re}\,\mathbf{k}+\mathbf{q}\}\end{aligned} \tag{8.25}$$

holds in the generalized sense with respect to the variables τ, $\mathbf{q}$ uniformly with respect to k. Exactly the same will hold in the case of the other functions $\tilde{F}_r$, $\tilde{F}_a$ appearing in expressions (8.22).

Let us construct a function $u(\tau)$ capable of being differentiated an unlimited number of times, in such a way that

$$u(\tau) = 0 \qquad \tau \leqq m_2$$
$$u(\tau) = 1 \qquad \tau \geqq m.$$

Then in virtue of (8.23) we may introduce the functions $u(\tau)$ and $u(-\tau)$ underneath the integral signs in the right-hand side of formula (8.21).

We also take an arbitrary function $f(\mathbf{q})$ from the class $C(r, s; 3)$ with sufficiently high indices r, s. Then in relations of the type (8.24) we may set

$$H(\tau, \mathbf{q}) = h_+(\tau)\,u(\pm\tau)\,\frac{f(\mathbf{q})}{k_0-\tau}$$

or

$$H(\tau, \mathbf{q}) = h_-(\tau)\,u(\pm\tau)\,\frac{f(\mathbf{q})}{k-\tau},$$

since the rate of falling off of the functions $h_+(\tau)$, $h_-(\tau)$ may be taken to be sufficiently great, while the denominator $k_0-\tau$ does not vanish inside the actual region of integration.

From this follows the existence of the limit

$$\lim_{\rho\to+0} h(k_0)\int \tilde{F}(k_0, \mathbf{k}+\mathbf{q};\,\rho)\,f(\mathbf{q})\,d\mathbf{q}$$

and therefore, since $h(k_0)$ is arbitrary, the limit

$$\lim_{\rho\to+0}\int \tilde{F}(k_0, \mathbf{k}+\mathbf{q};\,\rho)\,f(\mathbf{q})\,d\mathbf{q}, \tag{8.26}$$

exists; it may also be easily seen that the approach to the limit is uniform with respect to k in the sense indicated above.

We have established above the existence of improper convergence. We shall strengthen this result by showing that

$$\tilde{F}(k_0, \mathbf{k}; \rho) \to \tilde{F}(k_0, \mathbf{k}) \tag{8.27}$$

uniformly. In the complex planes of k'_α ($\alpha = 1, 2, 3$) we construct the circles C_α with centers at the points k_α and of radius δ.

We take the number δ to be so small that all the $\mathbf{k}'$ with components k'_α lying inside or on the boundary of C_α belong to the region (8.18).

Then in virtue of Cauchy's theorem we have:

$$\tilde{F}(k_0, \mathbf{k} + \mathbf{q}; \rho) = \frac{1}{(2\pi i)^3} \int_{c_1 \times c_2 \times c_3} \frac{\tilde{F}(k_0, \mathbf{k}' + \mathbf{q}; \rho)}{\prod\limits_{(\alpha)} (k'_\alpha - k_\alpha)} \prod_{(\alpha)} dk'_\alpha .$$

By replacing in the foregoing

$$\mathbf{k} \to \mathbf{k} - \mathbf{q}$$

we find that:

$$\tilde{F}(k_0, \mathbf{k}; \rho) = \frac{1}{(2\pi i)^3} \int_{c_1 \times c_2 \times c_3} \frac{\tilde{F}(k_0, \mathbf{k}' + \mathbf{q}; \rho)}{\prod\limits_{(\alpha)} (k'_\alpha - k_\alpha + q_\alpha)} \prod_{(\alpha)} dk'_\alpha . \tag{8.28}$$

Since in this integral

$$| k'_\alpha - k_\alpha | = \delta$$

then for

$$| q_\alpha | < \frac{\delta}{2}$$

the denominator does not vanish and in absolute value remains greater than

$$\left(\frac{\delta}{2}\right)^3 .$$

We now take some function $\varphi(\mathbf{q})$ of the real variables q_α belonging to the class $C(r, s; 3)$ with sufficiently high indices r, s and such that

$$\int \varphi(\mathbf{q})\, d\mathbf{q} = 1, \tag{8.29}$$

$\varphi(\mathbf{q}) = 0$ if for at least one α, $| q_\alpha | \geqq \delta/2$. Then from (8.28)

we obtain:

$$\tilde{F}(k_0, \mathbf{k}; \rho)$$
$$= \frac{1}{(2\pi i)^3} \int_{c_1 \times c_2 \times c_3} \left\{ \int \tilde{F}(k_0, \mathbf{k}'+\mathbf{q}; \rho) \frac{\varphi(\mathbf{q})}{\prod\limits_{(\alpha)} (k'_\alpha - k_\alpha + q_\alpha)} d\mathbf{q} \right\} \prod_\alpha dk'_\alpha . \tag{8.30}$$

But in virtue of (8.29) the function

$$f(\mathbf{q}) = \frac{\varphi(\mathbf{q})}{\prod\limits_{\alpha} (k'_\alpha - k_\alpha + q_\alpha)}; \qquad k'_\alpha \in C_\alpha$$

of the variables q_α also belongs to the class $C(r, s; 3)$, and we may apply to the right-hand side of (8.30) the result obtained earlier that the limit (8.26) exists and that the corresponding approach to the limit is uniform.

We thus see that within a sufficiently small neighborhood of an arbitrary point k from the region (8.18) the sequence

$$\tilde{F}(k_0, \mathbf{k}; \rho)$$

of analytic functions of k is uniformly convergent. Therefore, in virtue of well-known theorems, the limiting function

$$\tilde{F}(k_0, \mathbf{k}) = \lim_{\rho \to +0} \tilde{F}(k_0, \mathbf{k}; \rho) \tag{8.31}$$

will be an analytic function of the variables k_α ($\alpha = 0, 1, 2, 3$) regular within the region (8.18).

By noting that in our arguments we could have taken m_1 arbitrarily close to m we see that this function is regular within the whole region (8.1).

On the basis of (8.6) we can show that for real p from this region the function under consideration coincides with $\tilde{F}_r = \tilde{F}_a$, so that the proof of our theorem has now been completed.

§ 9.

Theorem IV, the proof of which was given in the preceding section, can be generalized in a trivial way to the case of functions which depend on two four-vectors x_1, x_2 and on the parameter t.

Moreover, in place of the centrally symmetric interval $|p_0| < m$ one can consider the more general interval $a < p_0 < b$. Then the inequality

$$|\operatorname{Im} \mathbf{k}|^2 < |\operatorname{Im} \sqrt{k_0^2 - m^2}|^2$$

must naturally be replaced by

$$|\operatorname{Im} \mathbf{k}|^2 < \operatorname{Im} \left| \sqrt{\left(k_0 - \frac{a+b}{2}\right)^2 - \left(\frac{b-a}{2}\right)^2} \right|.$$

Thus we demonstrate the validity of the following assertion.

LEMMA VI. Given the generalized functions:

$$f_{i,j}(x_1, x_2, t) \qquad (i, j = r, a)$$

which satisfy conditions (6.5).

Moreover, assume that

$$\begin{aligned} \tilde{f}_{r,j}(p_1, p_2, t) - \tilde{f}_{a,j}(p_1, p_2, t) &= 0, \quad \text{if} \quad \alpha < p_{10} < \beta; \\ \tilde{f}_{i,r}(p_1, p_2, t) - \tilde{f}_{i,a}(p_1, p_2, t) &= 0, \quad \text{if} \quad \alpha < p_{20} < \beta. \end{aligned} \tag{9.1}$$

Then there exists a generalized function of t

$$\tilde{f}(k_1, k_2, t)$$

which is an analytic function of the complex variables k_1, k_2 regular in the region

$$\begin{aligned} |\operatorname{Im} \mathbf{k}_1|^2 &< \left| \operatorname{Im} \sqrt{\left(k_{10} - \frac{\alpha+\beta}{2}\right)^2 - \left(\frac{\beta-\alpha}{2}\right)^2} \right|^2; \\ |\operatorname{Im} \mathbf{k}_2|^2 &< \left| \operatorname{Im} \sqrt{\left(k_{20} - \frac{\alpha+\beta}{2}\right)^2 - \left(\frac{\beta-\alpha}{2}\right)^2} \right|^2, \end{aligned} \tag{9.2}$$

such that within the domain of real p_1, p_2 satisfying the foregoing inequalities the following holds:

$$\tilde{f}(p_1, p_2, t) = \tilde{f}_{i,j}(p_1, p_2, t).$$

Making use of this lemma, and also of Theorem II, we shall prove the following assertion.

THEOREM V. If the conditions of Theorem III are fulfilled, then there exists such a positive ρ that the "domain of regularity" of the variables $z_1, \ldots, z_5$ may be described by the inequalities:

$$|z_1-M^2|<\rho\mu^2;\ |z_2-M^2|<\rho\mu^2;\ |z_3-\tau|<\rho\mu^2;\ |z_4-\tau|<\rho\mu^2;$$
$$-4\frac{M}{M+\mu}\mu^2 \leqq \mathrm{Re}\, z_5 \leqq 0;\ |\mathrm{Im}\, z_5|<\rho\mu^2\left(\frac{M}{t}\right)^2;\ -V\leqq\tau\leqq\mu^2. \tag{9.3}$$

PROOF. We consider separately the two cases:

$$-V \leqq \tau < 0 \tag{9.4}$$

and

$$0 \leqq \tau \leqq \mu^2. \tag{9.5}$$

We first take the case (9.4) and apply Theorem II with $\omega = 1$, $\delta = 0$. Since the whole extension of Theorem III being discussed at present refers only to the variable z_5, we shall agree to write out explicitly only the inequalities which refer to this variable.

In the case under consideration we have

$$|z_5 + 4a^2| < \rho\mu^2\left(\frac{M}{t}\right)^2; \qquad 4a^2 \leqq u^2 \tag{9.6}$$

where

$$u^2 = \left(M + \mu + \frac{M^2}{M + \mu}\right)^2 - 4M^2. \tag{9.7}$$

But the inequality (9.6) will be satisfied if

$$-u^2 \leqq \mathrm{Re}\, z_5 \leqq 0; \qquad |\mathrm{Im}\, z_5| < \rho\mu^2\left(\frac{M}{t}\right)^2.$$

On the other hand, from (9.7) we have:

$$u^2 = \left(M + \mu + \frac{\mu^2}{M + \mu}\right)^2 - 4M^2 > \frac{4M}{M + \mu}\mu^2.$$

Thus, in the case (9.4) the region (9.3) is actually included in the "domain of regularity."

We now proceed to the discussion of case (9.5).

We take a sufficiently small number $\sigma > 0$ (which will be specified in greater detail later) and construct within the class $C(0, \infty; 1)$ a function $h(t)$ such that

$$h(t) = 0, \qquad t \leqq \frac{M}{2} + \frac{3\mu}{4} - \sigma\mu;$$

$$h(t) = 1, \qquad t \geqq \frac{M}{2} + \frac{3\mu}{4}.$$

We set

$$f_{i,j}(x_1, x_2, t) = f_{i,j}^{(1)}(x_1, x_2, t) + f_{i,j}^{(2)}(x_1, x_2, t),$$

where

$$f_{i,j}^{(1)} = h(t) f_{i,j}\ , \qquad f_{i,j}^{(2)} = [1 - h(t)] f_{i,j}\,.$$

In the case (9.5) under consideration, we shall prove our theorem for $f_{i,j}^{(1)}$ and $f_{i,j}^{(2)}$ separately, since in such a case it will also hold for their sum, We take $f_{i,j}^{(1)}$ and make use of Theorem II with $\omega = 0$, $\delta = \frac{1}{2} - 2\sigma$.

We then note that the region

$$-u^2 \leqq \operatorname{Re} z_5 \leqq 0, \qquad |\operatorname{Im} z_5| < \rho\mu^2 \left(\frac{M}{t}\right)^2,$$

where

$$u^2 = \left[M + \mu(1+\delta) + \frac{M^2 - \mu^2}{M + \mu(1+\delta)}\right]^2 - 4M^2,$$

is contained within the "domain of regularity." Indeed,

$$u^2 = \left[2M + \frac{\mu^2(1+\delta)^2 - \mu^2}{M + \mu(1+\delta)}\right]^2 - 4M^2$$

$$> 4\,\frac{M\mu^2}{M+\mu}\,\frac{M+\mu}{M+\mu(1+\delta)}\,(2\delta + \delta^2).$$

Further, it is clear that

$$\frac{M+\mu}{M+\mu(1+\delta)}\,(2\delta + \delta^2) > 1 \tag{9.8}$$

for $\delta = \frac{1}{2}$. Therefore σ may always be chosen in such a way that

(9.8) will be satisfied also for $\delta = \frac{1}{2} - 2\sigma$. Then

$$u^2 > 4 \frac{M\mu^2}{M + \mu}$$

and the region (9.3) turns out to be a suitable one.

It remains now for us to examine $f_{i,j}^{(2)}$. Here we make use of Lemma VI. Since

$$\tilde{f}_{i,j}^{(2)}(p_1, p_2, t) = 0 \quad \text{if} \quad t < \frac{M + \mu}{2} \quad \text{or} \quad t > \frac{M}{2} + \frac{3\mu}{4}$$

we can restrict ourselves to the interval

$$\frac{M + \mu}{2} \leqq t \leqq \frac{M}{2} + \frac{3\mu}{4}. \tag{9.9}$$

We consider the inequalities

$$(k_0 + t)^2 - \mathbf{k}^2 < (M + \mu)^2, \; (k_0 - t)^2 - \mathbf{k}^2 < (3\mu)^2. \tag{9.10}$$

They will be evidently fulfilled if

$$- M - \mu < k_0 + t < M + \mu, \quad - 3\mu < k_0 - t < 3\mu,$$

i.e., if

$$t - 3\mu < k_0 < M + \mu - t.$$

Thus, (9.10) will hold provided

$$\frac{M + \mu(1 + \delta)}{2} - 3\mu < k_0 < M + \mu - \frac{M + \mu(1 + \delta)}{2}; \; \delta = \tfrac{1}{2}.$$

Taking into account relations (7.1), (7.2), we see from this that the conditions of Lemma VI are fulfilled in the case under consideration provided

$$\alpha = \frac{M + \mu(1 + \delta)}{2} - 3\mu, \; \beta = M + \mu - \frac{M + \mu(1 + \delta)}{2}, \; \delta = \tfrac{1}{2}. \tag{9.11}$$

But since in virtue of the conditions of our theorem, the functions $f_{i,j}^{(2)}$ must be invariant with respect to spatial rotations and reflections we see that the function

$$f^{(2)}(k_1, k_2, t)$$

regular in the region (9.2) can be represented in the form:

$$\Phi^{(2)}(z_1, \ldots, z_5, t)$$

where $z_1, \ldots, z_5$ are given by expressions (7.17).

By using the same arguments as for proving Theorem II, we express k_1, k_2 in terms of $z_1, \ldots, z_5, t$ by means of formulas (7.20), (7.22). Then the corresponding domain of regularity may be specified by the inequalities:

$$\begin{aligned} |\operatorname{Im} A|^2 + |\operatorname{Im} C|^2 &< \left| \operatorname{Im} \sqrt{\left(\frac{z_1 - z_3}{4t} - \frac{\alpha+\beta}{2}\right)^2 - \left(\frac{\beta-\alpha}{2}\right)^2} \right|^2, \\ |\operatorname{Im} B|^2 + |\operatorname{Im} C|^2 &< \left| \operatorname{Im} \sqrt{\left(\frac{z_2 - z_4}{4t} - \frac{\alpha+\beta}{2}\right)^2 - \left(\frac{\beta-\alpha}{2}\right)^2} \right|^2. \end{aligned} \tag{9.12}$$

Let us assume that the inequalities (9.12) hold for

$$z_1 = z_2 = M^2, \quad z_3 = z_4 = \tau, \quad z_5 = -4a^2, \tag{9.13}$$

where

$$a^2 \leqq \frac{M}{M+\mu}\mu^2. \tag{9.14}$$

Then, since the functions A, B, C are continuous in the neighborhood of (9.13), and the range of variation (9.9) of t is limited, we can always choose such a small positive ρ that the inequality (9.12) will hold for all z from the region (9.3). This would constitute a proof of our theorem.

It therefore remains for us to demonstrate the validity of the inequalities (9.12) for the values (9.13).

For all these values we have

$$\operatorname{Im} C = 0, \quad (\operatorname{Im} A)^2 \leqq a^2, \quad (\operatorname{Im} B)^2 \leqq a^2.$$

At the same time the right-hand sides of (9.12) are greater than μ^2.

Thus, the inequalities (9.12) are indeed fulfilled for the values (9.13) under the condition (9.14). This completes the proof.

§ 10.

LEMMA VII. We consider scalar generalized functions of three four-vectors:

$$F_{i,j}(y_1, y_2, y_3) \qquad i, j = r, a \tag{10.1}$$

satisfying the conditions:

$$\begin{aligned} F_{r,r}(y_1, y_2, y_3) &= 0, \quad \text{if} \quad y_1 \lesssim 0 \quad \text{or} \quad y_2 \lesssim 0; \\ F_{r,a}(y_1, y_2, y_3) &= 0, \quad \text{if} \quad y_1 \lesssim 0 \quad \text{or} \quad y_2 \gtrsim 0; \\ F_{a,r}(y_1, y_2, y_3) &= 0, \quad \text{if} \quad y_1 \gtrsim 0 \quad \text{or} \quad y_2 \lesssim 0; \\ F_{a,a}(y_1, y_2, y_3) &= 0, \quad \text{if} \quad y_1 \gtrsim 0 \quad \text{or} \quad y_2 \gtrsim 0; \end{aligned} \tag{10.2}$$

$$\left.\begin{aligned} \tilde{F}_{r,j}(q_1, q_2, q_3) - \tilde{F}_{a,j}(q_1, q_2, q_3) = 0, \text{ if } &\begin{cases} (q_1+q_3)^2 < (M+\mu)^2, \text{ and} \\ (q_1-q_3)^2 < (3\mu)^2; \end{cases} \\ \tilde{F}_{i,r}(q_1, q_2, q_3) - \tilde{F}_{i,a}(q_1, q_2, q_3) = 0, \text{ if } &\begin{cases} (q_2+q_3)^2 < (M+\mu)^2 \text{ and} \\ (q_2-q_3)^2 < (3\mu)^2; \end{cases} \end{aligned}\right\} \tag{10.3}$$

$$\tilde{F}_{i,j}(q_1, q_2, q_3) = 0, \text{ if } q_3^2 < \frac{(M+\mu)^2}{4} \text{ or } q_{30} < 0. \tag{10.4}$$

One can then construct a generalized function of the real variable z_6

$$\psi(z_1, \ldots, z_5, z_6)$$

which is an analytic function of the complex variables $z_1, \ldots, z_5$ and having the properties:

(1) ψ is regular within the region:

$$\begin{aligned} &|z_1 - M^2| < \rho\mu^2; \; |z_2 - M^2| < \rho\mu^2; \; |z_3 - \tau| < \rho\mu^2, \\ &|z_4 - \tau| < \rho\mu^2; \quad -\frac{4M}{M+\mu}\mu^2 \leqq \operatorname{Re} z_5 \leqq 0; \\ &|\operatorname{Im} z_5| < \rho\mu^2 \left(\frac{M^2}{z_6}\right); \; -V \leqq \tau \leqq \mu^2. \end{aligned} \tag{10.5}$$

Here V is an arbitrary fixed positive number, ρ is a sufficiently small positive number (which depends on V).

(2)

$$\psi(z_1, \ldots, z_5, z_6) = 0, \quad \text{if} \quad z_6 < \left(\frac{M+\mu}{2}\right)^2. \tag{10.6}$$

(3) For real q_1, q_2, q_3 for which the quantities

$$z_1 = (q_1 + q_3)^2;\ z_2 = (q_2 + q_3)^2;\ z_3 = (q_1 - q_3)^2;$$
$$z_4 = (q_2 - q_3)^2;\ z_5 = (q_1 - q_2)^2;\ z_6 = q_3^2,$$

satisfy the inequalities (10.5) we have:

$$\tilde{F}_{i,j}(q_1, q_2, q_3) = \psi(z_1, \ldots, z_5;\ z_6), \text{ if } q_{30} > 0.$$

Proof. We shall reduce the preceding assertion to Lemma VI and Theorem V. Let us consider the expressions:

$$\int F_{i,j}(y_1, y_2, y_3)\, e^{iq_3 y_3} dy_3, \tag{10.7}$$

where

$$q_3 = tl$$

while l is a timelike unit four-vector:

$$l_0 > 0, \qquad l^2 = 1.$$

We carry out a Lorentz transformation in such a way that l becomes directed along the time axis. We agree to denote corresponding quantities in the new coordinate system by the symbol "prime."

Expressions (10.7) may be regarded as functions

$$f_{i,j}(y_1', y_2', t).$$

It may be easily seen that in view of the conditions of our lemma, these functions satisfy all the conditions of Theorem V.

We can therefore construct a corresponding function

$$\phi(z_1, \ldots, z_5;\ t)$$

in which

$$z_1 = (q_{10}' + t)^2 - \mathbf{q}_1'^2;\quad z_2 = (q_{20}' + t)^2 - \mathbf{q}_2'^2;$$
$$z_3 = (q_{10}' - t)^2 - \mathbf{q}_1'^2;\quad z_4 = (q_{20}' - t)^2 - \mathbf{q}_2'^2;\quad z_5 = (q_1' - q_2')^2.$$

However, it it clear that

$$z_1 = (q_1 + q_3)^2,\quad z_2 = (q_2 + q_3)^2,\quad z_3 = (q_1 - q_3)^2,$$
$$z_4 = (q_2 - q_3)^2,\quad z_5 = (q_1 - q_2)^2,$$

in view of the scalar nature of these expressions. But

$$\phi(z_1, \ldots, z_5; t) = 0 \quad \text{for} \quad t < \frac{M + \mu}{2}.$$

Therefore we can introduce the function $\psi(z_1, \ldots, z_5; z_6)$ by setting

$$\psi(z_1, \ldots, z_5; z_6) \begin{cases} = \phi(z_1, \ldots, z_5; \sqrt{z_6}), & z_6 > 0 \\ = 0 & z_6 < \left(\frac{M + \mu}{2}\right)^2. \end{cases}$$

The validity of Lemma VII now becomes evident.

NOTE. Let us consider a more general case when the functions

$$F^{\nu}_{i,j}(y_1, y_2, y_3) \qquad \nu = 1, \ldots, l$$

satisfy all the conditions of Lemma VII, except for the condition of being scalar.

Instead of this condition, we shall assume that under transformations $\mathscr{L}$ from the Lorentz group our functions transform linearly among themselves

$$F^{\nu}_{i,j}(\mathscr{L}y_1, \mathscr{L}y_2, \mathscr{L}y_3) = \sum_{1 \leq \nu \leq l} A_{\nu,\nu'}(\mathscr{L}) F^{\nu'}_{i,j}(y_1, y_2, y_3) \tag{10.8}$$

with the aid of some representation $A(\mathscr{L})$ of this group which breaks up into the usual tensor and spinor representations.

From this it will follow that $\tilde{F}^{\nu}_{i,j}(q_1, q_2, q_3)$ can be expressed linearly (with coefficients that are polynomials in the q_i) in terms of scalar functions of q_1, q_2, q_3 which guarantees the applicability of Lemma VII.

It may be easily seen that the results of Lemma VII in this case undergo the following trivial change.

It is possible to construct a finite system of generalized functions of the real variable z_6

$$\psi_\lambda(z_1, \ldots, z_5, z_6) \qquad \lambda = 1, \ldots, s$$

which are analytic functions of the complex variables $z_1, \ldots, z_5$ and possess the properties (*1*) and (*2*). For real q_1, q_2, q_3 for which the quantities z satisfy the inequalities (10.5) we obtain a representation in terms of the sum of a finite number of terms of the type

$$q_{i_1}^{\alpha_1} \cdots q_{i_s}^{\alpha_s} \psi_\lambda(z_1, \ldots, z_5, z_6)$$

provided that

$$q_{30} > 0.$$

From this follows our fundamental theorem.

THEOREM VI. We consider the generalized functions, invariant under translation, of four four-vectors

$$F^{\nu}_{i.j}(x_1, \ldots, x_4) \quad i = r,\ a, \quad j = r,\ a, \quad \nu = 1, \ldots, l$$

which transform linearly under transformations $\mathscr{L}$ from the Lorentz group:

$$F^{\nu}_{i,j}(\mathscr{L}x_1, \ldots, \mathscr{L}x_4) = \sum_{1 \leqq \nu' \leqq l} A_{\nu\nu'}(\mathscr{L})\, F^{\nu'}_{i,j}(x_1, \ldots, x_\mu) \quad (10.9)$$

by means of some representation $A(\mathscr{L})$ of this group which breaks up into the usual tensor and spinor representations.

Moreover, we suppose that the functions introduced above satisfy the following conditions:

$$\left.\begin{aligned} F^{\nu}_{r,r}(x_1, \ldots, x_4) &= 0 \quad \text{for} \quad x_1 \lesssim x_3 \quad \text{or} \quad x_2 \lesssim x_4; \\ F^{\nu}_{r,a}(x_1, \ldots, x_4) &= 0 \quad \text{for} \quad x_1 \lesssim x_3 \quad \text{or} \quad x_2 \gtrsim x_4; \\ F^{\nu}_{a,r}(x_1, \ldots, x_4) &= 0 \quad \text{for} \quad x_1 \gtrsim x_3 \quad \text{or} \quad x_2 \lesssim x_4; \\ F^{\nu}_{a,a}(x_1, \ldots, x_4) &= 0 \quad \text{for} \quad x_1 \gtrsim x_3 \quad \text{or} \quad x_2 \gtrsim x_4. \end{aligned}\right\} \quad (10.10)$$

We consider the Fourier-transforms

$$\int F^{\nu}_{i,j}(x_1, \ldots, x_4) \exp i(p_1 x_1 + \ldots + p_4 x_4) dx_1 \ldots dx_4$$
$$= \delta(p_1 + \ldots + p_4)\, \tilde{F}^{\nu}_{i,j}(p_1, \ldots, p_4).$$

Here

$$\tilde{F}^{\nu}_{i,j}(p_1, \ldots, p_4)$$

are generalized functions of $p_1, \ldots p_4$ defined over the manifold

$$p_1 + \ldots + p_4 = 0. \quad (10.11)$$

We assume that they satisfy the conditions:

$$\left.\begin{aligned} \tilde{F}^{\nu}_{r,j}(p_1, \ldots, p_4) - \tilde{F}^{\nu}_{a,j}(p_1, \ldots, p_4) &= 0 \text{ for } p_1^2 < (M+\mu)^2, p_3^2 < (3\mu)^2; \\ \tilde{F}^{\nu}_{i,r}(p_1, \ldots, p_4) - \tilde{F}^{\nu}_{i,a}(p_1, \ldots, p_4) &= 0 \text{ for } p_2^2 < (M+\mu)^2, p_4^2 < (3\mu)^2; \end{aligned}\right\}$$
$$(10.12)$$

$$\left.\begin{aligned} &F^{\nu}_{i,j}(p_1, \ldots, p_4) = 0, \\ \text{if} \quad &(p_1 + p_3)^2 < (M + \mu)^2 \text{ or } p_{10} + p_{30} < 0. \end{aligned}\right\} \quad (10.13)$$

Then one can construct generalized functions of the real variable z_6:

$$\phi_\lambda(z_1, \ldots, z_5; z_6)$$

which are analytic functions of the variables $z_1, \ldots, z_5$ with the properties: *(1)* ϕ_λ are regular within the region (10.5). *(2)* $\phi_\lambda = 0$ if $z_6 < (M + \mu)^2$. *(3)* For real $p_1, \ldots, p_4$ from the manifold (10.11) for which the quantities

$$z_1 = p_1^2;\ z_2 = p_2^2;\ z_3 = p_3^2;\ z_4 = p_4^2;\ z_5 = (p_1 + p_2)^2;\ z_6 = (p_1 + p_3)^2$$

satisfy the inequalities (10.5) we have a representation of the form

$$\tilde{F}^{\nu}_{i,j}(p_1, \ldots, p_4) = \sum p_{i_1}^{\alpha_1} \ldots p_{i_s}^{\alpha_s} \phi_\lambda(z_1, \ldots, z_5; z_6) \text{ if } p_{10} + p_{30} > 0, \tag{10.14}$$

in which the sum contains a finite number of terms.

PROOF. Since the functions

$$F^{\nu}_{i,j}(x_1, \ldots, x_4)$$

are invariant under translations they may be regarded as functions of three variables, for example:

$$y_1 = x_1 - x_3;\ y_2 = x_4 - x_2;\ y_3 = x_1 - x_2 + x_3 - x_4.$$

We set

$$F^{\nu}_{i,j}(x_1, \ldots, x_4) = F^{\nu}_{i,j_1}(x_1 - x_3, x_4 - x_2, x_1 - x_2 + x_3 - x_4) \tag{10.15}$$

where $j_1 = r$ if $j = a$; $j_1 = a$ if $j = r$.

It is then clear that the functions

$$F^{\nu}_{i,j}(y_1, y_2, y_3)$$

satisfy condition (10.8) of the note to Lemma VII, and also satisfy conditions (10.2).

Further, it follows from (10.15) that

$$\tilde{F}^{\nu}_{i,j}(q_1+q_3,\ -q_2-q_3,\ q_3-q_1,\ q_2-q_3) = \tilde{F}^{\nu}_{i,j}(q_1,\ q_2,\ q_3).$$

By setting

$$p_1 = q_1 + q_3,\ p_2 = -q_2 - q_3,\ p_3 = q_3 - q_1,\ p_4 = q_2 - q_3$$

we have

$$q_3 = \frac{p_1+p_3}{2},\ p_1^2 = (q_1+q_3)^2,\ p_2^2 = (q_2+q_3)^2,\ p_3^2 = (q_1-q_3)^2$$

$$p_4^2 = (q_2 - q_3)^2,\ (p_1 + p_2)^2 = (q_1 - q_2)^2$$

From this we see that the other conditions of Lemma VII are also fulfilled.

By utilizing the note to Lemma VII, we obtain the proof of our fundamental theorem.

NOTE. In place of the condition (10.13) we can introduce the condition:

$$[(p_1+p_3)^2-M^2]\,\tilde{F}^{\nu}_{i,j}(p_1, \ldots, p_4) = 0, \text{ if } (p_1+p_3)^2 < (M+\mu)^2 \text{ or } p_{10} + p_{30} < 0.$$

Indeed, in this case in place of

$$F^{\nu}_{i,j}$$

we can consider the functions

$$\left[-\left(\frac{\partial}{\partial x_1} + \frac{\partial}{\partial x_3}\right)^2 - M^2\right] F^{\nu}_{i,j}(x_1, \ldots, x_4)$$

satisfying all the conditions of Theorem VI.

Relation (10.14) will then turn out to be multiplied by $[(p_1 + p_3)^2 - M^2]$. Moreover, we can divide by this factor in the region in which

$$(p_1 + p_3)^2 \neq M^2.$$

Therefore (10.14) continues to be valid if to the condition $p_{10} + p_{30} > 0$ one adds $(p_1 + p_3)^2 \neq M^2$.

References

1. Abrikosov, A. A., *JETP*, **30**, 96 (1956).
2. Akhiezer, A. I., and Berestetskii, V. B., *Quantum Electrodynamics*, Gostekhizdat, Moscow, 1953.
3. Akhiezer, A. I., and Pomeranchuk, I., *JETP*, **18**, 603 (1948).
4. Anderson, J. L., *Phys. Rev.*, **94**, 703 (1954).
5. Anderson, H. L., Davidon, W. C., and Kruse, U. E., *ibid.*, **100**, 339 (1955).
6. Baranger, M., Bethe, H. A., and Feynman, R. P., *ibid.*, **92**, 482 (1953).
7. Bethe, H. A., *ibid.*, **72**, 339 (1947).
8. Blank, V. Z., *Doklady Akad. Nauk USSR*, **107**, 389 (1956).
9. Blank, V. Z., and Shirkov, D. V., *Nuclear Phys.*, **2**, 356 (1956).
10. *Ibid.*, *Doklady Akad. Nauk USSR*, **111**, 1201 (1956).
11. Bleuler, K., *Helv. Phys. Acta*, **23**, 567 (1950).
12. Bloch, F., and Nordsieck, A., *Phys. Rev.*, **52**, 54 (1937).
13. Blokhintsev, D. I., *Principles of Quantum Mechanics*, Gostekhizdat, Moscow, 1949.
14. Bogoliubov, N. N., *Doklady Akad. Nauk USSR*, **81**, 757 (1951).
15. *Ibid.*, p. 1015.
16. *Ibid.*, **82**, 217 (1952); **99**, 225 (1954); *Izvest. Akad. Nauk SSSR, Ser. Fiz.*, **19**, 237 (1955).
17. Bogoliubov, N. N., Medvedev, B. V., and Polivanov, M. K., *Problems in the Theory of Dispersion Relations*, Fizmatgiz, Moscow, 1958.
18. Bogoliubov, N. N., and Parasiuk, O. S., *Doklady Akad. Nauk SSSR*, **100**, 25 (1955).
19. *Ibid.*, p. 429.
20. *Ibid.*, *Izvest. Akad. Nauk SSSR, Ser. Mat.*, **20**, 585 (1956).
21. Bogoliubov, N. N., and Shirkov, D. V., *Uspekhi Fiz. Nauk*, **55**, 149 (1955).
22. *Ibid.*, *Doklady Akad. Nauk USSR*, **103**, 203 (1955).
23. *Ibid.*, p. 391.
24. *Ibid.*, **105**, 685.
25. *Ibid.*, *JETP*, **30**, 77 (1956).
26. *Ibid.*, *Nuovo cimento*, **3**, 845 (1956).
27. Brown, L. M., and Feynman, R. P., *Phys. Rev.*, **85**, 231 (1952).
28. Cartan, E. J., *Leçons sur la théorie des spineurs*, Hermann, Paris, 1938.
29. Dancoff, S. M., *Phys. Rev.*, **78**, 382 (1950).
30. Dirac, P. A. M., *The Principles of Quantum Mechanics*, 2nd ed., Oxford, 1935; 3rd ed., 1947.

31. Dirac, P. A. M., Fock, W. A., and Podolsky, B., *Physik. Z. Sowjetunion*, **2**, 468 (1932).
32. Duffin, R. J., *Phys. Rev.*, **54**, 905 (1938).
33. Dyson, F. J., *ibid.*, **75**, 486 (1949).
34. *Ibid.*, p. 1736.
35. *Ibid.*, **85**, 631 (1953).
36. Edwards, S. F., *ibid.*, **90**, 284.
37. Edwards, S. F., and Peierls, R. E., *Proc. Roy. Soc. (London)*, A **224**, 24 (1954).
38. Fermi, E., *Nuovo cimento Suppl.*, **2**, 17 (1955).
39. Feynman, R. P., *Revs. Modern Phys.*, **20**, 367 (1947); *Phys. Rev.*, **74**, 1430 (1948).
40. *Ibid.*, *Phys. Rev.*, **76**, 749 (1949).
41. *Ibid.*, p. 769.
42. *Ibid.*, **84**, 108 (1951).
43. Fock, W. A., *Z. Physik*, **75**, 622 (1932); *Physik. Z. Sowjetunion*, **12**, 404 (1937).
44. Fradkin, E. S., *Doklady Akad. Nauk USSR*, **98**, 47 (1954).
45. Furry, W., *Phys. Rev.*, **51**, 125 (1937).
46. Gel'fand, I. M., and Minlos, R. A., *Doklady Akad. Nauk USSR*, **97**, 209 (1954).
47. Gell-Mann, M., Goldberger, M. L., and Thirring, W., *Phys. Rev.*, **95**, 1612 (1954).
48. Gell-Mann, M., and Low, F., *ibid.*, p. 1300.
49. Ginzburg, I. F., *Doklady Akad. Nauk USSR*, **110**, 535 (1956).
50. Goebel, C. J., Karplus, R., and Ruderman, M. A., *Phys. Rev.*, **100**, 240 (1955).
51. Goldberger, M. L., *ibid.*, **97**, 508 (1955).
52. *Ibid.*, **99**, 979.
53. Goldberger, M. L., Miyazawa, H., and Oehme, R., *ibid.*, p. 986.
54. Gor'kov, L. P., *Doklady Akad. Nauk USSR*, **105**, 65 (1955).
55. Gupta, S., *Proc. Roy. Soc. (London)*, A **63**, 681 (1950).
56. Haag, R., *Kgl. Danske Videnskab. Selskab, Mat.-fys. Medd.*, **29**, No. 12 (1955).
57. Heisenberg, W., *Z. Physik*, **120**, 513 (1943).
58. *Ibid.*, p. 673.
59. *Ibid.*, *Z. Naturforsch.*, **1**, 673 (1946).
60. Heitler, W., *The Quantum Theory of Radiation*, 1st ed., Oxford, 1936; *ibid.*, 3rd ed., 1954.
61. Hu Ning, *Phys. Rev.*, **74**, 131 (1948).
62. Hurst, C. A., *Proc. Cambridge Phil. Soc.*, **18**, 625 (1952).
63. Ioffe, B. L., *Doklady Akad. Nauk USSR*, **94**, 437 (1954).
64. Jost, R., and Luttinger, J., *Helv. Phys. Acta*, **23**, 201 (1950).
65. Källen, G., *ibid.*, **25**, 416 (1952); *Nuovo cimento*, **12**, 217 (1954).

66. Karplus, R., Klein, A., and Schwinger, J., *Phys. Rev.*, **86**, 288 (1952).
67. Karplus, R., and Kroll, N., *ibid.*, **77**, 536 (1950).
68. Karplus, R., and Ruderman, M. A., *ibid.*, **98**, 771 (1955).
69. Kemmer, N., *Proc. Roy. Soc. (London)*, A **173**, 91 (1939).
70. Khalatnikov, I. M., *JETP*, **28**, 633 (1955).
71. Klein, A., *Progr. Theoret. Phys. (Kyoto)*, **14**, 580 (1955).
72. Koenig, S. H., Prodell, A. G., and Kusch, R., *Phys. Rev.*, **88**, 191 (1952).
73. Kramers, H. A., *Atti congr. intern. Fisici, Como*, **2**, 545 (1927).
74. Krein, M. G., *Doklady Akad. Nauk USSR*, **105**, 433 (1955).
75. Kronig, R., *J. Opt. Soc. Am.*, **12**, 547 (1926).
76. Landau, L. D., Abrikosov, A. A., and Khalatnikov, I. M., *Doklady Akad. Nauk USSR*, **95**, 773 (1954).
77. *Ibid.*, p. 1177.
78. *Ibid.*, **96**, 261.
79. Landau, L. D., and Pomeranchuk, I., *ibid.*, **102**, 489 (1955).
80. Lee, T. D., *Phys. Rev.*, **95**, 1329 (1954).
81. Lehmann, H., *Nuovo cimento*, **11**, 342 (1954).
82. Lehmann, H., Symanzik, K., and Zimmerman, *Nuovo cim.*, **1**, 205 (1955).
83. Logunov, A. A., *JETP*, **30**, 793 (1956).
84. Low, F. E., *Phys. Rev.*, **97**, 1392 (1955).
85. Matthews, P. T., *ibid.*, **76**, 1657 (1949).
86. Matthews, P. T., and Salam, A., *ibid.*, **94**, 185 (1954).
87. Oehme, R., *ibid.*, **100**, 1503 (1955).
87a. *Ibid.*, **102**, 1174 (1956)
88. Ovsiannikov, L. V., *Doklady Akad. Nauk USSR*, **109**, 1121 (1956).
89. Parasiuk, O. S., *ibid.*, **100**, 643 (1955).
90. *Ibid.*, Thesis, Math. Inst. Acad. Sci. USSR, 1955.
91. Pauli, W., "Die Allgemeinen Prinzipien der Wellenmechanik" in *Handb. Phys.*, **24**(1), 1933.
91a. Pauli, W., "Relativistic Theory of Elementary Particles," *Rev. Mod. Phys.* **13**, 203 (1941).
91b. Pauli, W., *N. Bohr and the Development of Physics*, Pergamon – London, McGraw-Hill, – New York, 1955, p. 30.
92. Pauli, W., and Dancoff, S. M., *Phys. Rev.*, **62**, 85 (1942).
93. Pauli, W., and Villars, F., *Revs. Modern Phys.*, **21**, 434 (1949).
94. Pekar, S. I., *JETP*, **30**, 304 (1956).
95. Polivanov, M. K., *Doklady Akad. Nauk USSR*, **100**, 1061 (1955).
96. Polkinghorne, C., *Nuovo cimento*, **4**, 216 (1956).
97. Pomeranchuk, I., *Doklady Akad. Nauk USSR*, **103**, 1005 (1955).
98. Rivier, D., *Helv. Phys. Acta*, **22**, 265 (1949).
99. Ruijgrok, T. W., and Hove, L. van, *Physica*, **22**, 880 (1956).

100. Ryzhik and Gradshtein, *Tables of Integrals, Sums, Series and Products*, 3rd ed., Gostekhizdat, Moscow, 1951.
101. Salam, A., *Nuovo cimento*, **3**, 424 (1956).
102. Salam, A., and Gilbert, W., *ibid.*, p. 607.
103. Schwartz, L., *Théorie des distributions*, Hermann, Paris, 1950.
104. Schwinger, J., *Phys. Rev.*, **74**, 1439 (1948).
105. *Ibid.*, **75**, 651 (1949).
106. *Ibid.*, **76**, 790.
107. *Ibid.*, *Proc. Natl. Acad. Sci.*, **37**, 452 (1951).
108. *Ibid.*, p. 455.
109. *Ibid.*, *Phys. Rev.*, **82**, 914 (1951).
110. Serber, R., and Dancoff, S. M., *ibid.*, **63**, 143 (1943).
111. Shapiro, I. S., *Uspekki Fiz. Nauk*, **53**, 7 (1954).
112. Shirkov, D. V., *Doklady Akad. Nauk USSR*, **105**, 972 (1955).
113. Sobolev, S. L., *Mat. Sbornik*, **1** (43), 39 (1936).
114. Sokolov, A. A., and Ivanenko, D. D., *Quantum Field Theory*, Gostekhizdat, Moscow, 1952.
115. Stepanov, B. M., Thesis, Math. Inst. Acad. Sci., USSR, 1953; *Doklady Akad. Nauk USSR*, **100**, 889 (1955); *ibid.*, **108**, 1045 (1956).
116. Stueckelberg, E. C. G., *Phys. Rev.*, **81**, 130 (1951).
117. Stueckelberg, E. C. G., and Green, T., *Helv. Phys. Acta*, **24**, 153 (1951).
118. Stueckelberg, E. C. G., and Petermann, A., *ibid.*, **26**, 499 (1953).
119. Stueckelberg, E. C. G., and Rivier, D., *ibid.*, **22**, 215 (1949).
120. Sudakov, V. V., *JETP*, **30**, 87 (1956).
121. Svidzinskii, A. V., Thesis, L'vov State University, 1955; *JETP*, **31**, 324 (1956).
122. Symanzik, K., *Z. Naturforsch.*, **9a**, 809 (1954).
123. Takeda, G., *Progr. Theoret. Phys.* (*Kyoto*), **7**, 359 (1952).
124. Tamm, I. E., *J. Phys.* (*USSR*), **9**, 449 (1945).
125. Thirring, W., *Helv. Phys. Acta*, **26**, 33 (1953).
126. Tomonaga, S., *Progr. Theoret. Phys.* (*Kyoto*), **1**, 27 (1946).
127. Triebwasser, S., Dayhoff, E. S., and Lamb, W. E., *Phys. Rev.*, **89**, 98 (1953).
128. Umezawa, H., *Progr. Theoret. Phys.* (*Kyoto*), **7**, 551 (1952).
129. Van der Waerden, B. L., *Die Gruppentheoretische Methode in der Quantenmechanik*, Springer, Berlin, 1932.
130. Van Kampen, N. G., *Phys. Rev.*, **89**, 1072, 1953.
131. *Ibid.*, **91**, 1267.
132. Ward, J. C., *ibid.*, **78**, 182 (1950).
133. Wentzel, G., *Quantum Theory of Wave Fields*, Interscience, New York, 1949.
134. Wick, G., *Phys. Rev.*, **80**, 268 (1950).

Author Index

Subject Index